12271

THE APPLIED SCIENCE OF RUBBER

THE
APPLIED SCIENCE
OF RUBBER

*Prepared with the approval of the Institution of the
Rubber Industry*

Edited by
W. J. S. NAUNTON

LONDON
EDWARD ARNOLD (PUBLISHERS) LTD.

Printed in Great Britain by Richard Clay and Company, Ltd.,
Bungay, Suffolk

CONTRIBUTORS

A. F. Blanchard, M.Sc., A.Inst.P., A.I.R.I. of *Dunlop Tyre and Rubber Co. Ltd.*

G. F. Bloomfield, Ph.D., A.R.C.S., F.R.I.C. of *The Natural Rubber Producers' Research Association*

J. M. Buist, B.Sc., F.Inst.P., F.I.R.I. of *Imperial Chemical Industries Ltd.*

E. G. Cockbain, Ph.D. of *The Natural Rubber Producers' Research Association*

F. H. Cotton, Ph.D., F.R.I.C., F.I.R.I. of the *National College of Rubber Technology*

H. A. Daynes, D.Sc., F.Inst.P., F.I.R.I. of *Associated Electrical Industries (Woolwich) Ltd.*

J. W. Denson, F.I.R.I. of *Goodyear Tyre and Rubber Co. Ltd.*

A. C. Edwards of *Admiralty Materials Laboratory*

G. N. S. Farrand, B.Sc., A.R.I.C. of *Admiralty Materials Laboratory*

J. Glazer, Ph.D. of the *National College of Rubber Technology*

W. A. Gurney, B.Sc., A.Inst.P., A.I.R.I. of *Dunlop Tyre and Rubber Co. Ltd.*

M. M. Heywood, F.R.I.C., F.I.R.I. of *P. B. Cow and Co. Ltd.*

A. J. Hirst, B.Sc., A.M.I.Mech.E. of *Metalastik Ltd.*

C. H. Leigh-Dugmore, B.Sc., A.Inst.P., A.I.R.I. of *Dunlop Tyre and Rubber Co. Ltd.*

E. W. Madge, B.Sc., F.Inst.P., F.I.R.I. of *Dunlop Tyre and Rubber Co. Ltd.*

G. Martin, B.Sc., F.I.R.I. of *The Natural Rubber Producers' Research Association*

L. R. Mernagh, F.R.I.C., M.I.Mech.E., F.I.R.I. of *Firestone Tyre and Rubber Co.*

W. J. S. Naunton, Ph.D., F.R.I.C., V.P.I.R.I., *Consultant on Rubber and Plastics to the Admiralty*

F. C. J. Poulton, A.R.I.C. of *Dunlop Tyre and Rubber Co. Ltd.*

J. R. Scott, Ph.D., F.R.I.C., F.I.R.I. of the *Rubber and Plastics Research Association of Great Britain*

CONTRIBUTORS

J. F. Smith, Ph.D., F.R.I.C., F.I.R.I. late of the *Rubber and Plastics Research Association of Great Britain*

W. E. Stafford, A.M.C.T., A.R.I.C., F.I.R.I. of *Rubber Regenerating Co.*

R. N. Thomson, B.Sc., A.Inst.P. of *Dunlop Tyre and Rubber Co. Ltd.*

J. T. Watts, Ph.D., F.R.I.C., F.I.R.I. of *Imperial Chemical Industries Ltd.*

R. A. Wright, A.M.C.T., A.R.I.C., A.I.R.I. of *Rubber Regenerating Co.*

FOREWORD

THE need for an advanced comprehensive text-book of rubber technology which combined theory and practice has long been felt, and it was not therefore surprising that the Papers and Publications Committee of the Institution of the Rubber Industry on learning that the writer was contemplating editing such a treatise should give the venture their approval and enthusiastic support.   In compiling such a book it is essential that the contributors should have more than an academic knowledge of their subjects, and the question then arose whether the rubber industry would allow their experts to contribute frankly and without restraint to such a publication.   In no case was an invited contributor refused permission, and the opportunity is now taken to acknowledge the kindness of the rubber firms and organisations (listed in the index of contributors) which made the publication of this book possible.

Several distinguished rubber technologists who are not contributors have been willing to read and comment on the manuscripts before editing; for example, Dr. C. Falconer Flint on the latex sections and Dr. D. Parkinson on the reinforcement sections.

In order to keep the book within reasonable limits the editor has been compelled to cut down some of the manuscripts, but great care was taken not to delete essential information.   On the other hand, in such a book, where individual chapters will be studied for specific purposes, it is impossible completely to eliminate repetition, but an attempt has been made to reduce it to a minimum.

W. J. S. NAUNTON.

December 1960.

CONTENTS

chapter   *page*

CHAPTER I

PART ONE

NATURAL AND SYNTHETIC LATICES

by

E. G. COCKBAIN

In the rubber industry the term " latex " is restricted, with a few exceptions, to naturally occurring dispersions of rubber and to synthetic polymer dispersions in which the polymers have actually been synthesised in the form of very finely divided particles in an aqueous medium. In this way, a useful distinction can be drawn between latices, on the one hand, and dispersions prepared by comminution of a pre-formed polymer, such as reclaim rubber dispersions.

A large number of plant species secrete latices containing natural rubber or closely related compounds, but only *Hevea braziliensis* latex has assumed major industrial importance. In the synthetic field the growth of polymer chemistry and technology since 1940 has been so rapid that a large number of synthetic rubber latices is now available commercially. However, many of these latices produced by different manufacturers differ only very slightly in composition and performance. The most important of the synthetic latices in terms of consumption are the copolymers of butadiene with either styrene (SBR types) or acrylonitrile (nitrile rubbers), and polychloroprene (neoprene).

Other latices used on a relatively small scale for specialised applications are those of the acrylic rubbers and the Thiokols. The acrylic rubbers have good resistance to heat, ozone and mineral oils, while the Thiokols have excellent resistance to oils and solvents, excluding chlorinated solvents. The general elastic properties of the acrylics and Thiokols, however, are much inferior to those of natural and some of the synthetic rubbers.

A few terpolymer rubber latices are available consisting of three copolymerised vinyl monomers, one of which is usually employed in minor proportions. An example is the terpolymer of butadiene, styrene and 2-vinylpyridine, which is useful as an adhesive for nylon tyre cords.

In recent years latices have been introduced commercially in which the rubber phase consists at least partly of a graft polymer. This term signifies that a polymer B is attached as side chains to a different polymer A. The

B

I

whole graft polymer may be synthetic, or A may be natural rubber and B a synthetic polymer chain. Examples of this type are the graft polymers of natural rubber with methyl methacrylate or styrene.

Composition of natural (Hevea) latex

Freshly tapped latex, before preservation or concentration, is known as field latex. In addition to the suspended rubber particles, which range in diameter from less than 0·05 μ to about 3 μ, it contains a smaller number of easily deformable bodies named " lutoids " by Homans and van Gils [1,2] (Fig. 1.1). These lutoids, which consist essentially of a viscous aqueous

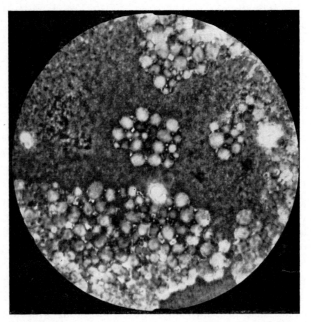

Fig. 1.1. Phase contrast photomicrograph of " Lutoid " particles in freshly tapped Hevea latex.   Magnification × 750.

solution or gel of non-rubber materials, probably surrounded by a membrane, break down on addition of ammonia, and most of their contents pass into the latex serum. The non-rubber constituents occurring in greatest quantity in field latex are proteins, lipids, quebrachitol and inorganic salts. The last two components occur entirely in the aqueous phase or serum, the lipids are nearly all on the surface or in the interior of the rubber particles, and the proteins are distributed between the serum and the rubber–serum interface.[3,4,5]

Structure and composition of the rubber particles

The rubber particles themselves, excluding surface-active materials adsorbed on their surface, consist almost entirely (*ca.* 99%) of rubber hydrocarbon [6] with which small amounts of oxygen may be combined.[7] Although the amount of rubber in field latex may vary considerably (about 32% by weight is a common concentration), the constitution of the rubber hydrocarbon is very uniform in its micro-structure. This term as applied to polymers means the sequence and detailed configuration of the monomer units comprising the polymer molecule. Natural rubber is a polymer of isoprene,

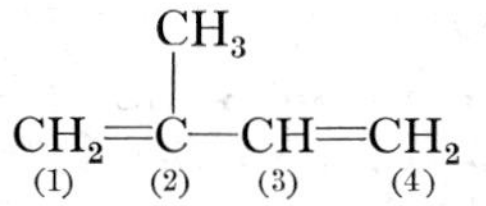

$$\underset{(1)}{CH_2}=\underset{(2)}{\overset{\overset{\displaystyle CH_3}{|}}{C}}-\underset{(3)}{CH}=\underset{(4)}{CH_2}$$

in which essentially all the isoprene units are linked together at carbon atoms 1 and 4 in a head-to-tail arrangement, and in which all or nearly all the repeating units possess the " *cis* " configuration. This regularity of micro-structure plays an important part in determining some of the most

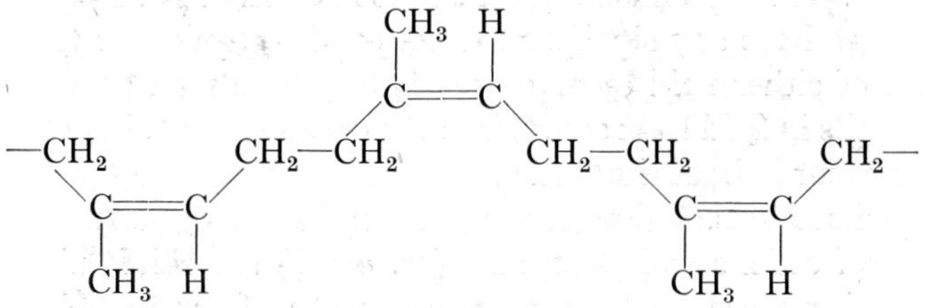

cis-polyisoprene

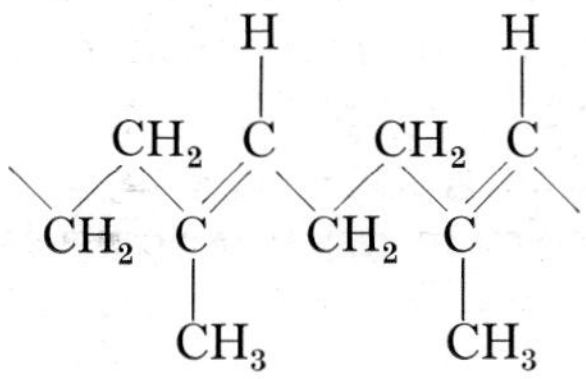

trans-polyisoprene

characteristic properties of natural rubber, such as its extremely high gum tensile strength. The main sources of variation in natural rubber hydro-carbon are due to differences in molecular weight and in the degree of cross-linking of the molecules,[8] which determines the sol-to-gel ratio, i.e. the fraction of the rubber soluble in a solvent such as benzene. In latex systems the gel rubber is referred to as micro-gel.

The surface-active compounds adsorbed on the rubber particles in field latex consist chiefly of proteins and phospholipids—mainly of the lecithin type.[9]   After addition of ammonia as preservative, the latex phospholipids are gradually hydrolysed to free bases (choline or hydroxyethylamine), glycerol and glycerophosphate, and fatty acid soaps.   The free bases, the glycerophosphate, and glycerol pass into the serum, but much of the fatty acid soap remains adsorbed.[10, 11]   Similarly, hydrolysis of some of the adsorbed protein slowly occurs in the presence of ammonia, forming amino acids and polypeptides which also pass into the serum.   Since the adsorbed materials are responsible for the stability of the latex, it is not surprising that their hydrolysis leads to changes in stability.   The mechanical stability actually increases, since the formation of fatty acid soap more than compensates for the loss of phospholipid and protein.   Fatty acid soaps, however, do not stabilise latex against inorganic or other water-soluble acids, and after ammoniation the latex coagulates more rapidly on acidification.

Serum constituents

In freshly tapped field latex, quebrachitol, inorganic salts, and proteins are the main constituents of the serum.   Quebrachitol is the monomethyl ether of *l*-inositol, which is one of the structural isomers of hexahydroxycyclohexane.   The quebrachitol content is fairly high (*ca.* 1%), but it does not appear to have any significant effect on the physical or technological properties of either field or preserved latex.   The total concentration of inorganic salts in field latex serum is of the order of 0·8%, but considerable variations occur in both the total salt concentration and in the proportions of the individual ions.[12]   Potassium (*ca.* 0·2%) and magnesium (*ca.* 0·05%) are the chief cations and phosphate (*ca.* 0·4%) the chief anion, all percentages being parts by weight per 100 parts of serum.   A small and variable amount of magnesium is also found at the rubber–serum interface. The relative proportions of the inorganic ions in the serum can have a marked influence on the stability of the latex and of the concentrates prepared from it.   In particular, an abnormally high ratio of magnesium to phosphate ion often results in a low mechanical stability.[13, 14]   Volatile fatty acids, such as acetic and formic acid, are formed in the serum if preservation of the latex is delayed.[15, 16]   Other constituents of technological importance are traces of copper ions, whose concentration in latex concentrates should not exceed 10 p.p.m. due to their effect on the ageing of rubber, and certain amino acids capable of forming complex salts with zinc oxide in the presence of ammonia.

The inorganic cations present in greatest amount in ammonia-preserved latex are those of potassium and ammonium.   Carbonate and bicarbonate ions are also formed by absorption of atmospheric carbon dioxide.   On the other hand, ammoniation results in the precipitation of magnesium and phosphate ions as magnesium ammonium phosphate, which is largely removed as sludge when the latex is concentrated by centrifuging. Depending on the relative proportions of magnesium and phosphate initially in the serum phase, ammoniated latices almost free from inorganic phosphate or magnesium ions can be obtained. Absorption of atmospheric oxygen by ammonia-preserved latex is an important factor influencing the mechanical stability and other properties of the latex.[17,18]

Field latex which has been preserved with ammonia but not concentrated is usually referred to as " normal " latex. It is still available commercially, but has been largely superseded by latex concentrates.

Concentrated natural latex

Apart from the fact that natural latex concentrates are more uniform in composition than normal latex, their chief technical advantage is that in the many manufacturing processes involving gelation of the latex their lower water content results in higher wet gel strength. Because of this, the use of concentrated latices is often essential. Four methods of concentration are used, viz. centrifuging, creaming, electrodecantation, and evaporation.

Centrifuged latex

Most of the latex exported from the Far East is of this type. As carried out commercially, centrifuging leaves most of the smaller rubber particles, i.e. those of diameter less than $0.15\ \mu$, in the skim. Although these particles account for only about 12% of the rubber by weight, they contain a much higher percentage of the adsorbed non-rubbers because of their large surface area-to-volume ratio. As a result, the non-rubber content of centrifuged latex is low, and less than that of the other types of concentrate *at the same DRC* (dry rubber content).

The nature and approximate concentrations of the main non-rubber constituents in ammonia-preserved centrifuged concentrates, a few months after production, are indicated in Table 1.1.

TABLE 1.1

APPROXIMATE CONCENTRATIONS OF NON-RUBBER CONSTITUENTS IN CENTRIFUGED LATEX CONCENTRATES

Constituent	Percentage by weight of latex
Fatty acid soaps (e.g. ammonium oleate)	0.5
Sterols and sterol esters	0.5
Proteins	0.8
Quebrachitol	0.3
Choline	0.1
Glycerophosphate	0.1
Water-soluble carboxylic acid salts (acetate, citrate, etc.)	0.3
Amino acids and polypeptides	0.2
Inorganic salts (ammonium and potassium carbonate and phosphate, etc.)	0.2

Creamed latex

Commercial creamed latices contain many more of the smaller rubber particles than centrifuged latex, and the content of adsorbed non-rubbers is correspondingly higher. However, since creaming is usually carried to 62% DRC or higher, as compared with 60% DRC for centrifuged latex, the proportion of *serum* constituents is somewhat smaller. Small amounts of added fatty acid soaps, which facilitate creaming, and the creaming agent itself (ammonium alginate) are present in creamed concentrates.

Electrodecanted latex

In concentrates of this type the proportion of small rubber particles is higher than in centrifuged but slightly lower than in creamed latex. Concentration is carried to 60% DRC. Approximately 0·1% of fatty acid soap, added as a stabiliser during electrodecantation, is partly retained in the concentrate and contributes towards the relatively high mechanical stability of electrodecanted latex. The ammonia content of the latex is also a little higher than in the other types of concentrate.

Evaporated latex

Evaporated concentrates are produced under the trade-names T-Revertex and Standard Revertex, which contain approximately 62% and 73% total solids respectively. Such " whole " latices possess a smaller number-average and weight-average particle size, a wider particle size distribution, and a higher proportion of non-rubbers than the other types of concentrate. Standard Revertex is preserved with fixed alkali (KOH) and T-Revertex with ammonia. Standard Revertex has an exceptionally high viscosity due to the high total solids content and small particle size; it also has a very high mechanical stability.

" Low ammonia " latices

To preserve latex concentrates adequately over long periods by means of ammonia alone, the concentrates must contain at least 0·7% by weight of ammonia (anhydrous). The search for alternative preservatives effective in smaller concentrations has resulted in the development of " low ammonia " latex concentrates in which the preservative system is a combination of ammonia, in comparatively low concentrations, e.g. 0·2%, with small amounts of a secondary bactericide. Among the bactericides which have been used successfully for this purpose are sodium pentachlorphenate, zinc dimethyldithiocarbamate and ammonium borate.[19] Because of the lower alkalinity of these latices, variations in latex composition due to the slow but progressive hydrolysis of non-rubber constituents is less marked than in concentrates containing 0·7% or more of ammonia. The lower alkalinity also avoids the necessity, in certain latex processes, of blowing off or otherwise removing excess ammonia from the latex.

Positively charged natural latex

In all the latices mentioned so far, the rubber particles carry a negative electric charge. If centrifuged ammoniated latex is first diluted with water and then poured into an aqueous solution of a quaternary ammonium salt of suitable concentration, reversal of the electric charge on the rubber particles occurs so rapidly that flocculation of the rubber does not take place. " Positex " is a natural rubber latex of this type, in which the quaternary ammonium salt is cetyltrimethylammonium bromide. The positive electric charge at the rubber–serum interface arises from the adsorption of this compound. The pH of " Positex " is on the alkaline side of neutrality, due to the presence of ammonia. The positively charged rubber particles have a high affinity for many negatively charged surfaces, and under suitable conditions the rubber can be completely exhausted on to such surfaces. As would be expected, " Positex " is incompatible with negatively charged latices, and special precautions must be taken in compounding.

Composition of synthetic latices

Nearly all the commercial synthetic rubber latices are manufactured by the same basic method of emulsion polymerisation, and as a result they have many similarities in respect of the non-rubber constituents. Due to the large number of synthetic latices and the fact that full details of the recipes used are seldom available, only the main features of their composition can be discussed. The basic constituents of all commercial emulsion polymerisation recipes are: (1) monomer(s), (2) emulsifiers, and (3) polymerisation catalysts. Other very common components are: (4) modifiers, (5) inorganic salts and free alkali, and (6) short-stops. A large literature now exists [20, 21] on the function of these different components and on the mechanism of emulsion polymerisation, but we need only note for the present that reagents (3), (4) and (6) are largely or completely consumed in the production process.

Structure of the polymer phase

The structure is essentially the same as that in the dry synthetic rubber, which is discussed in detail in the chapter on Synthetic Rubber (Chapter III).

Composition of the serum

Soaps. Many of the synthetic latices contain 7–10% of non-rubbers (on the weight of polymer), of which more than half is a soap or mixture of soaps.   One reason for this relatively high soap concentration, compared with natural latex, is that soap micelles containing solubilised monomer play a major role in the polymerisation process.   At present, a relatively high soap concentration is usually necessary to achieve a sufficiently rapid rate of polymerisation.   Secondly, a considerable fraction of the surface of the polymer particles must be covered by adsorbed soap, or equivalent stabiliser, to prevent flocculation of the latex during manufacture or subsequent use.   In the majority of synthetic latices the total surface area of the particles per unit weight of polymer is greater than in natural latex, and a correspondingly higher proportion of stabiliser is needed.

The most commonly used soaps are the sodium, potassium, or ammonium salts of oleic acid, stearic acid, rosin acids, or disproportionated rosin acids, either singly or in admixture.   Alkyl or alkaryl sulphates or sulphonates may also be present, a useful stabiliser of this class being the condensation product of formaldehyde with the sodium salt of β-naphthalene sulphonic acid.   All these stabilisers are anionic in type, and on adsorption confer a negative electric charge to the polymer particles.   Latices stabilised with cationic or non-ionic surfactants have been developed for special applications.   In spite of the high concentration of stabiliser in most synthetic latices, only a very small proportion is present in the aqueous phase; nearly all of it is adsorbed on the polymer particles.

Minor Constituents.   Neutral or alkaline salts such as potassium chloride, potassium sulphate, or trisodium phosphate are often present in synthetic latices in quantities of about 1% or less on the weight of rubber.   They play an important role during the emulsion polymerisation process in helping to control the viscosity of the latex and, in the case of the alkaline salts, the pH of the system.   Many polymerisations are carried out at a high pH value, requiring the use of fixed alkali (KOH).   Very small amounts of ferrous salts may be employed as a component of the catalyst system, in which case a sequestering agent, such as the sodium salt of ethylenediaminetetra-acetic acid, may be present to complex the iron.   Water-soluble " short-stops ", e.g. potassium dimethyldithiocarbamate, may also be present in very small concentration (*ca.* 0.1).

Synthetic latices of high solids content

For many applications latices of high solids contents are required, and polymerisation recipes have been developed which produce directly latices of 60% or more total solids.   To achieve this result a high conversion of the monomer is essential, and the recipes usually contain less soap and more electrolyte than those for latices of lower total solids.   These conditions favour the production of latices of relatively large average particle size, particularly if the soap is added in increments as polymerisation progresses.

The large particle size is important in preventing the viscosity of the latex from reaching abnormally high values.

Instead of polymerising directly to 60% total solids or higher, latices of low or medium solids content can be concentrated by evaporation or creaming. Again, the average particle size of the latex must not be so small as to give a concentrate of undesirably high viscosity, and polymerisation conditions are usually chosen accordingly. If, however, the original latex is of small particle size, it can be treated so that a limited and controlled degree of particle coalescence occurs. This can be achieved by a reduction in pH and/or the addition of salts, the latex being re-stabilised after sufficient coalescence of the particles has taken place. Another method which appears to have many advantages is to increase the particle size by freezing the latex under controlled conditions, as specified by Tallalay,[26] followed by concentration to 60% solids or higher.

SBR, neoprene and nitrile latices

SBR latices contain as the polymer phase either polybutadiene or co-polymers of butadiene and styrene in which the upper limit for the proportion of styrene is 50% by weight. Differences in the composition of SBR latices are mainly in respect of comonomer ratio, solids content, type and concentration of soap, and differences due to the polymerisation temperature, which is approximately 122° F for the hot polymers and 41° F for the cold. The hot latices are carried to 90% conversion or higher and are not normally short-stopped. The cold latices are usually short-stopped at 60–80% conversion, e.g. by a water-soluble dithiocarbamate. The total solids of SBR latices range from just over 20 to about 63%.

Neoprene is a generic name for polychloroprene (poly-2-chloro-1 : 3-butadiene) or for products in which polymerised chloroprene is the major constituent. There are several main types of neoprene latex, some of which are available at both high and intermediate solids contents. Differences in composition between the main types include the macrostructure of the polymer (e.g. sol or gel polymers), the type of stabiliser, and the total solids content.

Nitrile latices are copolymers of butadiene and acrylonitrile or products in which these copolymerised monomers are the major constituents. The latices differ mainly in respect of comonomer ratio and the type and concentration of stabiliser. Nitrile latices can be classified into low, medium and high acrylonitrile types. The latter contains 35–40% by weight of acrylonitrile in the copolymer, the medium types 25–33%, and the low types less than 33% acrylonitrile. Carboxylic acid modified nitrile rubbers, consisting of terpolymers of butadiene, acrylonitrile, and a small proportion of a polymerisable carboxylic acid, are also available as latices.

Graft polymer latices

Among the latices of this type which have been produced commercially are those containing graft polymers of natural rubber with methyl methacrylate or styrene.   G-Revertex 10 and G-Revertex K40 are 60% solids latices in which the polymer phase is natural rubber grafted with methyl methacrylate in proportions of 10 : 1 and 2·5 : 1 respectively.

Physical properties of natural and synthetic latices

Viscosity

The viscosity of a liquid is a measure of the resistance which it offers to flow.   If the flow is through a tube, for example, the layers of liquid near the centre move faster than the layers closer to the walls.   Thus, there is a velocity gradient at right angles to the length of the tube, and layers of liquid are sheared relative to one another during the flow.   If the shearing stress is F, then for many liquids it is found that the flow velocity gradient or rate of shear, G, is directly proportional to F at constant temperature (Fig. 1.2).   Such liquids are said to show Newtonian viscosity, and are called Newtonian liquids, since the above proportionality was first described by Newton.   The ratio $F/G = \eta$ is the coefficient of viscosity of the liquid.   The viscosity of many uncompounded rubber latices, including natural and SBR latices, approximates very closely to Newtonian behaviour at low total solids content, e.g. less than about 25% solids for SBR latices.[27, 28, 29]   At higher solids content, with all variables except F and G constant, F/G decreases as the rate of shear increases, and the equation of flow is often better represented by an exponential equation of the form

$$\frac{F^N}{G} = k^1 \quad . \quad . \quad . \quad . \quad . \quad . \quad (1.1)$$

where N and k^1 are constants for a given latex at constant temperature. With some SBR latices at relatively high solids contents, two separate exponential equations of the above form with different values of N and k^1 are necessary to describe the dependence of rate of shear on the shearing stress, one being applicable for low and the other for high shearing stresses.[27, 28, 29]

Compounded latices of high solids content are not only non-Newtonian but may possess a yield point F_c, defined as a critical shearing stress below which flow does not occur (Fig. 1.2).   They may also exhibit the phenomenon of thixotropy in which the apparent viscosity above the yield point depends on the length of time the system is sheared.

The flow of a latex at constant temperature depends on many factors besides the shearing stress, such as concentration of the disperse phase, primary particle size, particle aggregation, the viscosity of the aqueous medium and the nature of the adsorbed film of stabiliser. Particle shape also affects the flow behaviour when the shape deviates markedly from

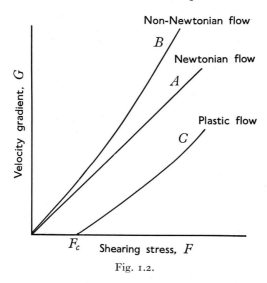

Fig. 1.2.

spherical. The concentration of the disperse phase is usually the most important factor. For very dilute suspensions of rigid spherical particles showing Newtonian viscosity, Einstein developed the equation

$$\frac{\eta_r - 1}{\phi} = 2 \cdot 5 \quad . \quad . \quad . \quad . \quad . \quad (1.2)$$

where η_r is the relative viscosity of the suspension, i.e. the ratio of the viscosity coefficient of the suspension to that of the continuous medium, and ϕ is the volume fraction of disperse phase (total volume of the particles divided by the volume of the suspension). Einstein's equation holds fairly well for dilute but not for high-solids latices. For some latices of the SBR and neoprene types,[30,31] the variation of η_r with ϕ over a wide range of polymer concentration can be expressed quite accurately by the equation

$$\frac{\eta_r^{\frac{1}{2}} - 1}{\phi} = a + b \left(\eta_r^{\frac{1}{2}} - 1 \right) \quad . \quad . \quad . \quad . \quad (1.3)$$

where a and b are constants requiring experimental determination.

A more general theoretical treatment of the flow behaviour of latices in both the Newtonian and non-Newtonian regions of flow has been developed by Maron *et al.*[32] This theory enables the viscosity of a latex to be calculated at any rate of shear over a wide range of temperature and polymer content, provided certain parameters are determined experimentally. An account of developments in the theory of the viscosity of colloidal suspensions, prior to 1956, has been given by Frisch and Simha.[33]

No theoretical treatment is available which takes adequate account of particle size and size distribution or the nature of the adsorbed film of stabiliser. For high-solids latices, the viscosity increases appreciably as the particle size is reduced. Aggregation of the primary particles can also increase greatly the viscosity of a latex. In most cases of reversible particle aggregation, suitable wetting agents will disaggregate the particles and reduce the viscosity.

One of the commonest methods of obtaining latex compounds of high viscosity is to increase the viscosity of the aqueous phase by the addition of thickening agents such as methyl cellulose, sodium carboxymethylcellulose, and the sodium or ammonium salts of polyacrylic or polymethacrylic acid. Many of these agents also increase the colloidal stability of the latex compounds.

The most reliable methods of measuring the viscosity of latices employ either capillary or rotating-cylinder viscometers. In the former the rate of efflux (v) of the latex is measured through a capillary tube of known length (l) and uniform radius (r). Changes in the rate of shear are obtained by varying the pressure head (P) of latex above the capillary. The viscosity, η, can be calculated from Poiseuille's equation

$$\eta = \frac{\pi P r^4}{8vl} \quad . \qquad . \qquad . \qquad . \qquad . \qquad (1.4)$$

Usually, it is more convenient to calibrate the viscometer with a liquid of known viscosity (η_2). The viscosity of the latex, η_1, under the driving pressure P, is then given by the simple expression

$$\eta_1 = \frac{\eta_2 \, \rho_1 \, t_1}{\rho_2 \, t_2} \quad . \qquad . \qquad . \qquad . \qquad . \qquad (1.5)$$

where ρ_1, ρ_2 are the densities of the latex and reference liquid and t_1, t_2 are the times of flow of the same volume of latex and liquid between the same points in the " reservoir " tube above the capillary. A suitable type of capillary viscometer for latex (Fig. 1.3) is described in ASTM D1076–49T. A capillary viscometer of improved design, which is particularly suitable for the study of non-Newtonian liquids, has been described by Maron, Krieger and Sisko.[34]

In the Zahn Cup method the time required for a given volume of latex to flow through the orifice in the bottom of a metal cup is measured. Cups with different diameter orifices are available to cover a wider range of viscosities. Although the method is not suitable for quantitative work, it is very simple and rapid and has been used for the factory control of viscosity.

In rotating-cylinder viscometers the latex is sheared between two con-centric cylinders, the outer one of which may be a cylindrical vessel containing the latex. In an apparatus of given dimensions in which the inner cylinder is rotated at constant speed, the torque exerted on the cylinder by the viscous drag of the latex is directly proportional to the viscosity of the latex at the particular rate of shear. In the Brookfield synchro-lectric viscometer, a cylinder or disc is placed in the latex and rotated (at constant speed) through a beryllium–copper spring, the deflection of the spring being read on a dial. The Brookfield viscometer is widely used for both laboratory investigations and factory control of latex viscosity.

The Ferranti viscometer (Fig. 1.4) con-sists of two co-axial cylinders, the outer one being rotated at constant speed by a syn-chronous motor. When the viscometer is placed in latex, a torque is transmitted by the latex from the outer rotating cylinder to the inner cylinder. The latter is free to rotate against a calibrated spring with pointer and dial to show its angular de-flection.

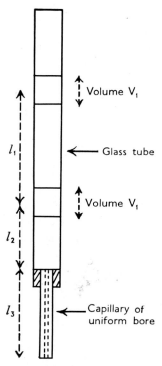

Fig. 1.3. Simple capillary viscometer for latex.

The dial readings in the Ferranti and Brookfield viscometers are multiplied by a numerical factor to obtain the viscosity of the latex in absolute units (poises). Both instruments are portable and are provided with cylinders of different diameters which may be rotated at three or more fixed speeds, thereby enabling a wide range of viscosities to be measured. The Ferranti viscometer has been designed to eliminate as far as possible viscous drag on the end of the rotating cylinder, thus en-suring uniform shear conditions.

A different principle is employed in the Hoppler viscometer, in which the time taken for a spherical ball of known radius to fall through a given height of latex is measured. The method is not so adaptable or accurate as those described above, but has been frequently used for determining the ratio of the viscosities of different latices.

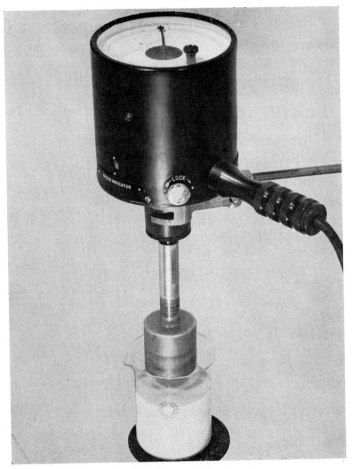

Fig. 1.4. Ferranti viscometer.

Surface tension

The surface tension of a latex is usually measured by the du Noüy ring method, in which the force required to pull a clean platinum–iridium ring out of the surface of the latex is determined. Other standard procedures for measuring surface tension, e.g. the Wilhelmy plate method,[35] can also be used satisfactorily.

The surface tension of pure water is 72 dynes/cm. Many soaps and synthetic detergents are capable of lowering this tension to 40 dynes/cm. or even less, provided the concentration of soap in solution is above a critical value, viz. the critical micellar concentration (cmc). The surface tension of 60% centrifuged natural latex is approximately 40 dynes/cm., while that of the synthetic latices may vary between 38 and 70 dynes/cm.

When the tension is higher than 60 dynes/cm., practically no free soap can be present in the aqueous phase—although considerable amounts will be adsorbed at the polymer–water interface to impart colloidal stability. Furthermore, the additional amount of soap or synthetic detergent necessary to lower the surface tension of the latex to about 40 dynes/cm. may be quite small, since the surface tension of soap or detergent solutions often decreases very rapidly with small increases in concentration, and the critical micellar concentration itself is usually small, e.g. less than 0·1 % for potassium oleate. Thus, even when the surface tension of a latex is very low, it should not be inferred that there is a considerable amount of " free " soap available for wetting out or stabilising finely divided powders. Whenever a latex is brought into contact with solids, liquids, or gases of large surface area, sufficient additional stabiliser should be present to prevent the transfer of soap from the rubber particles to the new interface, otherwise flocculation of the latex is liable to occur.

Particle size and size distribution

In natural as well as synthetic latices the particles have a shape sufficiently close to spherical for their dimensions to be characterised in terms of particle diameters. However, since the particles in any latex are not of uniform size, only an average diameter can be assigned to the particles as a whole. The term " average diameter " requires further explanation in that it can be defined in many ways, depending on the method of averaging, which itself depends on the relative statistical weights given to particles of different sizes. We shall consider here three average diameters: the number average (D_N), the weight average (D_W), and the volume to surface average diameter (D_S), defined as follows:

$$D_N = \frac{\Sigma n_i D_i}{\Sigma n_i}; \quad D_W = \left[\frac{\Sigma n_i D_i^6}{\Sigma n_i D_i^3}\right]^{\frac{1}{3}}; \quad D_S = \frac{\Sigma n_i D_i^3}{\Sigma n_i D_i^2}$$

In these expressions, n_i is the number of particles of diameter D_i. If all particles in a latex were of the same size, D_N, D_W and D_S would be the same. In actual latices D_W and D_S are often two or three times greater than D_N.

Four methods have been used successfully for determining the average particle size of latices, viz. electron microscopy, light scattering (turbidity), soap titration and rate of sedimentation of the particles.

The resolving power of an electron microscope enables all the particles of a latex sample to be photographed and measured, so that all the different average diameters referred to above can be calculated. In addition, the particle-size distribution can be determined. Distribution results are usually expressed either as an integral (i.e. cumulative) distribution curve or as a differential distribution curve (Fig. 1.5). The former shows directly the percentage by number, or by weight, of particles having diameters less than d_1, d_2, etc. The latter shows the relative proportions by number, or by weight, of particles having diameters d_1, d_2, etc. The differential distribution curve invariably has at least one maximum.

Determination of the rate of sedimentation or creaming of latex particles in a centrifuge, as described by Nisonoff, Messer and Howland,[36] gives D_W

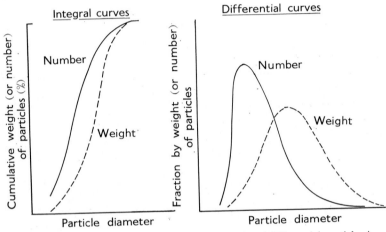

Fig. 1.5. Diagrammatic representation of integral and differential particle size distribution curves.

and the particle-weight distribution of the latex. D_N and the number-distribution curve can also be derived, as indeed can other averages and their distributions. The validity of Stokes Law for the rate of sedimentation of the particles is assumed in this method, which has the merit of simplicity.

In the soap titration method [37] the latex is titrated (at different concentrations) with a soap solution until a sharp break occurs in the surface tension or electrical conductivity of the system, corresponding to the critical micellar concentration of the soap in the aqueous phase of the latex. Provided the area occupied by each soap molecule adsorbed at the surface of the latex particles is known, D_S can be readily calculated. A modification of the method for use with natural latex has been described.[38]

Light-scattering measurements are capable of giving values of D_W in good agreement with those found by electron microscopy.[39,40] Neither the light-scattering nor the soap-titration method can be used to obtain particle-size distribution data unless the latex is first fractionated.

In comparing the average diameters of a number of latices, the type of average which is most useful will depend on the particular latex properties being considered. For example, if the adsorption of additional surface-active compounds on to the latex particles is of interest, then the volume to surface average diameter D_S is the most relevant. For many purposes, the weight average diameter is particularly important, since this average reflects more accurately than the others the size of the particles which constitute the bulk by weight of the rubber.

Film formation

Some of the oldest latex processes such as straight dipping and coating depend on the ability of the latex to form a coherent continuous film on evaporation. Other processes require the formation of continuous films on drying the latex after its shape has been set with a gelling agent. Film formation is thus a property of basic importance in natural and synthetic rubber latices.

No rigorous treatment of the problem of film formation from latices has yet been attempted, but approaches of a semi-quantitative nature have been made [41, 42, 43] which it will be useful to summarize. Some experimental facts to be accounted for are:

(1) Polymer latices which do not form continuous films can be rendered film-forming by plasticisation.

(2) Film formation is often enhanced by drying the latex at elevated temperatures, and by a slow rate of drying. These conditions can be achieved simultaneously by control of humidity.

(3) Formation of continuous films is favoured by a reduction in the particle size of the latex.

(4) Latices containing cross-linked polymers in which plastic flow is greatly reduced may still form continuous films.

The drying of a layer of latex can be considered in two stages: (a) loss of sufficient water to bring the particles into contact in a close-packed configuration, and (b) deformation of the particles with an increase in their area of contact, accompanied by further loss of water, leading to the formation of a continuous film. This does not imply that the individual particles need lose their identity completely. Indeed, electron-microscope photographs of dry latex films often show quite clearly the outlines of individual particles (Fig. 1.6). If the particles are flocculated during stage (a), they will not take up their closest possible packing, and discontinuities may occur in the dried film. This is one respect therefore in which the role of the stabiliser is important.

During stage (b) the forces required to deform the particles into a film arise as a result of the surface tension at the boundaries of the particles (this tension is a different one from that at the air–latex interface). For any curved surface of radius of curvature r and surface tension σ, the pressure on the concave side of the surface is greater than that on the convex side by an amount $P = \dfrac{2\sigma}{r}$.   In the case of fine pores or channels between the particles in a drying latex film, P may be of the order of several hundred kg./cm.^{2}.   This pressure difference across the walls of the pore has the effect of forcing the walls inwards, and hence forcing the liquid or vapour within the pore towards the top surface of the film.   Deformation of the particles comprising the pore walls may occur by means of plastic flow and/ or an elastic deformation, followed eventually by stress relaxation.   An expression for the rate of coalescence of uniform spherical particles by

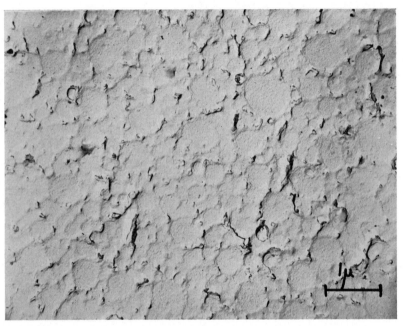

Fig. 1.6. Electron micrograph of uncompounded natural latex film dried at 50° C. Magnification × 15,000.

viscous flow has been derived by Frenkel,[43] in which the rate is directly proportional to the surface tension and inversely proportional to the viscosity and radius of the original particles.   Increase in temperature or addition of plasticiser would increase the rate of coalescence by reducing the viscosity of the polymer.

One of the factors influencing the tensile strength of the dried film is the extent to which the particles have merged together and eliminated small pores.   This explains why some polymer films show maximum tensile strength at critical plasticiser contents,[41] the reduction in the inherent viscosity or shear modulus of the polymer by *small* amounts of plasticiser being more than offset by the greater uniformity and coherence of the film. The closing of small pores with a corresponding increase in tensile strength may also be achieved, with some latices, by heating the dry or nearly dry film for short periods.

Colloidal stability

A colloidally stable latex can be defined as one in which no aggregation of the particles occurs under the conditions of test. In all commercial latices particle aggregation is prevented or retarded by an adsorbed film of one or more surface-active compounds surrounding the polymer particles. The molecules of surface-active compounds are characterised by possessing both polar (hydrophilic) groups and non-polar (hydrophobic) groups. Thus they have an affinity for both the polymer phase and the aqueous serum of a latex and satisfy these affinities by orienting themselves at the polymer–water interface.

The presence of an adsorbed film is not sufficient in itself to prevent rapid aggregation of the polymer particles. To do this, the film molecules must be ionised and/or strongly hydrated. Ionisable surface-active compounds may be of two types:

(1) $NP^-\ G^+\ (G^+ = Na^+,\ K^+,\ NH_4^+,\ \text{etc.})$, or
(2) $NP^+\ G^-\ (G^- = Cl^-,\ \frac{1}{2}SO_4^{--},\ \text{etc.})$

where N and P are the non-polar and polar groups of the surface-active ion, and G is the small counter-ion or gegenion which is not adsorbed appreciably. Compounds of type (1) are *anionic* stabilisers, and provide the polymer particles with a negative electric charge, while compounds of type (2) are *cationic* stabilisers which give a positive charge to the polymer particles. Non-ionisable or non-ionic surface-active compounds $NP(H_2O)_x$ owe their stabilising action to the strongly hydrated polar group(s). It will be appreciated that the ionised groups in stabilisers of types (1) and (2) are also hydrated. Some typical examples of the three classes of stabilisers are:

Anionic

Ammonium oleate, $C_{17}H_{33}COO^-NH_4^+$
Sodium cetyl sulphate, $C_{16}H_{33}SO_4^-Na^+$
Sodium dodecylbenzene sulphonate, $C_{12}H_{25} \cdot C_6H_4 \cdot SO_3^-Na^+$

Cationic

Dodecylamine hydrochloride, $C_{12}H_{25}NH_3^+Cl^-$
Cetyltrimethylammonium bromide, $C_{16}H_{33}N(CH_3)_3^+Br^-$

Non-ionic

Mono-oleylether of polyethylene glycol, $C_{17}H_{33}O(CH_2CH_2O)_nH$
Monododecyl ester of polyethylene glycol, $C_{12}H_{25}COO(CH_2CH_2O)_nH$
Monobutylphenyl ether of polyethylene glycol $C_4H_9C_6H_4O(CH_2CH_2O)_nH$

It is usually permissible to mix latices or dispersions containing non-ionic stabilisers with ones containing anionic or cationic stabilisers, but it is only under special conditions that systems containing oppositely charged stabilisers can be mixed.

Physical stability of latices

Stability towards high-speed stirring has been adopted as one of the standard test methods for natural latex. The mechanical stability as determined by this test can be greatly increased by the addition of 0·1–0·5% of a large number of anionic surfactants (Fig. 1.7). Increased

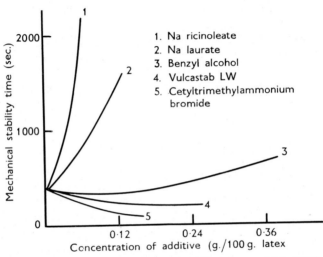

1. Na ricinoleate
2. Na laurate
3. Benzyl alcohol
4. Vulcastab LW
5. Cetyltrimethylammonium bromide

Fig. 1.7. Effect of surfactants on mechanical stability of natural latex (T.S. 59·5%, pH 10·3).

stability against frictional forces can be achieved in the same way. Non-ionic surfactants often decrease the mechanical stability of natural latex, while increasing its stability towards electrolytes. Natural and synthetic latices can be compounded readily with a wide range of water-insoluble solids and liquids which are normally first " wet-out ", dispersed, or emulsified. If the water content of the latex compound must be kept to a minimum, it is often possible to stir in the solids or liquids directly after first adding extra stabiliser to the latex. Fatty acid soaps, proteins, long-chain sulphates or sulphonates, polyethylene glycol ethers or esters, or formaldehyde condensation products, such as Daxad or Dispersol LN, are common additional stabilisers.

The stability of latices towards freezing, and especially intermittent freezing and thawing, is often very limited. High-molecular-weight colloidal materials, such as casein or copolymers of styrene with maleic anhydride, usually increase freeze–thaw stability.

Many organic liquids which are soluble in water coagulate latices due to dehydration of the adsorbed films.

Inorganic salts reduce the stability of positively or negatively charged latices by reducing the electrical repulsion between the particles. Even when the salt does not interact chemically with the adsorbed film of stabiliser, the attraction between the stabiliser ions and the oppositely charged ions of the salt has the effect of reducing the repulsion between the latex particles and thereby enhancing the probability of particle aggregation or coalescence. With negatively charged latices the destabilising effect of salts increases greatly with the valency of the positive salt ion.

Chemical stability

The addition to a latex of any reagent which alters the chemical nature of the adsorbed film affects the stability of the latex to a greater or less extent. If the reagent is one which precipitates an aqueous solution of the adsorbed material there is a very high probability that it will flocculate or coagulate the latex. Thus, latices stabilised with fatty acid or rosin soaps are coagulated by mineral acids or polyvalent metal salts. The free acids and polyvalent metal salts of long-chain alkyl sulphates or alkylarylsulphonates are often water-soluble, and latices containing these surfactants are more stable towards mineral acids and divalent metal ions than are latices containing fatty acid or rosin soaps. The destabilising effect of calcium and other polyvalent metal ions can be greatly reduced by adding to the latex sequestering agents, such as the sodium salt of ethylenediamine tetraacetic acid, which form uncharged or negatively charged complexes with the calcium ions. As would be expected, the stability of latices containing non-ionic surfactants is less affected by mineral acids and inorganic salts than is the stability of negatively charged latices.

Zinc oxide stability of natural latex

The stability of ammoniated natural latex towards zinc oxide is particularly important. When added to a latex in which it does not dissolve, zinc oxide behaves as a typical filler so far as stability is concerned. Even when a fixed alkali is present in sufficient amount to convert some of the zinc oxide into soluble zincate, the dissolved zinc does not influence appreciably the stability of a negatively charged latex, since the zincate ion (ZnO_2^{--}) is itself negatively charged. However, when zinc oxide is added to natural or any other latex containing ammonia, some of it goes into solution according to the equations:

$$ZnO + 2NH_3 + 2NH_4^+ \rightleftharpoons Zn(NH_3)_4^{++} + H_2O \quad . \quad . \quad (1.6)$$
$$Zn(NH_3)_4^{++} \rightleftharpoons Zn(NH_3)_x^{++} + (4\text{-}x)NH_3 \quad . \quad (1.7)$$

The positively charged zinc ammine ions reduce the stability of negatively charged latices, particularly when they are stabilised with soaps capable of forming insoluble salts with the zinc ammine ions, i.e.

$$Zn(NH_3)_x{}^{++} + 2R^- \longrightarrow Zn(NH_3)_x R_2 \quad . \quad . \quad . \quad (1.8)$$

where R^- is the soap ion. Destabilisation of the latex results in thickening or gelation, depending on the concentration of zinc in solution, the equilibrium between the different zinc ammine ions (eqn. 1.7) and the nature and concentration of the stabilisers in the latex. These three variables will now be considered in a little more detail.

The solubility of zinc oxide in ammoniated latex at pH values above about 8·0 increases with increase in (a) the free ammonia content and (b) the concentration of $NH_4{}^+$ ions, as would be expected from eqn. 1.6. Below pH 8·0, increasing amounts of zinc oxide dissolve in the form of simple zinc salts as the pH is reduced. The ammonium ions in eqn. 1.6 may be formed by dissociation of some of the ammonia, or ammonium salts may have been added to, or produced in, the latex. In any case, the ratio of the concentration of ammonium ions to undissociated (free) ammonia is approximately constant at a given pH and temperature, since

$$\frac{[NH_4{}^+]}{[NH_4OH]} = \frac{K}{[OH^-]} \quad . \quad . \quad . \quad . \quad (1.9)$$

where K is the dissociation constant of ammonia ($1·8 \times 10^{-5}$ at $20°$ C). Thus, in any latex at pH 9·25, where $[OH^-] = 1·8 \times 10^{-5}$, there will be equal concentrations of ammonium ions and free ammonia. Although the latter will be present almost entirely as ammonium hydroxide, it may be expressed as NH_3 for convenience.

Provided the total concentration of $(NH_3 + NH_4{}^+)$ is kept constant, eqn. 1.6 implies that the concentration of dissolved zinc will be a maximum when $[NH_3] = [NH_4{}^+]$, i.e. at pH 9·25 *after* addition of the zinc oxide. Such a maximum has been observed experimentally by van den Tempel [44] (Fig. 1.8).

In natural latex, the total concentration of free ammonia and ammonium ions approximates very closely to the total alkalinity as determined by standard methods, while the ratio of NH_3 to $NH_4{}^+$ depends on the pH of the latex in accordance with eqn. 1.9. The solubility of zinc oxide in commercial concentrates (60% DRC) preserved with 0·7% ammonia rarely exceeds 0·5 g./100 g. latex, which is substantially smaller than the zinc oxide content of most latex compounds.

The destabilising power of zinc oxide depends not only on the concentration of dissolved zinc but also on the relative proportions of the different zinc ammine ions which are formed according to the equilibrium expressed in eqn. 1.7. Whereas the zinc tetrammine ion $Zn(NH_3)_4{}^{++}$ is a relatively weak coagulant for natural latex, at least some of the lower zinc ammine ions such as $Zn(NH_3)_2^{++}$ are very powerful coagulants.[45] The dissociation of zinc tetrammine ions into the lower zinc ammine ions is promoted by an increase in temperature, and it is primarily for this reason that the coagulating power of zinc oxide increases rapidly with temperature.

Application of the Law of Mass Action to eqn. 1.7 shows that the fraction of the dissolved zinc which is present as lower zinc ammine ions increases

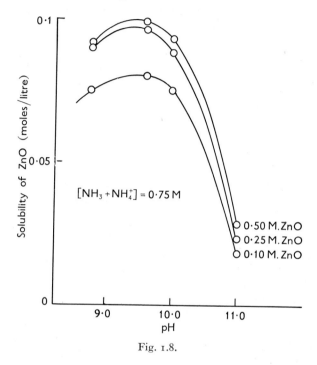

Fig. 1.8.

as the free ammonia content of the latex is reduced. If this is achieved by converting some NH_3 into NH_4^+, e.g. by addition of sodium silicofluoride, the actual concentration of lower zinc ammine ions will be greater than if the same reduction in free ammonia content is obtained by blowing off the ammonia, or by removing it with formaldehyde, since the total concentration of dissolved zinc is maintained at a higher level in the first process. The addition of fixed alkali to ammoniated latex increases the ratio of NH_3 to NH_4^+ in accordance with eqn. 1.9, thereby reducing both the relative concentration and actual concentration of lower zinc ammine ions, with a resulting reduction in the coagulating power of the dissolved zinc.

The nature and concentration of the stabiliser in a latex is no less important than the concentration of lower zinc ammine ions in determining its stability towards zinc oxide. Many synthetic surfactants which do not form insoluble zinc ammine salts, e.g. Igepon T (sodium salt of 2-(N-oleyl-N-methylamino) ethylsulphonic acid) [46] and numerous non-ionic surfactants,[47] markedly increase the zinc oxide stability of ammoniated latices over a wide range of experimental conditions. Fatty acid soaps may cause an increase or decrease in zinc oxide stability, depending on the structure and concentration of the soap,[48] as well as on the temperature and pH of the latex.[46] Newnham [49] has studied the surface tensions of a number of common fatty acid soaps, in the presence of zinc ammonium salts, as a function of pH. His results indicate that the solubilities of the soaps decrease rapidly as the pH is reduced below a limiting value which varies from pH 9 to pH 10 according to the nature of the soap. The amount of soap in solution also decreases with increasing temperature, due to the formation of reactive lower zinc ammine ions (eqn. 1.7) which precipitate the soap.

Gelation of latex compounds

During the manufacture of shaped articles directly from natural or synthetic latices by moulding or dipping, the latex compound must be converted from a fluid to a gel state possessing sufficient rigidity to retain its shape during subsequent processing. Gelation is a type of coagulation in which no gross separation of aqueous phase occurs during formation of the gel, i.e. the three-dimensional network of aggregated rubber particles constituting the framework of the fresh gel occupies essentially the same volume as the fluid latex from which it was formed. If the energy of adhesion between contiguous rubber particles in the network is large and the number of contiguous particles per unit volume is also large, permanent deformation or rupture will not occur readily when the gel is subjected to stresses. Such systems are said to possess good wet gel strength —a characteristic which is of primary importance in many latex processes. It is largely because of its excellent wet gel strength that natural latex can be used in such a wide variety of latex applications.

The destabilising agents most commonly used to gel latex compounds are acetic or formic acid, calcium salts, zinc ammonium salts formed *in situ* in the latex, sodium silicofluoride (Na_2SiF_6) and certain water-soluble polymeric ethers. The action of simple acids and salts in destabilising negatively charged latices has already been referred to. The action of sodium silicofluoride which is widely used as a gelling agent for latex foam is more complex. Its solubility in water at room temperature is a little less than 1%, and it is added to the latex as an aqueous dispersion. In a typical natural latex foam compound sufficient silicofluoride dissolves and hydrolyses to gel the compound in a few minutes (in the presence of zinc oxide). Hydrolysis of the dissolved silicofluoride occurs in accordance with the equation [50]

$$2Na^+ + SiF_6^{--} + 4H_2O \rightleftharpoons 2Na^+ + 4H^+ + 6F^- + Si(OH)_4$$

Both the hydrofluoric and silicic acid formed by hydrolysis contribute towards gelation of the latex.[51] A decrease in the particle size of the silico-fluoride dispersion increases the rate at which it dissolves in the latex, and thereby increases the rate of gelation. The addition of neutral salts, such as sodium or potassium chloride, decreases the rate of gelation by reducing the solubility of the silicofluoride in the latex [50] (Fig. 1.9). Potassium

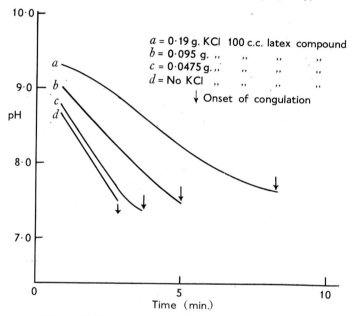

Fig. 1.9. Effect of KCl on rate of pH change in a latex compound containing Na silicofluoride.

salts are particularly effective because of the lower solubility of potassium silicofluoride as compared with sodium silicofluoride. With natural latex compounds, containing zinc oxide and ammonia, gelation normally occurs when sufficient acid has been liberated to reduce the pH value of the compound to about 8·3. Gelation is not due entirely, however, to liberation of hydrofluoric and silicic acid. Ammonium fluoride produced by hydrolysis of the silico-fluoride reacts with the zinc oxide and ammonia to form zinc ammonium ions, which assist in the destabilisation of the latex.

Two water-soluble polymeric ethers which are used for gelling natural latex compounds are polyvinyl methyl ether (PVME) [52] and polypropylene glycol (PPG).[53] Both are typical heat-sensitive gelling agents, i.e. they destabilise the latex only at elevated temperatures. When added to a latex compound, some of the PVME or PPG is adsorbed at the surface of the rubber particles, but the stability of the latex at room temperature is not appreciably reduced, since the adsorbed film of polymeric ether is strongly hydrated. On raising the temperature, however, dehydration of the ether film takes place, with a consequent decrease in the colloidal stability of the latex. To obtain a firm gel, the latex compound must be " sensitised " by addition of zinc oxide and/or a reduction in the ammonia content of the latex. High concentrations of other surface-active agents in the latex can greatly reduce the gelling efficiency of the polymeric ethers, probably by being preferentially adsorbed on the rubber particles.

Wet-gel strength

The strength and other mechanical properties (modulus, creep, etc.) of a latex gel depend on numerous factors, including the physical characteristics of the rubber component, the rubber content of the gel, the nature of the latex stabilisers, the conditions of gelation, etc. It is more significant, however, to consider the properties of the gels in terms of two basic quantities: (a) the total area of contact between particles per unit volume of gel, and (b) the specific adhesion energy of the particles, i.e. the energy of adhesion per unit area of true contact.

Freshly formed latex gels are not stable, and the gel network gradually contracts with the expulsion of water. This process, which is called synaeresis, causes an increase in gel strength due (at least partly) to an increase in the total area of contact between particles. This area may also increase as a result of plastic flow within the particles, as described in the section on film formation. Increases in wet-gel strength resulting from increases in the DRC of a latex can be attributed to the same cause.

The specific adhesion energy depends on the nature of the interfaces in contact, which may be polymer–polymer, polymer–colloid or colloid–colloid. The fact that latices whose compositions differ only in respect of the colloidal stabiliser often show appreciable differences in wet-gel strength indicates that at least part of the interfaces in contact, in the gel, consists of a film of colloid. De Vries and van den Tempel [54] consider this type of contact to be of predominating importance in fresh gels of natural latex. Evidence suggesting that polymer–polymer contacts are also important is provided by the reduction in wet-gel strength caused by cross-linking of the rubber in natural latex, and by the large differences in gel strength of different polymer latices stabilised with the same, or similar, surfactants. With many polymers it has been shown that diffusion of chain segments across the interfacial boundary can be a major factor in determining the specific adhesion energy.[55] For strong adhesion it is necessary that some restraint should operate to oppose removal of the chain segments back across the interface when the system is appropriately stressed. For polymers which crystallise under tension, inclusion of the chain segments in microcrystalline regions of the polymer may provide the above restraint.[56]

Vulcanisation of latex compounds

In the manufacture of vulcanised latex products the commonest procedure is to compound the latex with aqueous dispersions of the vulcanising components and other water-insoluble ingredients which may be required, e.g fillers, antioxidants, pigments, etc. Water-soluble ingredients of the latex compound will normally be added as aqueous solutions. The position and shape of the latex compound is then set and the product vulcanised after or during drying—except in the production of latex foam, which is vulcanised before the removal of any water. The procedure of compounding latex with vulcanising components and effecting vulcanisation after setting the shape and position of the latex compound is termed post-vulcanisation. The mechanism of vulcanisation in dry rubber compounds is discussed in Chapter XII, and identical mechanisms probably apply to latex products post-vulcanised after drying, provided the same type of vulcanising system is considered, e.g. sulphur, zinc oxide and a dithiocarbamate accelerator.

Since forming and setting the shape of a latex compound does not involve milling or any other treatment which would develop high temperatures locally, there is no danger of " scorch " and ultra-rapid accelerators can be used. They enable vulcanisation to be carried out at relatively low temperatures ($100°–120°$ C) in a reasonably short time. Low vulcanisation temperatures are generally preferred, rather than extra rapid cures, because of lower heating costs and the reduced risk of oxidative degradation.

Articles from natural, SBR, or nitrile latices are cured in a very similar manner. Almost invariably, sulphur is used in combination with zinc oxide as an activator and with one or more accelerators. With the same vulcanising ingredients, SBR latices cure a little more slowly than natural latex, and larger amounts of accelerator, with at least 2% of sulphur on the weight of polymer, are usually required. " Cold " SBR latices, however, tend to cure more rapidly than the " hot " types. Dithiocarbamates are probably the most widely used accelerators for natural, SBR, and nitrile latices. They produce a rapid cure at $100°$ C, show very little tendency to " overcure ", and give products with good ageing resistance. Thiazoles are slower accelerators than the dithiocarbamates, but are frequently used as activators for the latter, when products of relatively high modulus and good ageing characteristics are required. The zinc salt of mercaptobenzothiazole is widely used in conjunction with zinc diethyldithiocarbamate in latex foam compounds. The tendency shown by some of the thiazoles to destabilise and thicken natural latex compounds can be offset by the addition of stabilisers. Thiuram sulphide accelerators are usually intermediate in activity between the dithiocarbamates and the thiazoles. They produce vulcanisates of high tensile strength and good ageing properties. Thiuram polysulphides, i.e. the disulphides or tetrasulphides, can be used as vulcanising agents without the addition of further sulphur. The thiuram sulphides cause very little discoloration or odour and are used for the production of such articles as drug sundries.

The basic vulcanising agent for neoprene latices is zinc oxide in amounts of from 5 to 15%, or even more, on the weight of polymer. Besides acting as a vulcanising agent, zinc oxide combines with the hydrochloric acid which is slowly liberated from polychloroprene rubbers; it also improves the ageing and heat resistance of the rubbers. The use of approximately 1% of sulphur as a secondary vulcanising agent increases the rate of cure and reduces the tendency of neoprene products to harden with age. Some of the conventional accelerators for natural latex also increase the rate of cure of neoprene latex and improve its physical properties. Thus, thiocarbanilide as accelerator gives products of high modulus. The use of tetramethylthiuram disulphide and sodium dibutyldithiocarbamate, in combination, yields products of very high tensile strength with relatively low modulus.[57] Other accelerators sometimes used in neoprene latex compounds are zinc dibutyldithiocarbamate and polymerised p-dinitrosobenzene. Even with accelerated systems, neoprene must be cured at temperatures above 100° C to obtain optimum physical properties for many applications, and curing is usually carried out at 120°–140° C.

Pre-vulcanised latex

It has been known for many years that the addition of sulphur, zinc oxide and accelerator to natural latex caused cross-linking of the rubber within the individual latex particles. When such cross-linking is slight and the latex product is post-cured by conventional means, the pre-cure step is often referred to as a maturing process. When the pre-cure is considerable the latex is classed as a pre-vulcanised latex, although additional cross-linking normally occurs during drying of the finished article. Such latices are widely employed in the dipping and casting industries, where their use eliminates a compounding and post-vulcanising operation.

Pre-vulcanised latex is prepared by heating the latex with sulphur, zinc oxide, and an ultra-accelerator for about 2 hours at 70° C. Dispersions of the vulcanising ingredients should be of a particle size small enough to prevent rapid settling but large enough to enable unreacted sulphur, accelerator and especially zinc oxide to be removed by centrifuging after completion of vulcanisation. This can be achieved by passing aqueous suspensions of the ingredients through a colloid mill. The accelerators used are normally of the dithiocarbamate type. The zinc oxide and ammonia content of the latex are important, since zinc ammonium salts formed during the vulcanisation have a destabilising influence on the latex, which can be offset, however, by the addition of suitable stabilisers. Nevertheless, low proportions of zinc oxide, e.g. 0·5 %, are preferred. The combined sulphur content of commercially vulcanised latex is usually about 1·0%. Changes in the physical characteristics of the latex take place for several days after vulcanisation and centrifuging, but are almost complete after a week's storage.

Dried films of properly pre-vulcanised natural latex are comparable in tensile strength and modulus with post-vulcanised films prepared with the same vulcanising ingredients.[58] One of the advantages claimed for pre-vulcanised latex is that effective control of ultimate physical properties can be exercised before articles are actually manufactured from it. Disadvantages are that the wet-gel strength of the latex is not so high as that of unvulcanised latex and that the resistance of pre-vulcanised latex articles to hydrocarbon solvents is often inferior to that of post-vulcanised products.[59]

Although sulphur, zinc oxide, and accelerator are normally used to pre-vulcanise latex, effective pre-vulcanisation can also be obtained by the use of dicumyl peroxide, albeit at high temperatures. Dried films from such latex have a high clarity and good ageing characteristics. γ- or β-irradiation of natural latex can produce a similar pre-vulcanisation to that obtained with dicumyl peroxide.

REFERENCES

1. Homans, L. N. S. and van Gils, G. E. (1948) *Proc. Second Rubber Tech. Conf.*, 292.
2. Cook, A. S. and Sekhar, B. C. (1953) *J. Rubb. Res. Inst. Malaya*, **14**, 163.
3. Baker, H. C. (1940–41), *I.R.I. Trans.*, **16**, 165.
4. Archer, B. L. and Sekhar, B. C. (1955) *Biochem. J.*, **61**, 503.
5. Archer, B. L. and Cockbain, E. G. (1955) *ibid.*, **61**, 508.
6. Verghese, G. T. (1948–49) *I.R.I. Trans.*, **24**, 138.
7. Bloomfield, G. F. (1951) *J. Rubb. Res. Inst. Malaya*, **13** (Communication 273).
8. Bloomfield, G. F. (1951) *ibid.*, **13** (Communications 271, 272).
9. Smith, R. H. (1953) *ibid.*, **14**, 169.
10. Baker, H. C. (1942) *I.R.I. Trans.*, **18**, 115.
11. Tunnicliffe, M. E. (1954) *ibid.*, **30**, 97.
12. van den Tempel, M. (1953) *ibid.*, **29**, 312.
13. Madge, E. W., Collier, H. M. and Peel, J. D. (1950) *I.R.I. Trans.*, **26**, 305.
14. Philpott, M. W. and Westgarth, D. R. (1953) *J. Rubb. Res. Inst. Malaya*, **14**, 133.
15. Philpott, M. W. and Sekhar, K. C. (1953) *ibid.*, **14**, 93.
16. Cook, A. S. and Sekhar, K. C. (1954) *ibid.*, **14**, 407.
17. McGavack, J. and Bevilacqua, E. M. (1951) *Ind. Eng. Chem.*, **43**, 475.
18. Collier, H. M. (1955) *I.R.I. Trans.*, **31**, 166.
19. Philpott, M. W. (1958) *Rubb. Developm.*, **11**, No. 2, 47.

20. Whitby, G. S. *et al.* (1954) *Synthetic Rubber* (New York: John Wiley and Sons).
21. *High Polymers* Vol. 10 (1955) (Emulsion Polymerisation), Bovey, Kolthoff, Medalia and Meehan (Interscience).
22. Walker, H. W. and Mochel, W. E. (1948) *Proc. Second Rubb. Tech. Conf.*, London, 69.
23. Mochel, W. E. and Nichols, J. B. (1951) *Ind. Eng. Chem.*, **43**, 154.
24. Foster, F. C. and Binder, J. L. (1953) *J. Amer. chem. Soc.*, **75**, 2910.
25. Beatty, J. R. and Zwicker, B. M. G. (1952) *Ind. Eng. Chem.*, **44**, 742.
26. B.P. 758622 (1956) *Rubb. Age Lond.*, **80**, 114.
27. Krieger, I. M. and Maron, S. H. (1951) *J. Colloid Sci.*, **6**, 528.
28. Maron, S. H., Madow, B. P. and Krieger, I. M. (1951) *ibid.*, **6**, 584.
29. Maron, S. H. and Madow, B. P. (1953) *ibid.*, **8**, 130.
30. Maron, S. H. and Fok, S. M. (1955) *ibid.*, **10**, 482.
31. Maron, S. H. and Levy-Pascal, A. E. (1955) *ibid.*, **10**, 494.
32. Maron, S. H. *et al.* (1956) *ibid.*, **11**, 80; (1957) **12**, 99.
33. *Rheology; Theory and Applications* (1956) Vol. 1, Chapter 14 (Academic Press).
34. Maron, S. H., Krieger, I. M. and Sisko, A. W. (1954) *J. Appl. Physics*, **25**, 971.
35. Bikerman, J. J. (1958) *Surface Chemistry*, 2nd edition, Chapter 1 (Academic Press).
36. Nisonoff, A., Messer, W. E. and Howland, L. H. (1954) *Analytical Chem.*, **26**, 856.
37. Maron, S. H., Elder, M. E. and Ulevitch, I. N. (1954) *J. Colloid Sci.*, **9**, 89.
38. Cockbain, E. G. (1952) *I.R.I. Trans.*, **28**, 297.
39. Dandliker, W. B. (1950) *J. Amer. chem. Soc.*, **72**, 5110.
40. Burnett, G. M., Lehrle, R. S., Ovenall, D. W. and Peaker, F. W. (1958) *J. pol. Sci.*, **29**, 417.
41. Dillon, R. E., Matheson, L. A. and Bradford, E. B. (1951) *J. Colloid Sci.*, **6**, 108.
42. Henson, W. A., Taber, D. A. and Bradford, E. B. (1953) *Ind. Eng. Chem.*, **45**, 735.
43. Frenkel, J. (1943) *J. Phys. (U.S.S.R.)*, **9**, 385.
44. van den Tempel, M. (1955) *I.R.I. Trans.*, **31**, 33.
45. McRoberts, T. S. (1954) *Proc. Third Rubber Tech. Conf.*, 38.
46. Kraay, G. M. and Van den Tempel, M. (1952) *I.R.I. Trans.*, **28**, 144.
47. Flint, C. F. (1948) *Proc. Second Rubber Tech. Conf.*, 312.
48. Madge, E. W., Collier, H. M. and Newnham, J. L. M. (1954) *Proc. Third Rubber Tech. Conf.*, 67.
49. Newnham, J. L. M. (1953) *I.R.I. Trans.*, **29**, 160.
50. Twiss, D. F. and Amphlett, P. H. (1940) *J. Soc. Chem. Ind.*, **59**, 202.
51. Madge, E. W. and Pounder, D. W. (1947) *I.R.I. Trans.*, **23**, 94.
52. Cockbain, E. G. (1956) *I.R.I. Trans.*, **32**, 97.
53. Pole, E. G. and Cockbain, E. G. (1957) *Rubb. Developm.*, **10** (No. 2), 48.
54. De Vries, A. J. and van den Tempel, M. (1953) *Proc. 2nd Int. Congress on Rheology*, p. 291 (London: Butterworth, 1954).
55. Deryagin, B. V., Zherebkov, S. K. and Medvedeva, A. M. (1957) *Rubber Chem. Technol.*, **30**, 837.
56. Belorossova, A. G., Farberov, M. I. and Epshtein, V. G. (1956) *Koll. Zhur.*, **18**, 145.
57. Walsh, R. H. (1954) *Vanderbilt Latex Handbook*, p. 42.
58. Sutton, S. D. (1951) *I.R.I. Trans.*, **27**, 193.
59. Humphreys, N. C. H. and Wake, W. C. (1950), *I.R.I. Trans.*, **25**, 334.

CHAPTER I

PART TWO

MANUFACTURE OF ARTICLES FROM NATURAL AND SYNTHETIC LATICES

by

E. W. MADGE

Natural rubber latex

THE broad foundations of the latex manufacturing industry based on natural rubber latex were laid in the late 1920s and early 1930s. The vigorous research and development policy in the consuming countries, particularly in the United Kingdom, was matched by the coincident development of latex concentrate production in the producing countries, especially in Malaya. Centrifuged latex started to become available in relatively small quantities in 1928, and such was the rate of progress that the first bulk shipment to the United Kingdom was made in 1931. Latex manufacture in the United Kingdom is based principally on centrifuged latex, with Revertex supplying a smaller and more restricted requirement. In Europe some creamed concentrate is consumed, and in the U.S.A. a much larger proportion of creamed concentrate. Currently the largest proportion of world production of latex concentrate is by centrifuging. The amount of normal latex consumed, i.e. unconcentrated latex, is not large.

One large latex producer shipped for its own consumption appreciable quantities of latex concentrated by electrodecantation.

The world latex industry consumed approximately 162,000 long tons dry of natural rubber latex in 1957. Although this represents only 9·4% of the solid natural rubber consumption, this percentage is important as it represents a group of manufactures that cannot use normal rubber manufacturing methods. In standard rubber manufacture the raw material is received as a solid in the form of a tough rather intractable coagulum as crêpe, sheet, or slab. To produce articles the coagulum requires to be plasticised, shaped, and finally set to retain the shaped form. The plasticising, which is done principally by mechanical action and requires heavy machinery, reduces the molecular weight of the original coagulum. The average molecular weight of the raw coagulum may be taken as approximately 500,000 and approximately 100,000 after masticating. This is an oversimplification, but gives an idea of the orders of magnitude involved.[1]

The latex manufacturing industry, on the other hand, cuts out the intermediate step of producing the raw coagulum which has to be broken down, and arranges so that its products are made directly in the form of shaped coagula from the original fluid aqueous dispersion. This leads to advantages and disadvantages.

Advantages

1. Direct manufacture from latex gives a rubber of the highest molecular weight. This, other things being equal, leads to optimum physical properties in the final rubber.

2. Vulcanising, filling and conditioning ingredients are incorporated into a fluid. This does not involve heat and the use of heavy machinery.

3. Since heavy machinery is not required, a lower capital outlay is possible.

Disadvantages

1. In the direct manufacture of articles from latex the coagulated product contains water and must be dried. This drying limits the thickness and shape of the articles that can be made. The story of the latex industry is partly of how these limitations are circumvented.

2. It is still not possible to reinforce latex rubber with carbon black and other reinforcing fillers in the same way that it can be done with dry rubber. It has been shown [2] that at least part of the reinforcing action is concerned with the formation of free radicals at the chain ends of the rubber molecules during mechanical scission. The absence of a masticating process, therefore, precludes the possibility of normal reinforcement. As a result, special methods of reinforcement have been developed which are referred to later. These relate chiefly to reinforcement of hardness and modulus. Whether methods can ultimately be developed to reinforce with respect to abrasion has yet to be decided.

Comparison between latex mixings and solutions of rubber in organic solvent is also instructive, particularly when it is necessary to consider them in similar fields of application.

Rubber solutions are generally prepared from masticated rubber, and usually the solvents used are inflammable. For a given viscosity the total solids of a rubber solution are generally low. The outstanding characteristic is that of tack and ability to cement impervious surfaces, particularly rubber surfaces.

In contradistinction, latex mixings have a high total solids content for a given viscosity, are non-inflammable, and have special merit for the cementing of porous surfaces.

Direct manufacture of articles from rubber latex

This is logically concerned with the various ways of forming the co-agulum. The most important of these are:

1. By drying.
2. By ionic coagulation.
3. By hot or cold gelling.

(1) Direct manufacture from latex in which in the finished article the coagulum is formed by drying

Although this approach may seem to be somewhat elementary, it is surprising how many products are made by the employment of simple drying as the method by which the rubber phase is changed from the disperse to the continuous.

The processes under this main heading group themselves as follows:

(a) Impregnation and coating.
(b) Textile treatment other than under (a).
(c) General adhesives.
(d) Dipping.
(e) Rubberised hair.

(a) *Impregnation and coating.* In these applications the dried-out latex film functions as a binder, proofing agent and gap filler. Initially natural rubber latex was used extensively for proofing fabrics and impregnating paper, but the drawbacks of discoloration and surface drag have made these fields more the prerogative of synthetic latices, including those made from plastic materials.

A material that easily wets a fabric or cellulosic base layer will readily strike through the fabric. This is undesirable and has been prevented in two ways: (a) by giving the fabric a first skim coat of a rubber solution which does not strike through because of its viscosity; (b) by increasing the viscosity of the latex by foaming. The latter is practised on a large scale for combining fabrics, e.g. shoe cloths, where not only is a flexible bond obtained but also the combined cloth is itself porous.

In the manufacture of artificial suedes and other pile fabrics latex has been used as the adherent layer to which selected fibres are applied. It has not, however, completely replaced solution coatings, partly because of the difficulty of the correct control of tack and partly because in the electrostatic variation of such processes difficulties associated with the water

c

content were introduced.   Nevertheless, artificial suedes that " breathed " were produced experimentally by the use of a foamed latex as the adhesive coat to which the fibres were applied.

Natural latex has been widely used for rug and felt backing and in various types of carpet construction.   Its use has facilitated mass production of carpet, for example, of the type used in automobiles, and has led to economies in manufacture.

By the use of a latex binder the carpet tufts are stuck to a base fabric or are secured adhesively instead of being mechanically locked in the weave. As a result, carpets of this type can be cut to shape without the need for edge binding.   This is important for many transport applications.   There are various systems for producing a pile stuck to a base fabric or adhesively secured through its interstices.   It will be appreciated, however, that the very nature of the weaves used demands a latex of considerable viscosity, and in view of the gap-filling characteristics required, ability to take a high loading readily is also an advantage.   Revertex has, therefore, been widely used in carpet applications, but reclaim dispersions, often in admixture with latex, have also been extensively employed.   Cheaper felts which are backed with latex or reclaim compositions to lock the fibres usually employ heavily loaded compounds.   This also applies to the compounds applied to various types of rugs.   Apart from cost reduction, the deadness so achieved is advantageous in allowing the product to lie flat.   Non-slip characteristics are simultaneously obtained.

Foamed latices are also used in carpet construction and for the backing of various types of fabric in a similar way to loaded unfoamed latex mixings. Not only is air the cheapest filler that can be used but if the foam is used in the required thickness it adds its own resilience to the ensemble, and a composite construction is produced consisting of an upper carpet layer integrally united with its own sponge underlay.

(b) *Textile treatments other than those covered in* (a).   Of these the most important is that for cord for pneumatic tyres and for other rubber/ textile bonding where good adhesion between rubber and textile is required.   Natural latex is still extensively used, although synthetic latices have a special place in this field.   For tyre cord bonding natural latex is normally used in conjunction with an auxiliary adhesive, such as casein or a resorcinol resin.   Although formulations containing natural latex, whole cover reclaim and casein were widely used some years ago, most of them have now been superseded by formulations containing resorcinol resin.

The resorcinol resin is preformed in aqueous solution from resorcinol and formaldehyde activated by a small amount of caustic soda and mixed with the latex to form the finished dip.   In typical formulations the ratio of latex rubber to resorcinol is about 4 to 1.   The tyre cord is dipped into the prepared bath and the amount of pick-up carefully controlled.   After drying the treated cord is ready for " rubbering " and all the subsequent processes of tyre manufacture. Natural latex does not itself contribute appreciably to the static bond, but it has two functions of considerable importance. It imparts appreciable " green stick " to the treated cord, so that in pocket making and other operations rubber is not readily detached from the cord. It also has a marked influence on the dynamic adhesion, that is on the fatigue resistance of the bond. Moreover, for certain textiles, particularly cotton and rayon, an aqueous dip enables a tension-controlled stretch to be achieved during the dipping operation which reduces the elongation of the finished cord.

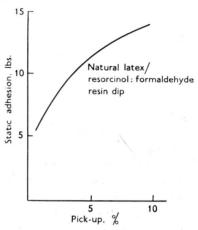

Fig. 1.10. Effect of pick-up on bond strength (rayon cord).

Fig. 1.10 shows the effect of varying the amount of pick-up of the dip on the bond strengths obtained.

A second textile application of a totally different type is the production of bonded non-woven fabrics. In this a carded web, usually of cotton, but rayon or other fibres can be used, is bonded by rubber latex. Natural rubber latex and synthetic rubber latices are used, the latter where resistance to dry-cleaning solvents is required. There appears to be some advantage in the extra flexibility imparted to the bond by the rubber latex, although bonded fabrics using other bonding agents, such as polyvinyl acetate emulsions, are also produced.

(c) *General adhesives.* A latex-based adhesive is of special value for cementing porous surfaces, chiefly on account of its ability to wet them. These surfaces, because of their porosity, allow the latex adhesive to dry out, thereby producing a strong, coherent film. Additives which are adhesives in their own right in aqueous systems, such as sodium silicate, glue, albumin, gums, starch, etc., are normally compatible with natural rubber latex, and usually have a stabilising action. The latex rubber in the adhesive film imparts flexibility and strength and protects the bond against dynamic fatigue.

One of the large users of latex-based adhesives is the shoe industry, where both temporary and permanent latex cements are employed. Although aqueous dispersions of solvents are sometimes added to latex to promote an after-tack in the dried film, extensive use has not yet been made of the inversion of such compositions by alcohol, which results in a high-viscosity rubber solution containing water as the disperse phase. The film from such a solution is exceptionally strong, as the rubber has not been masticated.

(*d*) *Dipping*.   This is one of the oldest applications of latex.   This is not surprising, as the original development consisted of the substitution with many advantages of latex in place of rubber solutions.   Dipping processes in which the film is formed by drying are chiefly used for the production of thin-walled articles.   Only articles of regular and simple shape are capable of being produced in this way.   As the products are thin, special care is taken in the preparation of the latex compound and in the avoidance of contamination during processing.   High-quality latex supplies are essential.   The deposit thickness depends on many physical factors of the latex mixing, e.g. viscosity, total solids, temperature and on other process factors, such as withdrawal rate, and nature and temperature of former.

In this type of production the biggest advances have been in machine and production development, and a substantial degree of automatic handling has been achieved.

(*e*) *Rubberised hair*.   Although this application can be considered as a further example of a bonded fabric, it has the important difference that probably the largest consumption of such materials is in moulded form. Both spraying and an immersion and teasing-out process have been employed in this manufacture, the former chiefly for sheet, the latter primarily for shaped products.   The resilience of the product arises both from the springy nature of the curled fibre used and the resilient nature of the bonding medium.

A stable rubber latex has for many years been used to lock the hair at cross-over points, and this bond is usually achieved by simple drying and vulcanisation.   In recent years other synthetic materials have been employed in auxiliary ways.

For upholstery rubberised hair has chiefly been employed in applications where the load-carrying demands are not high, e.g. in arm-rests, back squabs and so on.   Its other large application is in the protective packing of instruments, radio equipment, etc., because of its shock-absorbing characteristics and ability to be moulded to shape.

(2) Direct manufacture from latex in which the coagulum is formed by ionic coagulation

The introduction of a positive ionic coagulating system enables thicker articles to be produced than those in which the film was formed merely by drying.   The thickness, however, is still limited by the diffusion rate of the coagulant used, and this process again is a rate process.

The two most important processes using ionic coagulation are:

(*a*) dipping;

(*b*) extrusion.

The electrodeposition process in which a latex coagulum was formed on an anode by the migration of coagulating ions outwards under the influence of an electric current is of little importance today. It had special application to the deposition of a uniform film on difficult shapes, but in general could not compete in cost with alternative methods. The apotheosis of the electrodeposition process has been the electrodecantation process for the concentration of natural rubber latex and of certain synthetic latices.

(a) *Dipping*. The ionic coagulants used may be employed internally or externally. That is they may be applied to the former before dipping in the latex and/or the former carrying the deposit may be immersed in an external coagulant in order to set the deposit. The coagulants employed are normally volatile and based on alcohol/water mixtures of formic or acetic acids. The pre-treated former method is usually preferred for economic reasons. These coagulants have been used ever since coagulant dipping processes were first developed, and although a cyclohexylamine acetate/alcohol coagulant has been used more recently in certain cases, it has not generally superseded the earlier types.

A coagulant on a former has two functions. Its presence prevents the close approach of the individual latex particle to the former surface, and thereby facilitates subsequent stripping. It enables a more uniform deposit to be obtained, even on complicated shapes, as the film, due to its initial positive formation by the coagulant, is less affected by drainage.

The positively charged cations of the coagulant neutralise the negatively charged latex particles and bring about their coalescence. The coagulation is instantaneous in the immediate neighbourhood of the former, but diminishes both in rate and degree as distance from the former increases. Consequently the useful dwell time of the former in the latex bath is limited, and hence the total realisable thickness of deposit per dip. The skill of the latex technologist in recent years has been directed to a controlled destabilisation of the latex, so that for equal conditions of viscosity and total solids a maximum deposit weight per dip can be obtained. This is of considerable economic importance for thicker dipped articles.

Coagulant dipping processes are used for toy balloon manufacture and inflatable goods of many kinds and for a variety of glove types. These include surgeons' gloves, household gloves, industrial gloves, electricians' gloves, and variations in which the latex deposit is coagulated on a knitted-fabric base. Electricians' gloves and certain other dipped goods are required to have a minimum water absorption and to have recognised standards of insulation wet and dry. This necessitates careful washing procedures at certain stages in the dipping process to ensure the removal of electrolytes from the coagulum.

The production of seamless latex boots and other footwear by coagulant dipping methods has been one of the largest single commercial applications of such processes.

As in the more restricted non-coagulant dipping processes, the modern development has been chiefly in machine design and on the production side. The processes have been made semi-automatic, and the newer machines have enabled products of better quality to be produced.

(*b*) *Extrusion—elastic thread.*   The formation of a thread-like coagulum by the extrusion of a fine stream of compounded latex into a suitable coagulant is a special example of ionic coagulation.   The threads concerned may be considered in two general categories, which may be referred to as coarse- and fine-count threads respectively.   The former varies in diameter from $\frac{1}{20}$ to $\frac{1}{60}$ in., the latter from $\frac{1}{60}$ to a diameter approaching $\frac{1}{150}$ in.

Different types of plant are employed for the production of coarse- and fine-count threads for a very simple reason.   In the case of the coarse count an appreciable time is required for the thread to set throughout, so that the coagulant baths are long (approximately 30 ft.) and the thread is extruded substantially horizontally into the bath, the travelling coagulum removing it from the vicinity of the nozzle (Fig. 1.11).   The speed of travel in the coagulant bath is approximately 30 ft./min.

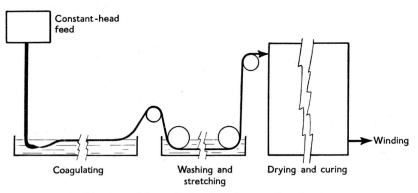

Fig. 1.11. Schematic drawing of coarse-thread unit.

As an outer membrane is formed initially at the surface of the thread and the coagulant has a high salt/acid concentration, in addition to the direct ionic coagulation, a measure of dehydration of the coagulum by osmotic action also takes place.   The bath is usually maintained at approximately room temperature.

The process is naturally a continuous one, and after coagulation the thread is washed in a hot-water bath.   At the same time the thread is stretched between differential-speed rollers, which assists the washing process and enables a reduced uniform diameter thread to be obtained.

Subsequent drying and vulcanisation in hot gas is carried out by standard methods.

The fine-count process (Fig. 1.12) differs in that the latex is extruded upwards into an acid coagulant, but due to the fineness of the thread,

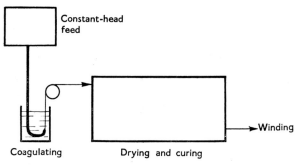

Fig. 1.12. Schematic drawing of fine-count thread unit.

coagulation is rapidly complete and the thread is removed vertically from the bath, which can be of a depth of 18 in. or less. The volatile acid disappears rapidly during the subsequent drying and vulcanisation, which is again continuous.

Latex thread manufacture demands a precision and an attention to detail which perhaps is greater than that required in any other latex manufacturing process. First of all, extrusion is required to proceed uninterruptedly for long periods. This is important, as a significant source of scrap is at the starting and stopping of extrusion runs. Secondly, the thread is required to have two types of uniformity: (a) uniformity in diameter, and (b) uniformity in physical properties. The first demands special selection and calibration of extruding nozzles and special attention to the conditions of extrusion. Constancy of flow through a fine orifice requires accurate maintenance of constant-pressure feed, and this is obtained in novel fashion. Uniformity in latex supply is another requirement, and special steps are taken in preparation of the mixing to see that coarse particles are removed before extrusion. Filtering through fine-mesh nylon gauze takes place at various points in the production sequence. Vibration and surface tension effects can all contribute to non-uniformity, and these have to be taken care of in plant design and construction. The maintenance of uniform physical properties is more simple but equally important. The state of cure is regularly checked by rapid methods, such as the T.50 type test, and continuous modulus testing of the finished thread is carried out.

As the chief uses of rubber thread are in combination with textiles, such threads have to be supplied in forms suitable for their subsequent handling.

In the case of coarse-count thread these are sometimes supplied in ribbon form produced by letting the wet threads stick together at an early stage. This coagulum attachment is also used for the production of a multi-filament thread from coarse-count threads and used, for example, for certain types of webbing.

The fine-count thread is normally covered with textile fibres of various types in special covering machines. The fine latex thread is covered at a controlled extension, and naturally the final thread is itself controlled by the covering thread in its physical properties. The covered threads are used in a variety of ways, but chiefly woven into foundation garments, swim-suits and other forms of wearing apparel.

(3) Direct manufacture from latex in which the coagulum is formed by hot or cold gelling

This group of processes is probably the most important commercially. They may be subdivided as:

(a) processes where the gel is formed locally, as, for example, against a hot former;

(b) processes where the contained latex volume is totally converted to a homogeneous coagulum.

The essential feature of hot or cold gelling processes is that the latex is conditioned in various ways so that either by a change in temperature or after a predetermined time interval the whole mass of the latex sets to a strong homogeneous coagulum retaining in its interstices the water that was originally the continuous phase. In other words, gelling is essentially a direct phase inversion.

(a) *Processes in which the gel is formed locally.* These processes depend on the labilisation of the latex mixing so that a hot former will cause a co-agulum to form in its vicinity but the bulk of the latex mixing will remain unchanged. Such labilisation can be carried out according to various principles.

The addition of ammonium salts to a latex containing zinc oxide, providing the addition is controlled and the other constituents of the mixing are suitably chosen, sensitises a latex such that it changes only very slowly at room temperature but rapidly gels at temperatures in the 80°–90° C range.

Increase in ammonium salt concentration increases zinc solubility, and increase in temperature increases both zinc solubility and the pH at which zinc soap formation commences. Zinc soap formation is an essential factor in obtaining a firm, strong gel.[3, 4, 5]

Provided that a slow rate of change of a latex mixing at room temperature is not ruled out, a sensitisation may be carried out by the addition of restricted amounts of agents which in larger amounts will cause the latex to gel in the cold. Heat then merely causes an acceleration of gelling. This kind of approach is not, however, very satisfactory.

Another approach was originally made in Germany but developed further in England. It used the fact that certain stabilisers were soluble in the cold but were precipitated as the temperature was raised. The substances originally used in Germany, the polyvinyl methyl ethers, are sensitive to the presence of certain surface-active materials, and need to be used under conditions of reduced pH obtained by reduction in the ammonia content of the latex. In England polypropylene glycol has been found to be effective in a similar manner, but is less sensitive to pH. Polyvinyl methyl ether is preferred for hot-dipping processes and polypropylene glycol for foam.[6]

The local heating processes based on heat sensitisation are hot former dipping and hot former moulding. In the latter case the heat-sensitised latex is introduced into a metal mould which is externally heated, and after a specified time the residual ungelled latex is poured out. The gelled layer is vulcanised and dried and removed from the mould.

A variation on the former moulding process that is currently practised is that in which the former is made from a porous material such as plaster of Paris. The deposit in this case is produced in a composite manner. It partly results from heat gelling, as the mould is usually used warm, partly by drying out in view of the porous nature of the mould, and to a small extent is ionically conditioned due to the active nature of the mould surface. Obviously special mixings, particularly those heavily filled or pre-aggregated, facilitate drying out by the porous mould.

The local internal casting processes lend themselves to the production of articles of intricate shapes, such as toys, advertising models, certain sports goods, etc.

(b) *Processes in which the entire latex charge is fully gelled.* This group of processes by definition includes foam rubber, but as this is such a large subject, it requires a separate section to itself. The more important of the other processes are those for hollow articles, where the total charge is gelled, and those relating to the production of microporous rubber.

In order that the total charge for a hollow article may be fully gelled, it is necessary during the gelling process for the latex to be mechanically distributed uniformly over the inner surface of the mould. The best-known process is that for the manufacture of meteorological and similar large balloons. A heat-sensitised mixing is distributed over the inner surface of a metal mould which is rotated about two axes in a steam atmosphere. The deposit is several millimetres thick, and on removal from the mould is inflated to a foot or more in diameter with warm air. The air pressure is maintained during the initial drying stage. The ingenuity of this process lies in the fact that the gel is controlled as to plasticity, so that it thins out uniformly during the inflation stage. After drying the balloon is chalked, deflated, and vulcanised, either in hot air or hot water. The method enables a large balloon to be produced with a small neck of a size ratio which would be extremely difficult to obtain by any other method. Although the gelled deposit is thick, after inflation it is thin and no drying difficulty is experienced.

In contradistinction, processes have been put forward and then abandoned for casting thick articles from latex, since it has been found virtually impossible to remove residual moisture. Tyre treads and shoe soles are particular examples. A considerable investigation was made in France of the production of tyre treads from rubber latices containing resorcinol formaldehyde resin. A total-heat-gelling process was employed using the " trypsin method " of heat sensitisation developed in France. This method of heat sensitisation is in effect the zinc oxide–ammonium salt method in which the ammonium salts are produced by the degradation of the latex protein by the trypsin. This process was finally abandoned after much work for several reasons, especially drying difficulties associated with thick coagula.

The production of microporous rubber, chiefly microporous ebonite for use as separators in secondary batteries, has been explored on several occasions. The basic principles of the method have been known for many years. Essentially a dilute latex mixing is heat sensitised, gelled, and the wet gel cured under such conditions that the moisture included in the gel is prevented from escaping during vulcanisation. As the mixing used is an ebonite one, the cured product does not shrink on drying out, with the result that microscopic channels are left where the water in the gel had originally been. The separators required for secondary batteries need to be mechanically strong, accurately dimensioned and contoured, so that gases can freely escape from the battery plates, acid can circulate, and any free solids be gravitationally removed from the vicinity of the plates.

A moulding process can technically be devised to meet such requirements, but as the annual requirements of battery separators run into millions, a process capable of mass production at low cost is needed. The original German process comprised the spreading of a heat-sensitised latex on profiled tin belts on which it was gelled. These were rolled up with superimposed felts, and vulcanisation then took place in autoclaves under water. The tin belts needed frequent re-profiling by heavy machinery. This particular process was dropped after the War, as the product could not compete economically with processes which did not involve the use of a tin belt.

Later developments,[7, 8] however, enabled the manufacture of separators to be put on a much more commercial footing, and millions of separators were made by the following mass-production methods.

In one process the heat-sensitised dilute latex was spread on to the surface of an accurately made neoprene-surfaced continuous belt and gelled during passage through a steam tunnel. The wet gel, kept wet by water jets, was detached from the belt and rolled up in wet fabric liners on an open drum. These drums were then immersed in water in an auto-clave and cured under steam pressure. The wet, but flexible microporous ebonite sheet was then continuously profiled and marked off to the required shape and sizes, the profiler also cutting the sheet longitudinally. The separators were then transferred to open baskets, in which they were washed by passing through a tank of warm water, after which they were dried, sorted and examined. The under-water cure, apart from main-taining the total water content of the gel, helped to remove water-soluble sulphides and surface-active materials from the gel, a process completed by the washing bath. In this way generation of hydrogen sulphide by battery acid was avoided and foaming during charging eliminated.

An alternative procedure [9] for contouring the microporous ebonite sheet was also developed for special types of separator which comprised a high-speed wet-grinding process using a contoured grinding stone under which the microporous ebonite sheet was fed.

The microporous ebonite separator products produced were of high quality and capable of out-lasting the battery plates themselves under service conditions.

Foam rubber

This, from many points of view, is the most important of all commercial latex processes so far developed. Not only is latex foam rubber produced in many countries of the world but its production consumes a high per-centage of the total natural rubber latex produced. It is an ideal example of a latex process, as it makes use of three fundamentals, i.e. it is a bulk user of latex, but despite the size of the products made it avoids the basic difficulty of drying out contained moisture by reason of the porous nature of the products and, moreover, it takes full advantage of the many high-quality physical properties of latex rubber itself.

The most important of the various processes used for foam rubber production is that known as the Dunlop process. Of the various ap-proaches that were covered by the original patents, the most generally adopted form of the process is relatively simple in conception.

A selected soap is added to a latex containing sulphur, accelerator, anti-oxidant, and filler or pigment if desired. By mechanical aeration the latex mixing is converted into a viscous foam of the required density.   Delayed-action gelling agents are then distributed throughout the foam.   The foam is poured into moulds or spread on suitable backings, where it sets without collapse in a given time interval at room temperature, or its setting is brought about by raising the temperature.

For many years the machines used for frothing were standard types of cake-mixing machines.   The charge of latex was weighed or measured-in and was then whipped to the required height by a wire whip rotating with a sun-and-planet motion.   The batch size, and hence the bowls of the machines, were selected in accordance with the size of the products re-quired.   Machines having more than one whip speed were developed, a fast speed for the main part of the frothing and a slower speed for a final refining of the bubbles.   The small- and medium-batch sizes did not present much of a problem, but the largest batches frothed in bowls of greater than 200-quart capacity introduced certain difficulties.   A very prolonged beating was undesirable, partly on account of the time involved and partly by reason of the resulting destabilisation.

The initial rate of rise of the foam during beating is rapid, but decreases as beating continues.   In certain instances after very prolonged beating continued frothing can lead to a diminution rather than an increase in froth height.   With large batches therefore, introduction of auxiliary air at the base of the whip was used, and in one particular machine alteration of the amplitude of the whip throw itself.   In the larger bowls the discharge of

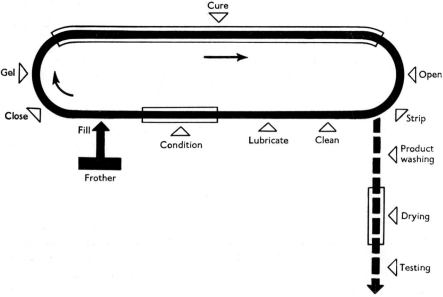

Fig. 1.13. Typical layout of conveyor system for batch foaming.

the foam was through a bottom valve rather than by direct pouring, and various mechanical runway devices were employed to assist the operators in bowl handling.

For the first decade the batch frothing process was the only one seriously employed, although just before the Second World War the first trials with continuous-foaming processes were being made.[10]

The considerable emphasis on batch frothing is understandable, as in latex foam production a unique opportunity is available of moulding products to special shapes and of predetermining their density. As a result, there was a tendency, except in certain groups, to tailor-make the products rather than to rationalise and fit them to limited mass-produced types.

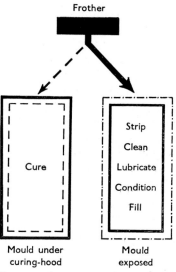

The pre-war production plants frequently used a conveyor layout. The moulds were all handled by a horizontal conveyor, and the various stages of mould preparation and conditioning, mould filling, lid application, gelling, vulcanisation, and product stripping were carried out in continuous cyclic fashion. The vulcanisation was carried out in hot water, atmospheric steam, or the moulds were transported to separate autoclaves, where they were vulcanised in steam under pressure.

There were certain difficulties with the conveyor system with the batch process, and a move to independent mould units in which the mould remained stationary was made.

Fig. 1.14. Arrangement for stationary moulds for batch foaming.

The advent of the continuous frother after the War, however, brought the conveyor system to the fore once more, although some independent mould units are frequently used alongside conveyors to give greater flexibility to the production.

The moulds used for foam-rubber production are either made from cast silicon–aluminium or constructed from sheet metal such as zinc. The requirements are robustness, good finish, non-corrosion by latex and latex serum, and minimum cost. The shapes are relatively complicated, and the lids to the moulds are usually fitted with hollow plugs to produce cavitied products and facilitate heat transfer. The mould-makers have improved considerably the quality of the castings in comparison with the earlier products, which were frequently porous.

Various types of mould lubricants are used which not only assist the release of the product but give a good surface finish.   These have included carbowaxes, silicones and sodium carboxymethyl cellulose.

The conditioning of the mould before pouring is twofold.   Any free water must be removed from the mould surface, usually by compressed air-jet, and the temperature must then be adjusted so that a differential temperature shock is not given to the sensitive foam on pouring.

The processes after stripping of the product from the mould are obvious ones.   In many cases it is desirable for the product to be washed in water, preferably hot water, excess of which is removed by squeeze rolls.   Some plants still use centrifuges to remove excess water from smaller products, and washing is frequently carried out in the centrifuge itself.

Drying is routine by forced hot-air draught, and the drying is considerably aided by the fact that the product itself is porous throughout and air can be blown through it.

The modern continuous frothing system has a number of special conditions to meet, although the principles employed are the same.   The most popular frothing machine is that known as the Oakes frother, which although it was originally used for latex almost unchanged, has since undergone some development.

The modern continuous frother does continuously almost exactly what is done in the batch process.   Whereas in the earlier Oakes frother the zinc oxide and gelling agent were introduced into the frothing head itself, they are now introduced into the foam *after* leaving the head, actually into a separate continuous blender (Fig. 1.15).

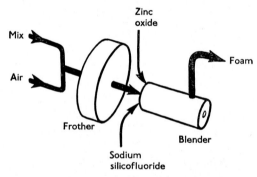

Fig. 1.15. Continuous foaming and blending.

In the continuous frother the air is introduced under pressure and distributed; it is not introduced as in the batch process by cavitation, and the whole process of air introduction is over in a few seconds.   One of the important features of the continuous frother is that it operates under a back pressure of up to 30 lb./in.^{2} built up by the long polyvinyl chloride discharge pipe.   The result is that in the frothing head the foam is of a high density and therefore more mobile than it is when it leaves the end of the discharge pipe.

The time from the introduction of the setting agent into the foam until the foam is in the mould is quite short, and very fast setting times are therefore possible, for example, of the order of 2 minutes. In the bowl process setting times of about 8 minutes were usually aimed at, although those employed were frequently longer.

The density is changed in the continuous frother by changing the rate of air influx with respect to the latex input. The rate of latex flow and of zinc oxide and silicofluoride introduction is controlled by pumps. The original pumps used were of conventional type, and required frequent dismantling and cleaning, as anyone who has worked with latex would anticipate. The newer types of pump of monopump design are much better, and run for longer times before cleaning.

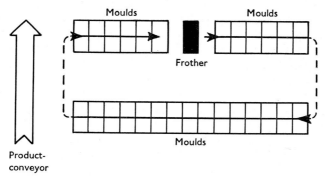

Fig. 1.16. Schematic arrangement for continuous foaming using stationary moulds.

Obviously a change in density in continuous frothing is not instantaneous as the change has to pass throughout the discharge system, but the amount of out-of-tolerance product has now been reduced to a minimum.

Other processes for production of foam rubber

The most important of these is known as the Talalay process.[11, 12, 13, 14, 15] This is an expansion process, the expanding gas (oxygen) being generated by an enzyme (catalase) from hydrogen peroxide added to the latex. The products are made in jacketed moulds. After the foam has expanded a refrigerating fluid is circulated through the jacket to freeze the water in the foam. Carbon dioxide gas is then injected through the frozen mass at moderate pressure and brings about coagulation. A second fluid at room temperature is circulated through the mould jacket for tempering after freezing and for cooling after vulcanisation. A third vulcanising fluid is circulated through the jacket for the vulcanisation itself.

The process developed by Cockbain for foam-rubber production employs the standard methods for frothing, but instead of the usual type of delayed action or heat-sensitising gelling agents, non-ionic substances are used, such as polypropylene glycol, which are soluble in cold water or ammoniated latex, but precipitate out on heating.[16]

Mechanism of the foam-rubber processes

The production of foam rubber from latex requires that the latex phase shall gel without a substantial breakdown of the dispersed air system. It is important, however, that a controlled breakdown takes place at a late stage in the gelling process sufficient to cause the bubbles to interconnect. If this has not occurred the product is likely to disrupt during vulcanisation, causing lamination and an internal feathery structure.

The change of pH during gelling with sodium silicofluoride, which is one of the gelling agents for foam-rubber production, follows a curve of the type shown in Fig. 1.17. It will be appreciated that such a major change

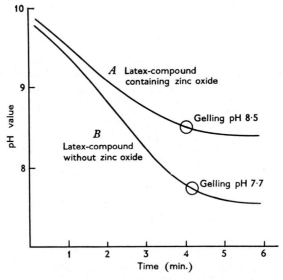

Fig. 1.17. pH changes during gelling with silicofluoride.

in pH also causes a major change in both surface and interfacial tensions.[17] When the full characteristics of the system are, however, known it is possible to deal separately with the rubber/serum and air/serum systems, stabilising the one and destabilising the other so that a properly balanced system is obtained giving rise to controlled products.

Heat-gelling processes using ammonium salt/zinc oxide gelling and systems of the polyglycol type mentioned earlier do not undergo appreciable changes in pH at the point of gelling, and consequently these systems yield products, particularly thick products, which are more prone to internal disruption during vulcanisation. Difficulties of this type are overcome by positively inducing a pH change by treatment of the set or partially set foam with carbon dioxide before vulcanisation.[18] The fall in pH thus brought about affects proper interconnection of the bubbles.

The parts played by zinc oxide and the zinc soap formed *in situ* under the correct pH conditions are fundamental to the whole mechanism.

In an ammonia preserved-latex system containing anionic soap and zinc oxide, zinc soap is progressively formed as the pH falls. When the pH fall is brought about by the hydrolysis of sodium silicofluoride an excess of zinc oxide is normally required for all the soap present to be converted to zinc soap with fall in pH to 8·0.[19]

The sodium silicofluoride hydrolyses according to the equation

$$2Na^+ + SiF_6^{--} + 4H_2O \rightleftharpoons 2Na^+ + 4H^+ + 6F^- + Si(OH)_4$$

and the colloidal silica formed may well adsorb some of the zinc amine ions which would otherwise take part in zinc soap formation.

Product characteristics

The important function of latex foam rubber is that it should carry a specified load at a predetermined deflection. This function is fulfilled when it is used as a mattress, or a full-depth cushion. When it is used as a topping on springs it is functioning more as a gap filler, and its mechanical properties are not quite so important or critical.

The hardness of foam rubber is defined as the load required to compress it to 60% of its original thickness, and naturally the simplest way of controlling this hardness or load-carrying capacity is to alter the density of the foam employed by controlling the amount of air beaten into the original latex mixing. Fig. 1.18 shows the characteristic hardness/density curve which fits an equation of the type $H = Ad^n$, where H = compression hardness at 60% of original thickness; d = density (weight per unit volume); A and n are constants which vary with the type of mixing employed. Talalay has given a somewhat more elaborate equation for a similar curve.[20]

In the early days of foam-rubber production a curve of this type was established for a given type of mixing, and subsequent to this a relative hardness or, conversely, a relative weight measurement may be made for any product which gives an indication as to whether the rubber is being more or less usefully employed.

As is well known, the moulding process for foam rubber facilitates the production of intricate cavitied shapes which provides a further means of altering the apparent density. Such a consideration, however, raises important questions of product design which are outside the scope of this book. Suffice to say, however, that such considerations of design affect the best use of the rubber employed, the distribution of support areas and

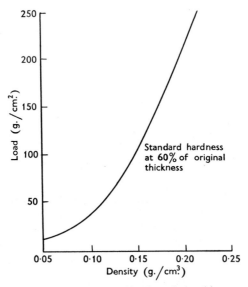

Fig. 1.18. Hardness/density relationship.

local high-pressure areas, and, in fact, constitute the design approach to the economic provision of comfort.

It is also important to remember that apart from these static considerations the dynamic properties of foam rubber are of the utmost importance. The products frequently need to undergo many millions of flexing cycles in service, and the passage of air through the pores during the deformation cycle produces a controlled damping and ventilation.

Compounding for foam rubber

The ability to use accelerator systems that produce high-modulus rubbers has been a feature of latex foam rubber from its early days. In fact, the type of mixings employed have not fundamentally changed since the early days.

The curing systems are those for vulcanising in atmospheric steam. Zinc diethyldithiocarbamate (Z.D.C.) is the generally preferred accelerator, frequently boosted by a secondary accelerator according to the curing cycle demanded. Z.D.C. has for very many years been the work horse of latex accelerators. It is an easily manageable insoluble product which gives fast cures and rubbers of good ageing properties. In contradistinction to many other latex manufactures, it is necessary to cure foam rubber largely in the wet-gel state in order that the product can be stripped from the mould without undue distortion. The ultra-accelerated foam curing system demands a relatively high sulphur addition, substantially all of which is employed in the cure, as only a very small free sulphur content remains in the average product.

The necessity of vulcanising in the wet-gel state demands that the hot-cured wet-gel strength is adequate for stripping, a factor which conditions both the use of current synthetic latices and of compounding. The amount of water present in the gel at the curing stage is important, as part of the product shrinkage takes place in drying after cure. The size and hardness of the product for a given foam expansion are interlinked. These, too, are influenced by the prematuring of the mixing.

The ageing properties of foam rubber are outstandingly good, even without any antioxidant addition, although non-staining antioxidants are employed to enhance the life still further, and to deal with special conditions of service. This outstanding ageing performance is all the more remarkable because the rubber is present in such thin films and at all times has free access to air. It has been a factor of major importance in such products as mattresses, household furniture, theatre seats, etc., where long life is necessary. A contributing factor, however, is the fact that foam rubber is almost always used in a covered condition. This is rather fortunate, as, in general, light has a deleterious effect, both on appearance and resistance to deterioration.

The compounding of foam rubber other than for vulcanisation, age resistance, and pigmentation has had as its object modification of load-carrying capacity. Attempts have been made to produce a higher-modulus rubber by various means in order to obtain a lighter product of the same load-carrying capacity or, alternatively, a higher modulus has been obtained by various filler loadings. In the latter case, although less rubber has been used, the overall weight of product has not necessarily been reduced.

One method of increasing the modulus of the rubber has been by graft polymerisation techniques of the type described by Bloomfield and Swift.[19] An analysis of the effect of filler loading has been made by Van't Wout and de Vries,[22] and reference has been made to the use of high-styrene resin latex for foam reinforcement.[23]

Oil additions, either to the mixing or as an after swelling of the finished product, reduce material cost, but in view of the greatly increased softening simultaneously occurring are not economic when viewed in the light of intrinsic load-carrying capacity. Other factors, such as pore size, are claimed to affect load-carrying capacity,[24] and these need to be borne in mind when assessing the price to be paid for good external appearance.

That so many uses of foam rubber require that it should maintain its characteristics under repeated flexing has a special significance in relation to the effects of compounding. Procedures that enhance modulus under single-cycle deformation are not necessarily advantageous under repeated flexing, and some compounding additions produce such shortness in the rubber that fatigue failures rapidly occur. In fact, minimum elongation at break figures for foam materials have been suggested with a view to obviating such difficulties in multiflex testing.

Other manufactures involving foam rubber

Latex foam rubber before cure but after gelling is to a large extent plastic, and may be shaped, such shaping being cured into the final product. This procedure has been employed for controlling density and finish of foam-rubber sheet, for continuously producing fluted or shallow cavitied toppings from foam-rubber sheet, and it obviously lends itself to the production of other shaped articles of simple and shallow contour.

The extreme of such a process is that in which the foam-rubber sheeting before cure is compressed in stages until the thin rubber films forming the bubbles are in contact and stuck to one another.[25] The resulting product after cure is a highly tear-resisting material which has had many special uses.

Cured foam rubber may be readily comminuted to a controlled crumb size, and as such has always been tempting as a filling material, although in so using it many of its advantageous features are lost. Nevertheless, if such crumb is combined with fresh mixing and applied to a suitable backing a high-grade underlay material is produced which for many years has been popular for use with carpets and other floor coverings.[26]

The underlay market since the original introduction of this form of underlay has grown to quite large proportions. This is a result not only of the improved feel but also of the improved wear properties given to the superimposed floor covering. Other forms of underlay have also been developed based on foaming processes,[27] some using appreciable quantities of dispersed reclaim as well as latex in their composition.

Synthetic latices

With the large-scale development of synthetic rubbers by emulsion polymerisation processes it was a natural consequence that the latices of such synthetic rubbers should be examined and developed. With a range of synthetic rubbers available, depending on the monomers employed in their manufacture, a range of types of synthetic latex has similarly arisen.

In the synthetic-rubber field two factors have conditioned growth: (a) the attainment of speciality properties which can command a higher price; (b) the economic relationship of synthetic to natural rubber under conditions of approximately equal performance.

As far as synthetic latices are concerned, speciality latices have won a recognised place, and for the particular applications for which they are employed command their higher price. The general-purpose synthetic latices, on the other hand, for reasons which will be described later, are not capable of replacing natural latex to the same extent as general-purpose synthetic rubber can replace natural rubber. This position will in due course improve, but it will take some time.

The consumption of the principal types of synthetic-rubber latices in 1957 was approximately 90,000 long tons dry, most of which was in the U.S.A. This represented approximately 7·8% of the world consumption of synthetic rubber. This indicates that the proportionate uses of both natural and synthetic latex expressed as percentages of the consumption of natural and synthetic rubber respectively are not greatly different.

When certain uses of synthetic latices are considered it becomes increasingly difficult to distinguish their function from that of the latices of other types of emulsion polymers, for example, polyvinyl acetate, polyvinyl chloride and latices of the polyacrylic and polymethacrylic esters. This is inevitable, but in this chapter the emphasis is chiefly on the more elastomeric polymers and copolymers and their more rubber-like uses.

(1) Direct manufacture from latex in which in the finished article the coagulum is formed by drying

(a) *Impregnation and coating.* Two special features of many synthetic latices, namely, their high mechanical stability and very small particle size, have made them particularly suitable for impregnation processes. In such processes the fact that it is easier to produce a synthetic latex at low total solids does not constitute a drawback. Synthetic latex normally produced at a particle size approximately one-tenth that of natural is particularly favourable for impregnation purposes.

Some of the important outlets for synthetic latices of various types are in the sizing and finishing of textiles to improve their durability and printing qualities, and in the production of non-woven bonded fabrics, where the butadiene/acrylonitrile latices have advantages of resistance to dry-cleaning solvents. Synthetic latices are also used in the manufacture of special-purpose papers and thin felted materials for lining purposes, particularly in the shoe trade. The latices have been added to the beater prior to sheet formation, or alternatively, have been used to saturate already formed papers. The addition of small amounts of synthetic latex to high pigment loadings, such as clay, improves pigment retention and printability in papers. The degree of rubberiness can be controlled, particularly in the case of the butadiene/styrene latices, by altering the butadiene/styrene ratio, thereby achieving a gradation in properties which is not possible with natural rubber latices.

Particular advantage has been taken of this in coating processes. Synthetic latices have been used as pigment binders in paper coating, particularly to enhance printing characteristics, and as leather finishes. One of the largest uses, however, has been in emulsion paints, particularly for indoor painting. It has been estimated that in 1956 approximately 40 million gallons of styrene–butadiene latex paint were used, chiefly in the U.S.A.[28]

(b) Butadiene–styrene latices are used extensively in tyre cord adhesives in place of natural latex. In a latex–resorcinol-resin type of rubber to textile adhesive butadiene–styrene latex performs the same function as natural latex in that it enhances the fatigue resistance of the bond. It does not, however, impart the same " green stick " as does natural latex. The terpolymer latex of butadiene–styrene–vinyl pyridine, however, although expensive, has particularly advantageous properties in rubber to textile bonding. The exact reason for this is not clear, but it is undoubtedly partly associated with the polar nature of the molecule. These terpolymer latices are used with resorcinol resin and applied to the bonding of rayon, nylon and other fibres to both natural and synthetic rubber compounds. With terpolymer latex–resorcinol-resin adhesive dopes static adhesion values may be obtained which are nearly twice those achieved with the natural-latex–resorcinol-resin dopes. Improvements in dynamic adhesion values follow the same pattern.

The processes using natural latex in the production of pile fabrics, carpets, and the like have also been adapted to the use of synthetic latices, either alone or in admixture with natural latex. Although claims have been made for improved ageing and dyeing obtained with synthetic latices, the preference is to a certain extent controlled by economic considerations, which also take into account the fact that natural latex will normally support larger filler loadings than, for example, butadiene–styrene types.

(2) Direct manufacture for latex in which the coagulum is formed by ionic coagulation

(a) Dipping. Neoprene latex is increasingly being used in a number of dipping applications, particularly for gloves. Neoprene latex coagulates well in coagulant dipping processes, and forms stronger products than do the butadiene–styrene type of latices. It is available generally in sufficiently high concentration. The acrylonitrile–butadiene latices are in general available at lower concentrations.

Gloves and other products made from neoprene latex are oil and heat resistant, the former being particularly advantageous under household conditions, where the use of modern detergents brings oil and fatty materials into close contact with the rubber.

Neoprene latex has also been used for the production of speciality foot-wear designed for use under oil swelling conditions that would be un-favourable to the use of natural latex.

In general, increased drying times are required for neoprene latex products in comparison with those produced from natural latex, as the water permeability is less.

(3) Direct manufacture from latex in which the coagulum is formed by hot or cold gelling

Several of the processes previously described for the production of articles by hot or cold gelling can be applied to butadiene–acrylonitrile latices, and particularly to neoprene latices. In view, however, of their increased cost, such latices are not usually employed unless some special feature is required. Butadiene–styrene latices are not normally employed in place of natural latex, although for economic reasons they can on occasion be used as diluents.

Synthetic latex in foam rubber

Part of the story of the development of butadiene–styrene latex has been the search for the improvements required to make it suitable for use in foam-rubber manufacture.

Both neoprene latex and butadiene–acrylonitrile latices had been used in bulk for foam-rubber production, particularly immediately after the Second World War when other latices were scarce, but the increased cost involved in their use made them unattractive, except for special applica-tions where features such as oil resistance were of importance. Neoprene latex foam has the added advantage of resistance to ozone. It also resists flame propagation. The high specific gravity of the neoprene polymer is, however, disadvantageous for foam uses.

The problems associated with the development of butadiene–styrene latex suitable for foam were the low wet-gel strength in general associated with butadiene–styrene latices, the small particle size, low total solids, and odour. The low hot wet-gel strength has been and still is one of the major problems associated with the use of butadiene–styrene latices. The use of " cold " latices has given some improvement together with special polymerisation procedures to increase particle size, and shallow products, such as automotive toppings, have been satisfactorily produced from 100% " cold " butadiene–styrene latex. For such shallow products stripping from the moulds is relatively easy, and the lower tear strength can be tolerated. Moreover, for such products flexing-performance condi-tions are not so stringent. As the weight of the product increases, blends of butadiene–styrene with natural latex are employed, the ratio synthetic to natural decreasing with product size and weight. This is particularly noticeable in the more or less automatic conveyorised production plants handling heavy deep products, such as luxury mattresses. For the static production-type processes, particularly the Talalay process, much higher ratios of synthetic to natural may in general be tolerated.

A high-solids synthetic latex is normally required for foam. The direct production of high-solids latex is not easy, as it involves stability problems during polymerisation and longer reaction times. A preferred procedure is to produce the latex at lower solids, usually not greater than 40%, and then to agglomerate and subsequently concentrate by heat evaporation. The content of non-rubber solids, which frequently approaches 6% of the polymer weight is often overlooked in making comparisons with natural latex, whose non-rubber solids are seldom more than 2·5% calculated on the polymer. The production of butadiene–styrene latices of increased particle size assists in the problem of reduced non-rubber solids.

The recent development by Talalay referred to earlier [29] proposes the production of low-solids latices, quick freezing, thawing, and final heat concentration if desired. The freezing of a SBR latex has the unusual property of increasing the particle size, which facilitates the subsequent operations. It is claimed that the overall cost of this series of operations is less than that of the usual process.

Odour in butadiene–styrene latices can come from residual styrene or butadiene dimer, and special care has to be taken in stripping such latices. Such precaution is not so necessary in automotive products, but in products such as mattresses the removal of odorous residues is important.

For certain special applications, on the other hand, the superior heat-resisting properties of foamed products made from synthetic latex are of value.

Apart from any strategic questions, the factors determining the relative use of synthetic and natural latices in foam will be largely economic ones.

Latex testing

Detailed specifications for latex tests have been published both by the American Society for Testing Materials [30] and by the British Standards Institution.[31] In addition, the mechanical stability test for latex has been approved by the International Standards Organisation, and other tests are under consideration by the same body. For full details of these tests reference should be made to the published specifications, but comment on the significance of certain of the tests is probably of value.

Natural rubber latex

Total solids and dry rubber content. These tests, although simple, are important, as they measure quantities on which the purchase of latex depends. The DRC is not, of course, an absolute measure of the dry rubber content, but represents the precipitated or coagulated insoluble material obtained under a standardised set of coagulating conditions. Nevertheless, the measurement is remarkably reproducible for certain classes of latex. In comparing natural and synthetic rubber latex concentrates the fact that the total solids of the latter usually contains a much higher proportion of non-rubber solids is frequently overlooked and not allowed for in product cost.

*VFA number and KOH number.** These quantities are to a large extent indicative of the state of preservation of the latex. Like all interpretative tests of this sort, they reach their optimum value when full data are available concerning the origin and treatment history of the latex in question. The VFA number refers to the volatile fatty acid content of the latex resulting from breakdown of non-rubber constituents by acid-producing bacteria. The acid is chiefly acetic. Its generation results in a fall in mechanical stability and a change in the zinc activity of a latex.

Natural latex contains a number of bacterial species, and acids are also produced other than those indicated by the VFA number. While with certain preservation systems which essentially maintain a high redox potential in the latex, the acid-producing bacteria are suppressed and the VFA remains low, other types of bacteria can still be active, bringing about a mechanical stability fall and a steadily rising KOH number. While, therefore, VFA generally indicates a state of preservation for ammonia preservation, the KOH number should always be consulted, particularly for those systems of preservation that do not rely solely on ammonia.

The electrical conductivity of latex has been used as a quick measure of its preservation, but this has now been largely superseded by the VFA measurement, as the level of conductivity can be strongly affected by ions arising from inorganic constituents.

For tests that measure a state of preservation the constancy of the values obtained are of importance quite apart from their actual magnitude. Satisfactory ammonia-preserved latex has a VFA of 0·03–0·1, and if the VFA is appreciably above 0·1 and is climbing the conditions of preservation should be examined. The KOH number is normally in the 0·5–0·7 range. Satisfactory figures for electrodecanted latex differ from those for centrifuged latex, as due to the average smaller particle size of electrodecanted latex the ratio of non-rubber to rubber constituents is greater. This factor influences a number of the test values for electrodecanted latex which would otherwise be suspect in a standard type of centrifuged latex.

Mechanical stability. This is one of the most important tests for latex

---

* VFA stands for volatile fatty acid content, and KOH number represents the number of grams of KOH required to neutralise the acids present in 100 g. of solids in the latex.

concentrate. Because it is an empirical test and measures an effect rather than a cause, it is surprisingly useful in providing an index of latex quality with respect to its average processing behaviour.

The influence of various factors, such as temperature, solids content, and ammonia content, are well known and standardised in the test. Various additives, such as soaps and protective colloids, increase the mechanical stability considerably, and the converse influence of various types of sensitisers and compounding ingredients, including, of course, zinc oxide, is most marked.[32]

In general, extremes of mechanical stability, both low and high, lead to processing difficulties in the sensitive types of latex processes. An intermediate stage is always to be preferred, and one which does not change appreciably in storage. Constancy in mechanical stability is of utmost value to the technologist controlling latex processes.

Ammonia content, total alkalinity, pH, colour and odour. These measurements are without subtle significance. Discoloration is usually an indication of iron contamination which has reacted with the high sulphur content of the latex protein.

Chemical tests for copper, manganese and magnesium. The measurement of the copper and manganese content is of importance in avoiding danger of active contamination leading to degradation in the final rubber. The magnesium content of a latex has, however, a different significance. An excess of magnesium in the latex can influence gelling, and a general unbalance of the magnesium–phosphate ratio can affect appreciably the mechanical stability of the latex.[33]

Tests involving the use of zinc oxide. Tests of many types aimed at assessing the behaviour of a latex in the presence of zinc oxide have been the subject of intensive investigation. They have involved thickening tests, chemical heat-stability tests, and chemical stirring tests,[34] but in general they have been inadequate, because the zinc complex involved under the conditions of the test has differed from that in the technological practice concerned. This state of affairs has arisen partly from insufficient attention to pH control and the part played by zinc soap. A greater understanding has, however, been obtained of the importance of zinc soaps since a number of more recent studies have been published.[3, 4, 34, 35]

It is still broadly true that the usefulness of zinc-activity tests, of whatever type, in latex is still largely confined to indicating conditions of inactivity towards zinc or, alternatively, is restricted to some specialised feature of a given process.

Synthetic rubber latices

The tests for synthetic rubber latex have not yet been developed to the same extent as those for natural latex, and their development has followed a different path.   One of the reasons for this is that the manufacturers of the latices know exactly what surface-active materials have been used and the processes employed in polymerisation.   Moreover, these are, or should be, reasonably reproducible.

The viscosity measurement for a synthetic latex is probably of greater significance than for a natural latex.   It reflects the average particle size of the latex, which in turn is conditioned by the polymerisation process used. Moreover, the viscosity at lower temperatures is influenced by the nature of the soaps employed.

In a similar way surface tension is of greater importance than for natural latex, as it reflects the nature and amount of surfactants and electrolyte employed in the polymerisation.   Mechanical stability testing is not easy, as so many of the synthetic latices are insensitive to the mechanical-stirring conditions of the natural latex text.   Modified tests have been proposed,[36,37] but none has yet been standardised.

In certain synthetic rubber latices it is important to be able to estimate monomer residues, as these will have a bearing on odour, inflammability and viscosity.

For certain applications of synthetic rubber latices it is important to have information about the polymer itself.   Two important factors are the Mooney viscosity value of the rubber and the gel content of the rubber obtained from the latex.   These are not latex characteristics as such, but will have a bearing on the strength of the raw coagulum.

General

When assessing the likely behaviour and characteristics of a latex it is important to examine as many of the various test results as possible in relation to one another, and better still, to consider them where possible in the light of the origin and the history of the latex in question.

The provision of a proper sample for testing is of such obvious importance that the various standardising bodies have laid down strict conditions for obtaining it.

In **general**, the most effective test for the suitability of a latex for a particular process is to try out the latex for that process.

References

1. Angier, D. J., Chambers, W. T. and Watson, W. F. (1957) *J. Polym. Sci.*, **25**, 133.
2. Watson, W. F. (1955) *Ind. Eng. Chem.*, 1281.
3. Newnham, J. L. M. (1953) *I.R.I. Trans.*, **29**, 171.
4. Kraay, G. M. and van den Tempel, (1952) *I.R.I. Trans.*, **28**, 144.
5. Newnham, J. L. M. (1953) *ibid.*, **29**, 170.
6. Cockbain, E. G. (1956) *I.R.I. Trans.*, **32**, 97.

7. Dunlop Rubber Co. Ltd., Ward, A. N., Madge, E. W. and Purkis, F. T. (December 1950) B.P. 698,613.
8. Dunlop Rubber Co. Ltd., Madge, E. W., Purkis, F. T., Ward, A. N. and Wesley, L. N. W. (October 1951) B.P. 699,415.
9. Dunlop Rubber Co. Ltd., Warren, F. W. (January 1955) B.P. 754,131.
10. Dunlop Rubber Co. Ltd., Madge, E. W., Murphy, E. A., Pounder, D. W. and Taylor, S. D. (March 1936) B.P. 471,899.
11. Talalay, J. A. (September 1946) B.P. 619,619.
12. —— (February 1950) B.P. 668,499.
13. —— (November 1936) B.P. 484,798.
14. —— (July 1950) B.P. 684,112.
15. Howard, J. A. and Talalay, J. A. (August 1951) B.P. 692,132.
16. Cockbain, E. G. (1956) *I.R.I. Trans.*, **32**, 100.
17. McKeand, D. J. (1951) *Ind. Eng. Chem.*, **43**, 415.
18. Dunlop Rubber Co. Ltd. and Calvert, K. O. (January 1955) B.P. 779,917.
19. Newnham, J. L. M. (1953) *I.R.I. Trans.*, **29**, 169.
20. Bloomfield, G. F. and Swift, P. McL. (1955) *J. App. Chem.*, **5**, 609.
21. Talalay, J. A. (1954) *Ind. Eng. Chem.*, **46**, 1531.
22. Van't Wout, J. W. F. and de Vries, A. J. (1955) Kautsch. u. Gummi, **8**, 130WT.
23. *Rubb. World* (1957) **136**, 738.
24. Talalay, J. A. (1954) *Ind. Eng. Chem.*, **46**, 1530.
25. Madge, E. W. (1946) *Ind. Rubb. World*, **114**, 803.
26. Dunlop Rubber Co. Ltd., Madge, E. W. and Payne, F. J. (December 1932) B.P. 413,284 and (March 1933) B.P. 414,814.
27. Durie & Miller Ltd. (November 1953) B.P. 767,957.
28. *Chem. Eng. News* (1957), **35**, 14.
29. Goodrich, B. F. (1953) B.P. 758,622.
30. A.S.T.M. Tentative specifications and methods of test for concentrated, ammonia preserved creamed and centrifuged natural rubber latices. D.1076-57T. Issued 1949, revised 1952, 1954, and 1957. Tentative methods of testing synthetic rubber latices (styrene and butadiene copolymers). D.1417-57T. Issued 1956. Revised 1957.
31. B.S.I. Methods of Testing Rubber Latex. B.S. 1672. Part I, 1950. Sampling and Basic Tests. B.S. 1672. Part II, 1954. Chemical and Physical Tests.
32. Madge, E. W. (1952) *I.R.I. Trans.*, **28**, 207.
33. Madge, E. W., Collier, H. M. and Peel, J. D. (1950) *I.R.I. Trans.*, **26**, 305.
34. Madge, E. W., Collier, H. M. and Newnham, J. L. M. (1954) *Proc. Third Rubber Tech. Conf.*, 67.
35. Dawson, H. G. (1956) *Rubb. World*, **135**, 239.
36. Maron, S. H. and Ulevitch, I. N. (1953) *Analyt. Chem.*, **25**, 1087.
37. Newnham, J. L. M. and Simcox, D. J. (1959) *Proc. Intern. Rubber Conf.*, *Washington D.C.*, p. 323.

CHAPTER II

PART ONE

CHEMISTRY AND STRUCTURE OF NATURAL RUBBER

by

G. F. BLOOMFIELD

The structure of natural rubber

TOWARDS the end of the first quarter of the nineteenth century Faraday [1] examined a sample of Mexican latex which he had obtained " through the kindness of Mr. Hancock " and obtained from it a sample of reasonably pure rubber by allowing the latex to cream spontaneously and subsequently washing the cream with successive lots of water. He recognised the rubber as a compound of carbon and hydrogen only, carried out the first recorded formal analysis, and reported that when heated it was resolved into substances which were more or less volatile.

The origins of systematic work leading to the elucidation of the chemical structure of rubber can be traced back to 1860, when Williams [2] found that the dry distillation of rubber gave a small quantity of a volatile liquid to which he gave the name " isoprene ". Williams drew attention to the fact that " the atomic constitution of caoutchouc appears to bear some simple relation to the hydrocarbons resulting from its decomposition by heat ". Tilden [3] correctly assigned to isoprene the composition C_5H_8 and suggested

$$CH_2{=}\overset{\displaystyle \overset{CH_3}{|}}{C}{-}CH{=}CH_2,$$

several possible structural formulae, including $CH_2{=}C{-}CH{=}CH_2$, which he later [4] regarded as the most probable in view of the ready conversion of isoprene to terpenes. Bouchardat [5] recognised in 1879 that isoprene could be regarded as the " foundation stone " of rubber, and he succeeded in converting it to an elastic, rubber-like material. Tilden [4] reported its spontaneous polymerisation; he had already foreseen [6] the possibility of synthesising rubber from isoprene if it were obtainable from another more accessible source, but another seventy-five years were to elapse before a successful commercial production of polyisoprene exactly duplicating natural rubber was to be achieved.

Towards the turn of the century it had become clear that rubber could be represented by the formula $(C_5H_8)_n$ in which the $C_5H_8{-}$ unit was structurally related to isoprene, and the next forward step was made by Gladstone and Hibbert,[7] who demonstrated the ability of rubber to add two atoms of bromine to every C_5H_8- unit to give the additive rubber bromide $(C_5H_8Br_2)_n$. This work, together with similar investigations by Weber,[8] who also added a molecule of hydrogen chloride to each C_5H_8- unit to give the hydrochloride $(C_5H_9Cl)_n$, established the presence of an olefinic double bond in each C_5H_8- unit. The disposition of the double bonds was shown by Harries [9] during the course of an extensive investigation of the action of ozone on olefins. Ozone reacts very readily at the double bonds of unsaturated substances (I) to form rather unstable, frequently explosive addition compounds (II) called ozonides

$$\underset{R_2}{\overset{R_1}{>}}C=C\underset{R_4}{\overset{R_3}{<}} + O_3 \longrightarrow \underset{R_2}{\overset{R_1}{>}}C\underset{O}{\overset{O-O}{<}}C\underset{R_4}{\overset{R_3}{>}}$$

(I)　　　　　　　　　(II)

which on cleavage by hydrolysis yield aldehydes or ketones according to the nature of the substituents R_1, R_2, R_3 and R_4. If one or both of the substituents on either of the carbon atoms is a hydrogen atom, then an aldehyde is formed at that carbon atom; if none of the substituents is hydrogen the products are exclusively ketonic

e.g.
$$\underset{H}{\overset{R}{>}}C=C\underset{R_3}{\overset{R_2}{<}} \longrightarrow RCHO + \underset{R_3}{\overset{R_2}{>}}C=O$$

(vinyl bonds accordingly give formaldehyde as one of the products: $CH_2=CRR^1 \longrightarrow HCHO + RR^1CO$).

Recent work [10, 11] on the action of ozone on an olefin suggests that a ketone and the zwitterion (III) are the primary products.

$$>C=C< + O_3 \longrightarrow >C=O + \overset{\ominus}{O}-O-\overset{\oplus}{C}<$$

(III)

Depending on the conditions and on the structure of the olefin, these may combine to give the ozonide (II) or a ketone, together with a keto-peroxide or polymer according to whether the zwitterion (III) dimerises or polymerises.

Since cleavage of the ozonolysis products of rubber gives high yields of levulinic aldehyde (IV) and its derivatives (levulinic acid (V) and its keto-peroxide (VI)) the structure of rubber has been unambiguously established as a 1 : 4-polyisoprene (VII).[9, 12]

The *cis*-stereoisomeric configuration (VIII) has been assigned to rubber, and the *trans*-configuration (IX) to gutta-percha, on account of the lower

$$\cdots -CH_2-\overset{\overset{\displaystyle CH_3}{|}}{C}=CH-CH_2-CH_2-\overset{\overset{\displaystyle CH_3}{|}}{C}=CH-CH_2- \cdots \quad \text{(VII)}$$

$$O_3 \Big\downarrow \text{ and hydrolysis}$$

$$\cdots -CH_2-\overset{\overset{\displaystyle CH_3}{|}}{C}=O \quad O=CH-CH_2-CH_2-\overset{\overset{\displaystyle CH_3}{|}}{C}=O \quad O=CH-CH_2- \cdots$$
(IV)

$$HOOC-CH_2-CH_2-\overset{\overset{\displaystyle CH_3}{|}}{C}=O \quad \text{(V)}$$

$$HOOC-CH_2-CH_2-\overset{\overset{\displaystyle CH_3}{|}}{C}\overset{O-O}{\underset{O-O}{<}}>\overset{\overset{\displaystyle CH_3}{|}}{C}-CH_2-CH_2-COOH$$
(VI)

specific gravity and lower melting point of rubber. This assignment is strongly supported by the X-ray pattern diagram, which reveals a shorter identity period in rubber (8·3 Å) compared with gutta-percha (9·6 Å).

cis-configuration (VIII)

trans-configuration (IX)

Although the structural difference between rubber and gutta-percha is mainly one of geometrical isomerism, gutta-percha is of lower molecular weight and is much more highly crystalline than rubber.

Commercial rubber

Raw rubber of commerce (crêpe or sheet) contains about 94% rubber hydrocarbon in the best grades, the balance consisting of proteins (2–3%), acetone-soluble resins (2%, including fatty acids), small amounts of sugars (mainly quebrachitol) and a little mineral matter (mainly consisting of compounds of potassium, magnesium and phosphorus).

Among trace elements, specific mention must be made of copper and manganese, both deleterious as promoters of oxidative degradation of raw and vulcanised rubbers. Both elements are normally present in rubber to the extent of 2–3 parts per million; the origin of the manganese is obscure, but the copper is mainly present in a copper-containing enzyme which may be involved in the biosynthesis of the rubber hydrocarbon itself. Lower grades of rubber contain rather more incidental impurities (e.g. dirt, sand, mineral matter), but copper and manganese must not exceed 8 and 10 p.p.m. respectively in any of the official types of rubber established by the R.M.A.

Physical properties of rubber

The principal physical properties of raw rubber are shown in Table 2.1. Most of the properties are affected to a greater or lesser extent by the non-rubber substances, and the tabulated values must be regarded as average values. The density of solid rubber has not been very precisely defined, due partly to variations introduced by non-rubber substances and partly to

TABLE 2.1

SOME PHYSICAL PROPERTIES OF NATURAL RUBBER

Density	0·92
Refractive index (20° C)	1·52
Coefficient of cubical expansion	0·00062/° C
Cohesive energy density	63·7 cal./c.c.
Heat of combustion	10,700 cal./g.
Thermal conductivity	0·00032 cal./sec./cm.^{2}/° C
Dielectric constant	2·37
Power factor (1,000 cycles)	0·15–0·2 *
Volume resistivity	10^{15} ohms/c.c.
Dielectric strength	1,000 volts/mil

* The power factor is reduced to 0·0015 and the resistivity substantially increased in deproteinised rubber.

variations in the degree of crystallinity. (When maintained at temperatures below 10° C natural rubber becomes stiffer, harder, and opaque as a result of crystallisation. This change is accompanied by an increase in specific gravity from about 0·92 up to 0·95.) The density of rubber in latex has been given as 0·900 ± 0·001 at 25° C and 0·9025 ± 0·001 at 25° C.[13]

The behaviour of rubber in solvents

The solubility of rubber is largely determined by the pre-treatment of the rubber. Broadly, it can be stated that hydrocarbons, chlorinated hydrocarbons, carbon disulphide, ethers, the higher ketones and higher fatty acids have solvent action on rubber, while the lower ketones, alcohols and lower esters are non-solvents. The first action of a solvent is that of swelling; on more prolonged standing in a solvent some soluble rubber is extracted from the swollen gel. This phenomenon gave rise to a two-phase theory of rubber, comprising " sol " and " gel " phases, and various methods have been proposed for increasing the proportion of either of these components at the expense of the other. The difference in behaviour is now known to be one of degree rather than of kind, the gel consisting of the more highly branched and lightly cross-linked components of the rubber closely intertwined with insoluble high-molecular non-rubber substances, such as proteins. Any factors tending to disaggregate the gel, such as mechanical shear or oxidative degradation, promote its dissolution.[14] Accordingly, masticated rubbers are generally wholly soluble, and some degree of milling or mechanical working is necessary for the preparation of technical rubber solutions or doughs. Conversely, a treatment designed to increase the cross-linking, such as a light vulcanisation or even quite a mild treatment, such as exposure to quinone vapour, substantially reduces the soluble component of rubber.[15]

From the equilibrium swelling of a rubber sample immersed in a solvent, its degree of cross-linking can be calculated.[16, 17]

Purification of rubber hydrocarbon

Acetone extraction of rubber provides an easy means of removing some of the non-rubber substances (e.g. quebrachitol, fatty acids and resins) and is a useful preliminary to any purification procedure. It does not effectively remove any of the proteins in rubber.

If to a dilute solution of rubber there is added a non-solvent (e.g. methanol) with efficient stirring to ensure its uniform dispersal, no material is precipitated until a certain critical ratio of solvent to non-solvent is reached. This critical ratio is dependent upon temperature, upon the molecular weight of the hydrocarbon, and to a lesser extent upon the solution concentration unless the latter is very low. If a substantial excess of the precipitant is added practically the whole of the rubber hydrocarbon is precipitated, together with some of its original nitrogenous impurities, but other non-rubbers soluble in the solvent–precipitant mixture are effectively eliminated. A partial purification of rubber was achieved in this way by some of the earlier rubber scientists. Later it was discovered that if the proportion of solvent to non-solvent was carefully adjusted so that only a part of the rubber was precipitated (say 20–25%), then the nitrogenous impurities were precipitated with this first fraction, and subsequent fractions were fairly pure hydrocarbon.[18, 19]

The dissolution of unmasticated rubber into a single solvent, or a mixed solvent, avoiding agitation, which would cause dispersal of gel, also gives

D

substantially nitrogen-free rubbers in the soluble fraction, and if this is subsequently precipitated from solution by addition of a non-solvent the hydrocarbon is recovered in a fairly pure condition.

Rubber hydrocarbon in crystalline form has been obtained from a very dilute solution (0·05%) of purified rubber in ether at −65° C.[20]

In all operations involving purified rubber it is essential to maintain an oxygen-free atmosphere, otherwise rapid degradation occurs. This condition can be achieved only by taking stringent precautions, either by carrying out all operations in totally enclosed evacuated apparatus, or in equipment which is liberally flushed with highly purified nitrogen or carbon dioxide.

Both dissolution and precipitation methods suffer from the disadvantage that the purified rubber represents only a portion of the original rubber, and from a research point of view is not at all representative of the total hydrocarbon. The first fraction, which is usually rejected on account of its high content of non-rubbers, contains the highest molecular species, and consequently molecular-weight determinations on the purer subsequent fractions are substantially below the true value for the whole rubber. A serious manipulative difficulty arises from the rapidity with which high-molecular fractions become insoluble, even when stored in the dark in sealed, highly evacuated tubes.[21]

Purified total rubber is best obtained by treatment of latex. Most of the acetone-insoluble non-rubber substances are located on the surface of the rubber particles or dissolved in the serum, and are accordingly readily accessible for displacement or chemical destruction. One method which has been used successfully to destroy these non-rubber substances is treatment with alkali, either over a long period at tropical temperatures [22] or for shorter periods at 50° C,[23, 24] but it is difficult to maintain adequate stability of the latex during the process, and it is also difficult to avoid degradation, to which rubber containing alkali is particularly susceptible. Hydrolysis with water alone at 190° C has also been attempted.[25] Trypsin has been used to digest protein, the debris being subsequently removed by multi-creaming,[20, 21] and the ether or petroleum-ether soluble portions of acetone-extracted rubbers purified in this way have been obtained in a high state of purity (Table 2.2.). More recently a much simpler technique has been proposed [26–28] in which the impurities at the surface of the latex particles are wholly displaced by soap, after which the latex is multi-creamed to eliminate all the substances then present in the serum. The latex may then be coagulated to give a rubber containing only soap and acetone-soluble impurities, and these are removed by acetone-extraction. In a further refinement the purified latex is taken up into hexane containing ammonium oleate, which solubilises both water and rubber; a homogeneous solution is obtained within a minute. On centrifuging, the remaining nitrogenous and mineral impurities separate, and from the supernatant solution the purified rubber is isolated by precipitation and finally is acetone-extracted.   Purified rubber obtained by this method is a water-white translucent solid, and is considered to be at least 99·9% pure rubber hydrocarbon.

TABLE 2.2

ANALYSES OF SOME PURIFIED RUBBERS AND RUBBER FRACTIONS

(T denotes total rubber, F denotes a fraction)

Method of preparation	% C	% H	% N	% O *	% Ash	Ref.
Diffusion into ethyl ether (F)	88·18	11·94	Nil	—	—	23
Diffusion into light petroleum (F)	87·65	11·85	0·09	—	0·065	29
Selective diffusion into mixture of acetone and light petroleum (F)	88·0	11·9	0·005	—	Nil	21
Alkali-treatment of latex (T)	—	—	0·004	—	—	24
Water at 190° C (T)	87·95	11·85	0·03	—	0·15	25
Trypsin-treatment of latex, diffusion into ether, and crystallisation (F)	88·10	11·85	Nil	—	—	20
Trypsin-treatment of latex, selective diffusion into mixture of acetone and light petroleum (F)	88·3	11·9	0·006	—	Nil	21
Fractional precipitation, multistage (F)	88·07	11·86	0·007	—	—	30
Single-stage fractional precipitation from benzene–isopropanol (F)	88·1	11·8	0·01	0·05	0·04	31
Soap-treatment of latex, and multicentrifuging (T)	88·0	11·8	0·02	0·2	Nil	32
Soap-treatment of latex, multicreaming, and precipitation (T)	—	—	<0·01	—	<0·01	26–28
Recrystallised gutta-percha (T)	88·1	11·8	Nil	0·1	Nil	

* O by direct determination.[33]

Some partially purified rubbers have been made on a commercial scale by processes based on simplifications of the above procedures.   A typical product " G crêpe " (J.P.P. Karet) has the following average composition:

Moisture	0·07%
Nitrogen	0·11%
Ash	0·03%
Acetone-extract	1·76%
Water-extract	0·04%
Water-absorption	63 mg./100 c.c.

Fractionation and molecular weight distribution of rubber

Fractionation of the rubber hydrocarbon has been accomplished by methods involving either fractional precipitation based on cooling a warm solution of rubber in a solvent–precipitant mixture of controlled composition,[18, 31, 34, 35] or fractional dissolution based on the decreasing rate of diffusion of fractions of increasing molecular weight when rubber is immersed in a single solvent [34] or in a mixture of solvent and precipitant.[21] Both methods have established that the major part of the hydrocarbon has very high molecular weight, i.e. in excess of 200,000.   A study of the molecular weight of freshly tapped rubber, by both viscometric and osmotic techniques (see below), has shown that the hydrocarbon has an average molecular weight in the region of a million, but with a considerable distribution into higher and lower regions.[31]   With increasing molecular weight the hydrocarbon molecules are increasingly branched or entangled, passing into " soluble " (i.e. colloidally dispersible) regions of limited cross-linking which have been termed " microgel ".[37]   The microgel is mainly responsible for the gel-component of rubber, and is a normal constituent of rubber in freshly tapped latex.[38]   Further spontaneous cross-linking reactions appear to take place on storage of latex or of dry rubber, for whereas the hydrocarbon in freshly tapped latex is readily soluble,[39, 40] it can no longer be taken up directly into a solvent after a few weeks' storage of ammoniated latex.   Similar reactions in solid rubber lead to more extensive regions of gel (macrogel) which are probably responsible for the gel-fraction of rubber to which reference has already been made.   These spontaneous changes also cause progressive hardening of rubber stored in bulk.[41]

In latex the regions in which spontaneous cross-linking can occur are of necessity confined to the dimensions of individual latex particles, and the latex which first issues from previously untapped or long-rested trees is usually almost wholly microgel.   Since microgel is a colloidal dispersion and not a true solution, its solution viscosity is relatively low.   Consequently, rubber solutions containing some microgel have a lower viscosity than they would have if no microgel were present, and molecular weights derived from viscosity methods are accordingly too low.   Microgel can be effectively removed by high-speed centrifuging or by absorption on to fine powders.[38]   Such treatments remove a substantial proportion of rubber from a solution without appreciably altering the solution viscosity.

The high microgel content of latex in untapped trees results in a rubber which is mainly insoluble (i.e. of high gel content) and very hard.   The latex itself can be colloidally dispersed in a solvent and gives a fairly low solution viscosity.   As tapping proceeds, the microgel content of the latex falls rapidly; intrinsic viscosity accordingly increases, while the Mooney viscosity (a measure of hardness) and gel content both decrease (Table 2.3). Latex samples taken from various parts of a tree reveal that these changes are accompanied by a progressive drop in microgel content in latex sampled from regions adjacent to the tapping cut.   In more remote regions the microgel content does not fall, and even in trees which have been regularly tapped for twenty years the latex found in samples taken 15–20 ft. above the tapping panel has exclusively microgel characteristics.   This shows

TABLE 2.3

CHANGES IN BULKED LATEX ON BRINGING 114 UNTAPPED TREES
INTO REGULAR TAPPING

Consecutive tapping number	Yield of latex, litres	Intrinsic viscosity of rubber	Mooney viscosity and gel content of resulting smoked sheet	
			Mooney ML4	Gel %
1	1·5	2·1	120	85
2	2·0	3·2	98	84
3	2·7	3·8	88	82
4	2·8	4·3	82	82
5	3·5	4·5	77	80
6	5·7	4·6	74	77
8	5·7	4·3	67	74
9	4·5	4·2	72	72
12	8·2	4·1	58	72
25	10·2	4·1	62	66

that the rubber withdrawn from trees in regular tapping has probably been synthesised in regions of bark adjacent to the tapping panel and has not been photosynthesised in the leaves and transported through the trees, as has sometimes been suggested.

The entangled, branched and microgel structures present in natural rubber are believed to be responsible for the exponential form of eqn. 2.1. relating intrinsic viscosity to molecular weight, which is undoubtedly

$$[\eta] = 5 \times 10^{-4} \, M^{\,0.67} \quad . \quad . \quad . \quad . \quad . \quad (2.1)$$

obeyed by the higher fractions of unmilled purified rubber.[31, 42] Masticated rubber, however, shows a more linear relationship [43] the change-

$$[\eta] = 10^{-5} \, M^{0.98} \quad . \quad . \quad . \quad . \quad . \quad (2.2)$$

over being attributed to breakdown of structure due to milling. Because of such structural modifications, a good correlation usually exists between Mooney viscosity and intrinsic viscosity of masticated rubbers,[44] whereas major anomalies exist between these parameters in unmasticated rubbers (Table 2.4).

TABLE 2.4

INTRINSIC VISCOSITIES AND MOONEY VISCOSITIES OF SOME SAMPLES OF
R.S.S.1 RUBBER

Intrinsic viscosity	Mooney viscosity
4·85	47
4·9	45
5·5	50
5·6	110
6·15	110
6·5	72
7·3	115

Methods of estimating the molecular weight of rubber

Owing to the high molecular weight to be measured, methods based on depression of freezing point or elevation of boiling point are quite useless for rubber. Measurement of osmotic pressure undoubtedly provides the least-complicated method for the estimation of a really high molecular weight, and for this purpose the small Zimm–Myerson instrument [45] is very suitable for masticated or degraded rubber, or for the lower-molecular fractions of an undegraded rubber,[31] since its upper limit of usefulness with any degree of precision does not exceed a molecular weight of 500,000. Larger osmometers of the Fuoss–Mead type can usefully extend the upper limit somewhat, and an estimate of 5×10^6 has been obtained in one of these instruments for a high-molecular rubber fraction.[46] Methods based on light scattering or on diffusion sedimentation are suitable alternatives in this higher range of molecular weight, but the experimental procedures are very involved, and little systematic work has been done with rubber. Some molecular weights obtained by the latter methods on selected rubber fractions are in fair agreement with values obtained from osmotic pressure and from viscometric data converted to molecular weight by eqn. 2.1.[35]

Viscosity methods can be used with advantage for obtaining comparative data for rubber samples whose history is known, but in converting the data obtained from a sample of unknown origin to an absolute molecular weight one is faced with the uncertainty as to whether to use eqn. 2.1 or 2.2. In viscometry the measurement actually made is the time of flow (t) of a solution through a fine capillary, and this is compared with the time of flow (t_0) of the solvent at the same temperature. The relative viscosity $\eta_r = t/t_0$ or the specific viscosity $\eta_{sp} = \dfrac{t - t_0}{t_0} = \eta_r - 1$ is then calculated. A series of values of η_{sp}/c obtained at different concentrations c (expressed in g. polymer per 100 c.c. of solution) extrapolated to zero concentration gives the intrinsic viscosity $[\eta] = \left[\dfrac{\eta_{sp}}{c} \right]_{c \to 0}$. The inherent viscosity $\eta_i = \dfrac{\log_e \eta_r}{c}$ varies much less with concentration than does η_{sp}/c, and some workers prefer the extrapolation of this function to zero concentration, the limiting value $\left[\dfrac{\log_e \eta_r}{c} \right]_{c \to 0}$ being identical with the intrinsic viscosity as just defined.[47] At sufficiently low concentrations (generally below 0·05 g./100 c.c.) the value of the inherent viscosity for rubber in benzene is fortuitously almost independent of concentration. Accordingly, within this range a single determination of η_r suffices to obtain the intrinsic viscosity with sufficient accuracy for routine measurements.[40]

The viscosity of solutions of freshly tapped hydrocarbon has been found to be very sensitive to additions of small amounts of polar or even non-polar substances, and when derived from viscometric data the apparently large molecular-weight differences observed between trees and between clones are more probably due to the extreme sensitivity of solution behaviour of the higher-molecular entities towards impurities rather than to any major differences in the basic natural-rubber hydrocarbon itself. In other words, the interpretation of viscometric data for natural rubber must be treated with extreme caution. The fine structure of natural rubber is indeed so complex that it seems improbable that further useful information can be obtained from conventional polymer characterisation studies, even with fresh latex, and less likely still with older rubber.

The heterogeneity of natural rubber

The most rigorous interpretations of the infra-red spectrum of rubber shows it to be at least 97% *cis*-1 : 4 polyisoprene (VIII).[48,49] There is a weak absorption band at 890 cm.$^{-1}$ which might be due to a few units per cent of a 3 : 4 addition unit (X) containing vinyl side-groups, but the evidence is by no means convincing, and there is no indication of absorption at 910 cm.$^{-1}$ corresponding to the 1 : 2 structure (XI).

$$CH_2\!=\!\underset{\underset{\vdots}{|}}{\overset{\overset{CH_3}{|}}{C}}\!-\!CH\!-\!CH_2\!-\cdots \qquad \cdots -CH_2\!-\!\underset{\underset{\vdots}{|}}{\overset{\overset{CH_3}{|}}{C}}\!-\!CH\!=\!CH_2$$

$$(X) \qquad\qquad\qquad (XI)$$

There is some evidence of a small content of oxygenated functional groupings in the rubber molecule itself, and the existence of some " weak links " has been suggested [43] to explain the fact that even under strictly oxygen-free conditions solutions of natural rubber maintained at 100°–120° C undergo a reduction in viscosity to a lower limiting value. On average, there is one such anomalous band per 13,000 monomer units (i.e. in molecular weight 900,000).

The best analytical data for rubber,[30] obtained from a highly purified fraction, gave the mean values C 88·07; H 11·86; N 0·007, O (by difference) 0·06%. The H/C ratio is 0·1346 and in view of the high degree of experimental accuracy this appears to be significantly higher than the value 0·13436 derived from the accepted calculated values C 88·16 and H 11·84, which are based on C = 12·0048, H = 1·0081 and O = 16·0000. (The theoretical ratio of 0·13436 becomes 0·13430 when recalculated with the 1953 international atomic weights C = 12·010 and H = 1·0081. The corresponding recalculation of the experimental analysis gives C 88·09; H 11·86; ratio 0·1346.) The significance of the departure from the theoretical ratio is supported by values obtained by the same analysts for alkali-metal polymerised polyisoprene, namely C 88·17; H 11·83; total 100·00% with H/C ratio 0·1342. The difference in the H/C ratios indicates an average excess over theory of one hydrogen atom in every 60–70 isoprene units. The excess tends to increase in lower molecular fractions of rubber, there being a trend towards a H/C ratio of 0·135 with decreasing molecular weight (one excess hydrogen in 20–30 units).[21, 37]

The oxygen content of rubber

The small oxygen content (0·06%) in the above analysis is not unambiguously established solely by the deficit in the C, H and N total without other evidence. The analysts also showed that the same highly purified fraction gelled in the presence of a Grignard reagent and liberated methane equivalent to 0·02% oxygen, whereas their synthetic polyisoprene was wholly unreactive. Similar positive indications of hydroxylic (or carboxylic) functional groups have been obtained by a sensitive micro-method for active hydrogen,[50] and 0·01–0·02% of peroxidic oxygen has also been reported in purified rubber.[29] Indications of a carboxylic group [51] have been obtained when extracted rubber containing zinc palmitate was heated in a molecular still; palmitic acid distilled off, and its amount indicated about 0·1% of oxygen in acidic functions.

The discovery that the lower-molecular fractions of natural rubber contain substantially greater amounts of combined oxygen [21, 37, 52] proved the presence of oxygen in rubber beyond any reasonable doubt, especially when the experiments were repeated in Malaya with latex tapped under conditions minimising its exposure to air.[37] The exact nature of the oxygenated groups is still open to question; based on the evidence of their reactivity towards methyl magnesium iodide and their behaviour on saponification, much of the oxygen appears to be in esterified hydroxyl or carboxyl groups. Only the low-molecular fractions, below 100,000 molecular weight, have an appreciable oxygen content, i.e. generally around 0·3% at 100,000, 0·5% at 50,000 and 1% at 30,000. Since the amount of these fractions is generally less than 5% of the total rubber, they make little contribution to the overall properties of rubber. Whether they are natural degradation products or naturally occurring polyisoprenic substances of molecular weight lower than that of rubber is still unknown.

The chemistry of natural rubber

The basic chemistry of rubber is essentially that of an olefin with internal double bonds, and it accordingly conforms with the classical reactions of olefins in its ability to undergo addition reactions at its double bonds or substitution of one or more of its hydrogen atoms. Indeed, much of the chemical behaviour of rubber can be forecast from experiments con- ducted with relatively simple olefins of low molecular weight, e.g. 2- methylbutene-2 (XII), which consists solely of one of the repeating units of the polyisoprene chain. However, in some of its reactions (notably thermal decomposition, autoxidation, halogenation and cyclisation) the be- haviour of any one of the repeating units cannot be considered apart from

$$\underset{\text{(XII)}}{CH_3\text{—}\overset{\overset{\displaystyle CH_3}{|}}{C}\text{=}CH\text{—}CH_3} \qquad \underset{\text{(XIII)}}{CH_3\text{—}\overset{\overset{\displaystyle CH_3}{|}}{C}\text{=}CH\text{—}CH_2\text{—}CH_2\text{—}\overset{\overset{\displaystyle CH_3}{|}}{C}\text{=}CH\text{—}CH_3}$$

its neighbour, and in its broader aspect the chemistry of rubber is that of the di-isoprenic unit $-CH_2 \cdot CMe{:}CH \cdot CH_2 \cdot CH_2 \cdot CMe{:}CH \cdot CH_2-$ rather than that of the simpler unit as exemplified by (XII). Hence a more appropriate low-molecular analogue of rubber is the hydrocarbon 2 : 6- dimethyloctadiene-2 : 6 (XIII), which can be synthesised in a high state of purity by the reduction of purified geraniol with sodium in liquid am- monia.[53, 54] Since this hydrocarbon can also be made quite readily (al- though spectroscopically less pure) by the reduction of myrcene obtained from bay oil (*Pimenta acris*),[55] it is also known as dihydromyrcene. Squalene (XIV) containing six isoprenic repeating units (although with a reversal of sense symmetrically about its centre) is also a convenient low- molecular analogue of rubber, but has the disadvantage of a higher boiling

$$CH_3 \cdot CMe{:}CH \cdot CH_2 \cdot CH_2 \cdot CMe{:}CH \cdot CH_2 \cdot CH_2 \cdot CMe{:}CH \cdot CH_2$$
$$\underset{\text{(XIV)}}{CH_3 \cdot CMe{:}CH \cdot CH_2 \cdot CH_2 \cdot CMe{:}CH \cdot CH_2 \cdot CH_2 \cdot CMe{:}CH \cdot \overset{|}{C}H_2}$$

point than dihydromyrcene. It is a major constituent of the liver-oil of the basking shark (*Symnorhinus lichia*), from which it is easily separated by high-vacuum distillation and purified by absorption of its impurities on alumina.[55]

Superimposed on the classical olefin chemistry of rubber are a few reactions specific to its high-molecular character, as will be apparent in later sections of this chapter.

An important factor governing the chemical reactivity of rubber is the reduction in the amount of energy required to rupture those bonds which, on breaking, produce allylic radicals. An allylic radical is an entity con- taining the structure (XV)

$$\underset{\text{(XV)}}{R_2\overset{*}{C}\text{—}CR\text{=}C{<}^R_R}$$

Radicals of this kind (XVII and XVIII) are formed either by breaking the C–C bond between atoms 5 and 1a in structure (XVI) or by removal of H atoms by breaking the H–C bonds attached to C atoms 1, 3, or 5, giving the structures XIX, XX and XXI respectively, the asterisk denoting the free radical. These bonds are therefore the energetically favoured seats of scission in rubber.

$$\cdots -CH_2-\underset{\underset{1}{|}}{\overset{\overset{3}{CH_3}}{C}}\underset{2}{=}\underset{4}{CH}-CH_2-\underset{5}{CH_2}-\underset{\underset{1a}{|}}{\overset{\overset{3a}{CH_3}}{C}}\underset{2a}{=}\underset{4a}{CH}-\underset{5a}{CH_2}-\cdots \quad (XVI)$$

$$\downarrow$$

$$\cdots -CH_2-\overset{\overset{CH_3}{|}}{C}=CH-\overset{*}{CH_2} + \overset{*}{CH_2}-\overset{\overset{CH_3}{|}}{C}=CH-CH_2-\cdots$$

$$\updownarrow \qquad\qquad\qquad\qquad \updownarrow$$

$$\cdots -CH_2-\overset{\overset{CH_3}{|}}{\underset{*}{C}}-CH=CH_2 \qquad\qquad CH_2=\overset{\overset{CH_3}{|}}{C}-\overset{*}{CH}-CH_2-\cdots$$

$$\text{(XVII)} \qquad\qquad\qquad\qquad \text{(XVIII)}$$

$$\cdots -\overset{*}{CH}-\overset{\overset{CH_3}{|}}{C}=CH-CH_2-\cdots \rightleftharpoons \cdots -CH=\overset{\overset{CH_3}{|}}{C}-\overset{*}{CH}-CH_2-\cdots$$

$$\text{(XIX)}$$

$$\cdots -CH_2-\overset{\overset{\overset{*}{CH_2}}{|}}{C}=CH-CH_2-\cdots \rightleftharpoons \cdots -CH_2-\overset{\overset{CH_2}{||}}{C}-\overset{*}{CH}-CH_2-\cdots$$

$$\text{(XX)}$$

$$\cdots -CH_2-\overset{\overset{CH_3}{|}}{C}=CH-\overset{*}{CH_2}-\cdots \rightleftharpoons \cdots -CH_2-\overset{\overset{CH_3}{|}}{\underset{*}{C}}-CH=CH-\cdots$$

$$\text{(XXI)}$$

None of these allylic radicals can be formally expressed in either of the two extreme configurations shown; they are to be regarded as oscillating between these structures. Molecules or radicals which behave in this way are thereby rendered more stable, and the phenomenon is known as " resonance ". An allylic radical gains energy equivalent to 19,000 cal./ mole in virtue of this effect,[56] hence the removal of H atoms to give structures (XIX–XXI) is facilitated by this amount of energy. The affected positions " next door to the double bond " are termed the α-methylenic positions, and on the relative ease of removal of the α-methylenic hydrogen atoms $(5 \gg 1 > 3)$ [57] depends the locus of substitive reactions of rubber.

When the C–C bond between atoms 5 and 1 is broken *both* of the radicals formed (XVII, XVIII) are allylic, and their combined energy level is $2 \times 19,000$ cal./mole greater than that of corresponding saturated or non-resonating fragments. Hence the energy of fission of the 1–5 bond is reduced by 38,000 cal./mole, whereas fission of the C–C bonds in any other position will not be facilitated in this way.[56] Obviously, in any scission reactions of rubber the 1–5 bond will be the most easily broken.

In addition to the structural influences determining the position of scission and location of substitutive attack, the unsymmetrically substituted double bond determines the direction of addition of unsymmetrical addenda, either in accordance with the well-known Markownikoff rule for ionic additions or in the contrary sense where radical additions are concerned.

Thermal behaviour of rubber

Although rubber oxidises rapidly when heated in air at temperatures much above 120° C, it has been found that rubber from which all traces of oxygen have been removed can be heated at temperatures up to 200° C for long periods without effect. At higher temperatures the rubber softens progressively into a viscous liquid and volatile products begin to appear. At the same time the degraded rubber becomes increasingly resinous as a result of cyclisation. The best yields of heat-cyclised rubber occur when the rubber is heated for several hours in the temperature range 250°–300° C, preferably in a solvent,[58] but even when volatile degradation products are continuously removed either by reduction of pressure or by passing a stream of inert gas as much as 30–40% of the rubber remains behind in this cyclised modification.

The volatile heat degradation products from rubber comprise a range of terpenoid hydrocarbons as exemplified by Table 2.5, which gives the results of a fractional distillation of the volatile products obtained from rubber maintained at 300°–350° C under vacuum; under these conditions 63·5% of the rubber degraded to volatile products and 36·5% remained in cyclised form.[59]

If the rubber is heated rapidly to temperatures in the region of 700° C so as to avoid more than a momentary exposure to the lower temperatures which favour cyclisation the yield of the more volatile degradation products is greatly increased, and the major constituents of the distillate are then isoprene and dipentene. Minor constituents of the distillate have been examined in detail.[60] Dipentene and probably other degradation products of rubber are themselves readily cracked to isoprene. The overall yield of

TABLE 2.5

DISTILLATION OF VOLATILE PRODUCTS OBTAINED FROM RUBBER AT
300°–350° C

B.° pt./0·03 mm. ° C	% of component present	Principal constituent
<45	5·6	Isoprene
45–46	11·6	Dipentene
46–60	4·4	
60–85	5·3	} $C_{15}H_{24}$
85–100	8·3	
100–150	8·1	
150–170	16·5	} Diterpenes $C_{25}H_{40}$
170–190	7·7	
190–220	14·7	
220–225	8·0	} Not identified
Residue	8·3	

isoprene from rubber has been increased to 60% by feeding the rubber continuously to a cracking tube packed with contact material of high thermal conductivity and maintained at 725° C under reduced pressure between 5 and 10 mm. of mercury.[61, 62] Under these conditions the rubber is degraded very rapidly and at the same time its isoprene-yielding degradation products are cracked to isoprene.

The preferential formation of isoprene and dipentene on pyrolysis of rubber follows logically from the ideas expressed above on the relative ease of fission of the various bonds in rubber. The normal amount of energy required to break a single C–C bond in a paraffin chain is 81,000 cal./mole, while a double bond requires 145,000 cal./mole. It has already been shown that the energy required to break the 1–5 bond is reduced by 38,000 cal., i.e. to 43,000 cal./mole. Once the initial scission has occurred, the splitting off of a complete isoprene unit is further aided, since the disappearance of two single C–C bonds and the formation of a C=C double bond means that the overall energy required to accomplish the scission of the second 1–5 bond at point P

$$\cdots -CH_2-\overset{\overset{\textstyle CH_3}{|}}{C}=CH-CH_2\overset{\overset{\textstyle P}{\downarrow}}{-}CH_2-\overset{\overset{\textstyle CH_3}{|}}{C}=CH-\overset{*}{C}H_2 \longrightarrow$$

$$\cdots -CH_2-\overset{\overset{\textstyle CH_3}{|}}{C}=CH-\overset{*}{C}H_2 + CH_2=\overset{\overset{\textstyle CH_3}{|}}{C}-CH=CH_2$$

is only 2 × 81,000 – 145,000 cal., i.e. 17,000 cal./mole, and this figure is reduced to about 10,000 cal./mole by the fact that an isoprene molecule is itself stabilised by about 7,000 cal./mole of resonance energy. Hence, once an initial break has occurred in a rubber molecule, the splitting of

successive isoprene molecules from the broken end occurs with considerable facility.

The formation of dipentene XXII arises from the addition of the radical
end of a once-broken molecule to the neighbouring double bond to form a
six-membered ring, accompanied by scission of the next adjacent 1–5 C–C
bond at P^1.

$$\cdots -CH_2-\underset{\substack{| \\ CH_3}}{C}=CH-CH_2\overset{P^1}{\downarrow}CH_2-\underset{\substack{| \\ CH_3}}{C}=CH-CH_2-CH_2-\underset{\substack{| \\ CH_3}}{C}=CH-\overset{*}{C}H_2$$

$$\downarrow$$

$$\cdots -CH_2-\underset{\substack{| \\ CH_3}}{C}=CH-\overset{*}{C}H_2 + CH_2=\underset{\substack{| \\ CH_3}}{C}-CH\begin{smallmatrix}CH_2-CH_2\\ \\ CH_2-CH\end{smallmatrix}C-CH_3 \quad (XXII)$$

Since one C–C bond is formed while another is broken, the heat of reaction
is zero, and probably the main factor in limiting the speed of this reaction
is the special steric configuration required of the radical end. Experiments
have shown that the rates at which isoprene and dipentene are formed are
respectively 25 and 100 times greater than would be the case if they were
produced only by splitting the appropriate groups from the ends of rubber
molecules.

Various proposals have been put forward from time to time for the preparation of motor fuels, diesel oils, lubricating oils, and solvents by the
thermal cracking of raw [63] or vulcanised scrap rubber.[64, 65] Resinification
of the products has presented some difficulty and has doubtless inspired
attempts to obtain products which are more saturated or more aromatic in
structure. The presence of 10–20% of aluminium chloride [66,67] enables
the cracking to take place at substantially lower temperatures and gives
mainly cyclic hydrocarbons (cyclohexane derivatives). Cracking accompanied by catalytic hydrogenation,[68-71] involving temperatures around
450°–480° C under 200 atmospheres hydrogen pressure in the presence of
molybdenum sulphide on alumina, gives 83·5% of saturated hydrocarbons
and 15% aromatic hydrocarbons.

The distillation products of rubber have not assumed commercial importance, even at times of very low rubber prices, although under the exceptional conditions prevailing during the Japanese occupation some
rubber was converted into fuel oil in Malaya and Burma.[72-74] " Caout-
choucine ", the fraction consisting mainly of dipentene, has been used to
denature alcohol.

Thermal degradation, aided by oxygen in the presence of suitable
catalysts, at temperatures below those of severe cracking has achieved some

importance in the manufacture of so-called " depolymerised rubber " or " liquid rubber " (see p. 80).

The action of light on rubber

When rubber solutions are exposed to light without free access to oxygen, gelation occurs after a period of time determined by the amount of oxygen adventitiously present and the nature of the solvent. The phenomenon has been aptly termed " photogelation ".[75-78] Gelation occurs most readily either in " active solvents " (ketones or chlorinated hydrocarbons) or in " inactive solvents " (ethers, hydrocarbons) containing small amounts of photosensitisers, but it has been observed with solutions in inactive solvents from which oxygen has been excluded. Photogelation in active solvents is usually accompanied by the combination of a substantial part of the solvent itself (or fragments thereof) with the rubber; thus the rubber recovered from photogels prepared in carbon tetrachloride contains 5–15% of combined chlorine which survives acetone-extraction. The gels have the characteristics of lightly vulcanised rubber and are undoubtedly cross-linked modifications of the rubber hydrocarbon with or without involvement of the solvent. Although the reaction details for the many systems empirically investigated are unknown and are almost certainly too complex to be readily resolved, the common features are clear. In the absence of oxygen cross-linking is initiated by free radicals produced photolytically from the active solvents, the sensitisers or the rubber. In the presence of oxygen, photo-oxidation first ensues with the usual degradation of rubber molecules; when the available oxygen is consumed the photolytic cross-linking reaction sets in, aided perhaps by the oxygenated centres, which may themselves provide photo-active centres for radical formation. Readmission of oxygen during irradiation may by degradation solubilise the gel already formed. Antioxidants or other substances capable of facile reaction with free radicals delay photogelation. The principal action of light on purified rubber hydrocarbon itself is one of cross-linking (diagnosed by insolubilisation and a swelling index comparable with that of a vulcanised rubber) accompanied by liberation of volatile gaseous products, of which the major constituent is hydrogen.[19] Since hydrogen is the major product, the α-methylenic C–H bonds are regarded as the principal dissociation sites in view of the reduced energy required to sever these bonds. Only those hydrogen atoms formed within a few atomic distances of the surface can be expected to escape and to combine to give molecular hydrogen; most of the latter more probably results from the reaction $H + RH \longrightarrow H_2 + R^*$, where R^* is an allylic rubber radical (again probably α-methylenic). The radical sites exposed both by this mechanism and by the original photolytic fission are the probable seats of cross-linking, either by mutual combination or addition to double bonds.

The action of high-energy radiation on rubber

The action of high-energy radiation (such as is present in atomic piles or is available from electron accelerators or waste fission products) on rubber is qualitatively very similar to that of light, but quantitatively considerably more intense. In fact, it can provide a technically practicable means of vulcanising rubber without the use of extraneous substances.[79] The principal reaction is again fission of C–H bonds, and hydrogen has been shown to be the major gaseous reaction product.[80] The amount of hydrogen evolved corresponds qualitatively with the degree of cross-linking deduced from swelling measurements, and this shows that the elimination of hydrogen atoms is responsible for much of the observed cross-linking.

The plasticity of rubber

As has already been made clear, the plasticity of a sample of freshly prepared rubber is very dependent upon the amount of microgel in the latex from which it is made. During coagulation, sheeting and drying some of the microgel undergoes conversion to macrogel, i.e. regions of cross-linking which exceed colloidal dimensions. Macrogel is revealed as residual gel when the soluble portion of the rubber hydrocarbon is allowed to diffuse into a solvent or a mixture of solvents, preferably under conditions permitting free access of solvent to the finely divided rubber;[81,82] a good correlation has been shown to exist between the plasticity of rubber and its gel content.[31] Cross-linking reactions responsible for gel formation slowly continue on storage of rubber, especially at low humidity, and both gel-content and hardness increase progressively.[41] Water has a marked effect, by an unknown mechanism, in retarding this change; intensive drying frequently leads to progressive insolubilisation of rubber.[36] This sort of hardening is not to be confused with hardening due to crystallisation on storage of rubber at low temperatures. Hardening of the former type is non-reversible, whereas that due to crystallisation is largely destroyed by warming long enough to " thaw out " the rubber. Rubber in this frozen crystalline state is commonly referred to as " stark " rubber.

There are several well-known methods of altering the plasticity of natural rubber to meet particular requirements. Hardening is brought about by any reagent which induces a small degree of cross-linking into the rubber, and treatments are very effective when applied to latex. Benzidine,[31,83] pyrogallol,[27] a light vulcanisation with sulphur [84] or the free-radical producing " peroxamine " system [85] are all effective reagents which may raise the Mooney viscosity to well over 150 units. The last-named system comprises an organic hydroperoxide (e.g. *tert*-butyl or cumyl) in conjunction with a polyethylene polyamine (e.g. tetra-ethylene pentamine).

Softened rubbers are produced by methods involving catalysed oxidative chain scission at temperatures in the range 110°–140° C in the presence of a chemical plasticiser,[86, 87] the function of which will be clarified later. These plasticisers (commonly called peptisers) are usually thiols, disulphides or the corresponding zinc salts and are used in a proportion of 0·05–0·5% on the rubber. Mercaptobenzthiazole, the well-known vulcanisation accelerator, is very effective in this role; other current proprietary materials include *o,o'*-dibenzamidodiphenyl disulphide, thio-β-naphthol, xylyl mercaptan and *bis*-pentachlorophenyl disulphide. The corresponding zinc salts are frequently active at lower temperatures; thus, whereas *o,o'*-dibenzamidodiphenyl disulphide requires a temperature of 120°–140° C to be effective, its zinc salt begins to soften rubber at 65° C.

Peptisers can be incorporated into latex before its coagulation so as to give rubbers either of greater plasticity or capable of rapid thermal plasticisation during processing according to whether the peptiser is active at the temperatures prevailing during estate drying or is effective only at the higher temperatures reached during processing.

Softened rubber has also been made by heating crumbed rubber at 170° in air.[88] This process is definitely oxidative, there being a gain in weight of about 2%.

Depolymerised rubber and fluid rubber compositions

If the thermal treatment of rubber containing a chemical plasticiser (e.g. mercaptobenzthiazole) is prolonged beyond that required for reasonable softening, highly degraded rubbers are produced without the introduction of appreciable oxygenated groups. The degradation may be carried out over a period of several hours at 140° C or a shorter period at 250°–300° C,[89, 90] and an analysis of a typical product (C 86·5; H 11·5; O 1·06; N 0·29; ash 0·4; Mol. wt. 2,000; unsaturation 81% of original rubber) shows that the degradation has been carried to an advanced stage without the introduction of an appreciable amount of oxygen into the rubber and without very much cyclisation. (The oxygen content of unpurified smoked sheet or crêpe rubber is usually around 1%.)

Commercial depolymerised rubber [91, 92] is available in England in two grades with viscosities at 20° C of 5,000 and 25,000 poises. These are pourable while hot, and when compounded with mineral oil they provide fluid compositions, pourable at room temperature, which are vulcanisable to soft rubbers or even to ebonite, and hence are suitable for making articles from rubber by a casting technique. Typical applications are potting of electronic components, brush-bristle cements, binders for abrasive in grinding wheels and battery boxes.

Mastication of rubber

It has long been known from practical experience that the breakdown of rubber on a mill or in an internal mixer occurs much more rapidly at either high or moderately low temperatures than it does at temperatures around 100° C, and this rather puzzling behaviour has only comparatively recently been satisfactorily explained.[44, 93] The explanation has fully justified an interesting suggestion put forward some years ago that mechanical rupture of primary bonds is possible under the stresses set up during mastication, and that the free radicals thus produced recombine unless stabilised by the addition of oxygen.[94] In the absence of oxygen, i.e. when mastication is carried out in an inert atmosphere, either in an internal mixer or on a boxed-in mill, little or no breakdown occurs under ordinary mastication conditions; indeed, in the early stages of mastication a slight hardening has been observed.[87, 95, 96] Under these conditions radicals resulting from mechanical shear recombine, although not necessarily with their original partners. Branching or cross-linking may result from the occasional interaction of a radical with another rubber molecule. The overall effect is a redistribution of chain lengths without much change in either plasticity or average molecular weight, although under more severe conditions of mastication obtained in laboratory machines there is evidence of preferential breakdown of the longer molecules, which causes an overall softening and lowering of average molecular weight, accompanied by a sharpening of the molecular-weight-distribution curve.[97]

Since the breakdown of rubber is now attributed to addition of oxygen to the rubber radicals to give oxygen-terminated fragments of lower molecular weight in accordance with the above suggestion, then many other known radical acceptors can be expected to react in an analogous manner. The demonstration that they do indeed promote breakdown of rubber in an inert atmosphere, and moreover, do so in a manner capable of quantitative interpretation, has provided adequate confirmation of the mechanical-rupture hypothesis. The type of additive which can be expected to function in this way may be forecast by known interactions of radicals with molecules, more especially in the field of vinyl polymerisations. Quinones, thiols, disulphides and the stable free radical diphenylpicrylhydrazyl are particularly effective (Table 2.6).

Colorimetric determination of the highly coloured unreacted diphenylpicrylhydrazyl, or radiochemical assay of labelled dinaphthyl [S^{35}]-disulphide in rubbers masticated under nitrogen in the presence of these additives has shown that the amount of reagent incorporated as end-groups is in close agreement with that calculated from the decrease in molecular weight.[98]

TABLE 2.6

BREAKDOWN OF RUBBER IN NITROGEN ATMOSPHERE IN PRESENCE OF ADDITIVES
(30 MINUTES MASTICATION) AT 55° C

Additive	Amount, % on rubber	Resulting Mooney viscosity, ML4
None	—	75
Thiophenol	1·0	22
Iodine	2·35	45
o,o'-Dibenzamidodiphenyldisulphide	4·2	33
Diphenylpicrylhydrazyl	0·01	55
Oxygen	150 mm. Hg	19

Whenever the primary product of addition of an acceptor to a rubber fragment is reactive towards another molecule, then branching or cross-linking may occur.   Examples of additives giving this type of reactivity are to be found in Table 2.7; the products are usually crumbs of high gel content.   With these additives both degradation and cross-linking reactions are occurring together.

TABLE 2.7

MASTICATION UNDER NITROGEN IN PRESENCE OF CROSS-LINKING ADDITIVES
(30 MINUTES AT 55° C)

Additive	Amount, % on rubber	Resulting Mooney viscosity ML4	Gel content, %
None	—	75	—
Chloranil	2·3	200	80
Maleic anhydride	0·9	120	75
m-Aminophenol	1·0	118	45
Benzidine	1·7	102	50
Trimethylene dimercaptan	0·7	98	73

Radical acceptors which promote breakdown of rubber are not to be confused with the chemical plasticisers (peptisers) referred to earlier.   The former are only effective under conditions of cold mastication and do not cause breakdown above 100° C in absence of oxygen.   Several of the common oxidation catalysts and peptisers (e.g. o,o'-dibenzamidodiphenyl disulphide) are also radical acceptors, and accordingly function as such in cold mastication; at higher temperatures they cause no breakdown in absence of oxygen but strongly catalyse oxidative breakdown, whereas some of the radical acceptors (e.g. pyrogallol, β-naphthol) retard it.   The behaviour of some substances which function in either one way or the other, together with some which function in both ways, is set out in Table 2.8.

TABLE 2.8

MASTICATION OF RUBBER WITH ADDITIVES SHOWING DIFFERENT TYPES OF ACTIVITY (30 MINUTES MASTICATION)

Additive	Type	Mooney viscosity after mastication in			
		Nitrogen at		Air at	
		55° C	140° C	55° C	140° C
None	—	75	75	19	10
Pyrogallol	Radical acceptor	63	75	37	43
α-Naphthol	,,	57	75	21	23
Azo-bis-isobutyronitrile	Oxidation catalyst	80	81	80	17
Co-naphthenate	,,	47	75	15	5
Mercaptobenzthiazole	Dual function	57	75	15	5
o,o'-Dibenzamidodiphenyl disulphide	,,	33	79	85	5

As the temperature reached in the rubber mass during mastication is increased the rubber becomes progressively softer, and the rate of mechanical rupture is correspondingly reduced. Hence the breakdown efficiency obtained with radical acceptors under nitrogen falls with increasing temperature (Fig. 2.1). A similar curve is obtained in oxygen, but in addition a second type of breakdown due to conventional oxidative scission becomes apparent a little above 80° C, and this increases rapidly with temperature. The overall behaviour of rubber masticated in air is expressed by the dotted curve in Fig. 2.1, in which stabilisation by oxygen of radicals formed by mechanical rupture is responsible for the left-hand part of the curve and oxidative degradation is responsible for the right-hand part. Degradation is at a minimum at 105° C. The different reaction mechanisms responsible for the two portions of the breakdown curve explain why the right-hand portion responds to additions of common oxidation inhibitors (antioxidants) while the left-hand portion is insensitive to such additions, and, although requiring the presence of oxygen, is not dependent upon the amount of oxygen present (i.e. the oxygen pressure) over a wide range. The left-hand curve also explains why rubbers of widely different oxidisabilities undergo cold breakdown at comparable rates.

With one or two exceptions (e.g. maleic anhydride, carbon black) radical acceptors are the effective terminators in cold mastication only when oxygen is absent. Oxygen generally predominates over other reagents in any

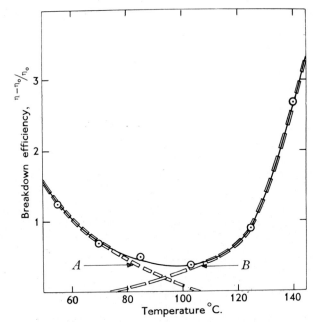

Fig. 2.1. Breakdown of natural rubber after 30 minutes mastication at different temperatures.

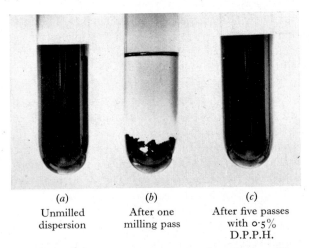

(a)	(b)	(c)
Unmilled dispersion	After one milling pass	After five passes with 0·5% D.P.P.H.

Fig. 2.2. Interaction of rubber and carbon black: milling strongly promotes the formation of a rubber–carbon black gel, which can be prevented by addition of radical acceptors (D.P.P.H. denotes diphenylpicrylhydrazyl).

competition for the primary radicals, hence the effects of other additives are undetectable in the presence of oxygen, since the maximum rate of plasticisation has already been attained.

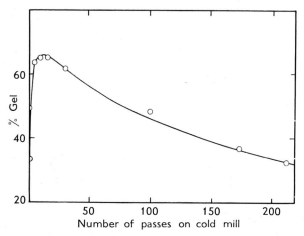

Fig. 2.3. Effect of milling natural rubber containing 50 p.h.r. Philblack O: 0·005 inch nip at roll temperature 25° C.

Carbon gel formation by cold mastication. The free radical character of ruptured rubber molecules makes a substantial contribution towards a better understanding of the mechanisms underlying the formation of

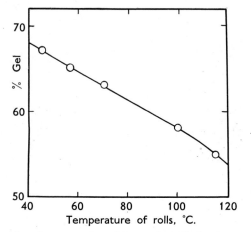

Fig. 2.4. Decrease in gel content of a rubber–carbon black mixture after five passes through 0·005 inch mill nip at increasing temperatures.

carbon gel. Carbon black is itself a radical acceptor, and since it is poly-functional, a network structure is built up by combination with rubber radicals.[99] This is easily demonstrated by a simple experiment. An intimate mixture of rubber and carbon black can be formed by freeze-drying a rubber solution containing dispersed black. This mixture is readily redispersible in benzene (Fig. 2.2(a)). Yet one pass through the tight nip of a mill gives a gel which is to a large extent insoluble. When placed in benzene (Fig. 2.2(b)) the supernatant liquid remains colourless, while the carbon black is contained in a coherent gel along with a considerable proportion of the rubber. The resistance of the gel to disintegration on shaking with the solvent increases up to approximately ten passes

Fig. 2.5. The production of interpolymers by milling. The upper test piece comprises rubber containing neoprene bound to it by milling in nitrogen, the lower test pieces are conventional mixtures of rubber and neoprene. All these have been given a " neoprene cure ".

through the nip (Fig. 2.3). The amount of gel decreases with increasing mill temperature (Fig. 2.4), as is to be expected from the lower rate of shear at higher temperatures.

If the proposed radical mechanism is correct, then competitive radical acceptors should reduce the formation of carbon gel. This is clearly shown by diphenylpicrylhydrazyl (Fig. 2.2(c)) of which the presence of a minute amount suppresses the formation of gel. Pretreatment of the carbon black with a radical acceptor, on the other hand, has no effect on its ability to form gel. Carbon black appears, however, to compete effectively

with oxygen, at least during the first few passes through the mill.   More
prolonged mastication reduces the amount of gel.

Formation of interpolymers by cold mastication.   Novel interpolymers
have been prepared by applying the above concepts to mixtures of elastomers.   If two rubbers which individually undergo softening on cold
milling in oxygen are mixed and cold milled *in oxygen*, then the result is
practically the same as if the two separately softened rubbers were mixed

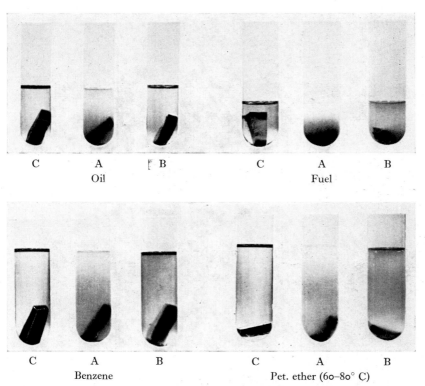

Fig. 2.6. Solvent resistance of inter-polymers produced by milling: the material pro-
     duced by vulcanisation in a neoprene recipe from rubber containing bound
     neoprene (Tube C) shows much better resistance to solvents than those obtained
     from rubber containing free neoprene (Tubes A and B).

together.   If, however, the mixture of the two rubbers is cold milled in
the absence of oxygen, then the reactive fragments formed from each
component combine randomly, and thus produce an interpolymer.   The
systems comprising natural rubber with neoprene, GR-S and acrylonitrile
rubber have been studied in this way,[100] and the behaviour of the neoprene system is illustrated in Figs. 2.5 and 2.6.   Of the rubber–neoprene
compositions described, only the interpolymer formed on mastication in

the absence of oxygen gives a satisfactory vulcanisate with a neoprene curing recipe (Fig. 2.5), and the solubility properties of this product are quite distinctive (Fig. 2.6). The technological significance of this work remains to be explored.

Fig. 2.7. A laboratory masticator for masticating rubber in a nitrogen atmosphere.

Formation of interpolymers by rubber—initiated polymerisation of vinyl monomers. Further proof of the radical nature of ruptured rubber molecules lies in their ability to initiate polymerisation of vinyl monomers, and the subsequent demonstration that the products consist of polymer chains attached to rubber molecules or sandwiched between them, i.e. block copolymers.[101] A considerable number of vinyl monomers has been shown to undergo this rubber-initiated polymerisation, with interesting effects on the properties of the product, but the technology of these novel materials has yet to be developed. The rubber (preferably acetone-extracted) is simply allowed to imbibe an uninhibited monomer, and the

Fig. 2.8. Preparation of a block copolymer of natural rubber and methyl methacrylate. Operator is feeding rubber-monomer mixture to a plastics extruder.

softened mass is submitted to mechanical shear in the substantial absence of air. Polymerisation proceeds rapidly, and with some monomers (e.g. methyl mechacrylate) is complete within a few minutes. Laboratory masticators (Fig. 2.7), a small sealed internal mixer and extruders (Fig. 2.8) have been used to obtain the necessary mechanical shear.

Isomeric modifications of rubber

Iso-rubber

This name is usually reserved for the rubbery substances which are obtained from rubber hydrochloride (XXIII) when it is heated either alone or with alkali or organic bases.[9] If this is done *in vacuo* or in an inert atmosphere to avoid oxidation most of the halogen is removed and the product contains practically the same amount of olefinic unsaturation as rubber itself. The unsaturation pattern is, however, rather different in that a substantial proportion of structure (XXIV) is revealed by the infra-red spectrum of iso-rubber.[48]   The elements of halogen acid are thus shown to be eliminated in the sense of either (XXIV) or (XXV); analogous behaviour has been observed with squalene hydrochloride.[102]   In accord-

$$
\cdots -CH_2-\underset{\underset{Cl}{|}}{\overset{\overset{CH_3}{|}}{C}}-CH_2-CH_2- \cdots \longrightarrow \cdots -CH_2-\underset{}{\overset{\overset{CH_2}{||}}{C}}-CH_2-CH_2- \cdots
$$

(XXIII)   (XXIV)

$$
or \quad \cdots -CH_2-\overset{\overset{CH_3}{|}}{C}=CH-CH_2- \cdots \quad (XXV)
$$

ance with the probable occurrence of both structures (XXIV and XXV), in iso-rubber, ozonolysis has been found to give ketonic products containing more than five carbon atoms, together with a substantial proportion of formic acid.[9]

Cyclised rubber

It has long been known that under the action of heat, especially in the presence of acidic catalysts, rubber is transformed into isomeric resinous substances with greatly reduced unsaturation.   This change is accompanied by increases in softening point, density and refractive index, and internal cyclisation has been proposed [103] to account for these changes, since the increases in the indicated physical properties are consistent with the already known effects of cyclisation of terpenes (e.g. dihydromyrcene [104]).

Cyclised rubber has been prepared by four different methods:

(1) by the action of heat on rubber;
(2) by the reductive dehydrohalogenation of rubber hydrohalides;
(3) by the action of halides of amphoterric metals on rubber;
(4) by the action of acidic catalysts on rubber at temperatures in the range 50°–150° C.

The properties of the fully cyclised products are very similar, and there is no basic reason to believe that any widely different structural features result from the various methods of preparation.   All four methods give products with softening points in the range 90°–120° C with a common density 0·992 and refractive index in the range 1·53–1·54.   Variation in product properties which have been described in the literature are attributed to differences in the degree of cyclisation rather than of its kind, although incidental oxidation or cross-linking side reactions undoubtedly make some contribution to product variability.

It will now be convenient to deal in turn with the various methods of cyclising rubber.

(1) *Thermal cyclisation.* Heat-cyclised rubber has already been described on p. 75. Although quantitative conversion to cyclised rubber has been reported when rubber was heated in solution,[58] recent work [105] has not confirmed this, the observed yield being around 40%, which agrees closely with the amount of cyclised rubber formed under similar conditions of time and temperature in the absence of a solvent.

Heat-cyclised rubber is a pale-coloured powdery material readily soluble in a number of solvents but insoluble in alcohol or acetone; cryoscopic determination of its molecular weight indicates a value in the range 2,000–2,500.

(2) *Cyclisation through reductive dehydrohalogenation.* Whereas the dehydrohalogenation of rubber hydrochloride or hydrobromide with alkaline reagents at 100°–150° C gives iso-rubber (containing displaced but undiminished unsaturation), reductive dehydrohalogenation with zinc dust and acid gives cyclised rubber,[103] which appears to be very similar to heat-cyclised rubber. Its molecular weight has been between 2,300 and 14,500, according to the conditions under which it has been prepared.[106]

Neither of the above methods of cyclising rubber have attained any commercial importance.

(3) *Cyclisation by halides of amphoteric metals: Plioform and Pliolite.* If stannic chloride is added to a rubber solution under an inert atmosphere at room temperature there is generally formed a coloured compound which is believed to be a complex of rubber with the halide.[107,108] The complex is rapidly decomposed on adding alcohol or water; the cyclised rubber is precipitated from the solution as an amorphous white powder when alcohol is added in excess, but is more conveniently isolated by removing the solvent with the aid of steam. Similar reactions occur with ferric chloride, antimony pentachloride, aluminium trichloride, titanium tetrachloride and allied compounds. Some attempts have been made to use these halides as Friedel–Crafts catalysts to bring about condensation of various halogenated substances (e.g. benzoyl chloride, carbon tetrachloride) with rubber, but these have met with little success, since cyclisation has been the predominant reaction and the products have contained insignificant amounts of the intended additives.

Hydrated chlorostannic acid has also been used to promote cyclisation; higher temperatures are required, but since the process is applicable to bulk rubber as well as to rubber solutions, it has assumed some commercial importance. The rubber is either refluxed in solution with 10% of its weight of hydrated chlorostannic acid or is heated in bulk after incorporation of a similar proportion of its weight of hydrated chlorostannic acid on the mill; some 2–5 hours at 130°–150° C are required.

The cyclised product is an amorphous powder, wholly soluble in rubber solvents if the rubber is pre-masticated and oxidation is avoided during the preparation; the presence of an antioxidant is a valuable aid in obtaining a soluble product. The crude reaction products usually contain a little chlorine (about 1%), together with some stannic oxide, and their specific gravity accordingly tends to be rather higher (1·02) than that of the purified materials (S.G. 0·96–0·98).

The main applications of this class of cyclised rubbers have been as thermoplastic moulding materials and in coating compositions.

4. *Cyclisation by acidic reagents—the Thermoprenes.* It is this class of cyclising agents which has assumed the greatest importance in the commercial preparation of cyclised rubber. The class includes sulphuric acid and its organic derivatives of the general structure $R–SO_2–X$, where R is an organic group and X is hydroxyl or a halogen (the most important examples are *p*-toluene sulphonic acid and its chloride),[109] phenols containing sulphuric [110] or phosphoric acids,[111] and various other acidic materials, such as hydrogen fluoride, trichloroacetic acid, and acidic earths or fillers. Doubtless an acidic exchange resin could similarly be used. Boron trifluoride in acetic acid,[112] boron trichloride and various halogen derivatives of phosphorus have also been used for cyclising rubber; possibly these reagents belong more appropriately to class (3), but a common mechanism of cyclisation is believed to underly the action of all these rather diverse reagents (see below).

The most popular acidic reagents for cyclisation of rubber in bulk have been sulphonic acids, sulphonyl chlorides and sulphuric acid itself; about 10 parts per 100 of rubber are incorporated on the mill, liquid reagents, such as free sulphuric acid, being conveniently dispersed on an inert filler. The mixture of rubber and cyclisation catalyst is then heated at 125°– 145° C for a period of 1–4 hours. The nature of the product obtained depends upon the temperature reached in the mass and the time of heating, probably in accordance with the degree of cyclisation produced under the particular conditions employed, and varies over a wide range from an elastic material resembling gutta-percha, through a tough material which is said to be more like hard balata, to a hard non-elastic and brittle resin not unlike shellac. The products have been given the general name " Thermoprenes ",[109] and have found an important application in adhesives and bonding agents.

Recently it has been discovered that the rate of cyclisation by *p*-toluene-sulphonic acid in bulk rubber can be strongly accelerated if a specific silicious filler (" Aerosil ") is also present.[113] So rapid is the reaction that complete cyclisation has been obtained in 10 minutes even with low grades of rubber, but owing to the amount of heat evolved in carrying the reaction to completion in so short a time, it becomes essential to conduct the reaction in an internal mixer so that some of the heat can be conducted away. The process has been reported to be very dependent on the grade of *p*-

toluenesulphonic acid, but good results have been obtained with technical p-toluenesulphonic acid monohydrate. In practice, the rubber, acid and filler are put into the internal mixer together and mixed at a starting temperature of 120°–140° C. The maximum temperature reached subsequently should not exceed 180° C, and the reaction should be complete within 10 minutes, as indicated by a fall in temperature and increase in stiffness.

Cyclisation in Phenol. Cyclised rubber resins which have been in commercial use for a number of years are made by carrying out the cyclisation in the presence of an excess of phenol containing a little sulphuric or phosphoric acid,[110, 111] under conditions causing little or no combination of phenol with the resin. This form of cyclised rubber is of comparatively low molecular weight owing to the severe degradation occurring during its preparation. Consequently it is readily soluble in a range of solvents and gives low-viscosity solutions of high resin content; it is used in the formulation of printing inks and in durable finishes which are resistant to heat and chemical attack.

Cyclisation of rubber in latex. In view of the readiness with which latex is coagulated on the addition of an acid, it seems a little strange even to consider a latex reaction which has to be conducted in a strongly acid medium. There are, however, well-established methods [114, 115] of stabilising latex towards the addition of inorganic acids and a restricted number of organic acids.

Ordinarily, latex is stabilised anionically so that its particles are negatively charged, and in this condition it is readily coagulated by acidification. However, latex can be rendered sufficiently acid to promote cyclisation if it is stabilised with either a cationic [116] or a non-ionic [117] stabiliser. The former class comprises stabilisers in which the hydrophobic part of the molecule forms a cation on ionisation, and typical examples are cetyltrimethyl ammonium bromide (XXVI) and laurylpyridinium chloride

(XXVII). A non-ionic stabiliser is one which remains unionised at any pH, and the most popular stabilisers in this class are obtained by condensing ethylene oxide on to one of the higher alcohols:

$$CH_3(CH_2)_n \cdot CH_2OH + x\ CH_2\!\!-\!\!CH_2 \longrightarrow$$
$$\underset{O}{\diagdown\!\!\diagup}$$

$$CH_3(CH_2)_n \cdot CH_2O[CH_2 \cdot CH_2O]_{(x-1)} CH_2 \cdot CH_2OH$$

The hydrophobic part of the non-ionic stabiliser molecule is the higher alkyl group as before, but the hydrophilic part is now the polyethylene oxide chain; its effectiveness in stabilising latex against acid depends mainly on the correct balance in the magnitudes of the alkyl group and the polyethylene oxide chain. For the conditions required for cyclising rubber the latter is in the region of 15–20 molecules of ethylene oxide when the alkyl group is stearyl, cetyl or oleyl.

Sulphuric acid is very effective for cyclising rubber in latex, but a fairly high concentration of acid is required in the serum—at least 70% w/w—before cyclisation proceeds at a reasonably practical rate. The kinetics of the reaction have been studied in some detail,[13, 118, 119] and the rate of reaction can be adequately expressed by eqn. 2.3, where k is expressed in

$$\log_{10} k = 6 + 0.17\,c - 7105/T \quad . \quad . \quad . \quad . \quad (2.3)$$

minutes^{-1}, c is the concentration of sulphuric acid expressed as % by weight and T is the absolute temperature. At 100° C cyclisation is reasonably complete within 2 hours when using 70% acid, but since from eqn. 2.3 either a 1% increase in c or a 3° C increase in T increases the reaction rate by 50%, it is necessary to control both variables carefully. The reaction is strongly exothermic, especially in its earlier stages, and cooling is necessary to prevent runaway conditions.

The high concentration of sulphuric acid required in the serum demands in the interests of economy that the latex shall be of the highest possible concentration; even so, the amount of acid required is substantial, and its disposal presents a considerable problem, since under the most favourable conditions $1\frac{1}{2}$ lb. of sulphuric acid are required per pound of cyclised rubber produced. Some attempts have been made to use a lower acid concentration at higher temperatures involving super-atmospheric pressure, and also to use a small amount of acid and to concentrate the acidified latex by evaporation, but neither alternative process has developed commercially.

After cyclisation the latex may be flocculated by pouring into aqueous alcohol, although cyclised latex stabilised by a non-ionic stabiliser can also be conveniently and more economically flocculated by pouring it into a considerable excess of boiling water. After filtration, washing and drying the cyclised rubber is obtained in the form of a very fine powder which softens above 130° C and can be compression-moulded at 140° C. The fineness of the powder (corresponding to the smallness of the original particles of rubber in the latex) renders its isolation costly and very laborious; it is easily redispersed in water to form a dispersion of cyclised rubber which has been used for stiffening dipped or foamed latex articles.[120] Since some of the more promising uses of cyclised rubber are as a reinforcing resin in admixture with raw rubber, a 50/50 mixture has been prepared in masterbatch form by mixing cyclised latex with ordinary latex containing an equivalent amount of rubber.[121] In order to avoid premature coagulation of the untreated latex on mixing with the strongly acid cyclised latex it is necessary to render the former latex also stable to acid by addition of a cationic or non-ionic stabiliser. Mildly cationic stabilisers made by the condensation of ethylene oxide on to higher alkyl amines are preferred in the production of the cyclised rubber masterbatch.[122,123] Cyclised rubber masterbatch has been used for shoe-soling, in industrial rollers and for rigid impact-resistant mouldings.

Partially cyclised rubber

From eqn. 2.3 conditions can be established for carrying out the process of cyclising rubber to any desired level. It is convenient to operate at a temperature substantially below $100°$ C in order to reduce the rate of cyclisation. For reproducibility it is essential that the acid concentration should be accurately known or, alternatively, that the rate of reaction should be experimentally determined during the progress of a run and the rate curve extrapolated to the time required for the desired extent of cyclisation. The degree of cyclisation can be speedily ascertained by determining the specific gravity of a flocculated sample, since the density increases steadily as the reaction proceeds.

Partially cyclised rubber is rather different in its properties from a mixture of fully cyclised and uncyclised rubbers. Rubbers containing a low degree of cyclisation are less stiff at room temperature than the corresponding mixtures, since the low-cyclised rubber has not yet assumed the characteristics of a reinforcing resinous filler. Only after a substantial degree of cyclisation is reinforcement obtained.

Considerable heterogeneity in partially cyclised rubber arises as an inevitable consequence of the spread of particle sizes in natural rubber latex. The rate-determining step is that of diffusion of acid (or a reactive ion-pair derived therefrom) into the latex particle, and it is to be expected that the smaller particles will undergo complete cyclisation in quite a short time, during which the large particles suffer only partial cyclisation.

The chemistry of cyclisation

There has been much speculation as to the nature of the cyclisation reaction. It is abundantly clear that it is an ionic reaction requiring the presence of a proton donor; the reaction is quite unresponsive to reagents which influence free radical reactions, and up to the present time no method has been discovered for cyclising rubber by a free radical mechanism.

From the readiness with which dihydromyrcene is cyclised by acidic reagents [124] there is little reason to suppose that the course of reaction is fundamentally different in rubber, and there is general agreement that cyclisation proceeds by protonation (XXVIII) and addition of the resulting carbonium ion to an adjacent double bond to form a six-membered ring XXIX, as has been proposed for dihydromyrcene.[125]

Cyclisation of rubber, after M. Gordon.[13]

Cyclisation by Friedel–Crafts reagents (class 3 reagents) may involve carbonium ion formation in a complex of the type (XXXI) or protonation

as above by the action of a co-catalyst such as is usually required in ionic polymerisations promoted by these reagents,[126] e.g.

$$H_2O + SnCl_4 \longrightarrow H\!-\!O\!\rightarrow\!SnCl_4 \rightleftharpoons \overset{\oplus}{H} + \overset{\ominus}{HOSnCl_4}$$
$$\underset{H}{|}$$

or
$$H_2SnCl_6 \rightleftharpoons \overset{\oplus}{H} + \overset{\ominus}{HSnCl_6}$$

It is now tempting to suggest that cyclisation is propagated to further adjacent units (XXXII) until terminated by a deprotonation step (XXXIII).[127] This formulation (XXXIII) of cyclised rubber is one of polycondensed cyclohexane rings, and it is necessary to assume that sequences of such condensed rings are distributed between segments of uncyclised polyisoprene to account for the residual unsaturation of fully cyclised rubber, since this is substantially greater than one double bond in the terminal ring of each cyclised sequence.

The kinetics of rubber cyclisation in latex are, however, more in accordance with the deprotonation step (XXX) completing a cyclisation involving two isoprenic units at a time [13, 119] rather than a propagating

(XXXII)   (XXXIII)

reaction involving sequences of propagating units as formulated above (XXXII). A direct consequence of such a reaction, involving at random adjacent pairs of isoprene units, is that the ultimate composition of fully cyclised rubber must be a " copolymer " of C_{10}-cyclic structures and isolated C_5-units, e.g.

$-C_{10}-C_{10}-C_5-C_{10}-C_5-C_{10}-$ · · · etc.   (XXXIV)

Such a random copolymer should contain $13 \cdot 5\%$ of the isolated C_5-units,[128] and if it can be demonstrated unambiguously that the unsaturation remaining in fully cyclised rubber corresponds to this composition the above cyclisation mechanism is further strengthened. If cyclisation paired up all of the available C_5-units in cyclic structures each containing one double bond the unsaturation of the original polyisoprene would clearly be halved, as indeed happens with the low-molecular analogue dihydromyrcene. The statistical distribution of cyclised and isolated units requires that the unsaturation shall be $56 \cdot 8\%$ of the original rubber instead of the 50% expected if each cyclised unit contains one double bond. The polycondensed structure (XXXIII), on the other hand, would retain only a small proportion of the original unsaturation of the rubber when cyclisation is pushed to completion. Supporting evidence for these structures is therefore critically dependent on the correct determination of the unsaturation of cyclised rubber, and unfortunately this cannot be determined with

E

complete certainty by the usual method of halogen addition owing to substitutive side reactions. The infra-red spectrum does not assist very much in the elucidation of cyclised rubber structure;[48] some features which are indicative of $C\!\!=\!\!CH_2$ groups have been found to survive ozonolysis. The spectrum gives some indication of residual unsaturation of the polyisoprenic pattern, but does not exclude the presence of unsaturation of the tetra-substituted ethylene type as formulated in (XXX); there are some features in common with the spectrum of 1 : 2-dimethyl-cyclohex-1-ene.[129]

Some of the earlier workers on cyclisation obtained, by halogen addition, unsaturation values corresponding to the presence of only one double bond in four or five cyclic units, and they accordingly proposed polycyclic structures.[58, 103] More recently further support for a polycyclic structure has been obtained by estimating the unsaturation by addition of hydrogen chloride,[127] which revealed only 17% of the original rubber unsaturation. On the other hand, there are several pieces of independent evidence for the statistical copolymer (XXXIV) based on units of structure (XXX); these are:

(1) Dilatometric experiments using latex showed that the reaction was more consistent with the statistical cyclisation law than with a first-order equation for the survival of stranded units.[13, 119]

(2) The most reliable unsaturation value obtained by addition of iodine chloride [130] was 57% of that of the original rubber.

(3) The reaction of phenyliododichloride, which adds chlorine quantitatively to double bonds, with latex-cyclised rubber gave additive chlorination corresponding to an unsaturation value 58·3% of that of rubber.[131]

(4) The unsaturation of samples of heat-cyclised and acid-cyclised (latex process) rubber, estimated by quantitative ozone-uptake, were respectively 55 and 58% of that of rubber.[132]

(5) Oxidation with chromic acid gave 25–30% of acetic acid instead of the 66% given by rubber, thus indicating about half of the unsaturation of rubber.[108]

Some rate abnormalities observed in the kinetics of latex cyclisation include an induction period of reduced rate, probably related to diffusion effects. A small volume change subsequent to cyclisation may reflect a prototropic shift of the double bond, and this may have some bearing on the structural features indicated by the infra-red spectrum.

Oxidation of rubber

Abundant evidence now exists indicating that the generalised reaction of oxygen with olefins proceeds in accordance with a radical chain reaction sequence which can be formally expressed as follows : [133]

Initiation: Any reaction leading to the formation of a free radical X·
or XO_2· (usually in presence of oxygen X· + $O_2 \to XO_2$·) and the reaction
thereof with the olefin RH (as in eqn. 2.6)

$$XO_2\cdot + RH \longrightarrow XO_2H + R\cdot \quad . \quad . \quad . \quad (2.4)$$

Propagation.
$$R\cdot + O_2 \longrightarrow RO_2\cdot \quad . \quad . \quad . \quad . \quad (2.5)$$
$$RO_2\cdot + RH \longrightarrow RO_2H + R\cdot \quad . \quad . \quad . \quad (2.6)$$

Termination:
$$2R\cdot \longrightarrow \left.\begin{matrix} \\ \\ \\ \end{matrix}\right\}$$
$$R\cdot + RO_2\cdot \longrightarrow \text{inactive products} \quad . \quad (2.7)$$
$$2RO_2\cdot \longrightarrow$$

The initiation step may involve decomposition of a peroxide which is
adventitiously present or formed as a product of reaction (eqn. 2.6), or it
may involve a photo-initiation step or even the direct attack of oxygen at a
double bond.[134]
In the very first initiating step the X· or XO_2· radicals are derived from
the olefin only if this step involves the direct addition of oxygen to the
olefin, but whatever the source of the first radical it, or the RO_2 radical
derived from it, is presumed to abstract α-methylenic hydrogen from the
olefin RH to give the chain-carrying olefinic radical R·. Once the
olefinic radical R· becomes involved in the propagation sequence (eqn.
2.5 and 2.6) the hydroperoxide formed takes the place of the original
initiator, the propagation sequence rapidly causes a build-up of hydroperoxide, and it is easy to see why the reaction becomes autocatalytic.
The stability of the hydroperoxide determines the nature of the final
products, and only rarely is a high yield of the hydroperoxide itself obtained. The simplest example of an oxidation which proceeds in this
manner is the formation of cyclohexenyl hydroperoxide from cyclo-

hexene.[135] The propagation sequence (eqn. 2.5 and 2.6) is usually of
considerable chain length, and involves the combination of oxygen with
the olefin without separation of the pairs of oxygen atoms comprising an
oxygen molecule, although the manner in which these pairs of atoms are
linked to the hydrocarbon is dependent upon the type of olefin.[133] Reaction (6) is aided by the reduced energy required to effect scission of an
α-methylenic carbon–hydrogen bond, and the structure of the products is
generally determined by the relative ease of capture of hydrogen from
different α-methylenic carbon atoms when more than one is present in the
olefin. In the polyisoprenes the relative numerical ease of detachment of
hydrogen has been shown to be 1 : 3 : 9·5 from the carbon atoms numbered
respectively 3, 1 and 5 in formula (XVI) (p. 74), and accordingly the

principal chain carrier is the radical (XXXV).   Because of the particular
1 : 5 spacing of neighbouring double bonds in polyisoprenes, cyclisation

$$\ldots -CH_2-CMe=CH-CH-CH_2-CMe=CH-CH_2- \ldots \quad (XXXV)$$
$$\underset{O_2}{|}$$

of the chain carrier (XXXV) occurs to the virtual exclusion of intermolecular α-methylenic hydrogen capture except in so far as this occurs
after the incorporation of a second oxygen molecule into the cyclised
unit;   reactions 2.8 and 2.9 therefore replace eqn. 2.6 in the special case of

$$\cdots -CH_2-CMe=CH-CH-CH_2-CMe=CH-CH_2- \cdots$$
$$\underset{O_2}{|}$$
$$\downarrow$$

$$\cdots -CH_2-CMe=CH \quad \overset{CH_2-\overset{*}{C}Me}{\diagup \quad \diagdown} \quad CH-CH_2- \cdots \quad . \quad (2.8)$$
$$O—O$$
$$\downarrow$$

$$\underset{\overset{|}{O_2}}{ } \atop CH_2-\overset{|}{C}Me$$
$$\cdots -CH_2-CMe=CH \quad \diagup \quad \diagdown \quad CH-CH_2- \cdots \quad . \quad (2.9)$$
$$O—O$$
$$\downarrow$$

$$\overset{OOH}{\underset{|}{CH_2-\overset{|}{C}Me}}$$
$$\cdots -CH_2-CMe=CH \quad \diagup \quad \diagdown \quad CH-CH_2- \cdots$$
$$O—O \quad (XXXVI)$$

polyisoprenes.   This type of peroxide has been shown to be given by
squalene [136] and dihydromyrcene.[137]

The formation of peroxides during the oxidation of rubber has often
been observed, but measurement of the amount formed presented considerable difficulty until a suitable analytical method was developed.[138]

The loss of unsaturation [29] which accompanies oxidation of rubber and the amount of hydroperoxide formed as measured by the active hydrogen content [50] are in reasonable agreement with the presence of the peroxidic structure (XXXVI) in the *early* stages of autoxidation of rubber.

As soon as the oxidation of rubber proceeds to a more advanced stage, corresponding to an uptake of more than a few units % of oxygen, the above generalised oxidation scheme is accompanied by secondary reactions of the initially formed peroxides, leading to the appearance of various functional groups, such as carboxyl, ester, hydroxyl, carbonyl and ethereal.[139, 140] These are the groups to be expected from decomposition of peroxides in the presence of polyisoprenic unsaturation. Only about half of the oxygen present in these more highly oxidised rubbers can be accounted for in carboxyl, hydroxyl, carbonyl, ester and residual peroxide groups (see Table 2.10), and the rest of the oxygen has been assumed to be in ether-type linkages either intra- or inter-molecular.[139]

Chain scission accompanies oxidation from its earliest stages, but its effect is most pronounced at the commencement of oxygen uptake, when only a few scissions per molecule are sufficient to reduce the viscosity of a rubber solution drastically. By estimating the molecular weight at any stage of the oxidation and comparing it with the original molecular weight of the rubber it is possible to calculate the number of scissions for a given uptake of oxygen. Only a very small proportion of the ingoing oxygen is responsible for chain scission in photochemical oxidation of rubber in solution at low temperature,[29] but a much higher efficiency (e.g. 0·17 scissions/mole of oxygen absorbed) has been observed in thermal oxidations conducted at temperatures in the vicinity of 140° C,[141] and the efficiency can be of a very high order in oxidations at similar temperature when aided by mastication in the presence of certain chemical plasticisers (see p. 82). The use of latex in a recent study of oxidation of rubber has enabled acidic oxidation products (specifically, carbon dioxide, formic acid and acetic acid) to be estimated.[142] When the results were combined with an estimate of the efficiency of scission the following ratios of acids (expressed in moles) were produced per mole of scissions:

Carbon dioxide	2·02
Acetic acid	0·92
Formic acid	0·83

These are in the approximate ratio 2 : 1 : 1, and it was concluded that five carbon atoms were eliminated per scission of the hydrocarbon chain. An appropriate explanation was advanced on the assumption that the initial rubber oxidation product contained the structure (XXXVI). The scheme requires six molecules of oxygen to effect each scission, and this is very close to the value found experimentally. This close agreement implies that under these particular conditions the oxidative attack is being directed entirely to chain scission, and the functional groups introduced should be located solely at the ends of ruptured chains.   This should be capable of experimental verification.

Some recent kinetic work with purified gutta-percha suggests that degradation is a secondary reaction intimately associated with one of the propagation steps.   This is contrary to any assertion that it is the decomposition of hydroperoxide groups, contained in the oxidation product, which is primarily responsible for scission.

Oxidation of rubber proceeds readily to a more advanced stage in the presence of various types of catalyst.   Acids are fairly effective in rendering rubber more easily oxidised, and for this reason the use of sulphuric acid or other non-volatile acid for coagulating latex has been criticised.   The activity of acids is probably due to the removal or destruction of the very potent natural protective agents normally present in natural rubber, but acid-catalysed peroxide decomposition may be a contributory factor.   If small pieces of rubber are suspended in boiling acetic acid and a stream of oxygen is passed through, a substantial proportion of the rubber is oxidised to a sufficiently advanced stage to pass into solution in the acid.   Evaporation yields products of high oxygen content separable by solvent extraction into oils and solids of low softening point.[143]   Much of the oxygen in these products is contained in acetylated groups (Table 2.9).   Acetic anhydride

TABLE 2.9
TYPICAL PRODUCTS OF OXIDATION OF RUBBER IN THE PRESENCE OF
ACETIC ACID OR ANHYDRIDE

Medium used:	Acetic anhydride	Acetic acid
Analysis of solid oxidation product		
% C	59·9	62·2
% H	6·9	7·3
% O	33·2	30·5
% acetyl (—OAc)	50·5	33·2
% carboxyl (—CO₂H)	6·0	8·2
% hydroxyl (—OH)	Nil	3·0
Iodine value	49	98

is an even more effective medium, and not unexpectedly gives an even higher proportion of acetylated groups in the products, although the total oxygen content is similar.   Much less degraded products containing only a small proportion of oxygenated groups (again mainly acetylated) have been obtained by conducting the oxidation at a lower temperature (80° C) in mixtures of acetic anhydride and benzene.[143]

Salts of some of the heavy metals, and, notably, the oil-soluble salts of cobalt, manganese and copper, powerfully catalyse the oxidation of rubber to resinous substances containing a high proportion of combined oxygen.[144-146] These are known as the " Rubbones ", and they have found applications in paints and heat-resisting finishes.

If cobalt linoleate ($2 \cdot 5 \%$ on rubber) is simply milled into rubber (mill temperature $60°$–$70°$ C) the latter is degraded sufficiently to give a pourable 50% solution in white spirit without any appreciable increase in its oxygen content. The viscosity of such a solution is about 3,000 poises at $25°$ C. Since the solution contains the catalyst, further oxidation to resinous products occurs on exposure to air, especially in thin films or coatings. This solution has been recommended as a paint additive.[147] The rubber enhances two specific properties—free flow and non-settling, and these improvements are particularly advantageous in flat paints and under-coatings, which are notorious for poor flow and hard settling of the pigments. By replacing part of the binder with rubber, both these defects are greatly ameliorated. The amount required depends to some extent on the other constituents of the paint, but for general purposes the binder should contain 50% of rubber. This amounts approximately to 4–5% of rubber on the finished paint. A flat paint prepared with a medium containing equal parts of rubber and oil requires no stippling to produce a smooth finish, but will flow out without showing the brush marks usually associated with standard flat wall paints. Similarly, with undercoatings, the elimination of brush marks is a distinct advantage, as no rubbing down is necessary before the application of the gloss finishing coat in order to obtain a ripple-free finish; this has the effect of enhancing the gloss. As an agent for improving flexibility the addition of rubber must be discounted, since it hardens to give a brittle film.

For the preparation of " Rubbone " cobalt linoleate or naphthenate ($2 \cdot 5 \%$ on rubber) is mixed into rubber on hot rolls and the milling is continued for 30 minutes. The degraded rubber is then dissolved in white spirit to give a 20% solution, which is oxidised by aeration at $80°$ C until a sample withdrawn from the bulk shows a quick separation of sediment and a clear supernatant solution of the resin. The solution is then clarified by centrifuging, and the solvent is distilled off by steam or under reduced pressure. The catalyst is removed with the sediment, and the Rubbone is then stable at room temperature. If it is desired to stop the oxidation at an earlier stage the catalyst may be removed by precipitation with thioglycollic acid.[145] If the oxidation is continued beyond the stage indicated above appreciable quantities of Rubbone C are precipitated from the solution.

Rubbone prepared as above is a viscous gum, yellow to orange red in colour, containing about 10% of oxygen. The material obtained on a commercial scale can be divided into three fractions designated Rubbones A, B and C, characterised by their differences in solubility in cold solvents and in their degree of oxidation, viz.:

Rubbone A.   Soluble in white spirit, aromatic hydrocarbons, ether and chlorinated solvents.

Insoluble in acetone and alcohol.

Oxygen content 5–6%.

Rubbone B.   Soluble in white spirit, aromatic hydrocarbons, acetone, ether and chlorinated solvents.

Insoluble in alcohol.

Oxygen content 10–11%.

Rubbone C.   Soluble in aromatic hydrocarbons, acetone, alcohol, ether and chlorinated solvents.

Insoluble in white spirit.

Oxygen content 15–16%.

Formation of the three Rubbones is not clear cut, and at any time mixtures will be present; commercial Rubbone contains 5% of Rubbone A, 80% of Rubbone B and 15% of Rubbone C.   The distribution of the oxygen between various functional groups in Rubbones B and C is given in Table 2.10.[139, 140]

TABLE 2.10

ANALYSES OF RUBBONES

Rubbone:	B	C
Molecular weight	3600	2400
Iodine value	290	260
Elementary analysis:		
% C	78·5	76·3
% H	10·5	10·4
% N	0·2	0·03
% O (diff.)	10·8	13·3
Distribution of oxygen between functional groups:		
in —OOH	0·001	0·06
in —COOH	0·3	0·3
in —COOR	1·5	0·6
in —COH	3·3	4·0
in =C=O	0·7	0·9
Total	5·8	5·9
% oxygen accounted for:	53	44

The highly oxygenated Rubbones A, B and C are not to be confused with Rubbone N or Rubbone P, which are degraded rubbers of *low* oxygen content prepared with the aid of the chemical plasticisers mercaptobenz-thiazole and Pepton 22 respectively.   Rubbones N and P are completely soluble in hydrocarbons but insoluble in acetone or alcohol, in marked contrast to B and C, and are more suitable than the oxygenated Rubbones for use in vulcanisable casting compositions.

In the above solution method of preparation of Rubbone there is a considerable induction period before oxidation occurs. This may be greatly reduced, with a consequent speeding up of the process, if oxidation is initiated by adding peroxides or a part of a previous charge.

An alternative method of preparing Rubbone has been developed using dry rubber. This depends on the powerful accelerating effect of cellulose on oxidation of rubber when catalysed by salts of copper and cobalt, which can present a hazard in applications of rubber to cellulosic textiles which may adventitiously contain copper (e.g. in a dyestuff). In this method of preparation chemical wood pulp is mixed at 80° C into well-masticated rubber containing cobalt linoleate in a mixer of the Werner–Pfleiderer type. As soon as exothermic oxidation sets in the temperature is regulated by water-cooling to 100°–120° C. After oxidation the mass is cooled and the Rubbone is extracted by a solvent, filtered and isolated by removal of the solvent. The extent of oxidation depends on the amount of wood pulp used, e.g.

30% wood pulp on rubber—Rubbone A predominates
40% ,, ,, ,, — ,, B ,,
50% ,, ,, ,, — ,, C ,,

The recovered pulp after filtration contains the spent catalyst and is liable to self-ignition.

The solubility of the Rubbones in a range of solvents is given in Table 2.11.

TABLE 2.11
SOLUBILITY OF RUBBONES

Solvent	Solubility of Rubbone		
	A	B	C
Methyl alcohol	i	i	i
Ethyl alcohol	i	i	S
Acetone	i	S	S
Methyl ethyl ketone	i	S	S
Diacetone alcohol	i	i	S
Dioxane	i	S	S
Ethyl acetate	S	S	S
Amyl acetate	S	S	S
Cellosolve	i	S	S
Benzene	S	S	S
Dekalin	S	S	i
White spirit	S	S	i
Carbon disulphide	S	S	i

The oxidation of rubber from the point of view of ageing is dealt with in greater detail in Part I of Chapter XIII.

Reaction of rubber with miscellaneous oxidising agents

Action of ozone

The principal interest in the reaction of ozone with rubber has been concerned: (*a*) with its application to the elucidation of the structure of rubber (see p. 62), and (*b*) with its remarkable effect in producing cracking in stretched rubber, even when present to the extent of only a few parts per hundred million in the atmosphere. The mechanism of ozone-cracking remains obscure, although it has recently been demonstrated that cracking requires the ozone to reach the surface of the rubber in a gaseous medium.[148] No cracking occurs when rubber is placed in a solution of ozone, but takes place immediately when a stream of either air or an inert gas is made to impinge on the surface of the rubber while immersed in the ozone solution. Furthermore, the reaction of ozone with rubber is not merely an ozone-catalysed autoxidation, since cracking occurs with equal facility in an atmosphere of inert gas containing oxygen-free ozone as it does ozonised oxygen.[149] Adequate protection of rubber against ozone-cracking has long presented a challenge to rubber chemists; recently it has been found that N-alkylated *p*-phenylenediamines show considerable promise in this direction.[150]

Much confusion has existed as to the chemical nature of the initial product of interaction of rubber with ozone, but the situation has been greatly clarified by the views of Criegee and his co-workers, to which reference has already been made (p. 62). The ozonide itself, when prepared by ozonising rubber in chloroform solution and isolating the ozonide by fractional precipitation, is a low-molecular product whose analysis and molecular weight correspond closely with the composition $(C_5H_8O_3)_5$.[151] It is soluble in benzene, alcohol, acetone, acetic acid, ethyl acetate, chloroform and dioxane, and is insoluble in ether, carbon tetrachloride, carbon disulphide and petroleum ether. On long standing at low temperature its solutions have been reported to deposit levulinic acid peroxide (VI).[152] Reductive cleavage of the ozonide yields mainly levulinic aldehyde and levulinic acid,[151] whereas hydrolytic cleavage yields mainly levulinic acid and its keto-peroxide (VI). When the ozonolysis is conducted in carbon tetrachloride the insoluble ozonide separates. Surprisingly, if ozonolysis is stopped short of completion the material remaining in solution has been shown to be only very lightly oxidised rubber,[151] although the precipitated material is the fully reacted ozonide. This suggests that once ozone attacks rubber the attack is propagated along the molecule to give preferentially a completely ozonised molecule before another rubber molecule becomes involved.

In the reaction of ozone with solid rubber the speed of reaction is controlled by diffusion of gas into the rubber; as a consequence, initial products formed near the surface are subjected to further action by ozone. This is minimised by the use of thin films, and infra-red characterisation of the products indicates that there is scission at the double bond with the production of aldehyde and/or ketone, and a peroxy-biradical.[153]

Oxidation with potassium permanganate

A solution of potassium permanganate is slowly decomposed by agitation with a solution of rubber at room temperature, but the products obtained are ill-defined materials ranging from elastic solids to friable resins, the latter containing 20% or more of oxygen.[154] Considerable degradation occurs, and the oxidation is accompanied by formation of formic, acetic, oxalic and levulinic acids, together with complex resins. Ill-defined resinous products have also been obtained when latex is treated with alkaline permanganate, but less extensive oxidation occurs than in the oxidation of rubber in solution.

Oxidation with hydrogen peroxide

When a rubber solution is shaken with dilute aqueous hydrogen peroxide somewhat less oxidised products are obtained than when permanganate is used, but the products are again rather ill-defined. Part of the oxidation product is water soluble, and has been isolated in the form of a white, tacky mass; the bulk of the oxidised rubber contains about 5% of oxygen and is partially soluble in ether.[155]

The rubber hydrocarbon in latex is not readily oxidised by hydrogen peroxide unless decomposition of the latter is promoted either by heat or by a catalyst, under which conditions the rubber is oxidised slightly to a very tacky but still rubbery product.[156] Hydrogen peroxide has a marked preservative action on latex, and provided that it is decomposed under conditions which do not liberate oxygen (e.g. by interaction with a sulphite) the rubber may be isolated from such treated latices in its original undegraded condition. If the hydrogen peroxide is not removed prior to coagulation the rubber undergoes rapid oxidative deterioration during drying.

Highly oxidised resinous products have been obtained by treating latex with hydrogen peroxide in the presence of sulphuric acid (see p. 129).[157]

Oxidation with peracetic acid and with mixtures of hydrogen peroxide and acetic acid

Water-white thermoplastic resins are readily obtained when rubber is treated with solutions of peracetic acid in acetic acid, or with mixtures of hydrogen peroxide and acetic acid which behave essentially as peracetic acid. Although the earlier work [158] with this system was carried out with the rubber in solution, the reaction may be brought about very simply by steeping shredded rubber in mixtures of hydrogen peroxide and acetic acid [159] or in solutions of peracetic acid in acetic acid,[160] whereupon the rubber passes into solution in the course of a few days at 40° C. The oxidation product may be isolated by diluting the solution, preferably with the addition of a little sodium acetate to aid flocculation. The product is a partially acetylated polyhydroxylated resin of fairly low molecular weight, containing minor amounts of carboxyl and peroxidic groups; the relative proportions of acetylated and free hydroxyl groups depends on the amount of water present in the oxidising system (Table 2.12).

TABLE 2.12

COMPOSITION OF SOME TYPICAL OXIDATION PRODUCTS OF RUBBER
OBTAINED BY THE REACTION OF PERACETIC ACID

Analysis of product	% *water in acetic acid*	
	13	27
Carbon, %	64·35	64·9
Hydrogen, %	9·0	9·4
Oxygen (diff.), %	26·65	25·7
Oxygen in —OAc, %	6·2	4·3
,, —OH, %	18·4	22·8
,, —COOH, %	0·4	0·3
,, as peroxide, %	0·6	0·3
Total oxygen accounted for	25·6	27·7

Saponification of the products yields the corresponding hydroxylated resins; treatment of the original or saponified materials with acetylating agents yields more highly acetylated products.

Formic acid with hydrogen peroxide behaves similarly, but less efficiently; the higher fatty peracids (e.g. perlauric acid) also enter into reaction when mixed into rubber and heated.

Latex can be similarly oxidised when treated with hydrogen peroxide and sufficient acetic acid to bring the product into solution; stabilisation of the latex with a non-ionic or cationic stabiliser is, of course, essential.[157]

The behaviour of rubber towards aliphatic peracids is in accordance with the general behaviour of olefins towards such reagents, whereby epoxides, diols and their acylated derivatives are formed,[161] according to the amount of free fatty acid present during the reaction.

Oxidation with perbenzoic acid

In the absence of any accompanying fatty acid the aliphatic peracids (in inert solvents) give good yields of epoxides when brought into reaction with olefins,[162] but the possibilities of this reaction with rubber have not been explored. Perbenzoic acid is, however, conveniently brought into reaction in a solvent and in the absence of free benzoic acid, and its normal mode of reaction with olefins is one of exclusive epoxidation.[161] Rubber is no exception, and reacts smoothly and fairly rapidly to give a rubbery product with the oxygen-content required by the poly-epoxide $(C_5H_8O)_n$.[163]

Reaction of rubber with organic peroxides

The action of organic peroxides on rubber is complex. Most peroxides are effective oxidation catalysts, and some are cross-linking agents. Hence the overall effect of treatment with a peroxide is very dependent on the accessibility of air during the reaction. Some peroxides also take part in additive reactions at the double bond, whereby some part of the peroxide becomes structurally incorporated in the products of reaction.

The cross-linking action of a peroxide is a direct outcome of the ability of the free radicals resulting from its thermal decomposition to capture hydrogen atoms from the α-methylenic positions of rubber molecules, the rubber radicals subsequently interacting to give a cross-linked structure (eqn. 2.10 and 2.12). Cyclic linkages have also been reported.[164] The

$$ROOR \longrightarrow 2RO^* \quad . \quad . \quad . \quad . \quad . \quad (2.10)$$
$$RO^* + rH \longrightarrow ROH + r^* \quad . \quad . \quad . \quad (2.11)$$
$$r^* + r^* \longrightarrow r \longrightarrow r \quad . \quad . \quad . \quad . \quad (2.12)$$

(rH here denotes the rubber hydrocarbon and r* a rubber radical.)

process is akin to photovulcanisation or cross-linking by high-energy radiation. It is at once apparent from eqn. 2.11 that in the presence of air molecular oxygen will intervene as in eqn. 2.5 and 2.6 to set up catalysed oxidation, but provided access of air is restricted, as in a press cure or in open steam (having purged the system of air by an initial flushing with steam), the cross-linking reaction can give a technically useful vulcanisate without appreciable degradation.[165] Radicals resulting from the decomposition products of some peroxides show a marked tendency to become incorporated in the product, either by a termination reaction (eqn. 2.13):

$$RO^* + r^* \longrightarrow RO \text{---} r \quad . \quad . \quad . \quad (2.13)$$

or by addition to a double bond (equation 2.14):

$$RO^* + \text{---}CH_2\text{---}CMe\text{=}CH\text{---}CH_2\text{---}$$

$$\downarrow$$

$$-CH_2\text{---}\underset{*}{C}Me\text{---}CH\text{---}CH_2\text{---} \quad . \quad . \quad . \quad . \quad (2.14)$$
$$\underset{}{\overset{|}{O}R} \qquad (XXXVII)$$

In the latter case the radical (XXXVII) may itself capture hydrogen (eqn. 2.15) or become involved in a cross-linking reaction (eqn. 2.16).

$$-CH_2-\underset{*}{C}Me-\underset{|}{C}H-CH_2- + rH \longrightarrow -CH_2-CHMe-\underset{|}{C}H-CH_2- + r^*$$
$$\qquad\qquad OR \qquad\qquad\qquad\qquad\qquad OR \qquad (2.15)$$

$$-CH_2-\underset{*}{C}Me-\underset{|}{C}H-CH_2- + r^* \longrightarrow -CH_2-\underset{|}{C}Me-\underset{|}{C}H-CH_2- \quad etc.$$
$$\qquad\qquad OR \qquad\qquad\qquad\qquad r \quad OR \quad (2.16)$$

Benzoyl peroxide shows all of the above three types of reactivity—as oxidation catalyst, as cross-linking agent and as a double-bond adduct.[166] The " grafting " of benzoate radicals on to rubber has been observed during vulcanisation by benzoyl peroxide.[48]

Dialkyl peroxides, on the other hand, show no tendency to incorporate alkoxy groups into rubber, the major products of the reaction being cross-linked rubber, *tert*-butyl alcohol and acetone.[167] *tert*-butyl perbenzoate shows the characteristics of both di-*tert*-butyl peroxide and benzoyl peroxide; the *tert*-butoxy radical reacts smoothly to give *tert*-butyl alcohol by hydrogen-capture, but combination of benzoate radicals with the rubber has been detected.[165]

Oxidation by oxides of chlorine

The decomposition of either sodium chlorite [168] or hypochlorite,[169] and the use of chlorine dioxide itself,[170] have been proposed as methods for controlled oxidation of rubber either in latex or in solution.

The oxidative chain scission of rubber by hypochlorite proceeds only at pH values in excess of 7, and is favoured by even higher alkalinity; in the low pH range the action of hypochlorous acid is primarily one of addition to double bonds (see p. 119).

Sodium chlorite is very suitable for use in latex, and the treatment should be carried out either in an acid medium or, preferably, in the presence of a chlorite-decomposing activator, such as formaldehyde, in a neutral medium. This process, requiring only low chlorite doses, can be used for the manufacture of latex cements and for preparing plasticised rubber without mastication. It is, however, essential that all of the chlorite is decomposed before coagulation, otherwise the presence of free chlorite in dry rubber leads to a highly oxidised and sticky product.

Hydrogenation of rubber

The rubber hydrocarbon has been hydrogenated only with considerable experimental difficulty, and the process has not been developed commercially in spite of a number of " use patents " for hydrogenated rubber. Some of the major difficulties which have to be overcome are:

(1) Processes for hydrogenating rubber require either the use of highly purified rubber in very dilute solution or, with unpurified rubber, the use of temperatures so high that severe degradation accompanies hydrogenation.

(2) A comparatively large amount of catalyst is required. This is understandable if one assumes that catalytic hydrogenation requires contact of each double bond in turn with a portion of catalyst surface. To bring all of the double bonds of a high polymer into such intimate contact requires a high proportion of catalyst, together with considerable agitation for a long period.

(3) Removal of the finely divided dispersed catalyst is difficult, but is essential, since hydrogenation catalysts frequently contain a metal (e.g. nickel) which can act as an oxidation catalyst if left in the product.

Rubber has been hydrogenated at room temperature [163] and at $70°$–$80°$ C [171] using platinum black with very dilute solutions of purified rubber. This has been accomplished only on a small scale, and cannot always be repeated; the hydro-rubber $(C_5H_{10})_x$ retained elastic properties and was of relatively high molecular weight. Very degraded hydrogenated rubbers have been obtained under high pressure at temperatures in the range $250°$–$300°$ C,[172] but rather more promising materials of molecular weight around 30,000 have been made using 0.1% solutions of rubber in methyl cyclohexane and a nickel catalyst at $150°$–$200°$ C under 100 atmospheres hydrogen pressure.[173] Hydro-rubber with a molecular weight of 90,000 has been claimed using nickel (5–10 times the weight of rubber present) at $50°$–$120°$ C during several days.[174] Gutta-percha and balata have been hydrogenated by similar methods; hydrogenation removes the assymetry, and the products are very similar to hydro-rubber, the density and refractive indices being practically identical.[175]

> Hydro-rubber: density 0.8585, n_D^{16} 1.4768
> Hydro-gutta-percha: density 0.8595, n_D^{16} 1.4770
> Hydro-balata, n_D^{16} 1.4762

The possibility that cyclisation accompanies hydrogenation has been suggested [176, 177] to account for some anomalies observed in hydrogenating rubber with the aid of platinum black; no anomalous behaviour has been observed with nickel catalysts.

More recently it has been found possible to hydrogenate rubber with very little degradation, provided that the temperature was controlled between fairly narrow limits ($170°$–$195°$ C) and oxygen was carefully excluded; only a moderate pressure of hydrogen (15–20 atmos.) was required.[178] The catalyst was nickel on kieselguhr, and 30–40 parts of nickel were required per 100 parts of rubber; crêpe rubber was used at a concentration of 2% in cyclohexane. After hydrogenation the catalyst was flocculated by the addition of 5 volumes of acetic acid per 100 volumes of solution and removed by filtration.   Hydrogenated rubber prepared in this way is a colourless, transparent, somewhat elastic waxy material (Fig. 2.9), having the peculiar property of pulling out into fine threads when stretched.

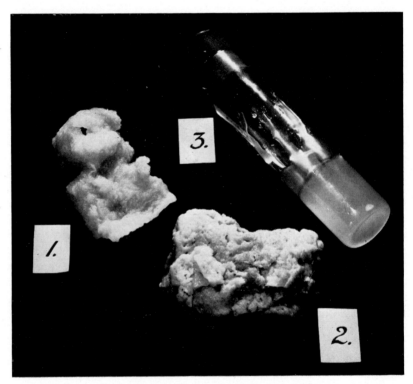

Fig. 2.9. Hydrogenated natural rubber.   (1) and (3) fully hydrogenated, mol. wt. 150,000 and 50,000 respectively;   (2) partially (60%) hydrogenated, mol. wt. 140,000.

(Reproduced by courtesy of *Endeavour* [179].)

The action of halogens on rubber

The reaction of chlorine with rubber

Considerable substitution and cyclisation accompany the reaction of elementary chlorine with rubber over a wide range of experimental conditions covering chlorination of rubber in solution or in latex, as well as the action of liquid chlorine on solid rubber at low temperature.

The reaction of gaseous chlorine when diluted with nitrogen and passed into a rubber solution in carbon tetrachloride at 80° C can be divided into three distinct stages represented by eqn. 2.17–2.19.[180,181] Under these experimental conditions the hydrogen chloride liberated during reaction is expelled rapidly from the solution, and the possibility of its addition to the double bonds of the rubber is minimised.

$$-C_{10}H_{16}- + 2Cl_2 \longrightarrow -C_{10}H_{14}Cl_2 + 2HCl \quad . \quad . \quad (2.17)$$

$$-C_{10}H_{14}Cl_2- + 2Cl_2 \longrightarrow -C_{10}H_{13}Cl_5- + HCl \quad . \quad (2.18)$$

$$-C_{10}H_{13}Cl_5- + 2Cl_2 \longrightarrow -C_{10}H_{11}Cl_7- + 2HCl \quad . \quad (2.19)$$

The reaction of chlorine up to the limit of one molecular proportion per C_5-unit is exclusively substitutive (eqn. 2.17), and most of the cyclisation is believed to occur during this stage, possibly by a carbonium-ion mechanism (eqn. 2.20–2.23) similar to that formulated above (2.17) for acid-catalysed cyclisation of rubber. The chlorination reactions at the two ethylenic centres of a pair of C_5-units involved in a cyclisation have not been formally separated, and they probably proceed simultaneously; thus fractionation of a product containing 18% of chlorine yielded only fractions containing at least 22% of chlorine together with unchlorinated rubber.[182] Fractionation of a more extended series of partially chlorinated rubbers has shown that up to an overall chlorine content of 35% (i.e. stage 1 chlorination) the products are very heterogeneous but always contain some material of 34–35% chlorine content, even when the overall average chlorine content is below 10%. Beyond the stage 1 chlorination reaction, the products become much more homogeneous.[183]

$$\cdots -CH_2-CMe{=}CH-CH_2-CH_2-CMe{=}CH-CH_2- \cdots + Cl_2 \quad . \quad . \quad (2.20)$$

$$\downarrow$$

$$\cdots -CH_2-\underset{+}{C}Me-CHCl-CH_2-CH_2-CMe{=}CH-CH_2- \cdots + Cl^- \quad . \quad (2.21)$$

$$\downarrow$$

$$\cdots -CH_2-CMe-CHCl-CH_2-CH_2-\underset{+}{C}Me-CH-CH_2- \cdots \qquad HCl$$

$$\downarrow$$

$$\cdots -CH_2-CMe-CHCl-CH_2-CH{=}CMe-CH-CH_2- \cdots + H^+ . \quad . \quad (2.22)$$

$$\downarrow Cl_2$$

$$\cdots -CH_2-CMe-CHCl-CH{=}CH-CMeCl-CH-CH-CH_2- \cdots + HCl \quad (2.23)$$

(XXXVIII)

The product at this stage of chlorination contains 34·6% Cl and is still somewhat rubbery. It has poor stability, especially towards heat. Some attempts have been made to use partially chlorinated rubber in oil-resistant compositions [184] without much success.   It still contains one ethylenic bond in the C_{10} structural unit XXXVIII, but changes in the infra-red spectrum during chlorination are indicative of a bond shift.[48]   No organic proof of the structure of stage 1 chlorinated rubber has yet been presented. The high reactivity of the chlorine atoms towards alcoholic silver nitrate [185] and towards organic bases [186,187] indicate that they are either tertiary or allylic, and this evidence is consistent with structure XXXVIII.

The stage 1 chlorination product may be very conveniently prepared by the interaction of sulphuryl chloride SO_2Cl_2 with rubber in the presence of a substance which will inhibit any tendency towards free radical additive chlorination (see below), e.g. an antioxidant.   The advantage of this reagent is it can be uniformly mixed with a rubber solution and reaction subsequently made to occur by heating to 60°–80° C.   This avoids the instantaneous and localised reaction which occurs when chlorine gas is led into a rubber solution, and consequently much more homogeneous chlorination products are obtained.

In the second stage of chlorination (eqn. 2.18) both substitution and addition proceed simultaneously, and by the time the C_{10}-unit has reacted with the further two molecules of chlorine no residual unsaturation remains and the product contains 57·2% Cl.   If isolated at this stage by precipitation from its solution the product is crumb-like and has no rubbery characteristics; it is of much greater thermal stability than the stage 1 product, and only about 30% of its halogen is reactive towards aniline. Obviously the chlorine atoms substituted in the first stage of chlorination have been stabilised by the addition of chlorine to the double bond in the second stage.   This is in accordance with the known stability of saturated polychlorides compared with allylic chlorides.

Beyond stage 2 further chlorination proceeds exclusively by substitution to give an ultimate chlorine content generally in the region of 65%. Fractional precipitation has shown that the product is homogeneous apart from a small first fraction of lower chlorine content.   All subsequent fractions contained 65·5 ± 0·3% in close conformity with the empirical formula $C_{10}H_{11}Cl_7$, which requires 65·42% Cl.[188]

The evolution of hydrogen chloride has been followed experimentally and agrees closely with the anticipated yields in each of the above three reaction stages.   The analytical compositions of the two intermediate products $C_{10}H_{14}Cl_2$ and $C_{10}H_{13}Cl_5$ and that of the final chlorination product $C_{10}H_{11}Cl_7$ have been found to agree closely with these empirical formulae, although some more recent analyses [189] of some fractions obtained from commercial fully chlorinated rubber show a H–C ratio in the region 12·5 : 10 rather than 11 : 10 as required by $C_{10}H_{11}Cl_7$.

The changes in the infra-red spectrum during chlorination of rubber have been interpreted as indicative of formation of vinyl groups rather than cyclisation.[48] This interpretation evolves mainly from the appearance of absorption at $11 \cdot 2\,\mu$ shifting towards $10 \cdot 9\,\mu$ as chlorination proceeds, but is not altogether conclusive, since the absorption persists at a very high level of chlorination, although tending towards still shorter wavelengths. Similar absorption at $11 \cdot 2\,\mu$ appears in rubber hydrochloride and at $10 \cdot 8\,\mu$ in the additive dichloride of rubber, in which unsaturation is unlikely; the $11 \cdot 2$-μ absorption of rubber hydrochloride disappears on chlorination, but absorption then appears in the $10 \cdot 8$-μ region.

The main evidence in favour of the cyclisation mechanism of chlorination is as follows:

(1) The evolution of hydrogen chloride through eqn. 2.17–2.19 shows that only one molecule of chlorine has added to the C_{10}-unit. On the basis of a non-cyclising mechanism this requires the presence of a residual double bond in the C_{10}-unit at advanced stages of chlorination, and for this there is no experimental evidence.

(2) The additive capacity of XXXVIII towards chlorine, iodine chloride and phenyl iododichloride indicates the presence of only one double bond in the C_{10}-unit. The failure to take up more than one molecule of these additive reagents cannot be explained by inhibition of additive reaction caused by the possibility of a chlorine atom substituted on the ethylenic carbon atom, i.e. as $-CH=CCl-$, since a chlorine atom so placed is unreactive to bases and silver nitrate. These reagents show that the chlorine is allylic or tertiary, and these types of substituted chlorine do not inhibit addition to the double bond. Hence only one double bond can be present in the C_{10}-unit.

(3) The products of ozonolysis during stage 1 chlorination show a substantial loss of unsaturation,[190] whereas a non-cyclising substitutive mechanism requires no loss of double bonds.

(4) An alternative interpretation of the infra-red spectra of partially and fully chlorinated rubber ascribes the 12-μ band to $-CH=CH-$ unsaturation in the early stages of chlorination, which together with $6 \cdot 1$-μ double bond unsaturation, disappears rapidly above 55% Cl. The absorptions around $8\,\mu$ and $11\,\mu$ are shown to be common to the spectral features of both cyclohexane and β-hexachlorocyclohexane.[183,189]

(5) The intrinsic viscosity of chlorinated rubber is much lower for a given molecular weight than is that of rubber.[183,191] This is indicative of a more compact molecule, and accordingly suggests a cyclised structure rather than a linear one.[192] This effect is already apparent at stage 1 chlorination; a sample of $(C_5H_7Cl)_n$ had an osmotic molecular weight of 240,000, but its intrinsic viscosity was only $1 \cdot 04$.[180]

(6) If the chlorination of rubber proceeds by a cyclisation mechanism it should be subject to the statistical effect of random cyclisation already

proposed for cyclisation of rubber.[119]   This requires the distribution of 13.5% of chlorinated C_5-units, each retaining its unsaturation, among the cyclised units.   The presence of one double bond in each cyclised unit requires the addition of two chlorine atoms per C_{10}-unit, i.e. one additive Cl per C_5-unit in cyclic structures.   Hence in the presence of 13.5% of uncyclised units, each with an additive capacity of two chlorine atoms, the theoretical limit of additive chlorine would be 1.135 atoms per C_5-unit.   An experimentally found value of 1.14 has been reported.[181]

The preparation of chlorinated rubber.   Various methods have been proposed for the preparation and manufacture of highly chlorinated rubber.[175, 193]   The most popular and, indeed, the only method to have reached a substantial scale of commercial production, is the direct chlorination of rubber in an inert solvent at temperatures around 80° C.   Products of better stability are obtained at this temperature than at room temperature.   In order to avoid gelation during chlorination and to obtain products of a sufficiently low viscosity to be practically useful, the rubber is usually degraded considerably, either by milling before putting it into solution or by exposure to light or oxidising agents either before or during chlorination.   After chlorination the product is usually isolated by volatilising the solvent with the aid of steam; it has also been proposed to evaporate the solution continuously on the surface of a heated drum from which the dried deposit could be removed by a scraper blade.   Detailed descriptions of these processes together with properties and uses of the product, and a comprehensive list of the patents involved, have appeared in the literature.[175].

Sheeted or finely-divided rubber has been treated with gaseous chlorine, sometimes in the presence of a little solvent or solvent vapour,[194] or with liquid chlorine at low temperature.[195]   If conducted under pressure at temperatures above 70° C the chlorine content can surpass that reached in gaseous chlorination of rubber in solution.   Chlorine contents approaching 70% have been reported.   A fine state of subdivision of the rubber is necessary to ensure homogeneity in the product, and an excess of liquid chlorine is advantageous, since it has a swelling action on rubber and a solvent action on the chlorinated product.   The reaction between rubber and liquid chlorine can proceed with considerable violence if not adequately controlled.[182]

Chlorinated rubber has also been prepared directly from latex.   Early attemps to chlorinate latex involved its prior treatment with hypochlorous acid or chlorine in an alkaline medium to saturate the double bonds, after which it could be further chlorinated without coagulation.[196]   These methods usually gave a rather insoluble product, and only by degradation of the latex have soluble products been obtained, using either promoted oxidation [197] or else making use of the oxidising power of chlorates, hypochlorites, permanganates, dichromates or peroxides added to the latex, which is then acidified with hydrochloric acid, whereupon the chlorine generated *in situ* reacts rapidly with the rubber.[198]   Recently it has been shown that the chlorination of latex can be accomplished directly at temperatures around 20°–30° C, provided that the latex is first stabilised by means of a non-ionic or cationic stabiliser.[199, 200]   A strongly acid medium is distinctly advantageous in avoiding incidental addition of hypochlorous acid and it is accordingly desirable to acidify the stabilised latex before chlorinating, thus if the serum is brought to an acid concentration of 8N-HCl or 6N-H_2SO_4 the chlorination product contains no combined oxygen.   At least 20 hours are required at 20°–30° C to reach chlorine contents approaching 60%.   At more elevated temperatures the product is discoloured and there is an adverse effect on its solubility.   It is undesirable to allow hydrogen chloride to add to the rubber prior to chlorination, as would occur if the serum were saturated with hydrochloric acid; rubber hydrochloride prepared in this way is much less amenable to chlorination than is rubber latex, or rubber hydrochloride when prepared in solution, and photolytic assistance is required to reach a chlorine content of 50–55%, which appears to be the upper limit obtainable by this procedure.   Nevertheless, chlorinated rubber hydrochloride containing 50–55% Cl is more stable than products of comparable chlorine content obtained by the direct chlorination of latex.

The chlorination of rubber in latex does not easily proceed to chlorine contents in excess of 60%.   In order to obtain a chlorine content, stability and solubility comparable with solution-chlorinated rubber an after-chlorination treatment is necessary.   This can be achieved by chlorinating the latex-chlorinated rubber in solution, suspension or swollen in carbon tetrachloride, but preferably by treating the dry, powdery product of latex chlorination with liquid chlorine under pressure at temperatures of 70° C or above.   Ultimate chlorine-contents of at least 70% can be achieved in this way.

Properties of chlorinated rubber.   Fully chlorinated rubber (with chlorine content at least 65%) is an almost white thermoplastic powder, S.G. 1·63–1·66, refractive index 1·596, which tenaciously retains small quantities of the solvent used in its manufacture.   For this reason foam-like masses of low density (e.g. 0·09) may be obtained by heating commercial chlorinated rubber in a press and releasing the pressure while hot.[201]   Solvent-free chlorinated rubber does not foam when subjected to the same treatment.   Chlorinated rubber is generally soluble in aromatic hydrocarbons and chlorinated solvents, in some esters and higher ketones (especially cyclohexanone), in dioxane and in nitrobenzene.   It is not soluble in alcohol, ether or petroleum solvents.   It is non-inflammable and is extremely resistant to many chemicals; it finds its principal applications in protective paints and coatings and as an adhesive.   It is not particularly resistant to organic bases, especially on heating, when a substantial proportion of its chlorine is removed.

The molecular weight of chlorinated rubber when made without extensive degradation can be quite high, and values in excess of 100,000 have been reported for commercial products, while a laboratory preparation had a molecular weight of 320,000.[191]

The additive chlorination of rubber.   Phenyliododichloride PhICl$_2$, and sulphuryl chloride SO$_2$Cl$_2$ in the presence of a peroxide, donate their chlorine additively to olefins, including those which are otherwise prone to substitution by elementary chlorine.   This type of chlorination shows the characteristic features of a radical chain reaction which, in the case of sulphuryl chloride, has been formulated as follows:

$$\text{Peroxide} \longrightarrow \text{R}*$$

$$\text{R}* + \text{SO}_2\text{Cl}_2 \longrightarrow \text{RCl} + *\text{SO}_2\text{Cl}$$

$$*\text{SO}_2\text{Cl} \longrightarrow \text{SO}_2 + \text{Cl}*$$

$$\text{Cl}* + {>}\text{C}{=}\text{C}{<} \longrightarrow {>}\overset{|}{\underset{\text{Cl}}{\text{C}}}{-}\overset{*}{\text{C}}{<}$$

$$\overset{|}{\underset{\text{Cl}}{>}\text{C}}{-}\overset{*}{\text{C}}{<} + \text{SO}_2\text{Cl}_2 \longrightarrow {>}\overset{|}{\underset{\text{Cl}}{\text{C}}}{-}\overset{|}{\underset{\text{Cl}}{\text{C}}}{<} + *\text{SO}_2\text{Cl}$$

etc.

The overall reaction is thus

$${>}\text{C}{=}\text{C}{<} + \text{SO}_2\text{Cl}_2 \longrightarrow {>}\overset{|}{\underset{\text{Cl}}{\text{C}}}{-}\overset{|}{\underset{\text{Cl}}{\text{C}}}{<} + \text{SO}_2 \quad . \quad . \quad . \quad (2.24)$$

Purified rubber (in solution) reacts smoothly with phenyliododichloride at 80° C and gives the additive dichloride (C$_5$H$_8$Cl$_2$)$_n$ (XXXIX), with only a trace of substitutive side reaction.   Sulphuryl chloride reacts similarly

$$\cdots -\text{CH}_2-\overset{\overset{\text{CH}_3}{|}}{\underset{\underset{\text{Cl}}{|}}{\text{C}}}-\overset{\overset{}{}}{\underset{\underset{\text{Cl}}{|}}{\text{CH}}}-\text{CH}_2- \cdots \qquad \text{(XXXIX)}$$

with purified rubber provided that a peroxide is present; in the absence of peroxide the reaction is largely substitutive and is wholly so with unpurified rubber.   Even with the addition of a peroxide, unpurified rubber gives a partially substitutive reaction.[185, 203]

As additive chlorination proceeds unsaturation is lost in proportion to the amount of chlorine added, and when one molecule of chlorine has reacted with a C_5-unit no unsaturation can be detected. The product has a chlorine content of 51%, and in contrast to materials of similar chlorine content obtained by the reaction of elementary chlorine the halogen in the additive dichloride is stable towards aniline and silver nitrate. Rubber dichloride is a white, crumb-like material with little elasticity; it is readily soluble in chlorinated solvents and in aromatic hydrocarbons, and it is reasonably stable. The infra-red spectrum is similar to that of ordinary chlorinated rubber, but in earlier stages of additive chlorination the spectrum shows some characteristics of fully chlorinated rubber while retaining part of the absorption characteristic of rubber.[204] The additive dichloride has not found any industrial application owing to the high cost of the reagents required for its manufacture.

The additive dichloride may be further chlorinated by the action of chlorine to give chlorinated rubber very similar to that obtained directly from rubber and chlorine, although the end product should be free from the cyclic structures believed to be present in ordinary chlorinated rubber. No comparisons have been made of the infra-red spectra or the intrinsic viscosity–molecular weight relationship of chlorinated rubber made by the two different processes. Both properties should reflect the anticipated structural differences.

A product (XLI) which is structurally very similar to the additive dichloride is obtained by chlorinating rubber hydrochloride (XL) until one atom of chlorine per C_5-unit has been substituted. Although the chlorine

$$\cdots -CH_2-\overset{\overset{\displaystyle CH_3}{|}}{\underset{\underset{\displaystyle Cl}{|}}{C}}-CH_2-CH_2-\cdots \xrightarrow{Cl_2} \cdots -CH_2-\overset{\overset{\displaystyle CH_3}{|}}{\underset{\underset{\displaystyle Cl}{|}}{C}}-\overset{}{\underset{\underset{\displaystyle Cl}{|}}{CH}}-CH_2-\cdots + HCl$$

(XL)   (XLI)

atom in rubber hydrochloride itself is very labile, it is stabilised by the introduction of the second chlorine atom in the dichloride XLI and the stability of this product towards aniline is comparable with that of the additive dichloride.[203] The more prolonged action of chlorine on rubber hydrochloride gives yet another fully chlorinated rubber, which, like that derived from the additive dichloride, should be free from cyclic structures.

The reaction of rubber with hypochlorous acid and its esters. Hypochlorous acid adds as expected to the double bond of rubber, but substitutive chlorination also proceeds readily to give highly chlorinated materials if an excess of hypochlorous acid is employed. This is not a normal feature of the addition of hypochlorous acid to olefins, and may perhaps be attributed to the readiness with which any free chlorine in the reagent can enter into substitutive reaction with the rubber, so liberating hydrochloric acid, which shifts towards the left the position of equilibrium in the system represented by eqn. 2.25.   Such a tendency is clearly cumulative and may well account for the readiness with which rubber is chlorinated by aqueous solutions of hypochlorous acid.

$$Cl_2 + H_2O \rightleftharpoons HOCl + HCl \quad . \quad . \quad . \quad (2.25)$$

Hypochlorous acid has a two-fold action on rubber, according to the pH of the system.   When on the alkaline side, especially in the pH range 10–12, the reaction is mainly one of oxidative degradation with little evidence of either addition of hypochlorite or of chlorination.   Under mildly acid conditions (pH 5–6) the addition of hypochlorous acid is the predominant reaction.   Neutral hypochlorous acid with pH around 7 gives both reactions.[205]   Hence the addition of a small proportion of neutral hypochlorous acid gives very tacky and obviously degraded hypochlorites. With larger proportions of hypochlorous acid the tackiness is less apparent, and, indeed, the initial degradation is advantageous in enabling readily soluble hypochlorinated and chlorinated products to be obtained.   The two competing reactions can be brought under control to achieve a desired combination of properties in the end product if the rubber is first treated with alkaline hypochlorite and then rendered feebly acid, e.g. by the addition of " dry ice " to liberate hypochlorous acid.

Both rubber solutions and rubber latex have been reacted with hypochlorous acid.[196]   Even at the early stages of addition (i.e. less than one mole of acid per C_5-unit), there is already evidence of some substitution of chlorine in that the chlorine content of the product is in excess of that corresponding to its oxygen content on the assumption of addition of hypochlorous acid in accordance with eqn. 2.26.   Thus the product of

$$(C_5H_8)_n + HOCl \longrightarrow (C_5H_9OCl)_n \quad . \quad . \quad (2.26)$$

interaction of one molecular proportion of hypochlorous acid per C_5-unit using a solution of rubber in chloroform had the composition C 57·4; H 6·4; Cl 27·1% and a corresponding product prepared from latex analysed C 53·2; H 6·4; Cl 29·8%.   The calculated composition of the molecular adduct C_5H_9OCl is C 49·9; H 7·5; Cl 29·4%.   With a considerable excess of hypochlorous acid a chloroform solution of rubber gave a highly chlorinated product (66% Cl) which was readily soluble in chloroform, benzene and acetone, and the presence of hydroxylic oxygen was revealed when its benzene solution was treated with methyl magnesium iodide.   With latex the maximum chlorine content obtained was 41·5%, and this product was insoluble.   Products of higher chlorine content could be obtained from latex only by the action of chlorine itself in a supplementary treatment.

No substantial commercial application of hypochlorinated rubber has developed, although it has found some application in cements and adhesives for bonding rubber to metal.

Esters of hypochlorous acid (other than *tert*-butyl) are rather unstable substances, but they can be handled in solution without hazard. Ethyl hypochlorite, for example, can be easily prepared by shaking carbon tetrachloride containing a little alcohol with an ice-cold solution of hypochlorous acid for a few minutes.[206] This solution reacts quantitatively with rubber in the course of a few hours and gives a product which is saturated to bromine and which has a chlorine content again somewhat higher than that of the expected adduct $(C_7H_{13}OCl)_n$, probably on account of some free chlorine in the reagent. An excess of the reagent does not cause further chlorination provided that the time of contact is not unduly prolonged.[207] The product is a somewhat rubbery material, solutions of which give very flexible mar-resistant films of reasonable stability. No commercial application has developed. Rather similar materials result from the reaction with rubber of the hypochlorites of the lower fatty acids.[208]

The reaction of bromine with rubber

There is much less tendency towards substitution when bromine is brought into reaction with rubber, especially if the reaction is conducted at low temperature in an inert solvent containing a little alcohol.[185] Addition of bromine to the double bond is very rapid and has been used to determine the unsaturation of rubber, although the results tend to be a little low. Alternatively, the brominated rubber solution may be added to alcohol to precipitate the dibromide, which may be subsequently dried and weighed. This procedure is the basis of some methods of estimating rubber in plant material.[209]

Rubber dibromide $(C_5H_8Br_2)_n$ is a pale yellow to white powdery material and contains $70 \cdot 1\%$ of bromine. Its properties have been much less extensively studied than those of chlorinated rubber, and it has found no commercial application on account of its high cost and poor stability, although surface treatment with bromine solution or bromine water is used quite commonly to impart surface hardness to rubber articles. It is not so readily soluble as chlorinated rubber, and its capability of dissolution is rather restricted to the solvents chloroform and carbon tetrachloride. One bromine atom is quite easily eliminated, either by heating or by the action of alkalis, organic bases or zinc; it reacts quite violently with sodium. Rubber dibromide undergoes an interesting reaction when heated with phenol at $140°-150°$ C. Hydrogen bromide is eliminated and a product (rubber dihydroxyphenyl) soluble in aqueous alkali is obtained. This has the composition $[C_5H_8(C_6H_4OH)_2]_n$.[210] The phenolic groups can be methylated or benzoylated, and this destroys the solubility in aqueous alkali; alternatively, they may be coupled with diazotised amines to give coloured substances based on rubber.[211]   The reaction with phenols is a general one, especially when aided by a catalyst such as ferric chloride, and a range of phenolic substances has been shown to react.   Gutta-percha and balata dibromides enter into similar reactions.[212] Rubber di-(hydroxyphenyl) is a coloured amorphous powder, soluble in acetone, esters, pyridine and aqueous alkali, insoluble in benzene, chloroform, petroleum ether and water.   It has also been stated that aromatic amines can be condensed with rubber dibromide in an analogous manner and reactions characteristic of the amino group (e.g. diazotisation) have been shown to take place.[213]

A substituted rubber monobromide $(C_{10}H_{15}Br)_n$ has been prepared directly from rubber by the action of N-bromosuccinimide (eqn. 2.27).[185]

$$-C_{10}H_{16}- + \quad \rangle NBr \longrightarrow -C_{10}H_{15}Br- + \quad \rangle NH \quad (2.27)$$

This reaction probably proceeds by a free radical chain mechanism in-volving the hydrogen-capturing radical $\rangle N*$, as has been established in corresponding substitutive bromination reactions between N-bromo-succinimide and various olefins.   The reaction is probably complex, since much gelling occurs, and the product when once precipitated from solution cannot be redissolved.   The bromide has an unexpectedly intense reddish-brown colour, and this may be the result of bond shifts which are com-monly observed in brominations by N-bromosuccinimide.   Its bromine is almost wholly reactive towards aniline and silver nitrate.

The reaction of rubber with fluorine

Fluorine reacts very violently and destructively with rubber.   By using greatly diluted fluorine, products containing up to 30% of fluorine have been obtained; they are quite rubbery and have been suggested for use as gaskets in fluorine generators in which the reaction could be carried out *in situ*.[214]

The reaction of rubber with iodine

No well-defined iodinated derivatives of rubber have been reported.   A greenish-yellow material of very poor stability is obtained when iodine is added to a solution of rubber; the solution gels and the product is in-soluble.[215, 216]

The reaction of rubber with iodine chloride

The main interest in this reagent is in its application to the determination of the unsaturation of rubber, in accordance with its wide general usage for this purpose in organic chemistry.

Determination of the olefinic unsaturation of rubber

It is perhaps convenient to consider this important topic at this stage on account of its close relationship to the mechanism of halogen addition to rubber. Unsaturation is in fact commonly defined in terms of the additive capacity for halogen exhibited by an olefin, and is expressed as an iodine number or iodine value, which is numerically equal to the weight of iodine equivalent to the halogen consumed by 100 g. of olefin. Thus in the example of natural rubber the theoretical iodine value is 373 (68 g. of rubber should add halogen equivalent to 2×127 g. of iodine, hence 100 g. of rubber requires 373 g. of iodine).

In determining the unsaturation of rubber by means of a halogen, the interpretation of the measured halogen uptake is complicated by its involvement in substitution and cyclisation reactions as well as the required addition reaction. Hence when based only on total halogen [217,218] consumption the result will be too high unless the substitution and cyclisation tendencies can be either corrected for or suppressed. Halogen acid arising solely from substitution is easily estimated by a simple extension to the normal experimental procedure. A halogen solution is added in excess to a solution of the olefin, and after reaction the excess halogen is estimated by the addition of aqueous potassium iodide and titration of the liberated iodine. This gives total halogen consumption. If potassium iodate is then added it will react immediately with any halogen acid which has been formed, liberating further iodine, which is estimated by a second titration. This is the well-known McIlhiney procedure.[219] For every molecule of halogen acid formed substitutively one atom of halogen has entered the olefin, hence one deducts twice the amount of halogen found by the McIlhiney procedure from the total halogen consumed to obtain the halogen added to the olefin. However, in a cyclisation reaction (eqn. 2.20–2.22) one double bond is lost, and one molecule of halogen is consumed, hence the halogen acid found by applying the McIlhiney procedure in this case must not be deducted from the halogen consumed.

In the reaction of rubber with iodine chloride in non-polar solvents halogen acid is formed by both substitution and cyclisation, and correction for substitution is impracticable, since it cannot be ascertained with certainty how much halogen acid is formed by substitution and how much by cyclisation. Unsaturation determination based on the use of iodine chloride in non-polar solvents is, therefore, of doubtful validity.

The use of iodine chloride in acetic acid (Wijs reagent) enables the substitutive reaction to be suppressed, and some excellent results have been obtained with this reagent.[220] Bromine has been used similarly in chloroform or carbon tetrachloride containing a very small proportion of alcohol,[185] but results with this reagent tend to be somewhat low.

Typical unsaturation values (calculated as iodine value) which have been reported for rubber are given in Table 2.13.

TABLE 2.13

SOME UNSATURATION VALUES FOR NATURAL RUBBER

Rubber	I.V. by Wijs method	I.V. by bromine addition
Purified hydrocarbon	372–3	364
Pale crêpe	348	—
Deresinated pale crêpe	361	358
Smoked sheet	351	—
Deresinated smoked sheet	360	—
Gutta-percha (white, purified)	365–370	352

The problem of determining the unsaturation of a vulcanised rubber is even more complicated, since further sources of halogen acid, accompanied by excessive uptake of halogen, arise from the tendency of halogens to add to sulphur atoms of mono- and polysulphides, leading to the formation of halogen acid by hydrolysis of the adduct [221, 222] (eqn. 2.28).   Hydrolysis of

$$
R \cdot S \cdot R^1 \xrightarrow{\ X_2\ } R \cdot \overset{\displaystyle X}{\underset{\displaystyle X}{S}} \cdot R^1 \xrightarrow{\ H_2O\ } R \cdot \overset{\displaystyle O}{S} \cdot R^1 + 2HX \quad . \quad . \quad (2.28)
$$

the sulphur–halogen adduct is facilitated by the presence of acetic acid, so that the Wijs reagent is unsuitable for vulcanised rubbers.   Fortunately the bromine adduct, in the absence of acetic acid, yields up its halogen fairly quantitatively (eqn. 2.29) to the strong potassium iodide, which is normally added in the later stages of an unsaturation determina-

$$
R \cdot \overset{\displaystyle X}{\underset{\displaystyle X}{S}} \cdot R^1 \xrightarrow[\ (H_2O)\ ]{\ KI\ } R \cdot S \cdot R^1 + I_2 \quad . \quad . \quad . \quad . \quad (2.29)
$$

tion, furthermore, substitutive reactions are practically absent with bromine in chlorinated solvents containing a little alcohol.   Consequently bromine in these solvents is a very useful reagent for vulcanised rubber, but it must always be remembered that results on unvulcanised rubber are somewhat low with this reagent.

The following procedures are recommended for iodine value determinations: [218]

(1) *Unvulcanised rubber.* The sample (*ca.* 0·1 g.) is dissolved in 75 ml. of pure carbon disulphide in a glass-stoppered flask or bottle. 25 ml. of 0·2N Wijs solution are added from a pipette while the contents of the flask are swirled around by a rotary motion of the flask. After standing for an hour at room temperature in the dark, 25 ml. of 15% potassium iodide are added, then 50 ml. of water, and the contents of the flask are titrated immediately with 0·1N-thiosulphate, adding starch indicator towards the end point. It is of the utmost importance that the Wijs solution should be anhydrous, and a test sample should give a clear solution on dilution with twice its volume of carbon disulphide. Water reacts with iodine chloride to give iodine and iodic acid (eqn. 2.30), which have a reactivity towards rubber quite different from that of iodine chloride, although their ability to liberate iodine from potassium iodide is of comparable magnitude, so that the deterioration of the reagent by moisture is not revealed by iodimetric determination of its strength. Moist reagent (especially when aged) gives low unsaturation values for rubber.

$$5ICl + 3H_2O = 5HCl + HIO_3 + 2I_2 \quad . \quad . \quad (2.30)$$

(2) *Vulcanised rubber.* The finely divided sample (0·1 g.) is dispersed as rapidly as possible in 50 g. of dichlorobenzene at 160°–170° C,[223] 70 ml. of chloroform containing 0·5 ml. of alcohol are then added, the solution is cooled to 0° C and 25 ml. of 0·2N-bromine in carbon tetrachloride are added. After standing for 15 minutes at 0°, 25 ml. of 15% potassium iodide are added and the above procedure is followed.

Recently some alternative methods for estimating unsaturation have been examined. Phenyliododichloride has been used as a purely additive reagent in an examination of cyclised rubber (p. 98). Hydrogen chloride has been used similarly, but suffers from the failure of this reagent to undergo quantitative addition to rubber in solution.[127] Perbenzoic acid is a useful additive reagent; the rubber in solution is treated with excess of the reagent, and the excess is subsequently estimated iodimetrically. It has a noteworthy advantage in that it reacts with terminal and pendant vinyl ($CH_2 = C$) groups more slowly than with internal double bonds, and so enables the relative proportions of each to be estimated. Although mainly of use in the examination of synthetic rubbers, the reagent has been applied in this manner to natural rubber and shows that at least 95 ± 2% of the double bonds of rubber are of the anticipated internal (i.e. 1 : 4-polyisoprenic) type.[224, 225]

Ozone has been used to estimate unsaturation in various olefins. For this purpose ozone is passed at a constant rate through a solution of the olefin, and the amount absorbed is measured by monitoring devices.[226] The method has recently been applied successfully to rubber.[132]

Rubber hydrohalides

The addition of hydrogen chloride to rubber.   Hydrogen chloride adds readily to rubber, either in finely divided solid form, in solution or merely swollen with a solvent, or in latex;[227] in the main the reaction is an orthodox addition at the double bonds (eqn. 2.31), but in hydrocarbon solvents the addition appears to be accompanied by some cyclisation, since the theoretical uptake of hydrogen chloride is not attained; in latex the addition of hydrogen chloride proceeds more or less to completion and the product contains almost the anticipated 33·9% of chlorine.   The kinetics

$$\cdots-CH_2-\overset{\overset{\displaystyle CH_3}{|}}{C}=CH-CH_2-\cdots + HCl- \longrightarrow \cdots-CH_2-\overset{\overset{\displaystyle CH_3}{|}}{\underset{\underset{\displaystyle Cl}{|}}{C}}-CH_2-CH_2-\cdots \quad . \quad . \quad (2.31)$$

of the hydrochlorination step have been recently studied.[228]   Hydrochlorination in solution is best conducted at low temperature (below 10° C), partly to avoid cyclisation and partly to obtain a higher concentration of hydrogen chloride in the reaction medium.   In *latex* an increased pressure of hydrogen chloride greatly increases the rate of hydrochlorination, especially if the temperature is also raised.   Hydrochlorination in solution is solvent-dependent, and is especially rapid in solvents containing a polar component which is capable of complex formation with hydrogen chloride. Dioxane and ethyl acetate suppress the cyclisation tendency when used in this way, and higher chlorine contents are obtained.

Manufacture of rubber hydrochloride is usually carried out in a solution of rubber, into which is passed a stream of dry hydrogen chloride.   The addition of a ketone or alcohol is advantageous to prevent gelling of the solution during reaction.   If it is required to use the rubber hydrochloride in solution it is sufficient to remove the excess hydrogen chloride, e.g. by air-blowing and neutralisation.   If the solid hydrochloride is required it may be precipitated from solution or isolated by steam distillation. Manufacture from latex has been recently proposed.[200]   It is generally necessary to incorporate an anti-acid stabiliser in formulations containing rubber hydrochloride.   The main application of the material is as cast film, of which " Pliofilm " is a well-known commercial example;   this application is a direct consequence of its low permeability to water vapour. Rubber hydrochloride has been made into thread, in which form it exhibits very good knot strength.   It has also been used in compositions for bonding rubber to metal.   Partially hydrochlorinated rubber has been considered for oil-resisting compositions, a chlorine content of 25–26% providing a suitable compromise between resistance to solvents and retention of rubbery properties.

Rubber hydrochloride made in solution usually has a chlorine content around 28–30% (the product from latex contains 32–33% of chlorine). Its solubility characteristics are similar to those of chlorinated rubber, but it is not soluble in acetone, ether or esters. It is incompatible with rubber. The S.G. is 1·16, and the refractive index is 1·533. Rubber hydrochloride is a highly crystalline material and undergoes marked orientation on stretching.[229,230] It " melts " at a similar temperature to polyethylene, i.e. *ca.* 115° C.

The infra-red spectrum of commercial " Pliofilm " reveals some residual unsaturation, which is consistent with the deficiency in its chlorine content. The spectrum has been examined in considerable detail.[231]

Rubber hydrochloride is not very stable to heat, and considerable loss of halogen occurs at 100° C. Its chlorine is very reactive towards organic bases,[186,232] but undergoes elimination rather than replacement (see " iso-rubber ", p. 89). If the chlorine atom underwent replacement reactions as readily as elimination, rubber hydrochloride would serve as a valuable intermediate in the preparation of a wide range of chemically modified rubbers. Unfortunately this is not the case.

Zinc dust in an acid medium removes most of the chlorine from rubber hydrochloride and gives a cyclised product (see p. 90).

Zinc diethyl reacts slowly with rubber hydrochloride in a cold toluene solution to give ethylhydro-rubber $(C_7H_{14})_n$.[103]

Chlorination of rubber hydrochloride can be carried out in solution or with liquid chlorine to give chlorinated rubbers of high chlorine content (see p. 119).

Comprehensive and detailed accounts of the preparation, properties and applications of rubber hydrochloride are to be found in the litterature.[175,193]

The addition of other halogen acids

Hydrogen bromide. The addition of hydrogen bromide proceeds similarly to that of hydrogen chloride, and the expected hydrobromide $(C_5H_9Br)_n$ has been obtained in the form of a yellowish powder, soluble in chloroform.[233,234] Its halogen atom is very labile.[232]

Hydrogen iodide. This addition has been little studied, and has not yet been carried beyond the stage $(C_{10}H_{17}I)_n$.[234]

Hydrogen fluoride. Considerable difficulty has been encountered in attempting the addition of hydrogen fluoride to rubber, owing to the very powerful cyclising action of this acid, especially in the anhydrous condition. Recently it has been shown that if the acid is brought into reaction with rubber in the presence of an oxygenated solvent with which it can form an " oxonium " complex, the cyclising tendency is largely suppressed and rubber hydrofluoride has been obtained containing 65–70% of the theoretical amount of the fluorine required by the product $(C_5H_9F)_n$.[235]

It is necessary to use an excess of hydrogen fluoride and the preferred "complexing" solvent is dioxane; a 50% solution of the acid in dioxane is recommended. This is added to a solution of rubber in xylene at low temperature, and the solution is allowed to stand for at least 6 hours; 16·7% of fluorine is obtainable in products made in this way below $-15°$ C. At 20° C addition is substantially less and cyclisation is apparent; above 40° C no addition can be obtained.

Rubber hydrofluoride is a non-crystalline rubbery material, although it has a tendency to become brittle at room temperature. The S.G. is 1·04. It exhibits fairly good thermal stability at temperatures up to 100° C and is surprisingly stable towards organic bases, thus with aniline only 2% of its fluorine is split off in 18 hours at 100° C. Indeed, basic substances have a stabilising action (probably by combining with and so neutralising the small amount of labile fluorine), and if magnesium oxide is added in compounding no hydrogen fluoride is split off at 140° C. Vulcanisation is therefore possible and the vulcanisates have good mechanical properties. Furthermore, they have three particular characteristics: they show absolute resistance to ozone, good stability to oxidation and low permeability to gases.

Acid-promoted condensations of rubber

Dispersions of rubber in fairly strong sulphuric acid, such as are obtained by the addition of sulphuric acid to an appropriately stabilised latex, react quite readily with a wide range of reagents which exhibit a tendency to condense with olefins by an ionic mechanism. The reaction involves conversion of the olefin to a carbonium ion, for which there is adequate spectroscopic evidence.[236] The marked cyclising tendency of the carbonium ion derived from natural rubber, however, imposes a limitation on what can be achieved in this direction, e.g. although the lower fatty acids can be very easily added to the double bond of mono-olefins in the presence of a small amount of perchloric acid,[237] rubber itself is merely cyclised when the same conditions are applied. Provided that cyclisation is avoided, either by limiting the concentration of sulphuric acid and keeping the temperature below that necessary for cyclisation, the use of acid latex opens up an interesting field of rubber modification, of which the following condensations are indicative.

1. *Reaction with phenols.* Evidence for the condensation of phenol itself with rubber is scanty. Even in cyclising rubber with acid in the presence of phenol, only a very little of the latter is incorporated in the product. It has been stated several times in the literature that β-naphthol readily condenses with rubber in the presence of sulphuric acid, and it has been suggested [238] that the reaction proceeds by the carbonium mechanism of eqn. 2.32 in conformity with that accepted for the alkylation of phenols

by olefins, e.g. isobutene. Inspection of the relevant patent,[239] however, does not give much indication of combination, and the reaction under the conditions specified therein appears to result mainly in cyclisation. Only

$$\cdots-CH_2-CMe\!=\!CH-CH_2-\cdots \xrightarrow{\ H^+\ } \cdots-CH_2-\underset{+}{C}Me-CH_2-CH_2-\cdots$$

β-naphthol

$$\cdots-CH_2-CMe-CH_2-CH_2-\cdots$$

. . . . . (2.32)

about 1–5% of β-naphthol enters into combination with the rubber. *m*-Cresol reacts much more readily, and a 63% addition of a molecule of *m*-cresol per C_5-unit has been obtained at 50° C in latex acidified to a concentration of 55% sulphuric acid in the serum. The product is not promising, since its vulcanisates have low tensile strength and the modulus is not increased as a result of combination with the *m*-cresol.

2. *Hydrogen peroxide.* The addition of strong hydrogen peroxide (90%) to latex acidified with sulphuric acid is violently exothermic and dangerous. More dilute peroxide (e.g. 100 volume) can be safely added to latex containing 50–55% sulphuric acid in its serum; the temperature rises to 40°–60° C according to the amount of peroxide added. Small amounts of peroxide give oxidised degraded rubbers, but higher proportions (giving up to 20% combined oxygen in the product) are apparently cross-linked resinous materials which are insoluble and unvulcanisable.

3. *Acetic acid.* Small additions of acetic acid were obtained when it (or the anhydride) was added to latex containing 50% sulphuric acid in its serum and heated to 80° C for an hour.

4. *Acetonitrile and acrylonitrile.* Several nitriles have been shown to add to olefins in the presence of sulphuric acid to give N-substituted amido derivatives in accordance with the generalised eqn. 2.33.[240]

$$>\!C\!=\!C\!< + \ RCN \xrightarrow[\;(H_2O)\;]{H_2SO_4} \ \underset{\underset{\overset{\displaystyle|}{R\cdot C\!=\!O}}{\overset{\displaystyle|}{NH}}}{>\!C\!-\!CH-} \qquad . \quad . \quad (2.33)$$

Various proportions of acetonitrile have been successfully condensed with rubber using the acidified-latex technique. The acid concentration in the serum was raised to 68% and the mixture was maintained for $2\frac{1}{2}$ hours at 50° C. The products were soluble and vulcanisable. Analysis

F

revealed a deficiency of nitrogen, and the appearance of more oxygen in the product than is required by eqn. 2.33. Acrylonitrile behaved similarly and gave a very substantial increase in modulus in the vulcanised addition products.

5. *Formaldehyde.* Condensation products of rubber with formaldehyde have been obtained by the action of various catalysts (sulphuric acid, borontrifluoride, zinc chloride, etc.) on mixtures of formaldehyde or its polymers with solutions of rubber,[241, 242] or by adding formaldehyde to appropriately stabilised latex containing a sufficiency of sulphuric acid.[175] The latex reaction proceeds very readily indeed when paraformaldehyde is stirred into stabilised acidified latex with the concentration of acid in the serum around 55% sulphuric acid. If hydrochloric acid is used chlorine is incorporated in the product.[157] The reaction in the presence of sulphuric acid is exothermic and the temperature of the mixture rises from room temperature to 50°–60° C during the course of an hour or so. The latex mixture gels, but the gel can be easily broken up and washed. The dried material is a crumb which consolidates into a coarse sheet on a mill, but is hard and boardy at a level of addition corresponding to 1 mole of formaldehyde per C_5-unit. The use of lower proportions of formaldehyde gives more rubbery products. The reaction products can be compounded and cured. The reaction with formaldehyde imparts to rubber a very high degree of stiffening with some reduction of tensile strength at the higher levels of formaldehyde addition; the elongation at break is comparatively low (100–200% at the level of 1 mole formaldehyde per C_5-unit). Hardness of well over 90° B.S.I. is obtainable in gum compounds, and the vulcanisates show very good resistance to swelling in benzene and in mineral oils.

The addition of formaldehyde to olefinic bonds in the presence of acetic and sulphuric acids is the basis of the well-known Prins reaction, which gives as major product the diacetate (XLII) of the 1 : 3-diol resulting from addition of both formaldehyde and acetic acid to the double bond (eqn.

$$>C{=}C< + HCHO + HOAc \longrightarrow >C\!-\!\overset{|}{\underset{OAc}{C}}\!-\!CH_2OAc \ . \quad (2.34)$$

(XLII)

2.34). There is also formed the cyclic formal (XLIII) (or substituted *m*-dioxane) resulting from addition of *two* moles of formaldehyde to the double bond (eqn. 2.35). The reaction has been discussed in the literature [243] and features in numerous patent applications which cover the addition of formaldehyde to various olefins, with or without acetic acid as a co-reagent, promoted by mineral acids or salts, the latter including both aqueous solutions and anhydrous applications of halides of tin, silicon, etc.

These patents variously describe either cyclic formals, $1:3$-diols (in the absence of an organic acid) or diesters of $1:3$-diols where organic acids are

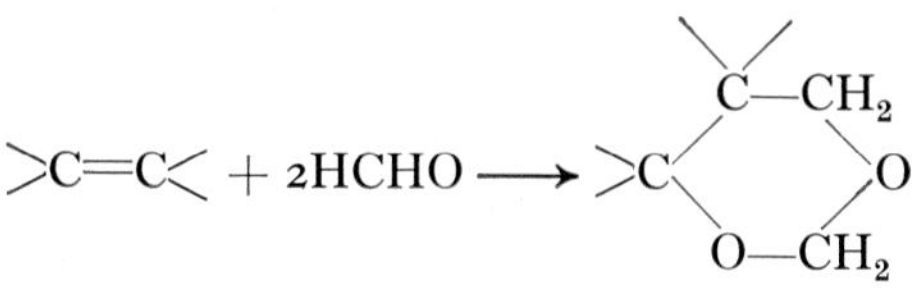

$$>C=C< + 2HCHO \longrightarrow >C \begin{array}{c} C-CH_2 \\ \diagdown \\ O \\ \diagup \\ O-CH_2 \end{array} \qquad . \quad . \quad (2.35)$$

(XLIII)

present, the relative proportions of formal to diol (or diol ester) being determined by conditions of reaction (temperature and nature of promoter).

There is strong evidence that the reaction proceeds by an ionic mechanism involving the entity $CH_2:\overset{+}{O}H$, which may react in one or more of several ways according to prevailing conditions: [244]

(1) Promotion by a strong mineral acid in the presence of acetic acid gives the diacetate (XLII) of a $1:3$-diol plus the cyclic formal (XLIII) and a cyclic ether.

(2) Promotion by a very dilute mineral acid at elevated temperature gives mainly the $1:3$-diols corresponding to (XLII).

(3) Promotion by strong mineral acids at moderate or room temperature gives mainly cyclic formals (XLIII). If hydrochloric acid is used as promoter both formaldehyde and hydrogen chloride add to the olefin to give a chloro-alcohol (XLIV) (eqn. 2.36).

$$RCH_2-CH=CHR + HCHO + HCl \longrightarrow RCH_2-\underset{\underset{Cl}{|}}{C}H-\underset{\underset{CH_2OH}{|}}{C}HR \qquad (2.36)$$

(XLIV)

(4) Promotion by stannic chloride (or similar halide) under substantially anhydrous conditions in the absence of acid gives mainly olefinic alcohols (XLV) together with cyclic formals (XLIII).

$$R-CH_2-CH=CHR + HCHO \longrightarrow R-\underset{\underset{CH_2OH}{|}}{C}H-CH=CHR$$

(XLV)

(5) Promotion by stannic chloride in the presence of an organic acid gives the ester of the olefinic alcohol (XLV).

It therefore appears most probable that the product formed in acidified rubber latex is mainly the cyclic formal (XLVI), and this is supported by the very limited reactivity of the product with phenyl isocyanate, which could be expected to react readily with hydroxylic groups. It is, however, not possible to proceed to the limit of addition of two molecules of formaldehyde per C_5-unit, and the highest addition which has been accomplished in latex is 1·67 moles per C_5-unit (product containing 22·5% oxygen). Technically useful products are not obtained beyond the addition of 1 mole per C_5-unit (product containing 16% oxygen).

$$\cdots CH_2{-}CMe{-}CH{-}CH_2{-}\cdots \qquad \cdots{-}CH_2{-}CMe{-}CH{-}CH_2{-}\cdots$$

(XLVI)

With the objective of causing formaldehyde to combine with rubber in hydroxylic form instead of as cyclic formal the reaction has been carried out both in solution and in dry rubber in the presence of acetic acid with zinc chloride as promoter.[245] The reactivity of the product towards di-isocyanates indicates the presence of some hydroxylic groups. There is also spectrographic evidence of the presence of a substantial proportion of hydroxyl groups when aluminium chloride is used as a promoter without the addition of acid.[246]

Higher aldehydes have been used in several of the above processes, but they do not stiffen rubber in the same way as formaldehyde, and the products do not appear to be of technical interest.

Miscellaneous reactions of rubber

Addition of thiols and thiol acids

In spite of the ease of addition of thiols to olefins and to SBR synthetic rubber the addition to natural rubber in bulk or in solution presents considerable difficulty.[247] A recorded reaction [248] of thioglycollic acid with rubber in solution has been since shown to be one of accelerated oxidation; in the absence of air no reaction occurred under the conditions described. However, addition of thiols occurs very easily in latex, and an interesting range of new elastomers has been obtained by addition of several n-alkyl thiols to natural and synthetic latices.[249] Isopropyl mercaptan was also successfully reacted, but the addition of tert-mercaptans still presents difficulty.

Thiol acids (R·COSH) react readily with rubber, either in solution, on the mill or in latex; the reaction needs the catalytic influence of a peroxide or of light and is believed to proceed by a radical mechanism [250] eqn. (2.37).

$$\cdots{-}CH_2{-}CMe{=}CH{-}CH_2{-}\cdots + R{\cdot}COSH \longrightarrow$$

$$\cdots{-}CH_2{-}CHMe{-}\underset{\underset{R{\cdot}C{=}O}{|}}{\overset{|}{\underset{S}{C}}}H{-}CH_2{-}\cdots \qquad (2.37)$$

Thiolacetic acid itself is not very reactive, but chloro-thiolacetic acids react readily and give rubbers containing sufficient polar groups to confer a substantial resistance to oil without too much sacrifice of rubbery properties. A small addition of a thiol acid (e.g. thiolbenzoic acid) provides a very effective way of retarding the crystallisation of rubber at low temperatures.[251, 252] It was at first thought that the retardation was due to the disorder introduced by the side groups (e.g. Ph—C—S—), but when the

$$O$$

reaction was carried out in latex the retardation was much greater than could be explained by the side-group theory. As little as 0·1% by weight of thiol acid on the rubber gave products which crystallised more than 1,000 times as slowly as the original rubber, and an effect was discernible at a level of addition of only one attachment per 400,000 molecular weight. Hence it was concluded that structural changes other than the simple attachment of side groups were taking place, and an explanation was suggested by the discovery that small amounts of thiol acids rapidly isomerise pure *cis*- and *trans*-trialkylethylenes to an equilibrium mixture of *cis*- and *trans*-isomers. Indications of similar changes in natural rubber have been reported after treatment of latex with thiol acids.[253]

Reaction with maleic anhydride and its derivatives

Three types of reactivity towards rubber are exhibited by maleic anhydride: thermal addition, peroxide-induced addition and addition induced by mastication. The thermal reaction requires a fairly high temperature, in excess of 160° C and preferably above 200° C and a considerable excess of maleic anhydride is necessary to obtain much combination. Esters of maleic acid also react. The peroxide promoted addition of maleic anhydride proceeds well in solution at much lower temperature (70°–80° C), high proportions of the anhydride have been combined, but a disproportionately high proportion of benzoyl peroxide (*ca*. 10% on the rubber) is required. Azo-*bis*-isobutyronitrile can be used as an alternative promoter, and its use reduces the gelation tendency of peroxides, but even so it is not practicable to exceed a concentration of 2% rubber in solution. Materials have been made containing up to 50% combined maleic anhydride (approaching 1 mole per C_5-unit); they range from elastic substances to resins according to the proportion of anhydride combined.[254, 255] Infra-red examination of an intermediate product (20% combined maleic anhydride) showed no reduction in the $>C=CH$ intensity and it is believed that reaction takes place at α-methylenic positions with hydrogen-migration (XLVII).

N-Methylmaleimide similarly adds either thermally [256] or under the influence of a peroxide,[257] and by making use of *p*-bromobenzoyl peroxide it has been shown that a substantial proportion of the promoter is combined in the product.

Up to 6% of maleic anhydride can be combined with rubber by passing a mixture of the two substances through the tight nip of a *cold* mill; several

$$
\cdots -\underset{\underset{\displaystyle CH-CO}{\overset{\displaystyle CH_3}{|}}}{C}=CH-CH-CH_2- \cdots
$$

(XLVII)

vinyl monomers react similarly but less efficiently owing to their volatility,[258] unless the mastication is carried out in an enclosed system moderately free of oxygen (see p. 81). A few passes through the nip are necessary to start the reaction with maleic anhydride, and the material then becomes lacy and crumbly; on further milling it consolidates and can then be compounded for curing. The limit of 6% combination on the mill is probably due to the crumbing, which prevents further shear in the nip; in the small masticator of Fig. 2.7 under nitrogen reaction proceeds very rapidly and to a considerably greater extent.

The thermal reaction has been re-examined within recent years following the discovery that cross-linking in the thermal reaction of maleic anhydride with synthetic rubbers could be prevented by inhibitors of free-radical polymerisation.[259] At 180° C and in the presence of selected antioxidants (2 : 6-di-tert-butyl-4-methylphenol and 6-phenyl-2 : 2 : 4-trimethyl-1 : 2-dihydroquinoline) natural rubber has been converted into succinic and anhydrosuccinic derivatives both in mass and in solution.[260] These derivatives have been successfully cross-linked with metal oxides, diamines and isocyanates and improvements in flex-life and tear resistance have been claimed in these novel vulcanisates.[261]

The reaction of rubber with sulphur dioxide

Many olefins add sulphur dioxide at low temperature in the presence of a radical-forming catalyst; there is usually a ceiling temperature above which no addition occurs. Rubber conforms with these general principles and the ceiling temperature is around 40° C. The reaction is best carried out at −10° to 15° C, either in solution, in latex or simply by immersing sheeted rubber in liquid sulphur dioxide, suitable catalysts being diazo-aminobenzene, lithium nitrate, oxides of nitrogen or peroxides. In the reaction of sheeted rubber with liquid sulphur dioxide the catalyst may be premixed with the rubber, or untreated rubber may be simply immersed in sulphur dioxide containing diazoaminobenzene. The maximum sulphur content which has been obtained is 22%, approaching that required by the addition of 1 mole of sulphur dioxide per C_5-unit, and the structure (XLVIII) has been proposed for the reaction product.[262]

$$\left[\begin{array}{c} -CH-CH_2-CH_2-CMe- \\ \diagdown \qquad \diagup \\ S \\ O_2 \end{array} \right]_n$$

(XLVIII)

With sulphur content up to 5% the products are elastic; with higher sulphur they become leathery. Products approaching full reaction (22% S, theoretical $24\cdot2\%$) are horn-like, insoluble and unprocessable owing to their small thermoplasticity, but they can be moulded at $150°$ C. They have not yet been satisfactorily stabilised against their tendency to undergo spontaneous decomposition, liberating sulphur dioxide, especially at elevated temperatures, otherwise they are potentially useful materials. It has been proposed to produce threads by extruding a rubber dough containing a catalyst into a coagulating bath saturated with sulphur dioxide.[263]

Above the reaction ceiling temperature sulphur dioxide has been shown to promote *cis–trans* isomerism. This provides a convenient alternative to thiol acids for introducing the necessary amount of disorder for retarding crystallisation.[253]

Complex formation with silver salts

Rubber forms a highly crystalline complex with silver nitrate or per-chlorate; there appears to be no isomerising action as the rubber can be recovered unchanged on decomposing the silver complex with pyridine. Crystallisation occurs spontaneously with complex formation when rubber into which silver nitrate has been milled is immersed in a solution of silver nitrate in aqueous dioxane. The complex is rigid, insoluble and swells only to a limited extent in solvents.[264]

Reaction with oxides of nitrogen and nitroso-compounds

The reactions with rubber of the various oxides of nitrogen (nitric oxide, nitrogen dioxide and trioxide), and of nitric acid have much in common in that the products are yellow unstable resinous materials in which a mole-cule of NO_2 or N_2O_3 per C_5- or C_{10}-unit has been incorporated. Although these reactions were among the earliest studied in the chemistry of rubber, they have contributed little to our knowledge and have found practically no application other than forming the subjects of a few adhesive patents. Atmospheric oxygen does not participate in the formation of the more highly oxygenated groups found in the reaction products of nitric oxide with both rubber and olefins. The reaction is complex, and a part (*ca.* 25%) of the nitric oxide is reduced to nitrogen, probably by a chain reaction involving the hydrocarbon. The rest of the nitric oxide is converted into higher states of oxidation, and these undergo addition and substitution reactions giving 1-nitro-substituted olefins, nitrosites and nitrosates.[265]

Nitrosyl chloride gives an insoluble adduct $(C_5H_8NOCl)_n$, which loses some chlorine and swells into a spongy mass in boiling water.

Rubber reacts readily with nitrosobenzene, with the participation of 3 moles of reagent per C_5-unit. Of these one enters into combination with the rubber to give the hydrogen-deficient adduct $(C_{11}H_{11}ON)_n$ (an amorphous yellow substance), another molecule is reduced to phenyl hydroxylamine by the two hydrogen atoms taken from the rubber and the third molecule reacts with the hydroxylamine to give azoxybenzene, which appears as an end-product.[266]

Tetranitromethane is a well-known reagent for unsaturation and gives an intense yellow colour with olefins. Some addition of the reagent to rubber has been reported.[267]

Reaction with azodicarboxylic esters (ROOC·N:N·COOR)

Ethyl azodicarboxylate (EAD) reacts readily with rubber in solution at $50°$ C to give one of the few known alcohol-soluble derivatives of rubber. One mole per C_5-unit can be added; the reaction has radical characteristics in being catalysed by azo-*bis*-isobutyronitrile and peroxides, and inhibited by some antioxidants. There is too much general absorption in the double-bond region of the infra-red spectrum for any valid estimation of the unsaturation; the spectrum reveals –NH groups and some conjugation. The EAD probably adds in an α-methylenic position with hydrogen migration (XLIX).[268] The NH-groups are not very reactive, they may be hydrogen-bonded or sterically blocked.

$$>\!C\!=\!CH\!-\!\underset{\substack{| \\ N\cdot COOEt \\ | \\ NH\cdot COOEt}}{CH-}$$

(XLIX)

Bis-azodicarboxylates have been used as cross-linking agents for rubber.[269]

Modification of natural rubber with other polymeric materials

Many attempts have been made to modify the properties of rubber by mixing it or attempting to combine it with other polymeric materials, both natural and synthetic. The attractiveness of this idea stems from the very different properties shown by various polymeric materials, and the hope that in combining or simply mixing them with rubber the properties of the product might reflect or even combine the individual properties of the rubber and polymer components. The polymers in which most interest has been expressed include the thermosetting resins, synthetic thermoplastic materials such as plastics derived from vinyl monomers and natural polymers such as lignin. There is an obvious advantage in the use of thermosetting resins in that their resistance to elevated temperature is enhanced, and these will be considered first.

Phenolic resins

A great deal of effort has been put into incorporating phenolic resins into rubber. The fully condensed resins themselves (unless specially modified for the purpose) are generally incompatible with rubber and give quite unpromising mixtures. Much better products are obtained if the condensation of the resin is carried out in the presence of rubber, e.g. by heating a mixture of rubber, phenol and formaldehyde in the presence of an acidic catalyst.[270] The reaction is facilitated and the product much improved if the rubber is somewhat oxidised, doubtless due to improved compatibility with the resin intermediates or with phenol itself, and technically useful rubber-modified phenolic resins have been obtained from Rubbone, phenol and formaldehyde with an organic acid catalyst (e.g. maleic or oxalic acid) [271] (see Fig. 2.10). The presence of the rubber enables the resin to be formed into any desired shape after condensation, and so imparts a new and desirable property to a phenolic resin.

There is a considerable likelihood that chemical linkage occurs between resin and rubber during the condensation of phenol with formaldehyde in the presence of rubber. Saligenin itself (L) has been shown to combine

$$\text{(L)} \quad + \quad \longrightarrow \quad + H_2O \quad . \quad (2.38)$$

with rubber with the formation of a chromane ring,[272] probably in accordance with eqn. 2.38, by analogy with the observed behaviour of 1-methylcyclohexene and of dihydromyrcene. From the point of view of resin formation it is very significant that a disaligenin compound has been observed to accompany the monosaligenin adduct, and in its derivation from rubber the former compound is probably (LI).   This compound

Fig. 2.10. Rubbone-phenolic resin laminates re-shaped after the original thermo-setting had occurred.
(Reproduced by courtesy of *Endeavour* [179].)

contains one atom of active hydrogen per molecule and apparently represents the simplest example of the linking of a polycondensed phenol–formaldehyde chain (i.e. a Novolak) to the rubber.   The interaction with

(LI)

rubber occurs quite easily at moderate temperature and results in a chromane ring at each resin–rubber junction.   Normal resin condensation occurs on heating if the compound is mixed with hexamethylene tetramine and used as the resinous component of moulding powders.

The interaction of rubber with resin intermediates forms the basis of a novel method of curing rubber. Dimethylol-*p*-cresol (2 : 6-di-hydroxymethyl-4-methylphenol, LII) is very effective in this role, but dimethylol

(LII)

phenol and allied resols are less effective, since they are too reactive in virtue of their unblocked para positions, and hardening takes place in preference to cross-linking.[273] The mechanism of cross-linking follows logically from the structure (LIII), the blocked para positions restricting further condensation to linear attachments in positions ortho to the hydroxyl group, although an alternative *o*-quininoid linkage has been

(LIII), $n = 0, 1, 2$, etc.

proposed. Vulcanisation with this type of reagent has recently assumed considerable importance in the curing of butyl rubber.

Polyhydroxyphenols (resorcinol, quinol or pyrogallol) readily condense with formaldehyde in the presence of an alkaline catalyst, and the partially condensed resins are miscible with latex. On heating the mixture the condensation of the resin is completed,[274] and if the process is carried out under suitable conditions the rubber is reinforced by the resin, i.e. it has high tensile strength, high modulus and good resistance to tear and abrasion.[275, 276] Resorcinol is the preferred phenol, and the partially condensed resin is added to a thermosensitive latex containing the necessary vulcanising ingredients. On heating, the resin is condensed and the mass gels; the gelation is preferably done in a mould of appropriate shape, and the cast article can then be dried and cured. Properties very similar to those of conventional black-reinforced rubber are obtained with resin contents around 10% with a resorcinol–formaldehyde ratio of unity. The reinforcement obtained in this way depends on the formation of a " structure ", and is largely destroyed by repeated deformations or by passing the cast material through a mill before cure.   Consequently the method is only suitable for the direct casting of objects from the resin-modified latex. Nevertheless, the method is novel in reinforcing rubber without the necessity of masticating it with a reinforcing filler.   The inability of conventional reinforcing fillers to reinforce articles made directly from latex is an obvious consequence of the mastication phenomena discussed on p. 81.   This ordinarily imposes a limitation on the field of application of latex, since it is not possible, simply by loading with fillers, to obtain articles combining medium or high modulus and hardness exceeding 45° B.S.I. with sufficiently high tensile strength and resistance to tear and abrasion.

Amine–formaldehyde resins

Reinforcement which survives mastication and compounding is obtained by condensing various aminoplasts (aniline–formaldehyde, urea–formaldehyde and melamine–formaldehyde) in latex, but not by merely incorporating the preformed resins on a mill or by attempting to carry out the condensation in dry rubber.   The resin-forming ingredients (e.g. aniline hydrochloride and formaldehyde) are added to an appropriately stabilised latex, and the condensation is allowed to proceed spontaneously at room temperature, with the exception of melamine, which requires to be heated to 80° C for completion of the condensation.   Although the latex is stabilised, it coagulates as the condensation reaction proceeds, and after the reaction has been carried to completion the coagulum (a rigid gel) is broken up, leached with ammonia, washed and dried.   The product can then be compounded on the mill and vulcanised provided that the resin content is less than 70% of the total polymer (rubber plus resin).   Products with resin content below 30% are rubbery and are suitable for production of light-coloured reinforced soft rubber articles; above 30% resin the materials become increasingly tough and leatherlike, and are then more suitable for rigid articles.   The aniline–formaldehyde resins have bad light stability, but those based on melamine, urea or the two in admixture are quite satisfactory in this respect.[276-278]

Graft polymers

Although the practicability of modifying rubber by polymerising vinyl monomers in its presence has been known for some time,[279] the graft-polymer nature of the products has only recently been established.[280] With a few exceptions polymerisation of vinyl monomers (conventionally initiated) is not inhibited by rubber or the impurities contained in it.   The notable exceptions are vinyl acetate and vinyl chloride, both of which are severely retarded even by pure polyisoprenes; there is a sound theoretical explanation of this behaviour.[281]   Polymerisation can be carried out in solution, in latex or in bulk rubber swollen with monomer.[282, 283]   When polymerisation is conducted in solution combination of polymer with rubber occurs only when peroxidic initiators are used and it appears to be essential that the initiator is capable of some direct action on the rubber (cf. cross-linking ability of peroxides), since polymerisation initiators (e.g. azo-*bis*-isobutyronitrile) which have no action on rubber give simply a mixture of rubber and vinyl polymer which can be separated by fractional precipitation.   This specific catalyst effect precludes a chain-transfer mechanism for graft polymerisation, and all other mechanisms involving prior attack of vinyl polymer radicals on the polyisoprene.   The cause of this specific initiator effect, and the mechanism of graft polymerisation, have been determined by using C^{14}-labelled initiators.   Benzoyl peroxide initiates graft polymerisation by prior reaction of the derived phenyl and benzoyloxy radicals with the polyisoprene by addition to the double bond, and by abstracting α-methylenic hydrogen atoms to give polyisoprenic alkyl and alkenyl radicals, respectively, which act as loci for methyl methacrylate polymerisation.   In the comparable system gutta-percha/methyl methacrylate, at 60° C, 35–45% of the grafted vinyl polymer side chains are initiated by hydrogen abstraction, and about 90% of the initiator radicals undergoing addition to the double bond are benzoyloxy. The modes of termination of the grafted and free polymethyl methacrylate radicals have been evaluated semi-quantitatively, and it has been found that, in the graft interpolymer, 13–27% of the polymethyl methacrylate chains have both ends attached to gutta-percha chains (i.e. have an " I " structure), while 73–87% are attached at one end only to gutta-percha chains (i.e. are " T " structures).[284]

The initiator specificity is less pronounced in polymerisations conducted in latex or in bulk rubber.[285]   Under these conditions the proximity of rubber and polymer molecules in a non-mobile system may permit chain transfer or other interactions to occur.[286]

Under favourable conditions of graft-polymerisation of monomers in rubber latex the polymerisation may be made to proceed wholly within the rubber particles, thus avoiding the formation of free polymer particles in the aqueous phase.[287, 288]   Electron micrographs of large-particle fractions of *Hevea* latex fail to reveal any of the small polymer particles which would be expected to result from such aqueous-phase emulsion polymerisation of monomer (Fig. 2.11).

Because the grafting of polymeric side chains on to rubber depends on the attack of initiator radicals and not vinyl polymer radicals with rubber molecules, there is inevitably competition between monomer and rubber for the available initiator radicals.   Since monomer–initiator interaction leads to conventional homopolymerisation not involving rubber, the products of graft copolymerisation are certain to contain some free homo-polymer.   Furthermore, even when using high monomer–rubber ratios only a part of the rubber undergoes the " grafting " reaction.   The product of the polymerisation reaction is therefore a mixture of free rubber,

Fig. 2.11. Large-particle *Hevea* latex after polymerising methyl methacrylate therein; mag. × 20,000.
(Reproduced by courtesy of Institut T.N.O., Delft.)

a graft copolymer and free vinyl polymer; these mixtures have been given the generic name " Heveaplus ".   The graft copolymer acts as an " alloy-ing " component, making difficult the separation of the free rubber; in fact, when an alcoholic precipitant is added to a solution of the crude product a stable colloidal solution is obtained, even when alcohol is added in amount far beyond that necessary to cause total precipitation of the rubber in a simple mixture of rubber and polymer.   The molecular weight of the polymer attached to rubber is comparable with that of the free polymer, and both are usually in the range 100,000–500,000.[289]   The combined polymethyl methacrylate in methacrylate graft copolymers has been shown experimentally to have molecular weight in this region by ozonolytic degradation of the rubber under conditions carefully adjusted to prevent degradation of the polymethyl methacrylate.[290, 291]

The proportion of free homopolymer in rubber-graft copolymers has been reduced to a low figure by the ingenious trick of using lightly per-oxidised rubber as the sole polymerisation initiator and ensuring that only the peroxy-rubber RO* radical derived from it is able to function in an initiating capacity.   This has been done very conveniently by the aeration of rubber latex prior to grafting.[292]   A trace of ozone has been said to in-crease the efficiency.[293]   A similar objective has been achieved with light [285] and γ-radiation [294] with or without the intervention of oxygen. In the latter case rubber radicals formed by loss of hydrogen are the effective initiators.

When water-soluble initiators are used in latex-monomer systems much of the graft-polymerisation occurs at or near the surface of the latex particles.   This results in a higher degree of grafting on to the smaller

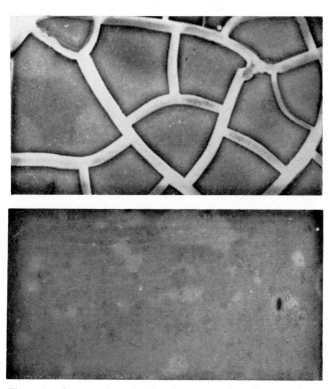

Fig. 2.12. Comparative film forming properties of conventional (upper sample) and rubber-initiated (lower sample) Heveaplus MG25 latices.

rubber particles than on to the larger ones,[287] and also reduces cohesion of the particles to such an extent that cast films from such latices are non-coherent and break up on drying (Fig. 2.12). With rubber-soluble initiators or, better, using direct initiation by the rubber itself as described in the preceding paragraph, coherent films are obtained.[294]   The latices also behave very differently in their behaviour on coagulation, the former type giving non-coherent crumbs or powders, and the latter type giving rubbery masses.

Vinyl monomers, which themselves polymerise to hard polymers (e.g. styrene, methyl methacrylate, acrylonitrile), give with rubber reinforced materials which have some novel properties;[295] the ability of the grafting of methyl methacrylate and styrene to proceed in rubber latex to give a stable dispersion of reinforced rubber particles is particularly valuable in the production of reinforced rubber goods directly from latex.   Acrylonitrile imparts to rubber some improvement in resistance to oil and solvents, but the processability of rubber generally suffers severely as a result of its interaction with acrylonitrile.

By suitable choice of solvent methacrylate–rubber graft polymer solutions may be made to yield cast films with pre-set configurations.   Thus from mixtures of benzene with methanol a hard, non-tacky film is obtained on evaporation, the rubber trunk molecules being collapsed with the polymethyl methacrylate side chains extended;   the complementary configuration is obtained as a soft, rubbery film on evaporation from solution in petroleum–benzene mixtures.[296]

REFERENCES

1. Faraday, M. (1826) *Quart. J. of Science and Arts*, **21**, 19.
2. Williams, C. G. (1860) *Phil. Trans.*, 241; (1860) *Proc. roy. Soc.*, **10**, 516, and (1862) *J. Chem. Soc.*, **15**, 110.
3. Tilden, W. A. (1884) *J. chem. Soc.*, **45**, 410.
4. Tilden, W. A. (1892) *Chem. News*, **65**, 265.
5. Bouchardat, G. (1879) *Comptes rendues*, **89**, 1117.
6. Tilden, W. A. (1882) *Chem. News*, **46**, 120.
7. Gladstone, J. H. and Hibbert, W. (1888) *J. chem. Soc.*, **53**, 682.
8. Weber, C. O. (1900) *Ber.*, **33**, 779.
9. Harries, C. D. (1919) *Untersuchungen uber die Natürlichen* and *Kunstlichen Kautschukarten* (Berlin), pp. 51 ff.
10. Criegee, R. *et al.* (1954) *Chem. Ber.*, **87**, 766; (1955), **88**, 1878; (1953) *Annalen*, **583**, 6; (1949) **564**, 9.
11. Long, L. (1940) *Chem. Rev.*, **27**, 437.
12. Pummerer, R., Ebermayer, G. and Gerlach, K. (1931) *Ber.*, **64**, 809; (1931) *Rubb. Chem. Technol.*, **4**, 386.
13. Gordon, M. (1951) *Ind. Eng. Chem.*, **43**, 388.
14. Kemp, A. R. and Peters, H. (1939) *J. Phys. Chem.*, **43**, 923.
15. Spence, D. and Ferry, J. D. (1939) *J. Soc. chem. Ind.*, **58**, 345; (1937) *J. Amer. chem. Soc.*, **59**, 1648.
16. Fletcher, W. P., Gee, G. and Morrell, S. H. (1952) *I.R.I. Trans.*, **28**, 85.
17. Mullins, L. (1956) *J. Polymer Sci.*, **19**, 225.

18. Midgley, T., Henne, A. L., Shepard, A. F. and Renoll, M. W. (1931) *J. Amer. chem. Soc.*, **53**, 2733.
19. Bateman, L. (1947) *J. Polymer Sci.*, **2**, 1.
20. Smith, W. H., Saylor, C. P. and Wing, H. J. (1933) *Bur. Standards J. Research*, **10**, 479.
21. Bloomfield, G. F. and Farmer, E. H. (1940) *I.R.I. Trans.*, **16**, 69.
22. De Vries, O. and Beumée Nieuwland, N. (1925) *Arch. Rubb. Cultiv.*, **9**, 694, 721.
23. Pummerer, R., Andriessen, A., Gundel, W. and Pahl, H. (1927) *Ber.*, **60**, 2152; (1928), **61**, 1583.
24. Cummings, A. D. and Sebrell, L. B. (1929) *Ind. Eng. Chem.*, **21**, 553.
25. McPherson, A. T. (1932) *Bur. Stand. J. Res.*, **8**, 751.
26. Baker, H. C. (1940) *I.R.I. Trans.*, **16**, 165.
27. Martin, G. (1948) *Proc. Second Rubb. Technol. Conf.*, p. 319.
28. Verghese, G. T. (1948) *I.R.I. Trans.*, **24**, 138.
29. Farmer, E. H. and Sundralingam, A. (1943) *J. chem. Soc.*, 125.
30. Midgley, T., Henne, A. L., Shepard, A. F. and Renoll, M. W. (1935) *J. Amer. chem. Soc.*, **57**, 2318.
31. Bloomfield, G. F. (1951) *Comm. no. 272 of the J. Rubb. Res. Inst. Malaya.*
32. Freeman, R. F. Rubb. Res. Inst., Malaya, unpublished work.
33. Chambers, W. T. (1948), *Proc. Second Rubb. Technol. Conf.*, p. 115.
34. Midgley, T. Henne A. L. and Renoll, M. W. (1932) *J. Amer. chem. Soc.* **54**, 3343.
35. Bywaters S. and Johnson, P. (1951,) *Trans. Faraday Soc.* **47**, 195.
36. Kemp A. R. and Peters, H. (1939) *J. Phys. Chem.*, **43**, 1063; (1941), *Ind. Eng. Chem.*, **33**, 1391.
37. Bloomfield, G. F. (1951). *Comm. no. 273 of the Rubb. Res. Inst. Malaya.*
38. Freeman, R. F. (1954) *Proc. Third Rubb. Technol. Conf.*, p. 3.
39. Van Essen, W. J. (1950) *Rec. trav. chim.*, **69**, 753.
40. Bloomfield, G. F. (1951) *Comm. no. 271 of the Rubb. Res. Inst., Malaya.*
41. Wood, R. I. (1953) *Rubb. Chem. Technol.*, **26**, 1.
42. Carter, W. C., Scott, R. L. and Magat, M. (1946) *J. Amer. chem. Soc.*, **68**, 1480.
43. Watson, W. F. (1953) *I.R.I. Trans.*, **29**, 202.
44. Pike, M. and Watson, W. F. (1952) *J. Polymer Sci.*, **9**, 229.
45. Zimm, B. H. and Myerson, I. (1946) *J. Amer. chem. Soc.*, **68**, 911.
46. Drake, G. W. (1953) *Arch. Rubb. Cultiv.*, **30**, pt. 2, 65.
47. Cragg, L. H. (1946) *J. Colloid Sci.*, **1**, 261.
48. Salomon, G., van der Schee, A. Chr., Ketelaar, J. A. A. and van Eyk, B. J. (1950) *Disc. Faraday Soc.*, **9**, 291; (1954) *J. Polymer Sci.*, **14**, 181.
49. Dinsmore, R. P. (1955) *Rubb. Age*, **78**, 99.
50. Bolland, J. L. (1941) *I.R.I. Trans.*, **16**, 267.
51. Craig, D., Juve, A. E. and Davidson, W. L. (1951) *J. Polymer Sci.*, **6**, 13.
52. Roberts, K. C. (1938) *J. chem. Soc.*, 215, 219; (1942), 223.
53. Chabley, E. (1917) *Ann. Chim.*, **8**, 195.
54. Dupont, G., Dulou, R. and Desreux, V. (1939) *Bull. Soc. chim.*, **6**, 84.
55. Farmer, E. H. and Sutton, D. A. (1942) *J. chem. Soc.*, 139.
56. Bolland, J. L. and Orr, W. J. C. (1945) *I.R.I. Trans.*, **21**, 133.
57. Bolland, J. L. (1949) *Quart. Rev.*, **3**, 13; (1950) *Trans. Faraday Soc.*, **46**, 358.
58. Geiger, E. and Staudinger, H. (1926) *Helv. chim. acta*, **9**, 549.
59. Fritschi, J. and Staudinger, H. (1922) *Helv. chim. acta*, **5**, 785.
60. Midgley, T. and Henne, A. L. (1929) *J. Amer. chem. Soc.*, **51**, 1215.
61. Boonstra, B. B. S. T. and von Amerongen, G. J. (1949) *Ind. Eng. Chem.*, **41**, 161.
62. B.P. 612,429.
63. Rubb. Res. Inst. Malaya (1932) *Annual Report*, pp. 34 and 111.
64. Pickett, F. N. (1940) *Rubb. Age, Lond.*, **21**, 75; and B.P. 444,654.

65. Marder, M. and Holzdräger, K. H. (1942) *Brennst. Chemie.*, **23**, 37.
66. Zelinsky, N. D. and Koslov, N. S. (1932) *Annalen*, **497**, 160.
67. B.P. 447,538.
68. Cawley, C. M. and King, J. G. (1935) *J. Soc. chem. Ind.*, **54**, 117T.
69. Kobayasi, R., Furihata, M. and Kajimoto, S. (1936) *Rubb. Chem. Technol.*, **9**, 589.
70. Zelinsky, N. D. and Rapoport, J. B. (1942) *Rubb. Chem. Technol.*, **15**, 33.
71. Ipatieff, V. N. and Schaad, R. E. (1940) *Ind. Eng. Chem.*, **32**, 762.
72. H.A. (1942) *India Rubb. J.*, **103**, 476.
73. Anon (1943) *Chem. Tr. J.*, **112**, 130.
74. Nightingale, W. H. (1946) *Chem. & Ind. (Rev.)*, 9.
75. Stevens, H. P. (1940) *I.R.I. Trans.*, **16**, 211.
76. Naunton, W. J. S. (1942) *Trans. Faraday Soc.*, **38**, 332.
77. Stevens, H. P. (1946) *Advances in Colloid Science* (New York: Interscience Publishers Inc.), **2**, 363.
78. Farmer, E. H. (1942) *Trans. Faraday Soc.*, **38**, 345, 361.
79. Charlesby, A. and Groves, D. (1954) *Proc. Third Rubb. Technol. Conf.*, p. 317.
80. Charlesby, A. (1954) *Atomics*, **5**, 12.
81. Fuller, C. S. (1946) *Bell Syst. tech. J.*, **25**, 351.
82. Medalia, A. I. and Kolthoff, I. M. (1951) *J. Polymer Sci.*, **6**, 433.
83. Philpott, M. W. (1947) *Proc. Eleventh Int. Congress Pure and appl. Chem.*, **5**, 355.
84. B.P. 730,864.
85. Bloomfield, G. F. (1952) *Rubb. Developm.*, **5**, 34.
86. Busse, W. F. and Cunningham, E. N. (1938) *Proc. First Rubb. Technol. Conf. (London)*, p. 288.
87. Blow, C. M. and Wood, R. I. (1950) *I.R.I. Trans.*, **25**, 309.
88. Schidrowitz, P. and Ungar, R. M., B.P. 368,902.
89. Rubber Technical Developments Ltd. (1953) *Broadsheet No. 2*.
90. Pike, M. (1953) *Rubb. Developm.*, **6**, 70.
91. Speight, C. (1955) *Rubb. Developm.*, **8**, 18.
92. Hardman, K. V. and Lang, A. J. (1950) *Ind. Eng. Chem.*, **66**, 419.
93. Watson, W. F. (1953) *I.R.I. Trans.*, **29**, 32.
94. Kauzmann, W. and Eyring, H. (1940) *J. Amer. chem. Soc.*, **62**, 3113.
95. Cotton, F. H. (1931) *I.R.I. Trans.*, **6**, 487.
96. Busse, W. F. (1932) *Ind. Eng. Chem.*, **24**, 140.
97. Angier, D. J., Chambers, W. T. and Watson, W. F. (1957) *J. Polymer Sci.*, **25**, 129.
98. Ayrey, G., Moore, C. G. and Watson, W. F. (1956) *J. Polymer Sci.*, **19**, 1.
99. Watson, W. F. (1955) *Ind. Eng. Chem.*, **47**, 1281.
100. Angier, D. J. and Watson, W. F. (1955) *J. Polymer Sci.*, **18**, 129.
101. Angier, D. J. and Watson, W. F. (1956) *J. Polymer Sci.*, **20**, 235.
102. Dauben, W. G., Bradlow, H. L., Freeman, N. K., Kritchevsky, D. and Kirk, M. (1952) *J. Amer. chem. Soc.*, **74**, 4321.
103. Staudinger, H. and Widmer, W. (1926) *Helv. chim. acta*, **9**, 529.
104. Semmler, F. W. (1901) *Ber.*, **34**, 3128.
105. Bloomfield, G. F., and McSweeney, G. P., unpublished results.
106. Staudinger, H. and Bondy, H. F. (1929) *Annalen*, **468**, 12.
107. Bruson, H. A., Sebrell, L. B. and Calvert, W. C. (1927) *Ind. Eng. Chem.*, **19**, 1033.
108. D'Ianni, J. D., Naples, F. J., Marsh, J. W. and Zarney, J. L. (1946) *Ind. Eng. Chem.*, **38**, 1171.
109. Fisher, H. L. (1927) *Ind. Eng. Chem.*, **19**, 1325.
110. Can. P. 282,778; D.R.P. 675,564; U.S.P. 2,200,715 and 2,363,654.
111. B.P. 498,311; 521,007; 572,768.
112. Stevens, H. P. and Miller, C. J. (1938) *Proc. First Rubb. Technol. Conf.*, p. 267.

113. Janssen, H. J. J. (1956) *Rubb. Age, Lond.*, **78**, 718.
114. Blow, C. M. (1938) *Proc. First Rubb. Technol. Conf.*, 186.
115. Hessels, J. H. E. (1940) *Chem. Weekblad*, **37**, 467.
116. B.P. 658,520.
117. B.P. 634,879.
118. van Veersen, G. J. (1950) *Rev. gen. Caoutch.*, **27**, 473.
119. Gordon, M. (1951) *Proc. roy. Soc.*, *A*, **204**, 569.
120. B.P. 663,807.
121. B.P. 713,481.
122. B.P. 713,482.
123. Bloomfield, G. F. and Stokes, S. C. (1956) *I.R.I. Trans.*, **32**, 172.
124. Simonsen, J. L. and Owen, L. N. (1947) *The Terpenes* (University Press), 2nd edition, Vol. I, pp. 111–113.
125. Bloomfield, G. F. (1943) *J. chem. Soc.*, 293.
126. Davies, B. L. and Glazer, J. (1955) *Plastics Derived from Natural Rubber*, Plastics Institute monograph, London, p. 70.
127. van Veersen, G. J. (1950) *Rec. trav. chim.*, **69**, 1365., (1951) *Rev. gén. Caoutch.*, **28**, 33.
128. Flory, P. J. (1939) *J. Amer. chem. Soc.*, **61**, 1518.
129. Ramakrishnan, C. S., Dasgupta, Sharda and Rao, N. V. C. (1956) *Makromol. Chem.*, **20**, 46.
130. Fisher, H. L. and McColm, E. M. (1927) *Ind. Eng. Chem.*, **19**, 1328.
131. Rao, N. V. C. (1955) *Makromol. Chem.*, **16**, 198.
132. Bloomfield, G. F. and Barnard, D., unpublished results.
133. Bolland, J. L. (1949) *Quart. Rev.*, **3**, 1.
134. Farmer, E. H. (1945) *I.R.I. Trans.*, **21**, 122.
135. Criegee, R., Pilz, H. and Flygare, H. (1939) *Ber.*, **72**, 1799.
136. Bolland, J. L. and Hughes, H. (1949) *J. chem. Soc.*, 492.
137. Bolland, J. L. and ten Have, P. (1949) *Trans. Faraday Soc.*, **45**, 93.
138. Bolland, J. L., Sundralingam, A., Sutton, D. A. and Tristram, G. R. (1941) *I.R.I. Trans.*, **17**, 29.
139. Hilton, F. (1942) *I.R.I. Trans.*, **17**, 319.
140. Naylor, R. F. (1943) *I.R.I. Trans.*, **20**, 45.
141. Bevilacqua, E. M. (1955) *J. Amer. chem. Soc.*, **77**, 5394.
142. Bevilacqua, E. M. (1955) *J. Amer. chem. Soc.*, **77**, 5396.
143. Bloomfield, G. F. (1943) *J. chem. Soc.*, 356.
144. Stevens, W. H. and Stevens, H. P. (1935) *I.R.I. Trans.*, **11**, 182.
145. Bloomfield, G. F. and Farmer, E. H. (1935) *J. Soc. chem. Ind.*, **54**, 125T.
146. Stevens, H. P. and Popham, F. J. (1938) *J. Soc. chem. Ind.*, **57**, 128T.
147. Stevens, H. P. and Heaton, N. (1933) *I.R.I. Trans.*, **9**, 247; (1935) *Bull. Rubb. Growers Ass.*, **17**, 119; B.P. 407,038 and B.P. 417,912.
148. Buist, J. M. (1955) *Rubb. Chem. Technol.*, **28**, 248.
149. Barnard, D., unpublished results.
150. Braden, M. and Fletcher, W. P. (1955) *Rubb. J.*, **129**, 709.
151. Pummerer, R. and Richtzenhain, H. (1937) *Annalen*, **529**, 33.
152. Pummerer, R. (1936) *Kautschuk*, **12**, 195.
153. Kendall, F. H. and Mann, J. (1956) *J. Polymer Sci.*, **19**, 503.
154. Robertson, J. M. and Mair, J. A. (1927) *J. Soc. chem. Ind.*, **46**, 41T.
155. Boswell, M. C., Hambleton, A., Parker, R. R. and McLaughlin, R. R. (1922) *Canad. Chem. Metall.*, **6**, 237; (1922) *India Rubb. J.*, **64**, 981.
156. Bloomfield, G. F., Farmer, E. H. and Schidrowitz, P. (1934) *Bull. Rubb. Gr. Ass. Rubb. Ser.*, **16**, 116.
157. Salomon, G., van Amerongen, G. J., van Veersen, G. J., Schuur, G. and de Decker, H. C. J. (1951) *Ind. Eng. Chem.*, **43**, 315.
158. Mair, J. A. and Todd, J. (1932) *J. chem. Soc.*, 386.
159. Bloomfield, G. F. (1934) *J. Soc. chem. Ind.*, **53**, 121T.
160. B.P. 369,716.

161. Swern, D. (1949) *Chem. Rev.*, **45**, 16.
162. Arbuzow, B. A. and Michailow, B. M. (1930) *J. prakt. Chem.*, **127**, 1, 92.
163. Pummerer, R. and Burkard, P. A. (1922) *Ber.*, **55**, 3458.
164. Farmer, E. H. and Moore, C. G. (1951) *J. chem. Soc.*, 142.
165. Braden, M., Fletcher, W. P. and McSweeney, G. P. (1954) *I.R.I. Trans.*, **30**, 44; (1955), **31**, 155.
166. Farmer, E. H. and Michael, S. E. (1942) *J. chem. Soc.*, 513.
167. Moore, C. G. and Watson, W. F. (1956) *J. Polymer Sci.*, **19**, 237.
168. Tournier, J. (1954) *Rev. gén. Caoutch.*, **31**, 46.
169. B.P. 732,932.
170. D.R.P. 898,512.
171. Harries, C. D. (1923) *Ber.*, **56**, 1050.
172. Staudinger, H. *et al.* (1930) *Helv. chim. acta*, **13**, 1334, 1339.
173. Staudinger, H. and Feisst, W. (1930) *Helv. chim. acta*, **13**, 1361.
174. Staudinger, H. and Leupold, E. O. (1934) *Ber.*, **67**, 304.
175. Le Bras, J. and Delalande, A. (1950) *Les Dérivés Chimiques du Caoutchouc Naturel* (Paris: Dunod).
176. Pummerer, R. and Koch, A. (1924) *Annalen*, **438**, 303.
177. Pummerer, R. and Nielsen, H. (1927) *Ber.*, **60**, 2171.
178. B.P. 577,472.
179. Farmer, E. H. (1944) *Endeavour*, **3**, 72.
180. Bloomfield, G. F. (1943) *J. chem. Soc.*, 289.
181. Kraus, G. and Reynolds, W. B. (1950) *J. Amer. chem. Soc.*, **72**, 5621.
182. van Amerongen, G. J., Koningsberger, C. and Salomon, G. (1950) *J. Polymer Sci.*, **6**, 639.
183. Troussier, M. (1955) *Rev. gén. Caoutch.*, **32**, 229.
184. Woods, D. E. (1949) *J. Soc. chem. Ind.*, **68**, 343.
185. Bloomfield, G. F. (1944) *J. chem. Soc.*, 114.
186. Salomon, G., Koningsberger, C. and Ultee, A. J. (1948) *Proc. Second Rubb. Technol. Conf., London*, p. 106.
187. Koningsberger, C. (1950) *Chimie et Industr.*, **63**, 562.
188. Allirot, R. (1950) *Comptes Rendus*, **231**, 1065.
189. Allirot, R. and Orsini, L. (1953) *Rev. gén. Caoutch.*, **30**, 42.
190. Ramakrishnan, C. S., Raghunath, D. and Pande, J. B. (1953) *I.R.I. Trans.*, **29**, 190.
191. Riou, M. and Pibarot, R. (1950) *Rev. gén. Caoutch.*, **27**, 596.
192. Staudinger, H. and Staudinger, H. (1943) *J. prakt. Chem.*, **162**, 148.
193. Nielsen, A. (1937) *Chlorkautschuk* (Leipzig).
194. U.S.P. 1,495,580; 1,544,531–5; B.P. 433,313.
195. B.P. 474,979; U.S.P. 2,072,255; 2,101,138.
196. Bloomfield, G. F. and Farmer, E. H. (1934) *J. Soc. chem. Ind.*, **53**, 43T, 47T.
197. B.P. 390,097.
198. Baker, H. C. (1938) *Proc. First Rubb. Technol. Conf.*, p. 209.
199. van Amerongen, G. J. (1951) *Ind. Eng. Chem.*, **43**, 2535.
200. de Decker, H. C. J., Nijveld, H. A. W. and Schuur, G. (1954) *Rev. gén. Caoutch.*, **31**, 43.
201. Schidrowitz, P. and Redfarn, C. A. (1935) *J. Soc. chem. Ind.*, **54**, 263T.
202. Kharasch, M. S. and Brown, H. C. (1939) *J. Amer. chem. Soc.*, **61**, 3432.
203. van Amerongen, G. J. and Koningsberger, C. (1950) *J. Polymer Sci.*, **6**, 653.
204. Ramakrishnan, C. S., Dasgupta, S. and Pande, J. B. (1956) *J. Polymer Sci.*, **19**, 323.
205. B.P. 732,932.
206. Taylor, M. C., MacMullin, R. B. and Gammal, C. A. (1925) *J. Amer. chem. Soc.*, **47**, 395.
207. B.P. 433,082.
208. B.P. 492,767.
209. Gowans, W. J. and Clarke, F. E. (1952) *Anal. Chem.*, **24**, 529.

210. Fisher, H. L., Gray, H. and McColm, E. M. (1926) *J. Amer. chem. Soc.*, **48**, 1309.
211. Geiger, E. (1927) *Helv. chim. acta.*, **10**, 530, 539.
212. Hardie, T. and Mair, J. A. (1935) *J. chem. Soc.*, 1242.
213. Low, R. (1937) *Congrés Intern. du Caoutchouc, Paris*, p. 203.
214. B.P. 456,536.
215. Weber, C. O. (1900) *J. Soc. chem. Ind.*, **19**, 218.
216. Caspari, W. A. (1905) *J. Soc. chem. Ind.*, **24**, 1275.
217. Kolthoff, I. M., Lee, T. S. and Mairs, M. A. (1948) *J. Polymer Sci.*, **3**, 66.
218. Bloomfield, G. F. (1950) *Thorpe's Dictionary of Applied Chemistry* (Longmans Green), pp. 566–567.
219. McIlhiney, P. C. (1899) *J. Amer. chem. Soc.*, **21**, 1084.
220. Kemp, A. R. and Mueller, G. S. (1934) *Anal. Chem.*, **6**, 52.
221. Bloomfield, G. F. (1945) *J. Soc. chem. Ind.*, **64**, 274.
222. Olsen, S. R., Hull, C. M. and France, W. G. (1946) *Ind. Eng. Chem.*, **38**, 1273.
223. Blake, J. T. and Bruce, P. L. (1937) *Ind. Eng. Chem.*, **29**, 866.
224. Kolthoff, I. M., Lee, T. S. and Mairs, M. A. (1947) *J. Polymer Sci.*, **2**, 206, 220.
225. Saffer, A. and Johnson, B. L. (1948) *Ind. Eng. Chem.*, **40**, 538.
226. Boer, H. and Kooyman, E. C. (1951) *Anal. chim. acta*, **5**, 550.
227. van Veersen, G. J. (1948) *Proc. Second Rubb. Technol. Conf.*, p. 87.
228. Gordon, M. and Taylor, J. S. (1953) *J. appl. Chem.*, **3**, 537.
229. Gehman, S. D., Field, J. E. and Dinsmore, R. P. (1938) *Proc. First Rubb. Technol. Conf.*, p. 961.
230. Bunn, C. W. and Garner, E. V. (1942) *J. chem. Soc.*, 654.
231. Checkland, P. B. and Davison, W. H. T. (1956) *Trans. Faraday Soc.*, **52**, 151.
232. Salomon, G. and Koningsberger, C. (1950) *Rec. trav. chim.*, **69**, 711.
233. Harries, C. (1913) *Ber.*, **46**, 733.
234. Hinrichsen, F. W., Quensell, H. and Kindscher, E. (1913) *Ber.*, **46**, 1286.
235. Tom, D. H. E. (1956) *J. Polymer Sci.*, **20**, 381.
236. Evans, A. G. and Meadows, G. W. (1950) *Trans. Faraday Soc.*, **46**, 327.
237. Knight, H. B., Koos, R. E. and Swern, D. (1953) *J. Amer. chem. Soc.*, **75**, 6212.
238. Gordon, M. (1951) *Ind. Eng. Chem.*, **43**, 386.
239. B.P. 520,985.
240. Ritter, J. J. and Minieri, P. P. (1948) *J. Amer. chem. Soc.*, **70**, 4045.
241. Kirchhof, F. (1923) *Chem. Ztg.*, **47**, 513.
242. Koide, T., Kubota, T., Kawanabe, M. and Umezawa, Y. (1951) *J. Soc. Rubb. Ind. Japan*, **24**, 242, 247, 272.
243. Price, C. C. (1946) *Mechanisms of Reactions at Carbon–Carbon Double Bonds* (New York: Interscience Publishers), pp. 44-46.
244. Baker, J. W. (1944) *J. chem. Soc.*, 296; (1948), 89.
245. B.P. 574,901.
246. Swift, P. McL., unpublished results.
247. Cunneen, J. I. (1947) *J. chem. Soc.*, 36.
248. Holmberg, B. (1932) *Ber.*, **65**, 1349.
249. Pierson, R. M. *et al.* (1957) *Rubb. World*, **136**, 529, 695.
250. Cunneen, J. I. (1947) *J. chem. Soc.*, 134; B.P. 580,514.
251. Ritter, F. J. (1956) *Kautschuk u. Gummi*, **9**, 187WT.
252. Cunneen, J. I. *et al.* (1959) *J. Polymer Sci.*, **36**, 77; (1958) *I.R.I. Trans.*, **34**, 260; B.P. 820,261 and 820,262.
253. Cunneen, J. I. (1959) *Rubb. Age*, **85**, 650.
254. Bacon, R. G. R. and Farmer, E. H. (1938) *Proc. First Rubb. Technol. Conf.*, p. 256.
255. Le Bras, J. and Compagnon, P. (1944) *Bull. Soc. chim.*, **11**, 553.

256. Delalande, A. (1951) *Bull. Soc. chim.*, **18**, 773.
257. Delalande, A. (1949) *Rev. gén. Caoutch.*, **26**, 426.
258. Le Bras, J. (1942) *Rev. gén. Caoutch.*, **19**, 43.
259. B.P. 739,634.
260. Le Bras, J., Pinazzi, C. and Milbert, G. (1958) *Rev. gén. Caoutch.*, **35**, 605, 931.
261. Paxton, H. W., Snyder, R. H., Gunberg, P. F. and Tawney, P. O. (1958) *Rubb. Age*, **83**, 127.
262. van Amerongen, G. J. (1950) *Rev. gén. Caoutch.*, **27**, 731; (1951) *J. Polymer Sci.*, **6**, 633.
263. U.S.P. 2,469,847.
264. Salomon, G. and Koningsberger, C. (1947) *J. Polymer Sci.*, **2**, 534.
265. Bloomfield, G. F. and Jeffrey, G. A. (1944) *J. chem. Soc.*, 120.
266. Pummerer, R. and Gundel, W. (1928) *Ber.*, **61**, 1591.
267. Pummerer, R. and Pahl, H. (1927) *Ber.*, **60**, 2159.
268. Rabjohn, N. (1948) *J. Amer. chem. Soc.*, **70**, 1181.
269. Flory, P. J., Rabjohn, N. and Shaffer, M. (1949) *J. Polymer Sci.*, **4**, 225, 435.
270. B.P. 507,995.
271. B.P. 538,992; 572,828; 573,049 and 573,114.
272. Cunneen, J. I., Farmer, E. H. and Koch, H. P. (1943) *J. chem. Soc.*, 472.
273. van der Meer, S. (1943) Communications Nos. 47 and 48 of the Rubber Stichting; *Rev. gén. Caoutch.*, **20**, 230.
274. Twiss, D. F., Neale, A. E. N. and Hale, R. W. (1941) *Rev. gén. Caoutch.*, **18**, 134.
275. Le Bras, J. and Piccini, I. (1951) *Ind. Eng. Chem.*, **43**, 381.
276. Pinazzi, C., Cheritat, R. and Billuart, M. (1956) *Rev. gén. Caoutch.*, **33**, 37.
277. Van Alphen, J. (1954) *Proc. Third Rubb. Technol. Conf.*, p. 670.
278. Houwink, R. and Van Alphen, J. (1955) *J. Polymer Sci.*, **16**, 121.
279. Le Bras, J. and Compagnon, P. (1941) *Comptes rendus.*, **212**, 616; (1944) *Bull. Soc. chim.*, **11**, 553; (1947) *Rev. gén. Caoutch.*, **24**, 281.
280. Merrett, F. M. (1954) *Trans. Faraday Soc.*, **50**, 759.
281. Allen, P. W., Merrett, F. M. and Scanlan, J. (1955) *Trans. Faraday Soc.*, **51**, 95.
282. Bloomfield, G. F., Merrett, F. M., Popham, F. J. and Swift, P. McL. (1954) *Proc. Third Rubb. Technol. Conf.*, p. 185.
283. Swift, P. McL. (1958) *J. appl. Chem.*, **8**, 803.
284. Allen, P. W., Ayrey, G. and Moore, C. G. (1959) *J. Polymer Sci.*, **36**, 55.
285. Cooper, W., Vaughan, G., Miller, S. and Fielden, M. (1959) *J. Polymer Sci.*, **34**, 651.
286. Bloomfield, G. F. (1959) *J. Polymer Sci.*, **34**, 669.
287. Bloomfield, G. F. and Swift, P. McL. (1955) *J. appl. Chem.*, **5**, 609.
288. B.P. 752,514.
289. Allen, P. W. and Merrett, F. M. (1956) *J. Polymer Sci.*, **22**, 193.
290. Barnard, D. (1956) *J. Polymer Sci.*, **22**, 213.
291. Kobryner, W. and Banderet, A. (1959) *J. Polymer Sci.*, **34**, 381.
292. Sekhar, B. C. (1958) *Rubb. Chem. Technol.*, **31**, 430.
293. Can. P. 549,110; B.P. 791,453.
294. Cockbain, E. G., Pendle, T. D. and Turner, D. T. (1958) *Chem. & Ind.*, 759.
295. Bloomfield, G. F. (1956) *Rubb. Developm.*, **9**, 34.
296. Merrett, F. M. (1957) *J. Polymer Sci.*, **24**, 467.

CHAPTER II

PART TWO

NATURAL RUBBER

by

G. MARTIN

Botanical sources

THE main source of natural rubber is a large tree, *Hevea braziliensis*, indigenous to forests in the Amazon valley. There are, however, many other plants which produce appreciable amounts of good-quality rubber. Like *Hevea braziliensis*, most of them flourish in damp, tropical areas, but a few are found in temperate zones. None provides such an abundant and continuous supply of such pure commercial rubber as *Hevea braziliensis*.

At the beginning of the century these other sources constituted the basis of a profitable and thriving industry, but with the passage of years their economic importance has faded into insignificance. They came to life again during the Second World War with the interruption of supplies from plantations in the Far East, but largely disappeared from the market at the conclusion of hostilities.

Among the most important sources in tropical Africa which have been exploited are the large tree *Funtumia elastica* and many of the *Landolphia spp.* of climbing shrubs. In Mexico rubber used to be obtained from another large tree *Castilloa elastica*. In South America *Manihot glaziovii* (the Ceara Rubber tree) was also a useful source. None could compete with *Hevea braziliensis* because yields were small, the rubber could not be extracted at frequent intervals and tapping sometimes involved the complete destruction of the tree or shrub. Moreover, Hevea rubber from the Amazon valley was marketed in a clean and wholesome condition, while that from other sources was usually dirty, often adulterated and generally prepared by primitive methods.

In Table 2.14 is a list of some of the principal rubber-bearing plants which at one time or another have achieved commercial importance.[1,2] The analytical results refer to carefully prepared material. Some of the rubbers contain less nitrogenous material (calculated as protein, $6 \cdot 25 \times N$) than Hevea rubber, but all contain more resinous, i.e. acetone-soluble, material. The very inferior rubbers contain large quantities of resin. A

TABLE 2.14

Name	Description	Indigenous source	Usual method of preparation	Approximate composition		
				Acetone extract, %	Protein, %	Ash, %
Hevea braziliensis	Tree	Amazon valley	Coagulation by acid	3	2·5	0·3
Funtumia elastica	Tree	Central Africa	Coagulation by heat	7	6	0·2
Manihot glazio-vii (Ceara)	Tree	Brazil	Coagulation by acid	4·5	10	1·4
Castilloa elastica	Tree	Central America	Creaming	7	3	0·2
Ficus elastica	Tree	India	Coagulation by heat	5·5	1	0·2
Ficus vogelii	Tree	Africa	Coagulation by heat	30	2	0·3
Landolphia spp. including:						
heudelotii	Climbing shrub	West Africa	⎱ Coagulation by heat or acid	6	1	1
owariensis	Climbing shrub	West Africa				
kirkii	Climbing shrub	East Africa				
klainii	Climbing shrub	Belgian Congo				
thollonii	Dwarf shrub	Belgian Congo	Maceration of rhizomes	6	1	1
Cryptostegia grandiflora	Climbing shrub	Mada-gascar	Coagulation	9	1·5	0·5
Euphorbia tirucalli	Shrub	Natal	Coagulation	Very resinous		
Parthenium argentatum (Guayule)	Shrub	Mexico	Maceration of shrub	25	10	1
Taraxacum kok-saghys and *krimsaghyz* (dandelion)	Small plant	U.S.S.R.	Maceration of roots	5·5	2·5	3·5

complete list of all the rubber-bearing plants would include hundreds of names, but most of them yield only small amounts of very resinous rubber. Typical examples are golden rod, milk weed and the common dandelion, the latter yielding minute amounts of highly resinous low-grade rubber.

A remarkable discovery of comparatively recent times is the species of dandelions (*Taraxacum koksaghys* and *Taraxacum krimsaghys*) whose roots contain about 10% of good-quality rubber, calculated on dry weight. *Taraxacum koksaghys* has been cultivated extensively in the U.S.S.R., where it was discovered in 1931 on the borders of China as a result of a deliberate search for indigenous sources of supply. The rubber is extracted by macerating the roots with water, which compacts the rubber and removes the debris. These dandelions have been grown on a small experimental scale in other countries, but have given no promise of being able to supply rubber which will compete economically with that from plantations of *Hevea braziliensis*. Attempts have been made to cultivate the Guayule plant (*Parthenium argentatum*) on a large scale in California and to grow the prolific shrub *Cryptostegia grandiflora* in Florida, but both had to be abandoned because of high cost in terms of rubber obtained.

The only important source of wild rubber which has survived the growth of the plantation industry is the *Hevea braziliensis* tree of the Amazon forest, but very little has been exported since 1945, chiefly due to inaccessibility of the trees and cost of collecting the latex. The usual procedure is to locate a number of trees in reasonable proximity, connect them by a jungle path and tap them by making a series of incisions in the bark. The latex is collected and then coagulated by repeatedly pouring it on to a paddle at the end of a long pole which is rotated in the smoke of burning Uricuri nuts, until a ball of rubber weighing about 50 lb. has been built up. Because of its high moisture content, which is about 15%, the ball, known as fine hard Para, has to be washed, crêped and dried by the consumer before use. The chemical composition of washed, fine hard Para is similar to that of coagulated plantation rubber and different from that of dried latex, which contains about 10%, calculated on the rubber, of additional non-rubber substances. Because of its reputed uniformity in technological behaviour and excellent keeping properties, fine hard Para has long maintained a reputation for quality.

Early history

The introduction of the Para rubber tree (*Hevea braziliensis*) into the East was an incident in United Kingdom government policy of obtaining from all over the world seeds of plants which might yield crops of economic importance when grown in British Colonies. Many of these importations were, however, shots in the dark, made without any assurance that commercial exploitation might ever be practicable. At that time there was sufficient rubber from wild sources to meet all demands, and it was not known that *Hevea braziliensis* could be tapped continuously to give better rubber than other trees, or that the tree would be a success outside its native habitat. Even as late as 1900 some planters were not convinced that *Hevea braziliensis* was a superior source of rubber to that from indigenous sources.

The first attempt to collect Hevea seeds and raise plants was a failure, none of the plants surviving their transfer to the East. The second attempt owed its success to the determined efforts of Wickham, who collected 70,000 seeds from the Tapajoz area of Brazil, chartered a ship which happened to be short of cargo, and rushed the seeds by special train from Liverpool to Kew Gardens, where glasshouses were cleared and the seeds planted. About 3·5% germinated, and the young plants were sent to Ceylon, where they grew vigorously but were largely neglected for over 10 years. A subsequent consignment in 1877 from Kew to the Economic Gardens in Singapore similarly failed to arouse interest.

When Ridley took charge of the gardens in 1888 he found the trees large and healthy but surrounded by tropical undergrowth. Very much ahead of his time, he appreciated that the introduction of the pneumatic tyre for bicycles meant that the demand for rubber would exceed the supply from wild sources. He therefore set about demonstrating to potential planters how the Hevea tree could be grown and economically tapped, how the rubber could be prepared in a clean, dry condition, ready for immediate use by consumers.

Ridley [3] showed that after the initial tapping, latex flowed more freely, a phenomenon known as wound response, and that the tree could be tapped continuously and economically at intervals of a few days, and that the excised bark renewed itself and could be tapped again after a few years. He was the first to use acetic acid to coagulate the latex, and the first to produce rubber in the form of quick-drying sheet instead of wet lumps and balls characteristic of wild rubber.

Ridley's efforts to popularise the planting of Hevea rubber were not immediately successful, and as late as 1900, when the total production of rubber from all sources amounted to 45,000 tons per annum, only a small quantity came from plantation sources.

Present Position

Today the total production of plantation rubber is nearly 2 million tons per annum. The growth of the plantation industry is shown graphically in Fig. 2.13, which is based on annual production at intervals of 10 years from 1900 to 1950. The production is spaced over a number of countries in South-East Asia, together with smaller amounts from Africa and still smaller amounts from other territories, including Latin America. Table 2.15 shows the maximum annual production in any one year since 1950 of all countries exporting more than 10,000 tons per annum. It will be seen that Indonesia and Malaya each produce more than all the other countries added together.

The total area planted with *Hevea braziliensis* is over 11 million acres, of which more than half consists of smallholdings, i.e. estates of less than 100 acres and often consisting of about 3 acres occupied by peasant proprietors.

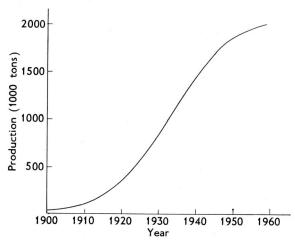

Fig. 2.13. Growth of plantation industry.

Some of the large estates occupy thousands of acres, but many of them devote the bulk of their output to producing concentrated latex and speciality products, so that much commercial dry rubber received by consumers is produced by relatively small proprietors.

TABLE 2.15

Country	Net exports, 1,000 long tons	Year
Indonesia	794	1951
Malaya	679	1949
Thailand	134	1956
Ceylon	119	1950
Vietnam	63	1956
Sarawak	43	1951
Liberia	38	1956
Nigeria	30	1955
Belgian Congo	26	1955
Cambodia	26	1955
British North Borneo	22	1951
Burma	14	1952

Development of modern plantations

The bulk of the trees now producing rubber are grown from seeds derived from the descendants of the original plantings in Ceylon and Singapore. The most important item in the cost of producing rubber is the labour involved in tapping the trees and collecting latex. Whether the trees are planted on estates or smallholdings, every endeavour has to be made to ensure that they yield as much rubber as possible per tapping. In the early days of the industry unselected seeds were planted (i.e. seeds collected at random), but it was found that the bulk of the yield of rubber came from less than half the trees, in spite of thinning-out operations to remove sub-standard material. The first attempts to improve yield were made by collecting seeds from trees which were known to be high-yielders. This had the disadvantage that the mother tree was likely to have been fertilised by pollen from a nearby low-yielder. Moreover, there was no evidence that yield capacity is an inherited characteristic. Nevertheless, trees from selected seeds were found to have appreciably higher average yields, although, as might be expected, not all the progeny were high-yielding.

The next step was the vegetative propagation of high-yielding trees by budding on to seedling stock on the assumption that the yield did not depend so much on the root system as on the anatomical structure of the trunk, which tends to conform to that of the parent tree from which the bud has been derived. Only a small percentage of high-yielding trees gave budded progeny with the yield characteristics of the mother tree, but the successes achieved were sufficient to encourage a widespread search for suitable high-yielding parents.

All trees which are derived by vegetative reproduction from a single mother tree are known as a clone, irrespective of the number of generations involved. The first high-yielding clones were propagated in Java, and some of those developed in the early 1920s are still of outstanding importance and compare favourably with later productions. An outstanding example is Tjirandji 1 (Tj1), which is widely planted not only in Indonesia but also in Malaya and other rubber-growing countries.

There was much scepticism at first about the future of budded rubber, in particular about the economic life of the tree and the quality of renewed bark. None of the fears was justified, and during the late 1920s official research organisations and some of the larger planting companies embarked on large-scale budding programmes which added appreciably to the number of high-yielding clones suitable for commercial planting.

Budded progeny is not likely to be better than the mother tree, and this limits yield-capacity to the best of the trees already in existence. Efforts were therefore made to obtain mother trees of improved genetic strain by cross-fertilisation where both parents are high-yielders. The results were somewhat of a gamble, as some of the trees proved to be poor parents. In fact, random seed from clonal areas was found to be little better than unselected seed. A few clones such as Tj1 proved, however, to be good parents, and in this way the Rubber Research Institute of Malaya has developed improved series of clones (RRIM 500 series and RRIM 600 series). Different clones have different characteristics by which they can be recognised, sometimes quite easily, from their general shape and branch and leaf cover. The character of the bark, the marking, shape and size of the seeds, and the colour and composition of the latex and the plasticity of the rubber tend to be uniform within a clone and different for different clones. Whereas commercial rubber used to be the average of that obtained from bulked latex yielded by thousands of unselected and genetically different trees, it now tends on progressive estates, and to some extent on smallholdings, to conform to the average of a few clones.

The following is a list of the best high-yielding clones recommended in Malaya for planting on a large scale, together with some notes on characteristics which are of interest to users of latex and rubber.[4]

Clone	Latex and rubber character
PB86	White latex of high mechanical stability suitable for concentration and pale crêpe.
Tj1	Latex usually yellow and rubber somewhat hard.
RRIM 501	Latex of low mechanical stability when first concentrated but increases to high value on storage for 2–3 months. Produces yellow crêpe and soft rubber.
RRIM 513	White latex of high mechanical stability suitable for concentration and pale crêpe.
PR107	White latex, but unsuitable for concentration because of low mechanical stability. Produces crêpe of average colour.
Glenshiel 1	White latex, but mechanically unstable and unsuitable for concentration.

No clone is the best in all circumstances of soil, climate, topography and type of material manufactured. For example, Tj1 grows well in average to poor soils, Glenshiel 1 is more suited to coastal and the better inland soils. In Java, LCB 1320 is widely planted but not in Malaya or on the East coast of Sumatra, because of a lop-sided crown which makes it susceptible to wind damage.

In Malaya the average yield of rubber from unselected seedling trees (i.e. trees grown from seed) is estimated to be 355 lb./acre/year, that from the older high-yielding clones is 650 lb/acre/year and that from the newer high-yielding clones is 940 lb/acre/year.[5] A few areas are yielding 2,000 lb/acre/year. For example, at the Rubber Research Institute of Malaya Experimental Station mean annual yields at the rate of 1,500–2,100 lb./acre have been obtained from selected clones over 10 years continuous tapping.

It is believed that breeding and selection will produce better trees with still higher yields than at present, but the development of new and improved clones takes many years before they can be recommended for large-scale planting. The first step is the selection of parents, followed by hand pollination and planting of the resulting seed, which is not ready for tapping until 5 years have elapsed. As the tree matures, yields continue to improve. Once in a while outstanding results are obtained and the decision is taken to multiply the tree by budding on to suitable stock. Again a period of about 5 years must elapse before tapping can commence, and it takes some years to establish that the trees are not only outstanding in yield but are also vigorous growers, with bark suitable for easy tapping, are resistant to storm damage and disease, and produce latex not likely to give rise to difficulty in preparing concentrated latex or dry rubber. Even when all these characteristics are satisfactory, experimental plantings have to be made under a range of conditions before any firm recommendation can be made about commercial plantings.

The operation of bud-grafting is one which can be carried out only by skilled labour. In Malaya alone there are 3,500,000 acres of rubber, corresponding to more than 200 million trees, many of which are of unselected origin and therefore relatively poor yielders. The size of the task and the fact that replacement with high-yielding material involves a period of up to 7 years with no yield determines that the rate of replanting is kept within reasonable limits. At present about 30% of the trees in Malaya consist of high-yielding clones.

A simpler alternative to bud-grafting, of special value to smallholders, is to replant with clonal seeds, which are seeds borne by bud-grafted trees. For the most part the Hevea tree is self-sterile, and consequently a mono-clonal block of rubber does not produce many seeds, and often these are poor in quality and the trees produced lack vigour and are deficient in yield capacity. The presence of other trees near the boundary increases the seed production, but illegitimate seeds with one of the parents unknown do not normally produce high-yielding trees. A notable exception is Tj1, which not only produces selfed seeds of superior quality but is also a good parent in association with other high-yielding clones. Isolated seed gardens which include a substantial proportion of Tj1 trees, in association with other high-yielding clones which are also good parents, are therefore useful sources of clonal seeds which can be planted with an assurance of high yields. An alternative is to plant " selfed " Tj1 seeds, but great care is needed to prevent contamination from other trees in the neighbourhood.[1]

Planting practices

Environment

Given a warm, damp climate and equable distribution of rainfall and temperature, rubber trees will grow almost anywhere and will survive a tremendous amount of ill-treatment, but vigour of growth and yield-capacity are appreciably affected by environmental circumstances. The ideal conditions are temperature about 80° F, seldom exceeding 95° F and seldom below 70° F, with a well-distributed rainfall of about 100 in. per annum. It is important that the rain should not usually fall during the early hours of daylight when the trees are being tapped. The soil should be acid in character, deep, of friable texture, and should contain a good supply of organic matter and mineral nutrients. If the land is flat or undulating, good drainage is required, and if it is hilly measures must be taken to prevent the loss of top-soil during heavy rain by planting a suitable cover-crop (which also helps to maintain the fertility of flat land) and by cutting terraces in the hillside. The rubber trees do not thrive above about 800 ft. elevation.

Conditions differ between and within rubber-growing countries, and are often far from ideal. For example, some rubber is grown in Ceylon at a height exceeding 1,000 ft., but yields, vigour and resistance to disease are poor. Indo-China has to contend with a somewhat prolonged dry season, but has a good depth of rich soil. On the whole, the soil in Java and Sumatra is superior to that in Malaya, which in turn is much better than that in Ceylon.

New planting

The area under rubber continues to increase, particularly in tropical countries not previously associated with rubber as a main crop. This involves felling, burning and clearing the jungle, preparing the land, and constructing roads, drains, terraces and dwelling-places for labour and staff. The greater part of new planting occurs, however, in well-established rubber-growing territories and consists in replacing old, poor-yielding, uneconomic trees with new materials capable of much higher yields. The first step is to tap the trees about to be replaced by a method which pays no attention to bark conservation, but which produces a maximum yield at a reasonable cost. No agreement has been reached about the best method, but a number of superimposed cuts at intervals of 2 or 3 days is a common practice.[6]

The labour and effort, including mechanical equipment, required to remove old trees is a considerable problem, particularly when root diseases are present which could spread to new plantings. The removal of old trees is facilitated by poisoning with sodium arsenite, which is applied in the form of a starch paste to a band cut round the trunk about 8 in. in height. Great care is needed in handling such a dangerous chemical. The heavy branches commence to fall after about 6 months, but the trunk may remain standing for a year or two.

In the meantime young trees have been grown in nurseries from seed, which may be clonal seeds or unselected seeds which are to be used as

stocks for bud-grafting.   The advantage of making a start in nurseries instead of in the field, where the trees are to grow eventually, is better supervision, more opportunity of selecting promising growths and, most important of all, the saving in time, as the plants can be placed in their final
position with a year's growth to their credit as soon as the ground is ready.
Transplanting, however, is expensive, involves some set-back to growth
and some failures which have to be replaced.

The operation of budding is one which is common in horticultural
practice and needs no description here.   It is carried out about 12 months
after the seed which produces the stock has been planted.   By this time the
young seedling tree should be about 9 ft. high with a girth of 3 in.   A bud
from a branch of the selected high-yielding clone is then applied as near the
ground as is practicable.   When the bud has taken the stock is cut back,
after which the scion starts to grow and forms the trunk and branches of
the new tree, while the original stock provides the root system.   The
suitably trimmed " budded-stump " is then transferred to its final quarters
in the field.

The optimum density of planting is a matter of opinion.   On smallholdings it often tends to be high, 200–300 trees per acre, and the trees are
consequently somewhat over-crowded and spindly in character.   On some
estates the number of trees is less than 100 per acre.   When the density is
high the trees require much longer to reach tappable size, and after they
have reached maturity they produce less latex per tree than well-spaced
plantings; nevertheless, the yield per acre is higher, but tapping costs in
terms of rubber obtained are also higher.   In the lifetime of a planting
some wastage from natural causes (e.g. thinning, lightning, wind damage,
disease) is inevitable.   Consequently, to ensure a stand of 100 trees per
acre during the most productive period it is desirable to start off with over
150 plants.[7]

Early growth

The rate at which trees grow depends on environmental circumstances
as well as on inherent characteristics.   For these reasons there is some
variation in the age at which trees are sufficiently large for tapping to
commence.   In good areas the trees may be tapped 5 years after
planting; in others it may be as long as 7 years.   Moreover, neighbouring
trees of the same clone do not necessarily reach tappable size at the same
time.   A tree is considered to be ready for tapping when it has a girth of
22 in. at 2 ft. from the ground, by which time it will have attained a height
approaching 30 ft.   As the tree becomes older, it naturally increases in
height and girth, with a larger surface of tappable bark, and consequently
gives higher yields which in 5 or 6 years reach several times those originally
obtained.

Manuring

During the early life of a new rubber planting, long before the trees are sufficiently large to tap, every effort must be made to keep the area free from weeds and the soil as fertile as possible. The latter is impossible if bare land is exposed to hot sun and rain. It is customary therefore to establish a suitable type of undergrowth which helps to aerate the soil and maintain, by cycles of growth and decomposition, equilibrium between losses and gains in organic and mineral nutrients in the top-soil. A popular type of cover-plant is a leguminous creeper, such as *Centrosema pubescens*, which is capable of fixing atmospheric nitrogen through its root-nodules. As rubber trees grow they develop more shade, so that cover-crops tend to become sparse, straggly and disappear. For this reason it is desirable to combine it with suitable types of indigenous covers.[8]

In Malaya the addition of phosphate fertilisers to the soil helps the growth of young trees. In some areas nitrogenous fertilisers improve growth and latex yields of mature trees, but this is a long-term effect, and the response is not immediate.[9, 10]

Diseases

Concentrations of the same crop over large areas encourage diseases which are rare when trees are widely scattered among other growths in tropical forests. Early attempts to establish rubber plantations in the Amazon valley, the original home of the rubber tree, were a failure, because the leaves were attacked by a fungus *Dothidella ulei*, which repeatedly defoliated and eventually killed them. This disease spread as far as Mexico and parts of the West Indies. A few trees were found to be resistant and have been multiplied on a large scale, each tree consisting of root-stock from seed, a budded-trunk derived from a high-yielding clone and a budded-crown from a *Dothidella ulei* resistant clone.[11] The Dothidella-resistant crown is not derived from trees which are usually regarded as high-yielders and tends to depress a little the yield of the trunk. For some reason which is difficult to understand, but which may be associated with small climatic differences, the disease has not spread to Africa and the Far East; strict precautions are now taken to prevent its accidental introduction.

Like trees in temperate climates, the rubber tree experiences an annual loss of leaf. This occurs during the early part of each year and is known as " wintering ". It is accompanied by a temporary reduction in yield and changes in the composition of the latex.

Secondary leaf falls sometimes occur due to fungus diseases, which in suitable conditions attack the young leaf. One of the most important is *Oidium heveae*, which is prevalent throughout the Far East but is absent in

G

Africa.   In Ceylon this disease causes repeated defoliation, seriously affecting the health and the yield of the trees, particularly those planted at high levels.   Some control is obtained by repeated dusting with sulphur, using power-driven machines, during the period when new leaves are forming after wintering.   In Malaya and neighbouring territories weather conditions are less suitable for the growth of the organism during the vital refoliation period.

Another cause of secondary leaf fall of importance in Southern India and Ceylon is *Phytophthera spp.*, which attack pods and spread to leaves. These fungi are unaffected by sulphur, and are therefore controlled by spraying with Bordeaux mixture prepared from copper sulphate and lime. It is obvious that great care must be taken to avoid contamination of bark and latex.

On the whole, most rubber areas are surprisingly free from serious diseases, but local conditions can favour attacks requiring immediate attention.   Of the stem diseases the most important is mouldy rot caused by the fungus *Ceratostomella fimbriatum,* which is liable to attack the tapping panel during the wet season.   Neglect leads to widespread infection and serious wounding, so that tapping on renewed bark becomes impracticable.   Spraying or painting the affected area with a tar-acid fungicide is found to be the most reliable remedy.

The rubber trees sometimes run dry due to a physiological condition of the bark tissues resulting in the death of the latex vessels.   This is accompanied by a brown discoloration, and hence the name " Brown Bast " disease.   Overtapping is a predisposing cause, but some trees are much more liable than others to acquire the condition, e.g. clone Glenshiel 1, which is therefore tapped more lightly than many other high-yielding clones.

The most important of the root diseases is *Fomes lignosus,* which produces fungus growths and feeds on the roots and on wood at ground level, completely destroying them.   Food and water supplies to the tree are cut off, and the tree is either blown over or dies of starvation.   If neglected, the disease spreads from tree to tree without obvious signs of its presence in the early stages.   The only remedy is the irradication of diseased roots and the construction of isolation trenches to prevent spreading.

Apart from accident and disease there is no reason why a rubber tree should not continue to yield latex for very many years, and specimen trees are still in existence which were planted in the early days of the rubber-growing industry.   The ravages of time are, however, responsible for many losses, and tapping on renewed bark can become more and more difficult, particularly if previous tapping has been done badly.   There comes a time therefore when the stand of trees is greatly reduced and the tapping of those which remain is no longer economic.   Moreover, better clones are continually being developed, and eventually the decision must be made to start again with new plantings. Nevertheless, much of the rubber in Indonesia and Malaya is over 30 years old.

Tapping

If any part of a rubber tree suffers mechanical damage involving fracture of tissues the injury is followed by an immediate exudation of latex, which dries on the wound and covers it with a thin film of rubber. The problem confronting planters is how to obtain the maximum yield with the minimum effort and the least damage to the tree. When rubber trees were first planted in the East the only guide was circumstantial information about the method used in Brazil. This consisted in making numerous oblique slashes in the bark of the trunk and catching the latex in suitable receptacles. Yields were not large, and damage to the bark was considerable, necessitating long periods for the trees to recover.

The first steps in introducing modern methods were taken by Ridley [3] (1889), who made a series of careful cuts in the bark to a herring-bone design, subsequently paring away, at intervals of a few days, thin shavings of bark from the lower sides of his original cuts. Little was known about the rate of growth of new bark to replace that cut away, and it has required years of experience to arrive at the best compromise between tapping intensity, yield, bark renewal, growth and health of the tree. The method used by Ridley is substantially the same as that employed today, but the herring-bone design has proved to be too drastic and has been replaced mostly by a single cut on half the circumference of the tree. Any system of tapping retards growth, and even the present system has its effects.

The removal of a thin slice of bark without damaging the tree unduly is a skilled operation which markedly influences the yield of latex, bark consumption and the quality of renewed bark. Shallow tapping leads to a loss of latex because it does not sever all the latex vessels. Maximum yield can be obtained only by cutting to within 1 mm. of the cambium. If the cut penetrates the cambium, severe wounding results, which causes formation of excrescences on renewed bark, making it difficult to tap.

The reason for such careful control of tapping depth is that the latex is contained in long vessels situated near the cambium and extending in a vertical direction with a slight inclination to the right. They may be likened to a series of concentric nets in the form of cylinders surrounding the cambium.[12] Each cylinder is embedded in soft tissue and is independent of its neighbour. When cutting horizontally into the bark, the severed ends of the latex vessels appear as a series of rows, more concentrated near the cambium than farther away and completely absent in the hard external portion of the trunk. The turgor pressure in the surrounding soft tissues forces the latex out of the severed ends of the vessels. At the same time water percolates into the latex vessels, thereby diluting the latex. The latex which exudes during the first 15 minutes is therefore more concentrated than that which flows later. As the pressure in the surrounding tissues diminishes the latex flows more slowly and eventually ceases to flow due to the formation of coagulum, which seals the cut ends of the latex vessels. In normal tapping, flow usually continues for about

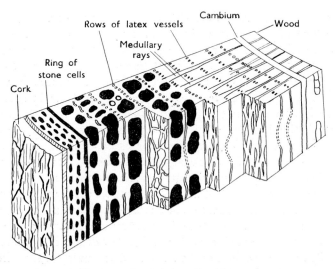

Fig. 2.14. Outer layers of rubber tree.

1–2 hours and sometimes much longer. Because turgor pressure commences to fall after sunrise, trees are tapped in the very early morning.

In a tree which has not been tapped the latex in the vessels contains about 60% rubber and the first tapping results in only a small flow of latex. As tapping is continued at intervals of a few days the latex becomes more dilute, flow is considerably increased and yields are much higher. This is known as " wound response ". An excessive rate of tapping leads to a greater dilution of latex, and a conservative rate of tapping to a more concentrated latex. A normal dilution for a tree in regular tapping is a dry rubber content of 30–40%. By noting the dilution which occurs in various parts of the tree it can be shown that latex is drawn from a distance of about 4 ft. below the tapping cut, but evidence has been obtained that changes occur in latex as far away as the branches in a freshly tapped tree.[13,14,15]

A common tapping system is a cut in the shape of a V on half the circumference of the trunk at intervals of 2 days. Another popular system is a single spiral cut at an angle of 25°–30° to the horizontal on half the circumference of the trunk at intervals of 2 days. The cut slopes from high left to low right so as to sever the maximum number of latex vessels, which as already explained are not quite verticle but inclined a little to the right. The steeper angle of cut is used on high-yielding trees so that latex will flow down it sufficiently quickly to avoid spilling over the sides. At the bottom of the cut the latex flows down a small vertical channel cut in the bark on to a metal spout, from which it drips into a cup immediately below.

Fig. 2.15. Using a gouge-like knife the young Tamil girl from Southern India in this picture is tapping a half spiral cut on a 30+ year old tree.

Porcelain cups are sometimes used, but more often than not the cup is a convenient half coconut shell.

All tapping systems not aimed at temporarily high yields, preceding the destruction of the trees preparatory to replanting, must ensure that bark is not consumed at a faster rate than that at which it is renewed.[16] A consumption of 10 in. per year, which is equivalent to about $\frac{1}{15}$ in. per tapping, allows 7–8 years before it is necessary to tap on renewed bark.

Seedling trees taper much more than buddings. The first tapping is therefore commenced at a comparatively low level, which permits tapping to be started a year earlier than would be practicable at a higher level. The usual procedure is to open the first cut at about 20 in. from the ground and proceed with tapping until the bark below has been consumed, after which the tapper opens a cut on the other side of the trunk. The next cut to be opened is at 30 in. and subsequently at 40 in. from the ground. The opening cut on budded trees is usually made at 40 in. or more from the ground without the need for divisions into three successive and increasing tapping heights.

A number of variations of the alternate-day, half-spiral cut is sometimes used. For example, a full-spiral cut every fourth day tends to reduce tapping costs, but has disadvantages associated with increased production of scrap and retardation of growth.

One of the effects of over-tapping is the complete cessation of latex yield due to the development of a physiological condition known as " Brown Bast " because of the characteristic appearance of the bark. As previously mentioned, some trees and clones are more liable to develop this condition than others, and should therefore be tapped more lightly. One method is a half-spiral cut every third day; another is a third-spiral cut every second day. These methods enable more trees to be tapped per day with a somewhat lower yield per tree. Some interest has also been taken in tapping systems involving long periods of rest, such as 6 months' tapping and 3 months' rest.

Tapping systems are conveniently represented in an abbreviated form by internationally agreed symbols, which are largely self-explanatory.[17] Thus s/2.d/2.100% refers to a half-spiral cut every second day, which is equivalent to normal tapping intensity. s/1.d/4.100% is a full-spiral cut every fourth day, and is approximately of the same intensity. s/2.d/3.67% indicates a half-spiral cut every third day; its intensity is two-thirds that of the standard. The following refers to a periodic system of tapping, c/2.d/2.6m/9.67%, where c/2 refers to a half-circumference cut which may be in the form of a V and 6m/9 refers to 6 months' tapping and 3 months' rest.

Although most estates use the c/2.d/2.100% tapping system, which at present appears to be the most useful compromise between all the factors involved, it is not necessarily one which will eventually survive.   Other systems with higher yields are at least being tried out commercially, and may become more general.

An interesting method is the use of two tapping cuts, preferably on opposite sides of the tree and separated by a vertical distance of 4 ft., which represents the distance from which latex is drained for each cut.   A combination of two cuts and the application of yield stimulants is capable of giving yields up to $2\frac{1}{2}$ times those obtained by the standard method.   It requires years of patient observation, however, to establish differences between the responses of different trees, and whether or not 2s/2.d/2.200% cuts can be continued indefinitely without unduly harming the trees.

High intensity or slaughter tapping is employed for about 12 months prior to the removal of trees which are to be replaced by new plantings. Cost of tapping in terms of yield chiefly determine which system is selected.   Superimposed cuts up to 3 or 4 at suitable intervals are generally preferred to daily tapping.[6]

Yield stimulation

Various methods of improving yield by bark treatments have been tried, some of which have been highly successful.   A recent development is the application of growth-regulators which are widely used in agriculture as herbicides by over-stimulation of growth.

The bark of a rubber tree is divided into three reasonably well-defined portions.   Next to the cambium is a layer consisting of soft tissue; outside this is a mixed layer of soft tissue and stone cells.   The third portion consists of the hard, corky material exposed to the atmosphere.   The soft tissues carry the latex vessels in addition to sieve tubes which are responsible for the transport of nutritional substances.

As early as 1912 it was found that the removal of the dead, corky layer by lightly scraping the bark below the tapping cut helped to increase the flow of latex and improve yield.   Later on, light scraping, followed by the application of proprietary and secret mixtures, some of which included cattle manure, were claimed to effect a further improvement.   In 1939 Baptist [18] showed that painting the lightly scraped bark with palm oil resulted in improved yields.   He suggested that the effect might be due to the presence of growth hormones in the palm oil.

In 1951 Chapman published data proving that the application of 2 : 4-dichlorphenoxy acetic acid (2 : 4-D, a well-known growth regulator) in palm oil markedly improved the yield of latex.[19, 20, 21]   Later Baptist and de Jonge showed that 2 : 4 : 5-trichlorphenoxy acetic acid (2 : 4 : 5-T), particularly in the form of its butyl ester, is at least as good as 2 : 4-D and possibly a little better.[22]   They also suggested that the efficacy of the growth regulator increases with the number of chlorine atoms in the phenoxy acetic compound.   Thus, 2 : 4-D is superior to *p*-chlorophenoxy acetic acid, but a little inferior to 2 : 4 : 5-T.

The treatment of trees with yield stimulants is a comparatively new development which is rapidly gaining in popularity and helping to increase the yield of rubber.   It is somewhat erratic in its effect on different trees, and much has yet to be learned about the circumstances and conditions which are necessary for optimum benefits.   The peak yield is usually obtained about 2 weeks after treatment.   Yield then slowly declines over a period of several months, after which further treatment is necessary.   Subsequent treatments are not as effective as the first, but continue to give appreciably higher yields than would otherwise have been obtained. Sometimes the increase in yield over 6 months after the first treatment is as high as 60%, and sometimes it is much smaller.   Best results are obtained by the application of a 1% solution of growth-regulator to a 3-in. strip of lightly scraped bark below the tapping cut.

The following figure is typical of the rate and duration of latex flow during the peak yield period in comparison with that of an untreated tree.[23]

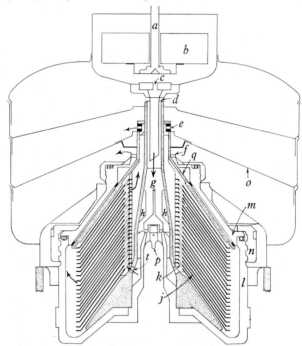

Fig. 2.16. Diagrammatic section of bowl.

a. Feed pipe. *b*. Feed control float. *c*. Inlet orifice. *d*. Overflow. *e*. Cream discharge. *f*. Skim discharge. *g*. Distributor. *h*. Distributor vanes. *i*. Discharge to bowl. *j*. Separator plates. *k*. Holes in separator plates. *l*. Bowl. *m*. Bowl cover. *n*. Locking ring. *o*. Collecting trays. *p*. Driving tongue. *q*. Top plate. *t*. Brake rim.

Secondary effects of yield-stimulation are an improvement in the rate of bark renewal after tapping, dilution of the latex by about 5% and a small increase in its copper content. Nearly all this extra copper is lost to the serum in the preparation of concentrated latex and of dry rubber. Detailed tests on vulcanising and ageing properties have failed to reveal any differences in the properties of rubber before and after yield-stimulation.

A novel method of improving yields is by the injection of several grams of copper sulphate into the bark near the tapping cut.[24] The yield results are comparable with those given by growth-regulators, and the copper content of the latex is no higher. It is evident that the copper sulphate does not penetrate into the latex vessels. Nevertheless, there is always a risk of accidental contamination, and planters in Malaya have been warned not to use this method of yield-stimulation.

Another interesting method of obtaining a substantial improvement in yield is by the treatment of the tapping cut with antibiotics, which it has been suggested are effective partly because they prevent the clogging of latex vessels with coagulum produced by bacteria.[25] There is no doubt that much has yet to be learned about the potentialities of chemical treatments, not only to improve yields but also the technical quality of the latex obtained.

The examination of latex at various points in the tree shows that yield-stimulants produce pronounced dilution of the latex at 2–3 ft. below the tapping cut, indicating a reduction in turgor pressure due to the movement of latex towards the tapping cut, and suggesting that these yield-stimulants are effective because they enable the latex to be drained from a greater area of bark. There is no indication that they are in any way responsible for increased synthesis of rubber within the tree. Even though they improve the growth of renewed bark, they do not influence the number of latex vessels in the soft tissues.

Latex collection

A tapper commences operations as soon as possible after daybreak, when turgor pressure in tissues, and consequently yields of latex, are at a maximum. Depending on local circumstances and conditions, his task is usually set at between 200 and 300 trees, from which he may collect 2 gallons or more of latex. As he arrives at each tree, he first peels off the dry residue of latex from the tapping cup and places it in a bag slung over his shoulder for subsequent washing treatment and conversion into brown crêpe. He replaces the cup, pares away a shaving of bark and proceeds to the next tree. When his tapping round is completed he returns to the first tree, which by this time has usually finished dripping. The latex in the cup is emptied into his bucket, and so he continues until he has collected all his latex, which he then carries to a receiving station, which may be the factory where the latex is to be processed or a more conveniently situated tank on wheels for transport to the main factory. Each tapper's latex is weighed and the approximate dry rubber content determined by a hydro-meter graduated in terms of dry rubber content (Metrolac). The latex as received is usually too viscous for direct hydrometer determination, and is therefore diluted with twice its volume of water. This method of estimating dry rubber content is not strictly accurate because of differences in the specific gravity of the aqueous serum in different localities, but is convenient and generally accepted.

From the moment that it exudes into the atmosphere the latex, which has a pH of 7·0, becomes contaminated with acid-producing bacteria and coagulating enzymes. Latex from some areas or some clones has a marked tendency to undergo complete or partial coagulation before it can be taken to the factory. The tendency is more marked during rainy weather and also immediately after wintering. Prematurely formed coagulum is only suitable for the preparation of lower grade rubber, such as estate brown crêpe, and must therefore be kept to a minimum. One explanation of the cause of premature coagulation is that enzymes liberate fat acids from the phospholipins around the rubber particles. These acids form magnesium and calcium soaps, which are responsible for premature coagulation. In wet weather water-soluble salts and tannins from the bark may also help to destabilise the latex.

The usual method of preventing premature coagulation is to add a dilute solution of mild alkali or a bactericide to the collecting buckets or cups. The conventional anti-coagulants are ammonia (about 0·01% on the weight of latex), sodium sulphite (about 0·05%) and formaldehyde (about 0·02%).[26] The latter is sometimes used in association with a little sodium carbonate.

Preparation of dry rubber

Ribbed smoked sheet

The process of preparing smoked sheet is essentially the same on estates and smallholdings, except that the latter treat latex in small quantities and have much simpler and locally extemporised equipment.

On large estates the latex as received from the tapper is strained through a 60-mesh sieve into a bulking tank. This removes leaves, pieces of coagulum, grass seeds and particles of sand which inevitably contaminate the latex. The finer particles are only partially removed by such a wide-mesh sieve. Sometimes an 80-mesh sieve is used, but anything finer than this is impracticable because of the viscosity of the latex. At one time brass sieves were used, but owing to the danger of contamination of the latex by copper, particularly in the presence of ammonia, Monel metal sieves are preferred and recommended.

After the whole of the day's supply of latex has been bulked it is diluted with water to the required dry rubber content. This allows the remaining heavy dirt to settle out more easily. The preferred dilution of latex is to a dry rubber content of about 15%. Sometimes a little greater dilution is found more suitable because it produces a softer and more easily machined coagulum, and sometimes a dilution of 20% produces a coagulum of the required firmness.

From the bulking tank the diluted latex is run into coagulating tanks, usually through a Monel metal sieve to remove particles of coagulum formed in the bulking tank. The coagulating tank is usually an aluminium-lined wooden rectangular container about 16 in. deep holding about 250 gallons of diluted latex. The sides of the tank are provided with vertical slots at intervals of $1\frac{1}{4}$ in. to receive removable aluminium partitions. Before the partitions are fitted into position the coagulant solution is added evenly over the surface of the latex and mixed into its bulk, being careful to avoid trapping air, which would lead to the production of bubbly sheets. A little foam forms on the surface and is skimmed off. The partitions are then placed in position and the latex slowly thickens and eventually forms a soft coagulum which occupies the upper spaces between the partitions. Sometimes a continuous sheet of coagulum throughout the length of the tank is obtained by leaving spaces between alternate opposite sides of the partitions and the tank wall.

The usual coagulants are acetic and formic acid. The dilution of the latex and the amount added determine the speed of coagulation. For 15% latex, which has to be coagulated over-night, it is usual to add about 100 parts of 1% acetic acid solution to 1,000 parts of latex. If the coagulant is formic acid the amount required is a little more than half that of acetic acid. To obtain coagulation the same day, the amount of acid is increased by 10–20% and a somewhat stronger solution is used. The addition of anti-coagulants in the field will also affect the amount of acid required.

Other coagulants have been used from time to time, but the only one to obtain any degree of popularity has been sulphuric acid, particularly when acetic and formic acids have been relatively expensive or difficult to obtain. Exhaustive tests in Malaya and the United Kingdom have failed to show that sulphuric acid has any harmful effects on the rubber except when used in excessive and uneconomic amounts, which have a marked retarding effect on the vulcanising properties of the rubber.

One of the advantages of acetic acid as a coagulant is that it is a weak acid, and variations in the amount used have relatively small effects on the pH of the latex-coagulant dispersion. The relation between pH of

coagulation and the vulcanising properties of the rubber in the ASC1
pure gum compound is shown in Fig. 2.17.[27]

When the latex is coagulated the partitions are removed and the coagulum fed as separate pieces or as a continuous sheet to a series of even-
speed rolls provided with water sprays and adjusted to give progressively,
tighter nips and corresponding faster speeds.   There are usually five pairs

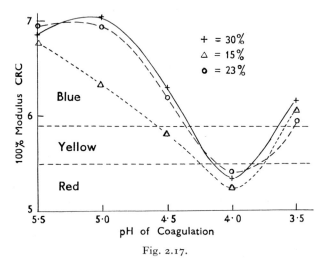

Fig. 2.17.

of rolls, the last pair being marking rolls, which impress a grooved pattern
on the sheets and sometimes the name of the estate.   During passage
through the series of rolls the thickness of the coagulum is reduced from
about $1\frac{1}{4}$ to about $\frac{1}{8}$ in. and serum is squeezed out and washed away.   The
grooved pattern developed by the final pair not only gives the sheet its
characteristic form but also facilitates drying because of the larger surface
exposed to the atmosphere.   In small-scale operations there is considerable
handling of sheets from the coagulum stage to the final grooving, but many
estates float the coagulum along chutes to the first pair of rolls and through
subsequent rolls which are geared together and arranged one behind the
other.

At the end of the machining operations the coagulum has become much
tougher and can be handled with less damage than previously.   It is hung
on racks to drip in the open for about 2 hours shaded from the sun.
During this time the moisture content of the sheet is reduced, partly by
superficial drying and partly by syneresis from about 60 to 40%.[28]

The sheets are finally dried by suspending them for about 4 days in an
atmosphere of smoke from the slow combustion of wood.   During this
process the sheets absorb smoke constituents, lose their white colour and
take on the dark amber shade characteristic of smoked sheet.   This

method of drying has the advantage that it can be done very cheaply with little or no capital expenditure, and the smoke constituents tend to prevent the growth of mould if the rubber is subsequently exposed to damp atmospheric conditions.

To smoke rubber on a large scale ranging from a few hundred to several thousand pounds per day, properly constructed smoke-houses are essential. These are usually rectangular tunnels with dimensions suitable to accommodate 4 days' output. The length of the smoke-house is traversed by rails on which are moved trolleys carrying wooden racks over which are hung the sheets of rubber. A day's output of wet rubber is pushed into the smoke-house through doors opening at the end farthest removed from the furnace. The next day a further supply is wheeled in and the previous day's crop moved another section nearer to the source of heat and smoke. At the end of 4 days the first day's output has been at the hot end of the smoke-house for 1 day and is then removed. The furnace which provides heat and smoke is built on the side towards one end of the smoke-house, the products of combustion being carried into the smoke-house by means of a flue which passes along the length of the smoke-house at floor level and has openings for smoke to emerge under the centre of each day's output. Adjustable flue apertures and roof ventilators are provided so that heat and smoke can be varied and directed to the required extent to each part of the house.

The first stage of drying consists in the removal of surface water. This is a comparatively rapid operation, but must be done at a relatively low temperature to avoid the formation of blisters due to the expansion of internal moisture. During its first day in the smoke-house the rubber is therefore kept at the cool end, where the temperature is about 110° F. Further drying involves the diffusion of water from within the sheet to the surface. This is a slow process which is inversely proportional to the square of the thickness. When the water content is reduced the rubber can be safely submitted to higher temperatures, which may reach 140° F at the furnace end of the smoke-house. Higher temperatures would tend to produce tackiness, which would reduce the market value of the rubber.

Smallholders who have only sufficient latex to produce a few sheets at a time cannot be expected to have the same equipment as large estates. Nevertheless, the method of preparation is essentially the same, and with care excellent results can be obtained. One method is to coagulate the latex in half a kerosene tin, followed by rolling in a hand mangle or even with a bottle and drying in the smoke of a kitchen fire. There is an increasing tendency in Malaya for a number of smallholders to combine in processing latex at a simplified type of central factory. The latex from a number of smallholdings is bulked, strained and coagulated in tanks with partitions. The machining is done on hand mangles, and the smoke-house consists of a cheap structure of gunny sacking hung over a wooden frame with smouldering wood providing smoke from below.   With adequate care and attention to cleanliness it has been found possible to convert nearly all the latex into the best grade of smoked sheet.

It is doubtful if any producer deliberately aims at preparing low-grade sheet, but even on good estates about 5 % of the total output is not up to the standard of appearance required for RSS1.

Approximately half the world's production of raw rubber comes from smallholdings, and a large part of their output is marketed in forms other than smoked sheet.   Some smallholders in Malaya produce excellent smoked sheet, and much of the first-grade rubber supplied by packing houses is made up of rubber from smallholdings.

Many smallholders are isolated from a knowledge of the requirements of terminal markets, and nearly all are financed by village dealers, to whom they sell their crude products.   Even in Malaya, where smallholders are encouraged to produce good-quality sheet, the fact that loose rubber passes through the hands of a succession of dealers before reaching a packing and shipping organisation does not encourage the production of the highest grade of sheet.   Moreover, some smallholders have not the equipment or the incentive to adopt all the precautions required to obtain a clean, dry product of the required colour and uniformity of appearance.   Failure to provide themselves with means of straining the latex to remove major contaminants is only one of the causes of the preparation of low-grade sheet.   Sometimes the local dealer has to dry and smoke the semi-dry sheet himself before passing it on to the next purchaser.   There are many other ways in which small-scale production can lead to the preparation of inferior sheet based on visual standards.   Nevertheless, apart from dirt, which is not the only cause of down-grading, this rubber is often of excellent quality, and because of its relatively low price is in large demand.

Pale crêpe

Crêpe rubber is made by heavily machining coagulum eight or nine times between grooved differential-speed rollers.   All latices contain yellow colouring matter consisting mainly of β-carotene, and in the absence of special precautions yield yellowish crêpe which has a distinct tendency to become darker during drying.[29]   The market requires that the best quality should be as white as possible, and this can be achieved only by using special techniques as follows:

(*a*) The addition of sodium bisulphite to the latex to prevent subsequent darkening of the crêpe due to the presence of oxidising enzymes.

(*b*) Fractional coagulation of the latex to remove yellow colouring matter in the first fraction.

(*c*) The addition of a chemical bleaching agent to the latex.

The addition of sodium bisulphite has little effect on the natural colour of dry crêpe, but it restrains the action of polyphenol oxydases which cause the crêpe to become darker on drying, sometimes markedly so.

When latex is partially coagulated by adding insufficient acid for complete coagulation the coagulum formed contains much of the colouring matter naturally present. Some latices contain more colouring matter than others, and for this reason latex from some clones is notoriously unsuitable for the manufacture of white crêpe. In extreme instances the amount of first-fraction rubber which must be removed to ensure a white second fraction may be as much as 50%. Because of its colour the first fraction commands a lower price than the second fraction, and must therefore be kept to a minimum.

An important increase in the amount of second fraction crêpe is obtained by the addition to latex of certain mercaptans and disulphides, which in addition to bleaching β-carotene are well-known peptising agents for dry rubber.[30] The most effective bleaching agent is xylyl mercaptan. The amount used is normally less than 0·05% of the weight of dry rubber and is insufficient to have more than a negligible effect on rheological properties. These bleaching agents are very effective, but sometimes fail to remove a slight greyish tinge retained by the crêpe. Although some consumers have tended to blame bleaching agents for alleged differences in the technical behaviour of present and pre-war crêpe, comparative tests on bleached and unbleached crêpe have not succeeded in demonstrating that such differences exist.

On some estates fractional coagulation is unnecessary, since white crêpe can be obtained by coagulating the whole of the latex after the addition of sodium bisulphite and bleaching agent. It is more usual, however, to remove a first clot and then coagulate the rest of the latex, the bleaching agent being added either to the whole latex or to the second fraction only. The great advantage of the bleaching agent is that it enables a larger proportion of the product to be converted into white crêpe.

The first step in preparing white latex crêpe is to dilute strained field latex to 20–25% D.R.C. This is a higher concentration of rubber than is required for the preparation of smoked sheet, for which the coagulum must be reasonably soft in order to respond to the machining received on light mangles. Crêpeing machines are of much sturdier construction, and in crêpe manufacture the coagulum is submitted to extensive maceration. The physical texture of the coagulum is therefore of less importance than in sheet manufacture, and the latex need not be diluted so much or to such exact proportions.

After dilution about 0·5% sodium bisulphite calculated on the rubber is added to the latex in the form of a 20% solution and well stirred.

The next step depends on local circumstances, and is best illustrated on the assumption that it is necessary to remove about 10% of the total rubber in the first clot and that the bleaching agent is not added until the first clot has been separated.

To produce the first clot somewhat less than 0·15% acetic acid calculated on the rubber is added as a 2·5% solution and well stirred. After a few hours a yellow clot is formed which is carefully skimmed off and subsequently machined to crêpe, which because of its colour may be graded as No. 3, fair average quality off-colour palish crêpe.

The residual latex is then strained through a 60-mesh sieve to remove small pieces of yellow coagulum still remaining in the latex, after which the bleaching agent is added. It is usually obtained in a self-emulsifying form, and an emulsion is prepared by diluting with four volumes of water. The amount of bleaching agent required can only be determined by trial and error, and in no circumstances exceeds 0·1% calculated on the rubber.

The latex is then coagulated by adding either dilute formic or acetic acid, the amount required being approximately four times that needed for partial coagulation. Sometimes the latex is coagulated in large jars, in which case the lumps of coagulum have to be cut into pieces which can be easily fed into the crêpeing machine. Sometimes coagulation is done in tanks with partitions about 3 in. apart.

The market recognises two distinct types of crêpe, based chiefly on the thickness of the commercial product. Thin pale crêpe is the type usually prepared in Malaya, and thick or blanket pale crêpe is the normal production of Ceylon.

For machining of coagulum to thin crêpe four sets of rollers are preferred, although some estates manage with two. Each machine consists of a pair of rolls revolving at differential speeds under a liberal spray of water. The usual sequence is a macerator with heavily grooved rolls, a crêpeing machine with lighter grooving and a lower gear ratio, followed by the finishing machine, which consists of plain rolls operating at higher gear ratios than crêpeing machines. The coagulum is passed through each pair of rolls several times, and two finishing machines are required to keep pace with the output of one macerator and one crêpeing machine.

The macerator rolls bite into the coagulum, squeeze out the serum and produce a rough, highly crinkled, thick blanket full of holes. The crêpeing machine produces a thinner sheet of more even texture, an operation which is completed in the finishing machine, which produces the lacy texture. Each successive rolling consolidates and toughens the coagulum by squeezing out and washing away serum, and it is obvious from the treatment which the coagulum receives that crêpe must be a purer form of rubber than sheet, but it is curious that there is no evidence of this when the two types are submitted to chemical analysis. The machining of the wet coagulum has no apparent effect on the plasticity of the dry rubber, and on an average pale crêpe is a little harder than smoked sheet.

On the whole, the cycle of milling operations performed on the wet coagulum is the same whether the final product is thin or thick crêpe. In both preparations the coagulum is converted into thin, lacy crêpe, but whereas thin crêpe is ready for packing when dry, that which is to be marketed as thick crêpe requires further machining, which is done by passing the dry crêpe about three times through smooth rolls revolving at slight friction speeds. The conversion of thin crêpe to thick crêpe has the advantage to the producer that not quite so much care and attention needs to be devoted to the form and texture of the milled coagulum when hung up to dry. It is essential, however, that it should be thin and coherent in order to dry quickly without damage, and care must be taken during dry milling to keep the rubber cool so that the colour of the crêpe is not damaged.

Crêped coagulum is dried in air and is much more prone to attack by fungi than sheet, which is dried in smoke. For this reason crêped coagulum must be dried quickly under reasonably hygienic conditions, and this is not always easy in the humid tropics, where drying houses quickly become infected with mould organisms. Moreover, crêpe cannot be dried at a temperature as high as that used for drying sheet in smoke, because a drying temperature above 100° F has an adverse effect on colour; for the same reason exposure to sunlight must be avoided. The usual procedure is to suspend long sheets of the thin crêped coagulum over horizontal wooden bars about 6 in. apart in large drying sheds with adequate ventilation. In fine weather the crêpe can be dried in less than a week, but many estates find it preferable and safer to dry at a temperature of about 95° F produced by means of artificial heat, such as can be obtained by the installation of hot-water radiators.

Sole crêpe

Apart from the attention given to appearance and dimensions, there is no essential difference between sole crêpe and pale crêpe marketed as a raw material for rubber manufacture. The market is excessively strict about obtaining a pale colour and requires that the thickness should be carefully controlled.

The crêpe is built up to the required thickness by superimposing a number of plies of thin crêpe which have been specially selected for colour and uniformity. The rubber is stretched slightly and the plies pressed together by hand rolling on a warm table and compressed a little further by passing several times between even-speed smooth rolls. When cool, the slabs are cut accurately to the required length and width and thickness checked by weighing. The trimmings are re-crêped and marketed as pale crêpe.   An alternative type of blanket sole crêpe is produced in Ceylon by lightly milling several layers of thin crêpe between even-speed smooth rolls.

Brown crêpes

The only type of plantation rubber in regular supply not marketed in crêpe form is smoked sheet.   All other types, ranging from pale crêpe to flat bark crêpe, are washed and crêped, the main difference between them being not so much in their final form as in colour, cleanliness and the degree of degradation of the rubber hydrocarbon.   Market quality largely depends on careful treatment, and because of its source estate brown crêpe is usually regarded as superior to brown crêpe from other sources, which in turn is superior to flat bark crêpe.

The largest source of brown crêpe rubber is native production in Indonesia, but all estates produce some scrap rubber which is eventually marketed as brown crêpe.   On well-conducted estates the percentage of scrap is between 5 and 10% of the total output.

It has already been explained that fresh latex is not very stable and that anti-coagulants are added to prevent premature coagulation.   Nevertheless, small lumps of coagulum tend to form in the latex during transit to the estate factory.   These clots are not sufficiently soft to machine to sheet and contain too much colouring matter to make into pale crêpe.   They are therefore converted into good-quality brown crêpe.   Another source of scrap rubber in the estate factory is the froth which is skimmed off the surface of diluted latex after the addition of the coagulating acid.   This also makes a superior type of brown crêpe.

A major source of tree scrap is the latex which dries on the tapping cut after flow has ceased.   The dried rubber is easily pulled off as a thin strip when the next tapping operation is due, and is for the most part reasonably clean.   Another source of relatively clean scrap, usually called cup scrap, is the dried film of latex left behind in the receptacle into which the latex has dripped.

The lowest grade of scrap is made from highly contaminated rubber which at some stage has been part of the debris at the foot of the tree-trunk.   For example, bark shavings removed in tapping contain dried latex in their tissues, and are collected from the ground where they have fallen.   Another source of dirty scrap is latex which has overflowed from the sides of the tapping cut, down the trunk and on to the ground.   With this kind of contamination and exposure, degradation of the rubber quickly occurs, but after treatment a moderately clean and reasonably stable product is obtained.   It is marketed as flat bark crêpe.

The number of estates producing crêpe rubber is relatively small, and it would be uneconomic for most estates to purchase expensive crêpeing mills for the treatment of the small quantity of scrap produced each day. Such rubber is therefore usually sold loose to remilling factories, which are normally situated at large ports. They treat not only locally produced and up-country scrap but also large quantities of crude, dirty and wet coagulum imported from overseas. The scrap is first sorted out into grades dependent on cleanliness and colour. Each lot is then soaked overnight in a solution of sodium bisulphite which helps to loosen the dirt and improve the colour of the rubber. It is then macerated in a Universal Washer, which consists of a hopper in which revolve paddles which chew up the rubber in a bath of water from which the rubber emerges in the form of lumps and corrugated rolls. The partly cleansed scrap is now ready for crêpeing, which is done on machines similar to those already described in the manufacture of pale crêpe. The rubber is then dried in air in sheds similar to those used for pale crêpe.

Smoked blanket crêpe

Before smoked sheet is packed, each sheet is usually examined by transmitted light and obvious specks of dirt and disfiguring marks which would tend to reduce the market view of its grade are cut out. These clippings are washed and made into smoked blanket crêpe.

Packing

Most plantation rubber is shipped in the form of approximately cubical bales occupying 5 cu.ft. of shipping space. The weight of a bale ranges from 250 lb., which is the maximum permitted for smoked sheet, to 160 lb., which is the minimum for crêpe, the latter being more difficult to compress to the required volume without loss of the characteristic appearance of crêpe. The normal procedure is to pile in carefully arranged layers the prescribed weight of rubber and to compress it in a box to the required dimensions. The rubber is then clamped overnight or otherwise submitted to pressure for a period which minimises recovery of shape and distortion in transit. The compressed bales are finally wrapped as shown in the following table: [46]

Rubber type	Range of wt. permitted, lb.	Wrapping materials permitted
Smoked sheet	224–250	Rubber
Thick pale crêpe	160–224	Hessian
Thin pale crêpe	160–224	Rubber or rubber and hessian
Brown crêpe	160–224	Rubber or hessian or no wrapper
Flat bark crêpe	204–224	Rubber or hessian or no wrapper

In the early years of the industry plantation rubber was packed in three-ply wooden cases, following the practice of the tea industry. Plank cases were somewhat cheaper, but gave rise to many splinters, which penetrated far into the bales. During the 1930s jute sacking or hessian gained in popularity. To prevent adhesion of jute fibres to rubber, the hessian was first treated with a starch–sodium silicate solution and then dried. Nevertheless, the hessian was sometimes difficult to remove and had to be burnt off. As shown in the above table, hessian is still used as a wrapping material for crêpe rubbers, and improved care in treating with anti-adhesives appears to have eliminated previous difficulties. Such rubber is usually strapped with metal bands.

Since the War sheet rubber has been shipped as " bare-back " bales in which the wrapping material is rubber of the same type and grade as the contents. Massing in transit is prevented by painting the exterior of the bales with a surface lubricant, such as talc, clay or whiting dispersed in a rubber solution. This type of dispersion has now replaced the popular water–glue dispersions, which led to the formation of hard agglomerates of the dusting powder which could not be broken up by mastication.

In the cleaner grades of smoked sheet (IX, 1 and 2) the bales may be dusted with a little talc before covering with wrapping rubber. This facilitates the removal by the consumer of the outside wrapping sheets if they happen to pick up dirt in transit.

Non-standard and inferior local wrapping materials are sometimes encountered with low-grade rubber, but most is now packed in accordance with the generally approved way. Attempts to improve the packing of rubber have not led to commercial developments, partly because of increased cost. Experimental shipments have been made from time to time with covering materials such as bituminised hessian and various types of paper bags, one of the most successful being a multi-wall paper bag with a polythene lining.[31] These bags hold about 75 lb. rubber and have apparent advantages in cleanliness and ease of stacking due to diminished liability to distortion in transit, but large manufacturers with the necessary mechanical equipment find large bales more convenient than small ones.

Market types and grades

Since 1945 much has been done by trade organisations throughout the world to reduce the number of market grades of plantation rubber and to define them in such a way that they will be understood everywhere. So far it has not been possible to reduce the number of recognised grades below 36, of which 24 have received international approval and 6 have two sets of standards because of differences of opinion about the material which should be included. The recognised market grades of rubber, including names of the standardising organisations, are shown in the following table: [32]

Type	Grade		
	International	R.M.A. (New York)	Singapore
Ribbed smoked sheets	1XRSS, 1RSS, 2RSS, 3RSS	4RSS, 5RSS	4RSS, 5RSS
Thick pale crêpes	1X, 1, 2, 3		
Thin pale crêpes	1X, 1, 2, 3		
Estate brown thick crêpes	1X, 2X, 3X		
Estate brown thin crêpes	1X, 2X, 3X		
Thick blanket crêpes (Ambers)	2, 4	3	C
Thin brown crêpes	1	2, 3, 4	2, 3, 4
Flat bark crêpe	Standard, Hard		
Pure smoked blanket crêpe	Standard		

Each of the above grades is defined by an approved brief verbal description and is normally covered by reference samples showing the range of appearances permitted.

The main differences between the grades of smoked sheet are in the amounts of mould and other blemishes permitted. Whereas RSS1 must be practically free of mould and visual defects, appreciable mould may be present in up to 30% of a consignment of RSS5, and rust, stains, large bark particles and bubbles are permitted to the extent shown by the reference sample.

The main difference between the grades of the different types of crêpe is in colour. The best pale crêpe, 1X, is very light and uniform in colour compared with No. 3, which is yellowish and variable in colour. In the brown crêpes the colour ranges from light brown in the best grades to dark brown in the poorest. In the lowest grade of estate and other thin brown crêpes specks of bark are permitted to the degree shown in the reference sample.

The lowest type of rubber is flat bark crêpe prepared by washing very dirty and badly deteriorated scrap rubber, usually after contact with the ground. There are two grades, both of which are dark brown to black in colour, the standard grade being described as hard to soft in texture and the hard grade as a thick, firm, comparatively tough crêpe.

No figures are available for the world-wide production of the different types of rubber, but the following table is a breakdown of shipments from Malaya in 1957, including rubber originally imported from Indonesia:

Type	*Per cent*
RSS and air-dried sheet	58·8
Pale crêpe	2·0
Sole crêpe, including cuttings	1·7
Thin remilled crêpe	12·0
Thick remilled blanket crêpe	14·2
Latex	10·7
Skim rubber	0·6
	100·0

The usual procedure for grading a consignment of rubber in a consuming country is based on the selection by experienced dock labour of a typical piece of rubber from each of 10% of the bales in a consignment. These samples may be used to ensure that the rubber has been correctly graded in the East, or for tendering the rubber for sale, or for grading the consignment by experienced assessors appointed by the appropriate Trade Association of Rubber Dealers.

All grading is based on visual inspection, and the reference samples are submitted to very critical and minute scrutiny before arriving at a decision. This method of grading is commercially convenient, and those who do it regularly acquire a considerable amount of skill, so that results are surprisingly reliable. To the consumer, however, visual grading can be very misleading. It provides no information about the vulcanising and other technical properties of rubber, and is even inaccurate in arranging samples in order of cleanliness. The reason for this is that while dirt such as bark is clearly visible when rubber sheet is viewed by transmitted light, sand is much more difficult to see because it has nearly the same refractive index as rubber. Consequently, while the cleanliness of rubber may be judged with a fair degree of accuracy in terms of bark content, the impression received is not closely related to the total dirt, which consists largely of minute particles of sand which are invisible except when examined by transmitted polarised light.

The presence of sand in rubber is not altogether due to carelessness, because it is inevitable that minute particles will be blown and washed into latex while it is exuding from the tapping cut. It is impractical to remove such fine particles by straining, and the most convenient alternative is to allow the diluted latex to stand for some time to give the sand an opportunity of sinking to the bottom of the containing vessel. Even such a simple operation as this leads to difficulties because of the tendency of fresh latex to coagulate on standing and to produce " bubbly " and therefore lower-grade sheet.

The relation between cleanliness and grading of smoked sheet is indicated in the table at top of p. 183.[33]

The dirt in the above samples is the insoluble non-rubber material which failed to pass a 325-mesh sieve. It consisted chiefly of fine sand.

Grade	No. of samples	Dirt content, %				Mean values, %		
		Average	Mini-mum	Maxi-mum	Ash, %	Acetone extract, %	Acid value of acetone extract, mg. KOH/ g. rubber	Nitrogen, %
1	12	0·04	0·02	0·07	0·21	2·51	1·84	0·37
2	10	0·04	0·02	0·05	0·32	2·64	1·94	0·41
3	6	0·09	0·03	0·19	0·43	3·06	2·35	0·41
4	10	0·06	0·03	0·08	0·43	2·37	2·21	0·40
5	10	0·31	0·05	1·39	1·01	1·91	1·08	0·36

The number of samples examined is too few to draw general conclusions regarding trends, but it is obvious that there is a certain amount of overlap between the cleanliness of such widely separated grades as 1 and 5. The low acid value of the acetone extract of grade 5 is characteristic of oxidised material, indicating that cleanliness is not the only technical factor affecting grading.

The following table shows the mean dirt contents of different types and grades of Indonesian rubber: [34]

Type	Grade	No. of samples	Mean dirt content, %
Ribbed smoked sheet	1	107	0·16
	2	68	0·14
	3	303	0·08
	4	251	0·11
	5	240	0·17
Pale crêpe	1	96	0·09
	2	130	0·08
	3	93	0·08
	4	20	0·12
Estate brown thin crêpe	1X	42	0·11
	2X	45	0·15
	3X	14	0·35
Thin brown crêpe	1	80	0·12
	2	91	0·20
	3	65	0·31
Blanket crêpe	B	13	0·24
	C	305	0·31
	D	257	0·40
	E	75	0·44
Flat bark crêpe	—	28	0·58
Remilled smoked sheet	—	9	0·24
Off crêpe	—	32	0·10

In all types and grades there is a considerable spread of results with much overlapping, but as expected, average cleanliness is usually related to grade. Smoked sheet appears to be an exception, but this may be due to the limited source from which samples have been obtained. The cleanest rubber is pale crêpe, followed by smoked sheet. There is surprisingly little difference in the cleanliness of estate and non-estate thin brown crêpe, and both are superior to thick blanket brown crêpe (amber). The dirtiest type of commercial rubber is, of course, flat bark crêpe.

For purposes where colour or purity or both are important, manufacturers use the finest grade of pale crêpe. For instance, it is used in the manufacture of surgical goods, cut thread, thin-walled articles generally and for making some chemical derivatives of rubber which are marketed in the form of transparent films. For purposes where traces of mechanical impurities are not likely to be harmful, and where colour is obtained in association with the addition of substantial quantities of compounding ingredients, the lighter grades of brown crêpe are satisfactory. Typical examples are play balls, extruded mechanical goods and flooring. For purposes where strength and toughness are far more important than colour (e.g. tyre treads) smoked sheet in association with carbon black is first choice. On the whole, there is no conclusive evidence that the lower grades of smoked sheet are inferior to the higher grades, but it is known that small particles of sand can be responsible for some reduction in tensile strength, and can initiate cracking under conditions of repeated flexing. It is also self-evident that less care is exercised in the preparation of the lower grades and that their use involves greater risk of variability due to non-standard methods of preparation.

Little information has been published regarding the comparative behaviour of different types and grades of rubber. An examination of 89 samples taken from rubber sold on the London market showed that differences between grades within types are irregular. The following table is therefore restricted to trends in types, and refers only to the 89 examples examined.[33]

Property	High → → → → → Low
Cleanliness	RSS → estate brown crêpe → (Singapore blanket) → flat bark
Mooney viscosity (ACS compound)	RSS → other types → flat bark
Tensile strength (all compounds)	RSS → (estate brown crêpe) → thin brown crêpe → flat bark (Singapore blanket)
Rate of cure (ACS compounds)	RSS → other types
Modulus (tread compound)	Little difference and no trend
Resistance to flex cracking (tread compound)	RSS → thin brown crêpe → (estate brown crêpe) → flat bark (Singapore blanket)
Resilience (tread compound)	All types except → flat bark

Vulcanising properties

When plantation rubber first appeared on the market in quantity there were many complaints about its unreliable quality, and more than a decade elapsed before manufacturers began to think of it as a satisfactory alternative to fine hard Para. It took some time to establish that the inferior results had nothing to do with the inherent strength and elasticity of the rubber hydrocarbon, but were due to incorrect vulcanisation arising from variability in rate of vulcanisation, which was much greater in plantation rubber than in fine hard Para. Eaton in Malaya and de Vries in Java made detailed studies of the effect of a wide range of preparational procedures on vulcanising properties, and showed that differences in the nature and amount of the natural non-rubber substances in commercial rubber were the main source of the variability experienced. Eaton in particular demonstrated that the non-rubber substances in wet coagulum underwent putrefactive changes which were responsible for a remarkable increase in rate of vulcanisation.

Much of this work was done before the use of organic accelerators had become fully established, and was accordingly based on a study of vulcanising properties in a compound containing rubber and sulphur only. During the last 20 years a pure gum test compound containing mercaptobenzthiazole and zinc oxide has been generally used to measure variability without affecting the main conclusions drawn by Eaton and de Vries. Nevertheless, pure gum compounds containing an alkaline accelerator, such as diphenyl guanidine, in place of mercaptobenzthiazole sometimes reverse the direction of variability, and the scale of variability is markedly affected by such factors as sulphur–accelerator ratio and carbon-black loading.

Numerous surveys have been made of the extent of variability in vulcanising properties of smoked sheet (RSS1) in the ACS1 compound consisting of 100 rubber, 6 zinc oxide, 3·5 sulphur, 0·5 stearic acid, 0·5 mercaptobenzthiazole. The following table is a summary of the results obtained: [35]

Date of survey	Country	Scope of survey	Coefficient of variation in modulus for fixed vulcanising conditions
1939	Malaya	157 estates	23·7
1940	Ceylon	72 ,,	22·5
1944	Malaya	262 ,,	26·6
1949	Malaya	48 ,,	21·2
1951	Ceylon	29 ,,	19·2
1946	Indo China	10 ,,	19·0
1940	U.S.A.	16,981 batches	12·7

The estate results refer to individual sheets, much of which, in common with sheets from smallholdings, is sold loose to packing houses, where they are sorted, graded and mixed with rubber from a range of sources before packing into bales. The most useful guide to consumer variation is provided by the U.S.A. results, which refer to blended bales from a wide range of supplies, and must include a large proportion of packing-house rubber.

It must be emphasised that the results refer to RSS1 only. Lower grades of smoked sheet and the brown crêpes might be expected to display more variation, but have not been studied extensively. Such evidence as exists, however, does not suggest that they are more variable than RSS1. Moreover, the cheaper types and grades of rubber are generally used for the manufacture of articles loaded with fillers, which have a marked effect in reducing the apparent variability as shown in the ACS1 compound.

Some high-grade soft-rubber articles, such as cut thread, are made from almost pure gum compounds, and the control of vulcanising behaviour is an important problem, which is solved by using technically classified rubber (*q.v.*), by blending of supplies or purchases from proved sources. If the article being manufactured is loaded with carbon black, differences in rate of vulcanisation tend to disappear. For example, although there is a significant correlation between variation in modulus of rubbers in a pure gum test compound and in a tyre-tread compound the variation in the latter is usually only a little more than the experimental error of the determination, as long as the rubber is not so abnormal that it is outside the range of technical classification.[32] The problem is, however, a difficult one, because the relation between modulus and other important mechanical properties is somewhat complex. Small differences in vulcanising behaviour can be responsible for serious difficulties when a critical balance is maintained between speed of vulcanisation and tendency to scorch during processing.

Rheological properties

The study of differences in the rheological behaviour of unmasticated rubber commenced with the advent of the parallel-plate plastimeter. Before then it was known that some rubbers appeared to be hard and somewhat difficult to process, and some others appeared to be particularly soft, but in the absence of a method of test it was difficult to establish that the differences were associated with the origin of the rubber or with the treatment received during preparation.

De Vries [36] showed that freshly prepared plantation rubber was somewhat variable in plasticity as measured by the parallel-plate plastimeter and that normal modifications of the method of preparation had only minor effects. He also noted that the plasticity of rubber often changed on keeping, and that hardness tended to increase with the amount of natural non-rubber substances present.   It is now clear, largely due to work by Bloomfield,[37] that whereas variation in vulcanising properties is mainly due to natural non-rubber substances, variation in plasticity is due to differences in the molecular size and structural arrangements of the rubber hydrocarbon.   Moreover, the average molecular weight of rubber from a tree in regular tapping is a specific characteristic of the tree, and varies from tree to tree.   Rubber with a low Mooney viscosity normally has a low intrinsic viscosity in solution, and rubber with a high Mooney viscosity normally has a high intrinsic solution viscosity, but the correlation between solution viscosity and Mooney viscosity is not as good as might be expected, due to the presence of microgel, which increases Mooney viscosity without contributing much to solution viscosity.   Latex in untapped trees or in trees which have been rested for a long period contains a considerable amount of microgel.   The rubber obtained is therefore hard, but its intrinsic solution viscosity is low.   The amount of microgel decreases as tapping continues, and for about 10 subsequent tappings the inherent solution viscosity of the rubber increases, despite the fact that it becomes progressively softer.   Similarly, latex from an upper tapping cut gives a much harder rubber than does latex from a lower tapping cut, although initially the intrinsic solution viscosities of the rubber from the two cuts are not very different.

The range of variation in sheet and crêpe from over 300 estates in Ceylon after the rubber has arrived in the United Kingdom is shown in Fig. 2.18.[38]   Despite the fact that each sample represents the average product

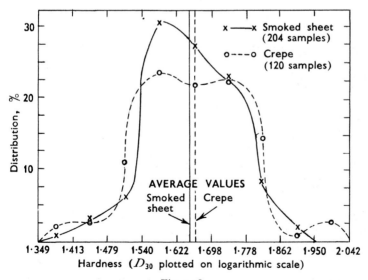

Fig. 2.18.

of bulked latex from thousands of trees, the variation is considerable. On an average smoked sheet is slightly softer than pale crêpe.

Martin and Baker showed that conditions of storage had marked effects on the plasticity of rubber. Thorough drying caused the rubber to become considerably harder, even when stored in the absence of oxygen. Moisture, air and temperatures in excess of $30°$ C favoured softening of the rubber.[39] This work was extended by Wood, who showed that the hardening and softening tendencies of purified rubber are similar to those of commercial smoked sheet and that storage-hardened rubber, when vulcanised in a pure gum compound, yielded a product a little stronger, harder and more resilient than the same rubber before hardening.[40] It is apparent that stored rubber undergoes considerable molecular change, including both cross-linking and chain scission, the ultimate effect being determined by temperature and atmospheric humidity as well as by access to oxygen and content of natural antioxidants.

A rheological property of considerable practical importance is the extent to which rubber compounds recover from deformation after extruding or calendering. Tests on uncompounded rubber masticated under fixed conditions have given no indications of appreciable variation in the shrinkage of different grades of smoked sheet, but some of the cheaper types of rubber, such as Singapore C and D blankets, are much more nervy. It is also of interest that rubber from latex skim (q.v.) produced during centrifuging and consisting mostly of small particles with a high proportion of non-rubber substances shrinks much less than rubber from the concentrate.[47]

Specialty rubbers

Technically classified rubber

This is any normal commercial grade of rubber which has been marked on the outside of the bale with a red, yellow or blue circle to show that it has a rate of vulcanisation which falls within certain limits as determined by approved tests in an approved laboratory. A yellow circle indicates that the rubber vulcanises at a normal rate, a red circle that it vulcanises somewhat slowly and a blue circle that it vulcanises somewhat quickly. Rubber which vulcanises very quickly or very slowly or which displays excessive variation from bale to bale is not classified.

The test compound (ASC1) is vulcanised for 40 minutes at $140°$ C and tested for strain under a load of 5 kg./cm.^{2}. Sampling, mixing, vulcanising and testing conditions are standardised, and regular co-operative check tests are carried out at all the Far Eastern testing stations.

For a consignment of rubber to be marked yellow circle, the average strain value must be between 73 and 85%, and the variability between the bales must be such that it is unlikely that a single bale will have a strain value outside the limits 67 and 91%. The upper and lower strain limits for the red and blue classes are 103 and 55% respectively. The inner limits are the outer limits of the yellow class.[41]

The main purpose of technical classification is to supply consumers with a reliable raw material which can be used without blending and without testing. Such rubber is particularly useful for the manufacture of lightly loaded articles, where variation in vulcanising behaviour is not ironed-out by loading and reinforcing materials such as carbon black. Another important use is in the manufacture of articles where speed of vulcanisation is critically balanced against tendency to scorch, so that even small differences in rate of vulcanisation cause difficulties.

Technical classification was first introduced in 1951, and was then based on both Mooney viscosity and rate of vulcanisation. As there were three grades of plasticity associated with three rates of vulcanisation, the original classification scheme embraced nine classes. Such a large number introduced supply and storage difficulties. Moreover, it was found that the Mooney viscosity of freshly prepared raw rubber changed appreciably during the first few weeks and was an unreliable guide to the plasticity of rubber as received by the consumer. From 1953 onwards classification was therefore confined to rate of vulcanisation. The only other change was made in 1954 when class limits were redefined so as to reduce the possibility of misclassification in borderline consignments.

The production of technically classified rubber amounts to about 50,000 tons per annum. About half comes from Malaya, one-third from Vietnam–Cambodia and a little from Indonesia. Over 90% of the rubber is RSS1 with a little No. 1 pale crêpe, the remainder being lower-grade sheet and some remilled brown crêpe. About 80% of the rubber from Vietnam–Cambodia is in the blue class, over 70% of Malayan classified RSS1 is in the yellow class. World production of the three classes is approximately 60% yellow, 30% blue and 10% red.

Classification of estate sheet rubber is based on a comprehensive study of day-to-day variation in the output of the estate which wishes to have its output classified. If the rubber is sufficiently uniform and within the prescribed limits the estate is permitted to mark its bales with the appropriate coloured circle. Regular testing is maintained and an estate control chart established. Permission to mark is withdrawn if the rubber becomes too variable or the colour changed if it drifts into another class.

The vulcanising characteristics of rubber from a group of trees may change for a number of reasons, some of which cannot be controlled. For example, wintering tends to raise the strain level and varies from year to year and place to place. Treatment of latex with a very small quantity of tetradecyl pyridinium bromide is occasionally used by estates to maintain the production of yellow rubber when output temporarily drifts into the red class.   Similarly, treatment of latex with formaldehyde is sometimes used to produce the opposite effect of prolonging vulcanisation.

Other means of changing the class of an estate's output is by altering the conditions of coagulation, viz. pH or dilution of latex.   Such changes introduce difficulties due to limitations of coagulating-tank capacity and adverse effects on the appearance of the sheet and related market price. Experience in Vietnam–Cambodia suggests that very uniform rubber can be obtained if pH of coagulation is carefully controlled.

The relatively small output of technically classified brown crêpes and lower grades of sheet is not due to technical difficulties, even though the rubber is bought loose from miscellaneous sources by packing houses and remilling factories, who treat it if necessary and then sort and grade it before packing.   It has been established that a simple system of blended packing results in the production of bales which are as uniform and regular from day to day as those produced in good estates.   The extra blending requires increased space and more handling, which leads to a small increase in costs, which is stated to be serious in a business operating on a small profit margin.   Nevertheless, about 5% of the Malayan output of classified rubber is in the lower grades.

Superior processing or S.P. rubber [42]

This is the name given to sheet and crêpe which has been prepared by coagulating a mixture of fresh and vulcanised latex, the latter usually constituting 20% of the mixture.   The appearance of the rubber is identical with that of sheet and crêpe prepared wholly from fresh latex, and in most respects its physical, mechanical and vulcanising properties are only a little different from those of normal rubber.   The outstanding feature of the rubber is a reduced tendency to recover from deformation when the masticated and mixed material is passed through a calender or extruder. For example, under conditions where masticated smoked sheet after calendering normally shrinks about 40% in length, with a corresponding increase in thickness, S.P. smoked sheet shrinks about 20%.   A consequence of this is that calender and extruder outputs are greatly increased, not only because they operate at larger apertures to allow for reduced shrinkage but also because they can be worked at higher speeds without developing surface corrugations due to uneven shrinkage.   In fact, calendered sheet and extruded profiles from S.P. rubber stocks are remarkably smooth.   Other advantages of the rubber are reduced wastage in extruding complicated shapes, better retention of unsupported shapes during vulcanisation, less cloth marking in wrapped vulcanisation and less water marking in open steam vulcanisation.

The vulcanising system used in the preparation of the vulcanised latex is 100 rubber (as ammoniated field latex), 2·0 sulphur, 0·75 zinc oxide, 0·2 zinc diethylidithiocarbamate, 0·4 mercaptobenzthiazole.[43] The vulcanising ingredients are added as a finely ground suspension with a dispersing agent in water, and the latex heated by the injection of live steam so that the temperature reaches 82°–85° C in 1 hour, at which temperature it is held for 2 hours. The vulcanised latex is then blended with diluted field latex, the mixture coagulated, the rubber machined, dried and packed as for normal rubber.

In some compounds superior processing rubber has a slightly increased tendency to " scorch ", and the vulcanisate may be harder by 1°–2° B.S.,

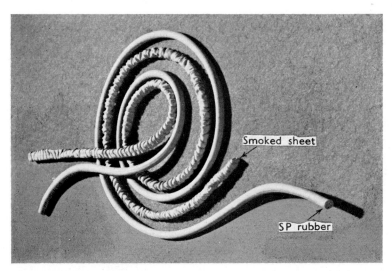

Fig. 2.19. RSSI and SP sheet pure gum compounds extruded under identical conditions.

with about 5% reduction in breaking strength and elongation and perhaps an improvement in resilience. Apart from such small differences, which are within the range of normal manufacturing variations and easily adjusted, the use of superior processing rubber involves no penalty in the way of ultimate service over a long period.

There are two ways of conferring superior processing properties on brown crêpes and lower grades of sheet. They both involve the preparation from a mixture of fresh and vulcanised latex of a masterbatch containing a high proportion of vulcanised particles.[44]

For the preparation of a product which is to be marketed as superior processing brown crêpe, the masterbatch is in the form of undried crumb containing 80% vulcanised particles. An appropriate amount is mixed with the appropriate grade of brown crêpe during remilling operations to give the usual 20% content of vulcanised particles.

The second method of conferring superior processing properties on low-grade rubber is by mixing it during mastication with an appropriate amount of a dry masterbatch containing 80% vulcanised particles. This masterbatch is precipitated and dried in crumb form from a mixture of fresh and vulcanised latex and is then pressed into bales weighing about 100 lb. before shipping to the consumer for mixing with standard grades of dry rubber.

Skim rubber

Skim sheet and crêpe are obtained by the coagulation of the diluted latex fraction obtained as a by-product during the centrifugal concentration of ammoniated field latex (*q.v.*). The composition of the rubber varies with the type of centrifuge, the rate of throughput and estate treatment, but all skim rubber which has not been specially purified contains a much higher proportion of natural non-rubber substances than normal rubber. This is partly due to the fact that skim rubber is mostly derived from small latex particles with a high specific surface carrying associated surface-active materials, and partly because many serum substances, such as proteins, have a higher specific gravity than rubber and migrate to the skim fraction during centrifuging. Whereas normal rubber contains over 90% rubber hydrocarbon with about 2% protein and 3% acetone-soluble material, skim rubber contains 75–85% rubber hydrocarbon, 9–18% protein and 5–10% acetone-soluble material. The high protein content tends to increase the specific gravity of the rubber, so that a quick test for skim rubber is to immerse a portion of the material in a mixture of alcohol and water made up to a specific gravity of 0·928. When thoroughly wet and free from air, skim rubber sinks and normal rubber usually floats.

Because of its dilution and ammonia content, skim latex is somewhat difficult to coagulate to a coherent coagulum. The usual coagulant is sulphuric acid, but calcium chloride, formic acid and spontaneous coagulation are also employed. The coagulum is machined to sheet and crêpe, and the appearance of the dried product is similar to that of smoked sheet or brown crêpe. In some instances the coagulum is soaked in water before and after crêpeing and treated with a fungicide such as formalin to obtain a lighter colour and freedom from mould.

The production of skim rubber is closely linked with that of concentrated latex and is of the order of 10,000 tons per annum. It is marketed as skim sheet or skim crêpe, and must on no account be marketed mixed with standard grades of rubber. The reason for this is partly the relatively low content of rubber hydrocarbon and partly difficulties which could arise in use if the rubber were passed off as a normal grade.

Because of the method of preparation, skim rubber is remarkably clean; it is somewhat easier to process than purer rubber, but its outstanding technological property is speed of vulcanisation in the presence of acidic accelerators with a corresponding tendency to scorch. With alkaline accelerators it vulcanises at a normal rate. The natural non-rubber substances present are also responsible for the production of vulcanisates which are several degrees harder than those from standard rubber. Although skim rubber usually contains less than 8 p.p.m. of naturally occurring copper, it sometimes contains up to 20 p.p.m. without apparently any effect on ageing properties. These are satisfactory.

The most serious disadvantage of skim is the variability of rubber from different sources, mostly due to difference in centrifuging conditions. That from a single source is, however, likely to be uniform. It is claimed that skim rubber is particularly useful in hard compounds, such as flooring and soling, and also for increasing the rate of vulcanisation of SBR.

Two proprietary processes have been developed for the production of skim rubber very similar in composition and vulcanising behaviour to normal grades.[45] In one skim, latex is treated with trypsin for 24 hours so as to decompose excess protein.[46] It is then deammoniated, coagulated, crêped and dried. In the other, clarified skim latex is allowed to coagulate spontaneously and the coagulum pulverised and treated with lime-water and caustic soda solution, followed by washing and drying.[47] Both processes are satisfactory and reasonably cheap to operate, but neither has so far achieved wide acceptance, chiefly because of complex economic factors largely associated with the relative market price of purified and normal skim rubber.

Hevea graft polymers (see also page 140)

One of the outstanding developments of recent years has been the preparation from latex of modified rubbers known as " graft polymers " made by polymerising vinyl monomers in latex under suitable conditions. The successful production of Hevea graft polymers as a commercial proposition is the culmination of much effort by many workers over the past two decades.[48] The so-called Heveaplus family includes both the true graft polymers and mixtures of already polymerised monomer with rubber by mutual coagulation of suitable mixtures of the synthetic and natural latices. Heveaplus M-G and Heveaplus M-M are the respective examples of the Heveaplus family where the modifying polymer is methyl methacrylate.[49] In the preparation of Heveaplus M-G from latex the preferred initiator for the graft polymerisation is a polyamine-activated hydroperoxide. The rubber chains containing a labile and methylenic hydrogen atoms act as transfer agents for the termination of the growing polymethyl methacrylate

H

chains to normal polymer molecules, with the formation of free radical centres on the rubber molecules, from which are formed polymethyl methacrylate side chains attached to the rubber.

To commercial ammoniated centrifuged latex concentrate is added an equal volume of water. Into this is stirred the required amount of monomeric methyl methacrylate (preferably washed free from inhibitor), to which has been added an amount of tertiary-butyl hydroperoxide (or similar hydroperoxide) calculated on the basis of 0·2 parts per 100 parts of rubber in the latex.

When a homogeneous dispersion is obtained, a similar amount of tetraethylene pentamine (conveniently used as a 10% solution) is stirred in. Stirring is then stopped, and the reaction vessel is covered. Provided the vessel is practically full, no additional precautions are necessary to exclude air. Polymerisation is usually substantially complete within 2 hours, during which time there is a gentle rise of temperature of about 5°–10° C. The product is isolated by running the modified latex into at least three times its volume of boiling water containing 0·1% of formic acid.[49]

With low ratios of polymethyl methacrylate to rubber the coagulum is sufficiently rubbery to be sheeted on a washing mill and dried in sheet form. With higher ratios the crumb is separated and washed by hydro-extraction and dried in shallow trays at 100° F. After partial drying the crumb is sufficiently coherent to be sheeted if desired for final drying. The yields of Heveaplus M-G by this process are practically quantitative (95–98%).

Besides Heveaplus M-G there are also available Heveaplus S-G types, where polystyrene is the modifying polymer.

Below 40% of modifying polymer, the M-G or S-G product resembles a fairly hard sheet which is, however, sufficiently softened at about 70° C to be readily processed and vulcanised by conventional natural-rubber techniques to give self-reinforcing vulcanisates. M-G23, for example (where the number indicates the percentage of modifying polymer in the product), when vulcanised with the sole addition of normal amounts of vulcanising ingredients, has properties resembling those of an HAF natural-rubber tread compound in many respects, such as tensile properties and hardness, and having a greatly increased flexing resistance in the de Mattia test. The promise of the self-reinforcing types of Heveaplus, however, has not at present been realised in practice, where flexing resistance, for example, has not proved superior, probably due to the poor thermal conductivity of the material.

Most use of the Heveaplus materials commercially has been made of the types containing the higher ratios of polymer/rubber, e.g. M-G50, which is obtained in the form of a crumb by the method already outlined.

The main features of Heveaplus M-G50 are its excellent physical properties at high hardness level ($>$90° B.S.), good hardness retention at elevated temperatures and good mould flow. In addition to the white and pastel shades that can be obtained, Heveaplus M-G50 can be tinted to give translucent effects. By suitable compounding of the self-reinforcing M-G50 attractive semi-rigid mouldings in a full range of colours can be obtained, possessing the impact resistance of rubber and the rigidity usually associated with ebonites and hard thermoplastic and thermosetting resins.[50] The excellent electrical properties make compounds based on M-G50 particularly suitable for electrical components such as wall plugs. Compounds can be formulated for moulding in conventional rubber multi-cavity moulds and multi-daylight presses, as well as for plastic moulding using tools with automatic ejection.

Heveaplus M-G latices containing between 5 and 10% of polymethyl methacrylate are of particular value in the production of foam latex upholstery, giving an appreciable reduction in density without loss of rigidity and load-bearing capacity.

Cyclised rubber (see page 90)

This is a hard, brittle resin originally prepared from dry rubber by heating it as an intimate mixture with either a strong acid, such as sulphuric, or an amphoteric halide, such as stannic chloride.[51] A rubbery material of the same name is, however, made on plantations from fresh latex.[52] It has an appearance and texture somewhat similar to that of brown crêpe and is essentially normal rubber in which is dispersed an equal proportion of cyclised rubber.

Cyclisation is effected on plantations by treating stabilised latex with strong sulphuric acid for about 2 hours at 100° C. The concentration of sulphuric acid must be at least 70% in the serum, and careful control of the temperature of the exothermic reaction is essential. A suitable stabiliser for the latex is a mildly cationic condensate of ethylene oxide and a primary amine, with a fairly delicate balance between the length of the polyethylene and the amine hydrocarbon chains.[53]

On the completion of the reaction the cyclised rubber latex is mixed with an equal quantity of untreated field latex or skim latex and the mixture coagulated by pouring into boiling water. The coagulum is then washed, crêped and dried in the usual way.

The main use of the brittle resin prepared from dry rubber is as surface coatings and as a rubber-to-metal adhesive; that of the masterbatch prepared in the East is as a raw material in the manufacture of synthetic soling material, when it behaves similarly to high styrene–butadiene resins in conferring hardness, strength and other desirable properties on compounded and vulcanised material.

Arctic rubber (see page 132)

All organic rubbers, both natural and synthetic, become hard and brittle when exposed to low temperatures. Owing to aircraft operations at high altitudes and man's encroachment on polar regions, there is an increasing demand for rubber which remains flexible under conditions of extreme cold. A useful type of " arctic rubber " is obtained by treatment of natural rubber, either in the solid or latex form, with very small quantities of thiol acids (RCOSH).[54] The latex process is the more efficient, and gives a modified rubber with better resistance to cold. Another promising method is the treatment of dry rubber at a temperature of about 140° C with sulphur dioxide or compounds yielding sulphur dioxide.[55] Both thiol acid and sulphur dioxide achieve their effects by a *cis–trans* isomerisation of the *cis*-polyisoprene molecule. A transformation of the double bonds as small as 5% leads to several hundredfold retardation of crystallisation, which is responsible for the " glassy " state of vulcanised rubber exposed for some time to temperatures between 0° and −40° C. In raw rubber, crystallisation occurs at even higher temperatures, and " frozen " rubber is a well-known condition in cool climates.

Peptised rubber

Small quantities of chemically softened rubber have been marketed from time to time, but none has achieved commercial importance.

The first of its kind was a product developed by Ungar and Schidrowitz, who oxidised rubber by heating it in crumb form, first in a vacuum oven and then in the presence of air. Subsequent processes acchieved a similar effect by adding to latex about 0·5% of a peptising agent, such as xylyl mercaptan or di-*o*-benzamidophenyl disulphide, followed by co-agulation, crêpeing and drying in the usual way. The former peptiser softened the rubber to a consistency approaching that produced by mastication (about 40° Mooney), and the rubber had to be packed in a somewhat rigid container because of its tendency to flow in transit. The special packing requirements obviously added to the cost of the rubber. The disulphide peptiser does not become fully effective until the rubber reaches a temperature of 120° C and so does not cause marked softening in transit.

Rubber powder

This is a misnomer, a more suitable name being granular rubber or rubber-crumb, since only the finest product passes through a 10-mesh sieve. Several methods of preparation are operated on a small scale. One consists in spray-drying preserved and concentrated latex in the presence of about 40% infusorial earth. The other methods depend on pulverising wet coagulum in a hammer mill in the presence of large quantities of a dusting powder such as talc. The amount of dusting powder required is greatly reduced by pulverising coagulum from vulcanised latex, and consequently this type of " powder " is usually slightly vulcanised. The powders are somewhat bulky to pack and tend to mass under small pressures.

The main use of this type of rubber is for dissolving in hot bitumen for road surfacing and similar applications. There is a recent tendency, however, to use concentrated latex in place of " rubber powder ", due regard being paid to the need to avoid excessive frothing.

REFERENCES

1. Brown, H. (1918) *Rubber. Its Sources, Cultivation and Preparation* (London: John Murray).
2. Martin, G. (1943) *I.R.I. Trans.*, **19**, 38.
3. Anon. (1955) *Rubb. Res. Inst. Malaya, Planters' Bull.*, **21**, 95; (1956), **23**, 39.
4. Anon. (1959) *ibid.*, **40**, 3.
5. Anon. (1957) *ibid.*, **28**, 2.
6. Anon. (1956) *ibid.*, **22**, 11.
7. Anon. (1956) *ibid.*, **22**, 14; (1958), **34**, 5.
8. Anon. (1954) *ibid.*, **13**, 64.
9. Owen, G., Westgarth, D. R. and Iyer, G. C. (1957) *J. Rubb. Res. Inst. Malaya*, **15**, 29.
10. Haines, W. B. (1949) *Commonwealth Bureau of Soil Science, Tech. Comm.*, **46**, 2117.
11. Anon. (1952) *Rubb. Res. Inst. Malaya, Planters' Bull.*, **3**, 54.
12. Bobiloff, W. (1923) *Anatomy of Hevea brasiliensis*, Zurich.
13. Riches, J. P. and Gooding, E. G. B. (1952) *New Phytologist*, **51**, 1.
14. Gooding, E. G. B. (1952) *ibid.*, **51**, 11, 258.
15. Bloomfield, G. F. (1951) *J. Rubb. Res. Inst. Malaya*, Comm. 273, VI.
16. Anon. (1953) *Rubb. Res. Inst. Malaya, Planters' Bull.*, **9**, 113; (1954), **11**, 32.
17. Anon. (1940) *J. Rubb. Res. Inst. Malaya*, Comm. 247, 26.
18. Baptist, E. D. (1955) *ibid.*, **14**, 355.
19. Chapman, G. W. (1951) *ibid.*, **13**, 167.
20. Chapman, G. W. (1951) *India Rubber World*, **125**, 94.
21. Chapman, G. W. and Chemera Plantations Ltd., B.P. 677,468.
22. Baptist, E. D. C. and de Jonge, P. (1955) *J. Rubb. Res. Inst. Malaya*, **14**, 372.
23. de Jonge, P. (1955) *ibid.*, **14**, 398.
24. Tixier, P. (1951) *ibid.*, **13**, 192.
25. Anon. (1958) *Rubb. Res. Inst. Malaya, Planters' Bull.*, **36**, 70.
26. Anon. (1953) *ibid.*, **6**, 61.
27. Anon. (1956) *Bull. d'information concernant l'Institut des Recherches sur le caoutchouc en IndoChine*, **15**, 17.
28. Anon. (1959) *Rubb. Res. Inst. Malaya, Planters' Bull.*, **37**, 74.
29. Eaton, B. J. and Fullerton, R. G. (1929) *ibid., Quarterly J.*, **1**, 135.
30. Philpott, M. W., B.P. 681,486.
31. Anon. (1956) *Rubb. Res. Inst. Malaya, Planters' Bull.*, **22**, 2.
32. *Type Descriptions and Packing Specifications for Natural Rubber Grades Used in International Trade* (1957), Rubber Manufacturers' Association Inc., N.Y.
33. London Advisory Committee for Rubber Research (Ceylon and Malaya), Private Report.
34. Heinisch, K. F. (1953) *Arch. Rubbercult. Ned.-Ind.*, Extra No. 2, 125.
35. Baker, H. C. (1954) *I.R.I. Trans.*, **30**, 162.

36. de Vries, O. (1929) *Arch. Rubbercult. Ned.-Ind.*, **13**, 283.
37. Bloomfield, G. F. (1951) *J. Rubb. Res. Inst. Malaya*, **13**, 273, Part I.
38. Martin, G. and Baker, H. C. (1932) *Rubber Res. Scheme (Ceylon)*, Bull. 52, 37.
39. (1932) *ibid., Quart. Circular*, **9**, 25.
40. Wood, R. I. (1952) *J. Rubb. Res. Inst. Malaya*, **14**, 20.
41. Anon. (1958) *Rubb. Res. Inst. Malaya, Planters' Bull.*, **35**, 28.
42. B.R.P.R.A. and Philpott, M. W., B.P. 803,013.
43. Anon. (1957) *Rubb. Res. Inst. Malaya, Planters' Bull.*, **32**, 83.
44. Sekhar, B. C. and Drake, G. W. (1958) *J. Rubb. Res. Inst. Malaya*, **15**, 205.
45. Anon. (1957) *Rubb. Res. Inst. Malaya, Planters' Bull.*, **33**, 108.
46. Paton, F. J., Newey, B. J., Barnwell, T. H. and Dunlop Rubber Co. Ltd., B.P. 695,813.
47. Firestone Tyre and Rubber Co., B.P. 739,750.
48. Bloomfield, Merrett, Popham and Swift (1954) *Proc. Third Rubber Tech. Conf.*, 185.
49. Anon., *B.R.P.R.A. Tech. Bull. No. 1.*   Heveaplus M.
50. Anon., R.T.D. Ltd., Broadsheet No. 6.
51. Davies, B. L. and Glazer, J., *Plastics Derived from Natural Rubber: A Plastics Inst. Monograph.*
52. B.R.P.R.A., Blow, C. M., Popham, F. J. W. and Bloomfield, G. F., B.P. 713,481 and B.P. 713,482.
53. Bloomfield, G. F. (1956) *Rubb. Dev.*, **9**, 34.
54. Cunneen, J. I., Fletcher, W. P., Shipley, F. W. and Wood, R. I. (1958) *I.R.I. Trans.*, **34**, 260.
55. Bateman, L. (1958) *B.R.P.R.A. Annual Rep. 27.*

CHAPTER III

PART ONE

SYNTHETIC RUBBER

by

W. J. S. NAUNTON

It should be emphasised that the term " synthetic rubber " does not imply a true synthetic product in the chemical sense of the word. The loose use of the word " synthetic " is justified inasmuch as the important (and in fact essential) property of a rubber is not chemical but physical, namely its ability to stretch to several times its original length *and to snap back after the removal of the stretching force to roughly its original length.* Chemists are beginning to realise that the shape of the molecule is more important than its chemical composition. Linus Pauling, for example, has pointed out that a molecule with the same shape as the camphor molecule would smell like camphor whatever its composition.

Any substance, whether organic or inorganic, which exhibits this type of elasticity is described as a " rubber ", and when produced chemically it is called a " synthetic rubber ". True synthetic rubbers have now been produced and are described in the rubber literature as " synthetic natural rubbers " to distinguish them from the broader group of synthetic products.

History of synthetic rubbers

Early scientific work

In the first half of the nineteenth century it was the ambition of chemists to determine the constitution of interesting natural products. Rubber, with its remarkable properties, offered a fascinating problem for investigation. Faraday, Leibig, Dalton and many other distinguished chemists made their contributions to the problem, but there was one stumbling block, namely that little was known about polymers, and it was therefore difficult for these chemists to correlate the simple empirical formula C_5H_8 with a product which was obviously of high molecular weight. The next step was the use of the commonly employed method of breaking down complex substances by destructive distillation. The chief product of this procedure was a hydrocarbon which was named by Greville Williams isoprene.[1] Since isoprene had the same empirical formula as rubber, Greville Williams put forward the idea that rubber was a polymer of isoprene. It must not be thought that these early chemists had very clear ideas of what constituted a polymer or that the monomer units were united chemically. They were prepared to leave it that there was some " simple relationship " between the parent substance and the product obtained by destructive distillation.

Bouchardat, Tilden, Wallach and others some years later showed that isoprene could be reconverted back into rubber by prolonged storage or catalysis with hydrochloric acid. Tilden proposed the formula $CH_2{:}C(CH_3){\cdot}CH{:}CH_2$ for isoprene and showed that it could also be produced by the destructive distillation of turpentine. So far therefore " synthetic " rubber had only been made from some plant product, but Euler in 1897 made isoprene synthetically, hence the synthesis of rubber (in the chemical sense) had been completed.

In 1900 Kondakov showed that 2 : 3-dimethylbutadiene could be converted into a rubber by standing or by catalysis with alcoholic potash. Thiele converted 1-methylbutadiene (as distinct from isoprene or 2-methylbutadiene) into a rubber, but it was not until 1910 that Lebedev showed that unsubstituted butadiene could give a less leathery rubber than its homologues.

Between 1900 and 1910 Harries of Kiel carried out his classical work on ozonolysis and showed that rubber was a polymer of isoprene units held together in the 1 : 4-position. It was, however, left to Pickles to show that the polymer consisted of long chains rather than rings and, furthermore, that the length of the chain was an important factor.

Industrial synthetic rubber

In the meantime the development of the motor car created such a demand for rubber that the price in 1910 reached over twelve shillings per pound. Work was commenced in England, Germany and the U.S.A. on the commercial production of synthetic rubber. The work in England was undertaken by the London firm of consulting chemists, Strange and Graham, with the help of several distinguished academic chemists, including Perkin and Ramsay.

Methods of obtaining the monomers were evolved from isoamyl alcohol, from butyl alcohol prepared by the Fernbach fermentation process and from alcohol by the aldol process. An interesting account of this work was published by Perkin in the *Journal of the Society of Chemical Industry*, 1912, **31,** 616.

F. E. Matthews of Strange and Graham discovered in 1910 the process of polymerising monomers by means of a metallic sodium catalyst. This became the basis of the technique used in Germany and Russia for synthetic rubber production and for the production in the U.S.A. of the true synthetic rubber. Harries independently discovered the same technique, and it has since been revealed that if the First World War had not intervened there would have been a pooling of interests.

In Germany work on synthetic rubber was centred round Fritz Hoffmann and K. Coutelle, who were working in the laboratories of the Bayer Company at Leverkusen. These chemists worked out methods of producing monomers and polymers on the factory scale, and their work was contemporaneously recorded in patents. The work carried out in the U.S.A. was kept secret, hence authenticated records are not available.

Synthetic rubber in the First World War

It took a war to bring about the first large-scale production of synthetic rubber. All attempts, including those of Synthetic Products Ltd., the firm founded by Strange and Graham, had ended in economic failure. Germany in 1914 was short of rubber, and the economic factor was no longer important. The Bayer Company produced dimethylbutadiene by the pinacone process and converted it into the so-called methyl-rubber discovered by the Russian chemist Kondakov in 1901. By polymerising at 70° C methyl-rubber W (W for *weich* or soft) and at 30° C methyl-rubber H (H for *hardt* or hard) were produced. About 2,400 tons were produced at a cost of about 14*s*. per lb. These rubbers were of poor quality and could not be used to the best advantage, since the reinforcing effect of carbon blacks was unknown in Germany.

The Inter-war period

As soon as natural rubber became freely available in Germany the production of synthetic rubber was abandoned. For some years it was generally accepted that it was most improbable that a synthetic product would ever be evolved which could compete with natural rubber, which used the cheapest form of energy, namely sunlight, in its production.

As soon as it was realised that synthetic rubber in the chemical sense was not required, but a better rubber than natural rubber, work recommenced in the middle 1920s. The most important economic stimulus was the realisation that the growing demand for an oil-resisting rubber would justify a far higher price than that of natural rubber and technically that vast quantities of raw materials were readily available from the petroleum industry. Added to these very sound reasons was the growing desire for national self-sufficiency which resulted, at least in Germany, in government subsidies for the development of synthetic rubber.

In Germany work under Ebert on sodium polymerisation was recommenced, and a continuous-screw process was evolved. At Leverkusen a careful evaluation of the position led to the conclusion that the old emulsion technique which had been tried out in 1910–12 might give results unobtainable by the sodium technique.

The brilliant work of Tschunker and Conrad led to the discovery of Buna S (1933) and Buna N (1934). It was soon clear that the emulsion technique offered great possibilities, since it not only made possible copolymerisation of two or more monomers, but by the use of modifiers (including in certain cases the second monomer itself) led to the building up of straighter chains.

In the U.S.A. the du Pont Company developed Duprene, now called neoprene, from the initial academic work of Nieuwland on vinylacetylenes. The announcement of the discovery in 1931 aroused great interest, since here was a rubber which was quite unconventional, as it was not a hydrocarbon but contained chlorine and showed remarkable oil resistance. It was therefore clear that it could command a far higher price than natural rubber, and it was undoubtedly this fact which influenced the du Pont Company to sanction the spending of millions of dollars in its development.

Simultaneously another group of oil-resisting products with even greater oil-resistance but far inferior elastic properties was developed in the U.S.A. by Patrick and in Switzerland by Baer. They were known in the U.S.A. as Thiokols and in Germany as Perdurens.

In Russia the drive for self-sufficiency had resulted in the development of SKA (made from petroleum by Byzov's process) and SKB (from butadiene by the Lebedev's alcohol technique). Polymerisation was carried out in bulk with metallic sodium as catalyst. These rubbers were hard, but could be employed with low-grade natural rubbers with a high resin-content (such as the rubber obtained from *Kok-sagiz*). Later the Russians made neoprene and Buna S by the German emulsification process.

In 1929 the Standard Oil Company of New Jersey entered into an agreement with the German I.G. to exchange information on " synthetic petrol and petroleum chemicals ". When the I.G. demonstrated that butadiene could be made from natural gas through acetylene it was clear the I.G. would have to give Standard information on synthetic rubber. Standard would have taken up the development of Buna S had General Tire not reported that it was difficult to process. To overcome this difficulty the I.G. developed special heat softening processes for Buna S, but it was not until Buna S III had been developed that Germany became largely independent of natural rubber for tyre production.

Synthetic rubber during the Second World War

Germany stepped up its production of Buna S III by producing 6,000 tons per month from carbide at Schopau, 4,000 tons per month from acetylene from coke-oven gases by the arc technique at Hüls and 2,500 tons per month by the Reppe process at Ludwigshafen. Perbunan and special Bunas together with their latices were produced in smaller quantities at Leverkusen.

In 1940 it was realised in the U.S.A. that a rubber shortage would soon develop, and the American Rubber Reserve Company was formed to undertake the production of a limited amount of synthetic rubber. With the fall of Singapore it was clear that the U.S.A. would have to supply not only its own needs but also those of the Allies. The recipe used was the outcome of the suggestions of all those firms who had special knowledge of the problem. It was called the Mutual Recipe and gave a rubber designated as GR-S, which was more workable than Buna S but slightly inferior in physical properties. Progress was at first slow, and the President of the U.S.A. created a Rubber Survey Committee to expedite matters. On the recommendation of this committee a rubber director was appointed with such powers that in 2 years he had established the new industry and returned it to the Rubber Reserve Company and later to the Office of Rubber Reserve. The rubbers produced were GR-S, GR-M (neoprene), GR-I (Butyl rubber) and GR-A (Buna N), and the total production was of the order of 800,000 tons per annum.

Post-war developments

The U.S.A. output was based on concentration on production of the standard products rather than upon dissipation of effort in the development of new products and processes. The end of the War ended this policy, and intense development work was undertaken.

The Germans had found that a better rubber could be obtained by lowering the temperature of polymerisation, but they did not go far enough in this direction, probably because of the greatly increased reaction time. With the application of reduction–oxidation (Redox) catalysis, a principle which had been known in biochemistry for some years, it was possible to carry out polymerisations at temperatures even below the freezing point of water in reasonable times. Rubbers made by such processes were called " cold rubbers ". These rubbers could be so tough that it was difficult or impossible to process them, but in 1950 the General Tire and Rubber Co. discovered that by blending the latices of such rubbers with emulsions of suitable mineral oils extended rubbers were obtained on coagulation, with properties at least equal to those of 100% rubber of similar viscosity. Such rubbers were called " oil-extended rubbers ".

In the meantime interest was renewed in metal-catalysed polymerisations, largely because it was found that structure could be more influenced by changes in the catalyst than in emulsion polymerisation. In this way the first true synthetic rubber (cis-polyisoprene) was made in 1954 and shown to be chemically identical with natural rubber. Similar rubbers were also prepared by Ziegler catalysts. It is also interesting to record that a synthetic gutta-percha (*trans*-polymer) was also prepared.

Another ionic technique, known as the Alfin process, in which metallic derivatives of an alcohol and an olefin are used as catalysts attracted great attention. The polymerisation is exceedingly rapid, and products of great chain length can be obtained. Since the reaction can be carried out in the presence of mineral oil, direct use can be made of the products in ordinary processing machinery in spite of their high molecular weights.

Work has been carried out with considerable success on condensation polymerisations. Silicone rubbers, for example, have made great progress, and are now generally used in applications in which resistance to high temperatures is essential.

Perhaps the greatest promise but the slowest realisation is shown by the isocyanate condensation rubbers. These rubbers have remarkable physical properties, including an amazing resistance to abrasion. Their structure is capable of greater chemical control than emulsion polymers, but in spite of some outstanding advances, they are not in general use in the rubber industry.

British production of synthetic rubber

The present indications are that in the next few years most countries will have their own synthetic rubber production. Several reasons have led to this state of affairs, notably the large increase in demand for rubber, dissatisfaction with the fluctuating prices of natural rubber, the probability of trouble (already evident in Indonesia) after nationalisation and the growing tendency to use special synthetic rubbers for special products.

A review of the position was published [2] in 1956. Synthetic rubber is already being produced in England.

The production of synthetic rubbers

In spite of the fact that this book is not concerned with the chemical technology of synthetic rubbers, it was thought advisable to include a brief account of production methods for the more important monomers and polymers.

The most important general-purpose rubbers are copolymers of butadiene and styrene. When true synthetic rubber was first made from isoprene it was thought that large-scale production methods for isoprene would have to be evolved, but later work by the Phillips Petroleum Co.[3] showed that similar products could be made from butadiene, which is cheaper and freely available. At present isoprene is not directly manufactured but obtained as a by-product in the production of butadiene.

After purification this isoprene is used in the manufacture of Butyl rubber.

Butadiene can be produced from petroleum, acetylene or alcohol, but since both acetylene and alcohol can be made from petroleum, there is little doubt that petroleum can be regarded as the primary raw material for synthetic rubber.

Monomer production

(1) Butadiene

Butadiene is a gas which boils at $-5°$ C. It can be stored under pressure at about $2\frac{1}{2}$ atmospheres pressure. It is produced:

(a) By the thermal cracking of higher hydrocarbons, such as the gas-oil fraction and naphtha.

(b) By the catalytic dehydrogenation at high temperatures ($1100°$ F) of butane to butene and then to butadiene. This is the main source of butadiene.

(c) By the simultaneous dehydrogenation and dehydration of alcohol with zinc oxide and aluminium oxide as catalysts at $825°$ F.

Fig. 3.1. The butadiene plant of Imperial Chemical Industries Ltd. at Wilton works.

(d) From acetylene by conversion into and dehydration of butylene glycol or by condensation with formaldehyde to form butinediol, which is reduced to butylene-1 : 4-diol, which is converted into butadiene by dehydration. These methods were used in Germany, where there was only a very limited supply of petroleum.

(e) By the chlorination and dehydrochlorination of butene. This method was similar to that evolved by Strange and Graham in London in 1909. It was used by the Shell Company in the U.S.A. in the early days of the Second World War.

Fig. 3.2. A manufacturing area at Du Pont's Louisville works where monovinylacetylene and hydrochloric acid gas are reacted to produce chlorobutadiene (CD). In turn the CD is converted to neoprene by polymerisation.

(2) Styrene

Styrene is a liquid which boils at 146° C. It is stabilised against auto-polymerisation by hydroquinone. It is produced by the cracking of ethylbenzene, which in turn is made by condensing ethylene with benzene in the presence of aluminium chloride.

(3) Acrylonitrile

Acrylonitrile is a water-soluble colourless liquid which boils at 78° C. It is produced by passing acetylene (10 pt.) and hydrogen cyanide (1 pt.) over heated activated carbon or by the use of a Nieuwland catalyst.

(4) Chlorobutadiene

The monomer for the production of neoprene. It is manufactured by interaction of monovinylacetylene and hydrochloric acid. (See Fig. 3.2.)

The production of polymers

(1) Emulsion polymerisation

The vast quantity of synthetic rubber produced during the Second World War was made almost entirely by this process.

Fig. 3.3. The butadiene copolymer plant of Imperial Chemical Industries Ltd.

This technique has two outstanding virtues, namely the fact that the viscosity of the reaction mixture hardly changes throughout the reaction, hence thermal control is simple, and the fact that monomers with different speeds of polymerisation can be effectively copolymerised.

Emulsion polymerisation was carried out in Germany by a continuous cascade (i.e. a " street " of five or six reaction vessels through which the reaction mixture slowly passed) process, and was so slow that catalysts were sought and found. The most effective was the Redox system. The mechanism of this system was thought to be due to the destruction by reduction of oxides formed on double bonds, with resulting loss of activity. This catalytic system was so effective that it was difficult to control the reaction, and the Germans experimented with externally cooled tube reactors. The real use of the Redox system became apparent only at the low temperatures used by the Americans in the production of *cold rubbers*.

Although the Germans had found that branching was reduced by lowering the reaction temperature, it was left to the Americans to complete this line of investigation by carrying out the polymerisation in non-freezing media (e.g. water–methanol) at really low temperatures. The resulting cold rubbers had high molecular weights and low branching.

Success in emulsion polymerisations depends upon the correct choice of the auxiliaries:

(*a*) *The emulsifier.* In the case of mixed monomers the mixture must be thoroughly mixed in a turbo-mixer. It is not generally realised how difficult it is to mix two liquids of different gravities.

The emulsifier determines the size of the particle and can affect the quality of the final product. It also influences the Vistex gel point.[4]

The commonly used emulsifier is potassium disproportionated rosin mixed with a small quantity of sodium alkyl naphthalenesulphonate.

(*b*) *The regulator or modifier.* In the case of copolymers of butadiene and styrene the latter acts to some extent as a regulator. The function of the regulator is to enable the chain to be built-up with as little branching as possible. The improvement in Buna S III (over Buna S) was effected by using Diproxid (di-isopropylxanthogen disulphide) as a regulator.

The present regulator in general use is tertiary dodecylmercaptan.

(*c*) *The initiator or reaction catalyst.* Before the use of the Redox system the common initiator was potassium persulphate.

At present for cold rubber the oxidising component of the Redox system is paramenthene hydroperoxide and the reducing component is ferrous sulphate. The whole system can be further activated by the addition of sodium ethylenediamine tetra-acetate.

Mention should here be made of the so-called *stereospecific* catalysts which are used in the production of largely oriented uniform chains. Such a catalyst may consist of 8 moles of triethyl aluminium to one of titanium chloride.[67]

(*d*) *The sequestering agent.* The agent employed must be one that not only sequesters the iron but also has no adverse effect upon the Redox system. The one in general use is sodium formaldehydesulphoxylate.

(*e*) *The electrolyte.* The electrolyte is added to keep the latex in a mobile condition for easy handling. Sodium phosphate is normally employed.

(*f*) *The short stop.* The stopper or short-stop must be instantly effective, non-toxic, water-soluble, non-discolouring and without effect upon subsequent batches. Hydroquinone used to be used, but has now been replaced by sodium dimethyldithiocarbamate.

(*g*) *The antioxidant.* More is required of the antioxidant than mere protection against oxidative degradation. It must protect against gel-

Fig. 3.4. An operator draws a sample of neoprene latex from a 400-gallon polymerisation kettle. Sample is used for production control tests. A part of the plant's production is shipped from Du Pont's Louisville works in this form; the remainder is processed into dry neoprene.

formation, be non-staining and protect against breakdown of oil-master-batches.

GR-S (*SBR*) *cold and oil-extended.* The early rubbers made without modifiers were tough and cross-linked. They could be processed only after degradation by heat treatment. After the discovery of modifiers more workable rubbers were produced, especially when the degree of conversion was kept low. The Mooney viscosity value of such rubbers was around 50–60.   With the development of cold rubbers polymers could be prepared with such long chains that they exhibited Mooney values up to 120.   Obviously such rubbers were difficult or impossible to process. The General Tire and Rubber Co.[5] found that such polymers could in the

Fig. 3.5. Neoprene looks like a gossamer lace curtain as it rolls off the dryer at Du Pont's Louisville works.   It is about one hundredth of an inch thick and nine feet wide.   The material is pulled through a roping machine which squeezes and shapes it into a solid material about an inch in diameter.

latex stage be mixed with a suitable quantity of an emulsion of suitable mineral oil and the mixture coagulated to give an oil-extended rubber of Mooney value 60 and with properties superior to those of a straight polymer of similar Mooney value.

A cold-rubber of Mooney 100 requires about 35 parts of oil to reduce the Mooney value to about 60.   It will therefore be seen that it is a valuable technique, since it not only extends the rubber without loss of quality but also allows such rubbers to be worked easily on standard rubber machinery.

Perbunan (*Buna N*) is another example of a rubber made by the emulsion technique. Its manufacture has been described in great detail in one of the official intelligence reports.[6] The butadiene and acrylonitrile are thoroughly mixed in a turbo-mixer and emulsified with di-isobutylnaph-thalene sulphonate. The catalyst is potassium persulphate and the regulator (di-isopropylxanthogen disulphide) is added stepwise. The reaction is carried out continuously in a battery of convertors at $33°-35°$ C and 8–9 atmospheres pressure. The reaction is stopped at 75% conversion. Anti-oxidant is added to the latex, which is stripped of unchanged monomer in cascade vacuum towers. The latex is shock coagulated, washed, filtered and dried.

Neoprene is another example of emulsion polymerisation. The purified chloroprene is emulsified with sodium rosinate soap and polymerised at $40°$ C with potassium persulphate as the catalyst and sulphur as the modifier.[7]

(2) Bulk polymerisation with the alkali metals

The method was discovered independently in England by Matthews and in Germany by Harries. It has been extensively used in Germany and Russia. The Russian technique was to use the sodium on a comb. The reaction was carried out at about $50°$ C for 60 hours. The Germans used sodium for Buna 32 and potassium for Buna 60. Later a continuous screw-feed process was evolved.

Interest was renewed in this process of polymerisation when it was found in the U.S.A. that the structure of the rubber could be influenced by the mixture of metals used.[8] The culmination of this work was the production of true synthetic rubber.[9] The difficulty in the way of the large-scale development of true synthetic rubber, which for the first time was a rubber which could completely replace natural rubber, was the limited supply of isoprene. The situation has, however, been ameliorated by the discovery of the Phillips Petroleum Company that similar rubbers can be produced from butadiene.[9] These polymers are not, of course, identical chemically with natural rubber, but they have similar physical properties.

Equally interesting is the claim by the same company that they have made the analogue of gutta-percha, namely *trans*-polybutadiene. It is a high softening resin.

Although metallic sodium is now available in the U.S.A. in large quantities at low prices, it is not particularly easy to handle. It is true that powdered sodium hydride has been shown to be an excellent catalyst for the bulk polymerisation of butadiene, but here again sodium hydride has to be carefully handled.

(3) Other ionic polymerisations

The announcement that the Goodyear Tire and Rubber Co. has succeeded in making *cis*-polyisoprene with the aid of a Ziegler catalyst (aluminium triethyl-titanium trichloride) is regarded as an important step forward. Similar results have been obtained with butadiene with a butyl lithium–titanium chloride catalyst.[10] A similar rubber called SKI has been synthesised in Russia. It was found if the polymerisation was carried too far, then mastication, as with natural rubber, had to be used to make the rubber processable.[66]

Since isoprene was not generally as available as butadiene, it was thought that *cis*-polybutadiene would be developed to compete with natural rubber, but the present view in the U.S.A. is that *cis*-polyisoprene, the true synthetic " natural " rubber, will *eventually* be available at prices below that of the natural product.

Another example of bulk and/or solution polymerisation is the Alfin polymerisations discovered in the late forties by A. A. Morton.[11] The name is derived from the nature of the catalyst, namely a mixture of the salt of a secondary alcohol and that of an olefin together with common salt. The preparation of the catalyst is rather complex: amyl alcohol is reacted with sodium and the resulting amyl sodium is half converted into sodium isoproproxide by treatment with the requisite amount of isopropyl alcohol. Propylene is then passed into the mixture to give the sodium salt of the olefin.

$$CH_3 \cdot CH_2 \cdot CH_2 \cdot CH_2 \cdot CH_2 \cdot Cl + Na \longrightarrow CH_3 \cdot CH_2 \cdot CH_2 \cdot CH_2 \cdot CH_2Na + NaCl$$

$$CH_3 \cdot CH_2 \cdot CH_2 \cdot CH_2 \cdot CH_2 \cdot Na + (CH_3)_2CHOH \longrightarrow (CH_3)_2CH \cdot ONa \ C_5H_{12}$$

$$CH_3 \cdot CH_2 \cdot CH_2 \cdot CH_2 \cdot CH_2 \cdot Na + CH_2 \vdots CH \cdot CH_3 \longrightarrow CH_2 \vdots CH \cdot CH_2 \cdot Na + C_5H_{12}$$

The presence of the sodium chloride is essential. The handling of the catalyst and the polymerisation requires great care, since it must be carried out in an atmosphere of nitrogen under scrupulously dry conditions.

The polymerisation is carried out with hydrocarbon dilution (up to 10 parts) at about 30° C, and with butadiene is complete in about 30 minutes.

The Alfin polymers are of high molecular weight and therefore very tough. They resemble, apart from chain length, the emulsion polymers rather than the alkali metal polymers, that is to say they contain a greater proportion of *trans*-1 : 4-structure and 1 : 2-additions than the new true synthetic rubbers.

Alfin polymerisations can be carried out in the presence of mineral oils to give workable rubbers. This is an advantage over the emulsion technique, although recent claims have been made that masterbatch emulsion polymerisations can be carried out in the presence of a liberal amount of organic peroxide.

Another example of bulk and solution polymerisation is the production of Butyl rubber, in which the ingredients are first of all in solution in a diluent and then separate out in a massive or granular form according to conditions.

Butyl rubber is a good example (another is nylon and terylene) of a large organisation overlooking the final step in a programme of development which should obviously have been made by them. The I.G. had discovered and developed the continuous low-temperature production of polyisobutylene. Furthermore, they were the pioneers of copolymerisation. Nevertheless, it was left to the Standard Oil Development Co. of New Jersey to discover that small proportions of dienes could be copolymerised with the isobutylene to give a vulcanisable rubber.

Butyl is produced by the almost instantaneous copolymerisation at low temperatures (150° F below zero) of a mixture of isobutylene with 4% isoprene. The catalyst is a dilute solution of aluminium chloride in methyl chloride. The reaction mixture is diluted with methyl chloride and cooled with liquid ethylene. The polymer as a slurry is dropped into water to flash off the diluent and unchanged monomers.

Butyl rubber analogues can also be produced from ethylene and propylene with 3% of isoprene by the aid of a Ziegler catalyst consisting of aluminium tri-isobutyl and titanium trichloride in tetralin.[12]

(4) Condensation polymerisations

The three most important condensation rubbers are: (*a*) the silicones; (*b*) the polysulphide rubbers; and (*c*) the ester and isocyanate rubbers.

(*a*) *The silicones.* The silicones are based on the pioneer work of Kipping on organo-silicon compounds, although Kipping did not realise the possibility of their development.

They are produced by the condensation polymerisation of silicols, which are obtained by the hydrolysis of chlorsilanes.

$$(CH_3)_2SiCl_2 + 2H_2O \longrightarrow (CH_3)_2Si(OH)_2 + 2HCl$$
$$n(CH_3)_2Si(OH)_2 \longrightarrow (-O \cdot Si(CH_3)_2 \cdot O \cdot Si(CH_3)_2 \cdot O-)n$$

The most difficult part of the production is the fractional purification of the methylchlorsilanes. The dichlorsilanes must be entirely free from trichlorsilanes, or cross-linking will take place during the polymerisation, with resulting loss of processability. The silicols themselves are so unstable that polymerisation commences during the hydrolysis of the chlorsilanes. In spite of this great activity, various catalysts such as butyl perbenzoate have been claimed in patents.[13]

The molecular weight of the silicone rubbers is of the order of 2,500,000, but very much lower-molecular-weight polymers are still rubbers but softer.

(b) *The polysulphide rubbers.* These rubbers are produced by the condensation polymerisation of an aliphatic dihalide and sodium polysulphide. Among the dihalides which have been used are ethylene dichloride, propylene dichloride, bis-2-chloroethyl, corresponding ethers, di-2-chlorethyl formal and others. Owing to their ease of manufacture, these rubbers have been made throughout the world. They are as rubbers comparatively inferior, for example their resilience is very low, but their unique oil-resistance has resulted in wide use.

(c) *The polyester and isocyanate rubbers.* These rubbers are of great interest on two main grounds, namely their outstanding abrasion and tear resistance, and the possibility of systematic variation in chemical construction.

The polyester (Paraplex) rubbers were produced on the pilot-plant scale in the U.S.A. during the Second World War. They were made by condensing mixtures of dibasic acids with mixed glycols. Molecular weights of 20,000 were reached in the unvulcanised rubbers. Vulcanisation and possibly chain lengthening were effected by heating with organic peroxides for 15 minutes at 20 lb./in.^{2} steam pressure.

The early isocyanate rubbers (J-Gummi and Vulcaprene) were developed in Germany and England. J-Gummi [14] was made by condensing adipic acid with ethylene glycol mixed with a small proportion of a trifunctional alcohol to give " the links " by which the chains could be linked together in the vulcanisation. Finished rubber articles were made by melting the polyester wax and stirring in the appropriate amount of a di-isocyanate diluted with dibutyl phthalate and heating for about 3 hours at 40 lb./in.^{2} steam pressure. Heels, for example, made in this way had excellent resistance to abrasion, but they were liable " to freeze " when the resistance to abrasion almost disappeared.

The Vulcaprene rubbers were similar to but an improvement upon J-Gummi inasmuch as they were far less liable to freeze, and chain lengthening by isocyanates was effected as a separate operation from vulcanisation which was brought about by treatment with nascent formaldehyde (from a formaldehyde-generating vulcanising agent). This did away with casting, since the rubber could be processed in the usual way.

The improvement in freezing had been effected by including some ethanolamine in the condensation to give a more complex mixed polyesteramide. This wax was then converted into the rubber by further lengthening the chain by joining them together with hexamethylene di-isocyanate.[15] The rubber could be vulcanised by further treatment with a di-isocyanate or better still with a formaldehyde-generating complex activated by an accelerator which generated a trace of acid (e.g. dichlor-naphthols).

The Vulkollan rubbers were developed by Otto Bayer and collaborators at Leverkusen during the Second World War.[16] The early work on these rubbers at first appeared to be non-reproducible until it was established that traces of water played a very important part in the process.

The build-up of the rubber molecule takes place (without taking into consideration the final cross-linking or vulcanisation) in three stages:

(1) The production of the polyester wax by condensing adipic acid with a glycol until a molecular weight of about 5,000 is reached.

(2) By linking these polyester chains together with excess of naphtha-lene-1 : 5-di-isocyanate to make sure that the end groups are isocyanate groups.

$$\text{OCN} \bigcirc \text{NH·CO·O·(Polyester)·O·CO·NH} \bigcirc \text{NH·CO·O·(Polyester)}—$$
$$—\text{O·CO·NH} \bigcirc \text{NCO}$$

This reaction is carried out by heating in an internal mixer for 30 minutes at 85° C with 15·5 parts of the isocyanate per 100 parts of polyester.

(3) By further linking together the molecules by means of urea bridges (with evolution of carbon dioxide) formed by the action of the water added at this stage upon the terminal isocyanate groups.

$$—\text{(Polyester)·O·CO·NH} \bigcirc \text{NH·CO·NH} \bigcirc \text{NH·CO·O·(Polyester)}—$$

This reaction is carried out by adding 1 % of water, very slowly, to the batch in the internal mixer which is kept at 85° C. This temperature is maintained for a further 45 minutes. The rubber can then be removed from the internal mixer and sheeted.

Now comes the real difficulty, which renders the use of these rubbers in the rubber factory almost impossible, namely, the fact that stage (3) above is not complete before stage (4), which is the vulcanisation proper, commences and proceeds simultaneously (but fortunately more slowly), with the result that there is a very limited time in which the rubber (or its compounded mix) can be shaped or processed before set-up.

(4) The vulcanisation, or conversion of the long chains into a three-dimensional structure, is brought about by the isocyanate group in one chain reacting with the imino group of a urea group in another chain to give a urethane bridge or, alternatively, some unchanged di-isocyanate may form urethane bridges between different molecules.

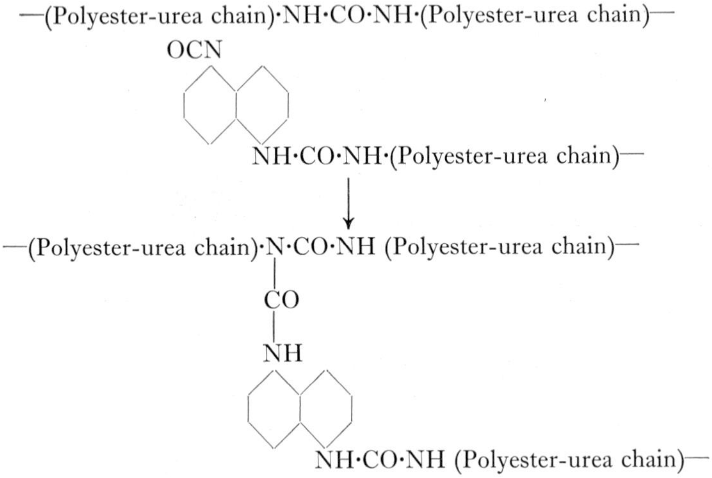

—(Polyester-urea chain)·NH·CO·NH·(Polyester-urea chain)—

OCN

NH·CO·NH·(Polyester-urea chain)—

—(Polyester-urea chain)·N·CO·NH (Polyester-urea chain)—

CO

NH

NH·CO·NH (Polyester-urea chain)—

This reaction, which would proceed slowly at room temperature, is carried out by rapidly moulding the uncured rubber for 10–15 minutes at temperatures around 160° C.

It will be realised from the above description of the process that the rubber factory would have to be a chemical factory or, alternatively, that the chemical factory would also have to be a rubber factory.

The evolution of carbon dioxide gas during the Banbury mixing makes high pressure essential in moulding the rubber, but later Bayer and his collaborators found that the water could be replaced by glycols which do not generate carbon dioxide but cross-link through adjoining urethane groups.[17]

Bayer suggested that the excellent tear resistance was due to the naphthalene " knots " in the chain, but later work by the Goodyear Co. showed that equally good results could be obtained when the naphthyl group was replaced by the phenyl group.

Further work by I.C.I. Ltd., the du Pont Co. and the Goodyear Co. has resulted in improving the stability of the rubber. The Wingfoot Corporation, for example, by careful control of quantities and operating conditions, especially reducing the quantity of isocyanate, has produced a rubber (Chemigum SL) which is more stable and processable. It is cured by adding further isocyanate (5·54 parts per 100 polymer) and moulding for 70 minutes at 149° C.[18]

The du Pont product, known as Adiprene B, differs from the other polymers inasmuch as the bricks (i.e. polymeric segments) from which the final chain is built are aliphatic polyethers rather than polyesters. Adiprene B exhibits high strength, abrasion resistance, solvent and ozone resistance, and has excellent low-temperature characteristics. In spite of its high viscosity (100 Mooney at 212° F), compared with 52 for SBR, it can be worked on ordinary rubber machinery. The molecular weight by intrinsic viscosity measurement is 30,000. It is cured with 6 parts of 3 : 3'-di-isocyanato-4 : 4'-dimethylcarbanilide in 20 minutes at 134° C.[19]

The types and uses of the synthetic rubbers

(1) The butadiene–styrene copolymers

(a) *SBR* (*Buna S, GR-S, etc.*). SBR is a general-purpose synthetic rubber which was intended by the Germans and the Americans to replace natural rubber. This did not prove to be possible, and it was found necessary to employ natural rubber to some extent. The Germans used natural rubber for springs for aircraft, for certain parts of giant tyres, for gas-mask valves and so on. In the U.S.A. giant tyres still contain a proportion of natural rubber (1957). When the Germans replaced Buna S with Buna S III the need for natural rubber decreased but did not disappear.

The demand for rubber for tyres in the U.S.A. has increased to such an extent that it was essential in 1955 to produce 2,261 million lb. of SBR (valued at nearly $700 million).

SBR can be used in admixture with natural rubber. The old Buna S was heat-softened before use, but this is not necessary with SBR. It can be masticated on open mills or in a Banbury or in a Gordon plasticator. Mastication and mixing should not be carried out too hot, or gel-formation will take place, with consequent difficulties in processing.

Since all processing operations are more difficult and slower with SBR, it is advisable to use a peptising agent. The Mooney value of the SBR compound should be adjusted by softeners or peptising agents to values from 50 to 60.

A vast amount of research work has been published on the use of various kinds of carbon black in SBR compounding. It is usual to employ blends of blacks (EPC and HMF) in order to offset good processability against ultimate physical properties. For tyre treads the best resistance to abrasion is obtained with HAF blacks.

The tack of SBR is poor, but when blended with even a small proportion of natural rubber it is sufficiently good for practical purposes. In the absence of natural rubber cements made of natural rubber or synthetic resins must be used.

Sulphur is less soluble in SBR than in natural rubber, hence the sulphur should be finely divided and uniformly incorporated. It is a remarkable fact that although the vulcanisation is slower than with natural rubber, less sulphur is required. The same accelerators and activators used for natural can be used with SBR. Only for applications in which the article will be submitted to exceptionally bad ageing conditions is it necessary to add more antioxidant.

Despite its inferior tensile strength, its poor cut-growth resistance when hot and its inferior resilience, SBR has found many applications in the rubber industry.

SBR vulcanisates are not as resistant to weathering as those of natural rubber, but the effect of wax and other anti-ozonants is more marked than with natural rubber, with the result that properly compounded SBR vulcanisates are actually better than those of natural rubber.

Many special types of SBR (i.e. GR-S) were put on the market during and after the War. Attention should be drawn especially to the types for use in the electrical industry: GR-S 65SP, for example, was purified by acid and water washing of the latex until its ash was only about one-tenth that of the ordinary grade. The resulting water absorption was, of course, correspondingly low. Such rubbers were ideal for the cable industry, with the result that about 75% of the rubber used in the U.S. cable industry was synthetic.

The tread-wear rating of SBR is as good or even a little better (especially on wet roads) than that of natural rubber. The rating of cold rubber is regarded as about 20% better. SBR treads are also better than those of natural rubber for skid resistance on wet but not icy surfaces.

Blends of SBR and natural rubber are used for tyre carcases to give less heat build-up and better building tack. Combinations of SBR and natural have also been found useful in the shoe trade as a means of reducing scorching and blowing.

SBR has proved to be highly successful in the production of black mechanicals. Its processing is easier, and the finished products are generally better.

Flooring and tiling manufacturers when compelled to use SBR during the War found many objections to its use, but now that natural is again available they have retained the use of SBR because of its greater resistance to ageing, discoloration and cleaning polishes. Furthermore, it does not develop the characteristic sour smell after prolonged ageing.

SBR is not identical with natural rubber. Its points of difference may be regarded in some cases as deficiencies, but in others as advantages.

(b) *High-styrene polymers* (*Pliolite, Butakon, Tred, etc.*). Since the styrene acts as a modifier, it is not necessary to use so much modifier in these polymerisations and, furthermore, the reaction rate is also faster.

The high-styrene polymers, which are resins, are available as crumb or free-flowing powder. They are thermoplastic, with a heat distortion point around 50° C.

Although these resins can be vulcanised to give hard products, their chief use is as reinforcing agents in soft rubbers.

The fact that these resins had a more pronounced reinforcing effect in SBR led to the view that they were more effective in synthetic than in natural, but it was soon realised that this was the outcome of the relative gum-stock characteristics of natural and synthetic rubbers.[20]

They can be used in heavily loaded stocks; in fact, they act in such stocks as plasticisers. Mixing is simple, since the powder can be added to the masticated rubber before the addition of the other compounding ingredients. In a Banbury the mixing will be complete in a few minutes.

With roughly half the weight of the rubber of resin and an equal weight of a reinforcing silicate plus the usual curing agents, including 3 parts of sulphur per 100 parts of rubber, a sole compound can be obtained which on curing for about 20 minutes at 60 lb./in.^{2} steam pressure gives all the desirable characteristics of a good soleing and about four times the wear of the best leather.

The latices of the high-styrene resins are used as water paints and finishes for paper, textiles and leather.

(2) Butadiene–acrylonitrile copolymers

The first members of the series were Buna N (25% acrylonitrile) and Buna NN (35% acrylonitrile). These rubbers were so successful that they have been produced and offered under a great variety of trade names (Butaprene, Chemigum, GR-A, Hycar, Paracril, Polysar N, Butakon A et al.). The generic name is nitrile rubber.

Although these rubbers can be worked in conventional rubber machines, in general the operations are slower, since they are less thermoplastic than natural rubber. Thorough mastication on a cool mill is necessary. Comparatively large proportions of softeners are desirable. Since these rubbers are oil-resisting, it is essential to use special softeners, such as the conventional ester plasticisers or higher nitriles. It is, of course, necessary to use reinforcing fillers, such as the carbon blacks, in compounding them.

Because of their lower degree of unsaturation, less sulphur or sulphur-donor is required than with natural rubber.

It has been claimed that vulcanisates cured with peroxides (e.g. 1·25 dicumyl peroxide per 100 of rubber) have better properties.[21] It is even possible to vulcanise these rubbers by heat alone.[22]

The nitrile rubbers can be mixed with other rubbers, thioplasts, P.V.C. or phenolic resins. The blends with P.V.C., including those in which the nitrile rubber is merely acting as a plasticiser for the P.V.C., have many applications.

The nitrile rubbers have outstanding oil resistance. Their heat resistance, especially with low sulphur, is good. It has recently been shown that their good heat resistance is due to the formation of a new powerful antioxidant from a decomposition product of the nitrile rubber with the existing antioxidant.[23]

A liquid nitrile rubber (Hycar 1312) has been made available. It can not only be used in the ordinary way but can also be used as a plasticiser for other nitrile rubbers or in P.V.C. plastisol compounding.

The new nitrile rubbers containing carboxyl groups are obtained either by partial hydrolysis or by including a small proportion of carboxyl-bearing monomers in the polymerisation. They have improved oil-resisting properties. They are also more compatible with synthetic resins.[24] Such rubbers are really examples of a group of rubbers known as " acid " or carboxylic rubbers.

(3) The carboxylic rubbers (" acid " rubbers)

The first example of a carboxylic rubber was the copolymer of butadiene with acrylic acid.[63] Carboxyl groups increase strength and oil resistance at the expense of elasticity. Copolymers based on methacrylic and sorbic acids have been studied. Tensiles as high as 11,000 lb./in.^{2} and 575% elongation have been obtained for such rubbers. They possess in addition good abrasion resistance.[64]

(4) Rubbers from basic monomers (" alkaline " rubbers)

Copolymers of butadiene with vinylpyridine and vinylpyridine derivatives show advantages over straight hydrocarbon copolymers. They possess good tensile strength, tear resistance and resistance to cut growth. They show a certain degree of oil resistance, which can be further improved by quaternising agents, such as active organic halides.

Just as with the " acid " rubbers, it is possible to produce terpolymers of butadiene/acrylonitrile/2-methyl-5-vinylpyridine. Such terpolymers after quaternising are more oil-resisting than the simple copolymers.[65] The latices of these rubbers are excellent agents for bonding rubber to synthetic fibres.

(5) Adduct rubbers

Adduct rubbers are made by the free-radical addition of aliphatic mercaptans to the double bonds of normal diene polymers by the emulsion polymerisation technique.

$$\text{RSH} + -\text{CH}_2-\text{CH}=\text{CH}-\text{CH}_2- \longrightarrow -\text{CH}_2-\overset{\displaystyle \overset{\text{R}}{|}\ \underset{}{\overset{\text{S}}{|}}}{\text{CH}}-\text{CH}_2-\text{CH}_2-$$

Naturally, the degree of unsaturation is reduced and they are defined by the degree of saturation in the individual product. It is remarkable that an 85% saturated product can still be vulcanised by the ordinary methods.

In general, they show better stress–strain properties, ageing, ozone resistance, impermeability and oil resistance.

Another interesting terpolymer of nitrile rubber is that containing a small amount of divinylbenzene (74% butadiene, 26% acrylonitrile and 0·25% divinylbenzene). In this case the improvement is not in oil resistance but in tensile strength and calender shrinkage. It is in fact a " chemically scorched " raw rubber. It is interesting to record that a similar modification of GR-S was available during the War. It was known as GR-S60 and was made by adding 0·5% divinylbenzene to the styrene.[25]

(6) The neoprenes

The neoprenes are among the earliest (1931) synthetic rubbers. They resemble natural rubber to a far greater extent than the other available (1957) synthetic rubbers, for example they give good physical properties in gum stocks, they show excellent tack, and mastication is so easy that it can virtually be omitted.

Although correct compounding for a particular purpose is essential, there are special grades for particular purposes. For example, neoprene AC and CG for quick-setting adhesives, Q for maximum resistance to oils, S for crêpe-soles or for stiffening other grades, and WHV for oil-extension. The general-purpose types are GN, GNA, GRT, W (non-discolouring) and WRT (maximum resistance to crystallisation).

Cure is effected with zinc oxide and magnesium oxide. In general, the magnesia should be the first and the zinc oxide the last ingredient to be added. This is because the magnesia is a mild peptiser and moderator for the more drastic action of the zinc oxide. If further retarding action is required, sodium acetate should be employed.

Special accelerators (with certain exceptions the aldehyde–amine class in the presence of litharge), such as Permalux, should be used with neoprene GN.

The addition of sulphur gives harder vulcanisates with lower elongations at break.

Since the neoprenes have a different curing system, it is often thought that they cannot be used in admixture. This is not the case, and the beneficial effect (e.g. improvement in heat stability, permeability, etc.) of even a small proportion of neoprene in other rubbers is most marked. Ten per cent of neoprene in Butyl rubber, for example, gives marked improvement in heat resistance. In general, when used in admixture with natural rubber no notice need be taken of the presence of the neoprene in fixing the quantities for curing the natural rubber.

When curing neoprenes the most frequent error is undercure, since the vulcanisates rapidly develop characteristics which are normally used in assessing cure in natural rubber. For this reason it is better to determine cure by a service test of some particular property (e.g. oil resistance) for which the final rubber is being designed.

Neoprene vulcanisates show good oil resistance, which in general is slightly inferior to that of the vulcanisates of the nitrile rubbers. On the other hand, they are more resistant to organic chemicals, such as alcohols, ketones, etc., than those of nitrile rubber.

Perhaps the most unique property is flame resistance due to their chlorine content. It is for this reason that neoprene is used for the construction of coal-mine conveyor belts. Fear was often expressed that neoprene might generate phosgene in the case of an underground fire, but it has been shown that no phosgene is produced when neoprene vulcanisates are decomposed at high temperatures.[26]

For detailed information on the compounding and processing of neoprenes the reader is referred to *The Neoprenes*, by Neil L. Catton, published by the du Pont Co. of Wilmington, U.S.A.

(7) The polyisoprenes and polybutadienes (Coral rubber, Ameripol SN, etc.)

The polyisoprene made by special alkali-metal or Ziegler catalysts is identical with pure natural rubber. After the addition of the usual additives it is identical in technological properties with crude natural rubber.

Giant tyres made exclusively from this rubber behave identically with those made from natural rubber.[27] These rubbers are not on the market at present, largely due to cost and the difficulty of obtaining supplies of isoprene.

The discovery by the Phillips Petroleum Co. that similar rubbers would be made from butadiene is important, since butadiene is freely available.[28] *cis*-polybutadiene is easily compounded. Heat build-up and resilience are 10–15% better than those of SBR.

(8) Butyl rubber

Butyl rubbers are available in several degrees of unsaturation. The grades with low unsaturation (1·45% isoprene) are for use in special applications where high ozone resistance is essential. The grades with

Fig. 3.6. Pilot plant production of Coral rubber at the Firestone Tyre and Rubber
Company's pilot plant at Akron, U.S.A.

twice as much unsaturation are the ones generally preferred, since they
vulcanise faster to tighter cures.

A vast amount of development work has been carried out during the last
few years on this rubber. This has been necessitated by the need to
extend the field of utility, since the major outlet for Butyl, namely inner
tubes, has largely disappeared with the development of the tubeless tyre.

Several symposia have been organised in the U.S.A. to discuss the
processing and applications of the rubber. A typical symposium was
organised by the Rhode Island Rubber Club and was reported in the
technical press.[29]

One of the most interesting developments has been the observation that
scorching Butyl rubber leads to higher tensiles and resiliences. The best
results, however, are obtained by heating after the addition of carbon
black. Alternate heating to 300° F for 30 minutes and cold milling of a
GMF furnace-black masterbatch are especially recommended. From a
study of the Mooney values, gel content, extrusion, stress–strain and
hysteresis it has been concluded that the beneficial effects result from the

presence of two continuous phases in the mix—one phase consisting of gelled polymer containing most of the black and the other of sol polymer containing little black.[30]   The best results are claimed to be obtained when a small quantity of " promotor " or curing agent is present in the master-batch.   The addition of a little isocyanate or dinitroso compound is advocated.[31]   Other workers have recommended the addition of N-methyl-N-4-dinitrosoaniline.[32]

The United States Rubber Co. advocate heat treatment in a Banbury at 300°–370° F in the presence of a small quantity of dimethylolphenol until at least 10% of the Butyl is rendered insoluble.[33]   The so-treated rubber can be compounded with large quantities of mineral oil to give good cold resistance and can be used for the production of inner tubes which do not show " cold-buckling ".   In general, scorched Butyl gives finished products of improved quality.

It was thought at one time that Butyl rubber could not be vulcanised in mixtures with more highly unsaturated substances (most rubbers and some softeners) due to the preferential absorption of the sulphur by the more highly unsaturated component, but this difficulty was overcome by treatment of the Butyl (in solution) with a little bromine.[34]   Later it was found that heat-treated Butyl could also be mixed with natural rubber, but it was left to Ford and Zapp to show that the trouble was due to high acceleration which enabled the natural rubber to absorb preferentially the sulphur, and that such mixtures could be successfully vulcanised by reducing the acceleration by using a slower accelerator or a retarder (e.g. lead oxide) in the presence of super-accelerators.[35]

In mixtures of Butyl and natural rubber the correct proportions should be used to get the best results.   Tensile strength and elongation are at a minimum in blends containing 75 parts of Butyl in 100 parts of the mixture. Better results are obtained with either higher or lower proportions of Butyl.   Far harder Butyl vulcanisates than were at one time thought possible have been obtained in admixture with SBR and high sulphur.

Owing to the low unsaturation, longer times of vulcanisation are required, and since it is undesirable in the presence of other rubbers to use super-accelerators, it is usual to shorten the time by using higher vulcanisation temperatures.

Since the solubility of sulphur in cold Butyl is low, there is a tendency to " bloom ".   If therefore it is desired to vulcanise with sulphur and yet get a non-blooming vulcanisate it is advisable to employ at least as part of the supply of sulphur an organic sulphur-donor.

By using other curing systems than sulphur the time of vulcanisation can be reduced.   Cures with quinone dioxime are so fast that unless cures are required for special purposes, such as self-curing cements, it is essential to use a retarder.   Butyl rubber can also be vulcanised with phenol–formaldehyde resins to give vulcanisates which are extremely stable, for example, curing-bags made in this way have five times the life of those cured with sulphur.[36] Cures with dimethylolphenol can be accelerated with an organo-sulphonic acid, such as p-toluenesulphonic acid. For example, a mix containing 50 parts of MPC black, phenol cured and accelerated with an organosulphonic acid can be cured in 30 minutes at 370° F to give a vulcanisate with tensile strength of 2,140 lb./in.^{2} and elongation 440%.[37]

Butyl rubber has been proposed for tyre treads because of its dynamic softness [38] and for mechanicals because of its good weathering and ozone-resisting characteristics. One slight objection to this rubber is its poor extrusion properties in the absence of heavy loading.[39]

It has seriously been suggested that all rubber articles which have to be stored for some time before use should be made of Butyl rubber.

A Butyl latex has recently been made available.

(9) The silicone rubbers

The silicone rubbers are the nearest approach we have on the large scale to true inorganic rubbers.

While they are unique in the range of temperatures over which they retain their rubbery properties, unfortunately they contain organic side

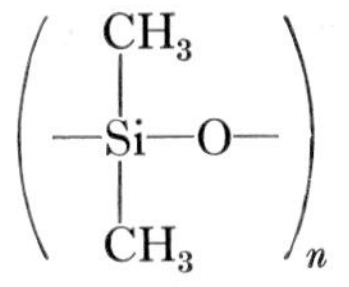

$$\left(\begin{array}{c} CH_3 \\ | \\ -Si-O- \\ | \\ CH_3 \end{array} \right)_n$$

chains which make them vulnerable to really high temperatures. Work, however, is proceeding in the U.S.A. on the possibility of protecting these organic side chains by fluorine substitution.

In the above formula n may be 2,000 or more. Increase in n results in better elastic properties, whereas decrease gives softer and more plastic characteristics. The high-molecular-weight polymers retain their flexibility over a range of $-130°-550°$ F.

The silicone rubbers can be purchased as already mixed stocks or as straight rubbers for compounding.

Silicone stocks are generally divided into five classes:

(*a*) general purpose;
(*b*) improved strength;
(*c*) low compression set;
(*d*) low moisture absorption; and
(*e*) extreme low temperature.

I

Not only the nature of the polymer but also compounding plays a part in attaining special qualities. For general purposes the usual filler is Santocel C, a pure aerogel silica. Improved strength can be obtained by increasing the Santocel C to 40 parts per 100 parts of rubber, and a further improvement is obtained by preheating the mix for 1 hour at 300° F before adding the curing agents.[40] Low-compression set compounds are made with Celite Super Floss with the addition of a small quantity of mercurous oxide as special additive. Some new polymers have enabled low-compression set compounds to be made without the addition of the poisonous mercury oxide.[41] Low water- and oil-absorption compounds are obtained by using high loadings of Celite and giving a long higher-temperature cure. Extreme low-temperature resistance cannot be obtained by compounding with plasticisers but by using a special polymer containing phenyl groups in the side chains.[42]

The best filler for volume resistivity, lowest power factor and dielectric constant in dry applications is Santocel CS, but in moist applications Celite 270.[43]

A good example of a special additive is Fluon (polytetrafluoroethylene), in the form of a fine powder, which if added to the mix to the extent of only 5% gives a remarkable increase in tensile strength, tear resistance and volume stability on oil immersion. The addition of the Fluon must be carried out carefully and slowly, or aggregates will be formed which are almost impossible to disperse. The compound is tough and difficult to handle, but the great improvement in properties more than justifies the extra trouble.[44]

Silicone rubbers are cured with benzoyl peroxide. From 1·5 to 3 parts per 100 parts of polymer are recommended. Since the peroxide is dangerous if not properly handled, it is sometimes purchased in the form of a harmless paste in silicone oil. The powder or paste is milled into the compound after the addition of the fillers.

Vulcanisation is usually carried out in two stages: partly in the mould and partly in an oven with circulating air. For certain purposes (high-tensile strength) the oven heating can be omitted, but for high-temperature applications the second heat is most important, and should be carried out for 24 hours at roughly the same temperature as that of the application for which the finished product is required. Since the decomposition products of the peroxide are discharged into the oven, it is important to ventilate it, or an explosive and poisonous mixture might be formed.

The initial mould cure (say 10–15 minutes at 250° F) is adjusted to give sufficient set-up to enable the moulding to be removed from the mould without damage. For thick articles it is sometimes necessary to cool the mould before removal of the moulding.

At one time the mechanism of vulcanisation was thought to be simple oxidation of the methyl groups with formation of siloxane bridges. The modern theory is cross-linking by the action of free radicals from the catalyst. The formation of these cross-links has been determined by tension and swelling techniques. As might be expected, the degree of cross-linking was found to be independent of the concentration of the silica filler, but a high degree of cross-linking was essential to utilise to the full the polymer-filler attachment. The most interesting observation was that, unlike the sulphur-curing rubbers, ageing at 150° C in air neither increased nor decreased the degree of cross-linking.[45]

Accelerators for the curing of silicone rubbers are not the usual rubber accelerators. Alkyl titanates are good accelerators which enable the vulcanisation to be carried out at temperatures as low as 50° C.[46] Even better is ammonium carbonate, which makes possible curing at room temperatures: for example, a compound of 100 parts silicone, 40 parts silica, and 1 part ammonium carbonate will cure at room temperature in 20 days to give a vulcanisate with tensile strength 280 lb./in.^{2} and 287% elongation at break.[47]

One of the disadvantages of silicone rubbers is the abnormally great shrinkage on vulcanisation (6% compared with about 2% for most rubbers), with the result that moulds used for producing mouldings from other rubbers cannot be used for silicones. It has now been found, however, that methylsiloxane type polymers can be vulcanised with bis-2 : 4-dichlorbenzoyl peroxide at 260°–340° F with minimum shrinkage.[48]

Ordinary silicones are incompatible with sulphur-curing rubbers, but special silicone rubbers have been prepared by the copolymerisation of dimethylsiloxanes with vinylsiloxanes to give rubbers which can be co-vulcanised with natural or other sulphur-curing rubbers.[49] Carbon black can be used in these special rubbers, although carbon blacks are unsuitable for use in compounds which have to withstand high temperatures due to gassing.

Silicone rubbers are so expensive that they can be used only for special applications. Such applications are those involving resistance to high temperatures, such as rings for high-pressure steam mains, or insulation for hot-running electric motors, or O-rings in high-temperature systems, etc. Since the silicone rubbers are odourless, tasteless and non-poisonous, they can be used in the machinery for the manufacture of foodstuffs. Another application is their use in surgery, in which these rubbers have proved to be highly successful.

Special silicone rubbers are under investigation, such as fluorine-protected polymers, polymers from polysulphide-yielding monomers to give rubbers with the low-temperature properties of the silicones and the oil resistance of the polysulphide rubbers and others.[50]

(10) Hypalon

Polyethylene and polybutylene are hard, flexible plastics devoid of rubbery properties except over a range of a few degrees just before the softening points. This hard crystalline structure is due to the close-packing due in turn to the regularity of the chemical structure in the long chains. When this regularity is destroyed by introducing at random other atoms or groups (such as chlorine or chlorsulphonic groups) this results in rubbery properties. The use of chlorine, for example, can result in a rubber which by simple hand-tests cannot be distinguished from pale crêpe (natural rubber), but the exact conditions of introduction and pro-portion of chlorine are extremely delicate. It was later discovered that by using chlorine and sulphur dioxide a more practical and reliable process was obtained. The du Pont Co. found that the best balance of rubbery properties was obtained by introducing 29% chlorine, equivalent to about 1 chlorine atom for every 6 carbon atoms, and 1·25% sulphur in the form of 1 sulphonyl chloride group per 100 carbon atoms.

This new product, called Hypalon 20, can be compounded and vul-canised to give vulcanisates which show remarkable resistance to oxygen, ozone and heat.

Since Hypalon is a saturated polymer, its method of vulcanisation is entirely different from that of the ordinary rubbers. Three ingredients are necessary:

(1) an organic acid such as hydrogenated wood rosin;
(2) a divalent metal oxide such as litharge; (but not zinc oxide); and
(3) an organic accelerator of medium activity such as mercapto-benzthiazyldisulphide.

The oxide reacts with the acid to give nascent water, which in turn hydrolyses the sulphonyl groups to give sulphonic acid groups, which in turn cross-link the molecules by reacting with the excess of metal oxide.

No antioxidant is required in Hypalon if the final product is not to be exposed to heat.

A typical practical mix (for acid-resisting hose) is:

Hypalon 20	100·0 parts
Hydrogenated rosin	2·5 ,,
Litharge	40·0 ,,
Clay	45·0 ,,
Process oil	5·0 ,,
Petrolatum	3·0 ,,
MBTS	2·0 ,,

The cure is 30 minutes at 307° F.

The tensile-strength is 1700, elongation 250% and Shore hardness 75.

Mixing and processing are easy, since Hypalon is much more thermo-plastic than other rubbers. All operations should be done on a well-cooled mill. The order of addition is usually litharge, other ingredients and lastly the accelerator.

One great virtue of Hypalon is its miscibility. It can be blended with other rubbers in all proportions.

The outstanding applications of Hypalon are those involving ozone resistance, resistance to a wide range of chemicals and weathering. An interesting application is for white sidewalls for tyres.

(11) The C 2.3 rubbers

Copolymers of ethylene and propylene in suitable proportions are not crystalline but are rubbers which can be cured with peroxides.

(12) The polysulphide rubbers

The main application of these rubbers is in the production of articles which have to withstand oil. They exhibit excellent resistance to oils and solvents, and have a high impermeability to gases.

The polysulphide rubbers are available as solid or liquid rubbers, latices, putties, powder and in solution.

They have been used for petrol hose, paint-spray hose, oil-tank linings and many other applications involving prolonged exposure to oils.

The powdered products can be flame sprayed and have found application in covering ships' propellers to prevent cavitation corrosion.

(13) The polyester and isocyanate rubbers

No really large-scale development of these rubbers has taken place, although small quantities have been produced and used for the last ten years in Great Britain, Germany and the U.S.A. The remarkable pro-perties of some of these rubbers are so outstanding that the rubbers have been hailed as the great synthetics of the future. For example, it is estimated that a tyre with a tread made of the best of these rubbers would last for 100,000 miles.[5] No carbon black would be needed in such treads. It is, however, unfortunate that the carcase of such a tyre could not be made out of the same rubber because of its high heat build-up. The difficulty in the past has been the attachment of the isocyanate tread to the natural-rubber carcase. The du Pont Co. has, however, evolved a method [52] of making the bond by painting the rubber carcase with a neo-prene cement and then placing a layer of polyalkylene ether glycol di-isocyanate in between the cemented surface of the carcase and the poly-urethane rubber tread and curing the whole structure.

The Rubber and Plastics Division of the American Society of Mechanical Engineers has discussed [53] the possibilities of these rubbers in engineering applications and come to the conclusion that they are eminently suitable.

They are already being used to some extent in Germany for lining pumps and pipelines, in which there is great abrasion, and for gear-wheels and small driving belts.

Another important application which is now rapidly forging ahead is in the production of foams. These foams can be produced and " fitted " into the mould in a few seconds. The advantages include its fire-retarding property, high tear strength, resistance to chemicals and fungi and controllable resilience.[54]

(14) The fluorocarbon rubbers

While the nitrile rubbers and neoprenes have proved to be successful for most oil-resisting articles, the demands of the aeronautical industry have led to the discovery and development of special rubbers, the fluorohydrocarbon rubbers, which at least at present are too expensive for general use but do meet *to some extent* the demands of this industry.[55]

The three methods of synthesising a rubber containing a large proportion of fluorine are:

(1) copolymerisation of butadiene with fluoro-olefins;
(2) polymerisation of partially fluorinated olefins; or
(3) copolymerisation of fluoro-olefins to produce a saturated polymer containing enough hydrogen to provide flexibility and polarity but not enough to destroy the flame resistance.

(1) Examples of rubbers made by the first method are the 70/30 copolymer of butadiene and 1-chlor-2 : 2-difluoroethylene and the corresponding rubber made from 1 : 1-dichlor-2-difluoroethylene.[56]

(2) The best example of a rubber made by the second method is Poly FBA (polyfluorobutyl acrylate) of the Minnesota Mining and Manufacturing Co. Chemically it is 1 : 1-dihydroperfluorobutyl acrylate.[57]

It can be processed in ordinary rubber machinery and cured with polyfunctional amines such as triethylene tetramine, ethylene diamine or trimethylenediamine (1 part per 100 parts of polymer). Fairly high tensiles can be obtained by reinforcing with furnace blacks.

The resistance of this rubber to reagents is remarkable. Vulcanisates give good resistance to lubricants up to 400° F. They resist ozone and even fuming nitric acid.

(3) Good examples of rubbers made by the third method are Kel F 5500 and 3700. These rubbers were developed by the Kellog Co. They are made by reacting trifluorochlorethylene and vinylidene fluoride at temperatures between 20° and 60° C in the presence of halogenated peroxides.[58]

Kel F is available as solid rubber or as a latex. It can be processed in ordinary rubber machinery. Even in gum stocks it gives tensiles of the order of 2,500 lb./in.^{2} and elongations of 600%. It can be reinforced with most reinforcing fillers, including reinforcing carbon blacks, and when reinforced with special silicas it gives tensiles up to 3800 lb./in.^{2}.[59]

Its processing has been fully described in the literature.[60] It can be vulcanised with peroxides, polyamines or isocyanates. For the best resistance to oxidation it should be cured with a peroxide.

Kel F	100	parts
Zinc oxide	5	,,
Hi-Sil C	20	,,
Benzoyl peroxide	1·5	,,

Set-up in press, then cure in oven for 48 hours at 240° F. Tensile strength of the vulcanisate 3,900 lb./in.^{2}.

Open cures (e.g. of extruded articles) must be carried out under a slight pressure to avoid blowing.

Kel F can be dissolved in certain ketones and used for coating fabrics to give proofings which can be dry cleaned with chlorinated solvents.

(15) Plastics of special interest to the rubber industry

Polyvinylchloride (PVC)

PVC is probably the most widely used plastic in the rubber and cable industries. When plasticised it is flexible and tough, but not elastic or resilient in the same way as a true rubber.

It is used for the construction of flame-resisting mine conveyor belts, small electric wires and cables, proofings, tank linings, flooring, tiles, etc.

Fig. 3.7. The olefine plant of Imperial Chemical Industries Ltd. at Wilton works at night.

Polyethylene (polythene)

Polyethylene is a hard, flexible, wax-like substance of great shock resistance. It is neither elastic nor resilient. It is completely non-smelling, non-tasting and non-swelling, hence it is used for tubing (water, beer, etc.) containers (especially where flexibility is required) wrapping-sheet, etc. It has become very popular for domestic ware such as non-breakable washing-up bowls.

It has outstanding electrical properties, hence is widely used for co-axial cables, submarine cables, etc.

Polyethylene made by the I.C.I. high-pressure process is less simple in structure than that made by the Ziegler technique.[61] The simpler structure allows of closer packing, and hence higher rigidity and strength. The Polythene Spectrum below (reproduced by courtesy of I.C.I. Ltd.) shows this variation.

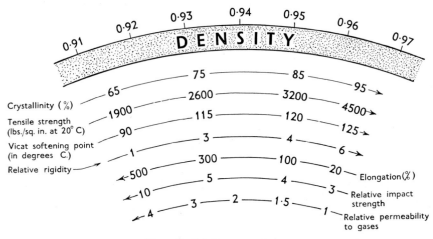

Fig. 3.8. Polythene spectrum.

Polypropylene

Polypropylene is made from the propylene obtained in petroleum refining. It is similar in properties to polyethylene, and only differs in ways which might be expected of a homologue.

Tetrafluoroethylene and trifluorochlorethylene

These polymers, which are hard and tough although flexible in thin sheets, have exceptional resistance to chemicals, solvents and heat. They require temperatures of the order of 500° F for moulding.

Vulcanisation of plastics

The plastics are, of course, thermoplastic, but due to their usually high softening points, they are seldom vulcanised.

Vulcanisation or chemical cross-linking is generally possible, but sometimes is not desirable in spite of the raising of the softening point. For example, an unvulcanised PVC mine belt is more fire resistant than a vulcanised one, since the unvulcanised PVC melts and saturates the textile core of the belt, thus rendering it fireproof. Impregnation during manufacture would greatly impair the flexibility of the belt.

Polymers containing halogens can be vulcanised with polyamines, peroxides, isocyanate or sometimes even with zinc oxide. Those containing carboxyl groups can be cross-linked by heating with a divalent metal oxide. Hydrocarbon saturated polymers can usually be cured by oxidation and oxygen-bridging brought about by irradiation. In the case of polyisobutylene unsaturation can be produced by oxidation, and the resulting product can than be cured with sulphur (1 part of butyl peroxide, 1 part of sulphur and 100 parts of isobutylene).[62]

REFERENCES

1. Williams, Greville (1860) *Proc. roy. Soc.*, **10**, 516.
2. Naunton, W. J. S. (1956) *Rubb. J.*, **131**, 744.
3. Phillips Petroleum Co. (1956) *Rubb. Age, N.Y.*, **79**, 322.
4. Larcher, T. B., Taft, W. K., Duke, J., Mooney, H. R. and Gynge, J. H. (1956) *Rubb. Age, N.Y.*, **59**, 791.
5. General Tire and Rubber Co., B.P. 737,086 (Application in U.S.A. 1950).
6. Naunton, W. J. S. *et al. B.I.O.S. Report No.* 1779, Item 22.
7. Walker, H. W. and Mochel, W. E. (1948) *Proc. Second Rubb. Tech. Conf.* • *London*, 69.
8. Dunbrook, R. F., Johnson, B. L., Binder, J. L., Willis, J. M. and Carr, E. L. (1954) *Proc. Third Rubb. Tech. Conf. London*, 139.
9. Stavely, F. W. (1956) *Ind. Eng. Chem.*, **48**, 778; Allinger, G., Willis, J. M., Smith, W. A. and Allen, J. J. (1956) *Rubb. World*, **134**, 549; Home, S. E., Kiehl, J. P., Chipman, J. J., Holt, V. L., Gibbs, C. F., Willson, E. A., Newton, E. B. and Reinhart, M. A. (1956) *Rubb. Chem. Technol.*, **29**, 687; Phillips Petroleum Co. (1956) *Rubb. Age, N.Y.*, **79**, 322.
10. Aries, R. S. (1956) *Rubb. World*, **134**, 719.
11. Morton, A. A. (1950) *Ind. Eng. Chem.*, **42**, 1488.
12. Aries, R. S. (1956) *Rubb. World*, **134**, 719.
13. Glass Works Corporation, B.P. 643,018.
14. Pinton, H. and Nobel Dynamit A.G. German Patent Application D90,260 of 1943.
15. Harper, D. A. and I.C.I. Ltd., B.P. 572,738.
16. Bayer, O., Müller, E., Petersen, S., Piepenbrink, H. F. and Windenuth, E. (1950) *Angew. Chem.*, **62**, 57.
17. Müller, E., Bayer, O., Petersen, S., Pieperbrink, H. F., Schmidt, E. and Weinbrenner, E. (1952) *Angew. Chem.*, **64**, 523.
18. Wingfoot Corporation, B.P. 694,982.

19. Hill, F. B., Young, C. A., Nelson, J. A. and Arnold, R. G. (1956) *Ind. Eng. Chem.*, **48**, 927.
20. Borders, A. M., Juve, R. D. and Hess, L. D. (1946) *Ind. Eng. Chem.*, **38**, 955; Thies, H. R. and Aiken, W. H. (1947) *Rubb. Age, N.Y.*, **61**, 51. Fox, K. M. (1948) *Ind. Rubb. World*, **117**, 487; Susie, A. G. and Wald, H. J. (1949) *Rubb. Age, N.Y.*, **65**, 537.
21. Lufter, C. H. (1956) *Rubb. World*, **133**, 511.
22. Zacharov, N. D., Sacharova, I. M. and Pavlov, S. A. (1955) *Legkaya Prom.*, **15**, 26.
23. Kuzminski, A. S. and Popova, E. B. (1956) *Rubb. Chem. Technol.*, **29**, 607.
24. Lufter, C. H. and Duke, N. G. (1956) *Rubb. Age, N.Y.*, **79**, 103.
25. Schone, D. L., Green, A. J., Burns, E. R. and Vila, G. R. (1946) *Ind. Eng. Chem.*, **38**, 1246.
26. Skinner, G. S. and McNeal, J. H. (1948) *Ind. Eng. Chem.*, **40**, 2303.
27. Reinhart, M. A. and Willson, E. A. (1955) *Rubb. World*, **133**, 82 and 635; Firestone Tire and Rubber Co. (1955) *Chem. Eng. News*, **33**, 3553 and 3716.
28. Phillips Petroleum Co. (1956) *Rubb. Age, N.Y.*, **79**, 322.
29. Rhode Island Rubber Club (1956) *Rubb. World*, **133**, 527.
30. Edwards, D. C. and Storey, E. B. (1956) *Rubb. Age, N.Y.*, **79**, 815.
31. The Goodyear Tyre and Rubber Co., V.S.P. 2690780 of 1954; Standard Oil Development Co., B.P. 724,792 of 1955.
32. Leeper, H. M., Gable, C. L., D'Amico, J. J. and Tung, C. C. (1956) *Rubb. World*, **135**, 413.
33. United States Rubber Co., B.P. 733,088 of 1955.
34. Morrissey, R. T. (1954) *Rubb. World*, **130**, 662.
35. Ford, F. P. and Zapp, R. L. (1955) *Rubb. World*, **133**, 81.
36. United States Rubber Co. (1954) B.P. 714,907.
37. United States Rubber Co. (1956) B.P. 752,868.
38. Zapp, R. L. (1955) *Rubb. World*, **133**, 59.
39. Thomas, R. M. (1956) *Rubb. World*, **133**, 527.
40. U.S. Government Contract, DA-44-109-QM-64.
41. Konkle, G. (1953) *Tlargi Yearbook*, **12**, 29.
42. Servais, P. C. (1954) *Rubb. Age, N.Y.*, **76**, 99; (1955), **77**, 265.
43. Nobble, M. G. and Lupfer, D. A. (1954) *Rubb. World*, **131**, 71.
44. Irby, G. S. (1955) *Rubb. Age, N.Y.*, **76**, 742; Crandall, W. H. (1955) *Rubb. World*, **132**, 72.
45. Bueche, A. M. (1955) *J. Polymer Sci.*, **15**, 105.
46. Union Chimique Belge, Belgian Pat. 500,963 of 1952.
47. General Electric Co. (1954) B.P. 714,471.
48. White, B. B. (1956) *Rubb. World*, **134**, 563; Deavy, J. J. and White, B. B. (1956) *Rubb. World*, **134**, 719.
49. Hurd, D. T. and Osterhof, R. C. (1954) *Rubb. World*, **130**, 662.
50. Montermoso, J. C. (1954) Proc. Joint Services (U.S.A.) Conference on Elastomer Research and Development, p. 14.
51. Seeger, N. V. (1955) *Rubb. Age, N.Y.*, **77**, 906.
52. du Pont Co., U.S.P. 2,713,884 of 1955.
53. R. and P. Division, A.S.M.E., Cleveland, June 1955.
54. Anon. (1955) *Upholstering*, **22**, 92.
55. Bartholemew, E. W. (1956) *Rubb. Age, N.Y.*, **79**, 84.
56. Gynge, J. M. (1955) *Rubb. World*, **132**, 608.
57. Bovey, F. A., Abere, J. F., Rothmann, G. B. and Sandberg, C. L. (1955) *J. Polymer Sci.*, **15**, 520.
58. Reanick, J. S. and Kellog Co. (1954) U.S.P. 2,684,959.
59. Conroy, M. E., Robb, L. E., Wolf, D. R. and Horn, F. J. (1955) *Rubb. Age, N.Y.*, **75**, 697.
60. Griffis, C. B. and Montermoso, J. C. (1955) *Rubb. Age, N.Y.*, **77**, 559.
61. Ziegler, K., B.P. 217,081 of 1951.

62. United States Rubber Co. (1955) B.P. 725,905.
63. I.G. (1933) French P. 701,102.
64. Brown, H. P. (1957) *Rubb. Chem. Tech. Rev.*, 1347.
65. Haws, J. R. (1957) *Rubb. Chem. Tech. Rev.*, 1387.
66. Anikanova, K. F., Betts, G. E., Zhakova, V. G., Komskaya, N. F., Karmin, B. K., Priss, L. S., Reznikovski, M. M., Chernikina, L. A. and Sketeyn, E. B. (1958) *Rubb. Chem. Technol.*, **31**, 30; Subbotin, S. A., Sanoletova, V. V. and Znamenskaya, A. K. (1958) *Rubb. Chem. Technol.*, **31**, 44.
67. Ziegler, K., Belgian Pat. 533,362 (1955); Adams, H. E., Stearns, R. S., Smith, W. A. and Binder, J. L. (1958) *Rubb. Chem. Technol.*, **31**, 838.

CHAPTER III

PART TWO

SYNTHETIC RUBBER RESEARCH AND THE DESIGN OF SYNTHETIC RUBBERS

by

W. J. S. NAUNTON

THE science of synthetic rubber is a part of the vast field of macromolecular chemistry. Included in this field are such important technological products as fibres, plastics and paint resins. These large molecules represent the building-stones of the animal and vegetable world and the small molecules (e.g. vitamins, rubber accelerators, etc.) are the regulating or processing agents (German: *Betriebstoffe*) for these structural molecules.

Macromolecules have certain characteristics in common, for example, they are fibrous, they swell rather than dissolve, but when dissolved they give viscous solutions. All these properties are the outcome of long-chain molecules. These long-chain molecules when aligned by stretching (" cold drawing ") give fibres, and in the presence of solvents swell by trapping the small solvent molecules in their coils, but if by extreme dilution the long molecules can be separated they give of necessity viscous solutions. In general, only very dilute solutions can be made.

Another characteristic of long-chain molecules is the vast number of possible isomers with only minute changes in chemical configuration. There are in addition five stereo-isomers of the dienes such as polybutadiene.

$I : 4\text{-}cis$ $-CH_2$ CH_2-CH_2 CH_2-CH_2 CH_2-
            $CH=CH$ $CH=CH$ $CH=CH$

$I : 4\text{-}trans$
     $-CH_2$
        $CH=CH$
           CH_2-CH_2
              $CH=CH$
                 CH_2-CH_2
                    $CH=CH$
                       CH_2-

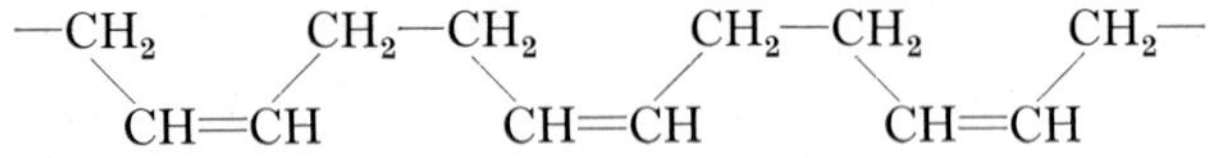

36

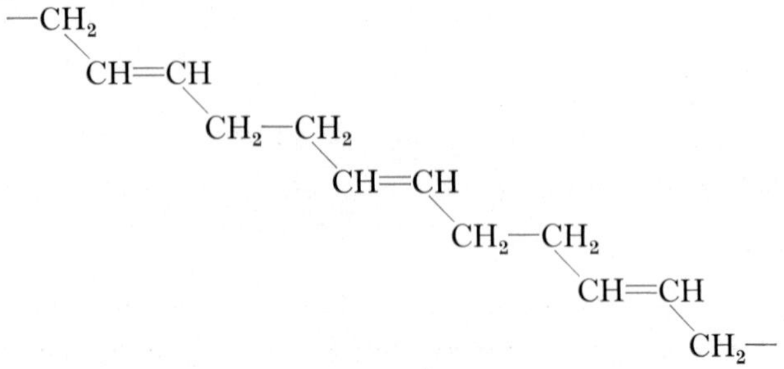

1 : 2-Head–tail

$$-CH_2-CH-CH_2-CH-CH_2-CH-CH_2-CH-$$
$$CHCHCHCH$$
$$CH_2CH_2CH_2CH_2$$

1 : 2-Head–head

$$-CH_2-CH-CH-CH_2-CH_2-CH-CH-CH_2$$
$$CH\ \ CHCH\ \ CH$$
$$CH_2\ CH_2CH_2\ CH_2$$

Mixed (non-crystalline) stereoisomer

$$-CH_2-CH-CH-CH_2-CH-CH_2-CH_2-CH-$$
$$CH\ \ CHCHCH$$
$$CH_2\ CH_2CH_2CH_2$$

It was at one time thought that only nature (the plant) could effect uniform polymerisation, but with the discovery by Ziegler,[24] Natta [25] and others [26] of *stereospecific* catalysts it has been possible to produce in the laboratory the five stereoisomers of such polymers as polybutadiene in a reasonable degree of stereouniformity. This has made possible the study of the influence of isomer structure on physical and indeed practical properties. One such study [27] was made of the effects of the *cis–trans* ratio on the properties of 1 : 4-polybutadiene. The high *cis*-content polymers require less sulphur to vulcanise them, have better resiliences and remain rubbery down to their brittle points (about $-85°$ C). They can also be used in combination with natural rubber.[28]

These so-called *tactic* polymers made with stereospecific catalysts are so important that great interest has been aroused not only in rubber-manufacturing circles but also in the academic world. Uelemann [29] has made a theoretical study of the mechanism of such catalysts. He concludes that such polymerisations are effected not by a free radical but by an intercomplex ion reaction on two metal atoms. A cationic initiation occurs on the cation of the transition element. The activated monomer orients towards and inside a negative complex ion, into which it migrates by adding a propagation starter. In this complex anion all further cationically activated monomers propagate anionically until termination occurs by H^- abstraction.

Conversion of isomers

Kurt Meyer in 1936 attempted to convert natural rubber (*cis*-polyisoprene) into gutta-percha (*trans*-polyisoprene) without success. But recent work [30] has shown that *cis*-polybutadiene can be transformed into *trans*- by ultra-violet irradiation in the presence of suitable sensitisers, such as organic bromides or organic sulphur compounds. Surprisingly, the isomerisation of natural rubber could not be effected by the same technique, but Russian workers [31] have shown, however, that natural rubber can be isomerised by the use of Ziegler catalysts.

Characteristics of long-chain molecules

Long-chain molecules produce materials which can be processed in rubber machinery (e.g. calendered into sheets), but if these long chains are

Fig. 3.9. Experimental emulsion polymerisation plant at Fort Dunlop.

cross-linked (i.e. vulcanised) the two-dimensional structure becomes three-dimensional and the material can no longer be processed.

Muscle fibre is made, for example, of long-chain molecules and is elastic in nature, but hair, on the other hand, can be regarded as " vulcanised ", and while it is flexible it is not rubbery.

The three-dimensional structure can be created either at the time of production of the material or later brought about by some treatment (e.g. sulphur vulcanisation), usually after the material has been shaped (i.e. processed). To make possible the production of the three-dimensional structure it is necessary that the initial monomer unit should have at least four active centres, two to form the long chain by polymerisation and two to act as one end of the final bridge structure. It should, however, be kept in mind that it is sometimes possible to create these bridge-forming active centres after the chain has been formed. For the purpose of this discussion one double bond is regarded as two active centres. There is a complication in the case of monomers containing four active centres (dienes), as distinct from those containing only two (vinyl monomers), namely the possibility of bridging simultaneously with chain growth. Theoretically one double bond is left in each monomer unit in the chain. This double bond should take no part in the polymerisation, but should remain free for later cross-linking. In actual practice, as the emulsion polymerisation proceeds there will be fewer and fewer monomer molecules and more and more lower polymers with which the monomer molecules can react by 1 : 2-addition as well as by 1 : 4-addition to give side chains and even cross-bridges. The point at which the complication of structure becomes of practical importance in rendering the rubber less soluble and more difficult to process is called the gel-point.

This is therefore the point at which the emulsion polymerisation is stopped. It therefore means that the unreacted monomers have to be recovered. It follows that the further the reaction can be pushed, the more economical the process. Intense studies have therefore been made of factors which influence the gel-point. Obviously the most important factor is the regulator, another factor is temperature, but recent work [1] has shown that even the emulsifier affects the gel-point.

The gel-point is not usually determined by actual solubility determinations but by determining the point of maximum intrinsic viscosity.

A very important principle of synthetic-rubber research must be introduced at this point, namely the importance of distinguishing between the state of the rubber in the emulsion (the latex) and the state of the same rubber after isolation (i.e. after the coagulating and drying operations). It is not always realised that the finishing processes may bring about profound changes in the rubber, even to the extent of rendering insoluble a rubber which was soluble in the latex state. For this reason the rubber is dissolved directly out of the latex in a 80/20 benzene–isopropanol mixture for the determination of its viscosity. In order to make it quite clear that this method has been employed, it is called the Vistex Gel Point.

Macromolecules have other characteristics, for example, they can be easily broken into shorter chains either chemically or even mechanically. Another characteristic is that small amounts of impurities during their build-up can have profound effects upon their ultimate properties: for example, as little as 0·002% divinylbenzene in the vinylbenzene can result in an insoluble polystyrene.

With regard to the points of chemical activity in long molecules, these can be either end groups (in which case they can be used for determining the molecular weight) or active centres throughout the long chain.

There is another characteristic of long chains, namely uniformity of structure which plays a great part in their behaviour. When the chains are uniform in structure, such as in polyethylene or nylon, the molecules can pack together, with the result that the material is very strong and

Fig. 3.10. Experimental coagulation plant at Fort Dunlop.

flexible but not elastic. When the uniformity is destroyed by the introduction of random atoms or groups the fibre changes into a rubber. Chlorinated or sulpho-chlorinated polyethylene, for example, is rubbery. The introduction of random methyl groups into nylon changes it into an elastic material, and on removal of these groups it changes back into a fibre.

There is another property originating in this ability " to close-pack ", namely chemical stability. Nylon, for example, becomes unstable to hydrolysis when converted into its rubbery form. The explanation probably lies in the fact that " close-packing " prevents access of the hydrolytic agent to the weak ester linkages.

Orientation as shown by X-rays should not, however, be taken as an indication of this " close-packing stability ", since orientation of aggregates as distinct from molecules will not result in chemical stability.

It is not necessary to modify chemically to bring about the plastic $\rightleftharpoons$ rubber conversion, since temperature plays a great part. A polymer is said to be a rubber when it is elastic at room temperature, but most plastics are rubbery over a small higher-temperature range and natural rubber itself when stretched cooled in liquid air and hit with a hammer breaks into non-elastic fibres (" racked rubber "). Cooling is in fact a reversible physical vulcanisation. Rubbers and fibres can be compared as follows:

Rubbers	*Fibres*
Long linear molecules	Long linear molecules
Unsymmetrical	Symmetrical
Elastic at room temperatures	Can be " cold drawn "
Internal and external Brownian movement	Physical alignment
Strength (natural rubber) 0·25 g./dernier	Strength (nylon) 5·50 g./dernier

Other factors which influence properties are: (1) chain length; (2) intermolecular forces arising from the chemical structure (hydrogen-bonding); and (3) flexible segment length of the chain.

Chain length is clearly seen in building up the Vulkollan rubber molecule: at first the polyester is liquid, then a solid wax, and finally when the chain length has been sufficiently lengthened by isocyanate condensation it becomes a rubber.

An example of hydrogen bonding is the attraction between long polyester–amide chains in which the NH group in one chain attracts the CO group in another chain.

All the physical characteristics of polymers, including tensile strength, elongation at break, flexibility, elasticity, brittleness, melting point, density and permeability to gases are affected one way or the other by these molecular features. Usually the effect can be predicted by commonsense principles, for example, the more orderly a long chain, the higher will be the tensile strength, brittleness, density and softening point, but the lower will be the elongation at break, flexibility, elasticity and permeability to gases. All these changes follow from the fact that the greater the order, the more closely packed will be the structure.

The synthetic rubbers are built up by the polymerisation, or joining together by chemical means, of many monomer molecules. The manner in which the monomer molecules join together is largely a matter of the nature of these molecules. It is true that modifying agents and physical conditions such as temperature have some effect upon build-up, but the possible control is very limited. The possible number of isomers by some slight modification of build-up is literally millions, and it has seriously been suggested that human personality may be the outcome of the millions of isomers possible in the long polypeptide chains which constitute the human body.

One method used in organic chemistry to confirm the structure of a chemical compound is to build it up group by group by known synthetic methods, but this technique would be far too tedious in the case of macromolecules. Resource is therefore had to the second or analytical method, in which the synthetic product is broken down chemically and shown to give the same fragments as the natural product. Confirmation is also obtained by demonstrating that the synthetic product has exactly the same physical properties as the natural product.

The new true synthetic rubbers were not built up step by step, but the most careful chemical, physical and technological examinations showed them to be identical with pure natural rubber (i.e. rubber from which proteins, sorbitol, etc., had been removed).

It follows therefore that methods of determining the structure of synthetic rubbers are most important, since their techniques of production are of little value as a guide to their structure. By systematically modifying these methods it is often possible to produce better rubbers. This would be mere progress by trial and error if it were not possible to determine by chemical and physical means how the structure is being modified by the variations.

The most important methods are given below:

(1) Chemical methods

Chemical methods are used to determine the number of double bonds in the structure, the proportion of 1 : 2- to 1 : 4-linkages and the general structure by breaking down into smaller fragments.

(a) Double bonds are determined by dissolving the rubber in nitrobenzene and reacting with iodine chloride. Only about 90% of the bonds react in a reasonable time, hence it is usual to apply a correction factor.

(b) The 1 : 4- to 1 : 2-ratio is determined by oxidation with perbenzoic acid. The method depends upon the fact that the 1 : 4-structure is more readily attacked than the 1 : 2-. Two separate determinations are therefore made: one after 20 minutes and the second after 24 hours.

$$C_6H_5CO_3H + \underset{|\;\;|}{C\!=\!C} \longrightarrow -\underset{|\;\;\;|}{\overset{\displaystyle O}{\overset{\displaystyle /\backslash}{C\!-\!-\!C}}}- + C_6H_5\!-\!COOH$$

$$\downarrow$$

$$-\underset{|\;\;\;\;|}{\overset{OH\quad OH}{C\!-\!-\!C}}-$$

(c) Structure in general is determined by oxidative breakdown either by ozone (ozonolysis) or by acid permanganate or by perbenzoic acid.

There are several ozonolysis techniques. The simplest method used by Harries [2] and Pummerer [3] was qualitative rather than quantitative. Later methods evolved by Rabjohn [4] in the U.S.A. and Yakubchik [5] in Russia were more quantitative, since volatile products were also examined.

The basic technique is to treat the rubber with ozone, steam distil, oxidise further with permanganate and esterify the acids so obtained with diazomethane. The esters are finally quantitatively separated by fractional distillation.

The method is not very attractive quantitatively, since results by different experimenters do not agree, and in any case not more than half the rubber is accounted for in the end products.

The German workers preferred oxidation of a solution of the rubber in nitrobenzene with an acid solution of permanganate. It was claimed that by this method it is possible to account for about 93% of the original polymer.

Kolthoff [6] recommends oxidation with perbenzoic acid.

(d) Structure can to some extent be determined by simple pyrolysis. This is perhaps the oldest method, since it was used in the 1850s to determine the structure of natural rubber.

By the use of the mass spectrometer for the analysis of the volatile constituents of the decomposition products the method has been made more useful. [7]

(2) Physical methods

(a) *Molecular-weight determinations.* These determinations are difficult, since in a given sample there may be many rubbers of widely different molecular weight and composition. It is known, for example, that in the production of SBR from a charge ratio of 25/75 the styrene content of the copolymer gradually changes from 17 to 26% at 70% conversion. In ionic addition polymerisations, however, the proportion of styrene in the polymer decreases as polymerisation proceeds. Since molecular size and composition affect different molecular-weight determinations in different ways, it is only to be expected that agreement is not reached by the different techniques.

The German workers at Leverkusen [8] took the view that since viscosity would be little influenced by side chains, whereas osmotic pressure depended on total size, the ratio of the two determinations should give a rough indication of the degree of branching in the molecule. They called this ratio the " Branching Number " of the polymer. It was admitted that the values obtained by this method did not often agree with those obtained by chemical methods, but nevertheless the technique proved

useful in directing their work. It should be mentioned that no importance was attached to this technique in the U.S.A., since so many factors
other than branching affected the result. More positive methods of
measuring cross-linking are based on the thickness of molecular layers
and swelling determinations.

The osmotic-pressure determinations were made with the apparatus
described by Schultz [9] and the viscosity measurements by the Ubbelohde
apparatus.[10] The rubber was dissolved directly from the latex, two
determinations were made at low concentrations and the values plotted
back to zero concentration. This value was used in the Fikentscher
equation to calculate the viscosity (or K value):

$$\log V = \left(\frac{75K^2}{1 + 1\cdot 5KC} + K \right)C$$

Where V is the relative viscosity, C the concentration in grams per 100 c.c.
and K is the intrinsic viscosity. Great importance was attached to the
K value by the German workers. At a time when they were investigating
literally hundreds of new rubbers in the laboratory it was obviously impossible to evaluate them fully by physical testing, and resource was had
to sorting by K values. A useful polymer would have a high K value
similar to that of natural rubber, but would have to be broken down to
make processability possible or, alternatively, a lower K value at the
beginning of the polymerisation to give a rubber with inherently better
processability.

Molecular-weight distribution is important, since as stated above
processability depends upon it. Yanco [11] has shown that fractions with
molecular weights below about 23,600 do not vulcanise under normal
factory vulcanising conditions but act as plasticisers or lubricants between
the larger molecules. " Cold rubbers " which consist of large molecules
(Mooney 80–120) are difficult to process unless mixed with lubricants at
the latex stage (oil-extended rubbers). Such " cold rubbers ", however,
could be made processable by arranging the polymerisation conditions to
give a proportion of low-molecular rubber, but in this way cheap mineral
oil would be replaced by expensive rubber. It has been contended that
the best results are obtained by combining the two methods.

Molecular-weight distribution is usually determined by taking samples
as the polymerisation proceeds or by the fractionation of the final polymer.
The latter procedure is usually carried out by extraction with a range of
solvents, for example, (a) acetone dioxane, (b) acetone, (c) acetone–
methanol and (d) methanol.

It is well known that a given polymerisation technique gives a more
easily workable rubber when produced in the laboratory than when made
in the factory. This led to the view that there was a " scale factor " in

emulsion polymerisations, but in fact it was due to a wider molecular-weight distribution under laboratory conditions.

Another method of determining molecular weights is based on light-scattering.[12] This involves determining turbidity and refractive indices at different concentrations. One difficulty in this method is ensuring freedom from foreign particles in the solutions.

Other methods are based on the use of the ultracentrifuge and the electro microscope.

(b) *Structure by infra-red absorption.* This method is the most useful of all the physical methods. It has been shown, for example,[13] that in SBR there are characteristic bands in the infra-red spectrum which allow measuring the proportion of 1 : 2-addition, *trans*-1 : 4-addition, *cis*-1 : 4-addition and styrene.

This method is, of course, also useful for identifying and even estimating the constituents in mixtures of rubbers.

(c) *Structure by ultra-violet absorption.* In general, this method is not as useful, although a method [14] has been evolved for estimating the content of styrene in SBR. One difficulty is the absorption in the ultra-violet of the processing agents used in the manufacture of the rubber.

(d) *Structure by X-ray diffraction.* Again this method is not as useful as infra-red absorption. In any case, it is only applicable to those poly-mers which can be induced to crystalline. In such cases it is useful for distinguishing between *cis*- and *trans*-structures.

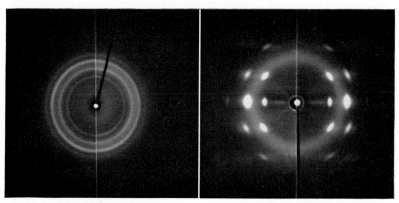

Fig. 3.11. X-ray diffraction picture of natural rubber and Coral rubber.

Fig. 3.12. X-ray diffraction picture of stretched natural rubber and Coral rubber.

X-ray-diffraction pictures of unstretched natural rubber and Coral rubber (Fig. 3.11) and of the corresponding stretched rubbers (Fig. 3.12) prove the structural identity of these rubbers.

(e) *Structure by light refractivity.* The refractive index of SBR has been used [15] in the U.S.A. factories for the routine control of styrene content. This determination was carried out with the solid rubber with the Abbé refractometer.

A method using a solution has been evolved by the Bell Telephone Laboratories, but this involved the use of the expensive Zeiss interferometric refractometer.

There are two physical properties which are important not so much from the point of view of determining structure as from the effect they have on the technological usefulness of the rubbers; they are: (i) crystallisation, and (ii) glass (or second-order) transition.

(i) *Crystallisation.* Certain rubbers crystallise under conditions such as stretching. The crystallised rubber is stronger than the non-crystallised, since crystallisation functions in the same way as reinforcement. The outcome of this is that crystallisable rubbers give good gum stocks, whereas the non-crystallisable ones do not, and strength has to be developed by the use of reinforcing agents (e.g. carbon blacks).

Natural rubber, neoprene, Butyl rubber, silicone rubbers, certain polysulphide rubbers, polyisoprene, polybutadiene and polyisobutylene are crystallisable polymers.

In copolymers of butadiene and styrene the styrene content plays a great part as well as the polymerisation temperature in determining the crystallisation behaviour. L. A. Wood [16] found that: (*a*) crystallisation is not found if the polymerisation temperature is over $60°$ C; (*b*) for polymerisation temperatures around $50°$ C a small amount of bound styrene inhibits crystallisation; (*c*) for polymerisation temperatures around $5°$ C the limit of bound styrene is 18% and (*d*) at $-40°$ C the limit is 30%.

As neoprene is predominantly *trans*-1 : 4- it crystallises with ease. A systematic study [17] of the effects of temperature (polymerisation) and other factors on the crystallisation of neoprene has been published. Dilatometric measurements were used on neoprenes polymerised over the range $40°$ to $-40°$ C. It was found that the melting point was influenced by temperature of crystallisation. The polymers were produced in a water–glycerol–methanol dispersion, with potassium ferrocyanide as promotor. The melting point of the $40°$ C polymer was $64°$ C. That of the $-10°$ C polymer was $55·2°$ C, which was depressed to $45·5°$ C by copolymerising with 6% methacrylonitrile. The melting point of the normal $40°$ C polymer is $40°$ C. The fall in melting point with rise in polymerisation temperature is due to the slight increase in *cis*-polymer.

Dilatometric and calorimetric measurements are more reliable than X-ray diffraction for the study of crystallisation phenomena.

(ii) *Glass (second-order) transition.* Rubbers can be regarded as liquids (or as described by Kurt Meyer as " two-dimensional liquids "), but on freezing they change to solids (non-rubbery). The temperature (or more usually the various range of temperatures) at which this change takes place is called the glass transition.   It is connected to some extent with the structure of the rubber, for example, the introduction of methyl groups or halogens raises the transition temperature but the interest in this change centres more round its bearing on the practical behaviour of the rubber on cooling than upon its contribution to determining structure.   It is in fact the temperature at which the internal molecular movements cease and the polymer is no longer a rubber.   This change takes place long after the

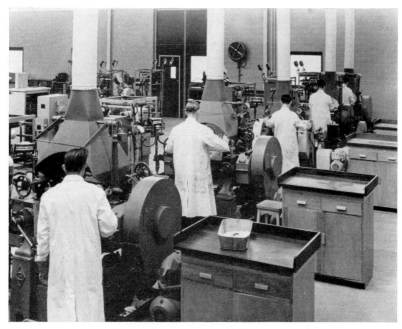

Fig. 3.13. Experimental laboratories of Imperial Chemical Industries Ltd. at Welwyn Garden City.   A battery of twin roll mixing mills in the compounding shop.   These machines are used for the preparation and pre-heating of compounds of standard or special formulae.   The compounds are then tested on calenders, extruders or injection moulding machines in other shops in the semi-technical laboratories.

rubber has ceased to function as a rubber in the practical sense of the word, hence it is not satisfactory as a measure of the resistance to freezing, although of course there is some connection.

The practical measure of freezing is called the brittle point, and is the temperature at which the rubber under some arbitrary test (bending moment, shattering under a sharp impact, etc.) undergoes the change looked for in the test.   It is not an intrinsic characteristic, since it depends on several conditions, such as rate of cooling, time cooled, etc.   Like other melting points, the transition temperature and brittle point are lowered by impurities as, for example, by plasticisers.

Rubbers which withstand low temperatures can therefore be made in two ways: either by altering the structure of the rubber (90/10 copolymer of butadiene and styrene) or/and by the use of suitable plasticisers.

Technological testing of new synthetic rubbers

In addition to the chemical and physical testing of new polymers it is essential to evaluate them technologically in an experimental rubber laboratory equipped with the plant used in a rubber factory.

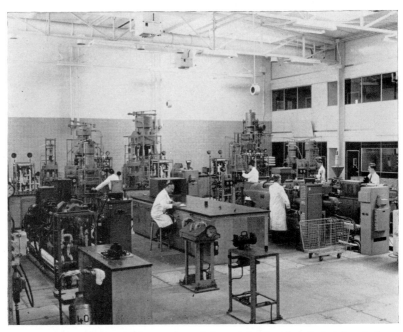

Fig. 3.14. Experimental laboratories of Imperial Chemical Industries Ltd. at Welwyn Garden City. A general view of the moulding shop showing some of the compression presses and injection moulding machines. This shop, which is one of the seven semi-technical laboratories, is equipped with 12 compression presses ranging from 10 tons to 250 tons (including a 100 ton side ram press) and with injection moulding machines of rated capacity from 2 oz. to 32 oz. The 32 oz. machine is a pre-plasticiser unit. Materials can thus be evaluated on equipment typical of that used in commercial moulding shops.

The design of oil-resisting synthetic rubbers

These rubbers were the subjects of more continuous investigation than the general-purpose rubbers, since even when the price of natural rubber was low, there was still a demand for such rubbers at a premium. Readers are referred to the work on neoprene by Carothers and Bridgwater [18] and on the polysulphide rubbers by Patrick [19] as examples of such investigations.

Since rubbers can be regarded as liquids, it follows that there is no distinction between a solution of the rubber and the rubber itself. They are both liquids, and it is conventional to speak of the viscosity rather than the plasticity of a liquid. If we measure the viscosities of solutions of a rubber as we gradually increase the concentration we shall find no break in the continuity up to that of the solid rubber. At first we have a few molecules which are so separated that they have no attraction, but as the concentration increases the interaction between the molecules will increase until we pass through the state in which the rubber can be regarded as swollen and finally solvent-free rubber. The graph of the viscosity–concentration gives no indication of the point at which inter-molecular forces come into play.

What happens when a rubber swells in oil? The small oil molecules diffuse into the spaces between the entwined long rubber chains and force the structure open, with the result that the rubber swells in size.

The oil molecules have to overcome the forces between the rubber molecules. The stronger these forces, the more difficult will it be for the oil molecules to enter the structure, or, in other words, the more oil-resisting will be the rubber.

The concept of rubber cohesive energy density

When a liquid evaporates it requires force to separate the molecules from the liquid, since they are held together by inter-molecular cohesive forces. This cohesive energy is measured in units called cohesive energy densities (C.E.D.) by the energies required to evaporate unit volume at constant pressure at room temperature. It follows that liquids with the same C.E.D. will be miscible, since further energy will not be required to insert one set of molecules between the other set.

Since rubbers are liquids, it follows that they will also have C.E.D.'s, and if a rubber with a certain C.E.D. is brought into contact with an oil or a rubber with the same C.E.D. they will be miscible.

Now obviously it is not possible to measure the latent heat of evaporation of rubbers, but fortunately it is possible to determine C.E.D. by other methods, for example, by finding a liquid of known C.E.D. in which the particular rubber shows maximum swelling.

It can also be calculated from expansivity and compressibility.[20] Since the C.E.D. of a rubber is a true characteristic of that rubber, it follows that it is independent of compounding.

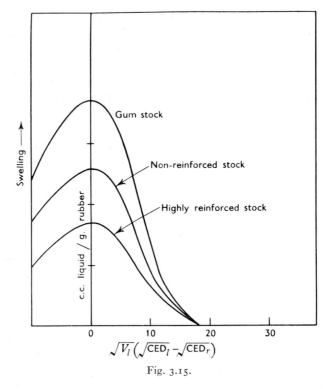

$$\sqrt{V_l}\left(\sqrt{CED_l} - \sqrt{CED_r}\right)$$

Fig. 3.15.

The actual swelling (calculated as c.c. liquid per gram of rubber in the compound) will be less with reinforcing fillers, which hold together the rubber structure very much in the same way as vulcanisation, but the maximum swelling for a given compound will always occur at the same interaction constant.

C.E.D. *of some rubbers*

Butadiene 95/styrene 5 copolymer	56
Natural rubber	64
SBR	65
Neoprene GN	86
Nitrile rubber	88
Polyfluorobutadiene	95

In the swelling curve the swelling is more accurately proportional to the expression which includes V_l the molecular volume of the liquid than to the simple C.E.D.

The swelling was measured as the c.c. of liquid taken up by 1 g. of rubber in 3 days. The rubber samples were lightly vulcanised, since it prevented disintegration and had little or no effect upon the results.[21]

The question now arises: How can this knowledge be used in designing oil-resisting rubbers?

Obviously if we can synthesise rubbers with a range of C.E.D.'s we can synthesise rubbers to resist oils or solvents. What are the factors which determine the C.E.D. of a rubber? Two factors at least are known, namely, polarity and " packability ". The most important is polarity. We should expect this, since a polar molecule will resist being opened by the attraction between the electropositive and electronegative portions of its structure.

Since the C.E.D.'s of oils are low the higher the C.E.D. of the rubber, the better is its oil resistance. The solvent resistance of the 95/5 butadiene–styrene copolymer is even less than that of natural rubber, hence it is used for the construction of bullet-proof petrol tanks.

The design of poly FBA

Let us take as an example the work carried out by the Minnesota Mining and Manufacturing Co. (with the support of the Wright Air Development Centre of Air Material Command of the U.S. Army) on the development of the above oil-resisting rubber. The monomer is a highly polar molecule with the right amount of hydrogen left to give polarity. It contains 133 parts of fluorine per 254 parts of monomer, hence it is not only polar but also highly flame resisting.

The 1 : 1-dihydroperfluorobutyl acrylate

$$CF_3 \cdot CF_2 \cdot CF_2 \cdot CH_2 \cdot O \cdot CO \cdot CH {=\!\!=} CH_2$$

is produced from perfluorobutyric acid, which in turn is made from butyric acid by fluorination in the Simons 3M electrochemical cell.

In order to select the best homologue the other members of the series were prepared. Up to the hexyl they are rubbers, but on reaching the octyl the polymer was either slightly rubbery or solid. On general grounds the butyl was selected.

The polydihydroperfluorobutyl acrylate had, however, poor low-temperature properties; in fact, it was rather sluggish even at room temperature. It had, however, excellent resistance to oils even up to 400° F.

There were several ways in which the brittle point could be lowered by chemical modification, for example, by making the main chain more heterogeneous by forming a copolymer with butadiene, or styrene or methyl methacrylate, or by making the side chains more flexible by introducing new groups.

The making of copolymers was not acceptable, because although it brought down the brittle point it also greatly reduced the oil resistance. The second method was finally employed by introducing an ether linkage into the side chain.

$$CF_3 \cdot O \cdot CF_2 \cdot CF_2 \cdot CH_2 \cdot O \cdot CO \cdot CH {=\!\!=} CH_2$$

The oxygen atom may be acting as a " swivel ", although the discoverers were not convinced of this simple explanation. Anyway, by this modification the brittle point was lowered 25° C.[22] Complete studies of the rubbers by light scattering and viscosity determinations and molecular weights of the order of 40 millions were determined. The freely jointed segment length has been calculated to be 15 carbon atoms, which is larger than that reported for any other rubber.[23]

REFERENCES

1. Larcher, T. B., Taft, W. K., Duke, J., Mooney, H. R. and Gynge, J. M. (1956) *Rubb. Age, N.Y.*, **79**, 971.
2. Harries, C. D. (1919) *Untersuchungen über die näturlichen und künstlichen Kautschukarten* (Berlin: Springer).
3. Pummerer, R. (1934) *Kautschuk*, **10**, 149.
4. Rabjohn, N. *et al.* (1947) *J. Amer. chem. Soc.*, **69**, 314.
5. Rakubchik, A. I., Vasiliev, A. A. and Zhabina, V. M. (1945) *Rubb. Chem. Technol.*, **18**, 780.
6. Kolthoff, I., Lee, T. S. and Mairs, M. A. (1947) *J. Polymer Sci.*, **2**, 199.
7. Madorsky, S. L. (1952) *J. Polymer Sci.*, **9**, 133.
8. Naunton, W. J. S. *et al.* (1945) PB32161 (CIOS XXXIII-19).
9. Schultz, G. V. (1936) *Zeit. phys. Chem.*, A176, 320.
10. Barr, Guy, *Viscosity*, p. 108.
11. Yanco, J. A. (1948) *J. Polymer Sci.*, **3**, 576.
12. Debye, P. (1944) *J. appl. Phys.*, **15**, 338.
13. Hampton, R. R. (1949) *Analyt. Chem.*, **21**, 923.
14. Mechan, E. J. (1946) *J. Polymer Sci.*, **1**, 175.
15. Madorsky, I., Wood, L. A. and Arnold, A. (1951) *Analyt. Chem.*, **23**, 1656.
16. Wood, L. A. (1954) *J. appl. Phys.*, **25**, 851.
17. Maynard, J. T. and Mochel, W. E. (1954) *J. Polymer Sci.*, **13**, 235.
18. Carothers, W. H., Williams, I., Collins, A. M. and Kirby, J. E. (1931) *J. Amer. chem. Soc.*, **53**, 4203; Bridgwater, E. R. and Krisman, E. H. (1933) *Ind. Eng. Chem.*, **25**, 280.
19. Patrick, J. C. (1936) *Trans. Faraday Soc.*, **32**, 347.
20. Gee, G. (1946) *Trans. Faraday Soc.*, **42**, 585.
21. Gee, G. (1943) *I.R.I. Trans.*, **18**, 266.
22. Bovey, F. A. and Abere, J. F. (1955) *J. Polymer Sci.*, **15**, 537.
23. Rathmann, G. B. and Bovey, F. A. (1955) *J. Polymer Sci.*, **15**, 544.
24. Ziegler, K. (1955) Belgian P. 533,362.
25. Natta, G. (1955) *Makronol. Chem.*, **16**, 213; (1956) *Angew. Chem.*, **68**, 393.
26. Adams, H. E., Stearns, R. S., Smith, W. A. and Binder, J. L. (1958) *Rubb. Chem. Technol.*, **31**, 838; Anikanova, K. F., Betts, G. E., Zhakova, V. G., Komskaya, N. F., Karmin, B. K., Priss, L. S., Reznikovski, M. M., Chernikina, L. A. and Sheteyn, E. B. (1958) *Rubb. Chem. Technol.*, **31**, 30.
27. Short, J. N., Thornton, V. and Kraus, G. (1957) *Rubb. Chem. Technol.*, **30**, 1118.
28. Railoback, H. E., Cooper, W. T. and Stumpe, N. A. (1959) *Rubb. Chem. Technol.*, **32**, 308.
29. Uelemann, H. (1959) *Rubb. Chem. Technol.*, **32**, 597.
30. Golub, M. A. (1957) *Rubb. Chem. Technol.*, **30**, 1142.
31. Dolgoplosk, B. A., Kropacheva, E. N. and Nelson, K. V. (1958) *Dokl. Akad. Nauk. S.S.S.R.*, **123**, 685.

CHAPTER IV

PART ONE

FUNDAMENTAL ASPECTS OF RECLAIMED RUBBER

by

W. E. STAFFORD AND R. A. WRIGHT

RECLAIM may be defined as a type of rubber prepared from waste or worn-out manufactured rubber articles, and the process of reclaiming is concerned with imparting the necessary degree of plasticity to vulcanised rubber and thereby enabling it to be blended with uncured natural or synthetic rubber. The removal of constructive fabrics, extraneous matter, etc., is obviously essential, as is a retention of a capacity for revulcanisation by orthodox procedures. World productive capacity for 1955 was estimated at 600,000 long tons,[1] and provides an important source of cheap rubber hydrocarbon.

Ball [2] describes the development of reclaiming, making clear that the utilisation of waste is almost as old as rubber manufacturing. In 1858 Hall [3] plasticised vulcanised rubber by means of heating in live steam at temperatures substantially higher than those used for vulcanisation. This patent cites a heating period of 48 hours (" more or less "), and steam pressure was probably of the order of 60 lb./in.^{2}, i.e. 307° F, whereas Charles Goodyear's patent for vulcanisation (1844) refers to temperatures up to 270° F. This degradation of the vulcanised structure, induced by heat, together with subsequent mechanical working, is still common to most modern processes. Periodic revisions of the degree of heating, etc., have been found necessary by reason of the improvements in curing and compounding, and also in order to upgrade the ultimate reclaim quality.

It has been pointed out [4] that while the operation of reclaiming may be regarded as relatively simple, to the fundamental chemist the processes are very complex. The methods of fabric removal, etc., will be dealt with subsequently, consideration being given first to the principles of restoring plasticity to vulcanised rubber, i.e., *so-called* " devulcanisation ". Scientifically the term devulcanisation is a misnomer, and is only justified in the sense that reclaiming is essentially a process of depolymerisation, while that of vulcanisation is one of polymerisation.

Basic steps in " devulcanisation "

Broadly speaking, the application of adequate thermal energy, normally assisted by suitable additions to destroy fibres and assist plasticising, may be regarded as inducing a sufficient measure of what has been described as " latent plasticity ", to enable reclamation to be completed by means of mechanical working. Various methods of applying this heat have been suggested, but in those cases where the scrap contains fabric, e.g. tyres, the use of digesters, in which the rubber is heated in an aqueous medium, is still predominant.

The high state of cure obtained by modern vulcanisation techniques and the use of antioxidants, together with those reinforcing pigments which induce strong surface forces, have greatly increased resistance to thermal plasticisation, as well as necessitating a more intense degree of subsequent mechanical working. The following typical digester formulations demonstrate some of the revisions which have been found necessary:

	1914	1954
Cracked natural-rubber motor tyre covers sifted:		
$\frac{5}{8}$-in. riddle	10,000	—
$\frac{1}{4}$-in. riddle	—	10,000
Mineral oil	100	—
Heavy naphtha	—	800
Pine tar oil	—	350
Reclaiming agent	—	20
Caustic soda	1,300	1,000
Water	16,000	16,000
	Heated 18 hours at maximum temp. of 175° C and pressure 150 lb./in.^{2}	Heated 7 hours at maximum temp. of 205° C and pressure 400 lb./in.^{2}

The " devulcanisation " reaction is stated to be doubled for each rise of 5·5° C,[5] but heat alone is not adequate for plasticisation, and techniques using swelling agents, plasticisers, reclaiming agents and sometimes the deliberate addition of oxygen have been developed. The complication of excessive free sulphur, which was adequately met by the well-known alkali process, has now largely disappeared. The diagram on p. 255 can be considered as describing the various steps and agents included in the present-day reclamation of natural-rubber waste containing fabric, e.g. motor tyres, by the Digester process.

Thermal energy

The use of higher temperatures is predominant, and the various additions made at this stage are designed to accelerate and amplify the changes

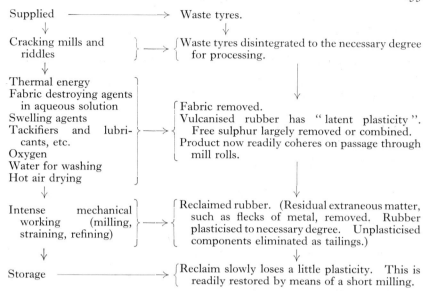

Supplied ⟶ Waste tyres.

Cracking mills and riddles ⟶ Waste tyres disintegrated to the necessary degree for processing.

Thermal energy
Fabric destroying agents in aqueous solution
Swelling agents
Tackifiers and lubricants, etc.
Oxygen
Water for washing
Hot air drying

⟶ Fabric removed.
Vulcanised rubber has "latent plasticity". Free sulphur largely removed or combined. Product now readily coheres on passage through mill rolls.

Intense mechanical working (milling, straining, refining)

⟶ Reclaimed rubber. (Residual extraneous matter, such as flecks of metal, removed. Rubber plasticised to necessary degree. Unplasticised components eliminated as tailings.)

Storage ⟶ Reclaim slowly loses a little plasticity. This is readily restored by means of a short milling.

induced and to modify the end product. This results in the necessary reduction in the resistance to deformation of the original waste, without which it would not be possible to complete regeneration by means of intense milling. If we accept the view that vulcanised rubber is of a three-dimensional net-work structure, it follows that plasticisation can be achieved only by breaking down this complex. This may be brought about by scission of carbon-to-carbon bonds in the original hydrocarbon chain, resulting in a reduction in molecular size.[6] The fact that combined sulphur is still present after reclaiming is an indication that this takes place. On the other hand, scission of sulphur bridges, etc., which hold the hydrocarbon chains together, would also tend to restore plasticity, and scientifically would constitute the ideal mode of attack. The chemistry of these depolymerisation processes has not been fully elucidated, but we can assume with certainty that thermal degradation, as practised in reclaiming, results in fragmentary molecules which do not arise from a reversal of the process of vulcanisation.

Houwink estimated that a good tyre reclaim, from a technological point of view, is equivalent to new rubber with a molecular weight of about 150,000. Many workers have pointed out that at reclaiming temperatures up to 50% of the vulcanised rubber is rendered soluble in chloroform.[5, 7, 8] This fraction usually takes the form of a viscous transparent fluid capable of revulcanisation with sulphur, and no doubt more highly depolymerised than the insoluble fraction. It is somewhat lower in combined sulphur than the latter, and the ratio of soluble to insoluble is normally accepted as a rough index of the degree of molecular disaggregation. The chloroform extract, however, is of greater academic than practical significance, since there is little relationship between it and subsequent workability (i.e. from a reclaimer's standpoint).

The structural changes induced at reclaiming temperatures, at least in the early stages of heating, must have similarities with those associated with reversion and heat ageing. There are, however, differences:

(a) In commercial operations the initial scrap is always oxidised to some degree.

(b) Operating temperatures are higher than those at which reversion is normally studied, or at which heat ageing tests are carried out.

(c) The availability of oxygen in the reclaiming atmosphere is limited.

These differences are perhaps exemplified in the behaviour of sulphurless TMT vulcanisates, which though usually considered as heat-resisting, are very readily reclaimed and yield abnormally high chloroform extracts.

Van Amerongen,[9] in a study of the non-oxidative breakdown of TMT sulphurless natural rubber gum stocks, reported a much stronger de-vulcanising tendency at $175°$ C than in the case of a similar type cured with 1% N-cyclohexyl-2-benzthiazylsulphenamide and 2% sulphur. He suggested that the former have comparatively few cross-links and no free sulphur to form additional ones, and hence if any links are broken down a *seemingly* unvulcanised rubber results.

The thermal stability of chain molecules is believed to be reduced by increasing chain length, irrespective of the state of aggregation. If this, as seems possible, can be taken to include segments of rubber chain molecules contained between the cross-links in the three-dimensional structure, the comparatively few junction points in a TMT cure would lead to a greater measure of thermal instability. Such considerations are essentially speculative, but it is reasonable to assume that molecular breakdown at reclaiming temperatures will at least be preceded by such changes as reversion, and hence the latter cannot be omitted from investigations into the mechanism of reclaiming.

It has been concluded that reversion involves the breakdown of cross-linkages, which predominates over any simultaneous reformation, and that the exclusion of oxygen will not prevent reversion, provided that the temperature is high enough to provide the necessary thermal energy for rupture.[10] The progress of the reaction of sulphur with dihydromyrcene at $141°$ C has been studied, and it was found that the ratio of polysulphide to cyclic linkages was decreased.[11] Other investigators envisage reversion and heat ageing as involving varying degrees of rupture of previously formed cross-links, together with chain scission.[12, 13]

It has been pointed out that the reversion of Butyl rubber vulcanisates, which occurs either at high temperatures or prolonged heating cycles, was at least partially dependent upon reaction with hydrogen sulphide, resulting in the conversion of sulphur linkages to mercaptan groups.[14,15] In spite of superior resistance to oxygen absorption and oxidation, Butyl waste plasticises in live steam more readily than natural, and much more so than SBR, which exhibits pronounced heat-hardening tendencies, necessitating special treatment.[16] In addition, Butyl reclaims are much closer to uncured Butyl than are natural-rubber reclaims to natural rubber. Possibly molecular disaggregation is not so extensive in the former, plasticisation being more dependent upon the severance of cross-linkages.

While present-day knowledge suggests that reclaiming of natural rubber leads to considerable modification in the cross-linkages, this alone is not sufficient to induce adequate plasticisation, and the ultimate reclaims always retain some of the elasticity and other characteristics associated with vulcanisation. Molecular disintegration consequent upon extensive chain scission is regarded as being the predominant result of thermal treatment, and the fate of the cross-links, together with such changes as may result from the reaggregation of fragments, is as yet imperfectly understood.

It has been pointed out that the deteriorating effect of heat as used in practical reclaiming is sufficient to remove one of the most serious variables in the initial scrap, i.e. tensile strength, and in an example quoted a tyre tread of original tensile strength of 3500 lb./in.² was reduced to 1,000 lb./in.², in 4 hours steaming at 350° C.[8] The economy of the milling processes which follow heat treatment and the quality of the ultimate products depend to some extent upon the degree of uniformity in the plasticity or workability induced in the various components of the scrap used.

Oxygen in thermal treatment

Modern theories regard the presence of at least traces of oxygen as essential for the breakdown of olefin polymers, and reclaimers have long known that the presence of air facilitates the thermal plasticisation of vulcanised rubber.[17,18,19] The application of heat is thought to lead to the formation of active radicals, followed by hydroperoxidation of the unsaturated hydrocarbon chains, and the breakdown of these unstable compounds leads to the extensive depolymerisation associated with " devulcanisation ". In the case of natural rubber it is suggested that breakdown is accompanied by a small degree of recombination of chain fragments, but with SBR and some other synthetic polymers aggregative reactions are pronounced and very seriously prejudice thermal plasticisation.[20,21,22] In spite of the importance of oxygen, infra-red spectrography proves that there is little or no increase in combined oxygen, over and above that present prior to reclaiming, the function of oxygen being characterised as " temporary ".[23]

K

Defibering agents

The type of defibering agent, e.g. caustic soda, zinc chloride, etc., exerts characteristic effects upon the course of depolymerisation and the properties of the ultimate reclaim, e.g. the use of caustic soda leads to rapid initial breakdown of the rubber and to softer though more nervy products, while metallic chlorides (neutral) give " deader " and " drier " end products.   Work has been published upon the specific influence of reclaiming atmosphere, thereby increasing our knowledge of the mechanism of " devulcanisation " and the treatments which give rise to the well-known Alkali, Neutral and Pan reclaims.[24]   Among other considerations, the character of decomposition of olefin hydroperoxides in acid and alkaline media and the greater availability of oxygen in open steam reclaiming are thought to be significant.

Swelling agents

A fairly wide range of materials is used, including terpenes, naphthas, petroleum fractions, etc.   They are usually sufficiently volatile to be substantially flashed off when the contents of the autoclaves are discharged, and in consequence are absent from the ultimate reclaim.   Their function appears to be more profound than that of assisting the penetration of the rubber by the less-volatile and more-viscous plasticisers which are normally present.   Wide differences in the efficiency of naphthas have been reported, certain constituents, e.g. indene and dicyclopentadiene, being particularly active.   Addition of naphthas and certain other swelling agents is identified with increased chloroform extract in the ultimate reclaim, and it has been suggested that activity in reclaiming is associated with their " autoxidative susceptibility ".[25]   Investigations of swelling [26, 27] have given valuable information which has been used in the selection of reclaiming oils.   In one instance, the increased swelling of certain unsaturated oils at $175°$ C was considered to arise from the transfer of sulphur from the rubber to the oils.

It is probable that the most important function of volatile swelling agents is to amplify the efficiency of thermal plasticisation, which appears to be linked with the activity of oxygen in promoting depolymerisation.   On the other hand, purely thermal breakdown will be facilitated by the swelling effects of organic solvents, since these reduce van der Waal forces between the molecules and assist chain scission by means of the swelling pressure. It has been stated that in the absence of oxygen, swelling in organic solvents at higher temperatures ($170°$ C) will dissolve vulcanised rubber because of thermal rupture of co-valent bonds.[28]   High ratios of swelling agents are particularly necessary with rubber which is highly reinforced with carbon black.

It has been claimed that the presence of naphthas does not change the basic characteristics of the mechanism of the particular breakdown associated with metallic chlorides, alkali, steam, water, etc.[29]

Tackifiers and lubricants

These cover a wide range, including mineral oils and tars, and are substantially retained in the ultimate reclaim. They serve to facilitate the mechanical working which follows autoclave treatment, and to enhance the properties of plasticity, tackiness, etc.

Reclaiming agents

The wide use of these compounds is of comparatively recent origin, and the impetus for development arose largely from the difficulties in handling synthetic rubbers. They are characterised by increasing thermal plasticisation even when used in relatively small amounts, and superficially their efficiency in aiding reclaiming can be compared to that of organic accelerators in vulcanisation. Rather curiously, the first to be proposed was aniline [30] and then the aromatic mercaptans,[31] which were already known to accelerate the plasticisation of natural rubber. Later came certain alkyl and arylamines [32] and the sulphur chloride–cresol reaction products.[33] Some polyalkylphenol sulphides, e.g. 4-6-*ditertiary*-butyl-*m*-cresol sulphide, have been found particularly effective for SBR. The use of such compounds is largely restricted to neutral treatments, but certain arylamine sulphides are effective catalysts under alkaline conditions.

A considerable amount of fundamental work upon the mechanism of these agents has been published, and several important references in the literature are recommended to those interested.[6,34,35,36] It has been suggested that they probably react chemically with vulcanisates and assist oxidative scission of hydrocarbon chains, i.e. they catalyse the type of breakdown largely accepted as being responsible for depolymerisation.[35]

It has been contended that the cross-links, themselves rather than the hydrocarbon chains between the cross-links, may be attacked, thereby opening up the network structure, and the possibility of direct reaction with sulphur of the cross-links was suggested.[6] However, since successful reclamation of SBR vulcanisates was accompanied by a small but definite increase in combined oxygen, oxidative scission at the sulphur cross-links catalysed by polyalkylphenol sulphides was thought to be the most important mechanism. The theory of cross-link attack receives support from the observation that alkylphenol sulphides were found to be less effective with vulcanisates obtained using *p*-benzoquinonedioxime, and from the evidence that these reclaiming agents tend to yield recured vulcanisates of lower modulus and high elongation.

The use of suitable reclaiming agents in the treatment of SBR, neo-prene and nitrile rubbers largely suppresses the pronounced heat-hardening tendencies, and this fact would appear to support the theory that they de-crease the degree of cross-linking in the ultimate reclaim.   The provision of a means of attack of cross-linkages would be a powerful tool in the re-claiming of polymers, where hydroperoxidative chain scission is so much less pronounced than with natural rubber and would constitute an ad-vance in the art of reclaiming.   On the other hand, it is thought that the breaking up of the network structure by either direct or indirect rupture of linkages is perhaps a rather idealised concept, more especially in the light of the possible modifications of the cross-links, such as are achieved by purely thermal agencies.   The use of hydrogen sulphide has been claimed for the reclamation of Butyl,[37] and this reagent probably functions by destroying cross-linkages by some means such as below:

$$R–S–S–R + H_2S \longrightarrow 2RSH + S$$
$$R–S–R + H_2S \longrightarrow 2RSH$$

In this sense H_2S can be regarded as a specific reclaiming agent for Butyl vulcanisates, just as dimethyldihalosilane is specific for silicone elastomers.

Mechanical working

In the foregoing some of the principles by which vulcanised rubber is plasticised have been described, but the plasticity so induced is in-sufficient to permit of uniform blending with uncured rubbers.   The mechanical working which follows and makes the latter possible must be regarded as an essential part of the reclaiming process.   Since milling does not materially increase either acetone or chloroform extracts,[5] it can be assumed that it does little to promote the degree of depolymerisation.   The various components of waste, e.g. tyres, can be expected to have different degrees of " latent plasticity " after autoclave treatment, and the necessity for thorough blending is obvious.   On the other hand, even waste of a single uniform composition also requires such treatment in order to com-plete the process of reclaiming.   The progressive increase in the degree of coherence which follows milling and refining suggests that the ultimate blending of the softer chloroform-soluble rubber with the harder insoluble portion is an important and necessary change, while the elimination of semi-plasticised particles on the refining mills, although essential to practical reclaiming, is not fundamental.

In addition, the further dispersion of the plasticisers added to the auto-clave charge is a factor of importance.   It has been suggested that low-temperature mastication of raw rubber leads to mechanical rupture of bonds,[38] and it is possible that the small increase in chloroform extract which attends abnormally low-temperature refining [5] may arise in the same way.

Storage of reclaim

Reclaim loses some of its plasticity on storage, especially if kept under warm conditions.[5] As a result of two years' storage, a whole tyre reclaim was found to fall from 27·23 to 19·86% in chloroform extract and to increase from 402 to 596 in Williams plasticity.[39] Open milling for 15 minutes restored chloroform extract to 28·07% and plasticity to about the original figure. It has been suggested that storage hardening may be a form of polymerisation involving oxygen, or of absorption of soluble by insoluble rubber, or of insolubilisation of chloroform extract by carbon black.[29] Significant losses in the unsaturation of reclaim take place on long storage. No means of effectively preventing storage hardening appears to be known, although digester treatment with adequate plasticisers appears to yield the type of reclaim less susceptible to this change.

General properties of reclaim

In spite of countless modifications of the basic principles of reclaiming, the degradation of the original vulcanised structure is fundamentally similar in most conventional types. They can be regarded as a particular type of depolymerised rubber, and hence their properties admit of a measure of generalisation. The ability to crystallise is completely lost except in reclaims prepared from sulphurless TMT vulcanisates. This difference is shown in the curves covering relationship between T-50 and combined sulphur.[40] The elasticity shown by all conventional reclaims is not significantly affected by milling. No doubt the long-chain molecules of new rubber are much more vulnerable to mechanical working than the already intensely milled fragmentary molecules of reclaim, and even prolonged milling does not change the plasticity of the latter to the same extent as that of raw rubber.[41]

Vulcanisation and vulcanised reclaim

Vulcanised reclaim rubbers have greatly inferior tensile strength, elongation, resilience, abrasion resistance, etc., as compared with the corresponding compounds in new rubber. For example, a tyre tread showing approximately 4,500 lb./in.^{2} tensile strength and 550–650% elongation will yield a reclaim of about 1,200–1,500 lb./in.^{2} tensile strength and 300–400% elongation. Natural reclaims cure faster than crude, and alkali reclaims faster than other types. The presence of combined sulphur in reclaim has been suggested as the reason for this general characteristic.

In a general way reclaims respond to organic accelerators in a manner similar to new rubber. In some instances up to 25% accelerator reduction can be effected with reclaim, while superior ageing can be achieved by means of reduced sulphur and more normal acceleration.[42] Zinc oxide (1–3%) is necessary for maximum vulcanisation in certain straight reclaims and in compounds containing them.[43] This indicates that residual zinc oxide is inadequate for full recure. In this connection it should not be overlooked that quite apart from other reactions, significant amounts of zinc oxide are converted to zinc sulphide in the original cure and in reclaiming.

The progressive vulcanisation of SBR, red tube reclaim and smoked sheet, using 40% sulphur on the hydrocarbon, have been examined. As might be anticipated on theoretical grounds, the maximum tensile in the soft-rubber region characteristic of natural rubber is not evident either with reclaim or SBR.[44]

Red Tube Reclaim. Tensile strength rises progressively from 0·36 kg./cm.² at 4·1% combined sulphur to 297 kg./cm.² at 32·3% combined sulphur.

Smoked Sheet. 246 kg./cm.² at 2·3% combined sulphur, 28 kg./cm.² at 13·6% combined sulphur and 169 kg./cm.² at 30·3% combined sulphur.

The replacement of new rubber by reclaim in ebonite has only a small depressing effect on impact strength.[45] In general, the use of reclaim in hard rubber results in much smaller loss in mechanical properties than that which occurs when it is incorporated into soft rubbers.

Ageing of reclaim

Reclaim is outstandingly stable in both the cured and uncured states. It has been characterised as a physical antioxidant much as one would regard factice.[46] Little change in acetone extract is found after 2 years' ageing.[39] The influence of reclaim on the accelerated ageing of natural rubber and SBR has been examined and it was found that a proportion is beneficial where this type of ageing is concerned.[47] It has been reported that alkali reclaim has a beneficial influence in suppressing frosting.[48] The compounding of reclaim with several types of elastomers has been studied, and among other conclusions it is stated that reclaim compounded with certain grades of neoprene has pronounced resistance to ozone cracking, weathering, cut growth, etc., and that an all-reclaim stock is better than its counterpart in SBR.[49] A reclaim stock of tensile strength, 1,050 lb./in.² shows practically no loss on heat ageing for 5 days at 100° C. The severe treatment to which reclaimed rubber has already been subjected includes oxidation, heating, digestion, washing and mastication in air, and these appear to stabilise the material against further changes.[16]

Finally, the authors [50] have recently made extensive tests upon the static atmospheric cracking of compounds containing reclaim. Crude rubber was progressively replaced with reclaim, and within the scope of their work this substitution appears to bring about a slight improvement. Although reclaim is inferior in rubber-like properties and further systematic work is needed, the overall conclusion appears to be that it is adequately stable for most applications.

REFERENCES

1. Ultsch, G. (1955) *Proc. Sveriges Gummitekniska Förenings*, p. 10.
2. Ball, J. M. (1947) *Reclaimed Rubber* (New York: Rubber Reclaimers Assoc. Inc.), Chapter 1.
3. Hall, H. L. (1858) U.S.P. 22,217.
4. Hader, N. and LeBeau, D. S. (1951) *Ind. Eng. Chem.*, **43**, 250–262.
5. Palmer, H. F. and Kilbourne, F. L. (1940) *Ind. Eng. Chem.*, **32**, 512–518.
6. Ambelang, J. C. and Smith, G. E. P. (1954) *Ind. Eng. Chem.*, **46**, 1716–1721.
7. Stafford, W. E. (1926) *India Rubb. J.*, **71**, 59.
8. Winkelmann, H. A. (1926) *Ind. Eng. Chem.*, **18**, 1163–1168.
9. Van Amerongen, G. J. (1955) *Ind. Eng. Chem.*, **47**, 2565–2574.
10. Shankar, U. (1952) *Rubb. Chem. Technol.*, **25**, 241–258.
11. Bloomfield, G. F. (1949) *J. Soc. chem. Ind.*, **68**, 66–68.
12. Flory, P. J., Rabjohn, N. and Shaffer, M. C. (1950) *Rubb. Chem. Technol.*, **23**, 27–43.
13. Gee, G. and Morrell, R. H. (1952) *Rubb. Chem. Technol.*, **25**, 454–467.
14. Zapp, R. L., Decker, R. H., Dyroff, M. S. and Rayner, H. A. (1951) *J. Polymer Sci.*, **6**, 331–349.
15. Baldwin, F. P., Turner, L. B. and Zapp, R. L. (1944) *Ind. Eng. Chem.*, **36**, 791–795.
16. Whitby, G. S. (1954) *Synthetic Rubber* (New York: J. Wiley & Sons Inc.), pp. 592–609.
17. Essex, W. G. (1939) U.S.P. 2,139,086.
18. Ioannue, J. P. (1937) U.S.P. 2,069,151.
19. U.S. Rubber Co., invs. Kirby, W. G. and Steinle, L. E. (1942) U.S.P. 2,279,047.
20. LeBeau, D. S. (1947) *Rubb. Age, N.Y.*, **62**, 51–55.
21. Firestone Tyre & Rubber Co., inv. Kilbourne, F. L., Jnr. (1943) U.S.P. 2,324,980.
22. Tobolsky, A. V., Prettyman, I. B. and Dillon, J. H. (1944) *J. appl. Phys.*, **15**, 380–395.
23. LeBeau, D. S. (1948) *Rubb. Chem. Technol.*, **21**, 895–908.
24. LeBeau, D. S. (1948) *India Rubb. World*, **118**, 59–65.
25. LeBeau, D. S. (1950) *Rubb. Age, N.Y.*, **68**, 49–56.
26. Scott, J. R. (1929) *I.R.I. Trans.*, **5**, 95–116.
27. Rostler, F. S. and White, R. M. (1947) *Rubb. Age, N.Y.*, **61**, 313–321.
28. Bergem, N. (1948) *Contributions to the Mechanism of Vulcanisation Chiefly Based on the T-50 Test* (Norway: A/S Askim Gummifabrik), p. 197.
29. LeBeau, D. S. (1948) *India Rubb. World*, **119**, 69–74.
30. Lutz (1910) *Gummi-Zeitung*, **25**, 120–121.
31. The B.F. Goodrich Co., inv. Garvey, B. S. (1940) U.S.P. 2,193,624.
32. Midwest Rubber Reclaiming Co., inv. LeBeau, R. V. (1947) U.S.P. 2,423,032.
33. U.S. Rubber Co., invs. Kirby, W. G. and Steinle, L. E. (1944) U.S.P. 2,359,122; (1944) U.S.P. 2,363,873; (1954) U.S.P. 2,372,584.
34. Webb, F. J., Cook, W. S., Albert, H. E. and Smith, G. E. P. (1954) *Ind. Eng. Chem.*, **46**, 1711–1715.

35. Cook, W. S., Albert, H. E., Kilbourne, F. L. and Smith, G. E. P. (1948) *Ind. Eng. Chem.*, **40**, 1194–1202.
36. Bennett, R. B. and Smith, G. E. P. (1954) *Ind. Eng. Chem.*, **46**, 1721–1726.
37. Standard Oil Development Co., inv. Baldwin, F. P. (1950) U.S.P. 2,493,518.
38. Pike, M. and Webster, W. J. (1952) *J. Polymer Sci.*, **9**, 229–251.
39. Stafford, W. E. (1942) *I.R.I. Trans.*, **17**, 264–267.
40. Bergem, N. (1948) *Contributions to the Mechanism of Vulcanisation Chiefly Based on the T-50 Test* (Norway: A/S Askim Gummifabrik), p. 77.
41. Ball, J. M. (1947) *Reclaimed Rubber* (New York: Rubber Reclaimers Assoc., Inc.), Chapter 8.
42. Carrington, J. H. (1942) *I.R.I. Trans.*, **17**, 255–257.
43. Ball, J. M. (Spring, 1955) Lecture 8A, Philadelphia Rubber Group.
44. Bergem, N. (1948) *Contributions to the Mechanism of Vulcanisation Chiefly Based on the T-50 Test* (Norway: A/S Askim Gummifabrik), p. 47.
45. Kemp, A. R. and Malm, F. S. (1935) *Ind. Eng. Chem.*, **27**, 141.
46. Naunton, W. J. S. (1930) *I.R.I. Trans.*, **5**, 317–335.
47. Ball, J. M. (1949) *Rubb. Age, N.Y.*, **64**, 718–722.
48. Beaudry, J. T. (1951) *Rubb. Age, N.Y.*, **69**, 429–432.
49. Torrance, M. F. and Schwartz, H. G. (1952) *Rubb. Age, N.Y.*, **71**, 357–360.
50. Unpublished work of the Rubber Regenerating Co. Ltd.

CHAPTER IV

PART TWO

PRACTICAL AND TECHNOLOGICAL ASPECTS OF RECLAIMED RUBBER

by

W. E. STAFFORD and R. A. WRIGHT

Rubber-reclaiming processes

Many excellent historical records and descriptions of modern rubber-reclaiming processes have already been published.[1, 2, 3, 4]

The more important processes of manufacture can be grouped as follows:

1. Digester (Neutral or Alkali).
2. Pan or Heater.
3. Acid.
4. Reclamator or Dip.
5. Thermal.
6. Thermodynamic or Hot Banbury.
7. Palmer or High Pressure Steam.

These processes are largely identified with methods of heat plasticisation and fabric removal, the mechanical treatment which follows being more or less common to all. An outline of general operations in reclaiming works operating the first and most important process will be given.

Scrap receiving and sorting

Waste collection, of which motor covers form by far the largest proportion, is almost exclusively in the hands of the merchants. Reclaimers do, however, hold considerable stocks, normally amounting to thousands of tons.

In addition to these, motor tubes, tread peelings, tread buffings, solid tyres, hose, sponge, etc., are all used as the basis of different grades of reclaim. The production of standard qualities obviously necessitates careful sorting and grading of scrap, as, for example, separation of passenger from truck tyres, and of natural from synthetic-rubber tyres. In the case of Butyl tubes a high degree of freedom from natural-rubber waste

265

is essential, and many other cases could be quoted indicating the importance of this primary stage of reclaim manufacture. Generally speaking, the scrap dealer works in close liaison with the reclaimer, and a large proportion of scrap is graded before the latter receives it.

Fig. 4.1. Digested scrap leaving 3-tier drier.

The very large volumes of waste make mechanical handling essential, and considerable capital expenditure is devoted to this aspect.

Cracking

The scrap is first sorted, then disintegrated in cracking mills and screened to size. Originally it was necessary to remove bead wire before cracking, but modern practice is to crack the whole tyre, releasing the bead wires during the operation.

More recently much larger crackers have been installed which are capable of handling larger truck tyres without any prior treatment. Any tyres which are still too big are either split longitudinally or cut transversely by means of heavy alligator jaws, so as to reduce them to a size which can be gripped readily by the rolls. The whole operation of cracking has been mechanised to a very high degree, hand operation between the entry of the scrap into the cracking mill to the final cracked stock storage bins being entirely eliminated.

Digesting

The ground scrap is heated in autoclaves, usually steam-jacketed, along with the necessary plasticisers and solutions for destroying fabric. Heating periods are in the region of 3–15 hours and temperatures 180°–205° C. Under these conditions the rubber is partly plasticised and the fabric destroyed. The contents of the claves are discharged into dump tanks and washed, dewatered and dried in hot-air currents. The wash liquor

Fig. 4.2. Battery of steam-jacketted autoclaves.

always carries fine particles of rubber and hydrolysed cellulose, etc., and necessitates treatment in settling tanks, where the solids are recovered prior to disposal of the effluent. The final moisture content after drying is usually left as high as practical (3–6%), by which means the efficiency of subsequent milling operations is increased. All processing up to this stage is designed to induce maximum efficiency in subsequent operations.

Milling, straining and refining

These treatments are common to most processes and provide the mechanical working essential for plasticisation. This is by far the most expensive section of the reclaiming operation and necessitates large capital investment, high power consumption and maintenance. It can be roughly broken down as follows:

(*a*) *Blending.* The dried stock is masticated in internal mixers or on open mills, at which stage it is not unusual to make small additions of

Fig. 4.3. Section of mill room showing refining mills.

carbon, clay, softeners, etc., to facilitate the subsequent operation and to modify the properties of the final product.

(*b*) *Sheeting.* The blended reclaim is now ground on tight mills, generally conventional refining mills, in order to render it suitable for straining. These machines exert very great pressure on the stock, thinning it out to about 0·01 in.

(c) *Straining.* This is carried out on large extruders, in which the sheeted rubber is forced through screens which vary from 16 to 40 mesh, according to requirements. Flecks of metal, particularly non-magnetic, and other foreign matter, are effectively removed, and the emerging stock is usually cut up by means of knives rotating at the head, to facilitate conveying for the subsequent treatment.

Fig. 4.4. Refining mill showing take-off drum.

(d) *Refining.* This, the final reclaiming operation, is most critical, and calls for considerable skilled supervision. The stock is passed through closely set rolls and compressed to a thickness of about 3–5 thousandths of an inch. At the settings employed, the less plasticised particles of rubber are either eliminated at the roll ends or removed periodically from the machine. The plasticised stock adheres to the fast roll and is scraped off by means of a doctor blade and wound up on a drum to form the familiar sheet of finished reclaim.

The high surface speed ratio and close setting of refiner rolls necessitate large volumes of cooling water, as unduly high temperatures lead to serious losses in efficiency.

The digester process can be subdivided according to the use of either caustic soda or metallic chlorides for the purpose of fabric destruction.

Alkali process

Patented by A. H. Marks,[5] this is a digester process in which scrap rubber is heated under pressure in caustic alkali solution, by which means fabrics are destroyed and the rubber is effectively plasticised. This process was particularly successful with the high-free-sulphur scrap of the early part of this century, but its importance has now receded, due in part to the tendencies for scorch with certain type accelerators, and more particularly to the introduction of SBR scrap, for which the neutral process of reclaiming is much more suitable.

Neutral process

Based upon an old patent of D. A. Cutler,[6] this treatment is similar to the alkali, except that dilute solutions of zinc chloride replace caustic soda. This is the most widely used process today. Its success lies chiefly in the following:

    1. Cheap fibre destruction.

    2. Subsequent millroom production, especially that of SBR, is normally superior to that of alkali cooks.

    3. Alkali inhibits the use of most reclaiming agents.

    4. Ultimate reclaims are much less " scorchy," are less tacky, and are " deader " than alkali types.

Digester cycles are similar to the alkali-process cycles.

Of late there has been a trend towards reducing heating to the minimum necessary for fibre destruction, with a view to minimising the serious heat hardening of the SBR components of tyre waste. The use of most reclaiming agents with mixed waste, i.e. SBR and natural, results in an over-softening of the natural and induces refining difficulties, whereas each can be advantageously treated separately by these agents. The addition of alkali towards the end of the digesting operation has the effect of hardening the oversoftened natural much more than the SBR.[7]

The reclamation of SBR and other synthetic types is less dependent upon heat and more dependent upon added plasticisers than with natural rubber. Hence it is usual to crack the initial waste to a much finer degree than is necessary with the latter, so enabling a better penetration of plasticisers. Many processes have been put forward for the reclaiming of synthetic scrap.[8, 9] Experience of SBR reclaiming has resulted in a trend towards a reduction in the amount of sorting of natural from synthetic rubber scrap and a search for better treatments capable of dealing with mixtures. The presence of SBR has complicated refining operations and necessitates a very high standard of technical control, while rolls and cooling facilities must be maintained in first-rate condition.

Pan devulcanisation

Fundamentally based upon the patent of H. L. Hall,[10] this process involves heating in live steam at pressures of 100–300 lb./in.² in large horizontal single-shell autoclaves, for varying periods of time. The treatment is used essentially for fabric-free scrap, e.g. buffings, tubes, etc., and it is usual to grind the waste to the requisite degree of fineness and to mix in a percentage of plasticising oils. The charge is contained in trays, boats or other suitable means, and after withdrawing from the autoclave it is usually broken up and air dried. Reclaiming is completed in the conventional manner.

Acid process

Originally introduced by Mitchell[11] and adequately described by Ball,[12] this process involves treating the fibre-containing scrap with hot dilute sulphuric acid in open tanks. Washing is usually effected by the use of a riffler with baffles, which serves to remove stones, metal, etc. The batch is ultimately neutralised with alkali and the rubber plasticised in live steam, as in the pan or heater process. The treatment is completed by means of milling, straining, etc., as in the digester process. Originally widely used for shoe scrap, its applications are now limited to unvulcanised friction scrap, etc., and for the production of certain types of reclaim having particularly dry and inert characteristics.

Reclamator or dip process

When vulcanised rubber is suitably heated there is a rapid initial rise in plasticity, followed by a sharp decrease and finally a slower steady increase. This process[13] rests upon the ability to arrest the softening process at the first point of maximum plasticity. Reclaiming agents are used to accelerate the process. In practice, fibre-containing waste is first defibred mechanically. The recovered fibres are ultimately baled and the fabric-free rubber is then fine ground, mixed with reclaiming agents and fed into a specially constructed extrusion-type plasticator which is provided with means of heating or cooling at any part of the travel of the rubber. Machine temperatures are of the order of 300°–400° F, with provision for rapid cooling before the stock emerges to atmosphere.

Thermal process

This procedure,[14] which gained popularity in Europe during the last War, results in the conjoint destruction of fibres and softening of vulcanised rubber in a medium of superheated steam. Temperatures employed are substantially higher than those used in the digester process. Tyre scrap is loaded into steam autoclaves in which are fitted electric heaters. Steam is raised to a low pressure (e.g. 60 lb./in.²) and the electric heaters located in the autoclaves increase the temperature to 220°–250° C. While opinions vary, it is thought that thermal reclaims are inferior to those prepared by more conventional processes and, moreover, the process is not readily adaptable to SBR and certain other synthetic scraps.

Thermodynamic or hot Banbury process

This process [15] employs a specially designed Banbury mixer which is more sturdily built and capable of handling higher load requirements. The raw cracked waste is loaded into the machine and subjected to intense shearing action by means of high pressure and power input. Ram pressures up to 180 lb./in.² are used, and temperatures may rise as high as 500° F, the batch being cooled somewhat before discharge. Plasticising agents, reclaiming agents, carbon black, etc., can be used to assist the process, and reclaiming cycles are of the order of 3–12 minutes, any fibres being charred and dispersed in the ultimate reclaim. Nitrile rubber and neoprene, as may be expected, do not handle well under these conditions. This process is said to be particularly useful in the case of scorched stocks, which cannot easily be cracked and so adapted to conventional treatments.

Palmer or high-pressure process

Fibre-free waste with reclaiming agents is loaded into a specially constructed closed container. Live steam at 800–1,000 lb./in.² is admitted and maintained for periods of up to 10 minutes. By means of a hydraulically operated valve in the bottom the pressure is suddenly released, the reclaim blown out and disintegrated, and finally finished in the conventional manner.

Among other treatments less widely used is the Dasher process,[16] in which fibres are destroyed by means of acid vapours.

Developments in plant, machinery and reclaim types

Strainers

The National Rubber Machinery Co.[17] claim that by the use of a conical nose screw, etc., output of strained stock is increased up to 30% and flow is more uniform.

Removal of bead wire and tramp metal

Ingenious methods for removing metals have been developed.[18]

Mill-strainer

This machine [19] is a standard rubber strainer which is modified to produce increased milling action over conventional strainers, and high-volume straining.

Uniblend process [9]

This was developed by Farrel-Birmingham Co. Inc., and Pequanoc Rubber Co., and uses a machine stated to be on the principle of a continuous Banbury or mill-strainer. The process is unique in so far as it enables the reclaim to be strained before milling and should be very economical in man-power, etc.

Mechanical removal of fibres

Dorris [20] describes processes for the mechanical removal of fibres from waste rubber, an achievement of considerable importance. Quite apart from the present and potential value of salvaged cotton, etc., the elimination of the high temperatures essential in conventional processes for fibre destruction is of great value in the handling of synthetic rubbers.

Premix [9]

This involves the compounding of reclaim in which the whole is passed through the strainer and refining mills, curing agents being omitted. An example given is: reclaim 194, fine calcium carbonate 50, FEF black 20, zinc oxide 5, fatty acid 5, asphaltic softener 5 and paraflux 5. Advantages claimed are faster mixing, less ingredients to be added by the manufacturer, improved processing and ultimate quality. Westhead [21] describes improvements in compounding value as a consequence of the refining of compounding ingredients into reclaim, and his work fully supports the advantages described for Premix.

Powdered reclaim

Reclaim is now produced in powder form and is free flowing and more readily adaptable to automatic weighing and handling.[22] Among advantages claimed are a wide range of plasticities, more uniform degree of reclaiming and cooler mixing at reduced power consumption.

Minimum staining reclaims

These are normally prepared by means of suitably modifying the basic scrap, reclaiming agents, etc., by the use of active carbons [23] and of formaldehyde or related compounds.[24]   The waste itself is usually treated by the digester process. The wider application of minimum staining types is of great importance in reclaim development.

Carboxylic rubbers

Among the latest developments in the use of waste rubber are the Bisonides, described as being a series of new polymerised materials produced from scrap vulcanised rubber.[25]   They are said to be prepared by combining unsaturated compounds containing an electrophilic group, such as a carboxyl group, alpha to the double bond, with natural or SBR scrap. Unique properties in oil resistance, cured hardness, tensile strength, etc., are claimed, and the products are suggested for blending with neoprenes in certain specific applications. While not a reclaiming process in the ordinary sense, such a development for the utilisation of scrap rubber may open up a wide field of usage.

Future trends in manufacture

These will probably be within three broad channels:

1. Further mechanisation and possible automation of the older processes, with economies in production costs.

2. Considerable shortening of " devulcanisation " cycles. These are already indicated in the dip and hot Banbury processes.

3. Fundamental improvements in processing, together with the utilisation of waste rubber as a basic material for other manufactures.

So long as high temperatures are necessary for fibre destruction, extensive chain scission must take place and result in a product consisting essentially of fragmentary molecules. Under these conditions there appears to be little prospect of any very pronounced improvement in reclaim qualities. Already it is evident that the employment of the digester process for SBR and other types of synthetic is introducing complications due to heat hardening, and this may be the main reason for the growth of the methods of mechanical fibre separation.

A further trend perhaps will be in the development of reclaiming agents more specific to the various types of rubber, thereby enabling better handling of mixed scrap, but this can be achieved only by a more comprehensive knowledge of the mechanism of reclaiming.

Testing of reclaim

Considerations of the testing of reclaim fall into two categories, namely, examination during the course of manufacture and that of the finished product. Obviously in some measure these are interlocked.

Testing during manufacture

A certain amount of testing is involved in the grading of waste. The sorting of various synthetic scraps, e.g. the separation of motor covers with SBR treads from those of natural, must be undertaken. Many such specialised operations are essential to present-day reclaiming and have been achieved only by training to a high degree of efficiency.

The " workability " of the batches after digesting, pan treatment, etc., is essential. This is usually determined by milling and refining small lots, and here again a high degree of skill and experience is necessary in the examiners. The uniformity of finished reclaim requires strict attention to the grading of waste, degree of cracking, heat processing and milling, etc., to accommodate changes in the processing characteristics of the scrap. It is usual to make frequent tests for specific gravity, Mooney viscosity, etc., during the millroom operations, since such factors as changes in refiner roll temperatures, adjustment of rolls, strainer temperatures, etc., can influence the ultimate quality.

Additional features of control involve the frequent testing of the various agents used in processing, together with that of the final effluents for efficiency of removal of suspended solids.

Regular analysis of finished reclaim, i.e. chemical and physical, is normally undertaken by the reclaimers.

Examination of finished reclaim

According to the purposes for which the reclaims are to be applied, the following are of importance:

1. Composition, especially rubber content, presence of synthetic, copper, manganese, etc.

2. Physical condition of unvulcanised reclaim, e.g. plasticity, colour, cleanliness (i.e. degree of freedom from insufficiently plasticised particles of rubber, flecks of metal, etc.), degree of tackiness, " body " and " nerve ".

3. Rate of cure, general compounding value, and ageing characteristics.

While exhaustive examination is often justified with a new reclaim, the control of the principal standard grades is usually maintained by a limited series of tests which experience has shown to be sufficient to ensure satisfaction.

Composition

A typical specification for natural rubber whole tyre reclaim is as follows:

Specific gravity	$1\cdot18 \pm 0\cdot02$
Alkali	$0\cdot05\%$ maximum
Acetone extract	$13\cdot5\%$,,
Ash	$14\cdot0\%$,,
Carbon black	$17-21\%$
Cellulose	$2\cdot0\%$ maximum
Heat loss at $105°$ C	Less than 2%
RHC content	$50-55\%$

Typical analyses of some other types are:

Type	S.G.	Acetone extract, %	Ash, %	Carbon, %	RHC, %
Tyre carcass (black)	$1\cdot17$	$13\cdot00$	$14\cdot00$	$15\cdot00$	55
Black inner tube	$1\cdot18$	$7\cdot00$	$17\cdot00$	$14\cdot00$	61
Red tube	$1\cdot20$	$8\cdot00$	$25\cdot00$	—	65
Mechanical	$1\cdot35$	$10\cdot00$	$32\cdot00$	$12\cdot00$	44

Specific gravity. Within limits, and especially in the hands of experienced technicians, this is a useful means of classification and control.

Alkali. This is usually done by aqueous extraction followed by titration or pH determinations. Other methods in which the reclaim is swollen with solvents, prior to aqueous extraction, are sometimes used. It has been claimed that up to 60 days' extraction is necessary for complete removal of alkali, and in consequence the tests as applied have only limited value for control purposes.[26] Winkelmann [27] has pointed out certain differences between alkali and other types of reclaim, which indicates the importance of establishing whether the alkali process has been employed.

Acetone extract and ash. These determinations serve to check uniformity and are necessary in determining an approximate " rubber by difference " figure.

Chloroform extract. With unvulcanised reclaim this extraction is indicative of the degree of molecular disaggregation, but since it tends to diminish with ageing, it is not a suitable determination for specification, and its value lies largely in the field of research. Kirchoff [28] reports a relation between chloroform extract and ageing, but there is no certainty that this is generally accepted.

Heat loss at 105° C. In addition to moisture, this includes any volatile residues, largely arising from added plasticisers used in reclaiming treatments.

Carbon content. This is necessary for a complete analysis, and in conjunction with other data it assists considerably in identifying the scrap of origin of the reclaim.

Cellulose. The procedure outlined in BS 903 [29] is normally used, and conventional reclaims usually yield figures below 2%. The degraded cellulose present in certain types of thermal reclaims is not fully estimated by this method, an important point to note is the examination of these qualities, which have been prepared from waste containing large proportions of cellulosic components.

Total fillers. This determination is especially valuable in reclaim analysis, being necessary for an accurate computation of rubber by difference.

Direct determination of RHC (rubber hydrocarbon content). When tested by the ASTM method,[30] reclaim tends to yield a lower RHC content than that obtained by earlier methods, but taken in conjunction with the RHC by difference, it is useful in arriving at an approximation of the SBR contents of mixed natural SBR reclaims. LeBeau[31] has investigated the chromic acid method of determining natural rubber in mixed synthetic/ natural reclaim.

Sulphur determinations. Free sulphur is almost invariably negligible, and its estimation is not normally carried out. Total sulphur sometimes appears in users' specifications.

The positive detection of reclaim in manufactured rubber is difficult. It has been suggested that high acetone extract, very diverse constituents of the ash (especially should their presence appear to fulfil no particular purpose) and the high water absorption associated with alkali reclaims are indicative of the presence of reclaim.[32] To these may be added the microscopic examination of very thin sections of the vulcanisates.

Examination of uncured reclaims

It is well known that the physical properties of uncured reclaims are most important to the compounder.[33]

Smoothness. With experience this can usually be examined directly, or by blending with a proportion of masticated rubber and calendering to a few thousandths of an inch thickness. Such tests should be interpreted with caution, since obviously the requisite degree of smoothness will vary greatly with the desired application, and highly refined reclaims are normally more expensive.

Plasticity. This is becoming increasingly important, more especially in view of the progress towards short standardised mixing cycles. The plasticity of reclaim has been examined in detail by Kilbourne, Misner and Fairchild.[34] They point out that it is by no means a truly plastic material, and at the same time emphasise the compounder's need for a numerical index for reclaim which will be indicative of the ease or difficulty in handling on conventional rubber machinery. They examined several methods, namely Williams, Mooney, Firestone Extrusion, Laboratory

Milling Test and Full-Scale Factory Processing Test of 3–5 minutes in a 3A Banbury.

Milling tests relate " knit time," i.e. the interval required for knitting together, and " smooth time," i.e. the period required to smooth out. The importance of correct sampling is evident from the 20% spread of Mooney values between the centre and edges of the reclaim sheets. They concluded that the Mooney viscosity method for measuring the plasticity of reclaim was more accurate than Williams or extrusion methods, and that milling measured some other property, probably elasticity. Finally, it was thought that a combination of milling and Mooney tests gave the maximum information on workability. Mooney tests alone are of limited value in testing reclaim.[35]

Colour and Staining Tendencies. Drab and coloured reclaims should be examined before and after vulcanisation. The so-called minimum staining types are usually examined as follows: Specimens are cured to optimum with 5% sulphur, and strips of the cured stock are dipped into a standardised solvent based white rubber paint, dried and exposed to ultra-violet light in a cabinet, which admits of careful control of operating conditions. The resultant discoloration is measured on a reflectance spectrophotometer.

Vulcanisation tests

The relation between tensile strength, etc., of straight-cured reclaims and that of the compounds into which they are incorporated, is as yet un-known.[36,37] Whereas in the past tests had largely been based on vul-canisates prepared from reclaim and sulphur only, the U.S. Reclaimers' Technical Committee suggested the following test formulation:[38]

Reclaim to	100 RHC
Zinc oxide	5
Sulphur	3
Stearic acid	2
MBT	0·5
DPG	0·2

Cure to optimum: 15, 20, 25, 30 minutes at 141° C.

Under these conditions, whole tyre reclaims usually yield 800–1,000 lb./in.² tensile strength and 350–450% elongation; black tubes yield 1,400–1,600 lb./in.² tensile strength and 500–600% elongation.

This formulation gives more uniform and informative results than those obtained by straight sulphur cures, but their value is essentially linked to that of control of uniformity.

With many consumers, a specific compound is preferred, an example of which is as follows:

Reclaim	100·00
Smoked sheet	50·00
Stearic acid	2·00
Zinc oxide	3·00
Antioxidant	1·00
Sulphur	3·00
MBT	0·75
SRF black	35·00
Tensile strength	2,000 lb./in.^{2} minimum
Elongation	450% ,,
Modulus at 300%	800–1,200 lb./in.^{2}

Butyl reclaim calls for a special test formula as follows: [39]

Butyl reclaim to	100 RHC
Zinc oxide	5
Sulphur	2
Tetramethylthiuram disulphide	1
MBT	0·5

Cured 30 minutes at 320° F

Butyl tube reclaims yield approximately:

| Tensile strength | 1,000–1,500 lb./in.^{2} |
| Elongation | 500–600% |

Various methods of dynamic testing of compounds containing reclaim have been examined [40] and an attempt has been made to establish a conversion factor for replacing new rubber by reclaim without serious impairment of physical properties.[41]   Typical analyses of many reclaims will be found in *Compounding Ingredients for Rubber*,[42] and elsewhere.

There is little doubt that reclaimers in the past have tended to produce more grades than are really necessary, and the advisability of reducing these to a minimum, so as to avoid undue complications in the production of reclaim with consequent increased costs, has been pointed out.[43]

Laboratory examination, at least with unknown reclaims or in the case of new compounds, is supplemented by works trials.   As yet the complexity of what is understood by " workability " can only be reliably assessed by more or less direct trials, but once suitability has been established, elementary chemical and physical tests usually suffice to control the uniformity of successive deliveries.

Advantages of reclaim

Reclaims can be regarded as compounds of a particular type of degraded rubber with unique properties.   When suitably used they offer specific advantages in rubber compounding.   Some of these are listed below: [33]

1. The price of reclaim is normally lower than that of raw rubber, and in the past has fluctuated much less than that of the latter.

2. Reclaim mixes faster than new rubber, partly because all the fillers of the original waste are already incorporated.

3. Power consumption in mixing is less than that for mixing new rubber, as might be inferred from (2).

4. Reclaim develops less heat in mixing than new rubber. This is important with compounds having high loadings of carbon black and other reinforcing pigments.

5. Use of reclaim results in faster processing during extrusion and calendering than new rubber. This is particularly useful in mass production, where smooth flowing, uniform stock with the minimum of defective goods is essential.

6. Reclaim enjoys an advantage over new rubber in that it promotes better dimensional stability to uncured compounds. It is claimed that the shrinkage of calendered stocks and the swelling of extruded compounds is reduced by its incorporation.

7. Reclaim, being less thermoplastic than raw rubber, gives rise to many advantages, e.g. less distortion in open cure, etc.

8. Reclaim vulcanises faster than either natural rubber or SBR.

9. The presence of reclaim reduces tendencies for reversion. One of the most successful pre-war natural-rubber truck-size inner tubes contained a moderate proportion of first-quality whole-tyre reclaim.[44]

10. Reclaim in both its raw and cured state has good ageing properties. As an example, large quantities are used in friction tapes, where retention of tackiness is important.

11. Reclaim properties can be modified in processing the waste, so enabling it to be more or less " tailor made " to specific compounding requirements.

Haehl [45] has surveyed the function of reclaim in rubber technology and claims that it facilitates the removal of gases formed during vulcanisation. " Superior processing rubbers " produced from field latex contain 0·41% combined sulphur, which has been introduced in a particular manner.[46] The object of deliberately creating a degree of cross-linking was drawn from analogy with certain butadiene–styrene copolymers in which this condition was produced by polymerisation in the presence of a little divinylbenzene, and for which improved processing properties were claimed. Superior processing rubber has advantages over first-grade crêpe and sheet, namely, less shrinkage after milling, extruding or calendering, smooth extrusion, less swelling, small reductions in Mooney viscosity during compounding, etc. These are in line with many properties which are identified with the use of reclaim, which certainly suggests that the presence of combined sulphur in the latter is responsible for some of its fundamental properties. This casts some doubt upon the desirability of removing combined sulphur, elimination of which was the aim of many seeking to perfect the reclaiming process.

Selection of reclaims for various applications

The economical and technical complexity of rubber manufacturing is such that it is not possible for reclaimers to specify all the possible uses of their products, and particular problems of compounding are frequently best solved by liaison between manufacturer and consumer. On the other hand, there is considerable standardisation of usage according to type. The following are among the most important characteristics to be considered in the selection for various purposes:

1. Composition, in particular rubber and carbon content, together with organic extractable matter, is important.

2. Price.

3. Reclaiming process, i.e. whether alkali or otherwise. Alkali grades often necessitate changes in curatives used.

4. Degree of smoothness, freedom from metallic and other hard particles. This is especially important in grades intended for extrusion or calendering.

5. Plasticity, nerve, body, tackiness and other characteristics which influence milling, calendering and extrusion, together with behaviour of uncured stock on maturing. While most of the unique properties of reclaim are generic properties, nerve is not so, and can be modified according to the reclaiming process employed. Normally nerve in uncured compounds is undesirable, since it induces undue swelling in extruded stocks, whilst in the case of friction compounds, reclaims of lower Mooney viscosity are usually preferred.

6. Tendencies for migratory staining. Only minimum staining type reclaim is suitable for passenger tyre carcass compounds of white side-wall tyres, etc.

7. Resistance to water absorption must be considered for many applications, e.g. radiator hose, water bottles, insulation stocks, etc.

8. Influence on such characteristics as rate of cure, tensile strength, elongation, modulus, flex cracking, etc.

A large number of commercial reclaims, together with suggested uses, have been tabulated.[9] As an example of the approach to selection, Goodrich [47] suggest that peel reclaim (tyre tread), in which the filler is predominantly channel or furnace black, is preferred for compounds requiring high abrasion resistance. Carcass or whole tyre is used for minimum hysteresis and heat build-up. The cost of pure gum and similar types of regenerates results in more expensive rubber hydrocarbon than in the case of whole tyre or similar grades, and in consequence their use is generally restricted to special applications, such as ebonite, in which they yield results only slightly inferior to those of new rubber.

A formula for evaluating reclaim against new rubber when used in cheap mechanicals is given below: [48]

$$\frac{\text{Specific gravity} \times \text{cost per lb.}}{\% \text{ Rubber content}} = \text{Equivalent rubber cost}$$

Many investigators have studied this problem with results which rate whole-tyre reclaim at about half that of new rubber. One difficulty in any such assessment is the necessity to take into account the technological advantages of reclaim and its limitations in usage. The true value is obviously related to the purpose to which it is to be applied. Taking extreme cases, reclaim has a high value when used for hard rubber battery containers, but its inferior resistance to abrasion makes it almost valueless in first-quality tyre treads.

Many examples of compounds containing reclaim are to be found in the literature. Formulations of graduated hardness, together with test results showing the changes in tensile strength and elongation which accompany the gradual replacement of whole-tyre reclaim by SBR and smoked sheet have been published.[44] Reclaim is used in varying proportions in goods requiring moderate rubber-like characteristics and finds limited employment in applications where small additions confer specific advantages.[49] Examples of the former class are soles and heels, in which its use is largely governed by consideration of raw-material cost and advantages in processing, while the latter is exemplified by the inclusion of a small amount in truck-tyre tubes, an addition mainly justified on technical grounds.

Industrial applications

The industrial uses of reclaim have been classified into the following broad channels, namely, Automotive, Building, Cement, Chemical, Clothing, Dye, Electrical, Highway Construction, Mechanical, Metallurgical, Mining, Plumbing and Pipefitting, Rayon and Therapeutical, giving detailed uses in each class. Major applications are tyres and tubes, battery cases, soles and heels, boots and shoes, friction tape, power-transmission belts, elevator belts, conveyor belts, jar rings, kneeling mats, garden hose and baby-carriage tyres.[50] The usage of American-produced reclaim is classified as follows: [44]

Tyres, tubes and camelback	More than 50%
Automobile floor mats	10–12%
Mechanical goods	10–12%
Automotive hard rubber battery containers	5–6%
Other automotive goods	5–6%
Soles and heels	Less than 5%
Solvent cements and water dispersions	,, ,, 5%

While a very considerable proportion of the reclaim consumed is linked with the production of motor vehicles, it also enters into a great variety of products outside this field, and its industrial applications are broad.

Summary and conclusions

The use of reclaim rests almost entirely upon considerations of price and technological advantages. Its employment has contributed materially to the growth of rubber manufacturing, and reclaiming is cited as one of its major developments.[51] Its importance should not be viewed as being limited to that of supplying a cheap raw material having certain favourable properties, but rather from the broader angle of successfully utilising rubber scrap. From the latter viewpoint, much remains to be achieved, and increasing employment depends largely upon three possibilities:

1. To find new outlets in rubber manufacture in which higher proportions of reclaim can be incorporated.

2. To improve quality, so enabling greater proportions to be used in orthodox formulations.

3. To find outlets for waste, outside those of conventional reclaiming.

The use of recovered rubber originally arose out of the necessity to augment the supplies of crude rubber, and later certain processing advantages became identified with it. The importance of the latter may diminish, more especially with the increasing range of materials available to the compounder, but its consumption can be expected to continue to grow with that of the industry as a whole, and new applications for its employment will be discovered.

REFERENCES

1. Ball, J. M. (1947) *Reclaimed Rubber* (New York: Rubber Reclaimers'Assoc.), Chapter 1.
2. Hader, N. and LeBeau, D. S. (1951) *Ind. Eng. Chem.*, **43**, 250–262.
3. Stafford, W. E. and Wright, R. A. (1954) *Proc. Inst. Rubber Ind.*, **1**, 40–53.
4. Alexander, P. (1938) *Proc. Rubber Tech. Conf., London*, Paper 55.
5. Marks, A. H. (1899) U.S.P. 635,141.
6. Cutler, D. A. (1913) U.S.P. 673,057.
7. U.S. Rubber Co. invs. Kirby, W. G. and Steinle, L. E. (1952) U.S.P. 2,612,479.
8. Whitby, C. S. (1954) *Synthetic Rubbers* (New York: J. Wiley), 592–609.
9. Drogin, I. (1953) *India Rubb. World*, **128**, 772–774; **129**, 63–68.
10. Hall, H. L. (1858) U.S.P. 22,217.
11. Mitchell, N. C. (1881) U.S.P. 249,970.
12. Ball, J. M. (1947) *Reclaimed Rubber* (New York: Rubber Reclaimers' Assoc.), Chapter 2.
13. *Rubb. Age, N.Y.* (1954), **75**, 548.
14. Bemelmans, E. (1935) B.P. 435,890.
15. Cotton, F. H. and Gibbons, P. A. (1946) B.P. 577,829; Comes, D. A. (1951) *India Rubb. World*, **124**, 175–177; (1943) *India Rubb. J.*, **105**, 339.

16. B.F. Goodrich Co., inv. Dasher, P. J. (1950) U.S.P. 2,498,398.
17. National Rubber Machinery Co. (1950) *India Rubb. World*, **123**, 271.
18. *Rubb. Age, N.Y.* (1950), **68**, 323–324.
19. Buecken, H. E. (1952) *India Rubb. World*, **125**, 435–437, 439, 442.
20. Dorris, T. B. (1952) *Rubb. Age, N.Y.*, **71**, 773–780.
21. Westhead, J. (1942) *I.R.I. Trans.*, **17**, 249.
22. LeBeau, D. S. (1953) *Rubb. Age, N.Y.*, **73**, 785.
23. Keilen, J. J. and Dougherty, W. K. (1953) *India Rubb. World*, **129**, 199–205.
24. Clayton, T. A. (1956) B.P. 747,997.
25. U.S. Rubber Reclaiming Co. (1955) Bulletin MD1.
26. Kilbourn, F. L. and Miller, G. W. (1930) *Ind. Eng. Chem.*, **22**, 69–73; (1930) *India Rubb. World*, **82**, 104–111.
27. Winkelmann, H. A. (1949) *Rubb. Age, N.Y.*, **65**, 57.
28. Kirchoff, F. (1949) *Kautsch. u. Gummi*, **2**, 151–153.
29. B.S. 903:1950, p. 73.
30. A.S.T.M. (1950), p. 146.
31. LeBeau, D. S. (1948) *Anal. Chem.*, **20**, 355–358.
32. Stern, H. J. (1954) *Rubber—Natural and Synthetic* (London: MacLaren), p. 478.
33. Ball, J. M. (1947) *Reclaimed Rubber* (New York: Rubber Reclaimers' Assoc.), Chapter 8.
34. Kilbourne, F. L., Misner, J. E. and Fairchild, R. W. (1950) *Rubb. Age, N.Y.*, **66**, 423–428.
35. Baader, T. (1955) *Rubb. Chem. Technol.*, **28**, 588–595.
36. Winkelmann, H. (1926) *Ind. Eng. Chem.*, **18**, 1163–1168.
37. Wallace, E. H. (1942) *India Rubb. J.*, **103**, 633–635.
38. Kilbourne, F. L. (1948) *Rubb. Age, N.Y.*, **62**, 541–542.
39. Busenberg, E. B. (1952) *Rubb. Age, N.Y.*, **70**, 608.
40. Randall, R. M. and Ball, J. M. (1954) *India Rubb. World*, **130**, 795–800.
41. Shaboyashi, G. (1942) *J. Soc. Rubb. Ind., Japan*, **15**, 514–528.
42. (1947) *Compounding Ingredients for Rubber* (New York: India Rubb. World), pp. 569–574.
43. Palmer, H. F. and Crossley, R. H. (1941/42) *I.R.I. Trans.*, **17**, 261–263.
44. Ball, J. M. (Spring 1955) Lecture VIIIA, Philadelphia Rubber Group.
45. Haehl, A. (1954) *Rev. gén. Caoutch.*, **31**, 891–893.
46. Baker, H. C. (1956) *I.R.I. Trans.*, **32**, 77–96.
47. B.F. Goodrich Co. *Reclaimed Rubber—Industrial Products*.
48. Schade, M. (1948) *Rubb. Age, N.Y.*, **63**, 498.
49. (1950) *Vanderbilt News*, **16**, No. 4.
50. Berliner, J. J. and Staff, *Latest Developments in Reclaiming*.
51. (1950) Goodyear Memorial Lecture, International Rubber Conf., Cleveland, Ohio.

CHAPTER V

PART ONE

FUNDAMENTALS OF PROCESSING

by

J. R. SCOTT

Introduction

IF by " processing " we denote those operations that come between the initial mastication of the rubber and the vulcanisation of the otherwise finished article, that is, the operations of mixing, calendering, frictioning, extrusion, moulding and combining with textile fabrics or cords, then we find that the basis of all these processes is the flow or viscous deformation of the rubber, or more precisely its rheological behaviour. In certain cases other factors of a more chemical nature come into play; thus, mixing with carbon black to achieve reinforcement involves a chemical reaction (or something very near it) between the black particles and the reactive ends of broken rubber chain-molecules; chemical factors enter also into the specific adhesion between rubber and textile fibres, and still more decisively in rubber/metal bonding. Nevertheless, the physical flow of the rubber is the one predominant factor, and it will therefore be instructive to consider briefly just how it is involved in each of the processes concerned.[1]

Mixing. In mixing a filler with rubber the surface of every particle should be thoroughly surrounded and wetted by the rubber. The surface areas involved are enormous; thus a 100-lb. batch of a tyre-tread stock made with a carbon black of particle size 25 mμ will contain some 10^{20} carbon particles, with a total surface area of about 1 sq. mile. Ability of the rubber to flow is obviously all-important, and a *low* viscosity would therefore appear desirable. On the other hand, filler aggregates have to be broken down; this is favoured by a *high* viscosity, so that the shearing action inherent in mixing will produce high shear stresses, and high stresses are likewise needed to produce the broken chain-molecules necessary for filler reinforcement. It is difficult to see how these conflicting requirements can be reconciled, so that the practical answer seems inevitably to be a compromise, but it is important that the right compromise be chosen.

Extrusion, calendering and frictioning all involve vigorous mechanical working, and hence considerable heat generation. The stiffer the stock, the greater the heat, and hence the greater the risk of scorching, so that from this point of view a soft stock is desirable. In calendering, a soft stock reduces the degree of bending of the bowls, and hence the degree of camber or other adjustment needed to get a uniform gauge; again in frictioning, a soft stock will more easily penetrate the interstices of the fabric. On the other hand, such penetration is a nuisance when calendered sheet is wrapped up in a fabric liner, so that a *high* viscosity is desirable. However, these apparently conflicting requirements may be reconcilable; the operations requiring a low viscosity involve high shear rates or stresses, whereas the stresses pressing calendered sheet against a liner are small; it is quite possible to have a rubber with low effective viscosity at high stresses and high viscosity at low stresses, indeed this type of rheological behaviour appears normal, as will be evident from the discussion below on the rheological properties of rubber; thus the data in Fig. 5.1 show that a rubber can have an effective viscosity of 2×10^4 poises at a shear stress of 2×10^6 dynes/cm.^{2}, rising to 10^8 poises when the shear stress falls to 2×10^4 dynes/cm.^{2}.

The so-called " swelling from the die " in extruded articles, and the corresponding increase in thickness of calendered sheet on leaving the nip, depend on the rheological characteristics of the stock; elastic recovery obviously plays a part, but these dimensional changes occur even in a material having no elastic character, as will be shown later in dealing with extrusion and calendering.

Two other troublesome phenomena, namely the after-shrinkage of calendered sheet and the deformation of extruded sections when cured in open steam, also depend on the rheological character of the stock. To minimise open-steam deformation the stock needs to have high viscosity at the low stresses set up by the weight of the article; it is fortunate that the natural rheological behaviour of rubbers tends strongly in this direction.

Building-up operations, involving the joining together of different pieces of stock, require easy flow (low viscosity) under small stresses, so that the inevitable irregularities on the mating surfaces can easily be flattened and so permit contact and fusion over the whole area.[2]

Moulding in its more conventional form is not critical in regard to rheological properties, but in the newer techniques of injection and transfer moulding these properties are directly involved.

Bonding to textiles has been shown to depend to an important extent on the loose fibre ends projecting from the fabric or cord.[3,4] For these fibres to be fully effective, however, the rubber must be able to surround and wet them, a requirement calling for the same rheological characteristics as the wetting of a large area of filler surface.

Rheological properties of rubber and effects of plasticisation

It would be out of place here to give any detailed account of the rheological characteristics of unvulcanised rubbers (see Chap. II, Part I). It will, however, be helpful, both as a supplement to what has been said above and as a background to the following discussions of individual processes, to summarise briefly what is known about these characteristics:

1. Rubbers are strongly non-Newtonian, that is, the rate of shear deformation is not proportional to the shear stress, except perhaps at *very* low stresses. Fig. 5.1 shows several typical " flow curves " (shear rate *versus* stress) plotted on logarithmic scales. The important points to note are that the slope of the curve is always greater than unity (i.e. shear rate increases more than proportionately to stress) and at high stresses the curves become very steep; indeed, some workers have obtained flow curves for natural rubber and butyl rubber (though not for neoprene or butadiene copolymers) that even appear to approach a vertical asymptote corresponding to a limiting stress of 2–$2 \cdot 5 \times 10^6$ dynes/cm.^{2}, which is independent of temperature.[6, 7, 8]

2. At any given stress the shear rate increases with temperature by a factor of roughly $1 \cdot 3$ per $10°$ C; the effect is, to a first approximation, to move the flow curve bodily upwards without changing its shape.[9]

3. The rate of flow under a fixed stress is time-dependent, i.e. rubber shows thixotropy, and this is very marked in stocks containing reinforcing fillers like carbon black.[10]

4. All rubbers and stocks show more or less elastic recovery when the deforming stress is removed.

The above summary of the rheological characteristics of unvulcanised rubber is necessarily in general terms, because these characteristics differ from one type of rubber to another and can be greatly changed by the treatments commonly referred to as " plasticisation ". It has long been a tempting idea that by proper choice of plasticising conditions a rubber could be given, at least in some measure, the rheological characteristics most suitable for a particular processing operation. This idea has never been pursued to its logical conclusion, and although it is probably overoptimistic to suppose that any given kind of rubber molecule can be adequately " tailored " merely by choice of plasticising treatment, the subject nevertheless deserves further study, and it is worth recording the main conclusions from work already done.

The general effect of plasticisation can be represented by moving the flow curve to the left and reducing its slope (see Fig. 5.1; compare curves 2–8, masticated, and with curve 1, unmasticated). Curves for successively increasing treatments by any one method do not cross (e.g. curves 2, 3, 4,

5 and 6), but those for different treatments may do so; thus *cold* mill mastication gives a steeper curve (curves 7 and 8) than the other methods tried (hot mill, hot or cold internal mixer, these three being indistinguishable). This crossing evidently arises from the fact that rubbers can

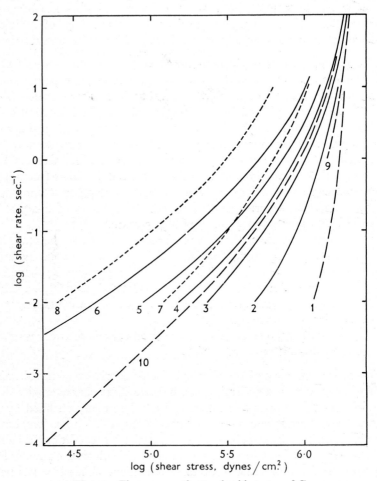

Fig. 5.1. Flow curves of natural rubber at 100° C.

Curve 1: unmasticated; Curves 2, 3, 4, 5, 6: hot-milled 2, 5, 10, 20, 40 minutes; Curves 7, 8: cold-milled 150, 300 passes (all from Refs. 5 and 8). Curves 9 and 10 from Ref. 6.

in general be softened, that is, their molecules reduced in size, by at least three distinct processes, viz.: mechanical breakage of the chain molecules, oxidation and heat, although the end products of these three processes do not necessarily possess identical molecular structures.[11] Moreover, there are exceptions; for instance, SBR cannot be softened by heat in absence of oxygen, since the effect is to produce cross-linking and hardening.[12]   The differences in molecular structure resulting from the various plasticising agencies lead to different rheological properties.   Thus it was found [11,12] with both natural rubber and SBR that mechanical plasticisation (i.e. cold milling) gave the product with the smallest elastic recovery, while heat plasticisation of natural rubber or oxidative softening of SBR (especially if the temperature was high) led to a greater degree of recovery.

Fig. 5.1 shows that the curves for rubbers plasticised to different extents converge markedly at high shear rates, in the sense that the range of shear stress (on a log scale) becomes less as shear rate is increased.   On the other hand, the *vertical* intercepts between the curves for any one method of plasticisation are roughly independent of stress, so that differences in shear rate remain proportionately just as large at the highest shear stresses;   in other words, the effect of plasticisation seems to be essentially to move the log stress/log shear rate curve bodily upwards, in which it appears to act in the same way as a rise of temperature.

Stocks containing fillers

The above discussion relates to rubber free from fillers or reinforcing powders.   The behaviour of filled stocks is similar in essentials, but with one important added complication, namely that the thixotropic character becomes very pronounced in stocks containing reinforcing fillers such as carbon black.   Indeed, investigations [10] make it clear that in any such stock undergoing a shear deformation the degree of " structure " present (which may be either filler–filler or filler–rubber) is a dynamic equilibrium between an ever-present tendency to form structure and the opposing tendency of the shearing motion to break down this structure;   hence if we are to understand the behaviour of such a stock in any processing operation the rheological properties must be measured at the shear rate obtaining in that operation, and after a sufficient period of shearing to reach equilibrium between the structure-building and structure-destroying tendencies.

Mixing

Hepner [13] and Welding [13a] have made an extensive study of the mechanism of mixing a powder into rubber on a two-roll mill.   It was shown that in absence of a bank the forces exerted on the rubber passing between the rolls are purely compressive, i.e. normal to the surface of the roll.   This compression produces a lateral shearing, that is, a mixing action in the circumferential direction, but gives no mixing in depth, i.e. through the thickness of the rubber sheet.

Effective incorporation of powders thus requires the presence of a bank

L

of rubber above the nip.   It was found, however, that even with a bank, if the rubber sheet passing round the front roll is not cut and folded back (as is usual in practice) the powder never penetrates through the full thickness of the sheet, the mechanism of mixing being as follows: On entering the bank the upper layer of the rubber becomes folded and forms

Fig. 5.2. Section through rubber batch showing filler (dark) entering corrugations in a *small* bank.

corrugations on the near or entry side of the bank.   Powder enters these corrugations and is drawn into the interior of the bank (see Fig. 5.2).   This process is responsible for radial or depthwise mixing within an active layer which never extends through the whole thickness of the sheet on the rolls. Indeed, with a sheet of normal thickness the active layer does not comprise

Fig. 5.3. Section through rubber batch showing " dead " layer (white) not penetrated by filler.

more than about two-thirds of the total thickness, the one-third in contact with the roll forming a dead layer into which powder added to the exposed surface does not penetrate; this is shown by the section of a batch in Fig. 5.3, in which the light portion represents rubber still unmixed with powder.   On the leaving, or left-hand (Fig. 5.2) side of the bank flow takes the form of streamlines, the rubber being sheared, especially in the upper layer, by the squeezing action of the rolls as the rubber approaches the nip.

This causes very efficient circumferential mixing of the powder with either even or differential speed rolls.

Thus, *in absence of cutting and folding*, the uniformity of a mixture is: (i) very good in the circumferential direction due to circumferential shear; (ii) good in the axial direction (except at the extreme edges), provided the powder is added uniformly across the roll face; (iii) poor radially because of the dead layer. It is also found, in absence of cutting, that a small bank is more effective than a large one, because a large bank has very few corrugations and the top part tends to roll round on its own axis (see Fig. 5.4).

Fig. 5.4. Section through rubber batch showing how filler (dark) fails to penetrate a *large* bank (cf. Fig. 5.2.)

For the fuller quantitative study of mixing efficiency with a bank, Hepner added lycopodium powder in amount sufficiently small to enable the number of particles to be counted microscopically in small samples cut systematically from the sheet. He calculated a " mixed fraction " (f), defined as the volume fraction of mixture throughout which all the added particles would have to be distributed uniformly (at random) to give a variance of number of particles per small sample equal to that obtained in the actual count. By plotting f against time of mixing (t) a curve was obtained which approximates to the form:

$$f = f_m \left(1 - e^{t/t_1}\right)$$

where f_m is the maximum (limiting) fraction of the sheet thickness penetrated by powder and t_1 is the "time-constant of mixing", an inverse measure of the rate of incorporation. The main conclusions from these experiments were:

1. If the sheet on the front roll is *not* cut and folded back, f_m only reaches about 71%, thus confirming that uniform mixing is *never attained without cutting*.

2. Cutting and folding raises f_m to 100% (i.e. gives uniform mixing) by bringing the dead layer to the top and so into the active zone.

3. The usual industrial technique of partial cutting and folding (i.e.

cutting across about half the width) gives about the same time constant t_1 as with no cutting.

4. Complete cutting across, with removal of the batch, folding over double and re-insertion as a sheet into the nip, gave t_1 about half of that for partial cutting, so that mixing was twice as quick, but unfortunately this is not a practicable method on an industrial scale.

5. The tests confirmed that with partial cutting and folding, even and friction speeds give about the same t_1.

6. With a constant size of bank (*without* cutting and folding) t_1 was independent of batch size between 300 and 700 g.; hence mixing is most efficient (i.e. the largest amount of mixed stock is produced in a given time) when there is maximum loading on the mill.

7. With partial cutting and folding the presence of a bank (or its size) has little influence on t_1; in other words, the advantage of the bank is lost when cutting is used, and in fact the bank merely wastes power (by churning the rubber round and round) without contributing to the mixing.

Hepner concludes that the partial cutting and folding process is inefficient because: (*a*) the radial mixing effect of the bank is hardly used, mixing being achieved largely by folding and compression rather than by convection on entering the bank, (*b*) the cutting and folding is only partial, and hence less effective than complete cutting. The manipulation involved increases operator cost, effort and variability, and safety considerations limit the speed of the rolls, and hence of mixing. The much more efficient complete cutting is industrially impracticable because of the additional manipulative effort.

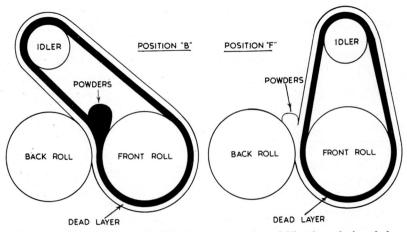

Fig. 5.5. Modified mixing mill, allowing incorporation of filler through the whole thickness of the sheet.

To satisfy the requirements that (i) the whole of the dead layer should be disturbed, (ii) the radial mixing power of the bank should be fully used, and (iii) this result should be achieved without handling the sheet, Hepner proposes a modified mixing mill having a third (idler) roll that can be positioned above either of the other two (see Fig. 5.5). The sheet of stock on the front roll passes over this idler. When the idler is above the front roll ("position F") the mixing action is similar to that obtained without the idler. To get powder into the dead layer, the idler is shifted to "position B"; powders added above the bank thus enter the previously unmixed dead layer; it is, of course, necessary to have a special device for distributing the added powder uniformly across the sheet when mixing in position B.

Experiments with the lycopodium powder test mix showed that this arrangement did in fact result in much quicker attainment of a uniform mixture; typical results were:

Normal mill, partial cutting/folding: $3t_1{}^* = 15$ minutes
    ,,   ,,   complete cutting/folding: 8   ,,
Modified mill, *no* cutting   3·6   ,,

It must be emphasised that in most of the tests only very small quantities of powder were used, so that the time of incorporation was negligible compared with the time to approach the ultimate uniformity of mixing. In using the measured times as a guide to what would happen with normal filler loadings, they should therefore be considered as indicating the time to blend after complete incorporation of the filler, and not the total mixing time. The saving of time in the blending stage was confirmed by tests with a heavily loaded whiting mix (90 parts filler per 100 rubber by weight) which showed improvements in time of blending (after completion of the incorporation of powder) of the same order as above.

Apart from Hepner's work, there has been little that can be described as fundamental investigation on the mixing process.

The rate of incorporation of powders (or its inverse, the mixing time) has been to some extent studied in relation to the nature and amount of the added powders. The general belief that fine powders take longer to mix than coarse powders was confirmed by quantitative experiments on the rate of incorporation of various fillers.[14] It was further shown that when a given amount of a filler (e.g. Q in Fig. 5.6) is added to rubber on the mill the rate of incorporation is at first constant, but later decreases, so that complete incorporation may take a long time, as shown at X on curve A. This observation suggested that it would be quicker to start with a larger amount of filler (P) than it is required to incorporate and to continue mixing till the residue equals the known excess, a stage that

* $3t_1$ is quoted because it is the time when f reaches 95%, i.e. practically uniform mixing.

would be reached at time Y on curve B. Experiments confirmed that this procedure could reduce the mixing time by as much as one-third.

The type of relationship illustrated in Fig. 5.6 could be explained on the basis of Hepner's observations, as follows: If rubber is running round the front roll, with a bank in the nip, and a large amount of powder is put on the mill, it will completely cover the bank. The rate at which this powder enters the rubber will depend entirely on the action of the bank in drawing powder into its corrugations; the amount of powder present will have no effect so long as it is sufficient to cover the bank,

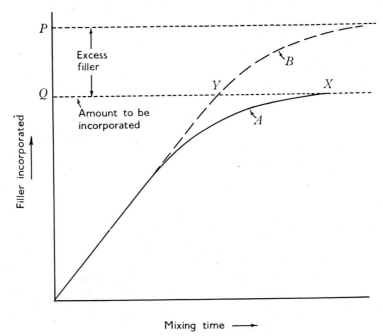

Fig. 5.6. Relation between mixing time and amount of filler incorporated.

and thus the rate of incorporation will be represented by a straight line. When the remaining powder is no longer sufficient to cover the bank completely the rate of incorporation will decrease because the bank is not being fully used; consequently the line will curve over and approach its maximum more or less asymptotically. If the initial amount of powder is increased (say, to P) the straight part of the graph will extend further (curve B instead of curve A), so that the required quantity Q is incorporated in time Y instead of X.

A more general relationship was found [15] that among a large variety of mixes made on the same mill the volume output per hour (which is the inverse of the mixing time for a batch of given volume) often bears a linear relationship to the logarithm of the total surface area of the added powders:

$$V = a - b \log S$$

where V = volume output per hour;

S = total surface area of fillers in unit quantity of stock;

a and b are constants characteristic of the mill used.

The relation is not exact, as the experimental points show some scatter about the regression line, and indeed sometimes the scatter is so great that no significant regression can be demonstrated. Some of this scatter is obviously due to the fact that factory mixing times are determined empirically and that surface areas of powders are not known precisely. Whether there are real causes of deviation from a simple relationship, such as the above equation, between filler surface and rate of mixing cannot be said definitely.

However, according to the work of Havenhill et al.,[16, 17, 18] there is at least one such cause, namely, the electrical contact potentials of the rubber and added powder. In the contact potential series rubbers (at least natural rubber and SBR) are at the negative end, while reinforcing fillers (carbon black, zinc oxide) are positive. The resulting electrostatic attaction between rubber and filler is considered to help the mixing process; the greater the potential difference, the quicker being the mixing, the less the power required, the lower the mix temperature (Banbury) and the softer the resulting stock. Anything that makes the rubber more negative or the filler more positive thus helps the mixing process; in Havenhill's experiments a zinc oxide that had been surface-treated to increase its positive contact potential did in fact mix more quickly and easily. Some softeners (e.g. lauric acid) make the rubber more negative, and so should be added before the filler; those that make it less negative (e.g. mineral oil) or positive (linseed oil) should be added after the filler.

Havenhill further claims that a reading of the contact potential between the rubber batch and a probe inserted in the mixing chamber shows when incorporation of filler or softener is complete. So long as any remains unmixed the reading is zero, but as soon as mixing is complete and there is no free filler or softener, the reading returns to the normal value corresponding to the composition of the batch.

Rubber-filler interactions (" carbon gel "; " bound rubber ")

An aspect of mixing that has been extensively studied is the breakdown and re-formation of filler structures and the formation of rubber-filler " gel ". As, however, this will be dealt with in Chap. 7 especially in relation to reinforcement, and the conclusions are in any case far from definite, it will be discussed only briefly here.

Carbon black, and doubtless to a certain extent other fillers also, exist in the form of aggregates of particles more or less firmly held together. The very high shearing forces set up in the rubber by the action of mixing break down these aggregates to a greater or less extent. It would be expected that this breakdown would be more complete the stiffer the rubber and the higher the rate of shear, since either of these factors increases the shearing stress. These expectations are in accord with general experience, and are directly confirmed, for instance, by the observations that breakdown of carbon black aggregates is increased: (i) by adding a cross-linking agent (Polyac) to Butyl rubber, so as to increase its stiffness and its " nerve " or elastic character; [19] (ii) by reducing the nip of a two-roll mill and so increasing the shear rate in the rubber passing between the rolls.[20]

However, other actions besides this mechanical breakdown of filler aggregates are involved in mixing. Investigations [10] on plasticity showed that in a rubber–filler mixture undergoing shear there is both a disrupting tendency of the shear stress and an opposing tendency to re-form structures of some kind; the view that these structures are filler aggregates has now given place to a different and more complete picture. It is known that milling of rubber breaks the chain molecules, producing free radicals that can attach themselves by chemical linkages to particles of certain reinforcing fillers such as carbon black.[21, 22] This results in the formation of a relatively stable combination of the filler with what has come to be known as " bound-rubber ", the whole forming (in the case of carbon black) a " carbon gel " insoluble in the usual rubber solvents. The amount of such gel depends on the mixing time and temperature, and may be increased by subsequent storage of the stock.[23] On the other hand, this gel can be broken down again by mechanical working, and the breakdown can be permanent if oxygen is present to react with the severed rubber chains.[22] Moreover, the formation or disruption of gel can be strongly influenced by certain softeners [10] or certain chemically reactive substances.[24]

It is thus clear that the ultimate result of mixing rubber with a surface-active filler is an equilibrium between, on the one hand, mechanical forces tending to disrupt both filler aggregates and rubber–filler combinations (" gel ") and, on the other hand, forces of a more chemical nature (ranging from van der Waals or adsorption forces to chemical linkages) tending to build up structures that are probably mainly rubber–filler rather than mere filler aggregates.

Extrusion

The theory of extrusion has been developed mainly for plastics that exhibit Newtonian flow (see, e.g., Rogowsky,[25] Rigbi,[26] Pigott,[27] Carley et al.,[28-34] Maillefer [35]), though it is claimed, and indeed shown experimentally, that the conclusions are valid for " mildly non-Newtonian " materials (Carley). It is unfortunate that this phrase is not further defined; it is thus not possible to say how far the conclusions would apply to such a strongly non-Newtonian material as rubber, though Pollett [36] has shown that some at least would need modification, and this is confirmed by the experimental results of Pigott.

Most of the theoretical treatments assume that there is no slippage of the plastic material over the walls of the screw or barrel. The question whether and to what extent plastic materials such as unvulcanised rubber slip over a metal surface is still open to considerable doubt, largely because no one appears as yet to have tackled the problem by direct experiment. All that can be given are statements based on indirect evidence from extrusion studies on rubbers and plastics. The general opinion is that slippage is either absent or slight (Atkinson and Nancarrow,[37] Storey,[38] Tunstall [39]); on the other hand, Mooney and Black [40] deduce from their experiments that slip does occur and increases with the shear stress at the rubber/metal interface, and Rogowsky also considers slippage to occur.

A further limitation of the studies hitherto made on extrusion is that they deal largely with the action of the screw in forcing material forward to the die. The very important problem (for rubber at least) of its behaviour while passing through the die and after leaving it, in other words the factors that determine the shape of the extruded material, has not been so fully studied.

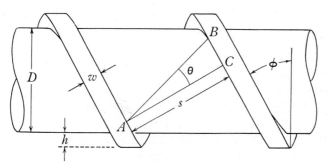

Fig. 5.7. Diagram of extruder screw.

AB = isobar (see p. 302), AC = perpendicular to thread.

Before describing the results of the various mathematical studies on extrusion it will be convenient to list the symbols used, as follows (see also Fig. 5.7):

L = length of screw
D = diameter of screw
n = number of flights on screw
s = width of thread channel (measured perpendicular to the thread)
w = ,, ,, land (,, ,, ,, ,,)

h = depth of thread channel
ϕ = helix angle
θ = angle between " isobar " and perpendicular to thread
N = number of revolutions of screw in unit time
P = pressure at extruder head
ΔP = pressure difference between opposite sides of one land
z = distance measured *along the thread or helix*
c = clearance between thread lands and barrel
η = viscosity of material extruded
S = shear stress
Z = power consumed in unit time
r = radius of die
l = length of die (in direction of flow)
W = width (long dimension) of slit-shaped die, *or* circumference of annular die
a = height (short dimension) of slit-shaped or annular die
ν, η^* = parameters in pseudo-viscous flow equation (15)

Basic flow mechanisms

Pigott [27] and Carley *et al.*[28-34] show that the movement of the material in the barrel of a screw-fed extruder is the resultant of four flow mechanisms. To appreciate these we must note that:

(*a*) Since the screw thread makes an angle ϕ with any generating circle of the screw cylinder, the rotational velocity (U) of the screw surface can be resolved into a " transverse " component $U \sin \phi$ (perpendicular to the thread) and a " longitudinal " component $U \cos \phi$ parallel to the thread.

(*b*) There is within the barrel a hydrostatic pressure which is a maximum (P) at the head (just inside the die) and falls to zero at the die orifice and the feed opening.

The four flow mechanisms are:

1. *Transverse flow.* Due to the transverse velocity $U \sin \phi$; since this acts *across* the screw channel, it does not affect flow *along* the channel, but only causes a circulating flow (see Fig. 5.8), which, however, can be important in equalising temperature.

2. " *Drag* " *flow* due to the longitudinal velocity $U \cos \phi$; seen in a longitudinal section of the channel, this can be represented by Fig. 5.9*a*.

3. " *Pressure* " *flow*; the falling pressure gradient from head to feed opening causes material to flow *backwards* along the channel; Fig. 5.9*b*. The resultant of this and the drag flow is as shown in Fig. 5.9*c*.

4. *Leakage*, being a backward flow through the clearance between the barrel and the screw lands, again due to the pressure gradient.

If we denote the drag flow by Q_D, pressure flow by Q_P and leakage flow by Q_L, then the output Q, i.e. the *useful* flow or amount extruded, is given by:

$$Q = Q_D - Q_P - Q_L \quad . \quad . \quad . \quad . \quad (5.1)$$

all quantities being expressed as volume per unit time.

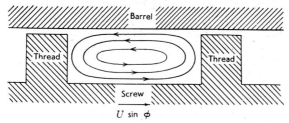

Fig. 5.8. " Transverse " (circulating) flow in screw channel.
(By permission of the American Chemical Society from *Industrial and Engineering Chemistry* (1953), **45**, 970.)

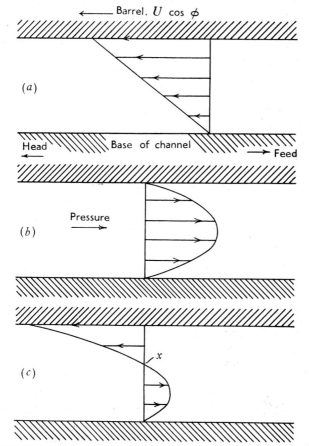

Fig. 5.9. (*a*) " Drag " flow, (*b*) " Pressure " flow, (*c*) resultant of Drag and Pressure flows along screw channel.

(By permission of the American Chemical Society from *Industrial and Engineering Chemistry* (1953), **45**, 970.)

Rigbi [26] points out that the resultant of drag and pressure flow produces a stationary layer at x, Fig. 5.9c, which might lead to trouble with a material having a limited heat life; however, the circulating transverse flow, Fig. 5.8, should help to overcome this by mixing this layer with the rest of the material.

Detailed consideration of flow mechanisms (Newtonian material)

We must now consider how the quantities Q_D, Q_P and Q_L depend on the characteristics of the extruder and the material passing through it. This has been worked out particularly by Carley et al.[28-34] and Pigott [27]; it must be noted that the mathematical treatment is only approximate, though doubtless adequate for practical purposes.

Drag flow (Q_D). For a screw with a rectangular-section channel:

$$Q_D = \pi n D N s^2 \cos \phi \, . \, F_D \qquad . \quad . \quad . \quad . \quad (5.2)$$

where F_D is a function of (h/s) given by Fig. 5.10. For a very shallow channel (i.e. as h/s approaches zero) F_D tends to the value $h/2s$.

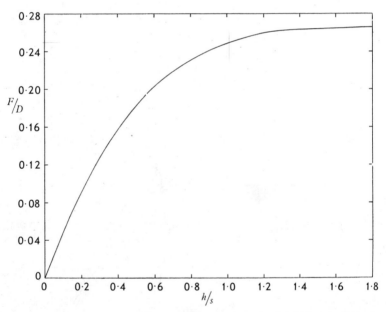

Fig. 5.10. Dependence of drag flow function F_D on depth/width ratio (h/s) of rectangular-section screw channel.

(By permission of the American Chemical Society from *Industrial and Engineering Chemistry* (1953), **45**, 970.)

It is important to note that Q_D is independent of the viscosity of the material and depends only on the dimensions and speed of the extruder.

Pressure flow (Q_P).   This is given by:

$$Q_P = (nsh^3/\eta F_P) \cdot dP/dz \quad . \quad . \quad . \quad . \quad (5.3)$$

where F_P is a function of (h/s) given by Fig. 5.11; when h is much less than s, F_P approaches the value 12.

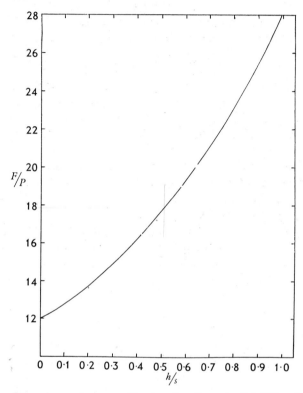

Fig. 5.11. Dependence of pressure flow function F_P on depth/width ratio (h/s) of rectangular-section screw channel.

(By permission of the American Chemical Society from *Industrial and Engineering Chemistry* (1953), **45**, 970.)

If the screw characteristics (diameter, helix angle, channel dimensions) and the temperature of the material are uniform along its length, $dP/dz = P(\sin \phi/)/L$, and hence:

$$Q_P = (nsh^3 P \sin \phi)/\eta L F_P \quad . \quad . \quad . \quad . \quad (5.4)$$

This flow is therefore proportional to the pressure gradient along the channel and inversely proportional to the viscosity; P depends, among other things, on the dimensions of the die because this same pressure has to force the material through the die (see section below on " Flow through Die ").

Leakage flow (Q_L). If the screw and barrel are perfectly concentric this flow is given by

$$Q_L = \pi Dc^3 \Delta P / 12\eta w \cos \phi \quad . \quad . \quad . \quad . \quad (5.5)$$

The pressure difference ΔP between opposite sides of the thread is due primarily to the pressure gradient along the channel, but as pointed out by Pollett,[36] the transverse (circulating) flow in the channel (see above) must also contribute to the pressure difference by an amount which, unfortunately, is not readily calculable.

Moreover, the main component of ΔP due to the longitudinal pressure gradient cannot be expressed with certainty because we do not know the direction of the lines of equal pressure (isobars) across the channel. These might be assumed to be perpendicular to the thread; the formula of Carley, Mallouk and McKelvey [29] corresponds to this assumption, while that of Pigott [27] corresponds to isobars parallel to the screw axis. Again, if the material in the extruder head is at a pressure circumferentially uniform it could be argued that the isobars run in a circumferential direction, though, on the other hand, the rotating screw end, with its projecting land or lands, might easily upset this uniformity.

It is thus only possible to deduce a formula involving the (unknown) direction of the isobars. If θ is the angle between the isobars, AB, and a line perpendicular to the thread, AC, (Fig. 5.7) then:

$$\Delta P = \frac{P \sin \phi}{L} \left\{ \frac{\pi D}{n} (\cos \phi - \sin \phi \tan \theta) + w \tan \theta \right\} . \quad (5.6)$$

whence from eqn. 5.5

$$Q_L = \frac{\pi Dc^3 P \tan \phi}{12\eta w L} \left\{ \frac{\pi D}{n} (\cos \phi - \sin \phi \tan \theta) + w \tan \theta \right\} . \quad (5.7)$$

The formula of Carley, Mallouk and McKelvey is the special case when $\theta = 0$ (and hence $\tan \theta = 0$), and Pigott's formula corresponds to $\theta = -\phi$, though he omits the $w \tan \theta$ term; this second term is generally smaller than the first because w is much less than $\pi D/n$. The other extreme case (isobars circumferential) is represented by $\theta = 90° - \phi$; here the first term disappears, and Q_L becomes $\pi Dc^3 P / 12\eta L$.

All these formulae, however, require correction for the unknown component due to transverse flow in the channel.

If the screw is eccentric, so that the clearance is not uniform, the expression in eqn. 5.5 or 5.7 has to be multiplied by a factor which increases from 1 (for concentricity) to 2.5 for the extreme case where the thread lands touch the barrel (Carley and Strub [28]); these authors suggest 1.2 as the factor for practical use, whence the 12 in the denominator of eqn. 5.5 or 5.7 becomes 10.

By using equations (2), (3) and (5), or the respective special forms (4) and (7), to give Q_D, Q_P and Q_L, and substituting these in equation (1) we thus obtain an expression for the net forward flow or output Q in terms of the dimensions of the screw, its speed, the viscosity of the material, the pressure at the extruder head and (if eqn. 5.7 is used) the angle θ.

Flow through die. Since Q is also the volume of material passing through the die, we have in the case of a cylindrical die (length l, radius r):

$$Q = \pi r^4 P / 8 \eta l \qquad . \quad . \quad . \quad . \quad . \quad (5.8)$$

For a slit-shaped die of cross-section W (long dimension) $\times$ a (short dimension):

$$Q = a^3 P W / 12 \eta l \qquad . \quad . \quad . \quad . \quad . \quad (5.9)$$

The same expression holds for an annular orifice, in which case W is the circumference (assumed much greater than a).

We thus have two expressions for Q, related respectively to the screw and the die, and by eliminating P from these, Q can be expressed in terms of the machine (screw and die) dimensions and speed only. For the case of uniform conditions along the screw:

$$Q = \frac{\alpha N}{1 + (\beta + \gamma)/k} \qquad . \quad . \quad . \quad . \quad (5.10)$$

where α, β, γ and k are functions solely of the machine dimensions:

$$\alpha = \pi n D s^2 \cos \phi \cdot F_D \quad . \qquad . \quad . \quad . \quad . \quad . \quad . \quad \text{(from eqn. 5.2)}$$

$$\beta = (n s h^3 \sin \phi)/L F_P \quad . \qquad . \quad . \quad . \quad . \quad . \quad \text{(from eqn. 5.4)}$$

$$\gamma = \frac{\pi D c^3 \tan \phi}{12 w L} \left\{ \frac{\pi D}{n} (\cos \phi - \sin \phi \tan \theta) + w \tan \theta \right\} \quad \text{(from eqn. 5.7)}$$

$$k = \pi r^4 / 8 l \quad . \qquad . \quad . \quad . \quad . \quad . \quad \text{(cylindrical die; from eqn. 5.8)}$$

$$\text{or } a^3 W / 12 l \quad . \qquad . \quad . \quad . \quad . \quad . \quad \text{(slit or annulus; from eqn. 5.9)}$$

Under these conditions, therefore, the output for a Newtonian material should be proportional to the screw speed (N) but independent of viscosity.

Dependence of output (Q) on pressure, speed and die dimensions. Eqn. 5.1 can be written:

$$Q = \alpha N - (\beta + \gamma) P / \eta \qquad . \quad . \quad . \quad . \quad (5.11)$$

An important conclusion from eqn. 5.11 is that for a given material and screw (i.e. η, α, β and γ being fixed) Q increases linearly with the screw speed (N) and decreases linearly with increasing head pressure (P). Hence the P/Q relationship is represented by a downwardly sloping line, termed by Carley, Mallouk and McKelvey [29] the " screw characteristic ", and with increasing N the line lies higher (Fig. 5.12).

However, eqn. 5.8 and 5.9 show Q is also a function of the die dimensions, pressure and viscosity; i.e. $Q = k P / \eta$, where k is $\pi r^4 / 8 l$ or $a^3 W / 12 l$.

Hence the Q/P relationship for discharge through the die is a straight line through the origin of Fig. 5.12 with a positive slope equal to k/η; this is called by Carley, Mallouk and McKelvey the " die characteristic ".

The intersection of this line with the appropriate " screw characteristic " gives the " operating point ", which defines the actual head pressure P and rate of discharge Q.

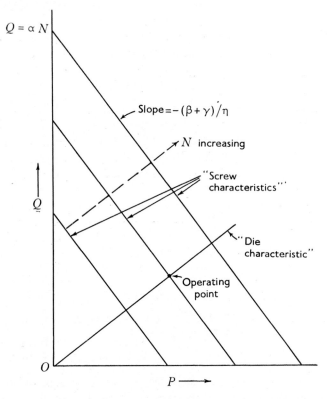

Fig. 5.12. Relationship between Head Pressure (P) and Output (Q).
(By permission of the American Chemical Society from *Industrial and Engineering Chemistry* (1953, **45**, 970.)

Experimental confirmation. McKelvey,[30] Pigott [27] and Maillefer [35] have checked certain of the above theoretical conclusions by experiments on Newtonian or nearly Newtonian materials; the results confirm the theory, and in particular:

(i) Viscosities calculated from the head pressure and die discharge rate (cylindrical die, eqn. 5.8) agree with these deduced from the screw dimensions and speed and the pressure (eqn. 5.11).

(ii) Pressure varies linearly along the barrel.

(iii) The dependence of Q on P and N is as shown by the " screw characteristic " lines in Fig. 5.12.

(iv) For free discharge (without a die), where $P = 0$ and Q is due entirely to drag flow, Q agrees quantitatively with the value calculated from the screw dimensions and speed, and is independent of viscosity, as predicted theoretically.

(v) With a closed head ($Q = 0$) P is proportional to the screw speed, as eqn. 5.11 indicates.

(vi) Observed values of P agree approximately with those calculated from viscosity and machine characteristics.

It can therefore be concluded that the theory outlined above gives a good representation of the behaviour of substantially Newtonian materials that do not slip over the barrel or screw surface, during extrusion at uniform temperature in a machine with a uniform screw and cylindrical die.

However, there can be marked deviation from these theoretical predictions if, for instance, the temperature (and hence viscosity) varies along the barrel, as it may do owing to the heat generated by the deformation of the material (Maillefer [35]).

Maximum output. Carley, Mallouk and McKelvey [29] show that for a given screw diameter and speed and given die dimensions, and neglecting the leakage flow, the maximum extrusion rate (Q) of a Newtonian material is obtained when:

(i) the helix angle $\phi = 30°$

(ii) the channel depth $h = \sqrt[3]{24kL/\pi D}$

where k equals $\pi r^4/8l$ for cylindrical dies or $a^3W/12l$ for slit-shaped or narrow annular dies; for other die sections k would be replaced by another die constant equal to $Q\eta/P$.

These results apply to either a single- or multiple-start screw, provided the land width is much less than the channel width.

Variable screw dimensions. Carley, Mallouk and McKelvey [29] derive expressions for Q and P for screws in which the helix angle and/or channel depth (assumed small) vary along the length. For example, in the common type with a uniform helix angle (ϕ) but having a rear section (length L_1) where the channel depth decreases uniformly from h_1 to h_2 followed by a section (L_2) of constant depth h_2, the output (again neglecting leakage flow) is given by:

$$Q = \frac{\pi^2 D^2 N \cot \phi \{(L_1/h_1 h_2) + (L_2/h_2^2)\}}{(\pi D/6k) + 2 \csc^2 \phi \{(L_2/h_2^3) + L_1(h_1 + h_2)/2h_1^2 h_2^2\}} \quad . \quad (5.12)$$

where k equals $Q\eta/P$, which for a cylindrical die is given by eqn. 5.8 as $\pi r^4/8l$.

Power consumption. The power consumed in the passage of a Newtonian material through an extruder has been deduced by Mallouk and McKelvey [31] for a uniform screw with a shallow channel (h much less than s) and assuming the temperature and hence viscosity to be uniform. If Z is the power per unit time, it can be represented by

$$Z = \pi^2 D^2 N\{(\pi D N \eta L/h) + \tfrac{1}{2}hP \tan \phi + n(N w \eta L/c \sin \phi)\}. \quad (5.13)$$

The three terms in the braces are respectively the energy consumed in:

(i) motions in the channel due to the screw rotation;
(ii) flow back along the channel due to the pressure gradient;
(iii) shearing of the material in the clearance between the barrel and the lands of the rotating screw. (This term, as originally given, omits the n, apparently because it refers to a single-start screw.) The increase of Z with N has been confirmed experimentally by Colwell.[41]

Eqn. 5.13 shows that the power consumption increases with P, and hence is greater if the outward flow is restricted by a die.

Owing to the very high shear rate in the narrow clearance (i.e. the small value of c), the power consumed here can be quite large; indeed, as Mallouk and McKelvey show, this third term can be two or three times as large as the first and second terms together. They calculate that for a material similar to molten polyethylene the following temperature rises could occur in a typical 2-in.-diameter extruder:

Clearance, mils: above	8	5	2
Temp. rise, ° C: below	10	40	100

This shows that the minimum desirable clearance will depend on the maximum temperature that the material will withstand. There is, however, a compensating factor in that a rise of temperature reduces the viscosity and hence the power dissipation, so that the actual heating effect would be less than as calculated.

Effect of machine size. Rogowsky [25] and Carley and McKelvey [32] point out that in a series of geometrically similar extruders, with the same screw speed, operating on the same material at the same temperature, Q and Z are proportional to the cube of any linear dimension (i.e. if all dimensions, including that of the die, are doubled, Q and Z increase eight fold), while P is independent of dimensions. These facts are useful in translating results from small-scale laboratory extruders to full-size machines.

It may be added that the equal-temperature condition is satisfied not only by working isothermally but also if operation is adiabatic, because the rise in temperature is proportional to Z/Q, and hence independent of dimensions, but not if there is cooling by radiation.

Efficiency of operation. Carley and Strub [33] define efficiency as the ratio of " useful power " to total power consumption; " useful power " is the product of volume extruded (Q) and the head pressure (P) against which it has to be forced along by the screw. Hence efficiency can be expressed as QP/Z. By using the expressions for Q, P and Z given in eqn. 5.8, 5.11 and 5.13, these authors derive an expression for efficiency in terms of the screw and die dimensions. From this they conclude that for maximum efficiency the following conditions must be fulfilled:

(i) Q_L should be about one-twentieth of Q;
(ii) $(Q_P + Q_L)$ should be half of Q;
(iii) the helix angle ϕ should be 22° (through a variation of 7° or 8° above or below this is not critical);
(iv) the land width w should be small.

Another definition of " efficiency " is given by Atkinson and Nancarrow [37] as the ratio of output (Q) to (swept volume $\times N$); it is not quite clear what is meant by " swept volume ", though it is probably the same as the denominator in the expression used by Pollett,[36] viz. $Q/hs\pi ND \cos^2 \phi$, described as " the ratio of the discharge rate to what its value would be if the material moved along the screw like a nut prevented from rotating ". Atkinson and Nancarrow's " efficiency " is said to have a maximum of 0·5 (that is, when $P = 0$; in practice, with $P > 0$, " efficiency " is less) and Pollett's expression also has a maximum of 0·5.

Heat transfer and generation. The heat needed to bring the material to a suitable state for extrusion may be supplied either from an external source (heating the barrel or other parts of the machine) or by the heat generated in the material by the work performed on it. Indeed, the latter may be so great that external cooling, instead of heating, is needed to avoid excessive temperatures. Carley and Strub [33] give an energy balance which can be stated thus:

$$Z = QP + \Delta E - HA\Delta t \qquad . \quad . \quad . \quad (5.14)$$

where $Z =$ mechanical energy input (per unit time);

$\Delta E =$ rate at which internal energy is being supplied to the material (i.e. $Q \times$ temperature rise $\times$ heat capacity);
$H =$ overall coefficient of heat transfer to or from the material;
$A =$ area of barrel and/or screw core available for heating or cooling;
$\Delta t =$ temperature difference between the material and the heating or cooling medium.

These authors give an example to show how this equation can be developed to guide the choice of screw dimensions and operating conditions when there is a maximum permissible temperature rise for the material in the extruder.

If heat has to be supplied to (or extracted from) the material by conduction this must lead to a non-uniform temperature distribution. Fortunately, this non-uniformity is lessened by two mechanisms:

1. If the barrel is heated or cooled the screw lands "wipe off" the heated (or cooled) layer next to the barrel wall; this action is the more effective the smaller the clearance, the greater the screw speed and the greater the number of starts on the screw.

2. The component of the rotational motion transverse to the threads mixes the material in each channel by a circulating motion (see Fig. 5.8) and so helps to even out temperature variations.

These facts suggest that it would be ideal if *all* the heat needed were generated by the mechanical working of the material but with no excess heat beyond that needed to balance unavoidable radiation losses. Such heating would give more uniform temperature because the heat is generated *in situ*, and would also avoid the need for large screw and barrel surfaces, that is, large heat transfer areas, to cope with a big output.

Non-Newtonian materials

So far the treatment has dealt only with materials that show Newtonian flow or do not deviate seriously from such flow.   However, as pointed out already by Rigbi,[26] the extrusion of actual materials may depend on many factors, which include the following (besides apparent density and bulk modulus, which are irrelevant for rubber-like materials fed in compact form, i.e. not as powder or chips):

(i) viscosity;
(ii) variation of viscosity with shear rate (or stress) and with temperature;
(iii) elasticity in shear;
(iv) yield point;
(v) recovery;
(vi) " maximum rate of stretch " (highest rate at which an extruded thread can be stretched without breaking);
(vii) frictional properties against a smooth metal surface (which determine whether it sticks or slips at the screw, barrel or die surface).

Rigbi considers *desirable* properties are: low viscosity; rapid change of viscosity with temperature (i.e. high $d\eta/dT$); small but definite yield-point; low recovery; short relaxation time.

As the extrusion of non-Newtonian materials has not been studied anything like so fully as that of Newtonian materials, it is only possible to give certain examples and general conclusions.

Atkinson and Nancarrow [37] have considered the case where shear rate is a general (undefined) function of shear stress, but have not been able to reach a solution entirely in terms of the basic parameters of the extruder. Mooney and Black [40] and Pollett [36] have studied the more limited case of pseudo-viscous flow represented by:

$$\text{shear rate} = (S/\eta^*)^{\nu} \quad . \quad . \quad . \quad (5.15)$$

where $S =$ shear stress;

$\nu =$ a number greater than 1;

$\eta^* =$ a constant allied to viscosity (and identical with it if $\nu = 1$, i.e Newtonian flow).

The quantities ν and η^* thus define the material.

For these pseudo-viscous materials it is only possible to give some general observations on the validity or otherwise of the equations deduced above for Newtonian materials. Although, as will be explained later, rubbers do not obey so simple a flow relation, many thermoplastic materials are said to do so (Atkinson and Nancarrow [37]), and it is possible by using the simple pseudo-viscous flow equation to indicate in what directions rubber will deviate from the equations deduced for Newtonian materials.

Drag flow (Q_D). For a shallow rectangular-section channel the form of eqn. 5.2 obtained by putting h much less than s would apply irrespective of the flow properties of the material, because the shear stress is uniform throughout the depth of the channel, and indeed the equation does not include any rheological parameters:

$$Q_D = \tfrac{1}{2}\pi n D N h s \cos \phi \quad . \quad . \quad . \quad . \quad (5.16)$$

Pressure flow, leakage flow and flow through die. Eqn. 5.3 and 5.4 for Q_P, 5.5 for Q_L and 5.8 or 5.9 for Q in terms of die dimensions would not apply to markedly non-Newtonian materials. Thus for pseudo-viscous materials we have: for *pressure flow* (assuming a shallow screw channel):

$$Q_P = \{(P \sin \phi)/L\eta^*\}^{\nu} h^{\nu+2} \, ns/2^{\nu+1}(\nu + 2) \quad . \quad . \quad (5.17)$$

for *leakage flow*:

$$Q_L = (\pi D/\cos \phi)(\Delta P/w\eta^*)^{\nu} c^{\nu+2}/2^{\nu+1}(\nu + 2) \quad . \quad . \quad (5.18)$$

for flow through a *cylindrical die*:

$$Q = \pi(P/2l\eta^*)^{\nu} r^{\nu+3}/(\nu + 3) \quad . \quad . \quad (5.19)$$

for flow through a *slit* or *annular die*:

$$Q = W(P/l\eta^*)^{\nu} a^{\nu+2}/2^{\nu+1}(\nu + 2) \quad . \quad . \quad (5.20)$$

Whereas for Newtonian materials the pressure flow, leakage flow and die flow are all proportional simply to the inverse of viscosity, and therefore change in the same ratio for a change of material, this is not so for pseudo-viscous materials having different values of ν; it follows that the output depends on the value of ν (though not on η^*), in contrast to Newtonian materials for which, by eqn. 5.10, Q is independent of viscosity.

Behaviour of rubbers

Experimental results. Pigott [27] studied various rubbers (compounded and pure gum; natural and synthetic) for which he found shear-stress–shear-rate relationships roughly corresponding to eqn. 5.15; his data give values of ν between about 4 and 10. He found that this very marked departure from Newtonian behaviour had the following consequences:

1. Head pressure (P) for zero discharge is no longer proportional to screw speed (N), as it is for Newtonian materials; the observed variation of P with N, indeed, agrees with the theoretical relationship derived for a material obeying eqn. 5.15, namely: $P = \text{const.} \times (N)^{1/\nu}$, using the experimentally deduced value of ν.

2. The influence of leakage (through the clearance between the barrel and screw lands) on the head pressure for zero discharge is greater than with Newtonian materials.

3. When a die is fitted, so that $Q > 0$, the relation between Q (output) and head pressure is no longer linear, as for Newtonian materials (Fig. 5.12), but is represented by a curved line convex to the Q and P axes. Pigott attributed this curvature to the fact that when P is small the screw-threads are incompletely filled and there is also slippage between the rubber and the barrel walls; indeed, at open discharge ($P = 0$) the mechanism is largely one of sliding friction, little or no viscous shearing taking place. As the discharge port or die is progressively closed, the pressure in the forward end of the screw increases enough to prevent slippage, and more and more of the stock undergoes viscous shearing.

It is not possible without further mathematical investigation to say whether this explanation of the curvilinear Q/P relation is acceptable, or whether it arises from the non-Newtonian nature of the flow of unvulcanised rubbers. The fact that Pollett [36] obtains theoretical Q/P curves (or more exactly, plots of the dimensionless quantities $Q/\pi hsND \cos^2 \phi$ and $Ph \sin \phi (h/\pi ND \cos \phi)^{1/\nu}/\eta^* L$) differing in shape from those of Pigott suggests that slippage or some other disturbing factor is in fact present.

Consequences of the rubber flow curve. Even the pseudo-viscous flow eqn. 5.15 probably represents an over-simplification, for other investigations (e.g. Whorlow,[5] Bulgin and Wratten,[6] Decker and Roth,[7] Hine,[8] and Mooney and Black [40]) have shown that for both natural and synthetic rubbers the plot of log shear rate (vertically) against log shear stress (horizontally) curves upwards. Indeed, the data of Bulgin and Wratten, Decker and Roth, and Hine even suggest that for natural rubber and butyl rubber the curve ultimately rises almost vertically as if approaching a vertical asymptote representing a limiting stress that cannot be exceeded. Whether this is in fact so or not, there is no doubt that at shear stresses of the order of $2-4 \times 10^6$ dynes/cm.² the shear rate can become extremely high.

Where flow is caused by a pressure gradient (i.e. pressure flow, leakage flow and flow through the die) the maximum stress occurs at the metal wall. If this maximum stress reaches the " critical " value of $2-4 \times 10^6$ dynes/cm.² the rubber at and near the wall must flow extremely quickly. From available data it seems likely that in the die, where the pressure gradient is high owing to the short length of the die, the shear stress near the wall will reach this " critical " value, whereas in the thread channel of the screw (which is much longer) this will not occur.

If the " critical " stress and hence a very high shear rate is reached at the

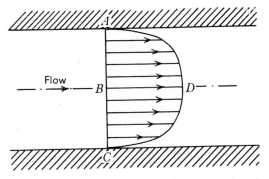

Fig. 5.13. Longitudinal section of die showing type of flow when shear rate at the wall is very high.

wall of an orifice, flow will be as represented diagrammatically in Fig. 5.13, where *ADC* is the profile attained by an initially plane section *ABC*. Thus, the motion is almost " plug flow ", in which the bulk of the material moves forward bodily with little or no shear. Such a regime differs strikingly from Newtonian flow (where the profile *ADC* would have the parabolic form shown in Fig. 5.14), and this difference must have an important influence on both the rate of extrusion and the deformation (swelling) of the extrudate on leaving the die (as indicated below).

Deformation after leaving the die.   The fact that rubber extruded through a die of given cross-section emerges as a uniform elongated body with more or less the same section as the die is always accepted as a natural and inevitable result, but a little consideration shows that there is no *a priori* reason why this should be so.

In the conventional case of telescopic flow of a Newtonian material, where the material adheres to the walls of the die, a section *ABC* takes on successively the profiles 1, 2, 3, 4, 5, . . . shown in Fig. 5.14.   So long as the material is *inside* the die it is constrained to assume these very elongated profiles, but once beyond the orifice of the die, this restraint ceases, and the extruded material will tend rather to accumulate as a more or less spherical mass of much bigger section than the die (Fig. 5.15).

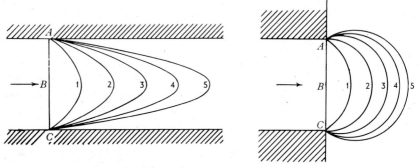

Fig. 5.14. Longitudinal section of die showing flow of Newtonian material.

Fig. 5.15. Flow of Newtonian material at orifice of die.

The reason why this does not occur when rubber is extruded is probably that adherence of the rubber to the wall does not persist right up to the orifice, but only to the point where the hydrostatic pressure has fallen below a limiting value, beyond which the rubber slips more or less freely over the metal (*note* that the pressure falls from P at the die entry to zero at

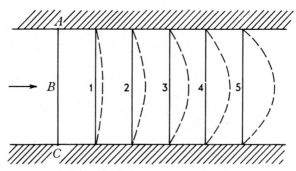

Fig. 5.16. Flow of material with perfect slippage over die wall (continuous lines) or with slight slippage (broken lines).

the orifice).   There must therefore be a point somewhere along the die where the regime represented by Fig. 5.14 ceases; if beyond this point there were *no* friction between the rubber and metal, the successive positions of *ABC* would be as shown at 1, 2, 3, 4, 5, . . . in Fig. 5.16; in fact, there probably still is *some* friction, causing the profiles to be somewhat curved as shown by the dotted lines, or in other words, giving a radial velocity gradient.   If, as is here postulated, the *extreme* case of telescopic flow, giving strongly curved profiles (Fig. 5.14), leads to the excessive " swelling from the die " shown by Fig. 5.15, then *any* curvature of the profiles as they reach the orifice will give *some* swelling.

Storey [38] has likewise pointed out how the existence of a radial velocity gradient (the centre moving more quickly) at the point of exit from the die will cause " swelling ", and that this gradient is made greater, and hence the swelling accentuated, by increasing the screw speed or the length/radius ratio of the die.

It thus appears that " swelling from the die " can occur even with a viscous material having no elastic recovery; presumably any elastic component of deformation would aggravate the swelling.   It also seems likely that the strongly non-Newtonian behaviour shown by rubber, causing a profound change in the shape of the profiles (Fig. 5.13 rather than Fig. 5.14), will markedly influence the degree of swelling.

The above is the merest outline of an approach that calls for fuller mathematical and experimental study.

Pollett [36] considers the radial velocity gradient to be the cause of the surface roughness often seen on extruded rubber; on leaving the die, this gradient must disappear, causing compression at the centre and stretching at the surface of the extruded material.   If stretching occurs locally to a degree where irrecoverable deformation occurs, an irregular surface will result.

Calendering

There is little work of a fundamental nature that helps towards a better understanding or control of the calendering of rubber.   Most theoretical studies have been concerned with the pressures developed when a relatively thick sheet of a viscous material is reduced in thickness by passage between rolls; the pressure concerned is that normal to the plane of the sheet and so tending to force the rolls apart.

The mathematical expressions so deduced are not directly applicable to rubber because they are usually based on the assumption that the material is Newtonian (i.e. strictly viscous), whereas rubber deviates very markedly from this type of flow.   Only Gaskell [42] and Atkinson and Nancarrow [37] have derived general expressions for more complex types of flow, but these are not developed to a directly usable stage.   Moreover, the different simplifying assumptions used by various workers have led to different forms of mathematical expression.

The essential point on which all the theoretical studies agree is that in the mass of material undergoing compression or thickness reduction (i.e. between X and Y in Fig. 5.17) the pressure increases progressively from X to a maximum at a point some distance in advance of the nip, as shown by (b) in the figure (Ardichvili,[43] Banks and Mill,[44] Eley,[45] Gaskell,[42] Hummel,[46]

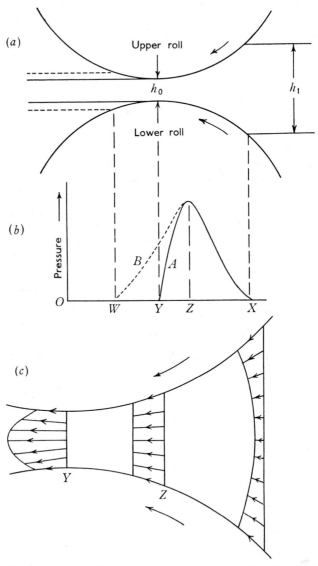

Fig. 5.17. (a) Cross-section of material passing between calender rolls, (b) distribution of pressure, (c) distribution of velocity through thickness at different points.

Atkinson and Nancarrow [37]). This has been confirmed experimentally by Bergen and Scott.[47] This variation in pressure is associated with changes in the relative rates of forward movement of the material at different points through its thickness, as shown at (c) in the figure. Before reaching the point of maximum pressure (i.e. between X and Z in Fig. 5.17) the velocity of forward movement is greatest at the roll surfaces (where, of course, it equals the peripheral roll speed) and least at the centre. As the material progresses forward this velocity difference gradually disappears until at the point of maximum pressure all parts are moving with equal velocity. Beyond this point the centre portions begin to move more quickly than those in contact with the rolls.

On the other hand, these various authorities differ as to whether the emerging sheet has a thickness equal to the nip spacing h_0 or greater than this. In the former case the pressure would drop to zero at the nip (curve A in Fig. 5.17b), whereas in the latter case it would not reach zero till some distance beyond (curve B). The latter, as postulated by Gaskell and by Atkinson and Nancarrow, seems the more likely and would indeed appear a necessary consequence of the unequal velocity distribution (centre moving most quickly) at the nip; an increase in thickness on leaving the nip is confirmed by the experiments of Bergen and Scott, which generally agree more closely with the theoretical formula of Gaskell than with those of Ardichvili and of Eley.

However, in either case the pressure distribution is such that the re-sultant vertical force exerted by the material passing between the rolls acts at some point (at or near Z) in advance of the nip. As the line of action of this force does not pass through the roll axes, the force produces a torque tending to oppose the rotation of the rolls.

For a given initial thickness (h_1) the force exerted is greater the smaller the minimum (nip) thickness h_0 and the greater the peripheral speed of the rolls. For given values of h_1, h_0 and speed the force exerted by a New-tonian material is proportional to its viscosity. Ardichvili expresses these relations in the form:

$$F = 2\eta VRL(1/h_0 - 1/h_1) \quad . \quad . \quad . \quad (5.21)$$

where F = total force exerted on rolls;
    η = viscosity of material;
    V = surface speed of rolls;
    R = radius of rolls;
    L = length of rolls;
  h_1, h_0 = initial and minimum (nip) thicknesses of sheet.

For rubber it is known that the shearing stress is proportional not to the rate of shear and hence to V, as with a Newtonian material, but to a fractional power $V^{1/\nu}$, where ν may be as high as 10 at high shear rates (Pigott [27]; see p. 304). Hence it would be expected that in calendering rubber the resultant force would be less dependent on roll speed than is indicated by eqn. 5.21. However, there is a further complication because, as pointed out by Ardichvili and Eley, the high rate of energy dissipation in the material approaching the nip raises its temperature and so lowers its viscosity, and hence the resulting force. The higher the roll speed, the greater this effect, which thus tends to counteract the effect of a high speed in increasing the force; indeed, Ardichvili states, and the experimental data of Bergen and Scott [47] show, that for a Newtonian material ηV is almost independent of variation in V.

Morrison [48] measured power consumption of a calender and its dependence on roll speed and nip. The variation with speed (V) was of the form ($aV^N + bV + c$), where a, b and c were constants depending on the rubber, and N was about 2·8; according to this relation, there should be an optimum speed, that is, one giving a minimum power/speed ratio. Power also increased with decrease of nip width (h_0), but at high speeds the power became almost independent of nip width. Neither the speed nor nip variation of the power can be reconciled exactly with eqn. 5.21 (bearing in mind that for a given calender the power should be proportional to FV), although the variation is in the right direction. However, it was clear from these experiments that much of the power being measured was that consumed by friction in the bearings, so that agreement with the theoretical equation can hardly be expected.

Eley [45] gives an interesting calculation of the temperature developed in a material undergoing compression by passage between rolls. Unfortunately, for our present purpose, he assumes that the material is free to

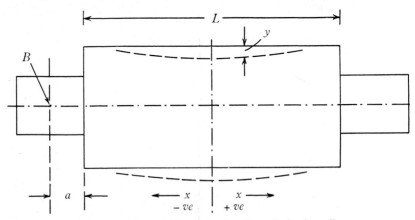

Fig. 5.18. Diagram illustrating bending of calender rolls.

expand laterally, which is not the case in calendering rubber, and the material he considers (cordite) differs markedly from rubber in its flow properties and thermal conductivity. It is, however, worthy of note that temperature rises of as much as 166° C at the centre of the sheet are predicted, although actual measurements gave lower values (about 70° C). The mathematical expression for the temperature rise is unfortunately an intractable one, even applied to a simple Newtonian material, and it seems doubtful whether for such a rheologically complex material as rubber any meaningful result could be deduced.

Roll bending, camber and skew-axis adjustment. One important consequence of the pressure exerted by the material passing between the rolls is that these are bent into a curve, which would result in a sheet thicker in the middle than at the edges unless steps were taken to counter this effect. The curvature of the roll can be expressed by the following formula (based on that of Ardichvili [43]):

$$y = (q/24EI)(x^4 - 3L^2x^2/2 - 6aLx^2 + 3aL^3/2 + 5L^4/16). \quad (5.22)$$

where y = deflection at distance x from the centre of the roll;
$\quad q$ = force exerted by the material, per unit length of the roll $(= F/L)$;
$\quad E$ = Young's modulus of the metal of the roll;
$\quad I$ = moment of inertia of the roll section;
$\quad L$ = length of roll;
$\quad a$ = distance of effective centre of roll bearing from end of working face (see Fig. 5.18).

The maximum deflection, at the centre $(x = 0)$, is:

$$y_{max.} = (5qL^4/384EI)(1 + 24a/5L) \quad . \quad . \quad (5.23)$$

Willshaw [49] gives a rather different formula which, however, becomes identical with eqn. 5.23 when a is much less than L.

For a Newtonian material q $(= F/L)$ can be derived from eqn. 5.21, giving:

$$y_{max.} = (5\eta L^4 VR/192EI)(1/h_0 - 1/h_1)(1 + 24a/5L) \quad . \quad (5.24)$$

In practice, two methods are used to counteract the effect of this bending of the rolls: (i) the rolls are made with a convex profile ("camber" or "crown"); (ii) one roll has its axis set at a small angle to the other (cross-axis or skew mounting) so as to widen the nip towards each end. The limitation of the first method is that the degree of curvature of the roll face is fixed, whereas eqn. 5.24 shows that the degree of bending depends on the viscosity of the material (and hence also on the working temperature), the roll speed and the nominal nip width (h_0). The second method is more flexible in that the correction can be varied by altering the angle between the roll axes. The variation of effective nip width along the roll, using skew axes, is given by the following expression (based on that of Ardichvili [43]):

$$h_x = \{x^2\alpha^2 + (2R + h_0)^2\}^{1/2} - 2R \quad . \quad . \quad . \quad (5.25)$$

where h_x = nip at distance x from roll centre;
$\quad\quad h_0$ = nip at centre;
$\quad\quad \alpha$ = angle (radians) between roll axes;
$\quad\quad R$ = radius of roll section.

It follows from eqn. 5.25 that the nip widening $(h_x - h_0)$ is given to a first approximation by:

$$(h_x - h_0) = Rx^2\alpha^2/(2R + h_0)^2 \quad . \quad . \quad . \quad (5.26)$$

(assuming α is very small and h_0 is much less than R). Hence if the widening is plotted against x the resulting curve is a parabola. On the other hand, the curvature produced by bending, eqn. 5.22, is not parabolic because the expression for the deflection at distance x from the centre involves terms in both x^2 and x^4. Consequently the skew-axis system cannot exactly compensate for roll bending. A practical compromise is to camber the rolls to a degree corresponding to the average working conditions and then use the variable skew-axis principle to apply further small (though approximate) corrections for variations in materials, speeds and temperatures (Chase [50]).

Moulding

The subject of moulding rubber has received very little attention from the theoretical standpoint, and indeed there appear to be few aspects of this process that are capable of theoretical or fundamental study. One obviously important matter is that of heat transfer to products that are vulcanised in moulds; as, however, this problem is common to all processes involving heating by an external medium and is capable of solution by the well-known laws of heat conduction, there is no point in elaborating on it here.

Another matter that has received something like a scientific approach is the effect of the thermal expansion of the rubber stock on being raised to curing temperature. Since rubber expands much more than the metal of the mould, it follows that if the mould is filled and closed before the curing temperature is reached, an enormous pressure will be developed as the temperature rises; Stangor [51] has recorded pressures as high as 10,000 lb./in.² in a two-part mould that allowed no outlet for the thermal expansion. Such high pressures produce an appreciable bulk compression, so that if the mould is opened hot there is a sudden expansion. In a mould of the type shown in Fig. 5.19*A*, this expansion can easily cause the rubber to tear at the " spew line " or line of separation of the two mould halves (*XX′*); this is the trouble known as " backrinding ". It can be avoided by using a plunger type of mould (Fig. 5.19*B*), or by cooling the mould

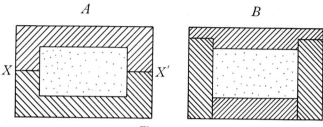

Fig. 5.19.

before opening, or by loading the mould with a volume of stock that will just fill the cavity *at curing temperature* (and hence is less than this volume when cold); low curing temperatures and compounding to reduce thermal expansion are also helpful (Stangor,[51] E. I. Du Pont de Nemours & Co. Inc.[52]).

Bonding of rubber to textiles

It is customary in discussing the adhesion of rubber to distinguish between adhesive failure and cohesive failure. The former refers to separation at the interface between the rubber and the other component of the bond, and the latter to failure within the rubber.

Both cohesion and adhesion between organic polymers (rubbers and textile fibres are examples of organic polymeric material) are functions of the intermolecular attractions between the various groups of which they are formed. It is convenient to refer to this aspect of adhesion as Specific Adhesion, being that which is independent of the geometrical form of the surface. This specific adhesion, arising from intermolecular attraction, could be due to:

(*a*) The London forces of electronic interaction, which decrease with increasing distance between the molecules by a sixth-power law.

(*b*) Dipole interaction if dipoles are present.

(*c*) Dipole interaction if a dipole is present in one molecule and another molecule near it is polarisable. The last two types of force decrease with increasing distance by a third-power law.

The forces depending solely on the London dispersion are small, and there is little adhesion between a plane surface, such as a foil, and a rubber if both substances are completely apolar. The London dispersion forces represent the only type of van der Waals field around a hydrocarbon chain and are the only forces available for adhesion of a non-polar rubber such as natural rubber and, say, a polyethylene foil.

Case (b) arises where both materials contain dipoles, e.g. adhesion of polar rubbers (neoprene, butadiene–acrylonitrile copolymers) to films of regenerated cellulose; as expected, the adhesion is relatively good.

The third case (c) arises if we consider the adhesion of rubbers to a polystyrene foil. A polar rubber, such as neoprene, shows marked adhesion to polystyrene, but natural rubber, which is apolar, shows no better adhesion to polystyrene than to polyethylene. In the first of these pairs the polarity of the rubber polarises the phenyl groups of the polystyrene; the resulting force field due to the dipoles and the induced dipoles is very much stronger than the London dispersion forces and, what is probably quite as important, does not fall away with the distance so rapidly.

Unlike polyethylene, most of the long-chain polymers with which adhesion to rubber is of interest are in the form of textiles. The complex form of the textile surface makes *mechanical adhesion* of greater importance, but *specific adhesion* still plays an important, even if secondary, role. If the fibres of a cotton fabric are coated with a non-polar waxy envelope of molecular dimensions, for instance by reacting the cellulose with a long-chain quaternary ammonium salt, the adhesion of rubber is much reduced. The adhesion of rubbers to smooth surfaces of nylon is probably less than would be expected from the polar nature of the nylon, because the action of

TABLE 5.1

COHESION OF POLYMERS PER 5 Å LENGTH OF CHAIN

Polymer		Molar cohesion kcal./mole/5 Å
Acrylonitrile/butadiene copolymers	(Hycar OR 15)	7·9
	(Hycar OR 25)	6·7
	(Perbunan, I.G.)	6·3
	(Butaprene NF)	6·1
	(Perbunan, Stanco)	6·7
Polychloroprene	(Neoprene GN)	6·4
Polyisoprene	(Natural *Hevea* rubber)	5·2
Polybutadiene	(Buna 115)	4·4
Butadiene/styrene copolymer	(SBR)	4·0

drawing the nylon fibres induces crystallisation, particularly of the surface layers, and this can occur only if there is hydrogen bonding between adjacent chains. This hydrogen bonding lowers the surface polarity.

If the surface to which rubber is adhering is kept constant, but the nature of the rubber is changed, we might expect that the force to separate the surfaces at a low rate of straining (i.e. so that viscosity differences are minimised) would be proportional to the force fields around the molecules of the rubber-like material. The latter forces can be estimated from the heats of evaporation of low-molecular-weight compounds or calculated from polarisabilities obtained from refractive-index measurements. Figures so obtained from the literature [53] have been calculated [54] and are given in Table 5.1.

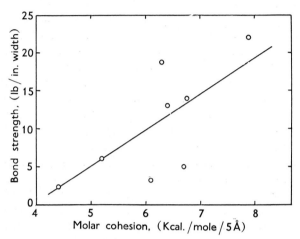

Fig. 5.20. Relation between molar cohesion of polymers and their bond strength to textile fabric (from Ref. 54).

Fig. 5.20 shows a plot of molar cohesion against the bond strength shown by the polymers when used in the unvulcanised state to cement together two pieces of closely woven fabric. The general trend of the results is convincing, even though the spread is large. The failures tended to be cohesive failures of the cements for polymers with low molecular cohesions, while above a molar cohesion of 6·0 kcal./mole/5 Å the failures were all adhesive.

Adhesion to textile fabrics and cords

Textile materials have geometrically complex surfaces, so that not only is the total surface greater than the plane area considered, but the nature of the geometry may influence the adhesion by permitting an interlocking of the rubber with the textile. There are, in fact, two levels of organisation to consider: (i) the organisation of the filaments (of continuous-filament materials) or fibres (of spun materials) into yarns, and (ii) the organisation of the yarns so formed into two-dimensional, and, sometimes, three-dimensional structures. The latter type of organisation results in interstices between the yarns caused by the crossing of warp and weft, and has

M

long been thought to provide opportunity for keying of the rubber into the textile. However, it has been shown,[3] by comparing two continuous-filament nylon weaves, one of which allowed penetration of rubber into and through the weave while the other did not, that this factor by itself has very little influence on adhesion. It is the first type of organisation that is of greatest importance in securing good adhesion of rubber to a textile surface, for it has been shown [4] that the protruding fibre ends from spun-staple yarn are responsible for the good adhesion of rubber to cotton fabrics, and that equally good adhesion can be obtained from other textiles if formed from yarns which either (a) have a large number of protruding fibre ends; or (b) have fibre ends of high individual tensile strength. In either case the fibre ends of the spun yarn protrude into the rubber and are gripped there, and in breaking the bond a number of these are fractured and remain embedded in the rubber while many more pull out from the rubber but only after they have also been pulled up from the yarn " surface " as well.[55] Fig. 5.21 shows the relation between the bond strength and (i) the number of projecting fibre ends on the woven fabric, and (ii) the number of fibre ends recovered from the rubber after breaking the bond (adhesion was measured by a direct tension test, which has been shown [56] to give a better indication of true bond strength than the conventional stripping test). The results were obtained from a series of fabrics in which the number of fibre ends protruding from the surface was varied by varying the amount of spun-staple nylon yarn and the nature of the weave employed.[4] It is of great interest that even from the fabric (A) formed entirely from continuous-filament material a few fibre ends are recovered from the rubber and that these are roughly proportional to bond strength when compared with the fabrics containing spun-staple yarn. It seems probable, therefore, that adhesion to continuous-filament material is substantially helped by small portions of individual filaments of the yarn becoming embedded in the rubber in a manner similar to the embedding of fibre ends from staple yarn, the filaments being broken in two places when the bond is broken, instead of a protruding end breaking off as with the staple yarn.

It follows from the results described above that a convenient means of obtaining good adhesion of rubber to fabric is to make the fabric with a proportion of spun staple in the face to which adhesion is required. This can be accomplished by using a continuous-filament warp and a suitable arrangement of picks of continuous-filament and spun-staple weft yarns; in a plain square weave every other pick of spun-staple yarn is a convenient arrangement, and 25% of the surface then contains projecting fibre ends. Alternatively, if there is no objection to spun staple in the warp, one in two or three of the ends can be of spun-staple yarn. With sateen weaves having a high proportion of the weft on one surface it is possible to use even smaller amounts of spun yarn, provided that it is the weft face that is to be bonded to the rubber. Where use depends on consumer appeal, these methods enable fabrics almost indistinguishable for sheen from continuous-filament material to have rubber adhesion characteristics and hence useful life as good as cotton.[57, 58]

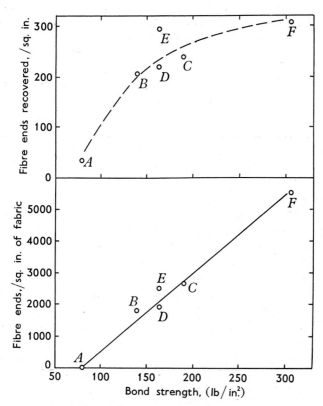

Fig. 5.21. Relation of rubber/fabric bond strength to (i) number of projecting fibre ends per unit area of fabric, (ii) number of broken fibre ends recovered from the rubber after breaking the bond. All fabrics had warp of continuous-filament viscose and weft of either continuous-filament or spun-staple nylon, as follows:

A: continuous-filament weft.
B: 3/1 twill, spun-staple weft, rubber applied to warp face.
E: ,,   ,,   ,,   ,,   weft   ,,
C: 4/1 sateen   ,,   ,,   ,,   warp   ,,
F: ,,   ,,   ,,   ,,   weft   ,,
D: 2/2 matt, spun-staple weft.

The increased strength resulting from the presence of projecting fibre ends has been demonstrated also with tyre cords. Using terylene cords made respectively from continuous-filament and $2\frac{1}{2}$-in. staple, without and with various bonding agents, the adhesion strengths shown in Table 5.2 were obtained;[59] the staple cords had about 50 fibre ends per cm.

The loose fibre ends may be obtained also by abrading a continuous-filament cord.   Gardner, Herbert and Wake [60] describe experiments in which with increasing severity of abrasion the bond strength (pull-through test) increased linearly from 5·3 to 9·3 lb. as the number of fibre ends

TABLE 5.2

ADHESION STRENGTH (LB., USING " H-BLOCK " PULL-THROUGH TEST)

Bonding agent:	None	Resorcinol–formaldehyde resin plus vinyl pyridine copolymer latex	Di-isocyanate	Tri-isocyanate
Continuous-filament cord	2·2	3·0	10·9	13·0
Spun-staple cord	5·8	7·2	16·4	14·5

increased from 0 to 300 per cm.; further abrasion, though it increased the number of fibre ends, did not further improve the adhesion, presumably because it resulted in fibres being broken in more than one place, so producing short lengths that easily pulled out and so did not contribute to the adhesion.

Adhesion of rubber and textile in technological practice

The introduction of continuous-filament materials with high tensile strength has led to difficulties of adhesion which did not exist with cotton. The way the industry has approached this problem is to alter the surface of the textile by treatment with dopes or tie-gums.   This seems like introducing a cement between the rubber and the textile, but it is certain that the matter is by no means as simple as this.   The following treatments are used technically:

(a) Impregnation with a mixture of rubber latex or a dispersed reclaimed rubber and casein.

(b) Impregnation with a mixture of rubber latex and resorcinol–formaldehyde resin (with or without casein) from aqueous suspension.

(c) Impregnation or surface coating with a resorcinol–formaldehyde resin (probably from an organic solvent).

(d) Coating with a polyisocyanate in admixture with rubber or chlorinated or hydrochlorinated rubber derivatives, application being from solution in an organic solvent.

In all cases the rubber is then applied to the treated and dried textile by means of a calender, never from solution in an organic solvent.   Now, it is well known that the level of adhesion obtained by calendering is markedly below that obtained by spreading of rubber on the textile from a solution in an organic solvent. Experiments have shown that calendering results in fewer fibre ends being embedded in the rubber than if the rubber is spread as a 20% dough in a solvent, the adhesion obtained being only about half that obtained with the dough. The embedding of fibre ends in the rubber involves " wetting " the fibre with rubber, and this is much more easily done by drying out from a solution or drying out an aqueous latex than expecting the very viscous rubber mix to " wet " the tiny fibres. Preliminary treatment with rubber latex and casein enables adhesion to be obtained with calendering equal to that obtained by coating with a rubber " dough " or solution.

In the case of polyisocyanates it is more probable that chemical reaction occurs between the isocyanate groups and the textile, on one hand, and the rubber, on the other. The reacting groups on the rubber are most probably the hydroxyl and hydroperoxide groups known to be introduced during mastication. In view of the highly reactive nature of the isocyanate grouping and the fact that both isocyanate groups and the power to form good adhesive bonds are destroyed by water vapour, this postulated chemical reaction is highly probable. Less certain is the nature of the changes responsible when resorcinol–formaldehyde resins are used, but the chemical reaction sometimes claimed may occur, even though at the present time there is no direct evidence for it. In this case, however, the best results seem to be obtained when latex is included with the resin in the " dip ".

A great deal of investigation is required to establish precisely the mechanism of adhesion in these cases, but the essential need for latex has suggested that mechanical rather than chemical factors are still more important. Attention has already been drawn to the fact that even with a fabric formed entirely from continuous-filament material, fibre fragments are recovered from the rubber when fabric and rubber are separated, and that the number of fragments recovered bears a relation to the load sustained by the bond. When latex impregnation is used some penetration between the filaments of a continuous-filament yarn occurs, and, during the subsequent coating with rubber on the calender, contact of the calendered rubber with the latex-deposited rubber is achieved. In this way the rubber matrix is established into the interstices of the filament bundle forming the yarn. We may regard this as the equivalent of embedding the fibre ends of a spun-staple yarn in the rubber, but further experimental evidence will be required before an explanation of the improved adhesion obtained can be worked out along these lines.

Bonding of rubber to metals

Our scientific knowledge of the bond between metals and elastomers is still imperfect, but broadly speaking, two different types of bond may be distinguished. In the first place there is a true chemical bond, caused by chemical reaction between the metal and a reactive group of the polymer, and secondly, there are bonds brought about by secondary forces. The two kinds of bond may be equivalent in strength at any given temperature, but obviously those bonds which are caused by the mere alignment of polar groups will be more dependent on temperature. Another distinction between the two types of bond is the effect of pre-treatment of the metal surface: for those bonds in which surface forces are involved, increase of surface area by etching or sand-blasting markedly increases the strength of the bond.

The rubber–brass bond

A review of the literature shows that the bond between vulcanised rubber and copper or cuprous alloys may be stated categorically to be due to primary chemical forces. Several authors have drawn attention to the fact that copper, cobalt and manganese will all bond to rubber, and that these same metals are the most effective catalysts for the oxidation of natural rubber. They have, however, neglected the equally pertinent observation that these metals will also bond to butadiene–styrene and nitrile rubbers, on the oxidation of which they have no catalytic effect.

The presence of a layer of cupric sulphide on the surface of brass which has been bonded to natural rubber has been shown by Robins [61] and Malden. [62] These authors separated the rubber from the brass by shearing after the unit had been cooled in liquid nitrogen, a process which gave a clean separation except for a green iridescent film on the brass. This was examined by electron diffraction and gave a clear pattern of hexagonal cupric sulphide. It is interesting to note that the cupric sulphide produced at room temperature by the action of hydrogen sulphide on solutions of copper salts is an allotropic modification, the transition temperature being about $75°$–$85°$ C.

The presence of cupric sulphide at the rubber–brass interface suggests that this compound is attached by co-ordinate linkages to the polysulphide cross-links, cleavage occurring at these more labile bonds.

It is known that in the simple rubber–sulphur vulcanisate the sulphur is present in both intermolecular and intramolecular compounds, the former cross-linking the molecules of the polymer by polysulphide chains, and the latter forming " nodules " of cyclic polysulphide on the molecular chains of the rubber hydrocarbon. According to the acceleration of the compound, the amount of uncombined sulphur and the amount of sulphur combined in each of these two forms will vary. In general, increase of acceleration causes the sulphur to be used more economically for crosslinking (i.e. the number of atoms of combined sulphur per cross-link decreases) and at the same time the adhesion to brass decreases in strength. The variation in adhesive strength to brass cannot, however, be a direct consequence of the amounts of the two kinds of polysulphide, because there will be no distinction between the sulphur atoms in each kind. It must be that both are governed by the rate of combination of rubber and sulphur. Gurney [63] measured the amount of copper removed from a copper sheet when various rubbers were bonded to it and then stripped. As the acceleration increased, so the attack of the rubber compound on the copper decreased: unfortunately no measurements of bond strength were made at the same time.

MBT content (p.p.h.)	0·25	1·0	2·0	0·16	0·65	1·3
TMT content (p.p.h.)	—	—	—	0·05	0·20	0·4
Copper removed from plate (mg./cm.²)	8·24	4·47	1·35	7·15	3·88	1·15

The bond strength obtained with different brasses is described in detail by Buchan.[64] The effect of the zinc in the brass is to modify the reaction rate between the copper and the sulphur. A good bond is obtained when the copper–sulphur reaction rate is adjusted to the rate of reaction between the rubber and the sulphur, and hence different compounds may be needed to give the best adhesion to different brasses. The same author also deals in detail with obtaining a good deposit when brass-plating, but a discussion of this aspect is scarcely relevant here. It is sufficient to state that the brass deposited (usually α-brass of 70% copper content) must be uncontaminated by other metals or by complex cyanides from the plating bath.

Neoprene will bond to brass, even when there is no sulphur in the molecule or the compound, but it is suggested that in this case the elastomer is sufficiently polar (dipole moment of CH_3CH_2Cl is 2·0 D) to adhere by surface forces alone in the same way as ebonite bonds to steel. When there is sulphur present in the compound, as is generally advised for bonding, there is usually insufficient to cause a rapid reaction with copper (see " ebonite " below), and the bond is probably caused by both primary and secondary forces.

Ebonite bonding

Rubbers may be bonded to non-cuprous metals by an inter-layer of ebonite, applied by means of a roller or painted on as a solution. Here the adhesion between the rubber and the ebonite is caused either by the sulphur cross-links or by the compatibility of the rubber hydrocarbon in each layer, and the adhesion between the ebonite and the metal is due to the polar nature of the ebonite, the $-C-S-S-S-C-$ group, for example, having a dipole moment of *ca.* $1\cdot6\ D$. Metals are extremely polarisable, and hence an opposite charge is induced on the parts of the metal nearest to the ebonite as the latter comes into contact with it. The strength of this bond is substantially unaffected by lowering the temperature, but at elevated temperatures it is progressively weakened until the bond fails completely at about $100°$ C, when the ebonite becomes soft. Bonds made with ebonites compounded from butadiene–styrene and acrylonitrile rubbers are more resistant to temperature.

The bond between ebonite and cuprous metals is weak, due to the presence in the ebonite of a large amount of sulphur, which reacts too quickly with the copper and gives a powdery interlayer of copper sulphide, thus preventing the surface action mentioned above.

Latex–albumen cements

Protein bonding agents have been known for many years, but it is only recently that the process has been extended in application by the addition of latex to the albumen to make it more elastic. The bond is thermoplastic, and hence comes into the same category as ebonite bonds.

Cyclised rubber (see Chapter II)

During the last few years the characteristic unit of cyclised rubber has been shown to be as inset, and as such it should have no polar groups of sufficient strength to cause bonding to metals, but it is likely that in the cyclisation there occurs some sulphonation of the molecule with the sulphuric acid or sulphonic acid derivative employed. The resulting sulphonic acid groups have sufficient polarity for adhesion to metals to occur. The bond is thermoplastic, but may be formed again by heating the constituent parts and cooling under pressure. It also shows resistance to shock in the same way as do rigid articles made from cyclised rubber.

$$H_2C—CH_2$$
$$H_2C \qquad C—CH_3$$
$$-CH_2—C—C—CH_2—$$
$$CH_3$$

Rubber hydrochloride and chlorinated rubbers (see Chapter II)

Both rubber hydrochloride and chlorinated rubber are employed as cements. The former is obtained by passing hydrogen chloride into a solution of rubber in benzene, when the chlorine content of the molecule is increased up to 34%.

$$-CH_2-\underset{\underset{}{\overset{\overset{CH_3}{|}}{C}}=CH-CH_2- \longrightarrow -CH_2-\underset{\underset{Cl}{\overset{\overset{CH_3}{|}}{C}}}{}-CH_2-CH_2-$$

Products of high chlorine content are brittle, those of chlorine content below 29% are soft and sticky. Hence compounds of about 30% chlorine content should give a flexible bonding material.

When chlorine is passed into a solution of rubber both addition and substitution occur, with the ultimate formation of the compound:

$$-\underset{\underset{Cl}{|}}{CH}-\underset{\underset{Cl}{\overset{\overset{CH_3}{|}}{C}}}{}-\underset{\underset{Cl}{|}}{CH}-\underset{\underset{Cl}{|}}{CH}-\underset{\underset{Cl}{|}}{CH}-\underset{\underset{Cl}{\overset{\overset{CH_3}{|}}{C}}}{}-\underset{\underset{Cl}{|}}{CH}-\underset{\underset{Cl}{|}}{CH}-$$

which contains 68% of chlorine. Chlorinated rubber of less than 65% chlorine content is said to be unstable, so presumably cements are made from the fully chlorinated product. This has lost most of its rubbery characteristics, but is nevertheless sufficiently flexible to provide resistance to shock.

In both cases the C–Cl bond is sufficiently polar (*ca.* 2 *D*) to cause adhesion by surface forces. The hydrochloride may be used for bonding natural and synthetic rubbers to a variety of metals, but chlorinated rubber can only be used for the direct bonding of polar rubbers (such as neoprene and nitrile rubbers) to metal; natural rubber and butadiene–styrene rubber require an interlayer of Neoprene, with which they are compatible. Copper, cobalt and manganese do not form good bonds with these cements.

Isocyanate cements

One of the first of these cements was a solution in methylene chloride of the isocyanate:

They may be used for bonding rubbers of all kinds to non-cuprous metals, the surface of which should preferably be roughened.[66] The bond is thermoplastic, but to a lesser degree than the cements described above. The evidence suggests that in part the strongly polar $-N=C=O$ groups (the dipole moment of CH_3CH_2NCO is $2 \cdot 8 \ D$) are responsible for the adhesion, although metal polyureides may also be formed (Buchan [64]). The isocyanate may polymerise inside the rubber network, or the $-N=C=O$ groups may react with active hydrogen groups in the rubber molecules:

$$R-H + \overset{\overset{\textstyle O}{\|}}{C}=N-R' \longrightarrow R-\overset{\overset{\textstyle O}{\|}}{C}-NH-R'$$

The bonds are resistant to oils and fuels.

Bonding vulcanised rubber

In addition to the compounds mentioned above, a variety of proprietary cements is marketed which may be used to bond metals to rubber which has already been vulcanised.

With Cycleweld cements the rubber surface must first be cyclised by immersion in sulphuric acid for a few minutes, a process which produces a crazing of the surface as well as cyclisation and sulphonation. The composition of the cement is not disclosed, and so its mechanism cannot be stated, but the bond does not appear to be sensitive to heat.

Similarly, phenol–formaldehyde resins may be used to bond vulcanised neoprene or nitrile rubbers to metals. Here the fact that only polar rubbers may be bonded suggests that surface forces are involved.

The use of ethoxyline resins is also suggested. These have a formula of the type:

and at an interface the molecules are probably arranged as shown at top of next page.[65]

$$H_3C \quad CH_3$$

(chemical structure)

non-polar medium

polar medium

At elevated temperatures the bond strength is reduced, a fact which suggests that it is the polar nature of the –OH groups which brings about bond formation. Although the cement has been used for bonding metals to a variety of substances as well as to each other, its use in rubber–metal bonding is in its early stages.

REFERENCES

1. Scott, J. R. (1944) *I.R.I. Trans.*, **20**, 8.
2. Scott, J. R. (1944) *Paint Technology*, **9**, 218.
3. Borroff, E. M. and Wake, W. C. (1949) *I.R.I. Trans.*, **25**, 190, 210.
4. Borroff, E. M., Khot, R. S. and Wake, W. C. (1951) *Ind. Eng. Chem.*, **43**, 439.
5. Whorlow, R. W. (1952) *RABRM Research Report No. 68*; (1954) *Rubb. Chem. and Tech.*, **27**, 20.
6. Bulgin, D. and Wratten, R. (1954) *Proc. Second Internat. Congress Rheology* (London), p. 191.
7. Decker, G. E. and Roth, F. L. (1953) *India Rubb. World*, **128**, 339.
8. Hine, D. J. (1954) *RABRM Research Memo. R396*.
9. Saunders, D. W. and Treloar, L. R. G. (1948) *I.R.I. Trans.*, **24**, 92.
10. Mullins, L. and Whorlow, R. W. (1949) *RABRM Research Report No. 61*; (1951) *I.R.I. Trans.*, **27**, 55.
11. Piper, G. H. and Scott, J. R. (1944) *RABRM Research Report No. 48*; (1947) *J. Rubb. Res.*, **16**, 151.
12. Piper, G. H. and Scott, J. R. (1947) *RABRM Research Report No. 55*; (1948) *J. Rubb. Res.*, **17**, 135.
13. Hepner, I. L. (1955) Thesis, University of London.
13a. Welding, G. N. (1957) Private communication.
14. Cotton, F. H. (1941) *I.R.I. Trans.*, **16**, 303, 322.
15. Wake, W. C. (1955) *RABRM Research Report No. 75*; (1957) *I.R.I. Trans.*, **33**, 71.
16. Havenhill, R. S., Carlson, L. E., Emery, H. F. and Rankin, J. J. (1951) *I.R.I. Trans.*, **27**, 339.
17. Havenhill, R. S., Carlson, L. E., Emery, H. F. and Rankin, J. J. (1953) *Ind. Eng. Chem.*, **45**, 1128.
18. Havenhill, R. S., Carlson, L. E. and Rankin, J. J. (1956) *Rubb. Age, N.Y.*, **79**, 75.
19. Dannenberg, E. M., Jordan, M. E. and Stokes, C. A. (1950) *India Rubb. World*, **122**, 663.
20. Ford, F. P. and Mottlau, A. Y. (1952) *Rubb. Age, N.Y.*, **70**, 457.
21. Watson, W. F. (1954) *Proc. Third Rubber Tech. Conf.* (Cambridge: Heffer), p. 553.

22. Watson, W. F. (1955) *Ind. Eng. Chem.*, **47**, 1281.
23. Parkinson, D. (1951) *Brit. J. appl. Phys.*, **2**, 273.
24. Gessler, A. M. and Rehner, J., Jr. (1955) *Rubb. Age, N.Y.*, **77**, 875.
25. Rogowsky, Z. (1947) *Proc. Inst. Mech. Engrs.*, **156**, 56.
26. Rigbi, Z. (1950) *Brit. Plastics*, **23**, 100.
27. Pigott, W. T. (1951) *Trans. Amer. Soc. Mech. Engrs.*, **73**, 947.
28. Carley, J. F. and Strub, R. A. (1953) *Ind. Eng. Chem.*, **45**, 970.
29. Carley, J. F., Mallouk, R. S. and McKelvey, J. M. (1953) *Ind. Eng. Chem.*, **45**, 974.
30. McKelvey, J. M. (1953) *Ind. Eng. Chem.*, **45**, 982.
31. Mallouk, R. S. and McKelvey, J. M. (1953) *Ind. Eng. Chem.*, **45**, 987.
32. Carley, J. F. and McKelvey, J. M. (1953) *Ind. Eng. Chem.*, **45**, 989.
33. Carley, J. F. and Strub, R. A. (1953) *Ind. Eng. Chem.*, **45**, 978.
34. Jepson, C. H. (1953) *Ind. Eng. Chem.*, **45**, 992.
35. Maillefer, C. (1954) *Rev. gén. Caoutch.*, **31**, 563.
36. Pollett, W. F. O. (Oct. 1956) Paper read at Symposium on *Extrusion of High Polymers*, National College of Rubber Technology, London.
37. Atkinson, E. B. and Nancarrow, H. A. (1951) *Trans. Plastics Inst.*, **19**, 23.
38. Storey, E. B. (1952) *Rubb. Age, N.Y.*, **72**, 377.
39. Tunstall, H. A. (1950) *Distribution of Electricity*, **23**, 330, 354.
40. Mooney, M. and Black, S. A. (1952) *J. Coll. Sci.*, **7**, 204.
41. Colwell, R. E. (1953) *S.P.E. Journal*, **9**, No. 6 (June), pp. 16, 67.
42. Gaskell, R. E. (1950) *J. appl. Mech.*, **17**, 334.
43. Ardichvili, G. (1938) *Kautsch. u. Gummi*, **14**, 23.
44. Banks, W. H. and Mill, C. C. (1954) *Proc. roy. Soc.*, **223A**, 414.
45. Eley, D. D. (1946) *J. Polymer Sci.*, **1**, 529, 535.
46. Hummel, C. (1956) *J. Oil Col. Chem. Ass.*, **39**, 777.
47. Bergen, J. T. and Scott, G. W. (1951) *J. appl. Mech.*, **18**, 101.
48. Morrison, J. (1928) *I.R.I. Trans.*, **3**, 480.
49. Willshaw, H. (1956) *Calenders for Rubber Processing* (London).
50. Chase, D. C. (1950) *Brit. Plastics*, **23**, 122.
51. Stangor, E. L. (1947) *Rubb. Age, N.Y.*, **60**, 439.
52. E.I. Du Pont de Nemours & Co. Inc. (1955) *Mechanical Moulded Goods: Neoprene and Hypalon* (Wilmington, U.S.A.).
53. Mark, H. (1940) *The Chemistry of Large Molecules* (New York); (1928) *International Critical Tables* (New York), Vol. 3.
54. Wake, W. C. (1954) *Adhesion and Adhesives, Fundamentals and Practice* (London: Soc. Chem. Ind.).
55. Wake, W. C. (1954) *Proc. Inst. Rubb. Ind.*, **1**, 176.
56. Borroff, E. M. and Wake, W. C. (1949) *I.R.I. Trans.*, **25**, 199.
57. Wake, W. C. (1953) *Manufacturing Clothier*, **15**, 163.
58. Research Association of British Rubber Manufacturers (1953) *Maker-Up*, **29**, No. 2, 105.
59. Gardner, E. R., Gundavda, S. P., Herbert, A. E., Hillier, K. W. and Wake, W. C. (1955) *RABRM Research Memo. R400*.
60. Gardner, E. R., Herbert, A. E. and Wake, W. C. (1954) *Proc. Third Rubber Tech. Conf.* (Cambridge: Heffer), p. 684.
61. Robins, W. G. H. (1946) D.I.C. Thesis, London University.
62. Malden, J. W. (1951) *I.R.I. Trans.*, **27**, 175.
63. Gurney, W. A. (1945) *I.R.I. Trans.*, **21**, 38.
64. Buchan, S. (1948) *Rubber to Metal Bonding* (London: Crosby Lockwood).
65. de Bruyne, N. A. (1953) *Research*, **6**, 370.
66. Buist, J. M. and Naunton, W. J. S. (1950) *I.R.I Trans.*, **25**, 380.

CHAPTER V

PART TWO

PRACTICAL PROCESSING

by

M. M. HEYWOOD

The treatment of rubbers on receipt at the rubber factory

Natural rubber is packed according to the specifications issued by the Rubber Trades Association, and the packing method varies with the grade. In the past cases were used for the high grades of white first latex crêpe and shoe soleings, but today cases are used only for white soleing crêpes. The other grades are either wrapped in sheets of rubber, fibre mats, plastic-lined paper bags or sacking, or sometimes without any protective cover. *Synthetic rubbers* are usually packed in paper bags or metal canisters. Suppliers of *reclaimed rubber* are now following the procedure of the natural-rubber producers and ship in bulk to the larger users such as the tyre industry. Since the advent of SBR, this industry uses a higher percentage of reclaim than hitherto and the bulk shipment procedure for tyre reclaims has been extended to the other types. Storage methods are similar to those of natural rubber and, of course, no heating is required to render this product ready for use.

The weight, the number of the bales in the consignment and shipping marks appear on the container or on a sheet of rubber attached to un-wrapped bales. On receipt the rubber is visually examined for obvious damage, such as that caused by water or contamination during transit. If damage has occurred or the quality is inferior for its type, this is noted, and a claim is made on the supplier.

Storage methods depend on available facilities. The rubber should be protected from the weather, and if inside storage is not available, then waterproof covers should be used, care being taken that water will not collect and that the bales at the top of the stack have an air space between them and the protective covering. When stacking the bales, a height of four bales is sufficient if they are to be man-handled, but higher stacks can be built up with the aid of mechanical handling appliances. If stacked in the open, the rubber in the lowest layer should be raised from the ground using a concrete base and duck boards. The grade of each stack should be identifiable, and stacks should be used in rotation.

Cleaning processes depend on the ultimate use of the rubber, and can take place, at the discretion of the user, either before or after the rubber has been warmed in preparation for cutting.   If the rubber is fully wrapped, then a good method is to pull off the wrappings and assign these sheets to a lower grade—for example, degrade the wrapper sheets on RSS1. or 1.X. to RSS3, or degrade crêpe wrapper sheets to a " C " blanket.   These wrapper sheets may, however, be washed and after drying used in their original grade, or they may be strained.   Also it is possible with some bales of smoked sheet to scrub the outside of the bale and use the whole bale in its original grade.   Sacking and matting coverings, particularly the former, are removed by cutting off with knives, and sometimes it is necessary to use water or a jet of steam to aid removal.   The " fuz " from both mats and sacking can be burned off, but obviously care must be exercised not to burn the rubber.

Unwrapped rubber can usually be well brushed and used afterwards without further attention; synthetic rubbers need only the removal of the paper covers or metal containers.   After preparation the rubber should be stored in clean receptacles.

Before cutting natural rubber it is desirable to bring the temperature of the rubber to about 80° F, and this can be accomplished by storing in suitably heated rooms for seven days at 100° F or in heated chambers for a few hours, taking care that the rubber does not remain heated long enough to become damaged.   Hot air blown over the rubber is a very safe procedure.   If the rubber is stacked on staging over heated pipes watch the surface nearest to the pipes; do not let the bales lie too long in the same position, but turn them over.   Other methods of warming may be applied, depending on facilities available.

Cutting and blending

The bales of rubber are now divided into pieces of a size suitable for weighing and in preparation for mastication before compounding. Dividing is accomplished in many ways, but chiefly by some form of guillotine, constructed to operate with a rising table or a falling knife, which may have one or more blades.

The power required to divide the bale depends on the number of blades cutting at the same time, the speed at which the rubber is cut and the temperature of the mass of rubber.   The centre of a bale may remain " frozen " even when the rubber up to 6 in. in from the sides is warm. The pressure on the piston actuating the knife (if down stroke), or the ram of the supporting table (if up stroke), varies with the type of machine, but pressures of 2,000 lb./in.² are quite common.   Speeds of cutting again vary.   For example, on a multiple-knife splitter bales can be split into eight pieces at one movement in 1 minute, and on a single-blade press the blade can be pushed through a bale of warmed smoked sheet in a tenth of a minute.

After cutting, the rubber can be stored in any clean receptacle suited to the output of the factory. If the rubber is warm, then quicker usage is desirable than if cold rubber only is available, as warm rubber forms a band quicker than cold rubber when premasticated or mixed in mills.

In an attempt to produce a uniform plasticity and rate of cure, rubber is blended, and many methods have been used with varied degrees of success. Naturally the larger the quantity available, the more easily a blend can be duplicated, and blending is often practised by large users making one product.

The smaller user has to be content by blending, say, ten bales, whereas a large tyre firm may blend many hundreds of bales, ending up with a random mixture on the floor of the blending room. This then needs quartering to pieces of such a size that at least four pieces from four different bales ultimately come together at the masticating point. It is hoped that technically classified rubber will eventually obviate blending in the user factory.

Mastication

The five major methods of mastication are Mill, Banbury, Intermix, Werner Pfleiderer and the Gordon Plasticator, the " tool " used being that most suitable for the particular requirement. The " through-put " depends on the size of the tool, and only the Plasticator is a continuous processing machine. According to the plasticity required, the rubber may be masticated once or a number of times, cooling of the rubber to room temperatures taking place after each successive mastication.

The maximum economical time for one or more than one mastication is determined by experiment, and depends on four items: tool size, batch size, grade of rubber and temperature of the rubber during mastication. A 84-in. × 22-in. mill takes 300 lb. of smoked sheet and after 18–20 minutes the rubber does not soften appreciably more. With a " C " blanket type of crêpe, 20–22 minutes is an economical time. A 60-in. × 22-in. mill masticates 200 lb. of rubber in the same time.

When the rubber has banded itself round the slow roll of a mill the mill man, with the aid of a short-bladed knife, cuts the rubber band from one end of the mill towards the middle and across the face to within 6 in. of the opposite end. All rubber passes through the nip and drops into the mill pan, except the 6-in. band to which the bulk still remains attached. The knife is then removed and the rubber climbs up the face of the slow roll back into the nip. This operation is repeated a number of times until the rubber has been masticated to the required degree.

An alternative method is to cut and roll the rubber, first from one end of the roll and then return the roll (sometimes called a " pig ") to the nip, repeating the operation from alternative ends of the front roll until mastication is completed. The thickness of the rubber covering the roll is about $\frac{3}{8}$ in.

On some mills a mechanical escalator takes the rubber from the mill in the form of a band, causing the rubber to travel through a set course in the air above the mill. On its travel it may be cooled by a spray of water and then returned to the nip for further milling.

There is also the use of the so-called mill apron, which is an endless belt placed between the mill rolls and the mill pan. When rubber is on the mill the belt is lying on the mill pan, and the rubber can be cut through across its width and dropped on to the mill apron. The belt is raised mechanically to the level of the crown of the front roll; the rubber is then raised on the belt, and the friction of the belt plus the rubber on the front roll causes the belt to travel in the same direction on the front roll, which in turn causes the rubber to be returned to the nip of the mill.

The rubber can be removed from the mill in rolls or sheets of a handy size, marked with the grade (a factory code is usual) and lightly dusted or wetted with a non-stick solution. A roll is not cooled before being placed in a suitable storage rack, but sheets are usually cooled before storage. Little value is obtained by premasticating synthetics. Mastication can also be carried out in internal mixers, such as the Banbury Mixer and the Intermix (or a plasticator can be used).

If high-temperature plastication is done in a Banbury the through-put is greater; 100 lb./min. is quite common, and the dumping temperature is as high as that obtained with a Gordon Plasticator.

In addition to the Internal Mixers referred to above, both of which are characterised by having a ram to hold the rubber in the rotors, there is the Werner Pfleiderer, a machine much used in Continental Europe. It is an internal mixer sometimes fitted with a top weight or ram.

The lay-out of the department where the raw materials are weighed varies widely from factory to factory, depending on the type of product made. Automatic weighing is possible where the through-put is based on a few stocks which are used in large quantities, such as in the tyre industry, but where, say, over 100 different stocks are in circulation, in weights of up to 1,000 lb. each, mechanisation is impractical. In the plants using big daily weights, particularly in those using carbon blacks, silo storage of black is practised. The black is fed by gravity to automatic scales set to the required weights, and delivered by conveyor to the internal mixer.

Rubber is not easily moved by machinery, and it is usually loaded manually on to a conveyor, of which the scale platform is a separate unit.

After weighing, the rubber is transferred to the mixing unit. Any master-batch can be similarly handled.

Solid fatty products can be melted, and materials normally liquid at room temperature are fed, via a measuring device, straight into the mixing chamber of the internal mixer. Variations on this method are numerous.

In the smaller compounding units use is often made of the packages in which the pigments are received at silos for measuring the pigments used in the greatest weights. The powders are taken from the containers by suitable scoops, and placed into a tared container situated on a scale pan. It is advisable to place the most important and vital ingredients in a separate container and to recheck their weights before delivery to the mixing unit.

Mixing

The feed stocks which are common to all products are natural and synthetic rubbers and reclaimed rubber, sulphur, accelerators, anti-oxidants, softeners, zinc oxide and fatty acids. Also the following are specified for the products in the table below. The list is not exhaustive.

Tyres	*Shoes*	*Proofings*	*Moulded mechanicals*
Carbon blacks	Carbon blacks	Reinforcing	Carbon blacks
Retarders	Mineral fillers	Mineral fillers	Mineral fillers
	Coloured pigments	Coloured pigments	Coloured pigments
	Oil substitutes	Oil substitutes	Oil substitutes

The weight required in a given period fixes the milling and storage capacity required. We must assume a figure for capacity per 24 hours before the calculation can be done.

Example of capacity calculation

Requirement: 100,000 lb. per 24 hours, with a stock containing 60% natural rubber. This would require 60,000 lb. of rubber. Assume the stock will be masterbatched mixed and that a carbon-black tread stock is to be mixed in the following proportions:

Smoked sheet	100
Black	50
Zinc oxide	5
Sulphur	2·75
MBTS	0·7
Stearic acid	2·0
Antioxidant	1·0
Pine tar	2·5
	163·25

The daily requirement is approximately:

	Lb.
Rubber	60,000
Black	30,000
Zinc oxide	3,200
Sulphur	1,600
MBT	240
Stearic acid	1,200
Antioxidant	600
Pine tar	1,600

An internal mixer plus mill is used for all mixing purposes.

Mixing plan

1. Pre-masticate 60,000 lb. rubber.
2. Mix a 40–60 rubber/black masterbatch containing also pine tar and stearic acid.
3. Mix ZnO and accelerator masterbatches.
4. Final mix—masterbatch, antioxidants, accelerator, and zinc oxide. Add sulphur in internal mixer 2 minutes before dumping.

Timing the operations

1. 60,000 lb. masticated rubber 300-lb. batches = 200 batches at 2,100 lb./hour = $28\frac{1}{2}$ hours internal mixer; $28\frac{1}{2}$ hours mill.

2. Mix black masterbatch—8 minutes per 350 lb. = 2,600 lb./hour for internal mixer and mill.

Note: Each 100 lb. of final stock requires 75 lb. of masterbatch, therefore 100,000 lb. final requires 75,000 lb. of black masterbatch, which will take 29 hours to mix.

3. It is essential to ensure a dispersion of certain of the compounding materials in the final batch. To individually masterbatch the zinc oxide and the accelerator, suggested proportions are 75% ZnO, 25% rubber, and for the accelerator a masterbatch of 25% accelerator and 75% rubber is advised.

Assuming the zinc oxide is mixed at the rate of 4,000 lb./hour and the accelerator at 1,500 lb./hour, together the time required to furnish the required amount will total 2 hours.

4. We still have to mix the final batch, which totals 100,000 lb., as 350 lb. are mixed in 6 minutes, this will take $28\frac{1}{2}$ hours.

Now total up the time for the complete mixing cycle:

	Hours
Mastication	28·5
Black masterbatch	29·00
Other ,,	2·00
Final ,,	28·5
	88·00

Additional time is taken between each change (and particularly after an accelerator masterbatch) in cleaning the mixing machines of any loose materials which may remain in the tool. This can be done by the masticating of one or two batches of rubber, care being taken that such "clean outs" are properly tagged to show what they are and disposed of by working away into suitable batches. For example, "clean out" after a zinc oxide masterbatch can be used as the rubber, or part of the rubber, when further zinc oxide batches are mixed. The rubber after an accelerator batch is worked away in a similar batch.

To the total time of 88·0 hours about 13 hours can be added for fatigue of personnel and other variables which occur in the most efficient of production units. We then have roughly 100 hours for the mixing operations, which in all require four mixing units and, although for economical production machines should be fully occupied, no production is possible if a major breakdown occurs. The question therefore arises, whether more units, each of lesser capacity, or duplicated units should be used.

The figures given are merely one example, and many factories mix tread stock final batches using masterbatches at the rate of 7,500 lb./hour, often using a high percentage of SBR.

A specification indicating to the mixing operator the sequence of operations should be available at the mixing unit to guide him. As an example, using an internal mixer to mix a stock using a masterbatch:

Add all rubbers and pigment masterbatch at 0 min.	Weight up.	
Add black	at 3 ,,	Weight down.
Mix for 3 minutes		
Add sulphur	at 6 ,,	Weight up.
Dump	at 8 ,,	Weight up.

In recent years, to facilitate quicker mixing in the internal mixers, air pressure has been increased on the piston actuating the weight. Also the speeds of the rotors have been increased, necessitating higher-powered motors to drive the machines, but in spite of an increase in the cost of power per 1,000 lb. of production, the faster machines are more economical, because the through-put per hour is greater.

Storage of mixed stocks

Again weights have to be considered, as well as servicing in preparation for the succeeding operation. If floor space is available and big through-put envisaged it is convenient to store on pallets, which can be moved mechanically. This allows easy checking of the work in progress and any sampling which may be required, such as the location of a batch of stock which is known to be unsatisfactory.

The use of racks, either alongside a wall or in the centre of a room, is a common procedure and is sufficient for small batches. However, the height of the compartments from the floor imposes a limitation on the ease of lifting the material. The bottom shelf should be above floor level to prevent contamination of the contents from the floor.

Whatever form of storage is used, the marks designating the quality of the material should be plainly visible. A periodical check should be made to guard against redundant mixed stocks, and if any are found, a system of disposal should be planned, depending on the condition of these stocks. They may be precured, in which event the only disposal is the scrap dealer or the reclaimer. All stocks which are known to be defective should be stored apart from the good stock when awaiting disposal.

In recent years extruders have been used besides the conventional mill to shape the mixed stock into a form suitable for storage. These can make a ribbon of a width up to 3 or 4 ft., according to the head used, or pellets. The volume per linear foot is such that the stock can be satisfactorily cooled to 80° F before storage, this being about the highest temperature at which stock should be stored. This temperature varies according to the rate of cure, and should be determined by finding the rate of set up on a plasti-meter. During the cooling operation " dopes " are applied to prevent the material sticking in a mass while in storage. With ribbon extrusions, the slabs can be cut to length after cooling; pellets are treated with anti-sticks and cooled after being formed and during transfer to silos. Excess anti-stick should be avoided in both instances.

Care must be exercised, when using such batching-out units as those mentioned, to see that they are cleaned out when stock changes take place, the method used being similar to that employed on the mixing units. If mills are used, cooling of the finished stock need not be a continuous operation, although if factory lay-out permits, it is better to allow for all cooling operations on the conveyor and deliver the cooled stock to the storage point, thus saving labour in handling. It is an advantage to use mills which have grooves cut in the faster roll when batching out.

Rubber stocks as mixed seldom leave the factory. If they do they are sold just as they leave the mill or slab-off unit, and are usually further processed in their unvulcanised state. There are exceptions, however, as when Camelback as is used in retreading of tyres or uncured shoe-soleing materials are cut to shape. More often stock is formed to a shape in preparation for a subsequent operation.

Shaping the mixed stocks

The machines used for shaping the mixed compound are called (1) mills, (2) calenders, (3) forcing machines, and (4) pelletisers, each having its particular application. Operating circumstances affect the choice of machine, and it may be necessary, for instance, to use an even-speed mill where a better job could be done using a two-roll calender.

(1) *The Open Mill.* The use of a mill is limited to cutting the sheeting from stock into a suitable shape for a moulding operation or to warming up stock before immersion in a solvent so as to make a dough or solution for spreading or for feeding a calender or an extruder.

The two major processing machines are the calender and the extruder (the latter often designated a *tuber*, particularly in America). These machines require to be fed with a warmed stock, and mills are either operated alone or in train with an internal mixer for this warming operation.

(2) *The Calender.* For precise work, a three-roll calender at least should be used and, when fabrics have to be coated on both sides with a film of rubber, a four-roll calender is the more expedient.

Many types of calenders are employed today and have rolls assembled in various ways: a three-roll machine usually has the rolls vertical. Four-roll machines are also made in this way, but sometimes have three vertical rolls and a breast roll or in a Z formation.

The roll faces are not parallel, but are cambered according to the intended use. Calenders have been developed recently with rolls askew to each other to accomplish the same results as the camber.

A calender operator should attempt to produce a flat sheet of material regular in thickness across its width and length. Many factors are involved in achieving this object, including stock temperature of the feed, roll temperature, float of the rolls in their bearings, speed and condition of the gears. A regular supply of feed stock is required, warmed up as nearly as possible to the calender temperature, and the supply to the nip must be consistent in quantity and temperature. All variations tend to bad production. A regular bank clearly gives a regular product, and blended batches aid this end.

In calenders with the rolls in line " float " is common and is caused by the opposing forces exerted by the stock in the " nips " and looseness of the bearings; even the lubrication of the journals is a contributory cause.

It was found in the plastics industry that the conventional rubber calender was unsuitable for the production of sheet PVC, and the machinery makers were asked to make new types of calenders. The rubber industry is now learning from the newer industry and installing machines which twenty years ago would not have been considered.

We now return to the operation of a calender and consider first the production of a sheet, and then the coating of a fabric with rubber.

The first essential is a regular feed of stock, employing a sufficient number of feed mills to produce as much stock as the calender requires. The gauge and running speed determine this requirement, of course, and calender speeds of up to 80 yards a minute when coating fabric and

60 yards a minute for certain sorts of sheet are not uncommon. As calender crews are expensive, the calender must be run at its maximum speed.

It is very desirable that calender rolls are capable of being warmed and cooled quickly and that roll temperatures can be held within the specified limits. In recent years calenders have been built with cored roll shells to facilitate temperature control. Many methods of heating and cooling are practised, and it is desirable that some record of the temperature of each roll is visible in a prominent place, so that the crew leader can see what is happening. If the rolls are too hot scorched stock and air blisters will result, and, although for many jobs slight blistering is unimportant (e.g. the rubber sheer built into the crown area of truck tyres) a blister in the rubber used for the leg of a Wellington boot or a football bladder is ruinous, and for such work plied-up stock is the rule. Even when running on to a face tape any noticeable blisters should be pricked on the middle roll. Sometimes small blisters can be eliminated by wrapping the roll of plied-up stock tightly in a liner.

Calender grain must be kept to a minimum, and this can be achieved by running at as high a temperature as the stock will stand without " setting up ".

One very important point to watch is that the final sheet is as cool as possible when it enters the liner. A liner or a face tape cannot be stripped immediately after calendering, but a hot sheet in a liner will toughen up, and when it comes to be assembled in succeeding operations jointing will not be easy if it is to be open cured, and the final product will, in many instances, assume a distorted shape.

In many factories plied-up sheet is run from a four-roll calender, with either four rolls in line or three in line and a breast roll. On such a machine two plies can be run at the same time.

During calendering operations it is necessary to determine the gauge of the sheet, and this is often done by cutting a piece out of the sheet as it passes round the middle bowl and gauging it on a dial gauge, making an allowance for the shrinkage which will take place in the sheet when it is removed from its carrier. There are other methods of measuring thickness which often employ electrical devices; there is the capacity gauge, in which the capacity of the condenser varies according to the mass between condenser plates, and the " Beta " ray gauge, where the mass of rubber affects the passage of rays across a gap. Visible recording on a gauge remote from the measuring point is used in these assemblies.

There are two ways of coating fabrics, i.e. by frictioning or by skim coating. Skim coating is the term used when a sheet of rubber is applied to a fabric surface by a calender; frictioning applies a film which penetrates the interstices of the fabric, i.e. the air space where the warp and weft threads cross over. Frictioning is usually done on raw fabrics without any previous treatment other than drying to remove the natural moisture held by the textile.

Skim coating is generally applied to fabrics which have been pre-treated to remove moisture, and the fibres treated with a suitable adhesive to " bond " to the hot coat or skim of rubber applied on the calender. The technique of coating varies as described below, but the general remarks expressed on the production of a sheet of rubber apply, that is feed, temperatures and so on. Exceptions will be noted.

Control of tension is most essential when coating fabrics, both in the feed to the calender and in the take up. Excessive tension will break the fabric, too little will allow the fabric to crease and enter the calender nip folded, thus causing the fabric to break. In recent years a new technique using pressure-sensitive tapes has been introduced. A few years ago all coating of fabrics, paper or cellulosic materials was done on the spreading machine; today the calender has ousted the table spreader and tapes are being made on the calender. However, the machine employed can be of a somewhat lighter construction than the regular tool, because the stock used for coating is less viscous, or softer than the rubber compound used generally for other purposes. Cellulosic film materials a few thousandths of an inch thick, PVC, glass fibres and polyethylene, are also now being coated on a calender. Such progress is due to the combined efforts of the technologists and the engineering side of the industry, who have at last realised that, in the long run, synthetic materials oust the natural ones. Today man-made fibres are used in tyres, whereas twenty years ago cotton was used. Tomorrow, the isocyanate sin combination with other synthetic materials or steel may be used, but all will need coating with an adhesive on the calender.

(3) *The Extruder.* The terms " extruder ", " tuber " or tubing machine refer to the same tool, which is merely a screw in a tube. Material goes in and either comes out or sets up in the head causing serious trouble.

As with the calender, to maintain a constant output the feed to the tuber must be constant, and this means that the machine must be fed with rubber of a closely uniform plasticity, at a regular weight per minute and with as constant temperature as possible.

The machine is used for many purposes, e.g. to provide material which is cut up to fill moulds for curing, for sections which are open steam cured, such as the surrounds of car windscreens, rubber tubing or tyre treads, which again are cured in a mould after attachment to a tyre casing, and the insulation of wire. In each case the die at the end of the machine away from the feed is shaped to produce the profile desired. Die-making is an art requiring high personal skill of the die-maker, especially where complicated sections are concerned. The method of " cut and try " plays a big part in making a die to give the desired result.

The machine must be capable of a variable speed for take-off, and the extruded section must be cooled before being delivered to the receptacle in which it will await the next operation.

The take-off must be capable of adjustment to the rate of delivery of the stock, so that tough stock will not be pulled down in overall gauge (or stretched), or soft stock will not be backed up (the converse of pulling down). The stock is allowed to shrink before being delivered to the storage receptacle. This increases the cross-sectional area because of the shrinkage in length.

The main parts of a tubing machine are the barrel, the screw and the head assembly. Included in the latter is the bridge plate or spider, which supports a piece of metal used for forming the hole or holes in an extrusion. This piece of metal is often called a mandrel and is made hollow to allow a dusting medium to be blown into the hole of an extrusion such as a rubber tube. The mandrel is sometimes capable of being heated or cooled. The screw, the barrel and the head of the extruder are so made that steam or water cooling can be applied when required.

The screws of the machines vary in form, some having a continuous groove from the feed end to the head (single flight), others having two grooves along the same length. Further modifications of the screw have two grooves at the feed end leading into one at the head. Screws can vary in pitch and depth of groove and also in the clearance between the barrel and the screw. This clearance is about one to one and one-half thousandths of an inch, per inch of diameter of the screw.

The head of the machine varies in shape according to the purpose of the machine. For a tyre tread, a so-called fish-tail head is used to extrude a relatively flat section, and the internal shape of this head is designed to restrict the flow near the centre line of the screw to some extent, and thus achieves uniform pressure on the die. Without restriction, the rubber would tend to flow very quickly in the middle of the die and slowly at the extreme width of the die, thus causing the edges of the extrusion to break and result in a saw-tooth form.

Although the head is heated or cooled by steam or water, the actual die is normally heated by a gas flame, which is often used for local as well as overall heating. The impingement of the flame on a particular part of the die causes change in appearance of the extrusion at the heated portions, a rough extrusion becoming smooth if the flame is applied where the extrusion is coming out rough.

When a run of extrusion is completed it is necessary to remove any stock remaining in the head of the machine. This can be a laborious operation on large machines using heads which are of complicated cross-section. An aid to cleaning is to feed into the machine warm uncompounded rubber which fills the head; on a restart with a new stock, the raw rubber is easily forced out of the head by the oncoming new stock. With machines using cylindrical or conical heads, the head is detached and the stock removed by suitable tools.

The extrusions may be cooled by water, by immersion or spraying, or if the stock is suitably compounded and not fast curing, cooling by the surrounding atmosphere is satisfactory.

(4) *The Pelletiser.* These are special types of extruders with a cutting device to give small pellets which are automatically dusted to prevent adhesion. The pellets are easily handled by belt or pneumatic devices, and hence can be automatically delivered to storage. This technique is used in the U.S.A., but has not been extensively used in this country.

In recent years, the demand for increased through-put, has caused some changes to be made in the construction of the internal mixer. Rotor speeds have been doubled, enabling shorter mixing cycles to be worked, and as the discharge time becomes a high proportion of the total time quicker operation of the discharging door has caused a change to the hinged type of opening mechanism in place of the slide, such a door will open in a few seconds. The mill servicing the mixer is now often replaced by a slab off unit, this in effect is a large extruder with a head producing a continuous ribbon of stock, which can be passed through a cooling trough, air dried and delivered to the storage point.

New methods of cutting extruded compound intended for mechanical moulding have replaced manual operations, and moulding blanks are now produced, according to size at many hundreds per minute, on the other hand there is a tendency to cut ribbons of compound taken off a mill into small cubes, and use this diced material for loading of moulds.

In conclusion, mention should be made of increasing *automation* in the industry. The first step was in mixing when the raw materials were automatically weighed and charged into the internal mixer. Those who have tried extending automation to other processes claim that increased maintenance of the expensive equipment more than offsets the saving in labour costs. With the development of modern instruments this objection will disappear.

CHAPTER VI

PART ONE

COMPOUNDING

by

J. T. WATTS

THE mixture of rubber and ingredients used in a particular rubber manufacture is known as a " *compound* " or " *mix* " and the art of making such a compound as compounding. A compound should be written so that final weight and volume cost are readily available. The order of ingredients in the formula should also represent approximately the order of mixing. Alternative formulae should be available to take advantage of price variations in raw materials.

Technology, developed in the past, has applied to the use of a single polymeric raw material. For example, the basic compounding was developed on natural rubber and applied with little modification to butadiene–styrene and butadiene–acrylonitrile co-polymers. Over the past few years, however, progress has been made in the compounding of mixed polymers, e.g. SBR and natural rubber and in the use of polymers and other organic materials as compounding ingredients. The use of nitrocellulose and cellulose acetate as additives to polyesteramides has been described by Harper *et al.*,[1] polyvinyl chloride additions to butadiene–acrylonitriles,[2] phenol–aldehyde condensates to latex rubbers by Le Bras and Piccini,[3] while work in the rubber service laboratories of Imperial Chemical Industries Ltd. at Blackley has resulted in useful mixtures based on polyethylene with natural or synthetic rubbers, particularly Butyl rubber. The most important polymeric compounding ingredients for natural or synthetic rubber are without doubt based on the high styrene–butadiene resins wherein the styrene content is at least 50%.

The processes available, in addition to those based on conventional rubber machinery, are now placing more emphasis on casting or other wet techniques. Wet processes have for many years been based on latices, the bulk of which has been natural rubber latex, but now developments are taking place which utilise solvent-free liquid materials, e.g. liquid rubber, butadiene–acrylonitrile and polyurethanes, in castings or solventless spreading techniques.

The basic design of rubber compounds is worked out by giving consideration to the following points:

(*a*) the type of polymer essential to give the service life required;
(*b*) the process by which the article will be fabricated.

Having decided on the type of polymer and the technique to be used in handling it, the components of a basic compound and functions are:

> Raw polymer
> Aids to and means of curing
> Aids to processing
> Aids to quality
> Aids to volume cost

It is essential that materials selected to fulfil one of these aims, contribute towards the performance of the compound as a whole. The skeleton described can be expanded to give greater detail, e.g.

> Raw polymer
> Curing agent ⎱
> Accelerator ⎬ Aids to and means of curing
> Activator ⎰
> Peptising agents ⎱
> Softeners ⎬ Aids to processing
> Fillers ⎰ ⎱
> Antioxidant ⎬ Aids to quality
> Special components ⎰

The raw polymer may be either natural, synthetic rubber or reclaimed rubber, mixtures of these, or a mixture of rubber and thermoplastic material. The curing agent for natural rubber, butadiene–styrene, butadiene–acrylonitrile or isobutylene–isoprene co-polymers is essentially sulphur, the insoluble form finding application where tendency to bloom in uncured stocks is of importance, e.g. tyre-repair materials. Alternative methods for the curing of rubber include the use of sulphur monochloride, S_2Cl_2, of particular interest in the production of proofings for the garment trade, and di-cumyl peroxide, where the heat resistance of the resulting cured stock may find commercial importance. Peroxide cures are also of importance with silicones, while in the case of Butyl rubbers alternatives to the sulphur cure are based on para-quinone dioxime or its derivatives.

For certain applications of Butyl rubber, fast cures can be obtained by using a mixed curing system based on sulphur, quinone dioxime, tetramethylthiuram disulphide and zinc diethyldithiocarbamate.

The compounder today is fortunate in having at his disposal a very wide range of accelerators varying in speed from slow to ultra-fast, together with a number of delayed-action types. In making a choice from this wide range, he is guided by the time of cure required, the safety or freedom from scorch of a stock curing in this time and cost. In addition to the range of accelerators, variation in the sulphur–accelerator ratio and the careful use of retarders all contribute towards the safe processing of a stock curing rapidly at higher temperatures.

The thickness of the article being cured controls the time–temperature cycle. Rubber compounds generally are poor conductors of heat and require time for the heat at the face of the rubber to penetrate through the mass. Otherwise, a significant gradient of cure will follow the temperature gradient through the rubber, resulting in serious overcure on the outside when the inside of the rubber has reached a satisfactory cure or, alternatively, serious undercure in the centre when the outside is cured to optimum. The meaning of terms related to curing was discussed by J. W. Schade.[4]

The volume cost of a compound is controlled by special attention to the following points:

(*a*) selection of the right rubber or blend of natural rubber grades which will do the job adequately;

(*b*) selection of the right type and amount of extender, e.g. reclaim, factice or oil; indeed, for many articles, reclaim may form the polymer base on which the compound is developed;

(*c*) selection of the right amount of activating oxide and avoidance of excess as an expensive filler;

(*d*) use the maximum amount of filler as permitted by service requirements; although the total number of ingredients in the compound should be kept as low as possible, thereby saving time in weighing out and processing.

From the previous pages therefore the skeleton of a rubber compound now appears as:[5]

Rubber	Natural Synthetic Reclaim
Peptising agent	
Filler	Reinforcing { Black / Non-black } / Extending
Softener	Processing aid / Elasticator / Extender / True softener
Accelerator	Slow / Medium / Ultra
Activator	Inorganic / Organic

Antioxidant
- Staining
- Non-staining
- Anti-flex-cracking
- Physical

Special components
- Blowing agents for sponge
- Abrasives, e.g. erasers
- Colour
- Stiffeners
- Retarders
- Flame-proofers
- Tack-producers

Vulcanising agent
- Sulphur
- Other materials

Particular attention must be given to all ingredients, including the base polymer, when non-discolouring and non-staining properties are required. These properties as related to compounding ingredients are discussed by Haworth and Pryer [6] and Williams.[7] Care must be taken to select a non-staining grade of rubber, to avoid the use of amine-type accelerators, to use only non-staining antioxidants and to avoid the use of certain discolouring softeners.

Compounds which have to stand up to conditions of sunlight, ozone, oil, solvents or chemicals known to attack rubber should be based on the appropriate synthetic.

Regarding the various sections of industry, processes and materials for rubber cables are discussed by Evans.[8] The methods of manufacture are described, together with the more important materials for use with both natural and synthetic rubber compounds and the properties which these raw materials should have. Types of continuous extrusion and vulcanisation plant for use on cables are described by Tunnicliff.[9] Some of the essential points in cable compounding may be summarised as follows:

Rubber of first quality must be used. In the U.S.A. SBR is used extensively for sheathing and insulation, but its employment for insulation purposes is not included in current British specifications, although it may be used in sheathing compounds. General-purpose sheathing to Specification BS 7 may contain up to one-third of the total elastomer as butadiene–styrene rubber. This includes the high-styrene resins, providing physical properties defined in the specification are met. Polychloroprene or neoprene is currently the next elastomer in importance for sheathing. Resistance to oil, heat, flame, ozone, weathering and attack by soil microorganisms are useful properties, when conditions of service make such demands. The use of Butyl rubber is expected to increase. It has excellent electrical properties, excellent heat resistance, lower water absorption than natural rubber, excellent ozone and weathering resistance and a specific gravity similar to natural rubber, i.e. lower than neoprene.

The effect of various accelerators on the volume resistivity of a high-grade insulation is shown in Table 6.1. The thiurams and dithiocarbamates give the highest order, the high figure with thiuram being maintained even though the sulphur content is reduced.

TABLE 6.1

Smoked sheet	100 parts by weight
Zinc oxide	25 ,, ,,
Stearic acid treated whiting	36 ,, ,,
Talc	36 ,, ,,
Paraffin wax	2 ,, ,,
Stearic acid	0·5 ,, ,,
Sulphur	1·5 ,, ,,
Accelerator	1·5 ,, ,,
Nonox B (diphenylamine/acetone condensate)	1 ,, ,,

Accelerator	Press cure at 141° C. minutes	Volume resistivity at 20° C. ohm/cm. × 10^15
Diphenylguanidine	30	0·11
	60	0·24
	90	0·40
2-mercaptobenzthiazole	15	10·6
	25	11·0
	35	11·4
Zinc salt of 2-mercaptobenzthiazole	15	19·4
	25	22·8
	35	24·3
Cyclohexylbenzthiazylsulphenamide	25	0·18
	35	0·20
Tetramethylthiuram disulphide	6	39
	9	39
	12	44
Zinc diethyldithiocarbamate	2	47
	4	44
	6	38
TMT, 3 parts Sulphur, nil	10	10·3
	20	10·9
	30	14·4

Blended accelerators are highly favoured to ensure the high level of physical properties required, together with safety from scorch hazards. Such blends are usually based on dibenzthiazyl disulphide activated with a guanidine and hexamethylenetetramine, thiuram or dithiocarbamate. Continuous vulcanisation processes utilise multi-accelerator combinations in which the zinc salt of 2-mercaptobenzthiazole is often included. A typical system utilises this accelerator in combination with dibenzthiazyl disulphide boosted with tetramethylthiuram disulphide or zinc diethyl-dithiocarbamate.

Open steam-cured insulations have been cured for a long time by means of tetramethylthiuram disulphide without sulphur. This produces a heat-resistant insulation with flat curing characteristics. The heat re-sistance of the stock and processing safety can be further improved by the addition of a small amount of a thiazole accelerator.

From the range of antioxidants, the performance of diphenylamine/acetone resin condensate (Nonox B) is outstanding in having the least in-fluence on volume resistivity of a series of materials tested, including phenyl α-naphthylamine, phenyl β-naphthylamine, sym-di-2-naphthyl p-phenylenediamine and several others of different trade names.

The essentials of a filler for the cable industry are that it shall maintain a high level of electrical resistance and effect some reinforcement. Talc is a popular filler, but while giving good electrical properties, other physical properties are improved by partial replacement by either stearic acid treated whiting or zinc oxide. In a series of mixes containing 50 volumes of filler the following values for volume resistivity were obtained:

TABLE 6.2

Smoked sheet	100 parts by weight	
Zinc oxide	5 ,, ,,	
Stearic acid	1 ,, ,,	
Sulphur	1·5 ,, ,,	
Vulcafor FN	1·5 ,, ,,	
Filler	50 volumes	

Filler	Parts by weight	Volume resistivity at 20° C, ohm/cm. $\times$ 10^{15}
Talc *	115	7·2
China clay	110	4·3
Titanium dioxide (rutile)	155	4·2
Zinc oxide †	240	2·74
Stearic acid treated whiting ‡	115	2·58
Lithopone	185	1·50
Whiting	110	1·44
Titanium dioxide (anatase)	155	1·16
Halloysitic clay	100	0·57

* At this loading physicals were poor.
† Additional to 5 parts in the mix.
‡ No stearic acid in this mix.

Carbon blacks are mainly used in sheathings. In heavy-duty sheathing, the black must impart a high degree of reinforcement, but nevertheless mix easily and extrude quickly. A GPF black combines these properties admirably, although for higher reinforcement FEF or HAF blacks are required.

Peptising agents when used in cable compounds should not influence the electrical properties. In general, softeners are used very sparingly with wax as the most common processing aid. It facilitates extrusion, and its bloom on the surface delays exposure cracking. BS 7 specifies a minimum wax content for natural-rubber general-purpose sheathing of 0·5% based on the compound or 1·5% on the elastomer. Some of the soft flexible sheathings can with advantage include petroleum jelly.

In the *Fundamentals of Rubber Technology* [10] a broad outline of tyre manufacture is given and the various parts of a tyre described. The parts taking the bulk of rubber are, of course, the tread, sidewalls and carcass. In designing tyre compounds it must be borne in mind that the modern tyre is required to perform satisfactorily as a unit, although composed of steel, fabric and rubber, and it must be designed to give satisfactory service, even though during that service it is continuously exposed to forces bringing about its destruction. Even when at rest, ozone containing air is attacking the sidewall and tread where these parts are in tension due to load.

Tyre compounding in Great Britain, consequent on the manufacture of synthetic rubber here, will be largely influenced towards an increased usage of SBR. Thus, as well as natural rubber, the tyre compounder will have a choice of raw materials for his selection, probably following the pattern:

Passenger treads	" Cold " SBR or blends with oil extended SBR
Camel back	Oil-extended SBR
Passenger sidewalls	Either SBR or natural rubber or blends
Passenger tyre casings	Blends of SBR and natural rubber
Truck tyre treads	Blends of " cold " SBR and natural rubber
Truck tyre sidewalls	SBR or blends of SBR and natural rubber
Truck tyre casings	Natural rubber or blends for smaller sizes

That " cold " SBR is capable of giving superior tread wear is now an accepted fact, but its performance is influenced by conditions of service. In the case of truck tyres the amount of SBR which can be used is controlled by the heat build-up and tread cracking. The attraction towards using SBR blends in carcass stocks is in part to ensure a balance of cure through the tyre when SBR is used as the tread and also because SBR has less tendency to scorch or overmill during the production of calendered fabric.

As reinforcement for the SBR stocks it is interesting to note that the relative behaviour of carbon blacks in SBR is similar to that in natural rubber, but the use of ISAF blacks may nevertheless be expected to increase with increased usage of synthetic. With SBR in casings, the tendency will be to use more reinforcing black instead of the softer or medium blacks, and attention must be given in compounding with anti-oxidants to give improvement in cut growth and ozone resistance of compounds.

Butyl rubber finds application in the tyre industry for inner tubes, tube-less tyre liners, curing bags, agricultural tyres, and development work is proceeding to establish Butyl rubber as a polymer for passenger tyres.

The use of neoprene in the tyre industry is very restricted, and appears to be limited to blends with natural rubber for sidewalls, tubeless-tyre liners and blends with Butyl rubber for air bags.

HAF blacks have inevitably become the standard tread black in this country, but there is an interest in future developments with ISAF types, especially with " cold " SBR. Where tread cracking, heat build-up and tread chipping are not a serious problem, as for example, passenger-tyre treads, maximum wear is obtained by the use of HAF or ISAF blacks. Where flexibility and cool-running properties are important advantage is taken of the superior wearing qualities of ISAF black at a reduced loading.

For natural-rubber sidewalls there is still a preference to use EPC blacks, but no doubt with the change to SBR polymer types in sidewalls HAF, FEF and possibly GPF blacks will become standard types for car-tyre sidewalls.

With the development of improved casings from bonded rayon or nylon cords it was possible to consider a higher reinforcement in casing stocks, truck casings in particular, by the use of channel blacks, HAF and FEF type blacks. With these compounds, although they develop a higher running temperature, modern casings are capable of withstanding these higher temperatures. Due to shortages, however, replacement of the above types of black has been made with blends of FEF and lamp black with successful results.

With the introduction of Butyl rubber in place of natural rubber for tubes, FEF or blends of FEF with SRF or GPF are preferred. FEF blacks are particularly useful on account of their good extrusion properties.

In certain sizes of tyre whole tyre reclaim is used in casing compounds.

With the introduction of HAF blacks the acceleration system has been based on cyclohexylbenzthiazylsulphenamide, mercaptobenzthiazole, di-benzthiazyl disulphide; CBS for treads and MBT and MBTS for casings. Certain manufacturers, however, use CBS in casings.

The safer types of sulphenamide accelerator will deal with scorch problems arising from the use of natural rubber compounds based on HAF, ISAF or SAF blacks.

For the acceleration of Butyl tube stocks mixtures of MBT and TMT are popular.

The use of retarders, such as n-dinitrosodiphenylamine, has brought the

N

freedom from scorching troubles with HAF, ISAF and SAF natural rubber stocks into line with natural rubber stocks containing channel blacks.

Of the antioxidants used in the tyre industry, those for use in natural rubber tubes are selected to confer heat resistance, and those for tyre stocks with special emphasis on the anti-flex-cracking properties and for SBR in particular, resistance to ozone attack.

Continuous vulcanisation with reference to flooring, belting, etc., is described [11] with particular reference to the machines utilised in this process. Additionally, belting or flooring can be manufactured by a discontinuous process, the acceleration of stocks for such modifications being slightly slower.

Belting may be divided into three types, conveyor, flat transmission and V belts. The raw polymers used in construction may be either natural rubber, SBR, neoprene or the nitrile types. Non-flam conveyor belting based on PVC [12] has been developed in England for use in the coal-mines, where it has been successful with elimination of the fire hazard ever-present with a rubber or SBR belt.

Conveyor belts consist of two parts, the textile carcass and the rubber cover. When the service life of the belt will be under moist conditions the textile used for construction of the carcass should be immune to fungal attack, e.g. " Terylene," or immunised against fungal attack by the use of a fungicide, such as dichlordihydroxydiphenylmethane, in the carcass stock.[13] Under these circumstances a damaged cover admitting moisture to the fabric will not cause deterioration of the belt by fungal attack.

The carcass consists essentially of friction-coated fabric built up to a laminated section which is finally encased in the cover. To ensure good building-up properties a stock should be used which is not highly loaded, and in certain cases the presence of reclaim is of assistance. Low-modulus fillers and safe accelerators are desirable. The acceleration used in the carcass must be compatible with that used in the cover, otherwise an over-cured condition may occur at the cover–carcass interface. It should also possess flat-cure characteristics, so that in the case of press-cured belting the ends of each section which have a double heat treatment do not suffer from over-cure.

Cover stocks are designed to withstand two types of service, abrasion and cutting. For high resistance to abrasion, a tyre-tread type of compound is used, but for resistance to cutting a more resilient stock usually gives better service. The rate of cure of the various parts across the section of the belt must be adjusted so that the centre of the carcass is adequately cured as well as the cover. This may be done by boosting the accelerator used in the centre of the belt.

Transmission belting usually consists of laminated plies of frictioned or frictioned and topped fabrics. Little filler is used, the aim of the compounder being to produce a cool-running stock with high adhesive qualities to the fabric over a range of temperature.

The footwear industry is one section of the rubber industry which continues annually to consume increasing quantities of polymers. These are used in the production of soles and heels and complete footwear. Whereas for many years footwear stocks were heavily loaded, the industry has developed to such a large extent for fashion as well as utility that demands exist now for a wide range of compounds and qualities. The range of compounds is well summarised in *Rubber Chemicals for Footwear*.[14] Suffice it to mention here that certain sections of the footwear industry lend themselves excellently to automatic production methods.

Accelerators

The types of accelerator in use today for natural rubber and butadiene co-polymers can be divided into two chemical classes, basic and acidic. Although the basic types were exceedingly popular years ago, their popularity was due to the fact that they could be used by the techniques then known, whereas the acidic types, the first member of which, zinc alkylxanthate, was patented by Ostromyslenski in 1915, were too scorchy. Although the use of diphenylguanidine, of the basic type, was patented by M. L. Weiss in 1922, other workers claim to have used it prior to that date. It is still very popular today, though in actual volume its usage is far surpassed by the acidic types.

The basic types of accelerator include:

(*a*) aldehyde–amine condensates;
(*b*) guanidine and thiocarbanilide.[15]

The aldehyde–amine condensates, which were once numerous, have now been reduced by competition from the acidic types, until there are only a few members left today. These include condensation products of toluidine and formaldehyde, aniline and butyraldehyde and a complex condensate of ethyl chloride, formaldehyde and ammonia, popularly known as " Trimene Base " or " Vulcafor EFA ".

Technologically, the resinous types of aldehyde–amine, as exemplified by the " toluidine–formaldehyde " complex, still find application today in the cure of massive articles requiring a long uniform cure.

The " butyraldehyde–aniline " condensation product, a reddish-amber-coloured liquid of characteristic odour, is a useful accelerator in mixes containing alkali reclaim, its speed of cure, or scorching, being less affected by increasing amounts of reclaim than when the thiazole types are used. It is also an accelerator for ebonite.

The " ethyl chloride–formaldehyde–ammonia " complex is used in the absence of zinc oxide for the manufacture of cut thread of low modulus and high elongation at break. It is also a stabiliser for latex foam, and may be used as an accelerator for polyacrylic rubbers (Hycar 4021) and fluorine-containing polymers (Kel F).

Thiocarbanilide (s-diphenylthiourea), $C_6H_5NH·C·S·NH·C_6H_5$ is unique among the accelerators of today, in being fast scorching but slow curing. It is chiefly used in natural rubber air-bag compounds, where its very slow flat-curing properties help to retard the deterioration of rubber during successive heating cycles. When used in adhesives, such mixtures are stable for long periods at room temperature but set up quickly at 100° C. or above. As a component of the accelerating system used in tube repair patches it is extremely useful, since its rapid set-up prior to cure, prevents excessive flow of the repair patch away from the damaged area.

Of the guanidines, two are commercially useful, diphenylguanidine and diorthotolylguanidine.

$$C_6H_5·NH$$
$$\diagdown$$
$$\qquad C{=}NH \quad \text{and} \quad$$
$$\diagup$$
$$C_6H_5NH$$
$$\text{DPG}$$

$$CH_3C_6H_4NH$$
$$\diagdown$$
$$\qquad C{=}NH$$
$$\diagup$$
$$CH_3C_6H_4·NH$$
$$\text{DOTG}$$

Diphenylguanidine, although still employed in certain cases as the sole accelerator, is chiefly used as a secondary accelerator for the thiazole class. Such mixtures are extremely popular for footwear, cables, etc. Alone diphenylguanidine may be used as an accelerator for ebonite. Diorthotolyl-guanidine as an alternative to diphenylguanidine is frequently used with dibenzthiazyl disulphide for hot air and open steam cures where a quick initial set-up, as an aid to prevent deformation, is essential. It may also be used as an accelerator for ebonite.

The class of basic accelerators may be summarised by the data given in Table 6.3.

TABLE 6.3

Chemical composition	Speed, minutes	Safety	Tensile strength, kg./cm.^{2}	Modulus at 500%	Notes
Thiocarbanilide	120–180	Scorchy	150	55	Sulphur 5 T.C. 1
Formaldehyde–para-toluidine complex	120	Safe	190	70	Sulphur 3·5
Ethyl chloride–formalde-hyde–ammonia complex	60	Fair	185	75	—
Butyraldehyde–aniline condensate	25	Scorchy	200	100	—
Diphenylguanidine	75	Safe	200	93	Sulphur 3
Diorthotolylguanidine	70	Safe	205	103	Sulphur 3

The above data are based on the following mix:

Rubber	100
Zinc oxide	5
Blanc fixe	75
Stearic acid	1
Sulphur *	2·5
Accelerator *	0·5

Press cured at 141° C. Time is indicated in the table as speed, assessed as the optimum.

With light-coloured stocks, all the above amine-type accelerators give significant staining and increased discoloration on exposure to light.

The acidic types of accelerator represent the popular classes today and may be divided chemically as follows:

Thiazoles
Sulphenamides
Thiurams
Dithiocarbamates
Xanthates

The first member of the thiazole series, mercaptobenzthiazole, was discovered by C. W. Bedford in 1921, who found that thiocarbanilide which had been heated with sulphur was much more active as an accelerator than thiocarbanilide itself due to the presence of mercaptobenzthiazole in the reaction products.[16] The first effect noted from the introduction of mercaptobenzthiazole as accelerator, other than the reduced time of cure, was that vulcanisates aged much better than previously.

Mercaptobenzthiazole and its derivatives are primarily accelerators for the tyre trade, giving good ageing properties and good abrasion resistance. MBT alone was widely used with channel blacks, but is too scorchy for use with furnace blacks.   It is extensively employed, boosted with a guanidine or with minor amounts of thiuram or dithiocarbamates for footwear and general rubber applications. When rubber is processed with MBT at temperatures above 100° C, a useful peptising action is developed. Di-

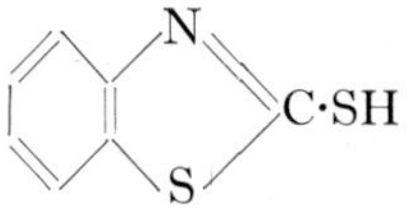

2-Mercaptobenzthiazole
MBT

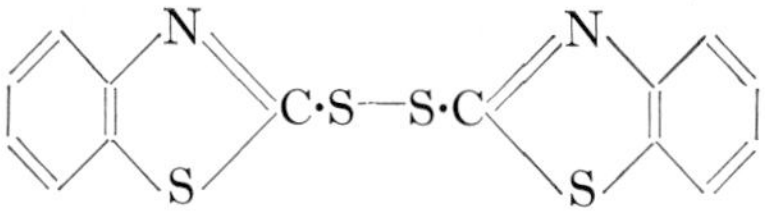

Dibenzthiazyl disulphide
MBTS

benzthiazyl disulphide can be produced from mercaptobenzthiazole by an oxidation process. As an accelerator, it is safer to use than mercaptobenzthiazole and may be regarded as the first *delayed-action accelerator*.[17]

* Higher amounts have been used in certain cases as indicated.

In the tyre trade, in conjunction with a retarder, it is capable of accelerating furnace-black stocks with safety. Other applications are as a general-purpose accelerator-boosted with guanidines, thiurams or dithiocarbamates. In neoprene GN stocks it functions as a retarder. The zinc salt

of mercaptobenzthiazole is sometimes used in camel back on the grounds that it does not bloom in uncured stocks. Used in combinations for the continuous vulcanisation of cables, it imparts high electrical resistivity. When used with zinc diethyldithiocarbamate in latex foam it improves the compression modulus.

The sulphenamides represent the popular type of accelerator used in the tyre industry today. They are manufactured from mercaptobenzthiazole by reaction with a selected amine. They can be regarded as delayed-action-type accelerators, varying in the amount of delay given in furnace-black stocks according to the amine part of the molecule. Accelerators of this type already in production are based on mercaptobenzthiazole reacted with:

Morpholine	n-Morpholylbenzthiazyl 2-sulphenamide
t-Butylamine	t-Butylbenzthiazyl-2-sulphenamide
Isopropylamine	N.N-Di-isopropylbenzthiazyl-2-sulphenamide
t-Octylamine	t-Octylbenzthiazyl-2-sulphenamide

Further safety from scorching may be achieved by the use of retarders. In addition to applications in the tyre industry these accelerators are excellent for compounds containing siliceous fillers, including high-styrene resin compounds, both solid and microcellular and also for flooring. In certain cases, where stocks are based on synthetic rubber, they may be boosted in action by diphenylguanidine additions.

Tetramethylthiuram monosulphide may be used as either a primary or secondary accelerator. As a primary accelerator in nitrile rubbers it is particularly useful to obtain low values for compression set in the vulcanisates. As a secondary accelerator with a primary of the thiazole type, it finds application in natural rubber, SBR and nitrile rubbers, for camel back, footwear and mechanical goods.

Tetramethylthiuram disulphide is the most popular member of this group, and is used as a secondary accelerator to boost the thiazole types or as a primary accelerator with low-sulphur or sulphurless cures in heat-resistant stocks. In sulphurless cures it is used at 2–4 parts per 100 rubber hydrocarbon. Butyl rubber compounds are also cured by TMT in combination with dithiocarbamates (e.g. ZDC).

Tetraethylthiuram disulphide may be used as an alternative to the methyl analogue as a secondary accelerator with thiazoles. If used alone in sulphurless cures a better performance is obtained in the presence of minor amounts of a thiazole-type accelerator.

$$\begin{array}{cc} CH_3 \quad\quad\quad CH_3 & CH_3 \quad\quad\quad\quad CH_3 \\ \backslash\;\;\;\;\;\;\;\;\;\; / & \backslash\;\;\;\;\;\;\;\;\;\;\;\;\; / \\ N-C-S-C-N & N-C-S-S-C-N \\ /\;\;\;\|\;\;\;\;\|\;\;\;\backslash & /\;\;\;\|\;\;\;\;\;\;\;\;\|\;\;\;\backslash \\ CH_3\;\;S\;\;\;\;S\;\;\;CH_3 & CH_3\;\;S\;\;\;\;\;\;\;\;S\;\;\;CH_3 \end{array}$$

Tetramethylthiuram monosulphide   Tetramethylthiuram disulphide

$$\begin{array}{c} CH_3{\cdot}CH_2 \quad\quad\quad\quad CH_2{\cdot}CH_3 \\ \backslash\;\;\;\;\;\;\;\;\;\;\;\;\;\;\;\; / \\ N-C-S-S-C-N \\ /\;\;\;\|\;\;\;\;\;\;\;\;\|\;\;\;\backslash \\ CH_3{\cdot}CH_2\;\;S\;\;\;\;\;\;\;\;S\;\;\;CH_2CH_3 \end{array}$$

Tetraethylthiuram disulphide

$$\begin{array}{cc} CH_2-CH_2 & CH_2-CH_2 \\ /\quad\quad\quad\quad\backslash & /\quad\quad\quad\backslash \\ CH_2 \quad\quad N-C-S-S-S-S-C-N \quad\quad CH_2 \\ \backslash\quad\quad/\;\;\|\quad\quad\quad\quad\|\quad\backslash\quad/ \\ CH_2-CH_2\;\;S\quad\quad\quad\quad S\;\;CH_2-CH_2 \end{array}$$

Dipentamethylene thiuram tetrasulphide

Dipentamethylenethiuram tetrasulphide may be used as a secondary accelerator for natural rubber or the butadiene co-polymers, also as a primary or secondary accelerator for butyl rubber. In low sulphur or sulphurless cures it gives a higher level of cure than is obtainable with tetramethylthiuram disulphide.

The dithiocarbamates include metallic salts of dialkyldithiocarbamic acid, e.g. sodium, zinc, lead, copper, bismuth, also the selenium, tellurium and organic derivatives.

The most important member of the series is zinc diethyldithiocarbamate, which may be used as the primary or secondary accelerator for natural rubber, SBR and nitrile rubbers. It is of particular interest in the latex industry, especially for latex foam. Used in conjunction with tetra-methylthiuramdisulphide or quinone dioxime, it forms very effective accelerating systems for Butyl rubber.

Zinc ethylphenyldithiocarbamate may be used as an alternative to the diethyl analogue in latex work. The soluble sodium dialkyldithiocar-bamates have also been used in latex work, but the interest is now chiefly in the dimethyl analogue for use in the synthetic-rubber-manufacturing industry. As accelerators of vulcanisation, they may both be used in natural rubber or SBR latices.

Other dithiocarbamates which are commercially available include: the bismuth salt for use with natural rubber or SBR; the cupric salt for SBR or Butyl; the lead salt for SBR, natural rubber or Butyl; selenium and

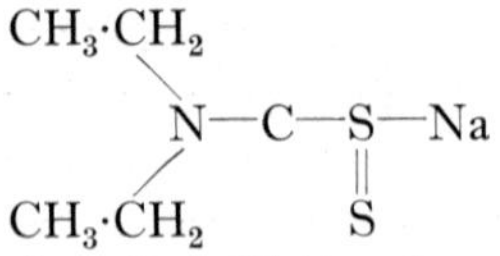

$$CH_3 \cdot CH_2 \diagdown N - C - S - Na$$

Sodium diethyldithiocarbamate

$$CH_3 \diagdown N - C - S - Na$$

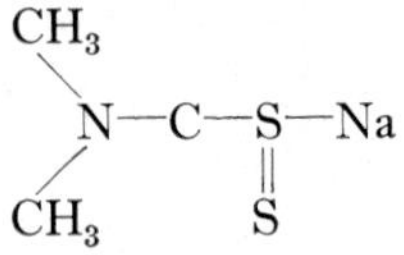

Sodium dimethyldithiocarbamate

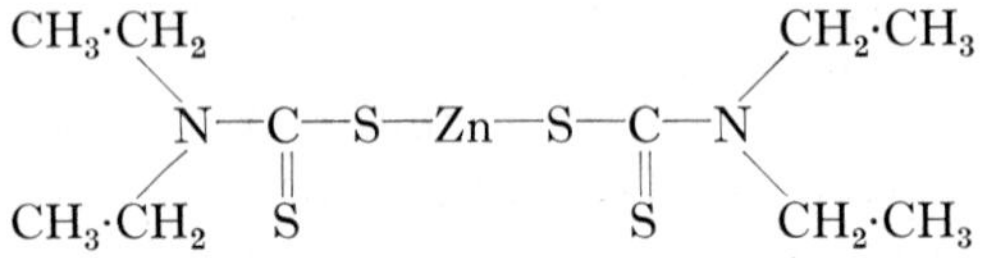

Zinc diethyldithiocarbamate

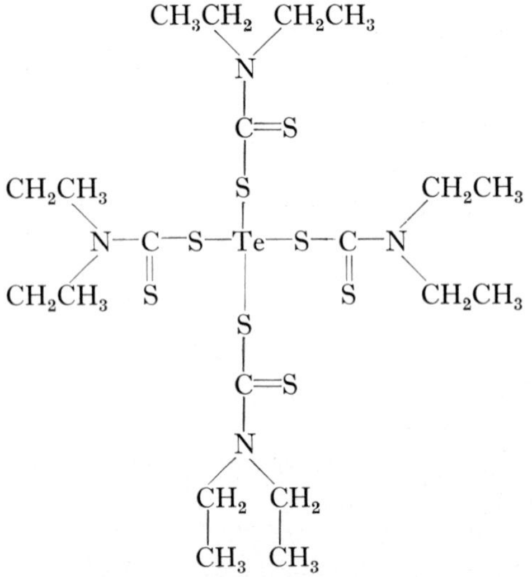

Tellurium diethyldithiocarbamate

tellurium salts of particular interest in compounding for heat resistance and piperidine pentamethylenedithiocarbamate. Selected members of the range of dithiocarbamates also find application in self-curing compounds.

The xanthates, which are extremely fast in acceleration properties, may be regarded as ester salts of dithiocarboxylic acid and are formed by the action of carbon disulphide on the appropriate alcohol in presence of alkali

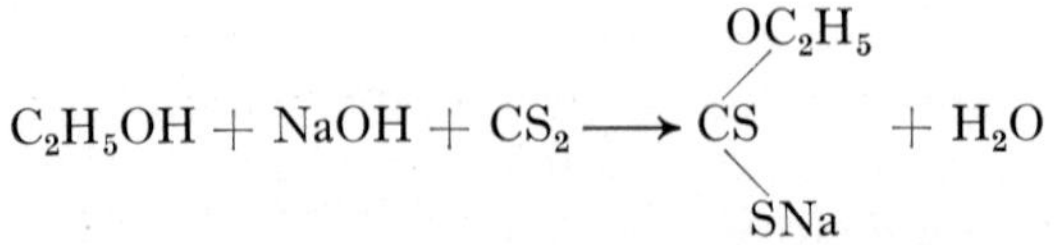

$$C_2H_5OH + NaOH + CS_2 \longrightarrow \overset{OC_2H_5}{\underset{SNa}{CS}} + H_2O$$

Sodium ethyl xanthate

Accelerators of interest to industry are zinc isobutylxanthate, zinc isopropylxanthate and sodium isopropylxanthate.

These accelerators are used primarily in room or low-temperature cures, either alone or in the presence of a second accelerator, such as a dithio-carbamate. The soluble sodium salts are chiefly employed in latex work, where a combination of sodium isopropylxanthate and diethylammonium dithiocarbamate gives room-temperature curing compounds in natural-rubber latex and rapid hot-air cures in the case of SBR latices. Quick-curing compounds based on natural-rubber latex may be prepared using these materials. Such compounds do not precure while ammonia is present, but cure very readily when the ammonia evaporates on drying.

The storage stability of xanthates is not of a high order, and lower still in the case of opened packages.

In the preparation of the modern range of accelerators carbon disulphide is a key intermediate, as will be seen from the following series of historical reactions:

Aniline and carbon disulphide are caused to react at a temperature of 46° C in the presence of a small amount of ammonia to produce thio-carbanilide in a process described by Carl N. Hand and Harold P. Roberts in 1929.[18] Thiocarbanilide may then be treated with excess of litharge in alcoholic ammonia to which soda has been added. This process was described by Ernest Wydler [19] in 1931 for the preparation of diphenylguanidine.

The early work on thiurams and dithiocarbamates was carried out by Bruni and Romani,[20, 21, 22] who discovered the activity of tetramethyl thiuram disulphide and the great activity of the metallic salts of dithio-carbamic acid. In a paper in 1922 published by Romani [23] he showed that the tetra-alkyl thiuram disulphides and their homologues were capable of curing rubber in the absence of free sulphur and gave rapid cures, classified by him as auto-ultra-acceleration. To prepare tetramethyl thiuram disulphide and cyclopentamethylene thiuram disulphide he passed chlorine through the aqueous solution of the corresponding dithiocar-bamate,

$$2(CH_3)_2\, N \cdot (CS)S \cdot NH_2(CH_3)_2 + Cl_2 \longrightarrow [(CH_3)_2\, N(CS)S-]_2 + 2NH \cdot (CH_3)_2 HCl$$

utilising the hydrochloride produced as a by-product for the preparation of more dithiocarbamate. The residue he converted into the desired di-sulphide by passing a current of air over it

Romani quotes the curing reaction as

$$[(CH_3)_2 \cdot N(CS)S-]_2 \longrightarrow [(CH_3)_2 \cdot NCS]_2\, S + S$$

where active sulphur is liberated. He also found that the curing activity was powerfully activated by zinc oxide, less so by magnesia. Reduced quantities of tetramethylthiuram disulphide with added sulphur could be used to produce the same level of cure. In the earlier publications the same workers revealed the discovery of the powerful activity of zinc dialkyldithiocarbamates. Bruni [21] had also found that if an amine were mixed into rubber with sulphur and zinc oxide and the mix exposed to carbon bisulphide vapour, rapid vulcanisation took place, presumably by the formation of a dithiocarbamate.

A secondary amine, such as dimethylamine, and carbon disulphide react to produce dimethylammonium¯dithiocarbamate

$$(CH_3)_2NH + CS_2 \longrightarrow (CH_3)_2-N-\underset{\underset{S}{\|}}{C}-S-\underset{\underset{CH_3}{|}}{N}\overset{H}{\underset{CH_2}{\diagdown}}H$$

The xanthates, as mentioned earlier, were known in 1915, and are also based on the use of carbon disulphide. The thiazole series originates from the work of Bedford in 1921. A patent [24] describes the production of mercaptobenzthiazole by mixing a solution of sulphur in carbon disulphide with aniline and heating the mixture under pressure at 200–275° C.

Developments have taken place in the field of thiazole chemistry, where the condensation products with amines have produced attractive delayed-action accelerators, useful for the fast but safe processing of stocks.

The first member of this series was cyclohexylbenzthiazylsulphenamide, a derivative of cyclohexylamine and 2-mercaptobenzthiazole. Compared with 2-mercaptobenzthiazole in a simple stock, the physical properties are as given in Table 6.4.

TABLE 6.4

Rubber	Pale crêpe	100
	Zinc oxide	5
	Blanc fixe	75
	Stearic acid	1
	Sulphur	2·5
	Accelerator	0·5

Physical properties	CBS	MBT
Tensile strength, kg./cm.²	220	150
Modulus at 500% Elongation	115	60
Elongation at break, %	675	700
Hardness, ° B.S.	52	36

Typical curing curves are given in Fig. 6.1, where the general high level of tensile and modulus are shown; scorching curves in Fig. 6.2.

Since the sulphenamide accelerators find particular use in the tyre industry with furnace black stocks, it is desirable to illustrate their use in such compounds.

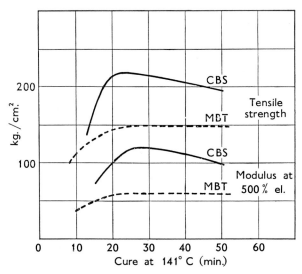

Fig. 6.1. Tensile and modulus curves for CBS and MBT (white stock).

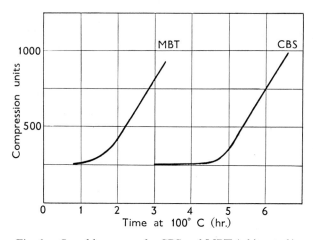

Fig. 6.2. Scorching curves for CBS and MBT (white stock).

Curves showing rates of cure and scorching of CBS, MBT and MBTS in the following furnace-black tread compound are given in Figs. 6.3 and 6.4.

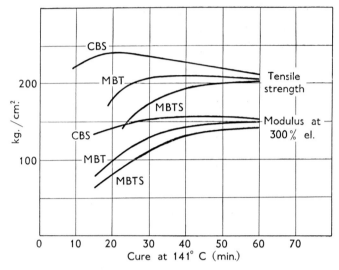

Fig. 6.3. Tensile properties in a furnace black stock (accelerator 0·65%).

The accelerator range can, therefore, be classified according to speed:

Slow accelerators	Formaldehyde paratoluidine condensation product, thiocarbanilide
Medium speed accelerators	Diphenylguanidine, diorthotolylguanidine
Semi-ultra accelerators	Butyraldehyde–aniline, mercaptobenzthiazole
Ultra accelerators	Tetramethylthiuram disulphide, tetramethylthiuram monosulphide, dipentamethylenetetrasulphide, the dithiocarbamates and xanthates

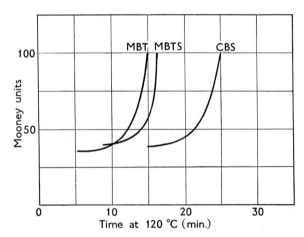

Fig. 6.4. Scorching of a furnace black stock at 120° C (accelerator 0·65%).

TABLE 6.5

Smoked sheet	100		
Zinc oxide	5		
HAF black	47·5		
Stearic acid	3		
Sulphur	3		
A. MBT ⎫			
B. MBTS ⎬ as below			
C. CBS ⎭			
Press cure at 141° C			

Properties at optimum cure	A	B	C
Accelerator content 0·85%:			
Optimum cure, minutes	30	30	15
Tensile strength, kg./cm.^{2}	224	224	248
Modulus at 300% elongation, kg./cm.^{2}	135	135	145
Elongation at break, %	460	480	525
Hardness, ° B.S.	74	75	75
Resilience at 50° C, %	62	58	64
Accelerator content 0·65%:			
Optimum cure, minutes	30	40–45	20
Tensile strength, kg./cm.^{2}	205	195	245
Modulus at 300% elongation, kg./cm.^{2}	130	130	140
Elongation at break, %	410	420	490
Hardness, ° B.S.	72	70	74
Resilience at 50° C, %	62	60	64

TABLE 6.6

Chemical composition	Speed, minutes	Safety	Tensile strength, kg./cm.^{2}	Modulus at 500%	Notes
2-mercaptobenzthiazole	30	Scorchy	160	60	
Dibenzthiazyl disulphide	30–35	Safe	160	60	
Zinc salt of 2-mercapto-benzthiazole	30	Scorchy	160	60	
Cyclohexylbenzthiazyl sulphenamide	25	Safe	220	115	
Tetramethylthiuram disulphide	8	Scorchy	210	103	
Tetraethylthiuram disulphide	10	Fairly safe	207	100	
Tetramethylthiuram monosulphide	10	Fairly safe	207	103	
Zinc diethyldithiocarbamate	12	Very scorchy	203	75	Cured at 125° C

A class of delayed-action accelerators would contain dibenzthiazyl di-sulphide, cyclohexylbenzthiazylsulphenamide and similar amine con-densates of 2-mercaptobenzthiazole.

Data on the use of common accelerators with increasing amounts of sulphur are given in the following tables.   The base mix was:

Pale crêpe	100
Zinc oxide	10
Blanc fixe	75
Stearic acid	1
Sulphur	Varied
Accelerators	

Chemical properties of some of the common accelerators are:

Sym-diphenylguanidine

$$C_6H_5-NH-\underset{\underset{NH}{|}}{C}-NH-C_6H_5 \qquad \text{(M.W. 211)}$$

Crystallised from ethanol or toluene gives material melting point 148° C. Very soluble in hot ethanol.   Soluble in carbon tetrachloride, chloroform, hot benzene, hot toluene, dilute mineral acids.   Sparingly soluble in water.   Aqueous solutions react strongly alkaline.

Di-o-tolylguanidine

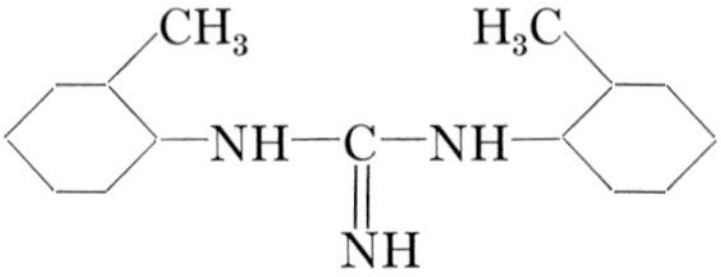

(M.W. 239)

Crystallises from aqueous ethanol to give material melting point 179° C. Soluble in ether.

2-mercaptobenzthiazole

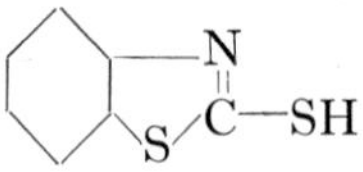

(M.W. 167)

Crystallises as needles from methyl alcohol.   Melting point 177–9° C.   It is sparingly soluble in ethyl alcohol and ether.   Insoluble in water, soluble in alkalis.   Readily oxidised to its disulphide.

Dibenzthiazyl disulphide

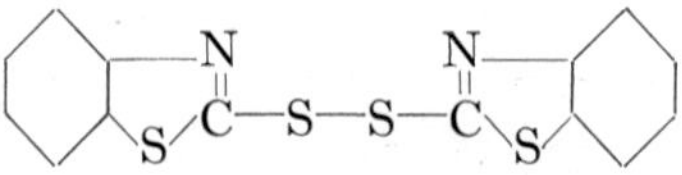

(M.W. 332)

Crystallises as needles from benzene.   Melting point 186° C.   Insoluble in ethyl alcohol and alkalis.

TABLE 6.7

BUTYRALDEHYDE–ANILINE

| Sulphur | 1 | 1 | 1 | 1 | 2 | 2 | 2 | 2 | 3 | 3 | 3 | 3 |
Butyraldehyde–aniline	2·5	1·5	1·0	0·75	1·5	1·0	0·75	0·5	1·0	0·75	0·5	0·375
Optimum cure 141° C minutes	10	20	30	30	20	20	20–30	50	20	20	30–50	50
Tensile strength, kg./cm.^{2}	180	177	158	165	212	195	186	190	195	188	182	180
Modulus 300% elongation	18	20	17	18	28	28	25	26	30	28	28	28
Modulus 500% elongation	66	74	64	66	88	92	86	90	103	94	91	88
Elongation at break, %	727	692	690	693	711	664	672	670	645	650	660	659
Hardness, ° Shore	39	43	39	39	49	46	43	44	48	42	44	45
Resilience at 50° C %	73	76	73	72	80	80	77	80	83	81	81	81

TABLE 6.8

DIPHENYLGUANIDINE

| Sulphur | 1 | 1 | 1 | 1 | 2 | 2 | 2 | 2 | 3 | 3 | 3 | 3 |
Diphenylguanidine	2·5	1·5	1·0	0·75	1·5	1·0	0·75	0·5	1·0	0·75	0·5	0·375
Optimum cure 141° C minutes	30	30–45	60	60	60	60	60	60	60	60	60–90	60–90
Tensile strength, kg./cm.^{2}	173	158	138	131	203	185	189	177	209	196	183	177
Modulus 300% elongation	20	20	16	16	27	24	22	20	34	26	26	20
Modulus 500% elongation	66	57	44	48	98	84	82	70	114	83	88	65
Elongation at break, %	709	735	751	727	655	670	675	693	655	686	665	725
Hardness, ° Shore	45	43	44	40	49	50	48	44	56	53	53	50
Resilience 50° C %	73	69	69	65	83	81	80	72	82	81	77	79

TABLE 6.9
2-MERCAPTOBENZTHIAZOLE

| Sulphur | 1 | 1 | 1 | 1 | 2 | 2 | 2 | 2 | 3 | 3 | 3 | 3 |
2-mercaptobenzthiazole	2·5	1·5	1·0	0·75	1·5	1·0	0·75	0·5	1·0	0·75	0·5	0·375
Optimum cure 141° C minutes	20	40	60–100	60–100	20–30	30	30–40	40	20–30	30	30	30
Tensile strength, kg./cm.²	139	136	117	112	175	174	155	142	177	175	161	145
Modulus 300% elongation	14	14	14	14	21	20	17	16	22	22	20	18
Modulus 500% elongation	39	38	33	33	56	52	46	40	56	52	46	42
Elongation at break, %	775	780	770	780	740	755	760	770	750	760	780	775
Hardness, ° Shore	38	38	39	39	41	42	44	44	46	45	42	39
Resilience 50° C %	63	65	61	61	74	71	67	70	79	77	72	68

TABLE 6.10
TETRAETHYLTHIURAM DISULPHIDE

| Sulphur | 1 | 1 | 1 | 1 | 2 | 2 | 2 | 2 | 3 | 3 | 3 | 3 |
Tetraethylthiuram disulphide	1·5	1·0	0·75	0·5	1·0	0·75	0·5	0·375	0·75	0·5	0·375	0·25
Optimum cure 125° C minutes	40	40	40	30–40	40	30	30	30	30	30	30	30
Tensile strength, kg./cm.²	177	191	187	186	176	209	213	202	206	186	220	198
Modulus 300% elongation	32	29	24	21	37	34	28	29	38	—	32	28
Modulus 500% elongation	101	92	77	66	101	100	86	85	112	127	95	81
Elongation at break, %	628	684	705	755	628	695	736	723	646	591	727	721
Hardness, ° Shore	53	50	49	46	59	56	56	54	56	59	56	53
Resilience 50° C %	83	83	79	77	83	82	80	79	81	84	84	84

TABLE 6.11

TETRAMETHYLTHIURAM MONOSULPHIDE

Sulphur	1	1	1	1	2	2	2	2	3	3	3	3
Tetramethylthiuram monosulphide	1·5	1·0	0·75	0·5	1·0	0·75	0·5	0·375	0·75	0·5	0·375	0·25
Optimum cure 125° C minutes	40	40	50	40–50	40	40	40	40	20	20	20	20
Tensile strength, kg./cm.²	185	176	183	183	166	159	176	185	199	205	215	204
Modulus 300% elongation	31	25	26	23	42	42	35	34	48	40	38	30
Modulus 500% elongation	94	83	84	70	124	120	102	100	144	123	117	99
Elongation at break, %	662	678	682	738	564	568	628	640	572	600	630	653
Hardness, ° Shore, %							No data					
Resilience 50° C	80	79	80	77	85	85	83	85	84	81	85	84

TABLE 6.12

ZINC DIETHYLDITHIOCARBAMATE

Sulphur	1	1	1	1	2	2	2	2	3	3	3	3
Zinc diethyldithiocarbamate	1·5	1·0	0·75	0·5	1·0	0·75	0·5	0·375	0·75	0·5	0·375	0·25
Optimum cure 125° C minutes	10	10	10	10	7½	7½	7½	7½	5–7½	7½–10	7½	7½–10
Tensile strength, kg./cm.²	193	190	197	178	218	219	205	213	219	224	225	212
Modulus 300% elongation	24	22	23	28	24	23	25	23	40	32	30	28
Modulus 500% elongation	77	72	80	74	59	67	70	64	122	96	86	80
Elongation at break, %	693	711	707	700	841	802	776	810	635	694	725	727
Hardness, ° Shore	45	44	44	42	50	49	48	48	55	50	49	48
Resilience 50° C %	77	76	76	74	80	76	79	79	83	81	82	80

Tetramethylthiuram disulphide

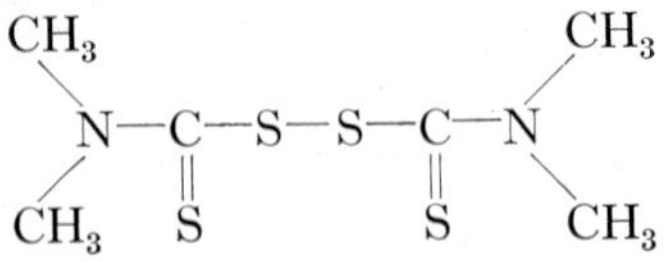

$$\underset{CH_3}{\overset{CH_3}{\diagdown}}N-\underset{\underset{S}{\|}}{C}-S-S-\underset{\underset{S}{\|}}{C}-N\underset{CH_3}{\overset{CH_3}{\diagup}}$$

(M.W. 240)

White crystals from chloroform, alcohol. Melting point 146° C, very soluble in ethyl alcohol and ether.

Tetramethylthiuram monosulphide

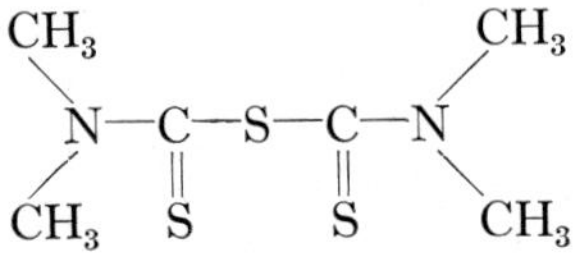

$$\underset{CH_3}{\overset{CH_3}{\diagdown}}N-\underset{\underset{S}{\|}}{C}-S-\underset{\underset{S}{\|}}{C}-N\underset{CH_3}{\overset{CH_3}{\diagup}}$$

(M.W. 208)

Yellow crystals from ethyl alcohol, melting point 104° C. It is very soluble in ethyl alcohol or chloroform and sparingly soluble in cold ether. Stable to dilute acids, but with alkalis yields dimethylamine.

Antioxidants

In all cases it must be borne in mind that the polymeric materials, used in bulk by the rubber industry, are perishable and suffer oxidative degradation in properties during their useful life due to oxygen or ozone. Secondary effects may be due to light, heat or fatigue. The degradation processes are broadly subdivided into the following types:

(1) shelf ageing;
(2) oxidation aided by metallic catalysts;
(3) effects of heat;
(4) effects of light;
(5) flex-cracking;
(6) atmospheric cracking.

This degradation may be retarded, but not entirely eliminated, by the use of materials falling into the class known as antioxidants.[25]

The terminology " antioxidant " is not exact, and a more accurate name would be " anti-oxygen ".

Chemically, the important antioxidants are divided into two classes:

(*a*) amines and their derivatives;
(*b*) phenols and their derivatives.

The essential difference in performance of these two classes, when incorporated into rubber, is the degree of staining imparted to the vulcanisate on subsequent exposure to light. As antioxidants their power is approximately the same, since improvements have been made in the phenol derivatives. A difference is, however, shown up in black stocks, where certain of the phenolic types tend to be adsorbed on the black and their antioxidant power reduced in consequence.

Amines and their derivatives are conveniently divided into the following groups:

> Ketoneamine condensates
> Aldehydeamine condensates
> Secondary aromatic amines

Condensates must not be regarded as chemical entities. In some cases, the impurities present, e.g. unreacted components, have significant and beneficial effects. A chemical description is, therefore, difficult, and today, when various physical forms of materials are available to the rubber industry, it is equally difficult to define physical appearance. Each manufacturer, however, maintains his production of antioxidants within a specification calling for close limits, so that uniformity of technical performance is assured.

Ketoneamine condensates

These products are usually based on acetone condensed with either aniline, diphenylamine, 4-substituted aniline or phenyl-β-naphthylamine. The physical state of the product obtained varies according to the condensation process. Representatives of this class are powerful antioxidants, characterised particularly by excellent heat resistance in loaded compounds, relatively moderate staining properties and some have useful anti-flexcracking or ozone-resistant properties.

The important members of this group are the acetone condensates with aniline, diphenylamine and *p*-phenetidine.

The acetone–aniline condensation product is 2 : 2 : 4-trimethyldihydroquinoline, which is capable of polymerisation to a form available either as powder liquid or resin. Compared with similar condensates of diphenylamine, these products are slightly inferior in respect of heat resistance and slightly inferior in flex-resistance. The substitution of aniline by *p*-aminodiphenyl or *p*-phenetidine brings about an improvement in anti-flexcracking properties and in the case of the *p*-phenetidine derivative, correctly compounded into natural rubber or butadiene–styrene types, an improvement in the resistance to ozone attack on the vulcanisate.

Diphenylamine condensed with acetone gives extremely complex resinous materials, which can be made as liquids or powdered resins, depending on the process. The liquids are generally superior in flex-resistance to the powders, the low-viscosity liquid products conferring flexcracking resistance of the same order as the speciality anti-flexcracking antioxidants.

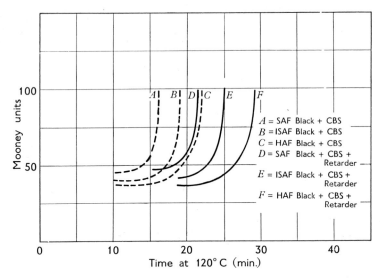

Fig. 6.5. Mooney Scorching of CBS with and without retarder in HAF, ISAF and SAF black compounds.

The difference in behaviour between solid and liquid acetone–diphenylamine condensates in rubber when tested by flexing is shown in Figs. 6.5 and 6.6.

The stock used was a typical tread type containing reinforcing black.

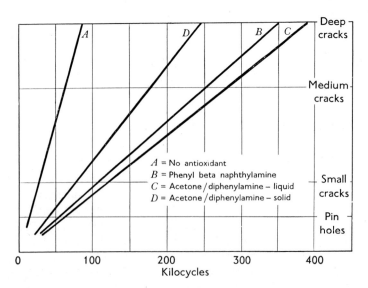

Fig. 6.6. De Mattia flexing test.

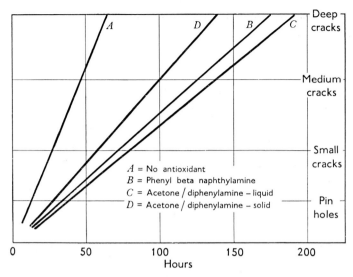

Fig. 6.7. Du Pont belt flexing.

Aldehydeamine condensates

Over the period of development of antioxidants, condensation products of aniline, toluidine and naphthylamines with formaldehyde, acetaldehyde and aldol (β-hydroxy-*n*-butyraldehyde) have been of commercial interest. Indeed, the condensation products of acetaldehyde or butyraldehyde with aniline function as accelerators as well as antioxidants, and the former is still in demand as such today. In the antioxidant class the most important have been the aldol α- and β-naphthylamines, particularly for heat resistance. The presence of traces of free β-naphthylamine in condensates based on that material has, however, necessitated their elimination from the rubber trade on account of causing papilloma. Similar remarks apply to condensates of 4-aminodiphenyl.

Secondary diarylamines

This group includes some of the most important, but staining, antioxidants known in industry, i.e. the phenylnaphthylamines, diphenylamine derivatives and *para*-phenylenediamine derivatives.

Phenyl-α- and phenyl-β-naphthylamines are among the oldest type of antioxidants. They offer a very balanced combination of properties as antioxidants and enjoy extensive usage for general purposes. Unfortunately, their staining properties are quite severe, but they do combine good all-round antioxidant properties with good antiflexing characteristics. They are, however, inferior to the liquid acetone–diphenylamine condensates in respect of heat and flex resistance. The greater solubility in rubber of the α-compound eliminates hazard of bloom, but at equal dosages the β-compound is the more effective.

Phenyl-α-naphthylamine   Phenyl-β-naphthylamine

A typical specification for phenyl-β-naphthylamine of commercial quality is as follows:

Appearance	Fine grey powder
Fineness 100 mesh	Not less than 98%
Crystallising point	105°C min.
Ash	0·5% max.
β-naphthol content	0·5% max.
Solubility	Soluble in acetone, benzene or chloroform

In view of the intense staining of light-coloured stocks containing phenyl-β-naphthylamine, its use is limited to black or dark-coloured compounds at a maximum concentration of 1·5 parts per 100 parts of rubber hydro-carbon. When stocks are mixed at a temperature approximating to the melting point or above, e.g. Banbury mixing, flake or agglomerated forms may be used without difficulty in dispersion.

Diphenylamine derivatives which are useful as antioxidants include those of the general formula

where R and R¹ may be alkyl, alkoxy, alkenoxy or styrene.

Diphenylamine itself, although volatile, has been used in admixture with other materials as an anti-flexcracking antioxidant. This property is greatly emphasised by the introduction of one or more alkoxy- or alkenoxy-groups in the para position(s), e.g. di-methoxydiphenylamine, an im-portant constituent of blended anti-flexcracking antioxidants. Alkylation in the *para* positions, usually with heptyl or octyl radicals, reduces the anti-flexcracking properties and also the tendency to stain, thus giving a series of products with powerful antioxidant properties capable of being used in light stocks in which some discoloration can be tolerated.

Structurally related to the diphenylamines, the most popular members of the *p*-phenylenediamine derivatives are the diphenyl, dinaphthyl and phenylcyclohexyl substituents

They are powerful antioxidants with good anti-flexcracking properties, though limited in the case of certain compounds by their low solubility in rubber, which when the chemicals are used at higher dosages gives rise to bloom. This is a particular weakness of diphenyl-*p*-phenylenediamine, which blooms at a concentration above 0·35 parts per 100 parts of rubber hydrocarbon. Replacement of one of the phenyl groups with cyclohexyl increases the solubility in rubber whereby dosages up to 2 parts can be used without the hazard of bloom and without loss of anti-flexcracking properties. The phenyl groups may also be replaced by naphthyl, in which case considerable loss in anti-flexcracking properties occurs but the staining characteristics are considerably decreased.

One interesting property of the phenylenediamines is their ability to retard the catalytic action of copper and manganese on the ageing of rubber. This effect will be discussed later.

Recent work, particularly on SBR, has shown that in combination with other antioxidants and waxes, some of the dialkyl-*p*-phenylenediamines retard significantly the attack by ozone on vulcanisates. This work has been extended to natural rubber, where a significant effect has also been shown. Some of these chemicals are, however, dermatitic, e.g. di-*sec*-butyl-*p*-phenylenediamine, so that care has to be exercised in handling. The materials also have a slightly basic reaction, so that accelerators of the acidic type will be activated, with resulting tendency to scorch.

The way in which amine-type antioxidants have developed around the aniline nucleus is shown in the diagram on page 376.

Phenols and their derivatives are mainly of interest on account of the low degree of staining which their use imparts to vulcanisates.[7] Substituted phenols are used to overcome the acidity of the phenolic group which retards the vulcanisation reaction, and include alkyl substituents and a popular class of " styrenated phenols ". As a class, the resistance which they impart to flexing and heat may be regarded as poor to moderate, but the resistance to natural ageing is in many uses adequate and their non-staining properties very good.

The condensates with aldehydes include some of the most powerful of the non-staining antioxidants, which although showing a slight tendency to stain, may still be regarded as non-staining antioxidants. Their general properties may be regarded as good against natural ageing, heat and staining, with fair to moderate performance against flexing and metal-catalysed oxidation.

Mention must be made of mercaptobenzimidazole, which although retarding cure to some extent, has useful antioxidant properties associated with non-staining. Le Bras has shown that the way to use this chemical most effectively is in combination with another antioxidant, phenyl-β-naphthylamine.

The types of ageing which bring about the degradation of rubber articles are:

(a) *" Shelf ageing "* is a term which covers the life of an article between manufacture and its being put into service. During this period, the article may have been stored in the dark or in green light or in sealed containers. Nevertheless, it can be shown that in the absence of antioxidant

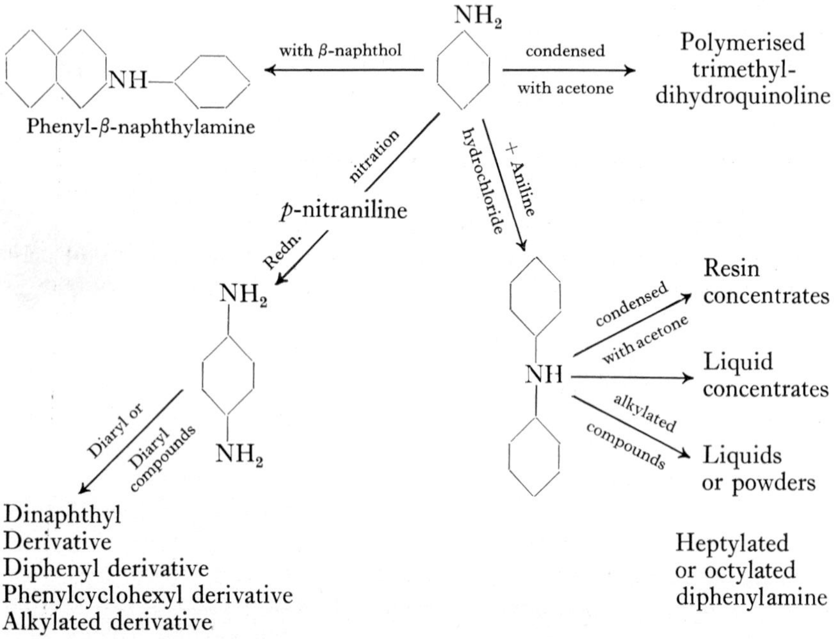

Phenyl-β-naphthylamine

with β-naphthol

NH₂

condensed with acetone

Polymerised trimethyl-dihydroquinoline

nitration

p-nitraniline

hydrochloride

+ Aniline

Redn.

NH₂

condensed with acetone → Resin concentrates

NH →→ Liquid concentrates

alkylated compounds → Liquids or powders

Diaryl or Diaryl compounds

NH₂

Dinaphthyl Derivative
Diphenyl derivative
Phenylcyclohexyl derivative
Alkylated derivative

p-phenylenediamine

Heptylated or octylated diphenylamine

Diphenylamine

considerable falling away of physical properties does occur. The extent of this deterioration depends to some extent on the accelerator system used in the original vulcanisation. In a diphenylguanidine accelerated mix, specially selected because this accelerator bestows no antioxidant properties on the cured stock, 50% of the original tensile strength had been lost after keeping in a drawer for 4 years at ordinary temperature in the laboratories at Blackley. The same stock, kept in an oven at 30° C, decreased in tensile strength by the same amount after 24 months, whereas the presence of 1 part of phenyl-β-naphthylamine per 100 parts of rubber gave the same decrease in tensile strength after 76 months in the oven at 30° C.

In addition to vulcanised rubbers, shelf ageing also applies to raw rubbers once they have been processed. For example, adhesive tapes which are manufactured from unvulcanised rubber, plasticised and compounded, may lose the properties of adhesion and cohesion unless suitably protected.

A study of the oxygen absorption of unvulcanised rubber shows that effective " antioxidants " for this class of goods include some of the normal accelerators, e.g. the dithiocarbamates, as well as selected materials of the conventional antioxidant type.

(*b*) *Oxidation aided by metallic catalysts*, such as copper and manganese compounds, exert a powerful catalytic effect on the degradation of rubber. In the case of copper, if this element is present as a co-ordinated compound, e.g. copper phthalocyanine of very low ionic copper content, no catalysis occurs. Recent work at Blackley has shown that metal sequestering agents in combination with certain antioxidants will give an antioxidant composition capable of inhibiting the action of considerable quantities of copper and/or manganese. This combination is particularly effective against copper contamination in fillers or other compounding ingredients and copper present in the dyestuffs or pigments associated with textiles used in the production of spread fabrics. An illustration of the copper-inhibiting properties is as follows:

Base Compound—Pale crêpe	100
Zinc oxide	10
Blanc fixe	75
Stearic acid	1
Cu stearate (equivalent to 200 p.p.m. Cu on r.h.c.)	0·2
Copper inhibitor/antioxidant (CGP)	2
Acceleration⎫ Cure ⎭	As indicated

In view of the known copper-inhibiting properties of *sym*-di-β-naphthyl-*p*-phenylenediamine (DNPD), this product has been included as a standard of comparison.

(*c*) *The effects of heat* on rubber parts are usually obvious in the case of ignition cables and hose which are subjected to a fair degree of heat during their service life. Less obvious is the effect of heat in the case of transmission belting, tyres and tubes, where heat is generated by continuous flexing, and in the latter case by conduction from the brake drums as well. Oxidation occurs, causing hardening, and in certain cases the process of vulcanisation is continued too at the higher temperature. The low thermal conductivity of rubber emphasises the effect of heat in the area nearest to the source. At the higher temperatures the rate of absorption of oxygen is greater than the rate of diffusion, so that some protection is afforded to the inner layers. Stiffness increases considerably, while elongation decreases. The net result being to increase the tendency to crack during manipulation or flexing.

The introduction of tubeless tyres has introduced an oxidation problem not present in a tyre-and-tube combination. Previously, air diffusing through the walls of the tube escaped via the rim. Now with the tubeless tyre, air is constantly diffusing through the wall of the tyre, tending also to "wick" along the cords. Oxidation at the cord–rubber interface can lead to ply separation.

TABLE 6.13

PHYSICAL TEST RESULTS (% RETAINED TENSILE STRENGTHS)

Acceleration, % on r.h.c.	S 3; DPG 0·5		S 2·5; MBT 0·5		S 2; ZDC 0·375	
Cure	30 min. at 153° C		30 min. at 141° C		12 min. at 125° C	
Antioxidant, % on r.h.c.	DNPD 2	CGP 2	DNPD 2	CGP 2	DNPD 2	CGP 2
Unaged	100		100		100	
After ageing in oxygen bomb:						
1 day	74	92	—	—	—	—
2 days	65	84	—	—	—	—
3 days	58	78	—	—	—	—
4 days	52	72	65	89	77	85
6 days	50	64	60	84	—	—
8 days	—	—	51	77	60	77
10 days	—	—	45	73	—	—
12 days	—	—	39	61	34	64
14 days	—	—	31	47	—	—
16 days	—	—	—	—	9	50

Heat-resisting antioxidants are usually of the staining type, and are based on amine derivatives. The effect of two typical antioxidants is shown by the data given on page 381.

Mention was made at the beginning of the chapter on the use of blends of polymers and their increasing possibilities due to their technical features. The following is an illustration of how the ageing resistance of natural rubber against the effects of heat can be improved by blending with polyethylene. Normal type antioxidants used for enhancing heat resistance give an added effect.

Thirty parts of polyethylene as illustrated in these compounds may not represent the optimum amount for a particular purpose, but significant increases beyond this level give a fall away in properties on unaged stocks.

(d) *The effects of light* visible only on non-black articles are well known, producing the appearance of crazing or " drying mud ". This is due to the production of an oxidised inelastic skin. In thin articles, such as proofings, the effect appears as a significant stiffening. Prevention can be obtained by the use of antioxidants and de-activators or by protection against light. Non-staining antioxidants from the phenyl–alkane class (phenolaldehyde condensates) afford useful protection. In a series of coloured mixes based on the same compound those coloured red or orange have resisted this surface crazing very much better than either blue, yellow or white.

(*e*) *Flexcracking* is an important factor, bringing about degradation of rubber-like materials in all dynamic applications. It is caused by fatigue

TABLE 6.14

Smoked sheet	100
Zinc oxide	5
H.A.F. black	47·5
Stearic acid	3
Sulphur	2·5
n-cyclohexylbenzthiazyl sulphenamide	0·65
Antioxidant	0 or 1

Cure: 30 minutes at 141° C

Antioxidant	None	Acetone–diphenylamine condensate	Phenyl β-naphthylamine
Tensile strength, kg./cm.²:			
Unaged	223	226	228
Aged—			
6 days in oxygen bomb	Perished	124	128
8 days in oxygen bomb	—	116	120
12 days in oxygen bomb	—	98	95
3 weeks in oven at 70° C	119	172	156
6 weeks in oven at 70° C	63	131	120
2 days in oven at 100° C	61	152	113
4 days in oven at 100° C	40	92	72
6 days in oven at 100° C	22	50	36
Elongation at break, %:			
Unaged	389	398	383
Aged—			
6 days in oxygen bomb	Perished	298	312
8 days in oxygen bomb	—	294	309
12 days in oxygen bomb	—	236	248
3 weeks in oven at 70° C	220	258	242
6 weeks in oven at 70° C	160	220	227
2 days in oven at 100° C	181	256	239
4 days in oven at 100° C	147	184	195
6 days in oven at 100° C	45	115	99

and oxidation. The influence of fatigue is emphasised, the nearer zero strain is approached on each cycle of flexing. In the development of cracks due to flexing, failure first appears as pinholes gradually developing into cracks at right angles to the direction of strain. When rubbers are flexed in an atmosphere of nitrogen the time taken to develop cracks is longer than when similar rubbers are flexed in the ordinary or an ozonised atmosphere. Considering a range of polymers, their resistance to flexcracking is similar to their resistance to ozone, e.g. butyl rubber is outstanding. Agents which readily improve the resistance of polymers to flexcracking rarely show any improvement in ozone resistance of these compounds.

Anti-flexcracking antioxidants are one of the most important branches of rubber chemicals, their importance arising from the demands of the tyre and belting industry, independent of whether the polymers are natural of synthetic rubber. Chemically, compounds which are technically useful

TABLE 6.15

Smoked sheet	100
Zinc oxide	5
Stearic acid	3
M.P.C. black	47·5
Sulphur	3
Mercaptobenzthiazole	0·85
Antioxidant	1
Cure: 45 minutes at 141° C	

Antioxidant	Acetone-diphenylamine condensate		Phenyl-β-naphthyl-amine	
	Tensile strength, kg./cm.^{2}	Elongation at break, %	Tensile strength, kg./cm.^{2}	Elongation at break, %
Unaged	231	494	220	480
Aged:				
4 days in oxygen bomb	127	380	132	348
6 days in oxygen bomb	108	322	109	335
8 days in oxygen bomb	95	295	97	309
12 days in oxygen bomb	64	245	73	284
3 weeks in oven at 70° C	213	355	134	276
6 weeks in oven at 70° C	153	276	62	140
4 days in oven at 100° C	193	299	160	290
6 days in oven at 100° C	139	225	94	182
8 days in oven at 100° C	75	124	54	105

are based on secondary amines and their derivatives, e.g. phenyl-β-naphthylamine, diphenyl-p-phenylene diamine, dimethoxyphenylene-diamine and condensates of acetone with diphenylamine or p-phenetidine. Commercially, products such as diphenyl-p-phenylenediamine or dimethoxyphenylenediamine, which are of either limited solubility in rubber or too expensive to use alone, are used to boost a good all-round antioxidant, such as phenyl-β-naphthylamine.

Without influencing the general antioxidant properties of the phenyl-β-naphthylamine, such mixtures show a significant effect on the

TABLE 6.16

BASE COMPOUND

Rubber	100
Zinc oxide	4
Stearic acid	1
Sulphur	2·5
Activated thiazole	0·5
Added to:	

Mix reference:	1 Control	2 Control	3 DNPPD	4 WSL	5 B
Alkathene Grade 2	—	30	30	30	30
Dinaphthyl-p-phenylene diamine	—	—	1	—	—
A phenol condensate (Nonox WSL)	—	—	—	1	—
Acetone/diphenylamine condensate (Nonox B)	—	—	—	—	1

Press cured: 10 minutes at 141° C

Physical test results	Mix				
	1	2	3	4	5
Tensile strength, kg./cm.^{2}:					
Unaged	176	159	145	162	165
Aged—					
4 days in oxygen bomb	20	173	180	192	200
12 days in oxygen bomb	9	86	128	127	138
6 weeks at 70° C Geer oven	P	37	144	120	134
8 weeks at 70° C Geer oven	P	34	116	90	130
12 weeks at 70° C Geer oven	P	26	104	75	113
Elongation at break, %:					
Unaged	803	715	709	738	725
Aged—					
4 days in oxygen bomb	396	692	686	686	686
12 days in oxygen bomb	261	640	673	660	643
6 weeks at 70° C Geer oven	P	346	591	578	588
8 weeks at 70° C Geer oven	P	317	526	503	542
12 weeks at 70° C Geer oven	P	304	516	500	442
Modulus at 500% kg./cm.^{2}:					
Unaged	23	53	52	50	53
Aged—					
4 days oxygen bomb	—	70	76	79	82
12 days oxygen bomb	—	47	57	60	69
6 weeks at 70° C Geer oven	P	—	91	82	81
8 weeks at 70° C Geer oven	P	—	105	85	104
12 weeks at 70° C Geer oven	P	—	89	75	94
Hardness, ° Shore:					
Unaged	40	50	46	47	49
Aged—					
4 days oxygen bomb	35	50	50	50	54
8 days oxygen bomb	—	43	45	46	50
6 weeks at 70° C Geer oven	42	53	53	56	57
8 weeks at 70° C Geer oven	39	53	56	54	56
12 weeks at 70° C Geer oven	35	49	54	51	57

anti-flex cracking resistance of compounds. A typical tyre-tread stock containing reinforcing carbon black gave the following results on test:

TABLE 6.17

Antioxidant	None	Phenyl-β-naphthylamine	Phenyl-β-naphthylamine + dimethoxy-p-phenylene diamine
Flexing on the De Mattia Machine			
Hours to produce:			
Pin holes	1	4	6
Small cracks	2	8	10
Medium cracks	3	16	20
Deep cracks	4	22	28
Flexing on du Pont Machine (belt)			
Hours to produce:			
Pin holes	11	41	53
Small cracks	18	65	82
Medium cracks	28	100	150
Deep cracks	41	135	210

(*f*) *Atmospheric cracking* refers to cracks which develop in rubber when stretched and exposed to the outside atmosphere. Light is not necessary. Ozone is one of the most effective agents for producing cracks in strained rubber, and the concentration normally present in the atmosphere is sufficient to produce cracking. How ozone attacks rubber is not clear, but it has been suggested that the act of stretching brings ethylenic linkages into juxta-positions where ozone attack brings about a rupture visible as a crack.

Various methods of compounding have been suggested as a means of combating this attack. For static applications, a small quantity of micro-crystalline wax in the rubber stock, which blooms to the surface and acts as a physical barrier, is very effective until broken. Varnish films behave in a similar way, but once such a physical barrier is broken, as by flexing, the ozone attack causes a few deep cracks which are dangerous, as opposed to a large number of fine surface cracks which represent the result of normal attack.

Increasing attention is being given to the use of alkyl substituted *p*-phenylenediamines, particularly in the U.S.A., where improvements in the ozone resistance of SBR are claimed by their use. The concentrations, however, to give a good effect are high, when judged by normal compounding standards, 2–4 parts per 100 of rubber hydrocarbon, and to obtain the optimum results it is recommended that they are used with normal dosages of antioxidant (for tyres the anti-flexcracking type) and wax. Their mode of protection is not understood, but since the effective agents tend to bloom from rubber and SBR and also, generally speaking, better results are obtained in the presence of wax, it seems probable that physical as well as chemical action is still an important factor in the protection they afford.

Materials selected on a basis of static tests carried out in a controlled ozonised atmosphere do not, of necessity, show up well when tested under service conditions. This may be due to the unavoidable stretching which occurs under these conditions.

It seems more than likely that the quickest way to eliminate ozone attack on rubber parts is, where possible, to change the polymer to one less sensitive to attack, e.g. Butyl rubber or a polyurethane.

The range of antioxidants available from suppliers all over the world is quoted by Buist.[26]

The protection of neoprene

The ageing of neoprene is discussed by Catton.[27] In the presence of air, neoprene stocks are slowly attacked by oxygen, with subsequent fall in physical properties. The process is catalysed by heat or sunlight, and an efficient antioxidant is recommended to ensure good ageing properties. In black or dark-coloured stocks phenyl-α- or phenyl-β-naphthylamine is useful. For light-coloured, non-discolouring stocks, a non-staining type is essential. The decomposition of neoprene through oxidation is accompanied by the liberation of hydrochloric acid, and the presence of zinc oxide and magnesia is recommended in addition to the antioxidants quoted above where stocks are in contact with or reinforced by textiles sensitive to hydrochloric acid.

Neoprene stocks under tension are attacked by ozone. du Pont have shown that a mixture of 50% phenyl-β-naphthylamine, 25% di-p-methoxydiphenylamine and 25% diphenyl-p-phenylenediamine imparts outstanding ozone resistance to neoprene vulcanisates. Phenyl-α- and phenyl-β-naphthylamine used in high dosages of 3–5 parts are also effective.

Additions of p-tolylsulphonylamidodiphenylamine give outstanding improvements as regards heat resistance. Other antioxidants which have been found beneficial include phenyl-β-naphthylamine and a mixture of phenyl-α-naphthylamine and diphenyl-p-phenylenediamine.

Chemical data on antioxidants

Chemical data on the pure variety of a few materials used as antioxidants are as follows:

Phenyl-β-naphthylamine or N-phenyl-2-naphthylamine

$$NH \cdot C_6H_5$$

(M.W. 219)

Crystallises as needles from methyl alcohol. Melting point 108° C. Boiling point 395–399·5° C, 237°/13 mm. Moderately soluble in ethanol, ether and benzene. Solutions show blue fluoresence.

Phenyl-α-naphthylamine or N-phenyl-1-naphthylamine

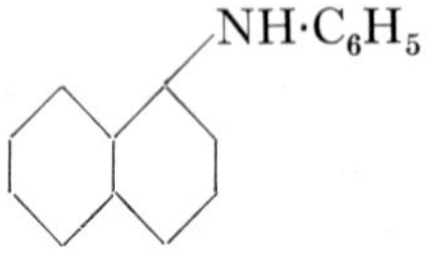

(M.W. 219)

Crystallises as needles or prisms from ethanol, leaflets from ligroin. Melting point 62° C. Boiling point 335°/528 mm, 200°/10 mm. Soluble in ethanol, ether, chloroform and benzene. The solutions show blue fluorescence.

Sym-diphenyl-p-*phenylenediamine*

(M.W. 260)

Silvery leaflets. Melting point 152° C. Soluble in ether, chloroform, hot benzene. Moderately soluble in hot ethanol, sparingly soluble in ligroin. Decomposes on distillation. Sulphuric acid + nitrite gives deep red colour.

Sym-di-2-naphthyl-p-*phenylenediamine*

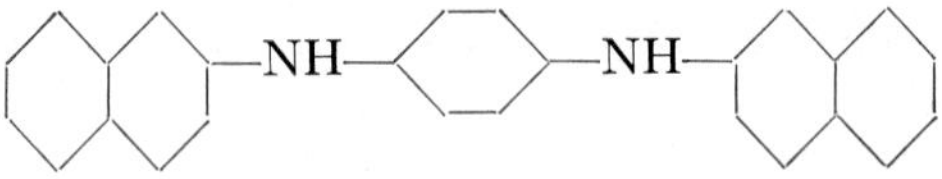

(M.W. 360)

Leaflets from hot aniline. Melting point 235° C. Soluble in hot nitro-benzene. Moderately soluble in hot acetic acid. Sparingly soluble in ethanol, ether and benzene.

2-Mercaptobenzimidazole

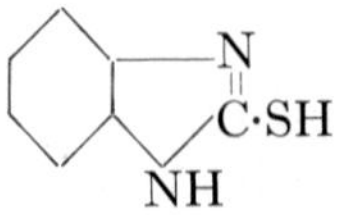

(M.W. 150)

Crystallises as plates from dilute ethanol or aqueous ammonia. Melting point 298° C. Soluble in ethanol. Less soluble in water.

REFERENCES

1. Harper, D. A., Smith, W. F. and White, H. G. (1948) *Second Rubb. Tech. Conf.* (London: I.R.I.) and Naunton, W. J. S. and Siddle, F. J. (October 1931) *I.R.J.*
2. Young, D. W., *et al.* (1949) *Ind. Eng. Chem.*, **41**, 401.
3. Piccini, I. (1951) *Rev. gén. Caout.*, **28**, 487.

4. Schade, J. W. (1952) *Ind. Rubb. World*, **126**, No. 1, 67.
5. Habgood, B. J. *Fundamentals of Rubber Technology* (Manchester: Imperial Chemical Industries Ltd., Dyestuffs Division).
6. Haworth, J. and Pryer, W. R. (1949) *I.R.I. Trans.*, **25**, No. 4, 265.
7. Williams, G. E. (1956) *Proc. I.R.I.*, **32**, No. 1, P.43.
8. Evans, B. B. (1953) *I.R.I. Trans.*, **29**, No. 1, 42.
9. Tunnicliff, E. (1953) *I.R.I. Trans.*, **29**, No. 2, 55.
10. Watts, J. T., *Fundamentals of Rubber Technology* (Manchester: Imperial Chemical Industries Ltd., Dyestuffs Division).
11. Bierer, J. M. (1950) *I.R.I. Trans.*, **26**, No. 4, 257.
12. Brazier, S. A. (1953) *I.R.I. Trans.*, **29**, No. 3, 115, 8th Foundation Lecture, I.R.I.
13. B.P. 750,513.
14. (1955) *Rubb. Chem. for Footwear* (Manchester: Imperial Chemical Industries Ltd., Dyestuffs Division).
15. Naunton, W. J. S. (1926) *I.R.I. Trans.*, **2**, 147.
16. Bedford, C. W. and Sebrell, L. B. (1922) *J. Ind. Eng. Chem.*, **14**, 25.
17. Naunton, W. J. S., Baird, W. and Bunbury, H. M. (1934) *Jour. S.C.I.*, **53**, 127.
18. Hand, C. N. and Roberts, H. P., U.S.P. 1,688,707. (1929) *Chem. Abs.*, **23**, 156.
19. Wydler, E., Swiss P. 145,148. (1931) *Chem. Abs.*, **25**, 5179.
20. Bruni, G., Italian P. 173,322. (1920) *Chim. et Ind.*, **4**, 663.
21. Bruni, G. (1921) *G. Chim. industr.*, **3**, 196.
22. Bruni, G. and Romani, E. (1921) *G. Chim. industr.*, **3**, 351.
23. Romani, E. (1921) *G. Chim. industr.*, **3**, 197.
24. B.P. 335,567; (1931) *Chem. Abs.*, **25**, 1539.
25. Naunton, W. J. S. (1930) *I.R.I. Trans.*, **5**, 317.
26. Buist, J. M. (1956) *Ageing and Weathering of Rubber*, Monograph (London: I.R.I.).
27. Catton, N. L. (1953) *du Pont Handbook on Neoprene*.

CHAPTER VI

PART TWO

PRACTICAL COMPOUNDING

by

J. W. DENSON

THE technical expert who practices practical compounding as a profession has no simple universal title by which he could be described in the English language. In various organisations he is described (among many other terms) as the chemist, compounder, process controller, engineer, technologist, all of which have to be preceded by the word rubber, and none of which convey precisely, harmoniously or with dignity the correct idea of his work or status. A simple harmonious word is needed which is as apt and descriptive as " metallurgist " in describing the expert in the science of producing and processing the metals and their alloys. For want of a better, the term *Compounder* will be used, although it suggests a narrower sphere of action than is actually the case and is capable of much misunderstanding.

In essence, the art of compounding consists of specifying the type and amount of the various ingredients in a mix, the manner of mixing, the processing of the finished mix, and the method and details of vulcanisation. All of the foregoing to be chosen with the following needs in mind:

1. To produce an article suitable for the service conditions it will be required to meet.
2. To ensure that the overall ingredient and manufacturing cost of the article is as economical as possible.

The first requirement usually determines the type of polymer to be used and the broad outline of the physical properties required, the second usually results in a compromise between ingredients, method of mixing, method of processing and vulcanisation. For instance, it would be uneconomical to produce a mix giving a high speed of vulcanisation and consequent low mould and heating costs if an undue proportion of scorched compound was produced in the mixing or processing, or vice versa, or to make a perfectly safe processing compound if it resulted in too high a vulcanising cost, remembering that mould costs can be high and a low mould turn-over means a higher capital investment in moulds to attain equivalent output.

It will be seen from the foregoing that the compounder needs to have not only an intimate knowledge of the service requirements of the article and physical effects of the materials at his command but also an intimate understanding of the processing equipment and vulcanising methods available, with a full knowledge of their advantages, disadvantages and relative costs if the most economical combinations of mix and conversion cost are to be attained. Since the compounder needs to be perpetually cost conscious as well as quality conscious, it would be well to discuss some of the costing details, and since these involve records, also to discuss the various methods of recording mix formulae and providing the factory with the desired information. The main ingredients are usually bought by weight, while rubber articles are normally sold as units rather than by weight. Since the rubber articles will have a constant volume, their weight will vary as the specific gravity of the mix used. Hence when comparing the relative costs of two or more formulae, it is essential to use the volume cost and not the cost per lb. A simple way of obtaining the volume cost is merely to multiply the cost per pound by the specific gravity. The figures obtained can be used to show the percentage increase or decrease in cost. Where the actual monetary increase or decrease is desired the weight of the articles using the various mixes is used in conjunction with the appropriate costs per pound.

It is necessary too, to ensure that the costing formula as well as the factory formula contains the proper allowances for dust losses according to the method of mixing used, since fly loss on mills is considerably greater than in internal mixers. These dust losses should be determined by weighing a suitable number of finished batches and determining the average loss. It is, of course, also necessary to determine which ingredients are being lost, usually it is the carbon blacks and the light fluffy materials such as magnesium carbonate. It is interesting to note that pelletising the blacks renders working conditions much better but does not eliminate entirely dust loses.

In certain processes the rubber is washed and dried before use in compounding. In other cases it is strained to remove dirt. In both cases a loss of weight occurs which should be added to cost of washing or straining and not shown on the mix formula as a shrinkage loss. This ensures that the appropriate comparisons can be made between, say, buying No. 4 smoked sheet with subsequent washing or straining and buying a cleaner grade of rubber.

In other processes rubber may be washed and used immediately without drying. The shrinkage on washing has already been taken care of in the washing cost, but since the rubber is still wet, the factory formula will show an evaporation loss, whereas the costing formula will show no evaporation loss, i.e. if 100 lb. of dry rubber is required, 105 lb. of wet rubber will show on the factory formula, and the overall weight of ingredients going into the mix will be 5 lb. higher than the finished batch weight. The costing formula, however, will show only 100 lb. of rubber.

The same sort of cost treatment is applied to rubber solutions to account for the inevitable solvent loss, i.e. the formula for 100 gallons of rubber solution may call for as much as 110 gallons of solvent plus 70 lb. of mixed rubber. These solvent losses vary with the type of solvent and kind of mixer used as well as the type of storage container and length of storage. In determining these losses it is obviously necessary to use average conditions as far as possible to avoid under- or over-recovery of the solvent costs.

Records

A logical and accurate system of recording all formulae is essential in all good compounding practice. It is necessary as a proof of prior art in the case of patents, essential for costing and of the greatest value in tracing outbreaks of service trouble due to formula changes. For development work the formula is usually shown based on 100 parts of rubber hydrocarbon. This ensures easy comparison of sulphur, accelerator and softener ratios, etc. It is also of advantage to record the volumes on 100 volumes of hydrocarbon. This allows a readier comparison of loadings where, for instance, the specific gravities of not only the polymers, i.e. neoprene and nitrile rubber, but also of the loading or reinforcing materials, i.e. clay, zinc oxide or blanc fixe, vary. The 100 lb. total formula renders costing easier and more accurate, while the 100 volume total formula gives a clearer picture of the make-up of a mix, since rubber mixes are essentially physical mixtures rather than chemical compounds.

Formula records using the metric system would be ideal if it were not for the fact that the ingredients are sold and bought on the avoirdupois system and considerable conversion work would be entailed in the stores and accounts records. An excellent compromise is to use the lb. decimal system, which renders formula and accounting calculations easy as well as simplifying factory weighing operations. The only requirement necessary is that all factory weighing machines be changed to read lb. and decimals of a lb. instead of cwt., lb. and oz. It is normally only necessary to go to the nearest 0·01 of a lb. except in the case of laboratory batches.

The compound numbering system chosen needs thought. The mere numbering or assigning of a series of hieroglyphics to new mixes regardless of other considerations is to be deplored. A good system will indicate the type of compound, the original basic compound, the modifications and, if possible, the basic polymer. For example, a neoprene hose mix could well be HN 63–10; H for hose, N for neoprene, 63 the original mix, 10 the 10th modification.

It is a matter of some judgement to decide whether a change in mix needs a new base mix number or merely a change in the modification number. Generally speaking, any change which causes a significant change in physical properties or service life should be given a new base mix number. Modifications which merely change the processing properties, such as changes in the grade of natural rubber used or type of softening or processing oil, can be given new modification numbers. The same also applies to new mix procedures, such as the introduction or removal of a remill or masterbatch.

It is essential to keep the number of digits used as low as possible, since the millman normally has to write this number on each slab, and this can become a hindrance to efficiency. It should be noted that whereas the numerical system has only 90 variants for two digits, the use of letters results in 26 × 26 or 676 variants. Thus the hose compound previously mentioned could become HN63-J, or where numbers such as 30731-10 are used XHS-J could save effort and still give the same number of variants. Certain digits when written carelessly in the factory are liable to be mistaken for others and cause mix-ups. Thus B475 and B478 can be confused, and such possibilities are best avoided.

The transmission of the mix information to the factory needs systematising to avoid errors and to enable the mix used at any time to be identified. The method will depend on the type of organisation in the millroom and the type of weighing equipment used. In small works a drug room will usually be available, and the mix information can be recorded on cards or loose leaves. In large concerns, where weighing is done by the Banbury operator, the card system may be used, or weighing rings marked in the appropriate places can be provided for clamping on the scales in lieu of the normal dial. In all cases, as changes are made, care should be taken to withdraw the obsolete formula and the date of the change logged for permanent record. It is rare that these records can be relied on to be accurate to a day or so, since there is usually a bank of compound to the old formula to be used up before the change becomes effective, but even so the information is invaluable in times of trouble.

Pigment coding

In the early years of the rubber industry secrecy regarding processes and materials was paramount, and among the devices used for this purpose was the practice of using code numbers and code names for various materials. While secrecy has lost its paramount importance, the use of a code system has advantages which justify its retention, for example, formulae become easy to write, concise and precise. Different sources of materials which can be used alternatively can be given the same code, and thus used conveniently. Different sources of the same materials which cannot be used alternatively are given different codes, and confusion thus avoided in the factory.

Material toxicity

Since the compounder is responsible for the materials used, he is also responsible for seeing that where toxic materials have to be used, proper precautions are taken in handling them in the factory. The dangerous materials are not so much those which are obviously dangerous but those which act insidiously. Materials such as benzidine, which have carcinogenic properties, should not be used. Solvents such as carbon tetrachloride, which have accumulative affects, should be replaced by trichlorethylene, etc. Every material used should be investigated from this angle of toxicity. Material suppliers are usually very co-operative in providing information on the dangers and the proper precautions to be taken.

Material control

The materials used for compounding in the rubber industry are not chemically pure but commercial materials containing impurities which vary in type and amount depending on their source. Their physical shape and properties may also vary. These impurities and physical differences can cause significant changes in their compounding behaviour, for example, the substitution of an American process zinc oxide for a French process one in a compound reinforced by zinc oxide can cause a significant slowing down in the rate of cure due to the much higher sulphate impurity of American process zinc oxide. The ratio of acicular particles to amorphous ones can also affect the physical properties of a zinc oxide reinforced compound.

With clays their various physical and chemical variations give products varying from the so-called soft clay giving soft, low-modulus compounds to the hard clays giving hard, high-modulus, abrasion-resisting compounds. The reinforcing properties of one variety of calcium silicate seems closely allied with its moisture content. Normally, this is around 10–12% of free and bound moisture. If it is dried down to around half this figure the reinforcing properties largely disappear.

These instances can be repeated for almost every material used in the rubber industry. It is obvious therefore that material control is an important function of the compounder if his formulae are to show consistent and repeatable results.

It is obviously impossible to allow the purchasing department to buy material from varying sources unless they have been previously tested and approved. Subsequent shipments also need checking to ensure that the correct material has been supplied and that the manufacturer has not changed his process or standards in a way which may have altered the compounding characteristics of the material.

It would obviously involve an uneconomic amount of testing to compound-test each shipment of all materials. In most cases resort is had to chemical analysis as a method of ensuring material consistency. Complete analysis is not usually necessary, but it is necessary to decide the salient points which, when determined, would indicate the compounding consistency or otherwise of the material.

Determination of optimum cure

The optimum cure of any compound depends upon the physical properties desired. If maximum resilience is required regardless of other properties it will be found that a higher state of cure is necessary than, for instance, where maximum tear resistance is wanted. Normally the optimum cure can be taken as being the shortest cure at which the maximum tensile strength is attained. This is an easily ascertainable point and suffices for most cases in determining the rate of cure and optimum cure on laboratory sheets.

For factory cured articles, where the emphasis is on rate of mould output, it is necessary to lay down limits for the minimum and maximum amount of cure any particular article and compound will stand and still be serviceable. Usually the minimum will be the optimum cure as above, but in some articles, i.e. moulded-on shoe soles, it may be a decided undercure. The maximum will depend on where the physical properties fall below the minimum required. Having fixed these limits, the amount of cure any particular portion of the article receives may be measured by means of thermocouples and the cure adjusted until the minimum and maximum limits are complied with. For speed, high temperatures are necessary, but inevitably in thick articles this means a wide spread in the amount of cure received by various parts of the article. Where the spread is too great a lowering of the temperature and an increase in time is indicated.

The choice of accelerator is very important in this respect, since whereas accelerators such as MBT have a long plateau effect with little or no fall away in properties on considerable overcure, others have a pronounced peak effect, and physical properties fall away rapidly on overcure. Thus the use of a fast but "peaky" accelerator, giving a laboratory optimum cure of, say, 20 minutes, may result in a slower factory cure than where an accelerator with a pronounced plateau effect is used, although the laboratory optimum cure on this latter may be only 30 minutes. This being due to the greater spread of the cure limits than can be tolerated, thus enabling higher curing temperatures to be employed. It is important to remember that rubber is a very poor conductor of heat, and consequently the cure time of an article varies not directly as the thickness but more nearly as the square of the thickness. Vulcanisation is a chemical reaction, and the rate of reaction is influenced largely by the temperature, the speed approximately doubling for every 10° C rise.

Design and development of the formula

As stated previously, service requirements normally determine the type of polymer to be used unless price considerations interfere unduly. Ten basic types of polymer are available with widely different properties. They are as follows: (see Chapter III)

Natural rubber
Butadiene styrene
Polybutylene
Polychloroprene
Butadiene acrylonitrile
Polysulphide
Hypalon
Fluorinated rubbers
Silicone based
Polyurethanes

Each basic type contains numerous modifications or grades, and since the polymers are considered in detail in another chapter, only general considerations will be discussed here. For general properties see Table 6.18.

The following service considerations, where severe, usually decide the basic type: exposure to (a) solvents; (b) heat; (c) atmospheric conditions.

Exposure to solvents

When exposure to solvents is involved, then neoprene, low acrylonitrile, high acrylonitrile and the Thiokols are indicated. The order given is that of increasing resistance to the aromatic- or ester-type solvents. For the non-aromatic or aliphatic types neoprene and the low-nitrile rubbers are approximately equal, and price or weathering considerations become the deciding factor. It should be noted, however, that simple exposure to solvents does not necessarily indicate the need for solvent-resisting synthetic rubbers. The important point is whether the exposure to oils or solvents renders the article useless for its particular purpose.

Printers' rolls are still being satisfactorily produced with natural rubber mixes despite the exposure to oils, solvents and catalytic driers of various types. One of the reasons for this is that comparatively little in the way of tensile strength or tear resistance is required in a printers' roll covering. In addition, the swelling induced by the solvents, provided it is uniform,

TABLE 6.18

GENERAL PROPERTIES OF THE POLYMERS

Properties	GRS			Buna N	Neoprene	Thiokol	Butyl	Standard natural rubber
	Hot	Cold	Oil extended					
Specific gravity	0·94	0·94	0·94	1·0	1·25	1·35	0·91	0·93
Tensile, lb./in.²:								
Black loaded	3000	3500	3500	4000	3000	1500	3000	4500
Unloaded	400	450	450	600	3500	300	3000	3000
Abrasion resistance	Fair	Good	Excellent	Good	Excellent	Poor	Good	Excellent
Ageing:								
Sunlight	Good	Fair	Fair	Poor	Excellent	Good	Excellent	Poor
Oxygen	Good	Good	Good	Fair	Good	Good	Very good	Good
Heat	Good	Good	Good	Good	Excellent	Poor	Good	Fair
Natural	Good	Good	Good	Good	Good	Good	Excellent	Good

makes a more satisfactory roll, since it becomes softer.   It is, of course, essential that the natural rubber mix be specially compounded for this purpose, and the use of factice and/or bone glue is indicated to reduce the swell to a minimum.

The high specific gravity of neoprene (1·23–1·25) is a serious disadvantage as far as cost is concerned, but can sometimes be overcome by the use of factice and/or rubber processing oil.

The nitrile rubbers suffer from the absence of building tack, which can cause trouble with lamination or ply separation defects, especially with the high nitrile rubbers.

The Thiokols have this disadvantage to an even greater degree, and in addition, an unpleasant odour when hot.   This is especially noticeable when hot mouldings are being removed from the mould.   In this instance the odour or gas given off has lacrimatory properties.

Great care has also to be exercised that small amounts of Thiokol scrap do not get mixed with other polymer mixes, since even traces can cause the articles to smell more offensively than a 100% Thiokol article.

The silicone rubbers also have a high degree of resistance to oils and solvents, but their high cost normally prohibits their use for this feature alone, and only where severe heat exposure in addition is experienced is their use justified.

Exposure to heat

For exposure to heat, neoprene, Butyl and the silicone rubbers are indicated in order of ascending resistance.

Neoprene normally stiffens on exposure to heat, while Butyl normally softens.   These two properties may be utilised to make a two-polymer mix which will be superior to either individually.   Once again the individual circumstances of the application need to be studied, since in some cases softening cannot be tolerated and stiffening is preferable.   In other cases stiffening may cause premature failure and softening may prove an advantage.

The silicone rubbers offer exceptional resistance to heat, but their high initial cost and the long vulcanising time necessary limit their uses to exceptional cases.

Atmospheric exposure

Where atmospheric exposure is the factor limiting service life, neoprene or Butyl are the indicated polymers, with Butyl usually enjoying a cost advantage.   With the exception of weather stripping, window fairing and possibly a few other applications, most articles are stressed in use.   Again, an analysis of the service conditions will repay the effort and, together with a knowledge of processing and handling difficulties, provide a solution.   A case in point is the hose used on a petrol pump.   The tube will be a low-nitrile polymer mix, since the aromatic content of the fuel can be considerable.   The cover is fully exposed to sun and climate and also to dragging over the ground, concrete or tarmac surrounding the pump.   It is also exposed to accidental oil exposure.   For this purpose neoprene is ideal, since not only will it withstand these conditions but it will also vulcanise satisfactorily with nitrile rubbers.

Where heat, oil, solvents and atmospheric exposure are not the limiting factors the choice lies with what may be termed the general-purpose rubbers.   Natural rubber, the butadiene–styrene types and to a lesser but growing extent the polybutylene rubbers.

Natural rubber is available in many grades classified by method of preparation, colour and cleanliness.

Plantation rubbers

Crêpes

    Pale—Thick or Thin 1X, 1 and 2
    Brown—1X, 2X and 3X
    Remilled—Thick or Thin 1, 2, 3, 4 and Roll Brown No. 1

Smoked sheets

    1X, 1, 2, 3, 4 and 5

Wild rubbers

Small amounts of wild rubbers, such as Upriver fine Para, are still available, but are of little significance except for highly specialised applications.

For applications requiring the utmost cleanliness or where pastel shades are required, pale crêpe is essential.   For other applications it becomes a question of choosing the cheapest grade or grades consistent with requirements of cleanliness, physical requirements and ageing.   The lower grades contain bark, leaf or sand in increasing amounts, and the ageing properties of the lowest grades may also be poorer.   The dirt usually results in lower tensiles, leaks in air, water- or solvent-retaining articles and failure due to separation in textile-reinforced articles subjected to rapid reversals of stress, etc., while the softer more oxidised grades may have higher hysteresis losses.   For consistency over long periods it is best to use a mixture of the off-grades rather than rely on one only, and if possible use a blend of sheets and brown crêpes.

This point of economical usage of the available grades of natural rubber is one of major importance, since appreciable savings in cost can be made without loss of quality if the best use is made of the off-grades.

General-purpose synthetics

The butadiene–styrene rubbers represent an easier choice than natural, since they are all clean, packaged in such a way as to prevent contamination during transit and reasonably consistent in their physical properties. There are three main types—hot, cold and oil extended.

These three types have numerous modifications and can be staining or non-staining. They can also be obtained masterbatched with various blacks. Various manufacturing differences also result in slight processing differences. The oil-extended polymers are available with extensions of 25, $37\frac{1}{2}$ and 45%.

The present numbering system, while giving a good idea of their make-up, does not, however, mean that one manufacturer's 1710 will process the same as someone else's.

The system is as follows:

1000–1099	Hot rubber series unpigmented
1100–1199	,, ,, ,, pigmented
1500–1599	Cold rubber series unpigmented
1600–1699	,, ,, ,, pigmented
1700–1799	Oil extended series unpigmented
1800–1899	,, ,, ,, pigmented

Individual specifications are available for each modification of the basic types.

The hot rubbers are rapidly being replaced by the cold rubbers by virtue of their superior tensile strength at both normal and elevated temperatures, elongation, flex life, resilience and ageing. They do appear, however, to be more resistant to exposure cracking than the cold rubbers.

Pure gum SBR compounds show low tensile strength, and it is neces-sary to use channel blacks or fine furnace blacks to develop optimum physical properties. Mineral fillers give low tensile strength in SBR. Vulcanisation of SBR is similar to natural except that, due to the lower unsaturation, a smaller sulphur ratio is used (2 parts per 100) and more acceleration. MBT, MBTS, thiurams or sulphenamides being the pre-ferred accelerators.

The cold rubbers are superior to natural in abrasion, approximately equal in processing and inferior in flex cracking, tensile and tear, par-ticularly hot tear.

SBR compounds give good heat ageing and low water absorption. The freezing point is higher than that of natural rubber.

The oil-extended rubbers represent a highly significant saving in cost. With this reduction in cost go higher abrasion resistance than cold rubber, slightly higher hysteresis loss and processing which requires more care. The use of the oil-extended polymers will undoubtedly grow rapidly in view of the potential advantages.

Building and processing tack are noticeably absent with SBR compounds, and where necessary have to be supplied by a film of natural rubber cement. Combinations of natural rubber with up to 30% of SBR may, however, have sufficient tack for use, depending on the degree of tack considered desirable or necessary.

The choice between the SBR types and natural rubber can be summarised as follows, if SBR is cheaper than natural, does it have the required properties and can it be handled in the factory? If natural is cheaper than SBR, then only if a higher degree of abrasion resistance is required will SBR be used.

Vulcanising materials

Sulphur is still the preferred curing agent, and will probably continue to be so, with selenium, tellurium and the peroxides being used only in special cases. Sulphur ratios for natural rubber are normally around 2·25–3·0 parts per 100 of r.h.c. for natural rubber, with emphasis on the lower ratio where the abrasion-resistant furnace blacks are used for reinforcement. With SBR a ratio of 1·75–2·0 parts per hundred of r.h.c. is more normal.

Care is needed when compounding the oil-extended SBR types. It should be remembered that only the butadiene is reactive and that the oil is not. The sulphur ratio should be calculated therefore only on the butadiene–styrene portion, i.e.

$$137·5 \text{ O.E. polymer } (37\tfrac{1}{2}\% \text{ extension})$$
$$(100 \text{ rubber hydrocarbon, } 37\tfrac{1}{2} \text{ oil})$$
$$2 \text{ sulphur}$$

Conversely, when calculating reinforcement the oil acts as polymer and volume loadings should be calculated on the entire polymer.

In certain cases it is essential to have a good tacky surface on the uncured compound for a considerable period after mixing. With normal rhombic sulphur a sulphur bloom will appear which can completely destroy all tack. Where this is undesirable the allotropic modification known as insoluble sulphur may be used, since this form will not bloom. It should be noted, however, that this form is not stable, and undue exposure to ammonia or to processing temperatures above 200° F will produce reversion to the rhombic or blooming type.

Bloom is primarily caused by the formation of an unstable supersaturated solution of sulphur in rubber during processing. The solubility of sulphur in rubber at room temperature is about 0·7%. To prevent bloom it is necessary therefore to keep the percentage of soluble or rhombic sulphur below this figure. Commercial insoluble sulphur usually contains a proportion of rhombic sulphur, and when comparing different sources they should be evaluated on the basis of their insoluble sulphur content. Where this is high, it is often possible to use a small amount of regular sulphur in the formula to reduce cost and still keep the percentage of soluble sulphur in the mix below 0·7%.

Insoluble sulphur is insoluble in carbon disulphide, and thus easily estimated.

Due to the instability of this allotrope, traces of iodine, sulphur dioxide or sulphuric acid are sometimes used as stabilisers, and material control should ensure that no excess is present.

Dispersion difficulties are sometimes encountered with sulphur, particularly with the insoluble type. Oil treatment of the material is usually helpful, and there is available a special sulphur, surface treated with magnesium carbonate, which is also useful particularly in Butyl.

Activation

Zinc oxide is the most widely used activator, and since it has a high volume cost, care should be taken to see that no more than necessary is used. For normal cases, 3·5 parts per 100 r.h.c. are sufficient and represent a significant saving over the traditional 5·0 parts. For special cases, up to 10 parts may prove advantageous, but these cases are few and far between.

Fatty acid requirements

Natural rubber normally contains a small amount of fatty acid, principally in the form of stearic acid. It is the variability in the amount of this acid in the various lots and types of natural rubber which account for a large proportion of the variability in rate of cure of compounds made from them. Nearly all synthetic rubbers contain fatty acid from the soap used as the emulsion stabiliser, and consequently less cure-rate variation is experienced, even so, it is normal to use from 1 to 4 parts of stearic acid to smooth out possible cure variations and further activate certain accelerators.

There are other sources of fatty acids than stearic acid, among them being oleic, palmitic and lauric acid and their salts, such as zinc stearate and zinc laurate. The latter two are expensive sources of fatty acid and zinc oxide. The efficiency of the various fatty acids is approximately equal to their acid number. Hence a more expensive stearic acid with a high acid number of, say, 210–230 may be more economical than a cheaper one with an acid number of 170–180. For this reason they should be compared on the basis of pence per acid number. The difference between the acid value and the saponification value indicates the amount of unsplit fat present, and should be low, giving a difference of not more than 10–15. The amount of unsaponifiable matter should also be low, since this indicates mixture with mineral oils.

Acceleration retarders

For certain purposes, it may be found advantageous to use a retarder to prevent premature vulcanisation or scorch during processing.   Normally it is better to do this by the correct choice of accelerator, especially now that the sulphenamide type of accelerators are available.   Where, however, it is desirable, organic acids, such as benzoic, salicylic, phthalic and the phenols, together with various organic compounds, such as the nitrosamine types, may be used to procure an increase in processing safety. Aspirin (acetyl salicylic acid) has been known to cure rubber headaches as well as mental ones.   A word of warning is necessary, however.   These materials can act at the curing temperature as well as at the processing temperature, and it may be necessary to adjust the acceleration when they are used.   Additionally, certain parts of the article may get no more than a scorch cure, anyway, and thus the use of safe accelerators and/or retarders would result in lack of cure.   An article of this description is the moulded-on sole and heel of a shoe made by such processes as the Cema, Pinto and Ferrari.   These machines apply heat to the bottom only of the sole and heel, which may be up to $\frac{3}{8}$ inch thick, and since the shoe manufacturers demand a vulcanising time of not more than 8–10 minutes in order to keep their capital investment low, an extremely fast curing compound is necessary.   These compounds are so fast that they will normally cure at room temperature in a few weeks.   Any attempt to remove this speed at low temperatures will result in poor bonding to the leather upper.   The only answer is to suit the processing to the compound.   Mixing on cool mills and strict control on the time allowed to elapse between mixing and use by the shoe manufacturer.

The above discussion relates to natural, SBR and butadiene acrylonitrile rubbers.   The neoprenes, which have different curing systems, react differently, and certain natural rubber accelerators, such as MBT, are used as retarders.   Again, different accelerators act differently.   The acid types, such as MBT, are retarded by acidic materials but not basic types such as the guanidines.

Accelerators

A full discussion of the chemistry of accelerators is included in Part I of this chapter.   A recent check showed that at least 150 different types of chemicals are in use as accelerators.   This does not take into account those of similar composition sold under different trade names.   For instance, MBT is sold under at least 17 different trade names, while a further 9 consist of mixtures of MBT with other accelerators.   The following principles may help, however, in their efficient use.   No rubber works or compounder can operate efficiently with a plethora of accelerators.   It is far better for the compounder to concentrate on a few accelerators and get thoroughly acquainted with their properties and capabilities than to spread his energies thinly over a great number. From the works point of view, the economy of using three or four accelerators in large quantities, rather than small amounts of a larger number, is undoubted. Store-keeping is simplified, there are less chances of error in the factory and purchasing economies can be effected. Fortunately, modern organic accelerators lend themselves to this kind of flexibility in use. Accelerators can be divided into two main types—inorganic and organic.

The inorganic ones, white lead, litharge, zinc oxide, lime, magnesia, selenium and tellurium, are now used only for speciality articles, such as ebonite, etc. The lead compounds, unless purchased as masterbatches, should not be used, due to the danger of lead poisoning.

The organic ones are extremely numerous, and classification is difficult unless on a chemical basis which is of small value for compounding purposes. For general compounding, MBT can be made to satisfy an amazing variety of requirements.

In speed, it lies between the high-speed ultra accelerators, such as the thiurams and dithiocarbamates, and the medium-speed guanidines, at the same time it imparts flat curing properties with a large plateau effect and good ageing properties. Increased speed can be obtained by activation with small amounts of DPG or TMT. Larger quantities of DPG will produce an air-curing compound. Energetic activation of the MBT is also possible by PbO, CaO, amines, etc. For increased safety, MBTS can be used, and any point in between obtained by simple mixtures of MBTS and MBT. The increased use of the abrasion-resistant furnace blacks and the demand for increased processing safety has largely influenced the introduction and demand for the sulphenamide type of accelerators, and they are now beginning to replace the thiazole type for large-scale useage in the tyre world. It is all the more interesting, since they are chemical derivatives of the thiazole type.

For heat resistance, a low sulphur ratio with a low uncombined sulphur in the vulcanised article is desirable, and one of the best ways of attaining this is to use a sulphur-containing type of accelerator, such as the thiuram disulphides. Of these tetramethylthiuram disulphide contains, for instance, 13.3% sulphur that is available for vulcanisation on heating, and products resulting from the use of $3-4\%$ TMTS and no other form of sulphur are among the best heat- and age-resistant compounds obtainable.

For sheer speed, the dithiocarbamates and xanthates can be used.

Protective agents

These comprise a wide range of materials, varying from paraffin wax to complex chemicals capable of retarding atmospheric oxidation or sequestrating harmful catalysts of oxidation or depolymerisation. They can roughly be divided into three classes.

(a) The waxes which by blooming to the surface form a protective film against surface deterioration.

(b) Chemicals which retard oxidation or depolymerisation and which are further subdivided into two more classes—

(i) Staining,
(ii) Faintly staining or non-staining.

(Class (i) obviously cannot be used in white or pastel-coloured articles.) A full discussion of antioxidants is included in Part I of this chapter.

(c) Sequestrating agents.

These materials are capable of combining with oxidation catalysts, such as copper and iron, to form complexes in which the copper or iron becomes inert. Usually they are specific in their action, but care in use is necessary, because it is possible that some materials in sequestrating copper may activate iron, or vice versa.

The waxes are obtained during the refining of lubricating oil. Chilling brings out first of all paraffin wax or crystalline wax, and secondly, after prolonged chilling, the microcrystalline waxes. Their protective effect lies in their ability to bloom to the surface of the article and form a very thin continuous film and to replenish that continuous film if removed under the specific conditions of service of the article. The rate of bloom is governed by the amount of wax present, the temperature of the article in use and the type of wax used, i.e. crystalline or microcrystalline.

Most of the proprietary waxes consist of mixtures of crystalline and microcrystalline waxes, and hence vary in their value from article to article. For some, paraffin wax works splendidly without the production of an unsightly thick waxy bloom, in others the microcrystalline blends are better. If the film cracks in service, then failure is usually due to concentration of oxidation and stress at the crack.

The second class of chemicals which retard oxidation are numerous. Some 90 basic types have been, or are, in use, with as many as 9 different trade names for the same basic material, in addition to various mixtures sold under trade names and some 30 of completely unknown compositions. Together they form a truly formidable task to one engaged in obtaining the optimum protection at the minimum cost. Fortunately the same remarks can be applied here as to accelerators. Keep the number in use as few as possible. Standardise on a good all-round one, such as PBN (phenyl-β-naphthylamine), and diverge only where found essential.

In amounts over 1 part on 100 PBN forms a disfiguring bloom, and if more than this amount is required the additional should be added as PAN (phenyl-α-naphthylamine), which has the same properties but is non-blooming. Difficult applications, involving excessive exposure to heat, sun, ozone or flexing, can be catered for by materials excelling in these specifics. For white or pastel shades, a non-staining or faintly staining type should be used. It is unfortunate that none of the non-staining types are quite equal to the staining types in protective power. The third class, consisting of sequestrating agents, are in their infancy as yet, but may be of value where thin films or dyed fabrics are concerned.

Peptisers

Natural rubber and SBR are usually too tough and nervy to process without some degree of mastication. The class of materials known as peptisers enable mastication to be done on a very efficient basis when internal mixers are available for this operation, and provided the cooling is restricted to allow temperatures of around 300°–350° F to be attained by the batch before dumping. That ever-useful accelerator MBT is a most efficient peptiser for natural rubber in these circumstances when used at a rate of 0·25 parts per 100 on the rubber. It would appear to act as a catalyst only, since after peptising it is also able to take its normal part in accelerating vulcanisation. Thus no peptiser cost is involved. Where the abrasion-resistant furnace blacks are concerned, however, MBT is usually regarded as too scorchy, and even 0·25 parts on a 100 RHC can cause trouble.

The specific peptisers, usually mercaptans or chlorinated thiophenols, are efficient even at 0·1 parts per 100, provided high-temperature mastication is used. Peptisers are extremely efficient, and where very soft rubber is desired they will produce it efficiently in one operation and so save possibly several mastication operations with their attendant power and labour costs.

Softeners

These consist of various oils, resins, pitches and tars used for producing compounds with good calendering, extrusion and other processing properties, such as good tack in natural rubber. The traditional one is Stockholm tar or pine tar, an excellent softener and tack producer. Care should be taken to see that the tar is not too acid, or undesirable interference with the acceleration may be caused.

Where tack is not an important factor the oil-residue type of material is much cheaper.

Hardwood pitch and mineral rubber also promote good processing without unduly softening the finished product.

The cumarone resins and the wood resins can, in certain circumstances, provide the tack required.

With SBR, it is not normally possible to obtain tack, anyway, and here the softener can be light lubricating oil.

Softeners reduce the tensile strength, tear resistance and abrasion, and increase the hysteresis loss, hence are normally used only in restricted amounts of not more than 5–10 parts on the rubber.

Stiffening agents

It may be necessary to increase the stiffness of an uncured vulcanisate or retain the viscosity of a rubber solution which in certain solvents, such as carbon tetrachloride, sometimes becomes excessively fluid. For these purposes, p-amino-phenol or even sulphur, where not otherwise present, are used.

Pigments or colouring agents

For white articles the choice lies between zinc oxide, zinc sulphide, lithopone (a mixture of zinc sulphide and barium sulphate precipitated when solutions of barium sulphide and zinc sulphate are mixed in molecular proportions) and titanium dioxide, either pure or diluted with an inert material such as calcium sulphate.

Their whitening powers vary considerably from zinc oxide, the weakest, to titanium dioxide, the most powerful. Although titanium dioxide has the highest cost per lb., its whitening cost per lb. may be the least. If reinforcement is required as well, however, zinc oxide may be the cheaper. All of them are improved by a small addition of ultramarine blue to eliminate the slight creamy tinge of the rubber.

The inorganic colours, with the exception of the iron oxides and ultramarine blue, have largely been replaced by the organic dyestuffs, since more delicate shades can be obtained and lower concentrations used, thus allowing either softer products or the use of more low-cost inert fillers.

The iron oxides can provide colours varying from crimsons to yellowy browns. Care should be taken to see that the copper and manganese contents are below 0·05% and that the chlorine content is also low, otherwise ageing may be adversely affected.

Colour matching in rubber goods is still very much an art depending on the skill and experience of the compounder. The type and amount of cure can be very important, and it is extremely difficult to vulcanise a repair in a white-sidewall tyre without the repair having a different colour from the surrounding material, due primarily to the different states of cure.

Reinforcing agents

For some applications pure gum or unloaded compounds are used, although these applications are relatively few. Most conditions of service demand increased hardness, stiffness, strength, tear resistance and resistance to abrasion.

To obtain these properties reinforcing agents are used. With SBR and the nitrile rubbers, the use of these materials is especially important, since they rarely have enough strength in the pure gum form to satisfy service conditions.

Whereas the action of vulcanising agents is a chemical one resulting in a physical change, the action of these materials is purely physical and dependent on their particle size and surface energy. For these reasons, a high degree of dispersion is necessary. For natural rubber, SBR, the nitriles and Butyl, the most important reinforcing agents are the various carbon blacks, ranging from the soft thermal blacks to the highly reinforcing oil furnace blacks.

They are given various names, some indicating their method of manufacture, some their main property in rubber. The following chart will be of help in sorting them out into some sort of order.

Channel Process Blacks
Harsh Processing Channel   (HPC) ⎫
Medium Processing Channel (MPC) ⎬ abrasion-resistant compounds
Easy Processing Channel   (EPC) ⎭
Conductive Channel   (CC)   abrasion plus electrical conductance

Furnace Blacks

Abrasion-resistant types
SAF   Super abrasion furnace
ISAF   Intermediate super abrasion furnace
HAF   High-abrasion furnace
CF   Electrical conductance

Non-abrasion resistant types
FEF   Fast-extruding furnace
FF   Fine furnace
GPF   General-purpose furnace
HMF   High-modulus furnace
SRF   Semi-reinforcing furnace
LME   Low-modulus furnace

Thermal Decomposition Blacks
MT   Medium thermal   Low-cost soft filler
FT   Fine thermal   High resiliency, good tear (inner tubes, etc.)

Incomplete Combustion Blacks
Lampblack   Low hysteresis loss

Acetylene Black
Electrically Conducting   Good abrasion resistance

The channel blacks have lost their importance in the abrasion-resistant group, having been supplanted by the abrasion-resistant furnace types. Providing good dispersion is obtained, the abrasion resistance increases from the Easy Processing types to the Harsh Processing types. The thermal-decomposition blacks give soft, highly resilient compounds. The FT blacks give in addition good flex properties, and for this reason are very useful in natural rubber inner tubes.

The abrasion-resistant furnace types are named in the order of abrasion resistance. Unfortunately, at the present time flex properties fall off with increasing abrasion, and in consequence, while the ISAF blacks are used for tyre treads, the SAF blacks still present problems in this respect.

Some people will object to the title " non-abrasion-resistant blacks " with justice, since they do confer some degree of abrasion resistance, however, they are rarely used for this purpose, and only when some other reason compels their use. An instance of this is in solid tyres, where a low hysteresis loss is imperative to prevent heat build up in service. They are a miscellaneous group which can be grouped in one way for modulus, another for tensile and still another for hysteresis loss. It is necessary to consider what compounding properties are desirable in the article and pick out a suitable one. Again, a warning is necessary against using every kind. Two or at most three types should suffice for the average factory.

Lampblacks vary considerably from mere fillers to semi-reinforcing blacks. The best should have properties somewhat similar to an SRF black with a slightly lower hysteresis loss.

Acetylene black is used mainly for its electrically conducting properties, but is being replaced by the conducting furnace black for this purpose. For the more detailed effects of the carbon blacks in natural rubber and neoprene see Tables 6.19 and 6.20.

The non-black reinforcing agents are varied and growing in importance. The traditional types are zinc oxide, clay, magnesium carbonate and blanc fixe. The more recent ones are surface-treated whitings, calcium silicates, aluminium silicates and silica itself, together with a group of organic reinforcing agents which are growing in importance. Due to its high specific gravity, zinc oxide is an expensive reinforcing agent and is now rarely used for this purpose. Its electrical properties render it useful in the cable industry, and its adhesive and therapeutic properties are useful in surgical compositions. Two main types are available. The French-process and American-process types. The French process results in a purer zinc oxide, since metallic zinc is distilled and oxidised to zinc oxide. In the American process the zinc ore is mixed with charcoal in the retort and the metal reduced, distilled and oxidised in one operation. As a result, the zinc oxide contains more impurities, such as sulphates, etc., which produce a slower-curing compound than when French process zinc oxide is used. This appears only when the zinc oxide is used for loading, activation amounts do not show this difference.

The clays are useful and are classified as hard or soft, depending on their reinforcing properties. Clays native to England are intermediate or soft.

TABLE 6.19

EVALUATION OF VARIOUS TYPES OF CARBON BLACK IN NATURAL RUBBER

Type	SAF	ISAF	HAF	MPC	FEF	FF	GPF	GPF	GPF	HMF	SRF	FT	MT
Carbon black	Kosmos 85, Dixie 85	Kosmos 70, Dixie 70	Kosmos 60, Dixie 60	Kosmobile S-66, Dixie-densed S-66	Kosmos 50, Dixie 50	Statex B	Kosmos 35, Dixie 35	Sterling V	Kosmos 45, Dixie 45	Kosmos 40, Dixie 40	Kosmos 20, Dixie 20	P-33	Thermax
mµ [handwritten]	17	20	26		40	41	60		55	55	73	190	300
Processing, Banbury:													
Maximum stock temperature, °C	114·6	115·0	117·8	98·9	117·8	103·9	111·1	109·4	103·0	101·1	97·8	98·9	95·6
Total power, watt-hours	2,275	2,230	2,235	1,970	2,210	2,015	2,090	1,950	1,875	1,840	1,840	1,705	1,690
Plasticity:													
Mooney, compound (ML, 4 minutes at 100° C)	72	69	51	51	48	38	38	36	35	35	33	28	26
Williams, h_1, mm.	3·05	2·80	2·39	1·95	2·18	1·78	1·78	1·75	1·73	1·65	1·60	1·55	1·46
Dillon, seconds	9·9	5·9	3·4	2·1	2·7	1·6	1·6	1·3	1·2	1·2	1·2	0·8	0·8
Extrusion:													
Grams/minute	17·7	24·3	26·6	26·4	27·5	29·1	28·2	29·7	30·5	31·2	30·2	30·4	29·7
Metres/minute	5·4	6·4	6·0	6·5	7·5	6·8	7·2	7·7	7·1	7·1	7·4	6·0	5·9
Grams/metre	3·27	3·78	3·87	4·05	3·68	4·28	3·94	3·85	4·34	4·41	4·09	5·08	5·02
Shrinkage and swell:													
Mill shrinkage, %	28	26	23	40	21	36	26	28	34	37	37	63	54
Extruder shrinkage, %	62·3	67·4	68·2	69·6	66·5	71·2	68·7	68·0	70·8	72·0	69·8	75·7	75·4
Extruder swell, %	148	190	193	204	176	220	190	186	212	223	201	276	276
Dillon swell, %	60	73	76	111	76	111	82	89	104	107	111	152	152
Williams recovery, h_2, mm.	4·06	3·22	2·74	2·31	2·44	2·13	2·11	1·91	2·03	1·91	1·83	1·64	1·55
Scorch, MS at 121·1° C, minutes	22	22	26	26	30	40	41	43	43	43	49	43	48
Reinforcement at 27·8° C:													
Modulus at 400% elongation, lb./in.*	3,395	3,225	3,325	2,085	3,175	2,075	2,660	2,390	2,220	2,100	1,955	880	965
Tensile strength, lb./in.²	4,340	4,175	3,080	4,445	3,715	3,825	3,535	3,420	3,375	3,645	3,305	3,650	3,450
% Elongation at break **	497	510	468	632	465	578	512	518	540	572	507	663	655
Shore hardness *	62	61	59	57	59	54	57	55	52	52	52	46	45
% Rebound at 26·7° C *	46·7	47·7	55·3	48·7	59·0	58·7	61·3	61·0	63·0	62·7	64·3	65·7	68·3
Tear resistance at 26·7° C, lb./in.*	964	906	822	944	669	718	651	604	581	625	544	509	425
Heat build-up, Goodrich flexometer, ° C †	123·9	131·1	107·2	120·0	83·4	92·2	78·3	80·0	77·2	81·6	78·9	80·0	77·8
% Compression †	21·0	33·3	15·2	27·2	3·5	9·8	2·1	3·4	3·6	5·7	3·9	6·1	5·7
% Set †	11·2	12·0	9·4	14·8	4·8	8·6	4·2	4·2	4·0	5·2	4·6	9·4	8·4
Heat build-up, Firestone flexometer, ° C †	98·9	96·7	84·5	85·0	85·0	77·2	73·4	71·6	70·0	68·9	67·2	59·4	56·1
Flex, cut growth, De Mattia, flexes to failure ‡	8,490	9,593	11,657	8,040	12,727	14,783	13,950	10,023	11,090	13,673	12,917	13,498	14,665
Abrasion, g. loss/hr.†	12·4	14·4	16·2	21·6	21·9	26·2	26·6	30·0	31·0	29·8	34·0	42·7	52·8
Electrical resistance, megohms/cm.³	0·0021	0·0013	0·08	14	861	1·0	4·2	11·06	1,784	408	2,526	—	—

Reinforcement at 121.1° C:													
Modulus at 400% elongation, % of original properties	48	45	44	43	48	45	49	48	46	45	46	41	44
Tensile strength, % of original properties	59	58	73	50	53	50	49	44	43	38	41	30	30
Elongation at break, % of original properties	130	136	136	129	121	130	111	113	114	113	118	127	128
Rebound, % of original properties	122	123	110	113	115	114	116	114	113	111	108	113	112
Tear resistance, % of original properties	49	47	50	40	52	57	50	47	43	40	45	27	37
Reinforcement after oven ageing 14 days at 70° C:													
Modulus at 400% elongation, % of original properties	114	112	108	141	108	127	111	115	116	125	124	127	129
Tensile strength, % of original properties	96	98	99	97	96	98	96	89	88	89	93	90	93
Elongation at break, % of original properties	88	89	93	79	91	89	90	78	84	83	87	95	93
Shore hardness, % of original properties	106	108	105	111	105	107	105	107	108	106	108	111	100
Rebound, % of original properties	94	103	102	98	101	100	100	102	101	102	100	99	98
Tear resistance, % of original properties	99	92	92	94	103	98	106	94	84	92	89	92	90
Heat build-up, Goodrich flexometer, ° C†	132.7	128.9	85.6	119.4	78.7	78.3	75.6	71.6	71.6	71.6	69.4	67.2	65.6
% Compression †	30.9	27.6	3.4	27.9	1.1	2.3	1.2	0.9	0.6	0.9	0.6	0.6	0.6
% Set †	13.0	16.2	4.2	15.0	3.4	3.6	3.0	2.0	2.0	2.2	2.4	1.8	2.6
Heat build-up, Firestone flexometer, ° C†	102.2	102.2	85.6	93.4	78.9	77.2	72.2	70.0	68.9	66.1	65.0	57.8	55.6
Flex, cut growth, De Mattia, flexes to failure	4,223	6,173	8,573	5,847	9,434	10,413	9,857	8,323	9,373	11,503	11,413	9,010	12,645
Abrasion, g. loss/hr.†	15.0	17.6	19.1	21.7	24.2	27.5	29.0	32.1	33.4	31.1	36.8	50.1	62.9
Electrical resistance, megohms/cm.³ §	0.0023	0.0010	0.13	72	138	0.6	0.8	5.88	128	28	1.401		—
Cure:													
T-50, ° C ||	-5.5	-6.1	-6.5	-6.6	-7.4	-7.1	-0.5	-7.3	-8.4	-8.8	-6.9	-12.1	-12.7
Torsional hysteresis, K × 10³ ||	262	259	148	203	103	168	98	94	95	108	103	93	60
% Free sulphur ||	0.31	0.28	0.29	0.56	0.28	0.38	0.34	0.30	0.43	0.42	0.43	0.38	0.53

FORMULATION. Channel: Natural rubber, 100; zinc oxide, 100; stearic acid, 3; Santoflex 35, 1; Paraflux, 6; sulphur, 2.50; Santocure, 0.6; carbon black, 50. Banbury mix.

Furnace: Natural rubber, 100; zinc oxide, 100; stearic acid, 3; Santoflex 35, 1; Paraflux, 6; sulphur, 2.25; Santocure, 0.5; Vultrol, 1; carbon black, 50. Banbury mix.

* Average of 40-, 60- and 80-minute cures at 137.8° C.
† Average of 60- and 80-minute cures at 137.8° C.
‡ 60-minute cure at 137.8° C.
§ Average of 30-, 40-, 60- and 80-minute cures at 137.8° C.
|| Average of 20-, 30-, 40- and 60-minute cures at 137.8° C.

We are indebted to the Institution of the Rubber Industry and Dr. I. Drogin for permission to reprint this table which forms part of the publication entitled *The Role of Intermediate Level Carbon Blacks in Rubber*, presented by Dr. Drogin to the Third Rubber Technology Conference, London, 22nd-25th June, 1954.

Table 6.20
Neoprene Type GN Filler Loading Table

Sheet cure 35/307° F — Pellet cure 40/307° F — Pellet cure 45/307° F

Filler	Vols./100 vols. Neoprene	Parts/100 parts Neoprene	Specific gravity	Stress at % strain, lb./in.² 200	400	600	Tensile strength, lb./in.²	Elongation at break, %	Tear, lb./in.	Hardness, Shore A	Volume swell, % 70 hr. at 212°F ASTM No. 1 oil	No. 3 oil	Compression set, % ASTM Method B, 30% defl. 22 hr. at 158°F	Resilience, %	Yerzley oscillograph Load at 20% defl., lb./in.²	Static mod. at 5%, lb./in.²	Static mod. at 20%, lb./in.²	Eff. dynamic mod., lb./in.²	Goodrich flexometer, 150 lb./in.², 1800 cpm, ⅛ in. stroke, 20 min., °F rise	Compressive stress at ½ in./min. % deflection, lb./in.² (0·75-in.-dia. × 0·50-in. sample) 10	20	30	40	50
Base stock	0	0	1·30	150	250	650	3600	950	95	41	14	159	27	81	85	440	450	615	30	50	120	210	380	650
MT carbon black	20	29·3	1·38	425	900	1475	2850	920	240	50	13	117	27	70	130	605	760	900	35	85	190	320	530	875
	30	43·9	1·42	500	1200	2000	2425	660	270	54	12	104	26	77	160	800	830	1100	50	100	230	370	645	1050
	40	58·5	1·48	625	1475		2200	575	300	58	11	96	27	75	200	975	900	1250	70	125	280	450	765	1260
	60	87·7	1·52	750	1725		2000	475	340	66	10	84	27	72	250	1110	1190	1650	110	175	370	600	975	2010
	80	117·0	1·55	1050			1900	320	365	73	8	73	28	66		1510		2000	150	280	580	1000	1375	2700
	100	146·4					1800	240	330	80	6	64	25	62		1815		2500					1900	
FT carbon black	20	29·3	1·38	400	875	1450	3100	950	250	50	13	115	30	80	125	620	800	950	40	85	180	310	510	860
	30	43·9	1·42	475	1000	1625	2975	920	315	55	12	102	25	78	150	850	890	1150	50	105	220	385	625	1000
	40	58·5	1·44	575	1175	1850	2200	680	360	58	11	95	26	76	180	1065	1050	1350	70	125	265	460	740	1260
	60	87·7	1·48	1200			1600	350	400	68	10	82	26	70	225	1220	1285	1700	100	160	340	550	950	1870
	80	117·0	1·52				1450	240	410	76	8	71	27	63		1760		2100	130	220	450	740	1250	2525
	100	146·4	1·55				1350	150	405	84	6	62	26	57		2375		3100		280	550	910	1700	
SRF carbon black	10	14·6	1·34	350	1050	1850	3600	920	155	48	14	130	26	79	120	570	710	800	40	80	170	205	460	750
	20	29·3	1·38	725	1675	2550	3450	800	230	55	13	109	26	78	160	720	920	1200	55	110	235	395	660	1100
	30	43·9	1·42	1275	2750	2775	3200	600	365	61	12	93	25	75	200	920	1100	1800	70	135	305	500	830	1400
	40	58·5	1·44	1850			3000	440	450	68	11	82	24	72	250	1210	1280	2250	95	175	365	605	1075	2100
	60	87·7	1·46	2250			2850	300	440	74	10	74	20	69		1610	1620	2700	115	230	470	810	1700	
	70	102·3	1·50	2800			2800	200	250	85	9	62	18	61		2340		3200	125	350	590	1100		
HMF carbon black	10	14·6	1·34	350	1050	1950	3550	860	230	50	13	131	27	80	140	600	725	900	40	90	200	290	470	810
	20	29·3	1·38	725	1900	2850	3350	720	350	58	12	100	26	77	170	790	930	1200	55	110	245	400	650	1140
	30	43·9	1·42	1340	2850		3100	500	460	66	11	94	24	73	220	1066	1260	1555	80	160	325	520	800	1500
	40	58·5	1·44	2075			2900	320	520	73	10	82	23	68		1325	1600	1975	105	200	420	675	1300	
	50	73·0	1·46				2800	230	500	79		74	22	61		1875		2550	130	250	530	900	1850	
	60	87·7	1·48				2750	160	435	85		66	21	57		2490		3350		350	750	1670		
MAF carbon black	10	14·6	1·34	460	1425	2600	3850	770	220	52	13	120	27	70	145	730	865	1000	40	100	210	360	590	1000
	20	29·3	1·38	1125	2900	2850	3800	560	330	62	12	100	25	75	195	1120	1250	1400	60	145	300	475	865	1850
	30	43·9	1·42	2175			3650	380	340	71	11	86	23	70	220	1500		1950	80	190	410	660	1210	
	40	58·5	1·44	3100			3400	260	270	78	10	74	22	66		2410		2700	105	240	600	1200		
	50	73·0	1·46				2850	180	230	84	9	65	21	62		3275		3750	130	420	930	2050		
	60	87·7	1·48					120		88		55	20	59		5325		5350		825	1650			1850

FF carbon black	10 20 30 40 50 60	43·9 58·5 73·0 87·7	2350 3300 — —	— — — —	1·42 1·44 1·46 1·48	4200 3400 3050 2750	320 220 150 100	415 300 300 240	74 82 88 92	11 10 0 8	80 66 57 48	22 21 20 19	67 61 57 54			1700 2825 3900	790 940 1300	2350 3200 4750 7800	95 110 135	215 300 475 880	435 655 1050 2260	725 1280	1365	825 1200 1615
EPC carbon black	10 20 30 40 50 60	14·6 29·3 43·7 58·5 73·0 87·7	390 750 1350 2150 3075 3500	1220 2275 3350	1·34 1·38 1·42 1·44 1·46 1·48	4700 4500 4000 3750 3625 3500	840 620 440 400 260 280	250 390 460 400 315 280	51 59 67 74 80 86	13 12 12 10 0 8	122 105 89 70 70 63	26 24 22 21 19 17	70 75 71 66 60 54			650 920 1190 1700 2200 3050	950 1300 1700 2200 3000 4250	40 60 75 100 120 130	85 120 155 215 280 375	185 335 445 550 765	300 415 525 730 940 1720	480 660 850 1400 2050	825 1200 1400 2050
MT carbon black Process oil	60 11	87·7 8·0	825 —	1650 —	1·48	1775 —	500 —	330 —	60 —	5	74 —	27 —	76 —			865 —	965 —	1200 —	60 —	130 —	275 —	430 —	735 —	1400 —
Hard clay	20 40 60 80	42·2 84·4 126·6 169·0	600 1050 1250 1450	900 1200 1400 —	1·51 1·65 1·77 1·86	3200 2600 2100 1550	900 800 625 300	185 290 340 385	56 66 75 83	13 11 10 8	132 114 100 87	27 29 34 39	78 74 69 63	145 220 —	630 1210 1790 2365	875 1250 — —	1050 1750 2325 2850	55 95 155 210	85 125 180 230	205 290 380 475	350 485 645 —	600 820 1060 —	1015 1400 1950 —
Natural whiting	20 40 60 80 100	44·0 88·0 132·0 176·0 220·0	175 185 200 250 200	350 360 325 300 250	1·53 1·69 1·82 1·91 1·98	2300 1550 1150 900 700	880 820 780 750 700	140 100 90 60	51 59 66 73 76	12 11 10 7 5	147 127 108 98 90	31 34 38 44 49	81 77 69 62 55	135 210 270 — —	670 930 1200 1480 1800	750 975 1180 1420 —	940 1350 1580 1890 2050	55 120 135 — —	75 105 160 205	190 260 340 530	285 380 510 940	510 640 805 1550	930 1200 1475 —
Calcium silicate	20 40 60 80 100	17·1 34·2 51·3 68·4 85·5	275 350 450 675 900	500 800 925 1225 1325	1·38 1·43 1·48 1·52 1·56	3250 2850 2500 2150 1850	825 800 750 700 660	205 325 340 345 355	50 59 68 78 86	11 9 8 7 6	138 118 99 82 67	27 30 35 43 56	80 77 74 71 66	140 190 245 — —	560 875 1080 1245 1415	810 1090 1165 1400 —	940 1210 1350 1040 2500	35 55 70 — —	75 105 150 200 270	205 340 425 530	350 485 700 940	510 805 1040 1550	785 1000 1325 1810
Blanc fixe	20 40 60	70·0 140·0 210·0	300 450 600	450 650 775	1·79 2·12 2·39	2500 1950 1400	825 780 690	130 180 185	52 60 71	13 11 10	130 108 97	27 26 26	80 78 72	140 190 235	610 810 1180	725 950 1225	920 1200 1575	35 60 75	105 160 205	200 280 355	320 425 525	540 710 870	930 1200 1475
Zinc oxide	5 10 20 30	22·6 45·3 90·6 135·9	225 300 475 600	350 575 875 1250	1·49 1·67 1·99 2·25	3400 3350 3000 2600	930 920 875 850	185 300 310 330	46 48 55 62	13 13 10 8	151 143 128 115	29 31 32 34	81 82 79 77	105 125 160 200	490 550 680 840	560 640 820 1020	730 820 1050 1360	30 35 55 75	60 70 105 145	140 170 225 290	245 285 385 495	435 500 650 835	750 855 1105 1395
Titanium bioxide	5 10 20	15·8 31·6 63·2	200 275 350	325 450 600	1·42 1·53 1·72	3550 3325 2725	925 920 860	175 250 255	45 49 55	13 12 10	148 139 125	28 28 29	80 78 72	100 115 150	480 540 720	540 660 825	710 795 980	25 30 35	55 65 95	140 160 210	235 260 335	430 475 585	715 785 975
Magnesia	5 10 20	13·0 26·0 52·0	350 450 600	750 925 1225	1·38 1·47 1·60	3900 3575 3250	840 785 775	260 270 305	51 54 62	13 14 15	131 110 98	19 22 29	85 84 81	110 130 180	615 680 975	770 900 1135	850 960 1440	20 25 35	60 75 110	150 185 250	270 320 440	450 530 690	775 905 1170
Clay Process oil	15 5·9	31·7 8·0	375	650	1·44	3300	930	275	45	8	127	26	83	105	520	650	750	40	65	145	650	450	770

We are indebted to the Rubber Chemicals Division of the Dupont Co., of Wilmington, U.S.A., for permission to reproduce this table, which forms part of the publication entitled *The Neoprenes*, by Neil L. Catton.

No indigenous hard clay is available.   Surface-treated clays are now being used successfully and are intermediate between a hard clay and the calcium silicates in reinforcing properties.   Their price is usually attractive if something better than clay is wanted and calcium silicate proves too expensive.

Magnesium carbonate has a medium specific gravity, but is usually expensive and used only where reinforced translucent articles are desired.

The surface-treated whitings prove useful where soft, resilient articles are required with a good tear strength.   The flex properties, however, are not usually as good as when FF black is used.

The silicon materials appear to fall into three classes, calcium silicate, aluminium silicate and the finely divided silicas.   Their reinforcing properties increase in the order given, as does their price.

Blanc fixe (precipitated barium sulphate) gives a fair degree of reinforcement, but suffers the disadvantage of a high specific gravity.

The organic reinforcing agents are lignin, cyclised rubber and the high styrene butadiene resins.

All have the advantage of low specific gravity approaching that of rubber itself.   Lignin is difficult to use and varies considerably from source to source.   The only method so far revealed of obtaining reinforcement appears to be either by co-precipitation with the latex or its incorporation while in a highly hydrolised state.

The high-styrene resins are good reinforcing agents for SBR in things such as shoe soleing, where hardness and ability to flex is required with a low gravity, and protective helmets and pads for sports use, where extreme hardness without brittleness is required.

The normal high-styrene resins are 85% styrene with 15% butadiene. With natural rubber this type of resin is of little value, since their reinforcing properties seem to appear only with SBR or the nitrile rubbers. They also require care in obtaining dispersion.   For these reasons resins with lower styrene and higher butadiene contents were introduced.   They vary from 50/50 styrene–butadiene to 60/40 and 70/30 styrene–butadiene. A convenient method of using and comparing them is to regard them as masterbatches of 85/15 resin and SBR.   Thus the 50/50 version can be regarded as comprised of approximately 42% high-styrene resin and 58% of SBR.   While the 70/30 version would be approximately 75% high-styrene resin with 25% SBR.   They should be compounded on this basis, adding the SBR portion to the vulcanisable hydrocarbon.   This method of approach also helps to explain their behaviour in both SBR and natural rubber.

In SBR their only advantage over the normal 85/15 resin is possibly easier dispersion, although this is questioned.   They provide an expensive solution to the dispersion problem, which a little heat during mixing will normally do.   With natural rubber, the situation is different.   The 85/15 resin is of little value in natural rubber for reinforcement, but the lower-styrene versions will provide some reinforcement by virtue of the SBR they contain.   In actual effect, it can be said that it is not so much that the 50/50 type resin reinforces the natural as that the natural can be used to dilute some of the SBR present (58%) in the 50/50 resin.   It is, however, an expensive method of buying SBR.

Cyclised rubber is obtainable either in its 100% form or as a masterbatch with 50% of natural rubber.   Good results can be obtained with the masterbatch in natural rubber, although not quite up to the highest combinations of hardness and flex which can be obtained with the 85/15 resin and SBR.   The price factor also tends to be high.

Inert fillers or loading materials

Many materials fall into this category, adding little or nothing to the tensile strength, tear or abrasion resistance but are frequently used for cost-reducing purposes or to obtain better processing or some specific physical property.   Since cost considerations are usually a major consideration when using these materials, their volume cost should be compared rather than their actual cost per pound.

Some of the common ones are whiting, barytes, talc, kieselguhr, slate powder, hard rubber dust, wood flour, cotton or rayon flock and mineral rubber.   Whiting is available in three forms, ground whiting, precipitated whiting and surface-treated whiting.   These are arranged in order of price. The more expensive surface-treated whitings are noted for giving much better tear resistance than the ground or precipitated varieties.

Barytes consists of finely ground naturally occurring barium sulphate with the disadvantage of high specific gravity.

Hard rubber dust is used mainly in ebonite for improving processing and reducing cost.

Wood flour, cotton and rayon flocks are used for reducing cold flow and stiffening purposes in sports soles and upholstery.   Mineral rubber is a residue from the distillation of crude oil, and can be obtained in several melting points and hardnesses.   It has a low specific gravity, and since it is thermoplastic, aids processing.

Rubber substitutes

This term is applied to a series of materials made by vulcanising various unsaturated oils with either sulphur or sulphur chloride.

When sulphur chloride is used the reaction is exothermic and the mixture has to be cooled in order to retain as light a colour as possible.   All of the so-called white substitutes are made by this method.   There should be no free hydrochloric acid present, otherwise the rate of cure and ageing will be unduly affected. Heating the oil with sulphur is the method used to prepare the brown substitutes, the colour varying from brown to black. These materials are useful in producing oil-resistant natural rubber products and for cost reduction in both natural rubber and neoprene. They have the advantage of a low specific gravity and a noticeably good effect on processing, but effects on ageing should be carefully checked.

Blowing agents

For blown sponges, porous or microporous articles, blowing agents are used which decompose with the evolution of gaseous products during hot vulcanisation. Sodium bicarbonate and ammonium carbonate were the common ones, but are now being replaced by more complex organic chemicals, such as various hydrazides and carboxylic acid esters.

The production of a good sponge depends on two other factors beside the correct formation of gas. First, the compound must be correctly plasticised; a hard compound will not blow properly. Secondly, the correct type of acceleration. This should be of the delayed-action type so that the blow can take place in the early part of the cure, followed by a rapid increase in the rate of cure to avoid the formation of large pores.

Fungicides

Some articles comprised of rubber with a cotton reinforcement, such as conveyor belting, have to work in wet locations, where trouble can be experienced with mildew rotting the fabric. Various fungicides are available which can be compounded into the rubber without adversely affecting its properties but which will inhibit the growth of fungi and mildew.

Reclaimed rubbers (see Chapter IV)

A more accurate name for these materials would be *reworked rubbers*, since the rubber is not regenerated but merely put into a usable form. Furthermore, the combined sulphur is not removed from the rubber. Large quantities are used for many good reasons such as:

1. Low cost.
2. Uniform cost with far less fluctuations than natural rubber.
3. Lower power consumption and faster mixing.
4. Good processing properties.

The two main varieties are ground rubber scrap, known as " springs ", or rubber crumb and the depolymerised rubbers.

The first variety is usually produced in the consuming factory from cured waste and, depending on which point of view is taken, is either a low-cost inert filler, extremely useful in soles, heels, pedal rubbers, etc., or as a means of recovering the material cost of the cured scrap, in which case it may not reduce the material cost of the article. In either case, no allowance need be made for effects on cure, although the view has been put forward that an increase in acceleration may reap benefits in wearing properties.

The compounding differences of depolymerised reclaims are due to traces of the treatment chemical remaining. The alkali ones are faster curing with acid accelerators such as MBT, the acid ones slow curing, while the neutral ones are intermediate. In no case should a reclaim have more than 0·10% of either acidity or alkalinity calculated as NaOH or H_2SO_4 where extracted with water.

The acetone extract gives an idea of the amount of softening oil added, while the chloroform extract indicates the amount of depolymerisation which the reclaim has undergone.

Both natural rubber and SBR articles are used for reclaiming and the normal grades are:

Whole-tyre reclaim	General-purpose reclaim
Tube reclaim	Solution and high-grade mechanical
Mechanical reclaim	Low-grade articles, flooring, etc.

When compounding, it should be remembered that part of the reclaim hydrocarbon is reactive and should form part of the rubber hydrocarbon. Part is softener, part is inert load and in the case of whole-tyre reclaim, part is active reinforcing black. An approximation for whole-tyre reclaim would be 50% vulcanisable hydrocarbon, 20% inert load, 10% softener and 10% carbon black.

CHAPTER VII

PART ONE

THEORETICAL AND BASIC PRINCIPLES OF REINFORCEMENT

by

A. F. BLANCHARD

In rubber technology the term reinforcement is often used generally without any reservation as to the character of the improvement in the properties of the rubber. It is then taken to imply " the incorporation into rubber of substances having small particles which give to the vulcanisate high abrasion resistance, high tear and tensile strength and some increase in stiffness ".[1] Parkinson's formulation of the problem is here similar to that of Cotton [2] almost 30 years ago, and of J. R. Scott in 1951,[3] who stressed that unless a filler enhances all of these properties (except stiffness) it is not a true reinforcing agent. The disagreements and confusion which have sometimes arisen are not so much caused by any basic disagreement as by failure to make proper reservations in the use of the term, when these are necessary. Rubber technologists are agreed that colloidal carbon is the best example of a truly reinforcing filler; and basic studies of reinforcement have been mainly concerned with this material.

It was in 1920, when channel black was the only highly reinforcing filler, that the first considerable scientific study of the problem was published by Wiegand,[4] who discussed " Some Aspects of the Rubber Stress–Strain Curve ". Since then the basis for scientific studies has been widened by the development of semi-reinforcing and high-modulus furnace blacks in the 1930s, medium and high-abrasion furnace (HAF) blacks in the 1940s, and both super (SAF) and intermediate (ISAF) grades up to the present time. In addition, the last decade has seen the development of finely divided silicas capable of producing quite a high degree of reinforcement. Resins [5] have also been introduced as fillers in special cases for compounds which do not experience exacting conditions of wear and tear.

Characteristics of colloidal fillers

Carbon black consists of spherical or spheroidal particles which range from 5 to 500 mμ in mean diameter according to the type of black. Esti-

414

mates of particle size were very crude and indirect before the first use of the electron microscope in 1940.[6] Emmett and Brunauer's technique of low-temperature nitrogen adsorption isotherms was later used by Emmett and DeWitt [7] and Smith, Thornhill and Bray [8] to determine the surface area of colloidal carbons. Dannenberg and Collyer [9] discovered porous surfaces in some carbon blacks by their study of the relationship between surface areas measured by nitrogen adsorption and areas calculated from electron-microscope data.

The observations of Hatch and Choate,[10,11] on particle-size distributions in general have been applied to carbon blacks by Leigh-Dugmore,[12] who considers the distribution can be taken as log-normal in carbon blacks. He concludes that any two parameters, such as mean diameter and specific surface (area of unit mass), are adequate to specify particle size. Fig. 7.1

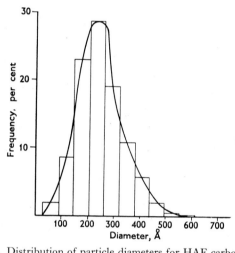

Fig. 7.1. Distribution of particle diameters for HAF carbon black.

shows a typical distribution of particle diameters obtained from measurements on high-abrasion furnace (HAF) black. Data for a wide range of carbon blacks are given in Part II of this chapter. Flemmert[13] discovered that the size distributions for silicon dioxide, aluminium oxide and ferric oxide could not be safely taken as log-normal in every case. He noted deviations from sphericity in the case of titanium dioxide, aluminium oxide and ferric oxide, but they were too rare to involve correcting calculations of specifice surface from diameter measurements. There has been much interest recently in 10–30-mμ-diameter silicas.[14,15,16]

The studies of White and Germer [17] with electron diffraction and Biscoe and Warren [18] with X-ray diffraction have indicated that colloidal carbons are two-dimensionally crystalline, consisting of graphite layers arranged roughly parallel, but otherwise in random orientation. The structure and physical parameters of a graphitic crystallite are as shown in Fig. 7.2. A carbon particle consists of a cluster of such crystallites. Typical crystallite dimensions obtained by Biscoe and Warren for a channel carbon were (in Å) $L_c = 12\cdot7$, $L_a = 20$, $a = 2\cdot45$, $c = 6\cdot82$. Flemmert [13] has studied the internal structure of several inorganic fillers by X-ray and electron diffraction, concluding that particles of titanium dioxide, aluminium oxide and ferric oxide consist of single crystals, but that silicon dioxide is non-crystalline.

A tendency for carbon particles to be grouped in chain-like structures [19,20,21] can be seen in electron micrographs (Fig. 7.27), especially in the case of lampblack and acetylene black;[22,23] and this feature influences

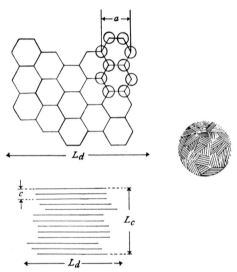

Fig. 7.2. Structure of quasi-graphitic crystallites in carbon black.

the electrical conductivity and stiffness which the black imparts to rubber. Chain structure has been found to be related to oil absorption, and a " structure index " has been suggested based on a combination of oil-absorption and surface-area determinations.[22] Other methods of assessing structure are based on carbon tetrachloride absorption, shrinkage of rubber black stocks,[24,25] and electron micrographs.[26] It must be admitted that there is really no satisfactory way of assessing chain structure in fillers.

Channel blacks for rubber contain more than four times the chemisorbed oxygen in furnace blacks, and this reduces the pH of a water sludge to about 5, whereas the pH for high-abrasion furnace (HAF) black is slightly alkaline at about 8. Table 7.1 shows the composition of various blacks, according to Studebaker.[27] Studebaker and co-workers [28] have concluded by detailed analysis that 18% of this oxygen may be present in

1 : 4-quinone form, and that in furnace and channel blacks carboxyl groups account respectively for 5 and 9% of the total oxygen.

TABLE 7.1

CHEMICAL COMPOSITION OF CARBON BLACKS (STUDEBAKER)

Type of black	% carbon	% hydrogen	% oxygen
HPC	96·76	0·41	2·77
MPC	96·68	0·51	2·78
EPC	96·33	0·65	2·99
HAF	98·54	0·30	0·62
FEF	98·99	0·36	0·19
SRF	98·89	0·44	0·30
Acetylene	99·72	0·07	0·14

Synopsis of filler effects on rubber properties

In this chapter comparisons of carbon reinforcement are made with the same compound ingredients and with equal or roughly equal cure times at about the optimum. Between 0·2 and 0·3 parts more accelerator (cyclo-hexylbenzthiazylsulphenamide) for channel than furnace blacks is used because oxygen-rich surfaces influence vulcanisation by absorbing or otherwise interacting with accelerator.

The stress in rubber at a fixed extension is commonly referred to as the static " modulus ", and it increases progressively with filler concentration, but is little affected by filler particle size. On the other hand, van Amerongen [29] has obtained a marked increase in dynamic modulus with diminishing particle size of carbon blacks. The change in static modulus with measurement hampers basic investigations, but the difficulties can be partially overcome by discriminating mathematically that part of the stiffness which is removable by stretching.

Fig. 7.3 illustrates the general trend of abrasion resistance with particle diameter of ungraphitised carbon blacks. For a given polymer such measurements on a Constant Power Lambourn Abrader reflect differences in tyre tread wear if the differences in compound quality are fairly wide. With the best laboratory tests on sulphur vulcanisates it is only on the finer points of comparison between similar blacks that service conditions and the arbitrary character of the tests obscure discussion of reinforcement. But, in general, a warning should be expressed against extending conclusions to apply to conditions which are too far removed from those experienced in tyres, e.g. very low rates of wear. The conditions of abrasion testing are important.[30, 31]

Abrasion resistance of both natural and synthetic rubber passes through a maximum at a moderate concentration of reinforcing black or silica

P

(Hi-Sil). For natural rubber this is shown by the data of Fig. 7.4, selected from Parkinson's monograph.[1]

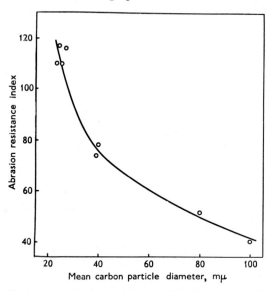

Fig. 7.3. Variation of abrasion resistance with carbon particle diameter in natural rubber.

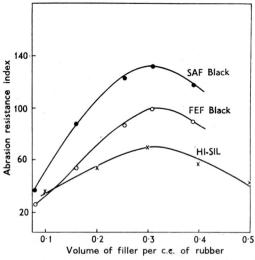

Fig. 7.4. Variation of abrasion resistance with filler concentration in natural rubber.

Fig. 7.5 shows the effect of carbon particle size on the tensile strength of SBR, which does not crystallise, and is very weak prior to reinforcement. Small particles also impart the highest tear resistance to rubber. There is an optimum filler concentration for both tensile and tear strength, as in Fig. 7.10 and 7.11. High tensile and tear strengths can be obtained with fine silicas with average particle diameters between 20 and 30 mμ,[13,14,15,16] but even the finest silicas impart much less abrasion resistance than the most reinforcing furnace blacks. Lignin and certain resins are capable of

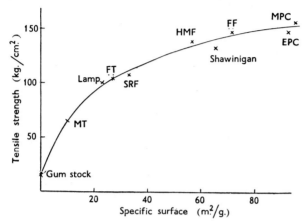

Fig. 7.5. Effect of carbon particle diameter on tensile strength of SBR rubber.

enhancing the tensile and tear strength of SBR and natural rubber, but the abrasion resistance is very poor compared with carbon reinforcement.

Other noteworthy effects of fillers are the fall in resilience with increasing filler concentration and decreasing particle size, and corresponding increases in B.S. hardness of the vulcanisates and Mooney viscosity of the unvulcanised rubber.

The optimum filler concentration

Wiegand [32] suggested that there is a severe limitation on the quantity of black which can associate closely with the rubber, and so be active in reinforcement. He postulated relatively large discrete rubber units (" macromolecules "), each surrounded by a layer of carbon particles bound to the rubber, and with loose associations of carbon particles filling the voids between the " macromolecules ". This early picture of black in rubber contained part of the truth, as will appear later (p. 443); but as Parkinson [33] pointed out, the linear decrease of resilience to well above the optimum does not suggest that pockets of loose black are being formed; and the undiminished increase in modulus beyond the optimum loading indicates that the attachment of rubber to filler is continuing to increase. These points can be appreciated by reference to Fig. 7.7 and to Fig. 7.8. Moreover, it is evident from Fig. 7.11 that the optimum loading for tear resistance is increased simply by tearing at 100° C instead of 20° C, i.e. without associating more particles with the rubber.

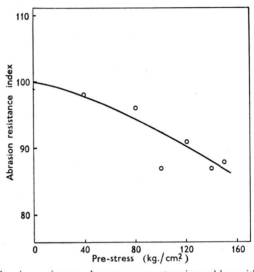

Fig. 7.6. Abrasion resistance changes on pre-stressing rubber with more than the optimum filler concentration.

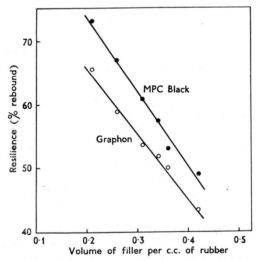

Fig. 7.7. Variation of resilience with volume concentration of MPC and Graphon black.

At high filler concentrations it could be that abrasion reinforcement is impaired by an excessive stiffness and concentration of filler-induced linkages. An increase in abrasion resistance might then be expected when linkages are broken and the rubber is softened by pre-stressing the test piece. However, Fig. 7.6 shows that the effect of pre-stressing with 0·42 c.c. of HAF black per c.c. of rubber is similar to that obtained when the black concentration is below optimum.[34]   Moreover, Figs. 7.4 and 7.10 show that the silica Hi-Sil does not have a higher optimum concentration than carbon black, although relatively low moduli before and after pre-stressing are characteristic of silica reinforcement.   It should also be noted that the exceptional tendency of Shawinigan (acetylene) black to stiffen rubber does not result in a lower loading for optimum abrasion resistance.

As a basis for theoretical interpretation of the optimum loading it is proposed: (1) that there is a balance of opposed tendencies at optimum reinforcement; and (2) that the positive tendency of additional particles to reinforce varies widely with particle diameter.   Both assumptions are reasonable, the latter one being encouraged by the profound effect of particle diameter on the level of reinforcement at all filler concentrations. The positive tendency to reinforce is neutralised by opposed factors at a filler concentration which is remarkably similar for abrasion reinforcement by various fillers.   This feature is illustrated by Figs. 7.4 and 7.8.   Thus it appears that the opposing factor or factors increase with reinforcing ability as well as filler concentration, and so must be greater for small particles.

Taking low resilience as the adverse factor limiting abrasion resistance would not conflict with the above principles.   But Fig. 7.7 shows that the rebound resilience is much reduced by partially graphitising MPC black to form Graphon, and yet this does not lower the optimum filler concentration (Fig. 7.8).   A compensating increase in the tendency to reinforce does not explain this result of the writer's experiments; in fact, reinforcement by Graphon at all concentrations is relatively quite poor. Moreover, decreasing resilience is unlikely to impair tear resistance, and so could not provide a convincing explanation for any of the optima, since all probably reflect the same basic conflict in tendencies.   The relative strength of these tendencies and the filler concentration when they become equal are likely to depend on the particular property and the temperature at which it is measured.

It is suggested that all the optima are due to interference of high particle concentrations with the mobility and alignment of rubber chain segments when the vulcanisate is strained.   Such interference would probably increase with reduced spacing of the particles, and this accords with the conclusion that the tendencies opposing reinforcement are greater for small particles.   The writer's later experiments have tended to confirm this view.   They show decreased tear and abrasion reinforcement as carbon particles in oil-extended (OEP) vulcanisates are brought closer together by extracting part of the oil.   The abrasion resistance of thin extracted test-

pieces was measured by glueing them to buffed test-wheels—after allowing
time for the distribution of unextracted oil to become uniform.   No change
is observed on acetone extraction of the control, i.e. SBR rubber com-

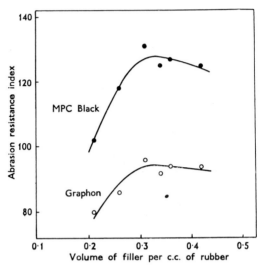

Fig. 7.8. Variation of abrasion resistance with volume concentration of MPC
and Graphon blacks.

pound without oil; and any effects which oil may have on mixing and
vulcanising the experimental OEP compound are irrelevant, because the oil
content was varied only after vulcanisation.   Thus Fig. 7.9(a) is evidence
that at high particle concentrations, e.g. volume $V = 0.36$ c.c. of filler per
c.c. of rubber, there is a steady decrease in reinforcement as the spacing of
particles is reduced.   Tear-resistance measurements indicate the same
conclusion.   With a lower concentration $V = 0.29$ c.c. of carbon black,
Fig. 7.9(a) shows an increase in abrasion resistance as oil is extracted.   In
this case the spacing of the particles is adequate without oil, and oil has the
normal adverse effect of a diluent.   Oil and polymer are interchangeable
in their effects on the spacing of particles; and Fig. 7.9b shows that they
are also equivalent in determining the optimum amount of reinforcing
filler.   This provides some theoretical justification for counting oil as
polymer when formulating filler contents for OEP compounds.

We may envisage restrictions and flaws due to an excessive particle concentration without assuming proper crystallinity in the stretched polymer;
and it is the final degree of van der Waal's association of chain segments at
high extensions which is involved.   Consequently, the interpretation is
not inconsistent with Gehman and Field's discovery that X-ray-diffraction
spots appear at lower elongations with reinforced than with unreinforced

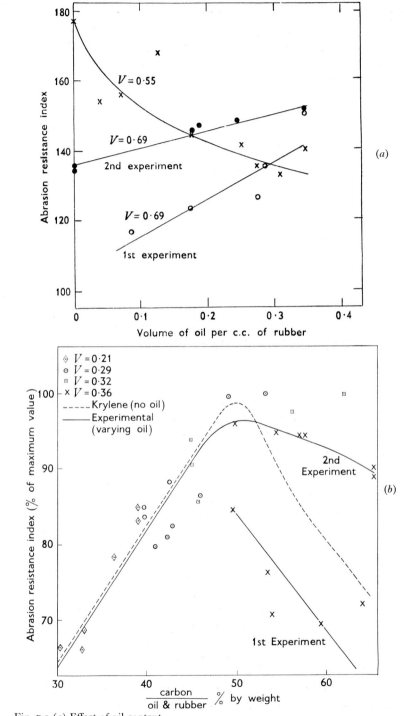

Fig. 7.9 (a) Effect of oil content.
(b) Optimum filler concentration with varied proportions of SBR and oil.

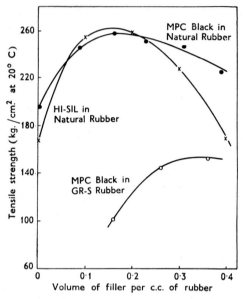

Fig. 7.10. Variation of tensile strength with filler concentration.

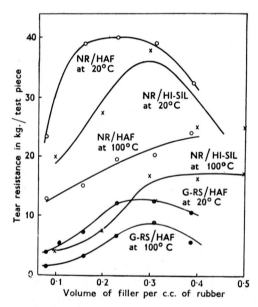

Fig. 7.11. Variation of tear resistance with filler concentration.

natural rubber.[35]   A decrease in the number of filler-induced linkages may reduce the adverse influence as well as the positive tendency to reinforce; and this could explain why partially graphitised black has an unchanged optimum loading (Fig. 7.8).   Modulus is therefore not considered very important, and so these ideas differ from Zapp's concept [36] of excessive cross-linking in highly cured rubber, but the distinction disappears when we are considering the spacing of sulphur linkages instead of filler particles.   Zapp has claimed that his concept is supported by higher abrasion resistance of Butyl rubber at low states of cure.

When natural rubber is ordered by stretching, the association of chain segments by alignment becomes so close that they actually unite to form crystallites, and this accounts for the high tensile and tear strengths shown in Figs. 7.10 and 7.11.   Interference of fillers with the crystallite mechanism of tear resistance at low temperature could explain the lower optimum concentrations at 20° C than at 100° C in Fig. 7.10; and it could also explain why the optimum concentrations at 20° C in Figs. 7.10 and 7.11 are lower for natural rubber than SBR.   Fig. 7.11 shows relatively little effect of temperature on the optimum filler concentration in SBR, presumably because that polymer does not crystallise.   These conclusions suggest that the restricted time for crystallisation in high-speed tests would increase the optimum concentration of filler.

Stress–strain theories of reinforced rubber

Approaches to this problem can be divided roughly into two types, the deductive kind, which develops mathematically a number of assumptions to obtain a solution without initial recourse to experiment, and the inductive or empirical kind, which grows more from experiment and quantitative descriptions of phenomena.

Theories of the first type which consider stresses in rubber around spherical particles have been developed by Weiss,[37] Rehner,[38] Smallwood,[39] Guth,[40] Guth and Gold,[41] and more recently by Hashin.[42]   By computing the hydrodynamic interaction of pairs of particles, Guth and Gold added the term $14 \cdot 1 C^2$ to Smallwood's equation, thus obtaining:

$$E^* = E(1 + 2 \cdot 5C + 14 \cdot 1 C^2) \quad . \quad . \quad . \quad (7.1)$$

where E^* is Young's modulus for the reinforced rubber, E is Young's modulus for the rubber matrix itself and C is the volume of filler per unit volume of rubber and filler.   To take account of chain-like groupings of carbon particles Guth has considered rod-shaped particles and obtains the equation:

$$E^* = E(1 + 0 \cdot 67 fC + 1 \cdot 62 f^2 C^2) \quad . \quad . \quad . \quad (7.2)$$

where f is the shape factor of the rod ($f \gg 1$). Among the assumptions made are: " non-specific " wetting between rubber and filler particles [43] with no localised bonds between pigment and elastomer;[44] and it is presumed [43] that " the adhesion of rubber to the surface of the filler particles will persist " when the rubber is stretched. Eqn. 7.1. and 7.2 do not fit in with changes on heat-treatment of rubber-black stocks, or with the effects of furnace treatment of carbon black, but Schaeffer, and Smith [45] suggest that Smallwood's equation may hold for carbon blacks after furnace treatment.

These theories take no account of the stiffening of the matrix itself when this consists of elastomer chains which may be linked by attachment at or to the surface of colloidal particles. The more inductive or empirical theories have been much concerned with the drastic softening of filled rubber by prestretching, and this was first studied in some detail by Mullins.[46,48]

Mullins obtained substantial softening only at elongations less than the previous stretch, the stress–strain curve at higher extensions being similar to that of rubber not previously extended.

Effects of previous deformation on stiffness have been considered by Naunton et al.[47] from a different standpoint from that of Mullins. To study rubber-to-metal bonding they designed an impact test which gave constant energy inputs for each deformation, and they showed that under these conditions tread stocks develop increased stress with successive blows, except at low stresses. That the " hardening " (increasing stress) at constant energy input is in accord with the softening caused by " static " prestressing is demonstrated in the paper. Care must therefore be taken to avoid misapplying theoretical conclusions on the effect of previous deformations by not appreciating the deformation conditions.

Mullins [46] proposed a dual mechanism of softening by bond rupture, but with emphasis on the increase in electrical resistivity as evidence for breakdown of chain-like groupings of filler particles as the primary mechanism.[48] Previously Ladd and Wiegand [20] had presented evidence that the chain structure of black in rubber has survived during severe milling, and this view is supported by Blanchard and Parkinson [49,50] who maintain that it is mainly filler–rubber bonds which are broken by prestretching, and that this is the cause of softening. A distinction is made by Blanchard and Parkinson between " characteristic " structure and weak structure formed by contacts between fortuitously adjacent particles. The unstable structure (contacts) could be disturbed and broken by stretching and remade by heating, in accord with electrical evidence of breakage and reformation of conducting paths. Physical contacts between spherical particles with contaminated surfaces can reasonably be expected to form this weak structure. Exceptional stiffening by the high structure acetylene black remains after pre-stressing, and so presumably does the characteristic structure which previously survived milling of unvulcanised rubber. Rubber–filler bonding during vulcanisation would increase stress transmission to characteristic chains, so that a few may break down on pre-stressing, and this may apply particularly to lampblack.   But in general the mechanism of pre-stress softening appears to be breakage of rubber–filler linkages rather than chain structure.[49, 50, 51]   Some evidence for this conclusion will appear later (p. 435).

For theoretical studies it seems wise to examine the material under

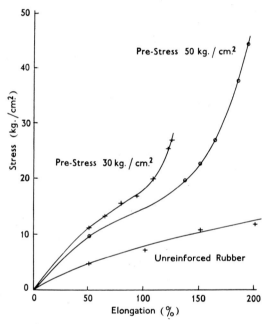

Fig. 7.12. Stress–strain curves of reinforced natural rubber after low pre-stresses.

conditions such that it is not basically changed during the measurements. Mullins [46] showed that softening with strain occurs mostly in the first extension, and that it is very small, for example, after three successive extensions to a stress greater than that reached in measuring the modulus. Blanchard and Parkinson [50] therefore conditioned reinforced rubber by three successive pre-stresses.   The character of the subsequent stress–strain curves is shown by Figs. 7.12 and 7.13 for pre-stresses between 30 and 160 kg./cm.[2].   An interesting feature of these curves is the sharp upturn, which is at much lower extensions than in unreinforced rubber, and begins at extensions approaching the pre-stretch.   To describe these curves Blanchard and Parkinson modified the theoretical relation for un-reinforced rubber, introducing an empirical parameter μ to take account of the upturn. The modified equation contained a parameter corresponding roughly with the modulus G in the relation of Guth and James (eqn. 7.5), and it adequately represented extensions 70–400%. The derivation and form of the modification will not be considered here in view of later advances.

Mullins and Tobin [52] also take the stress–strain curves after pre-stretching as their starting-point, but they propose a model comprising regions

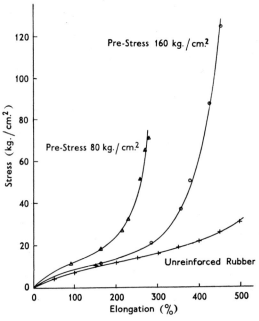

Fig. 7.13. Stress–strain curves of reinforced natural rubber after high pre-stresses.

of hard and soft rubber in series, and featuring a sharp upturn of the stress–strain curves with the soft regions highly extended. With this model the pre-stress softening is represented by breakdown of hard regions into soft regions. Mullins and Tobin apply eqn. 7.3 of Rivlin, Thomas and Saunders [53] to the fraction of rubber in soft regions needed in each case to reconcile the equation with data for a wide range of extensions of reinforced rubber. This procedure assumes that the deformation can be treated as occurring essentially in soft regions, and a substitution is therefore made in the following eqn. 7.3:

$$f = 2A_0 \, (\alpha - 1/\alpha^2)(C_1 + C_2/\alpha) \qquad . \quad . \quad . \quad (7.3)$$

where f is the force, A_0 the original cross-sectional area, α the extension ratio, and C_1 and C_2 are constants. The substitution made by Mullins and Tobin is:

$$\alpha = \frac{\alpha_m - \text{I}}{\sigma} + \text{I} \qquad \cdots \cdots \quad (7.4)$$

where α_m is the overall extension ratio and α refers to the soft region alone, σ being the fraction of soft rubber needed for eqn. 7.3 to fit the curves.

Blanchard [51] later questioned impressions from earlier work that fillers influence the form of stress–strain curves in the special manner which the above model is intended to represent. Experiments with reinforced natural rubber and Butyl showed that the stress–strain curves after pre-stretching could be matched by gum rubber with increased vulcanisation, both in respect to modulus and the sharp upturn which occurs at high extensions. Hard and soft regions are indeed formed by uneven distribution of particles and linkages (p. 440); but theoretical discussions of stress–strain curves in terms of the overall linkage concentration in filled rubber are supported by similar results with evenly distributed sulphur linkages. It appears that filler and sulphur linkages equally limit the extensibility of the network, and that continued extension of reinforced rubber beyond the pre-stretches in Figs 7.12 and 7.13 is possible only because more rubber–filler bonds are broken. Empirical modifications of theory to take account of the upturn of the curves are therefore best abandoned in the case of pre-stressed rubber. The discussion here will therefore be concerned with the lower extensions in Figs. 7.12 and 7.13, as in treatments of the elasticity of gum vulcanisates. However, mention should be made of the work of Skinner et al.,[54] who investigated the Blanchard–Parkinson equation [50] for high extensions. For reinforced Butyl they discovered invariance with extension for the product of the modifying parameter μ and the modulus from the empirically modified equation. This is a further illustration of the fact that the upturn of the stress–strain curves is related to the constraints (linkages) which determine the modulus at low extensions. Skinner et al. show that their development of the Blanchard–Parkinson approach gives estimates $6\text{–}30A^2$ for the area per constraint similar to those of Bueche, who has treated the problem rather differently.[55]

A theoretical equation for gum vulcanisates in simple extension was derived by Guth and James [56] and later by Wall,[57] who used a different method, and also by Treloar,[58] who showed that it follows from Kuhn's model [59] when suitably modified in detail. Using α to denote the extension ratio, i.e. the ratio of the extended length to the initial length, this equation for low and moderate extensions is written:

$$F = G(\alpha - \text{I}/\alpha^2) \qquad \cdots \cdots \quad (7.5)$$

in which F is the force per unit area of original cross-section.   Fig. 7.14 shows the result of applying the equation to natural rubber reinforced by HAF black and pre-stressed to both 50 and 140 kg./cm.^{2}.   The modulus G is not constant at extensions approaching the pre-stretch, and it also increases sharply if the extension falls much below 70%.   Therefore the extension should be fixed or limited, and the writer has adopted 70 or 100% extension for determining the moduli G.   The contribution of filler linkages to these moduli is taken proportional to the number of points of attachment linking the molecules, or more strictly to the number of rubber-chain segments bounded by linkages.   This accords with the theoretical derivation of eqn. 7.5 for unreinforced rubber.

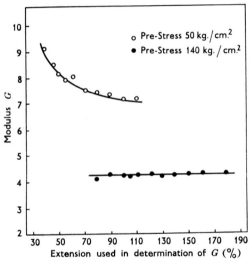

Fig. 7.14. Variation of modulus G with the extension used in experimental determinations.

A quantitative treatment of modulus changes with pre-stressing has been put forward by Blanchard and Parkinson.[50]   This attributes the softening to breakage of rubber–filler linkages; and it assumes that a measure of the strength of a linkage would be provided by the force per link required to rupture that linkage.   The force per linkage is taken to depend on the stress applied to the rubber and on the number of linkages U per unit volume.   An expression for the force per linkage in terms of these quantities must have the dimensions of force, i.e. $(M)\ (L)\ (T^{-2})$.   Therefore, since the force per linkage will be directly proportional to the pre-stress S, which has dimensions $(M)\ (L^{-1})\ (T^{-2})$, we may write:

$$\frac{(M)\ (L^{-1})\ (T^{-2})}{(L^{-3})\rho} = (M)\ (L)\ (T^{-2})$$

where (L^{-3}) is the dimension of linkages U per unit volume and ρ is some power of U. This condition is satisfied provided that $\rho = \frac{2}{3}$, which indicates that if the modulus G is taken proportional to the linkage concentration U it is probable that the force per linkage may be satisfactorily expressed in terms of the quotient $S/G^{\frac{2}{3}}$. The next step in the argument is to assume that the concentration of filler affects the number of rubber–filler linkages, but not their strength distribution. Conformity with this principle is then made an experimental test of measures of linkage strength. If the pre-stress S is expressed in terms of the cross-section before extension, as is customary in rubber technology, the ratio $S/G^{\frac{2}{3}}$ is obviously inadequate by the above test when for different filler concentrations it is graphed against the number of linkages as reflected in modulus measurements. But this difficulty is removed if the measure of linkage strength is the value of $\alpha S/G^{\frac{2}{3}}$ required to break the linkage, where α is the extension ratio at the pre-stress S. The ratio α is dimensionless, so that $\alpha S/G^{\frac{2}{3}}$ still has the appropriate dimensions for a measure of force per linkage, and should determine the degree of softening following the application of stress.

By the quantity $\alpha S/G_{\,\frac{2}{3}}$ we have defined a linkage strength factor X which should reflect the strength of the strongest linkages broken by the pre-stress S. The distribution of linkage strengths has been established empirically,[50] using values of dG/dX from tangents to experimental curves, and postulating distributions for trial which seemed broadly consistent with experimental trends in the pre-stress range 40–200 kg./cm.[2]. In this way it can be shown that the proportion of secondary or easily breakable linkages with strengths between X and $X + dX$ is:

$$dG/G_r = -(K^3 X^{\frac{1}{2}}/4) \exp(-KX^{\frac{1}{2}})dX \quad . \quad . \quad . \quad (7.6)$$

The above distribution is described by two parameters. One of them, G_r, is a measure of the number of secondary linkages before stress is applied; the other K describes their strength. A rough plot of the distribution is shown in Fig. 7.15 for $G_r = 4 \cdot 0$ and $K = 0 \cdot 276$ in order to illustrate the general shape of the curve. The ordinate ΔG is a measure of the number of linkages having strengths in the range $X \pm 5$, values of $X \pm 5$ being plotted as abscissas. The strength distribution may be due mainly to differences in the number of adsorbed chemical groups involved when the links are broken.[60] It represents a law of softening which can be expressed by the equations:

$$G = G^* + G_r F(X) \quad . \quad . \quad . \quad . \quad . \quad (7.7)$$

$$F(X) = (K^3/4) \int_x^{\infty} X^{\frac{1}{2}} \exp\{-KX^{\frac{1}{2}}\}\, dX \quad . \quad . \quad (7.8)$$

where G^* is the residual modulus after high pre-stresses, K is a constant; and theoretically for low pre-stresses $F(X) \to 1$ and after high pre-stresses

$F(X) \to 0$. Eqn. 7.7 therefore resolves the modulus into one component $G_r F(X)$ which is a function of the pre-stress and is due mainly to filler, and

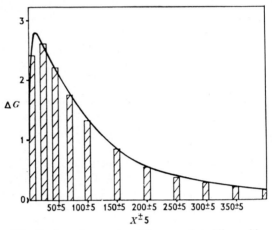

Fig. 7.15. Distribution of strengths of the secondary filler–rubber linkages.

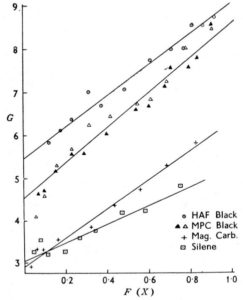

Fig. 7.16. Application of theory to pre-stress softening for various fillers in natural rubber.

a component G^* attributed to strong (primary) linkages formed by sulphur and by carbon blacks. To make a rough correction [60] for the volume V of the filler per c.c. of rubber these modulus components should be multiplied by $(1 + V)$.

The strength distribution parameter $K = 0.276$ is independent of the filler concentration [60] and common to secondary linkages formed by many types of filler in natural rubber [50] (Fig. 7.16); it is also the same for both SBR and Butyl rubber.[51, 60] The value of $F(X)$ is therefore uniquely determined by X and can be obtained from graphs after working out X from the experimental data.   This treatment is not necessarily dependent

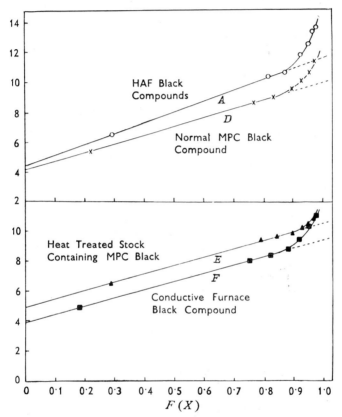

Fig. 7.17. Failure of the law of pre-stress softening at low force per linkage factors X (low pre-stresses).

on Eqn. 7.5; it could be applied using any stiffness parameter P that is proportional to the linkage concentration U.   For instance, if $G = \Psi\, U$ and $P = \varepsilon\, U$ we have $G^{\frac{2}{3}} = (\Psi\, U)^{\frac{2}{3}} = (\Psi/\varepsilon)^{\frac{2}{3}} P^{\frac{2}{3}}$ so that $X = (\varepsilon/\Psi)^{\frac{2}{3}} X^1$, where X^1 is calculated from P instead of G.   Since $F(X)$ comes out as a function of $KX^{\frac{1}{2}}$, if we are to use X^1 instead of X it is evident that a new value K^1 is needed in place of K such that:

$$K^1 = K(\varepsilon/\Psi)^{\frac{1}{3}} = K(P/G)^{\frac{1}{3}} \quad . \quad . \quad . \quad . \quad (7.9)$$

With this modification and $P = C_1$, for example, it is possible that the same treatment of the problem could be applied using eqn. 7.3. instead of eqn. 7.5.

For very low pre-stresses when $F(X) > 0.9$ there is a departure from eqn. 7.7, as can be seen in curve A of Fig. 7.17, which represents natural rubber containing 50 parts by weight of HAF black.[51]   Curves A of Figs. 7.17 and 7.18 show that an additional softening mechanism at pre-stresses

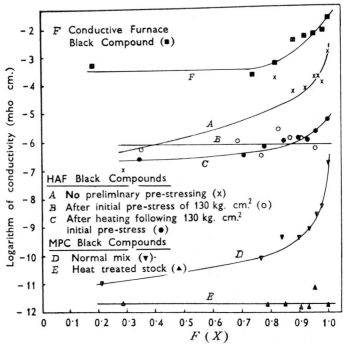

Fig. 7.18. Electrical conductivities of reinforced natural rubber test piece obtained for different $F(X)$.

below 40 kg./cm.² might be breakage of electrical contacts between particles.   After breaking the contacts by a preliminary pre-stress to 130 kg./cm.² there is no anomalous softening by low pre-stresses and no breakage of contacts (decrease in conductivity) with pre-stressing.   The contacts broken by the preliminary pre-stress are reformed to a limited extent by heating for 20 minutes at 100° C, so that a few contacts are broken by subsequent pre-stressing, and there is a corresponding break in the modulus graph at low pre-stresses.[51]   When natural rubber and MPC black are heat treated for 45 minutes at 158° C there are few contacts to break in the remilled and completed mix, and the vulcanisate shows no evidence of breakage of contacts by pre-stressing (Fig. 7.18, curve E).

Curve E of Fig. 7.17 shows correspondingly little evidence of anomalous softening by low pre-stresses. It therefore appears that contact forces between particles in chance contact are weak, but contribute to the modulus after very low pre-stresses; and that disruption of these contacts by pre-stresses between 15 and 40 kg./cm.^{2} is mainly responsible for the departure from the law of softening when $F(X) > 0.9$. This can be linked with the conclusion of Gessler and Rehner, who discovered that heat treatment of butyl–silica stocks removes a tendency of the vulcanisates to be very " stiff or boardy " at low extensions, and attributed the change to elimination of an undesirable pigment structure.[61] Waring [62] interpreted his studies of the dynamic properties of reinforced rubber as confirmation of the presence of a non-coherent (fortuitous) type of carbon chain structure.

There is some ambiguity in interpreting the modulus components G^* and G_r in the above theory, because modulus is influenced by coherent (characteristic) carbon chains as well as the bonding activity of the filler surface. On the other hand, chain structure was much overestimated at one time as a main factor determining modulus; for example, it is now known that removal of surface oxygen and hydrogen by furnace treatment eliminates much of the stiffening power of carbon black.[45] In recent years it has even been suggested that coherent chains in rubber do not exist except as adjacent particles joined by rubber.[63] Additional complications are envisaged by Houwink and Janssen,[64] who suggest that the lowering of modulus by pre-stressing is due to formation of linkages in new positions as well as to destruction of linkages during deformation. They believe this would make a negative contribution to the modulus by tending to maintain the pre-stretch of the test piece, and Houwink [65] suggests such a mechanism would solve the theoretical problem of the apparently slow restoration of broken bonds on resting. The importance of this concept appears limited by the fact that large sets are not normally obtained after pre-stressing.

Optical stress analysis has been applied by Kruse [66, 67] to examine filled rubber, and he has inferred that " the rubber is not bound firmly to the surface of the filler particles . . . it slides from their surface on deformation ". Kruse's microscopic investigations have also led him to describe a break-up of carbon black " clouds " (gel structure) on stretching.[63] There is evidence from volume increases under strain that in the case of very coarse mineral fillers vacuoles are formed by the rubber pulling bodily away from the particles, as was first demonstrated by Schippel.[68] Green,[69] Depew and Easley,[70] and Jones and Yiengst [71] found that this effect diminished as the particle size of the filler decreased. These observations have been interpreted by Kruse,[67] who showed that zones of high stress in the direction of elongation occur round particles with diameters exceeding $1\ \mu$. There is no evidence of vacuole formation with carbon blacks.

Bryant and Bisset [72] have discovered a "stress-plateau" with large volumes of very coarse mineral fillers. Their explanation is that the material softens so much by progressive "de-wetting" of the filler that the tendency of stress to increase with extension is counteracted (see Fig. 7.19). They conclude that separation of rubber from filler to form vacuoles by stretching occurs less readily with small particles.

More recently, Andrews and Walsh have used electron microscopy to study the number of particles extracted by replication of the rupture surface of reinforced rubbers. Even with carbon black as the reinforcing

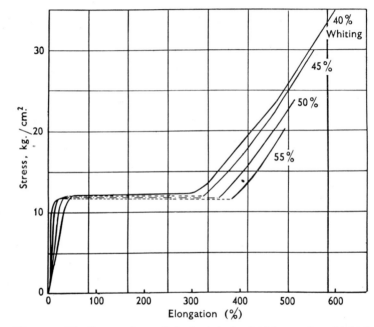

Fig. 7.19. The "stress-plateau" obtained during initial extension with high concentrations of mineral filler and very large particles.

filler they found that many particles were extracted from torn surfaces, and the proportion extracted was dependent on the mode of rupture and the type of black. Their method was to estimate the proportion of the area of the replica occupied by extracted particles and the proportion of carbon black originally in the rupture surface. The amount of black extracted was greatest in slow tearing and least in brittle fracture, and was less the more reinforcing the black.

A model comprising the spring and dashpot elements of visco-elastic theory has been applied by Marshall, Walker and Smith, [73] who note that "the behaviour of black-loaded rubber at large extensions differs in some fundamental respects from a simple visco-elastic material". These authors conclude that within the experimental limits ($\pm 10\%$) all the energy used in softening their black-loaded rubbers appears as heat. According to Zapp and Guth,[74] equilibrium stresses in reinforced butyl can be resolved into contributions made by internal energy and entropy. A greater internal energy contribution to stress is attributed to carbon blacks than to mineral fillers, especially if the particles are small.

The work of retraction of filled rubber was investigated by Barron and Cotton,[75] who concluded that the energy returned is not much greater than with gum vulcanisates. More recently Stearns and Johnson [76, 77] conditioned their test pieces at the highest temperature and the largest deformation to be experienced in the experiments. The test pieces were then retracted in small increments, allowing about 45 minutes for stress

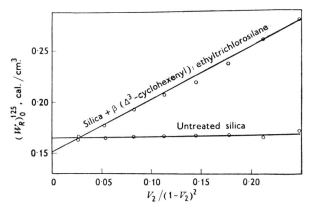

Fig. 7.20. Application of the Stearns and Johnson equation to the work of retraction of rubber reinforced with finely divided silica.

recovery after each 10% reduction in elongation. The area under the resulting " equilibrium " stress–strain curve is then measured with a planimeter to give the work of retraction, keeping the limits of integration between o and 125% elongation. The maximum initial elongation is limited to 150% of the unstrained length and the temperature kept constant. For these experimental conditions the following equation is given:

$$W_r = W_r{}^0 + \phi V_2/(1 - V_2)^2 \quad . \quad . \quad . \quad (7.10)$$

where W_r is the work of retraction between 125 and 0% elongation, $W_r{}^0$ is the work of retraction of the gum stock between the same limits. V_2 is the volume fraction of filler present and ϕ is a constant. According to Stearns and Johnson, ϕ is related to the surface concentration g of active sites capable of immobilising polymer segments, the relationship being:

$$\phi = b(g)^{\frac{1}{2}} \quad . \quad . \quad . \quad . \quad . \quad (7.11)$$

where b is a constant. For carbon blacks ϕ is an appreciable quantity and for non-reinforcing fillers $\phi \simeq 0$. The application of eqn. 7.10 to silica before and after treatment with chlorosilane is shown in Fig. 7.20 taken from a paper by Stearns and Johnson.[77]

Tear resistance and reinforcement theory

The early contribution of Busse [78] contains a number of deductions about the structure of stretched rubber, including some notable conclusions about the effect of carbon black. Reference should also be made to the important studies of Buist [79] on the tear resistance of reinforced natural and synthetic rubbers, which generally supported the work of Busse. Busse concluded that a structure was formed on stretching, and attributed this to crystallisation. He drew attention to " knotty tearing " of carbon-reinforced rubber, noting that the compound tends to fail in a direction at

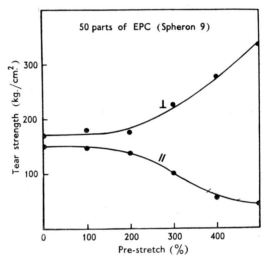

Fig. 7.21. Effect of pre-stretch on tear strength in two directions of a natural rubber–EPC black compound.

right angles to the initial cut. Busse recognised that this behaviour implies the " development of a mechanically fibrous structure in these compounds on stretching ". More recently Houwink and Janssen [64] have suggested that anisotropy of tear resistance of pre-stretched rubber in their experiments implies formation of some kind of structure by pre-stretching, and Janssen [80] has clarified this by postulating some persistence of rubber crystallites after pre-stretching.

Fig. 7.21 from Janssen's paper shows the influence of degree of pre-stretch on the tear strengths in two directions of a natural rubber–EPC black compound. The tear strength at right angles to the direction of pre-stretching can be seen to increase as the pre-stretch increases, whereas in the other direction it falls to the value for a pure gum compound. The effect does not occur in non-reinforced compounds, and it is absent from reinforced polymers which do not crystallise. Janssen points out that if there is good adhesion between rubber and filler the crystallites will tend to be drawn into straight lines connecting the filler particles. He suggests that " if certain requirements of size and amount of filler particles are fulfilled, a continuous network of crystallites and filler particles could be formed that

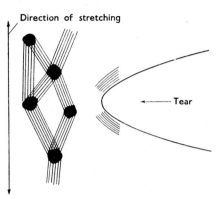

Fig. 7.22. Network in pre-stretched rubber of crystallites and filler particles (according to Janssen).

would protect the weaker regions against the stress concentration at the tip of the tear " (Fig. 7.22).

Greensmith and Thomas [81] have recently measured an energy for tearing T as a function of the rate $R = dc/dt$ of tear propagation, T being the energy per unit length of tear per unit thickness. For test pieces as in

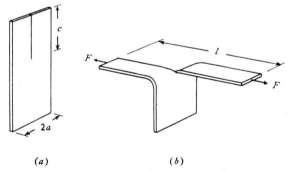

(a)   (b)

Fig. 7.23. Tear test pieces used by Greensmith and Thomas.

Fig. 7.23 and sufficiently wide, it is shown that T may be derived from the tearing force F by means of the relation

$$Th = 2F \quad . \quad . \quad . \quad . \quad . \quad (7.12)$$

where h is the thickness of the test piece; the rate R of propagation of the tear can be obtained from the rate of separation dc/dt of the grips, the relation being

$$de/dt = 2dc/dt = 2R \quad . \quad . \quad . \quad (7.13)$$

" Stick–slip " behaviour as shown by marked fluctuations in the tearing force is attributed to a strengthening structure at the tip of the tear which is due to crystallisation in the case of gum vulcanisates and takes an appreciable time to form. Where stick–slip tearing is observed it undergoes a transition to steady tearing with increasing rates of propagation in the range $2 \cdot 4 \times 10^{-5}$ to 25 cm./second.

Greensmith [82] has shown that stick–slip or knotty tearing under some conditions is a feature of the behaviour of reinforced SBR and natural

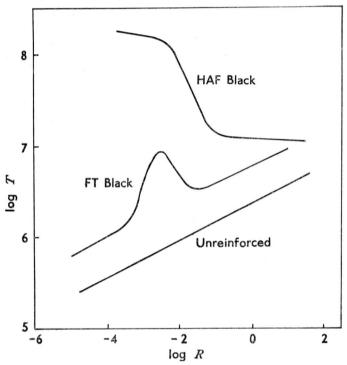

Fig. 7.24. Tearing energy T as a function of the rate R of tear propagation in SBR at 50° C.

rubber. It is associated with a negative gradient in the graph of tearing energy versus rate of tear propagation. Fig. 7.24 illustrates the behaviour at 50° C of SBR vulcanisates containing a highly reinforcing filler, a poorly reinforcing filler and no filler at all. Greensmith suggests that increasing the rate of propagation tends to increase the stress and extension at the tip, and therefore to increase the development of a strengthening structure at the tip. On the other hand, he argues that " the rate of extension at the tip, also governed by the rate of propagation, has the opposite effect so that in suitable instances a maximum of structure development should be apparent for a particular rate of propagation " (cf. Fig. 7.24).

According to Greensmith, " knotty tearing is an important aspect of the reinforcing action of carbon black, and a measure of reinforcing ability can be obtained by determining the conditions of temperature and rate of propagation under which knotty tearing develops ". Figs. 7.25 and 7.26 from Greensmith's paper show these conditions respectively for SBR vulcanisates containing HAF and FT blacks, and for natural rubber vulcanisates containing HAF, FT and MT blacks. Greensmith suggests that the less restricted conditions for natural rubber are due to formation of a crystallite structure.

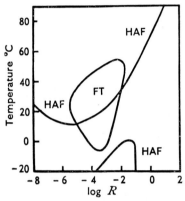

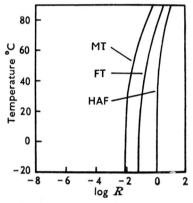

Fig. 7.25. Conditions of temperature and rate R of tear propagation for knotty tearing of reinforced SBR (the conditions occur within the closed or partially closed curves).

Fig. 7.26. Conditions of temperature and rate R of tear propagation for knotty tearing of reinforced natural rubber (the conditions occur to the left of the appropriate curve).

This view supports in part the suggestion of Ira Williams [83] that reinforcing fillers increase the degree of " organisation " of polymer molecules when the rubber is stretched. There would seem to be a close relationship with the work of Dogadkin and Sandomirski [84] and Bartenev and Belostotskaya.[85] These latter authors were concerned with the tensile break of unreinforced polymers, but an understanding of the behaviour of unfilled polymers is obviously important in studying the reinforcing action of fillers. Greensmith has been able to relate his tear measurements with the data of Dogadkin and Sandomirski on the variation of tensile strength with rate of extension of SBR gum vulcanisates. Bartenev and Belostotskaya have concluded that " elastic fracture consists of two stages—slow and rapid. The slow stage produces a rough, and the rapid a smooth zone on the fracture surface. . . . The slow stage of elastic fracture is characterised specifically for polymers by the ' fibrous ' mechanism of destruction,

and the rapid by the mechanism of the ' clean break ' of bonds. . . .
The smaller the load or rate of elongation, the longer the fracture process,
and the larger the rough zone. . . . With very slow fracture the rough
zone occupies the complete fracture surface and the smooth zone disappears.''

There appears to be some agreement between this theory that fibre
formation leads to rough rather than clean breaks and the theory associating
knotty tearing with structure formation. In work awaiting publication
Greensmith has shown that roughness of the torn surfaces reflects a
broadening of the tip of the growing tears. The replica electron microscopy of Andrews and Walsh has indicated that the rupture path tends to
meander from particle to particle, especially in the case of slow tearing.
Interpretations of tear and tensile strength in terms of ability to relax
stresses have come to the fore since Brown's work provided evidence of
high strength due to vulcanisation of carboxylic polymers by labile cross-
links (see supplementary references). Mullins recently suggested that
relaxation of stress ahead of the tip of a growing tear may result in broadening of the tip of the tear and lead to increased strength. Relaxation of
newly formed structures could play a part in this, and so it is not necessarily inconsistent with the foregoing hypothesis of structure formation.
Nevertheless, it should be understood that ability to promote stress relaxation has long been recognised in most rubber fillers, and that it is not a
sole criterion for tear reinforcement by filler particles.

The structure of reinforced rubber

Wiegand's discrete rubber regions

The discrete rubber theory of Wiegand [32] pictured units of rubber
(macromolecules) containing relatively little filler, but surrounded by bound
carbon particles, which form conducting paths for an electric current, and
dissipate energy when the rubber is stretched. Electron micrographs later
demonstrated an important element of Wiegand's theory, namely clear
regions which are practically free of carbon. With this feature there is less
rubber to space out the particles and so impair electrical conduction in the
loaded part of the matrix. The tendency of carbon particles to be grouped
in chain-like aggregates, and the speed and firmness of their association
with the rubber, are generally considered important influences on electrical
conduction, and they may determine the appearance of discrete rubber
regions.

Kruse's concept of carbon black " clouds " (p. 444) would appear to
follow from the idea of discrete rubber, but the relationship appears better
expressed the other way round. It is necessary to explain what has prevented black from penetrating regions of discrete rubber, and what there

is to prevent soft, unbound rubber in such regions from penetrating the clouds. Generally, the answer would seem to be that binding of black and rubber forms the clouds and gives them resistance to penetration by rubber not brought into early contact with black during mixing. The cloud configuration of reinforcing particles in rubber therefore appears to be the more fundamental feature, with discrete rubber regions appearing as a consequence.

Chain aggregation of particles

From observations with the electron microscope Ladd and Wiegand [20] concluded that carbon chain structures in rubber are aggregates which have persisted during mixing and milling. This is supported by Parkinson and Blanchard,[86] who used electrical conductivity tests to examine and reject the idea that carbon chains are reformed by flocculation of particles in rubber after being initially broken by milling.[87, 88] Evidence that chain structure in acetylene black can be destroyed by ball milling before mixing into rubber has been presented by Dobbin and Rossman [89] and by Sweitzer.[22] Contacts between particles appear to be broken temporarily by flexing or remade by heating; and Blanchard and Parkinson [49] are supported by Waring [62] in distinguishing structure formed by these fortuitously adjacent particles from characteristic differences in aggregation ("characteristic" structure). Sweitzer [22] considers that characteristic structure consists of carbon particles fused together by the carbon linkages or necks which Ladd demonstrated and Watson confirmed.[20, 90] Sweitzer supports his conclusions with Grisdale's theory of structure formation in flames by collision of droplets of hydrocarbon which later change into carbon.

Fig. 7.27 shows an electron micrograph of high structure (acetylene) black in rubber. Sweitzer's interpretation of his electron micrographs is that " numerous rod-type linkages are evident in Thermax with the chain length short, whereas with lampblack the fused junctions are generally thick with the chain length long ". He found that treatments which partially break down the chain structure magnify the difference between these blacks. In private communications C. H. Leigh-Dugmore and H. W. Davidson have noted that the particles in chain structures are of the same size—and they infer that this structure was formed with the particles at an early stage of manufacture. Blanchard's study [91] of compressed blacks has indicated that a kind of structure may be formed after manufacture if the surfaces of contacting particles are cleaned by high temperatures ($ca.$ 1000° C). This form of structure gives the black high resistance to compression and high absorption of carbon tetrachloride (p. 416); it does not impart high modulus to rubber, but it survives mixing inasmuch as it leads to a highly conductive configuration of particles. There may be an application here for Leigh-Dugmore's concept that characteristic structure may persist without remaining strictly intact during mixing. This idea is discussed below in the context of its origin, but the writer believes that it

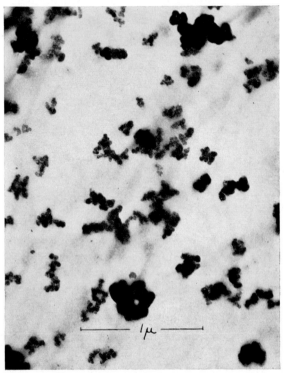

Fig. 7.27. Electron micrograph showing chain structure of Shawinigan (acetylene) black in rubber ($1\mu = 10^{-3}$ mm.).

should be understood also in the light of the discrete rubber theory of Wiegand.

Cloud configuration of particles

The above picture of carbon chains in rubber is rather idealised, and a more realistic view must take account of the important concepts evolved by Kruse.[63, 66, 67] From stereo photographs taken with light and electron microscopes Kruse has described cloud-like arrangements of particles in rubber. These carbon " clouds " are regions where the filler concentration is relatively high, and superficially they may appear in the light microscope as undispersed aggregates of particles not wetted by rubber. Kruse has probably gone farther than is justified in interpreting his stereo pictures when he states: " It was not possible to observe particles cohering in chain fashion in either vulcanisate. We certainly see particles close to each other, but there is always rubber in between ".[63] Even so, his ideas and observations do indicate the presence of another kind of conductive structure in rubber mixes, i.e. chains of particles bound by rubber. Or, as Kruse puts it, " the rubber is penetrated by drawn-out carbon black clouds which are often intertwined in a net formation . . . we recognise in the greatest propinquity small cloudlets whose length is less than 1μ, partly overlapping each other, and giving as a whole the lengthy cloud-form or network structure ".

In a private communication Leigh-Dugmore has suggested that characteristic structure should therefore be taken to include chains of particles which do not strictly remain intact during mixing, but which have their configuration maintained by bonding to the rubber. This idea appears feasible if bonding of particles into chains is envisaged at the outset of mixing when black agglomerates are being dispersed, and conditions are probably critical in determining the initial configuration of dispersed particles. Otherwise it conflicts with the well-established conclusion that carbon–rubber bonds are formed at the expense of carbon–carbon contacts and conducting structure (see p. 449).

Carbon clouds are presumably influenced by the aggregation before mixing, the speed and firmness of bonding between black and rubber, and the breakdown with remilling. More research is needed to establish a clear understanding of the factors involved.

Bound rubber or carbon gel

According to Goldfinger,[92, 93] there is preferential adsorption of SBR on carbon particles so as to leave a tougher than average rubber fraction between particles. For many years it has been known that after mixing certain fillers into rubber a portion of the rubber becomes insoluble in benzene. Fielding [94] used the term " bound rubber " to denote all the rubber in unvulcanised filler–rubber stocks which is insoluble in benzene. Later the term " carbon gel " was introduced by Sweitzer, Goodrich and Burgess [95] in their studies of reinforcement by carbon black.

As predicted by Fielding, the carbon gel formed under controlled conditions of processing is a function of particle size. Dannenberg and Collyer [9] found a linear relationship between bound rubber values and specific surface areas as measured by the electron microscope. J. W. Watson [96] has also obtained a reasonably good relationship between bound rubber and specific surface, and this is shown in Fig. 7.28. Sweitzer et al.[95] showed that the fraction of bound rubber increases with mixing time and temperature, as in Figs. 7.34 and 7.35 for SBR mixes.

W. F. Watson [97] has shown that gel can be produced by cold as well as by hot milling of fillers into natural rubber. This was done by freeze-drying filler suspensions in benzene solution to form initial dispersions of carbon black in rubber without milling. Gel contents were found to

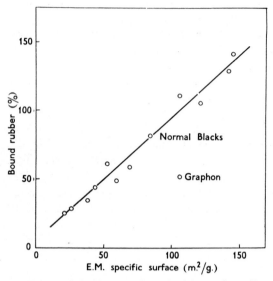

Fig. 7.28. The correlation between bound rubber and specific surface.

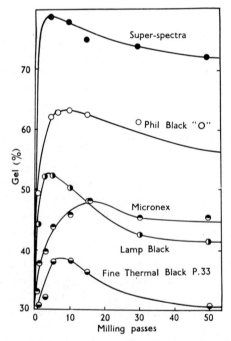

Fig. 7.29. Gel production on milling with different grades of carbon black.

increase with subsequent milling to maxima, depending on the grade of black (Fig. 7.29). Watson supports Sweitzer *et al.* in attributing bound rubber to chemical combination; and he presents evidence of a free radical mechanism.

A mathematical theory of bound rubber has been presented recently by Villars.[98] Electron microscopical examinations of bound rubber have been made by Ladd and Ladd,[99] Endter [100] and Kruse,[63] and these are discussed below.

Integral features of mix structure

Sweitzer, Goodrich and Burgess have pictured bound rubber in SBR mixes as a three-dimensional lattice structure joined together by additional rubber through primary and/or secondary valence forces.[95] Sweitzer refers to particles with adsorbed rubber molecules as " colloidal carbon-gel units " which become knitted by additional carbon–rubber bonds or polymer cross-links into " an insoluble lattice structure co-extensive with the unvulcanised stock ".[101] A similar picture of the whole mix in the case of natural rubber is advanced by Endter,[100] who speaks of " a three phase system in which the filler particles, the bound rubber component, and the unchanged natural rubber are present as three co-existing phases ".

The concept of a bound rubber component and unchanged natural rubber as co-existing phases has been modified by Blanchard and Wootton,[102] who suggest that bound rubber should not be considered as a whole or uniform entity in the carbon–rubber mix. This conclusion is based on the effect of heating the mix up to 16 hours in air at 100° C in the case of natural rubber containing 60 parts by weight of HAF black. There is a marked decrease in Mooney viscosity and elastic modulus of the unvulcanised stock, but a very substantial increase in cross-linking is indicated by reduced swelling in solvents (Fig. 7.30). To resolve this apparent conflict of evidence it is suggested that there is a complex (fragmentary) structure of carbon and rubber with internal cross-linking of carbon gel fragments largely determining swelling in solvents. On the other hand, the quality of the connection between gel fragments by entangled or attached rubber chains is believed to have a predominant influence on the viscosity and elastic modulus of the unvulcanised rubber. Oxidation by prolonged heating in air presumably weakens and breaks down the connection between carbon gel fragments, while cross-linking by carbon particles predominates over chain scission within the gel fragments and so reduces swelling. These conclusions are supported by measurements of soluble rubber, which in similar circumstances provide evidence of the formation of a degraded (sol) fraction. The fragmentary structure is a natural consequence of mill or Banbury mixing in which a mild tendency to cross-link is offset and rendered ineffective before vulcanisation by oxidative and mechanical breakdown. The process of vulcanisation will clearly tend to knit together the gel fragments to form a thoroughly interconnected structure comprising the whole of the mix.

The above ideas are complementary to those advanced by Ladd and Ladd [99] and by Kruse.[63] Carbon gel fragments can be identified with the

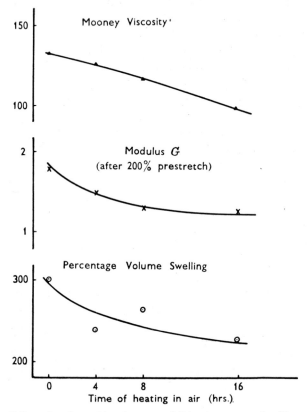

Fig. 7.30. Effect of prolonged heating at 100° C in air on natural rubber containing HAF black and no antioxidant, etc.

carbon black clouds, which Kruse regards as " coherent structure in which rubber has the gel structure well known from the literature ". Fig. 7.31 shows a diagrammatic representation of the structure of carbon–rubber mixes.

Ladd and Ladd have pointed out that the mix structure can also be influenced by cross-linking of the molecules to form polymer gel. This can occur much more readily in SBR than in natural rubber, and it is found that carbon black in low temperature SBR gives more homogeneous dispersions when mixed at 200° F than at 400° F.[99] High-temperature mixing produces both carbon gel and polymer gel free from carbon, the result being " highly pigmented carbon gel units separated by polymer gel and areas of low carbon concentrations ". Previously Baker [103] had concluded from studies of reinforced SBR that " even fine carbon black will

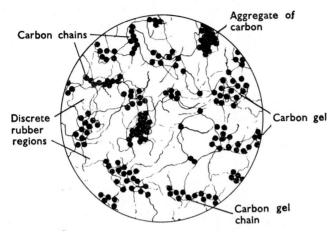

Fig. 7.31. Diagrammatic representation of the structure of carbon–rubber mixes.

not penetrate microgel ". Evidently in SBR Wiegand's discrete rubber regions may take on the character of structural units and have a considerable resistance to disruption.

Structural variations and their effects

Changes in aggregation of filler particles

Poor reinforcement is obtained when the filler is present as large aggregates of particles not wetted by rubber. Normally dispersion is satisfactory when rubber is masticated in the presence of filler, e.g. in a Banbury and on a mill. Chain aggregation of carbon blacks is one aspect of mix structure which tends to break down with milling treatments, and this change would be expected to affect electrical resistivity measurements. Stability of conductivity in various circumstances has been shown by Boonstra and Dannenberg [104] to vary with the type of black. Martin and Parkinson [105] obtained an increase in resistivity with mixing temperature of HAF and conductive channel black in natural rubber, and also an increase with mixing time in the case of HAF black.

An interesting method of making structural changes in rubber–black masterbatches was discovered by Gerke et al.[87] This involved heat treatment in the range 140°–190° C either during or subsequent to the mixing operation. The masterbatch is usually heated in steam or a limited supply of air, although short-period treatments, for example hot milling, can be done in air. Parkinson [106] confirmed that heating stiffens channel black

Q

stocks and decreases their electrical resistivity, and that remilling then causes a spectacular increase in resistivity. Resilience is improved by a steam heat treatment for 45 minutes at 158° C or by including a small quantity of benzidine in the stock. Parkinson and Blanchard [86] concluded from resistivity tests that changes in configuration of the particles on heating were only slight and temporary, and probably due to removing the effect of strains. They suggested that the stock is stiffened by heat or benzidine treatments, which probably attach particles to the rubber, and so cause decatenation by the additional shear on carbon chains during milling. A similar interpretation is proposed by Barton, Smallwood and Ganzhorn [107] and by Gessler and co-workers.[108,109,110,111]

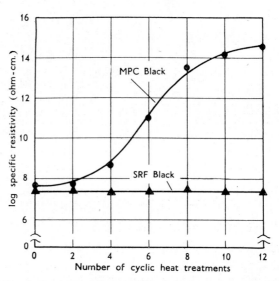

Fig. 7.32. Electrical resistivity changes with cyclic heat treatment of butyl rubber and channel black.

Gessler [108] considers that heating mixes of carbon black and butyl attaches the polymer to clusters of particles, and that subsequent milling disaggregates the carbon clusters by virtue of the polymer attachments. This process is believed to expose a new carbon surface, which can then be bonded to the polymer by further heating; hence, it is argued, there are progressive effects with successive treatments. Some of these effects are shown in Figs. 7.32 and 7.33, where the term cyclic heat treatment denotes consecutive heating and milling stages. Gessler suggests that black particles are " anchored " by forces which develop between polymer and black during heat treatment, and they " cannot then be re-formed into the carbon chain structure when the mass is heated ". Although these conclusions are fairly consistent with the general picture which has been presented of carbon black in rubber, they appear to imply that the chain structure can be formed in rubber by heating, which is contrary to the conclusions of some other workers.[20, 22, 86]

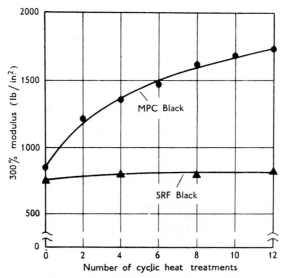

Fig. 7.33. Modulus changes with cyclic heat treatment of butyl rubber and channel black.

General variability of mix structure

The general structural features of reinforced rubber are evidently much influenced by filler–rubber bonding in the unvulcanised mix. Sweitzer, Goodrich and Burgess,[95] Braendle, Estelow and Wiegand,[112] and more recently Sweitzer[101] have considered the changes in carbon–rubber association when mixes of black and rubber are heat treated by raising the temperature during or after mixing. As illustrated in Figs. 7.34 and 7.35, the heat treatment increases bound rubber by forming more carbon gel in both natural and SBR rubber, and it may form polymer gel as well if the temperature is sufficiently high. The work of Gessler and co-workers on butyl mixes likewise revealed an increase in bound rubber with heat treatment. Heat treatment has much less effect with furnace black than with channel black; but Gessler and Ford[109] have shown that with furnace black the response to treatment can be chemically promoted by including a little sulphur or p-dinitrosobenzene (Polyac). A chemical mechanism for the structural changes is also suggested by the work of Barton, Smallwood and Ganzhorn[107] on the effect of time and temperature of treatment. Chemical promoters of various types have been demonstrated by Doak, Ganzhorn and Barton,[113] who suggest that a free radical action is involved. Braendle[114] has considered various heat-treatment procedures for carbon

black in natural rubber. He discusses (1) milling 50 parts of black at
340° F in a Banbury for 28 minutes, cooling overnight and completing mix
on a mill (" Gerke method "), comparing this procedure with the " Bradley

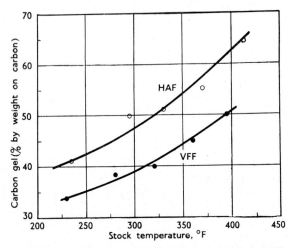

Fig. 7.34. Effect of mixing temperature on bound rubber in SBR mixes.

method ", i.e. (2) mixing 67 parts of black for 15 minutes on a mill at
200°–225° F, oven treating at 300° F for 2 hours in nitrogen, and diluting
the cooled stock with rubber when completing the mix on a mill. Both

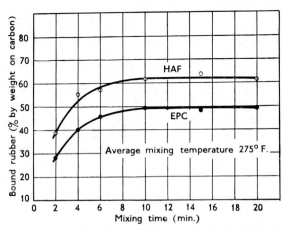

Fig. 7.35. Effect of mixing time on bound rubber in SBR mixes.

methods are compared with a preferred procedure; (3) in which stocks
containing 75 parts black are prepared by Banbury mixing for 10 minutes
at 370° F, and then cooled and compounded with diluent rubber and other
ingredients by means of a second Banbury stage employing cooling water.

It is noted that Bradley pictured " clumps of highly pigmented tough rubber dispersed in a matrix with relatively less carbon reinforcement ", this view being supported by electron micrographs.[115]   Braendle suggests that: " (*a*) Gerke makes a carbon gel lattice and destroys it by overmilling; (*b*) Bradley makes such a tight lattice that he tears it up upon addition of diluting rubber ".   The preferred procedure is believed to form " a more open lattice into which the diluting rubber can be put ".   With regard to point (*b*) the present writer believes that carbon gel fragments may be too highly cross-linked for subsequent milling to improve their distribution in the diluted mix by *partial* breakdown.   The effect of milling in breaking down gel structure is illustrated by Fig. 7.36 from the paper of Sweitzer, Goodrich and Burgess.[95]   In some circumstances this effect may mask

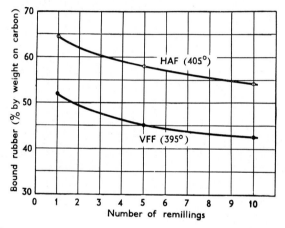

Fig. 7.36. Breakdown of bound rubber by remilling SBR mixes.

tendencies for carbon gel to increase with mixing time and temperature (cf. Figs. 7.33 and 7.35).   The resulting sol rubber lubricates the gel fragments and so acts as a plasticiser.

Drogin [116] obtained a decrease in Mooney viscosity with mixing time of carbon black in a Banbury after an increase during the first minute as the particles became wetted and disaggregated.   He showed that the greatest change in plasticity takes place in the first 4 minutes of mixing.   Mullins and Whorlow [117] have used plasticity measurements to trace changes in the structure of unvulcanised natural rubber during storing, heating and shearing.   They used the term " filler structure " to denote interactions either between filler particles or between filler and rubber, or both.   An initial increase in torque with shearing indicated growth of " filler-structure ", and a later decrease in torque indicated breakdown of that structure with continued shearing.   The stock stiffened on standing, suggesting that " structure " builds up again, the rate at which it recovers increasing with temperature.   Although structure forms more rapidly as temperature increases, the ability to form structure is reduced after prolonged storage in the region 100°–120° C.   In the case of several fillers Fig. 7.37 shows the value of the torque after 1 minute's shearing following various periods of recovery at 100° C.   Acetylene black showed the highest torque before any build-up of structure, and much less change on standing at 100° C

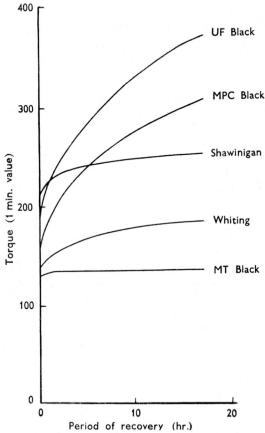

Fig. 7.37. Changes in plastometer torque with recovery time at 100° C after shearing natural rubber stocks containing various fillers.

than with channel black or a furnace black then known as UF black. Mullins and Whorlow confirm Wiegand's view [118] that acetylene black has a strong structure not easily broken down by shearing; and they show there is little structure reformation of acetylene black on standing. Parkinson [1] has pointed out that any disagreement between the conclusions of Mullins and Whorlow and those of Parkinson and Blanchard [86] is probably more apparent than real.   He comments that " Changes in particle to particle association will affect electrical resistance; changes in particle to rubber association may or may not do so. . . . The simultaneous breaking down and building up of structure as indicated by plasticity changes . . . may well mean that as the carbon chains disrupt, some carbon–rubber structure (either physical or chemical) is formed, as has been postulated to account for some of the resistivity changes. On such an interpretation subsequent changes would not be truly reversible, though their influence on plasticity might make them appear to be so ''.

The complex changes in mix structure indicated by Blanchard and Wootton's study of prolonged heating in air were discussed on p. 447. It appears that prolonged heating of the stocks, particularly if followed by addition of further rubber (cf. Bradley's treatment, p. 452), should lead to a relatively coarse structure of large gel fragments.

Relation of mix structure to reinforcement

There is no general agreement on the influence of structural features in reinforcement, but it is important to take note of viewpoints and to consider what might give rise to the conflicting impressions.

Parkinson [119] makes the point that breaking down carbon chain structure by severe remilling does not generally decrease abrasion resistance, and that high structure acetylene black imparts poor tear and abrasion resistance in relation to particle size. Parkinson and Blanchard [86] destroyed the electrical conductivity of rubber–channel black mixes by heat treatment and remilling, but without decreasing reinforcement; and Gerke, Ganzhorn, Howland and Smallwood even noted increased reinforcement in their experiments. Thus it appears that chain structure does not have an essential or very important role in reinforcement, though Sweitzer [22] may be right in maintaining that it makes some contribution.

The structural changes produced by heating and remilling are, of course, over-simplified by the concept of decatenation of carbon chains. Gessler [108] has shown that after heat treatment of butyl a combination of increased bonding with improved dispersion and distribution of black, leads to substantially increased resilience and reinforcement. He considers that the low unsaturation and therefore high chemical stability of butyl makes it suitable for a wide range of thermal treatments; and that improvement of natural rubber and SBR mixes by heat treatment is largely confined to resilience, because oxidative effects compete with the interaction of carbon and polymer. On the other hand, increased reinforcement with hot mixing procedure has been claimed for SBR by Sweitzer, Goodrich and Burgess;[95] and for natural rubber Braendle, Estelow and Wiegand [112] claim improvements with a high black loading in the hot-mixed stock. Experiments described by Martin and Parkinson [105] and by Parkinson [1] have not supported such conclusions on the effect of increasing mixing temperature. Drogin, Bishop and Wiseman,[120] and Dannenberg [121] likewise noted a decrease in tensile and tear strength at room temperature as the mixing temperature is raised, although Dannenberg did note an improvement in abrasion resistance. The improved abrasion resistance conflicts with experiments reported by Parkinson,[1] and also with the writer's own experiments on Banbury mixing temperatures in the range 140°–180° C. Experience with OEP has shown that the oil content of SBR can vary widely without seriously affecting reinforcement; and this may be true also of the variations in bound and soluble rubber which accompany heat interaction.

The carbon gel feature of mix structure came into particular prominence in discussions of reinforcement following the work of Sweitzer, Goodrich and Burgess [95] and also of Sperberg, Svetlick and Bliss.[122]   Sweitzer et al. consider that carbon gel is a fundamental factor in reinforcement, and a similar view is held by Endter,[100] whose studies include rubber bound by fine silica fillers.   Braendle [114] maintains that carbon gel is the basic factor in toughening rubber and increasing wear resistance; he believes that " a homogeneous particulate dispersion of carbon black in rubber is contrary to the very nature of the two materials, and unsuitable for best performance, in tyre treads, for example ".

The above views on carbon gel are not supported by J. W. Watson,[96] who found that bound rubber and swelling index are related to reinforcement only to the extent of their dependence on specific surface. For instance Watson discovered that: (1) bound rubber is higher for MPC than HAF black, although the latter imparts better abrasion resistance; (2) bound rubber is unaffected by pre-treatment of HAF black by hydroxyl free radicals, although this markedly reduces reinforcing ability; and (3) bound rubber formed by Graphon is markedly increased by pre-treatment with hydroxyl radicals, but without increasing abrasion reinforcement. These experiments do not justify a conclusion that bound rubber has no influence on reinforcement; but evidently there must be important aspects of the structure of vulcanised rubber–filler mixes of which bound rubber takes no account.

One difficulty is that uncured mixes may contain widely different numbers of real cross-links and yet have the same measured (effective) cross-linking and the same bound rubber. During vulcanisation these differences will become apparent because many ineffective linkages with free chain ends will be made effective as resilient networks when supplemented by vulcanisation. Higher resilience after heat interaction may thus be due to tying of carbon particles into elastic networks and to separation of particles by rubber film. The problem of estimating cross-linking is discussed in a following section.

Bound rubber may include polymer gel as well as carbon gel.   In so far as a polymer gel component of the mix structure may prevent rubber from accepting reinforcing particles, it can be considered as a harmful element, as was pointed out by Baker.[103] Ladd and Ladd [99] have concluded that black will reinforce gelled SBR rubber provided the gel is generated in the presence of the carbon. Although discrete regions of polymer gel in SBR are not a desirable feature of the mix structure, compensating factors may be present in particular cases.

Quantitative and well-established conclusions on the role of mix structure in reinforcement are not yet available. The present writer believes that initial formation of carbon gel fragments during mixing reflects an interaction between black and rubber which can contribute to the reinforcement of vulcanised rubber. Accordingly, it is considered that Braendle [114] is probably right in arguing that a perfect distribution of particles does not represent an optimum condition for reinforcement. On the other hand, formation of very coherent, tightly linked gel fragments could lead to a rather coarse structure of large gel fragments which did not give optimum reinforcement. In the writer's opinion best results will be shown by a fine structure comprising small carbon gel fragments, with a proportion of single particles dispersed and attached to rubber chains and with good connection between gel fragments in the vulcanised state. A compromise of this kind for the ideal structure may account, together with the adverse effects of oxidation, for some of the conflicting impressions at the present time.

Chemical aspects of reinforcement

Naunton and Waring [123] appreciated that unsaturation of the filler surface and the polymer might be important, and they postulated a chemical bond between carbon black and rubber " like the sulphur bridge in vulcanisation ". Stearns and Johnson [76] inferred that double bonds are present on the carbon surface by studying heats of reaction with bromine; and they postulated linkages to rubber through sulphur molecules. However, J. W. Watson and D. Parkinson [124] have shown that reinforcement by channel black is unaffected by bromination and hydrogenation, although this would eliminate unsaturated groups on the carbon surface.

Smith, Beebe and co-workers [125,126,127,128,129,130] adsorbed on to carbon blacks certain model compounds, such as dihydromyrcene, which has an unsaturation pattern similar to natural rubber. These experiments did not show any chemical reaction of carbon black with unsaturated groups which could account for reinforcement. All the highly reinforcing blacks were shown to have sites of high adsorptive activity, and it was suggested that strong physical adsorption of rubber at these points might be important.

An influence of polymer unsaturation on the response of polymer–black mixes to heat treatment is suggested by the work of Sweitzer,[101] and was established by Rehner and Gessler,[110] using butyls of varied unsaturation. As heat treatment markedly improves the abrasion resistance of reinforced butyl, polymer unsaturation is evidently an important factor in the reinforcement of this polymer.   Fig. 7.38, taken from the paper of Rehner and Gessler, shows how unsaturation influences the effectiveness of heat treatment as reflected by electrical resistivity changes.

Researches by Pike and W. F. Watson [131] have shown that milling can cause rupture of the rubber molecules into free radicals, and W. F. Watson

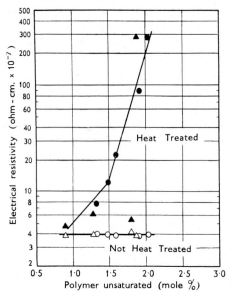

Fig. 7.38. Effect of unsaturation of the polymer on the response to heat treatment of butyl mixes.

has presented convincing evidence [97] that some of these react chemically with carbon black to form a cross-linked network.   Garten and Sutherland [132] have also argued that reinforcement is due to carbon particles acting as radical acceptors for the rubber molecules; and Wake [133] has associated Pike and Watson's discovery with his view that milling is essential for reinforcement.[134]   Watson postulates a tendency to equilibrium between chain scission and recombination, and he claims that this is reached under nitrogen, but is otherwise upset by oxygen acting as a radical acceptor. Thus oxygen terminates rubber radicals without their combining with neighbouring chains, and Watson shows that adding other radical acceptors to the mix reduces the gel content in the way which would be expected from his theory. The theory of Watson is clearly of great importance in explaining bound rubber formation when reinforcing fillers are milled into rubber. It is supported by the researches of Garten and Sutherland,[132] who have shown that carbon black can accept free radicals from solution. However, a different mechanism of formation of bound rubber has been suggested by Endter,[100] and more recently elaborated by Endter and Westlinning. These authors suggest that cross-linking is brought about by C–C bonds under the influence of electrostatic surface forces of the filler particles. According to this view the double bonds of rubber molecules can be polarised by coming within the range of marked instability of the electric field at the surface of filler particles.

Electron spin resonance in carbon blacks has been studied recently by Kraus and Collins, who note a correlation between odd electron concentration and the modulus the blacks impart to rubber. These authors present measurements on heated rubber and carbon black as evidence that carbon black radicals may react with the polymeric free radicals formed during processing or vulcanisation. They estimate about 10^{20} unpaired electrons per gm. of black. Donnet and Henrich have calculated $1·47 \times 10^{20}$ electron accepting centres per gm. from stirring carbon black with 22'-azodi-isobutyronitrile in benzene at 80° C.

Garten and Weiss [135] have obtained evidence that part of the chemisorbed oxygen on the carbon surface is in the form of semi-quinones, which are known to be radical acceptors. Earlier Barton, Smallwood and Ganzhorn [107] had suggested that the presence of semiquinone groups on the carbon surface determined the response of a carbon–rubber mix to heat treatment. A study of the character of the oxygen-containing groups on carbon black has been made by Studebaker, Huffman, Wolfe and Nabors,[28] who conclude that " analysis of 12 carbon black samples with diazomethane and other reagents indicates that 18% of the oxygen may be present in 1:4-quinone form ". Garten and Weiss claim that semi-quinones are mainly responsible for the superior reinforcing ability of carbon blacks over other fillers. The results of furnace treating blacks (see below) appear to contradict this idea, but they support the more cautious view of Barton and of Studebaker et al. that oxygen-containing groups determine the response when rubber–black mixes are heat treated. The chemical action during heat treatment is not an answer to the problem of reinforcement, although it is an important mechanism in the reinforcement of butyl. Recently Gessler has obtained increased reinforcement of butyl by ball milling the carbon black before mixing. The " attrited " black has greatly increased oxygen content and surface area as well as broken chain structure.

J. W. Watson [96] has pointed out that bound rubber formation by free radicals during milling does not necessarily account for reinforcement. He

studied the effect of pre-treating black with free radicals in order to eliminate radical acceptor sites and so reduce reinforcement. The sulphate-
free radical treatment described by Garten and Sutherland did lead to the
black accepting free radicals, but these were hydroxyl and not sulphate
radicals. A radical-treated MPC black gave about 30% less abrasion
resistance, and Watson concluded that at least 30% of the reinforcing
ability is due to chemical effects involving radical acceptor sites on the
black. Furnace treatment to form Graphon yields similar results, and
Watson suggests that the residual reinforcement might be largely physical
in nature. Radical treatment of HAF black did not alter the swelling index
or bound rubber obtained with an unvulcanised natural rubber mix, but
reinforcement was again substantially reduced. Watson concludes that
the treatment did not alter the interaction between the blacks and the
rubber during milling, but in some way altered the black's influence
during vulcanisation.

In a recent publication Donnet and Henrich propose a mechanism
whereby oxidation during vulcanisation may activate carbon black with
new free radical sites for polymer–carbon bonds. Studebaker has suggested that the most important catalytic action of carbon black during
vulcanisation is in catalysing the dehydrogenation of rubber by sulphur.
On the other hand, Garten and Weiss suggest that there is dehydrogenation
of rubber by quinone structures of the carbon. A better understanding
of vulcanisation may be needed before speculation on the action of carbon
black during vulcanisation can be replaced by a proper understanding.

One way of varying surface chemical composition without altering
particle size is by furnace treating black. Schaeffer, Smith and Polley [130]
have studied the effect of heating four grades of carbon black to temperatures from 1,000° and 3,300° C. They show that the temperature of
maximum evolution of hydrogen is 1,000° C, and that carbon crystallite
growth begins at this temperature. The interplanar spacing of graphite is
never obtained even at 3,300° C, although three-dimensional ordering of
the crystallites has been observed for this temperature.[18] Schaeffer and
Smith [45] later showed that a drastic fall in the modulus imparted to rubber
occurs principally after temperatures below those which cause appreciable
crystallite growth. With support from ultimate analyses they conclude
that this fall in modulus is mainly due to removal of surface hydrogen, and
so occurs below 1,500° C. When oxygen and hydrogen are removed in
this way resilience and abrasion resistance are much decreased, electrical
conductivity is greatly increased and the response of rubber–black mixes
to heat treatment is eliminated. Zapp and Gessler [111] have shown that the
effect of heat treating butyl mixes is reduced by removing oxygen from the
black and increased by putting it back on again.

Carbon fillers have been shown to influence the oxidation of polymers.

Kuzminskii *et al.*[137] concluded that increasing the loading of channel black leads to a reduced rate and amount of oxygen uptake. They consider that adsorption of added antioxidant explains the contrary conclusions of Winn, Shelton and Turnbull [138] and presumably of van Amerongen,[29] who all agree that oxidation increases with the concentration and specific surface of carbon black. Sweitzer and Lyon [139] and Lyon *et al.*[140] have shown that under some conditions carbon blacks inhibit the oxidation of un-vulcanised SBR, and that the effect increases with the volatile content of the carbon. Garten, Eppinger and Weiss [141] have suggested that carbon blacks can reinforce by acting as polyphenol-type antioxidants or in a catalytic fashion through " temporary stabilisation of broken rubber chains on their surface ". The importance of such mechanisms of reinforcement would seem to be very limited, if only because of the effect of particle size noted by Winn *et al.* and van Amerongen.

The role of particle diameter and linkage formation in reinforcement

Dannenberg and Boonstra [142] have shown that if the surface of carbon black is etched by oxidation during manufacture the black has a high specific surface in relation to particle diameter and imparts high electrical conductivity and low resilience to rubber. They discovered that rein-forcement is not affected if porosity is caused by varying the conditions of normal manufacture, but that oxidising a non-porous black in the labora-tory increases its ability to reinforce. The surface area excluding pores is known to be the important factor in determining ability to reinforce. Many years of experience with carbon blacks and other types of filler have indicated that fine particles are essential for obtaining a high degree of reinforcement. If, nevertheless, it is suggested that particle size may not be important, then some related feature of the chemical composition or structure of the surface must be substituted. But the known chemical composition is not related to particle size, and crystallite size, porosity of surface or chain structure are all variables which cannot be substituted for particle size without destroying all relationship with reinforcement. Moreover, particle size is theoretically expected to be a basic factor because: (1) it determines the filler surface in contact with the rubber, and (2) it profoundly affects the distribution of filler activity in the rubber because the number of particles in a given volume is inversely proportional to the cube of their size. It seems beyond reasonable doubt that the trend of reinforcement with particle diameter in Fig. 7.3 is a causal relationship showing the influence of a basic factor.

Linkages induced by fillers in rubber may be considered another basic factor in reinforcement.The question how far cross-links are additive will now be considered in order to make clear some limitations on the validity of treatments of cross-linking. This difficulty can be understood by reference to the accompanying diagram of a polymer molecule PQ, the molecule being straightened out for convenience of representation.

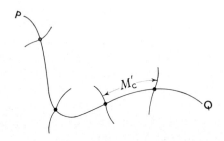

Let M_1 = original molecular weight, i.e., the chain length between molecule ends P and Q.

M_c' = initial average molecular weight between cross-links.

n = initial number of cross-links per molecule.

M_c'' = average molecular weight between some new cross-links.

m = number of new cross-links per molecule.

M_2 = final molecular weight when some chain scission occurs as the new cross-links are introduced.

M_c = average molecular weight between all cross-links after the new cross-links have been added.

A = Avogadro's number.

In one molecule the initial n cross-links divide the molecule into $n + 1$ segments. In one gram of polymer there are A/M_1 molecules, A/M_c' segments, and nA/M_1 cross-links.

Each molecule has one more segment than it has cross-links and so for a number A/M_1 molecules we have:

$$A/M_c' - nA/M_1 = A/M_1$$
$$\therefore \ 1/M_c' = (n + 1)/M_1 \ \ . \ \ . \ \ . \ \ . \ \ . \ \ (7.14)$$

If a further m cross-links are added per molecule and the molecular weight is reduced to M_2

$$1/M_c'' = (m + 1)/M_2 \ \ . \ \ . \ \ . \ \ . \ \ . \ \ (7.15)$$

The number of pre-existing cross-links per molecule has also changed from n to nM_2/M_1 because each molecule is shorter. Therefore, considering the two sets of cross-links together:

$$1/M_c = (1 + m + nM_2/M_1)/M_2$$
$$= (M_1 + mM_1 + nM_2)/M_1 M_2 \ \ . \ \ . \ \ . \ \ (7.16)$$

Whereas simple addition of these components gives:

$$1/M_c'' + 1/M_c' = (M_1 + nM_1 + (n + 1)M_2)/M_1M_2 \quad . \quad . \quad (7.17)$$

Therefore the cross-links are roughly additive if $n + 1 \simeq n$, in which case eqn 7.16 and 7.17 combine to give:

$$1/M_c = 1/M_c' + 1/M_c'' \quad . \quad . \quad . \quad . \quad . \quad (7.18)$$

The condition for simple additivity of cross-links is therefore $n \gg 1$ and this will be satisfied in properly cured rubber.

For unvulcanised and for lightly cured rubber the equations give

$$1/M_c = 1/M_c' + 1/M_c'' - 1/M_1 \quad . \quad . \quad . \quad (7.19)$$

Therefore cross-link densities can still be added provided that a molecular weight correction $1/M_1$ is subtracted from the result.

It must be emphasised, however, that this calculation is concerned with real cross-links, i.e. it assumes that the influence of molecular weight on effective (measured) cross-linking is either negligible or already taken into account. Otherwise the presence of substantial numbers of ineffective cross-links will cause further non-additive contributions through mutually increased effectiveness of cross-links. The influence of molecular weight and entanglements on effective cross-linking will be considered later. Neglect of these factors is permissible in rough calculations on properly cured rubber, i.e. vulcanisates having a few ineffective cross-links.

Blanchard and Parkinson distinguished two kinds of filler linkage in vulcanised rubber by means of stress–strain studies. One type is present with all fillers, and such linkages are termed weak or secondary linkages. The other type is shown to be present with carbon black, and these are termed strong or primary bonds because they are not ruptured by pre-stressing. In his research on pre-stretching[46] Mullins argued that the bonds broken by pre-stretching do not contribute appreciably to tensile strength, and Blanchard and Parkinson[50] have concluded that such bonds are secondary factors in tear and abrasion reinforcement. These conclusions are supported by Blanchard's later work which showed: (1) that reinforcing ability cannot be explained by considering particle diameter together with either secondary linkages or the energy dissipated in breaking them;[60] and (2) that breakage of linkages by pre-stressing has little effect on abrasion resistance.[34] These views may require modification in the light of recent work showing that tensile strength can be greatly increased by vulcanising carboxylic polymers with labile cross-links. Carboxylic polymers are usually made by copolymerising an unsaturated carboxylic acid with olefins or dienes. In reinforced rubber the strongest of the secondary linkages may have a role similar to that of labile cross-links in carboxylic polymers. But a significant contribution could be made only by the primary linkages G^* and by a few bonds to the far right of the distribution curve in Fig. 7.15.　Blanchard and Parkinson associated their modulus component G^* with strong rubber–filler linkages and with reinforcement.　The effect of filler loading on $(1 + V)G^*$, which represents strong (primary) linkages,[60] is shown in Fig. 7.39 from a later paper by Blanchard.[34]　Fillers with little effect on abrasion resistance (e.g. Calcene, magnesium carbonate, calcium silicate) differ from carbon blacks (e.g. MPC, FEF or HAF black) in having little or no tendency to introduce some form of strong-type linkage.　This indication of the part played by strong linkages comes from studying vulcanised rubber; and this is important

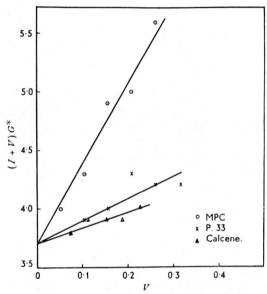

Fig. 7.39. Effect of filler concentration on the strong (primary) linkages in vulcanised rubber.

because J. W. Watson [96] has deduced that vulcanisation plays an important part in reinforcement by carbon black.

The cross-linking of vulcanised rubber can also be studied by measuring either its equilibrium swelling in a solvent or modulus when swollen. These methods are theoretically superior when the requirement is for a measure of strong cross-links in reinforced rubber.　The solvent then minimises such complications as uncertain equilibrium moduli, possible reformation of labile cross-links in extended positions, and semi-permanent set.　Cross-linking is related to the equilibrium volume fraction v_r of polymer in swollen gels by the equation:

$$M_c = F(v_r) = \frac{-\rho V_1(v_r^{1/3} - v_r/2)}{\mu v_r^2 + 1n(1 - v_r) + v_r} \qquad . \qquad . \qquad (7.20)$$

where V_1 is the molar volume of the solvent, ρ is the density of the polymer, M_c is the molecular weight of the average length of chain between cross-links and μ is the interaction constant between polymer and solvent. This equation represents Flory's refinement of the well-known Flory–Rehner theory. To take account of entanglements and molecular weight Blanchard and Wootton have recently derived the equation:

$$\frac{1}{M_c} = \frac{1}{F(v_r)} + \frac{2(1 + \sigma M_c)}{M} - \sigma \quad . \quad . \quad . \quad (7.21)$$

where $\sigma = 0.414 \times 10^{-4}$, M = molecular weight, and $F(V_r)$ is given by eqn. 7.20. The swollen modulus method will not be considered here. Blanchard and Wootton have shown that swollen modulus appears to be complicated by a steric hindrance effect, which is of considerable significance in measurements on reinforced rubber (see later references).

In unvulcanised rubber W. F. Watson obtained gel formation on cold milling reinforcing blacks or silicates, but not with the non-reinforcing fillers, whiting, barytes, lithopone, kieselguhr and Devolite china clay. The linkages in this gel structure presumably persist during vulcanisation. The experiments of Blanchard and Wootton [102] with unvulcanised mixes indicate that only a few linkages with strength to resist swelling are weak enough to be broken by stretching. The remaining linkages presumably contribute to the modulus component G^* of the rubber after it has been vulcanised and pre-stressed, and they can be expected to play a part in reinforcement. On the other hand, J. W. Watson has concluded that reinforcement by free radical interaction of rubber and black occurs mainly during vulcanisation. He shows convincingly that bound rubber for a given particle size does not correlate with black reinforcement, and is unaffected by a hydroxyl-free radical treatment which reduces abrasion reinforcement by 30%. In the light of J. W. Watson's work it is suggested that reinforcement linkages associated with the filler are greatly augmented during vulcanisation, at least in the case of untreated carbon fillers.

There is no reinforcement by fillers which form negligible bound rubber and show no evidence of primary linkage formation in vulcanised rubber. But with bound rubber present there is considerable reinforcement even when stress–strain measurements have not detected strong filler linkages in vulcanised rubber. This is particularly true of the very fine silicas, which give quite low modulus [16] and prevent even rough stress–strain estimates of primary filler linkages by interfering markedly with sulphur cross-linking during vulcanisation. A convincing demonstration of strong linkages induced by Graphon in vulcanised rubber is also difficult because the number of filler linkages is very much less than with normal blacks. Nevertheless, J. W. Watson [96] has obtained the same bound rubber for Graphon as for FEF and acetylene black (see Fig. 7.28). Linkage formation by Graphon therefore appears to take place in the unvulcanised stock, though stress–strain evidence for it in vulcanised rubber is slight (Table 7.2); and this may well be connected with the appreciable reinforcing action of Graphon.

With constant mixing procedure and conditions, Blanchard[34] obtained a rough correlation for a given particle diameter between abrasion resistance and primary linkages as reflected by stress–strain measurements. This is shown by Fig. 7.40, in which A-15 is the amount by which the

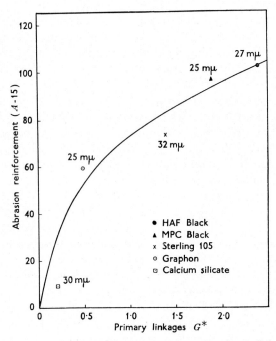

Fig. 7.40. The dependence of abrasion reinforcement on primary linkages induced by fillers of similar particle size.

abrasion resistance on the Constant Power Lambourn Abrader exceeds that for an equivalent volume concentration $V = 0.26$ of inert fillers of large particle size. In Fig. 7.39 the value of G^* when there is no filler is 3·7, and for Fig. 7.40 this has been subtracted from $(1 + V)G^*$ to give a rough measure, G_r^*, of the linkages introduced by fillers of similar mean particle diameter in the region 25–30 mμ. All the fillers in this comparison were well dispersed, and they were compounded similarly with only a slight accelerator adjustment for the channel blacks to give a common optimum cure after 55 minutes at 138° C. Both Fig. 7.40 and the tear data in Table 7.2 indicate that a much smaller number of primary linkages than is normally introduced by carbon blacks can do much to reinforce rubber if the filler particles are small. Unpublished work has shown a fair correlation between changes in the modulus component $G*$ with furnace pre-treatment of various blacks at $1,400°$ C and the resulting drop in abrasion resistance; but changes in $G*$ with mixing conditions and procedure bear no relation to reinforcement.

TABLE 7.2

EFFECT OF FILLER PARTICLE DIAMETER

Type of filler	Mean particle diam., mμ	Modulus G_f* due to primary filler linkages	Abrasion resist., A	ASTM tear resist. at 20° C
Conductive channel black (Spheron C)	23	1·1	110	43·7
HPC black (Spheron 4)	24	1·6	117	44·0
MPC black (Spheron 6)	25	1·9	110	38·7
Graphitised MPC black (Graphon)	25	0·5	74	30·3
HAF black (Vulcan 3)	27	2·4	116	40·8
FF black (Sterling 105)	32	1·4	87	39·2
FF black (Sterling 99)	39	1·7	74	36·8
Shawinigan acetylene black	40	2·4	78	33·7
SRF black (Sterling S)	80	1·8	52	24·9
Lampblack	100	1·8	41	19·7
Calcium silicate	30	0·2	24	18·2

Table 7.2 from Blanchard's paper shows that primary linkages, as reflected by the residual modulus $G*$ after high pre-stresses, are unrelated to particle diameter; and it illustrates the dominant influence of particle diameter on tear and abrasion reinforcement. Kraus [143] has used measurements of equilibrium swelling to investigate the cross-linking of reinforced vulcanisates, and he also concludes that " the number of apparent strong linkages contributed by the filler is not generally dependent on surface area ". Kraus has shown (Table 7.3) that the contribution of carbon black to cross-linking is roughly proportional to the degree of cure, and he concludes that vulcanisation is an important factor. Kraus suggests that the filler-induced linkages are mainly between rubber molecules, the number of filler-to-rubber linkages being relatively small (though important in reinforcement). He points out that linkages of the former type would increase with the level of cure if they were formed by an " interaction of the vulcanisation reaction with carbon black ". As the interaction during vulcanisation could equally be supposed to form attachments between black and rubber, the evidence for this interesting hypothesis is based on an assumption that filler-to-rubber linkages will be proportional to the surface area of the filler.

A distinction between real and effective cross-linking of partially vulcanised rubber may perhaps explain Kraus's discovery (Table 7.3) of an effect of vulcanisation on the linkages contributed by carbon black. In uncured rubber a given balance between real cross-linking and molecular breakdown may be reached with quite different levels of real cross-linking. The differences will become apparent as this balance is destroyed by vulcanisation, many ineffective links to carbon black being made effective by

TABLE 7.3

EFFECT OF VULCANISATION ON PRIMARY LINKAGES INDUCED BY SAF BLACK
(KRAUS [143])

Time of cure, min.	Cross-linking with carbon black/cross-linking without carbon black			
	1·25 p.h.r. sulphur	1·50 p.h.r. sulphur	1·70 p.h.r. sulphur	2·25 p.h.r. sulphur
20	1·36	1·30	1·40	1·30
30	1·37	1·33	1·36	1·32
45	1·41	1·38	1·36	1·42
75	1·41	1·38	1·41	1·41

vulcanisation. Thus the filler contribution to cross-linking can be expected to increase with cure. Chain entanglements and molecular weight will be major factors determining the effective (measured) cross-linking of uncured rubber. For molecular weight ca. 300,000 eqn. 7.21 gives $1/M_c = 0·07 \times 10^{-4}$ and 280 cross-links per carbon particle in a typical tyre tread mix. The carbon surface area per induced cross-link is then about $2200A^2$, which is very different from the estimated $6–30A^2$ per constraint given by Bueche [55] and Skinner et al. [54] for vulcanised mixes. This indicates a direct contribution of vulcanisation to filler-induced cross-linking; it could not be explained by changed effectiveness of filler cross-links. Boonstra and Dannenberg showed that the number of cross-links estimated in the bound rubber gel are far too small to account for the increase in cross-link density that is caused by the presence of carbon black in the vulcanisate (see later references). The above calculation allowing for molecular weight and entanglements only strengthens this conclusion. Taking the cross-sectional area of isoprene to be $50A^2$, the calculation would imply about 2% coverage of the carbon surface if all induced cross-links were to carbon particles. The same effective (measured) cross-linking before vulcanisation would be obtained with 6% coverage if the molecular weight was only 150,000. And in this latter case the substantially higher real cross-linking before vulcanisation would be reflected by an increase of only $0·1 \times 10^{-4}$ in the cured $1/M_c$ e.g. from $1·5 \times 10^{-4}$ to $1·6 \times 10^{-4}$. Thus a substantial degree of carbon–rubber bonding could easily go undetected and yet make a major contribution to reinforcement. This may account for the satisfactory reinforcement by the low modulus types of black now available e.g. Regal 600.

Partly on the basis of the data in Table 7.2 Blanchard [34] has questioned the view that poor reinforcement with coarse blacks of low specific surface is due to the relatively low interfacial area for linkage formation. He considers that a plausible explanation of the effect of specific surface in terms of linkages would require the drastic reduction in linkages with furnace-treated black (Graphon) to change reinforcement much more than is the case in practice. It is argued that there are other reasons for thinking that particle diameter and linkage formation are distinct though interacting factors in reinforcement. Any theory of reinforcement based on the concept of total surface available to the rubber suffers from the objection that it implies increasing reinforcement with diminishing particle diameter, no matter how small the particles. This is difficult to accept because it suggests that chemical cross-linking by molecules (e.g. sulphur) would be the best means of reinforcement, whereas all our experience suggests that incorporation of small filler particles is necessary to obtain a large improvement in abrasion resistance. For good wear resistance the particles, though small, probably need to have macromolecular dimensions.

From this line of reasoning Blanchard [34] goes on to propose that reinforcement for a given dispersion and concentration of filler can be interpreted in terms of the number of particles N per c.c. of rubber $+$ filler, and u, the number of primary linkages per particle. A tentative mathematical postulate is used to illustrate how this concept of reinforcing action could be quantitatively consistent with theory and with experimental findings. On this view a decrease in particle diameter has opposed effects in increasing the number of particles and reducing the number of linkages per particle. The concept therefore implies that reinforcement increases with diminishing particle diameter until an optimum is reached, and thereafter decreases to become negligible for particles of molecular dimensions. The probable influence of number of particles on tear and abrasion reinforcement can be appreciated by picturing one layer being torn away from the body of the material so that " the linkage forming particles of diameter d closely involved by the separation will have their centres lying within a distance $d/2$ on either side of the line of cleavage, i.e. within a volume d if unit areas are separated ". The number of particles Nd closely involved by the rupture for unit area separated would clearly be expected to influence the reinforcement, and this number is proportional to the reciprocal of d^2 for a given concentration of filler. On the other hand, the number of strong bonds per particle will influence the aggregate resistance to tear propagation round each particle, and it could be expected to increase with particle size.

Mullins' interpretation of reinforcement is that increased hysteresis is associated with increased strength when there is strong adhesion between the rubber and filler. Breakdown at the interface leading to flaws is then apparent only at large stresses, and Mullins suggests that " multiple internal failure gives rise to extra interfacial surfaces and a consequent increased dissipation of energy. . . . The net result of fillers which adhere strongly is an enlarging of the volume of rubber which must be highly strained during the process of rupture ".

The effect of particle size and linkage formation in tear and tensile reinforcement by resins has been discussed by Houwink and van Alphen.[144] They attribute a superiority of aniline over urea resin to more chemical bonding as indicated by bound rubber measurements; and they support the interpretation given here of the role of particle diameter by showing that cyclised rubber particles in natural rubber can be too small to have any reinforcing action. Little more can be said on these theoretical aspects of resin reinforcement because they have received relatively little attention, and the problem is a complex one. It should be noted that when the resin is first formed in latex the particles are much larger than those of a reinforcing black; and the cyclo-rubber particles considered by Houwink and van Alphen are so large that in some respects they are more analogous to the carbon gel fragments of p. 449 than to carbon particles. The discussion on p. 447 of the relation of mix structure to reinforcement may therefore ultimately prove to have a limited bearing on the problem of resin reinforcement (and vice versa).

The above ideas can be given additional support by a purely theoretical consideration of the role of particle diameter. Consider the system of filler particles in rubber, the volume concentration being fixed at any value for the purpose of the argument. On the assumption that reinforcement is due to linkage formation, the simplest and least questionable additional assumption is that reinforcement will be some function of the basic variables number of linkage u per particle and number of particles N per unit volume of the mix. This simple assumption of two basic variables is open to criticism on the ground that particle size may be important in another way by affecting the geometry of linkage formation by each particle. But at least no assumptions about the manner of the dependence of reinforcement on the two basic variables are involved. Whereas it now becomes clear that to interpret reinforcement in terms of specific surface for linkage formation involves two special assumptions, one of which certainly cannot be justified. These additional assumptions are: (1) that the influence of number of particles and number of linkages per particle can be expressed by a function of their product Nu; and (2) that the number of primary linkages u per particle is proportional to the particle surface area πd^2, which would make Nu proportional to $1/d$, i.e. to the specific surface. There is really little justification for using an interfacial area to interpret how such properties as tear and abrasion resistance are affected by a large number of discrete spherical interfaces formed by particles in rubber.

REFERENCES

1. Parkinson, D. (1956) Monograph, *Reinforcement of Rubbers* (Cambridge: W. Heffer).
2. Cotton, F. H. (1930) *I.R.I. Trans.*, **6**, 248.
3. Scott, J. R. (1951) *India Rubber J.*, **121**, 344, 384, 424, 478, 513.
4. Wiegand, W. B. (1920) *Can. Chem. J.*, **4**, 160; (1920) *India-Rubber J.*, **60**, 379, 423, 453.
5. Van Alphen, J. (1954) *Proc. Third Rubb. Technol. Conf.*, London, 670.
6. *Columbian Colloidal Carbons* (1940), **2**; (1942), **3**.
7. Emmett, P. H. and De Witt, T. (1941) *Ind. Eng. Chem., Anal. Ed.*, **13**, 28.
8. Smith, W. R., Thornhill, F. S. and Bray, R. I. (1941) *Ind. Eng. Chem.*, **33**, 1303.
9. Dannenberg, E. M. and Collyer, H. J. (1949) *Ind. Eng. Chem.*, **41**, 1607.
10. Hatch, T. H. and Choate, S. P. (1929) *J. Franklin Inst.*, **207**, 369.
11. Dallavale, J. (1948) *Micromeretics: The Technology of Fine Particles* (New York).
12. Leigh-Dugmore, C. H. (1953) *I.R.I. Trans.*, **29**, 92.
13. Flemmert, G. (1952) *Communication of the Division of Applied Inorganic Chemistry, Royal Institute of Technology, Stockholm.*
14. Schmidt, E. (1951) *Ind. Eng. Chem.*, **43**, 679.
15. Wolf, R. F. and Stueber, C. C. (1955) *Rubb. Age*, **77**, 399.
16. Harris, J. D. (1956) *Proc. Inst. Rubb. Ind.*, **3**, 145.
17. White, A. H. and Germer, L. H. (1941) *J. chem. Phys.*, **9**, 492.
18. Biscoe, J. and Warren, B. E. (1942) *J. appl. Phys.*, **13**, 364.
19. Wiegand, W. B. and Ladd, W. A. (1942) *Rubb. Age, N.Y.*, **50**, 431.
20. Ladd, W. A. and Wiegand, W. B. (1945) *Rubb. Age, N.Y.*, **57**, 299.
21. Hall, C. E. (1948) *J. appl. Phys.*, **19**, 271.
22. Sweitzer, C. W. (1955) *Proc. Inst. Rubb. Ind.*, **2**, 77.
23. Benson, G. (1946) *Rubb. Age, N.Y.*, **58**, 461.
24. Dannenberg, E. M. and Stokes, C. A. (1949) *Ind. Eng. Chem.*, **41**, 812.
25. Dobbin, R. E. and Rossman, R. P. (1946) *Ind. Eng. Chem.*, **38**, 1145.
26. Cohan, L. H. and Watson, J. H. L. (1951) *Rubb. Age, N.Y.*, **68**, 687.
27. Studebaker, M. L., Bulletin P.10 of the Phillips Chemical Company (Philblack Sales Division).
28. Studebaker, M. L., Huffman, E. W. D., Wolfe, A. C., Nabors, L. G. (1956) *Ind. Eng. Chem.*, **48**, 162.
29. Amerongen, G. J. van (1955) *I.R.I. Trans.*, **31**, 70.
30. Powell, E. F. and Gough, S. W. (1954) *Proc. Third Rubb. Technol. Conf., London*, 460.
31. Schallamach, A. (1956) *Rubb. Chem. Technol.*, **29**, 781.
32. Wiegand, W. B. (1937) *Can. Chem. and Met.*, **21**, 35.
33. Parkinson, D. (1946) *Advances in Colloid Science, New York*, **2**, 389.
34. Blanchard, A. F. (1954) *Proc. Third Rubber Technol. Conf., London*, 592.
35. Gehman, S. D. and Field, J. E. (1940) *Ind. Eng. Chem.*, **32**, 140.
36. Zapp, R. L. (1955) *Rubb. World*, **133**, 59.
37. Weiss, J. (1942) *I.R.I. Trans.*, **18**, 32.
38. Rehner, J., Jr. (1943) *J. appl. Phys.*, **14**, 638.
39. Smallwood, H. M. (1944) *J. appl. Phys.*, **15**, 758.
40. Guth, E. (1945) *J. appl. Physics*, **16**, 20.

41. Guth, E. and Gold, O. (1938) *Phys. Rev.*, **53**, 322.
42. Hashin, Z. (1955) *Bull. Res. Council of Israel*, **5C**, 46.
43. Guth, E. (1948) *Proc. Second Rubb. Technol. Conf., London*, 353.
44. Cohan, L. H. (1948) *Proc. Second Rubber Technol. Conf., London*, 365.
45. Schaeffer, W. D. and Smith, W. R. (1955) *Ind. Eng. Chem.*, **47**, 1286.
46. Mullins, L. (1947) *J. Rubb. Research*, **16**, 275.
47. Buist, J. M., Lindsey, C. H., Naunton, W. J. S., Stafford, R. L. and Williams, G. E. (1951) *Ind. Eng. Chem.*, **43**, 373.
48. Mullins, L. (1950) *J. Phys. and Colloid Chem.*, **54**, 239.
49. Blanchard, A. F. and Parkinson, D. (1948) *Proc. Second Rubb. Technol. Conf., London*, 414.
50. Blanchard, A. F. and Parkinson, D. (1952) *Ind. Eng. Chem.*, **44**, 799.
51. Blanchard, A. F. (1956) *I.R.I. Trans.*, **32**, 124.
52. Mullins, L. and Tobin, N. R. (1954) *Proc. Third Rubb. Technol. Conf., London*, 397.
53. Rivlin, R. S., Thomas, A. G. and Saunders, D. W. (1951) *Phil. Trans. A.*, **243**, 251.
54. Skinner, S. M., Bobalek, E. G., Blum, G. W. and Ling, T. H. (1956) *Ind. Eng. Chem.*, **48**, 2086.
55. Bueche, A. M. (1955) *J. Polymer Sci.*, **15**, 105.
56. Guth, E. and James, H. M. (1941) *Ind. Eng. Chem.*, **33**, 624.
57. Wall, F. T. (1942) *J. chem. Phys.*, **10**, 485.
58. Treloar, L. R. G. (1943) *Trans. Farad. Soc.*, **39**, 36.
59. Kuhn, W. (1936) *Kolloid-Z.*, **76**, 258.
60. Blanchard, A. F. (1954) *J. Polymer Sci.*, **14**, 355.
61. Gessler, A. M. and Rehner, J., Jr. (1955) *Rubb. Age, N.Y.*, **77**, 875.
62. Waring, J. R. S. (1951) *Ind. Eng. Chem.*, **43**, 352.
63. Kruse, J. (1953) *Kautsch. u Gummi*, 6, WT140–1, WT202–5.
64. Houwink, R. and Janssen, H. J. J. (1954) *Kautsch. u Gummi*, 7, WT82–7.
65. Houwink, R. (1956) *Rubb. Chem. Technol.*, **29**, 888.
66. Kruse, J. (1952) *Kautsch. u Gummi*, **5**, WT1–3.
67. Kruse, J. (1951) *Kolloid Zshr.*, **122**, 65.
68. Schippel, H. F. (1920) *Ind. Eng. Chem.*, **12**, 33.
69. Green, H. (1921) *Ind. Eng. Chem.*, **13**, 1029.
70. Depew, H. A. and Easley, M. K. (1934) *Ind. Eng. Chem.*, **26**, 1187.
71. Jones, H. C. and Yiengst, Y. A. (1940) *Ind. Eng. Chem.*, **32**, 1354.
72. Bryant, K. C. and Bisset, D. C. (1954) *Proc. Third Rubber Technol. Conf., London*, 655.
73. Marshall, D. G., Walker, D. L. and Smith, J. G. (1955) *I.R.I. Trans.*, **31**, 115.
74. Zapp, R. L. and Guth, E. (1951) *Ind. Eng. Chem.*, **43**, 430.
75. Barron, H. and Cotton, F. H. (1931) *I.R.I. Trans.*, **7**, 209.
76. Stearns, R. S. and Johnson, B. L. (1951) *Ind. Eng. Chem.*, **43**, 146.
77. Stearns, R. S. and Johnson, B. L. (1956) *Ind. Eng. Chem.*, **48**, 961.
78. Busse, W. F. (1934) *Ind. Eng. Chem.*, **26**, 1194.
79. Buist, J. M. (1945) *I.R.I. Trans.*, **20**, 155.
80. Janssen, H. J. J. (1954) *Proc. Third Rubb. Technol. Conf., London*, 351.
81. Greensmith, H. W. and Thomas, A. G. (1955) *J. Polymer Sci.*, **18**, 189.
82. Greensmith, H. W. (1956) *J. Polymer Sci.*, **21**, 175.
83. Williams, I. (1952) *India Rubb. World*, **126**, 359.
84. Dogadkin, B. A. and Sandomirski, D. M. (1952) *Rubb. Chem. Technol.*, **25**, 50.
85. Bartenev, G. M. and Belostotskaya, G. I. (1954) *Zhur. Tekh. Fiz.*, **24**, 1773–85.
86. Parkinson, D. and Blanchard, A. F. (1948) *I.R.I. Trans.*, **23**, 259.
87. Gerke, R. H., Ganzhorn, G. H., Howland, L. H. and Smallwood, H. M. (1938), U.S.P. 2,118,601.
88. Bulgin, D. (1946) *I.R.I. Trans.*, **21**, 188.
89. Dobbin, R. E. and Rossman, R. P. (1946) *Ind. Eng. Chem.*, **38**, 1145.

90. Watson, J. H. L. (1949) *J. appl. Phys.*, **20**, 747.
91. Blanchard, A. F. (1958) Conference Proceedings " Industrial Carbon and Graphite ", Society Chem. Ind., London.
92. Goldfinger, G. (1945) *Rubb. Chem. Technol.*, **18**, 286.
93. Goldfinger, G. (1946) *J. Polymer Res.*, **1**, 58.
94. Fielding, J. H. (1937) *Ind. Eng. Chem.*, **29**, 880.
95. Sweitzer, C. W., Goodrich, W. C. and Burgess, K. A. (1949) *Rubb. Age, N.Y.*, **65**, 651.
96. Watson, J. W. (1956) *I.R.I. Trans.*, **32**, 204.
97. Watson, W. F. (1954) *Proc. Third Rubb. Technol. Conf., London*, 553.
98. Villars, D. S. (1956) *J. Polymer Sci.*, **21**, 257.
99. Ladd, W. A. and Ladd, M. W. (1951) *Ind. Eng. Chem.*, **43**, 2564.
100. Endter, F. (1954) *Rubb. Chem. Technol.*, **27**, 1.
101. Sweitzer, C. W. (1952) *Rubb. Age, N.Y.*, **72**, 55.
102. Blanchard, A. F. and Wootton, P. (paper in preparation).
103. Baker, W. O. (1949) *Ind. Eng. Chem.*, **41**, 511.
104. Boonstra, B. B. S. T. and Dannenberg, E. M. (1954) *Ind. Eng. Chem.*, **46**, 218.
105. Martin, B. J. A. and Parkinson, D. (1955) *Rubb. Chem. Technol.*, **28**, 261.
106. Parkinson, D. (1940) *I.R.I. Trans.*, **16**, 87.
107. Barton, B. C., Smallwood, H. M. and Ganzhorn, G. H. (1954) *J. Polymer Sci.*, **13**, 487.
108. Gessler, A. M. (1953) *Rubb. Age, N.Y.*, **74**, 59.
109. Gessler, A. M. and Ford, F. P. (1953) *Rubb. Age, N.Y.*, **74**, 397.
110. Rehner, J., Jr. and Gessler, A. M. (1954) *Rubb. Age, N.Y.*, **74**, 561.
111. Zapp, R. L. and Gessler, A. M. (1953) *Rubb. Age, N.Y.*, **74**, 243.
112. Braendle, H. A., Estelow, R. K. and Wiegand, W. B. (1950) *Rubb. Age, N.Y.*, **67**, 64.
113. Doak, K. W., Ganzhorn, G. H. and Barton, B. C. (1955) *Canad. J. Technol.*, **33**, 98.
114. Braendle, H. A. (1952) *Rubb. Age, N.Y.*, **72**, 205.
115. Bradley, H. P., U.S.P. 2,239,659.
116. Drogin, I. (1948) *Proc. Second Rubb. Technol. Conf., London*, 385.
117. Mullins, L. and Whorlow, R. W. (1951) *I.R.I. Trans.*, **27**, 55.
118. Wiegand, W. B. (1944) *Canad. Chem. Proc. Inds.*, **28**, 151.
119. Parkinson, D. (1951) *Brit. J. appl. Phys.*, **2**, 273.
120. Drogin, I., Bishop, H. R. and Wiseman, P. (1954) *Rubb. Age, N.Y.*, **74**, 707.
121. Dannenberg, E. M. (1952) *Ind. Eng. Chem.*, **44**, 813.
122. Sperberg, L. R., Svetlick, J. F. and Bliss, L. A. (1949) *Ind. Eng. Chem.*, **41**, 1641.
123. Naunton, W. J. S. and Waring, J. R. S. (1939) *I.R.I. Trans.*, **14**, 340.
124. Watson, J. W. and Parkinson, D. (1955) *Ind. Eng. Chem.*, **47**, 1053.
125. Beebe, R. A., Kingston, G. L., Polley, M. H. and Smith, W. R. (1950) *J. Amer. chem. Soc.*, **72**, 40.
126. Beebe, R. A., Polley, M. H., Smith, W. R. and Wendell, C. B. (1947) *J. Amer. chem. Soc.*, **69**, 2294.
127. Beebe, R. A. and Young, D. M. (1954) *J. phys. Chem.*, **58**, 93.
128. Polley, M. H., Schaeffer, W. D. and Smith, W. R. (1953) *J. phys. Chem.*, **57**, 469.
129. Polley, M. H., Schaeffer, W. D. and Smith, W. R. (1955) *Canad. J. Chem.*, **33**, 314.
130. Schaeffer, W. D., Polley, M. H. and Smith, W. R. (1950) *J. phys. Chem.*, **54**, 227.
131. Pike, M. and Watson, W. F. (1952) *J. Polymer Sci.*, **9**, 229.
132. Garten, V. A. and Sutherland, G. K. (1954) *Proc. Third Rubb. Technol. Conf., London*, 536.
133. Wake, W. C. (1954) *Discussion, Third Rubb. Technol. Conf., London*, 549.

134. Wake, W. C. (1950) *Rubb. Age*, **31**, 298.
135. Garten, V. A. and Weiss, D. E. (1955) *Aust. J. Chem.*, **8**, 68.
136. Schaeffer, W. D., Smith, W. R. and Polley, M. H. (1953) *Ind. Eng. Chem.*, **45**, 1721.
137. Kuzminskii, A. S., Lyubchanskaya, L. I., Khitrova, N. G. and Bass, S. I. (1952) *C.R. Acad. Sci. U.R.S.S.*, **82**, 131.
138. Winn, H., Shelton, J. R. and Turnbull, D. (1946) *Ind. Eng. Chem.*, **38**, 1052.
139. Sweitzer, C. W. and Lyon, F. (1952) *Ind. Eng. Chem.*, **44**, 125.
140. Lyon, F., Burgess, K. A. and Sweitzer, C. W. (1954) *Ind. Eng. Chem.*, **46**, 596.
141. Garten, V. A., Eppinger, K. and Weiss, D. E. (1956) *Aust. J. appl. Sci.*, **7**, 148.
142. Dannenberg, E. M. and Boonstra, B. B. S. T. (1955) *Ind. Eng. Chem.*, **47**, 339.
143. Kraus, G. (1956) *Rubb. World*, **136**, 67, 254.
144. Houwink, R. and van Alphen, J. (1955) **16**, 121.

ADDITIONAL REFERENCES

Andrews, E. H. and Walsh, A. (1958) *J. Polymer Sci.*, **93**, 39.
Greensmith, H. W. (1960) *J. Polymer Sci.*, in press.
Brown, H. P. (1957) *Rubb. Chem. Technol.*, **30**, 1347.
Dolgoplosk, B. A., Reikh, V. N., Tinyakova, E. I., Kalaus, A. E., Koryushenko, Z. A. and Sladkevich, E. G. (1959) *Rubb. Chem. Technol.*, **32**, 328.
Mullins, L. (1960) *Proceedings, International Rubb. Conf.*, p. 389.
Endter, F. and Westlinning, H. (1957) *Rubber Chem. Technol.*, **30**, 1103.
Kraus, G. and Collins, R. L. (1958) *Rubb. World*, **139**, 219.
Donnet, J. B. and Henrich, G. (1958) *Compt. Rend.*, **246**, 3230.
Gessler, A. M. (1960) *Rubb. Age, N.Y.*, **86**, 1017
Studebaker, M. L. (1957) *Rubber Reviews, Rubb. Chem. Technol.*, **30**, 1400.
Garten, V. A. and Weiss, D. E. (Nov., 1959) *Indust. Chemist*, pp. 525.
Blanchard, A. F. and Wootton, P. (1959) *J. Polymer Sci.*, **34**, 627.

CHAPTER VII

PART TWO

PRACTICE AND TECHNOLOGY OF REINFORCEMENT

by

C. H. LEIGH-DUGMORE

IN the early days of rubber technology when tensile strength and modulus were the only properties which could be measured objectively with any reliability, it was natural that their enhancement should be regarded as reinforcement. In 1920 Wiegand [1,2] suggested that a better measure of reinforcement was the work of extension to breaking, which is sometimes known as the proof resilience or resilient energy, and is proportional to the area beneath the stress–strain curve. In 1937 Shepard, Street and Park [3] pointed out that tearing also must be taken into account in evaluating reinforcement, but, because resistance to tearing was so difficult to measure accurately, many rubber technologists relied on hand-tearing. The same authors stated that " one of the most important effects of the addition of powders to rubber is the increase of abrasion resistance ", but, as with tearing, the art of measurement was so little developed they could scarcely say more.

Improvements in methods of measuring tear strength and abrasion resistance (though these methods are still far from perfect) have shown that high levels of these properties are not necessarily obtained either when tensile strength or when the work of extension is high.

Because of this and because most of the world's rubber (both natural and synthetic) is used to make tyres for which, in the treads at least, resistance to wear and tear is a necessary requirement, reinforcement now implies to most technologists increased abrasion resistance and tear strength.

But not every rubber product requires these properties: some, such as engine mountings, need resistance to deformation, with the result that stiffening alone is sometimes regarded as reinforcement. This can be achieved without improvement in abrasion resistance or tear or tensile strength and, indeed, even at their expense; and the stiffness of reinforced compounds can be markedly decreased merely by pre-stretching.[4]

In the following pages reinforcement will be understood to imply improvement of abrasion resistance, tear strength and tensile strength, and it will be seen that this is usually accompanied by increased stiffness.

Stiffening alone will not be regarded as reinforcement, but because it is technologically important it will not be ignored.

The adoption of this definition does not mean that reinforcement for tyre-tread compounds alone will be considered. Different degrees of reinforcement are required for other purposes: belting and hose need reinforcement against wear and tear under conditions of service sometimes similar to those in which tyre treads operate; tyre-carcass stocks need reinforcement against tearing, especially at high operating temperatures; shoe-soleing and flooring compounds against wear and tear of a kind different from those in tyre service.

In achieving reinforcement there are concomitant effects which cannot be overlooked: processing of the unvulcanised stock is often made more difficult and scorching becomes a hazard; resilience is almost always lowered, and as a consequence heat build-up in dynamic service is a danger that has to be guarded against; flexcracking, crack-growth and cut-growth, permanent set, fatigue resistance and electrical properties all change with reinforcement. Changes in any of these properties often set a limit to permissible reinforcement.

Methods of reinforcement

Without reinforcement few polymers are adequate for other than the more trivial applications; they have to be compounded with other materials to give them the reinforcement necessary for service requirements.

Before classifying these materials it is necessary to review the terms that have been used to describe them. The name " filler " is now given widely to almost all materials which are added in sufficiently large quantities to reduce the amount of rubber needed. If at the same time they reinforce the rubber they are described as reinforcing or active fillers; if not, as inert or inactive fillers. Other terms in use are reinforcing agent, reinforcing material and reinforcing ingredient. Inert fillers are sometimes called diluents or described merely as fillers if the context allows no doubt; the word " filler " originally had only this limited meaning, but custom has broadened it.

Reinforcing materials can be divided into three classes: carbon blacks, inorganic materials and organic materials.

The inorganic materials include the fine silicas, the silicates and the inorganic inert fillers, such as clay and whiting.

The carbon blacks and the inorganic fillers are used in the form of fine particles which retain their identity as particles after addition to the polymer. The reinforcing power of each increases as its particle size is diminished, and the reinforcement they provide improves as the loading in the polymer is increased to an optimum concentration. Beyond this loading reinforcement will fall off, though some properties, such as hardness, will go on increasing and others, such as resilience, will continue to decrease.

Although the organic fillers, such as cyclised rubber, the high-styrene resins and the phenolic resins, may be added to or formed in the elastomer in the form of discrete particles to give tear-reinforcement and stiffness, they can be used in much higher proportions than carbon black or the inorganic fillers. At high loadings their particles coalesce and become the continuous matrix in which particles or fragments of the rubber are dispersed. Compounds of rubber and resin have different combinations of properties from those containing carbon or inorganic fillers: they can be made with hardness anywhere in the range from soft to very hard, with good tear strength and tensile strength; and however hard the vulcanisate, the unvulcanised stock is soft and easily processed.

The formation of graft or block polymers must also be considered as a way of stiffening and improving tear strength. A polymer, such as natural rubber, is activated in the presence of a monomer, such as methyl methacrylate, so that it forms free radicals which initiate polymerisation of the monomer. This monomer then forms polymer blocks grafted on the molecules of the original polymer. Graft polymers of this kind have characteristics similar to rubber-and-resin compounds.

Because reinforcement cannot be defined in terms of a single physical property, it is not always possible to say, without fear of contradiction, that one material reinforces more than another. Even if we use the definition of reinforcement given on p. 473 to classify reinforcing ingredients in order of merit, we shall still tend to arrive at different orders, depending on whether we regard abrasion resistance or tear strength or tensile strength as the most important of the three properties involved.

General considerations

When deciding which reinforcing agent and how much of it to use for a particular purpose there are technical factors to consider other than merely the desired degree of reinforcement. There will be other properties that the product should, or should not have, and it must be possible to handle the unvulcanised material easily and safely in the manufacturing processes. Also the colour may have been specified, and there will normally be an upper limit to the cost.

The problem of colour is difficult only when the product must not be black. The variety of carbon blacks available enables a wide choice of degree of reinforcement and level of other properties. If for any reason it is decided not to use carbon as the reinforcing agent it can be used as a pigment: a few per cent of a fine carbon black will make any compound as black as may be required. The choice of degree of reinforcement is less wide if black must be avoided, but it is wider now than it was before the development of fine-particle silicas. Many of the non-black materials give white or light-coloured stocks which can be pigmented to any desired colour.

Cost can rarely be ignored; in fact, it may dominate other considerations. There are several aspects to this problem. The first and most obvious is the cost of the materials used. If the merits of two reinforcing agents are being judged it may be necessary not only to compare their own volume costs but to take into account also the costs of the different amounts of other compounding ingredients that they may require, as for example, processing aids and curatives. There are other factors too which influence cost more or less directly and whose effects will vary from one reinforcing agent to another: the power, the time and the labour necessary for the mixing and processing operations; the risk of scrap material if scorching is likely, if moulding is difficult, if extraction from the mould is likely to cause damage, or if a rigid specification has to be met; the time and heat for vulcanising and, should it be necessary, the cost of cooling the mould before extraction.

When reinforcement is the dominating requirement natural rubber or the SBR types or Butyl rubber will be used, and the choice between them may have to be made on grounds of economy or policy. When some other requirement is equally important or more important than reinforcement a special-purpose polymer may be chosen. This choice will affect the degree of reinforcement that can be reached, and may limit the selection of reinforcing agents that can be added to the polymer.

Even after the polymer and the reinforcing material have been selected the level of reinforcement to be attained can still be modified to some extent by varying the type and amount of other compounding ingredients and the procedures for mixing and processing.

In the sections which follow these factors will be discussed. The different classes of reinforcing agents will be taken in turn, beginning with the carbon blacks, and their value in natural rubber and other polymers will be described. Special sections will be devoted to the effects of milling and processing and to such general considerations as the importance of dispersion.

Carbon black

Carbon black, the most widely-used reinforcing material, is produced in a variety of grades. These differ in the way they are manufactured, in their particle size, in the amounts they contain of matter other than carbon, chiefly oxygen and hydrogen, and in the extent to which their particles tend to agglomerate in chain-like structures.

An account of these differences has been given by W. R. Smith,[5] and shorter accounts have recently been given by Parkinson.[6, 7]

There are five methods of manufacture.

In the channel or impingement process natural gas is burnt in small flames which play on iron channels on which the carbon is deposited. The particle size of the product can be varied from about 10 to about 30 mμ. Those smaller than 15 mμ are used in paint and varnish but not in rubber: they are difficult to mix into rubber, and the resulting stocks are hard and difficult to process. Channel blacks with particles sizes between 17 and

TABLE 7.4

RUBBER-GRADE CARBON BLACKS

Type	Symbol	Mean particle diam.,* mμ	Surface area,* M²/g.	Vola-tile matter, %	pH	Nigro-meter index
Reinforcing carbon blacks						
Super-abrasion furnace	SAF	14–20	120–140	1	9–10	83–85
Intermediate-super-abrasion furnace	ISAF	18–24	110–120	1	8·5–9·5	87–89
High-abrasion furnace	HAF	24–28	75–95	1	8–9	88–90
Hard-processing channel	HPC	22–25	100–110	5	3·7–4·0	82–84
Medium-processing channel	MPC	25–29	90–105	5	3·8–4·5	83–86
Easy-processing channel	EPC	29–33	80–95	5	3·8–5·0	85–87
Medium-reinforcing carbon blacks						
Fast-extrusion furnace	FEF	30–50	45–70	<1	9·0–9·5	92–96
Fine furnace	FF	40–45	55–70	<1	9·0–9·5	90–92
General-purpose furnace	GPF	50	45	<1	9·0–9·5	96
High-modulus furnace	HMF	45–65	30–60	<1	9·5–10·0	93–96
Semi-reinforcing furnace	SRF	60–85	25–45	<1	9·5–10·0	98–100
Lamp	LB	100–150	13–25	—	4	—
Conductive carbon blacks						
Superconductive furnace	SCF	16–20	120	1–2	9·5	84–88
Conductive furnace	CF	24	110	1–2	9·0	86–88
Conductive channel	CC	17–23	100–150	5	3·5–4·5	73–80
Acetylene	—	40–55	40–70	<1	7–9	92–96
Other carbon blacks						
Fine thermal	FT	120–200	15–35	<1	8·5–9·5	106
Medium thermal	MT	250–500	5–10	<1	7–9	115

* These estimates are from measurements of electron-microscope images of the particles.

23 mμ can be mixed into rubber, though processing is not easy, and are used to make electrically conductive stocks. The hard-processing, medium-processing and easy-processing channel blacks (HPC, MPC and EPC), the most important rubber-grade impingement blacks, have particle sizes between 24 and 33 mμ (see Table 7.4).

Furnace blacks are made by burning natural gas or oil or a mixture of the two in furnaces in a controlled supply of air. All grades can be used for rubber compounding. The original furnace blacks were much coarser than can be made by the channel process, but furnace blacks are produced now with mean particle sizes nearly as small as those of the finest channel blacks.

The furnace and channel processes produce most of the black used in the rubber industry. The channel process has been established longer, but is being supplanted by the furnace process for both technical and economic reasons. Technical differences are discussed below; the economic reasons have been described by Parkinson.[8]

The other three processes give lampblack, thermal black and acetylene black, each of which has its own special uses, but consumption of them is small compared with the furnace and channel blacks.

For this discussion carbon blacks are divided into the four groups shown in Table 7.4. The ranges of values shown give an idea of the variability between the products of different manufacturers.

Carbon black in natural rubber

Reinforcing carbon blacks

When the fullest possible reinforcement is needed, as in tyre treads or conveyor belting, one of the following grades of black is generally used:

SAF	Super-abrasion furnace black
ISAF	Intermediate-super-abrasion furnace black
HAF	High-abrasion furnace black
HPC	Hard-processing channel black
MPC	Medium-processing channel black
EPC	Easy-processing channel black

Until after the Second World War the three channel blacks were alone in this group, and MPC and EPC were widely used. For a variety of reasons they are being supplanted by HAF and ISAF. SAF is little used yet because of its cost and its adverse effect on processing. All three furnace blacks are made from oil, and HAF and ISAF blacks are being produced in the United Kingdom.

The general trend of abrasion resistance (Dunlop–Lambourn constant-power test [9]) with increased loading of these carbons is shown in Fig. 7.41; at any loading this decreases in the order in which they are named above.

Any of these furnace blacks provides greater resistance to wear than the channel grades, even when they each have the same particle size, and this seems to be not because they are made by the furnace process but because they are made from oil instead of gas.[10]

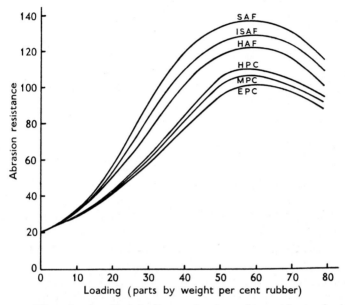

Fig. 7.41. Effect of carbon black loading on abrasion resistance of natural rubber.

Comparisons of tear strength (Fig. 7.42) are less straightforward. Except at loadings higher than would ordinarily be considered for any of these 6 grades, SAF black probably gives the highest tear strength of all at room temperature; at loadings below those more commonly used differences between the other 5 are not considerable. In any case, at loadings at or near the optimum for this property, 40–60 parts, room-temperature tear strength is usually more than adequate to meet the demands of service.

Tear strength is of greater consequence at higher temperatures when it is usually lower than at room temperature. Fig. 7.42 shows also tear strength measured at 100° C. No reliable distinctions can be made within either the channel or furnace groups, but the furnace blacks have an advantage which, though it looks small, is sufficiently real to be important.

Tensile strength has little practical importance in natural rubber, whose inherent (gumstock) strength is already high, so though the furnace blacks give lower tensile strength than the channel blacks, this does not offset their superiority in imparting abrasion resistance and hot tear strength.

Furnace-black compounds are stiffer (Fig. 7.43) and harder (Fig. 7.44) than similarly-loaded channel-black compounds.

R

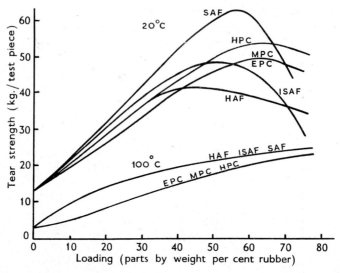

Fig. 7.42. Effect of carbon black loading on tear strength of natural rubber.

In dynamic service resilience (Fig. 7.45 shows results from the Dunlop–Healey pendulum) plays an important part in governing the temperature to which the rubber will be raised, and here again the furnace blacks have an advantage over channel blacks of equivalent particle size. This is especially true of the HAF grade, which has largely replaced MPC as the principal black for tyre-tread compounding.

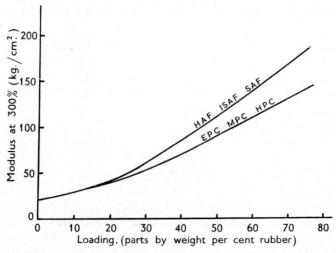

Fig. 7.43. Effect of carbon black loading on modulus of natural rubber at 300% elongation.

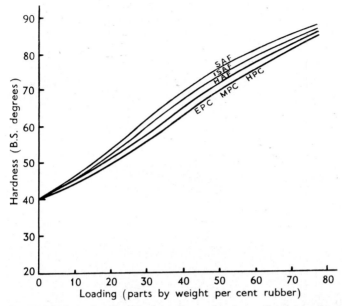

Fig. 7.44. Effect of carbon black loading on hardness of natural rubber.

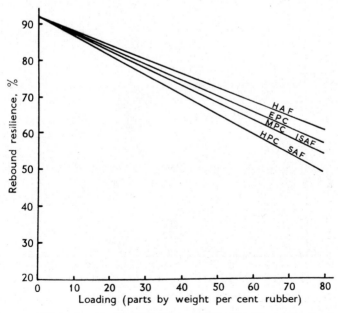

Fig. 7.45. Effect of carbon black loading on rebound resilience of natural rubber at 50° C.

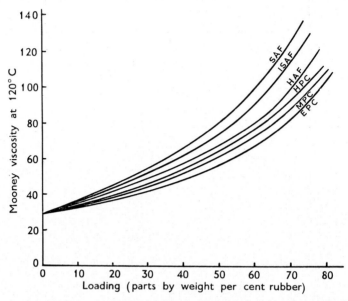

Fig. 7.46. Effect of carbon black loading on Mooney viscosity of natural rubber at 120° C.

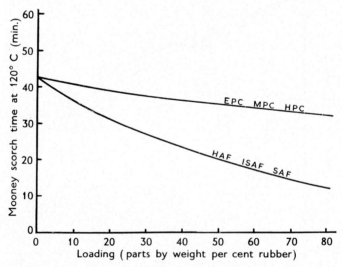

Fig. 7.47. Effect of carbon black loading on Mooney scorch time of natural rubber at 120° C.

Though their enhancement is not essential to reinforcement, unvulcanised properties vary, as hardness and resilience do, with changes in the level of reinforcement. Mooney viscosity (Fig. 7.46) increases with black loading and is higher, at the same loading, for furnace than for channel blacks. Mooney scorch time (Fig. 7.47) is shorter for furnace-black than for channel-black stocks, and the difference between the two increases rapidly with loading. In practice, this difference in scorch time is aggravated, and there are also differences in processability within these two groups, because higher viscosity increases processing temperature and makes scorching more likely.

When designing a reinforced-rubber compound for a particular service a compromise often has to be made between these conflicting trends in properties. Greatest abrasion resistance and highest tear strength at room temperature are usually given by loadings of about 50–60 parts of carbon black. If the corresponding levels of resilience, hardness, Mooney viscosity and scorch time can be accepted such levels can be used; if not, some sacrifice in reinforcement may be enforced to allow safety in processing or to reduce heat build-up in service.

Compounds for tyre treads usually contain about 50 parts of HAF or ISAF black; this loading gives nearly maximum reinforcement and tolerable levels of the other properties. With such compounds scorching needs most attention, but ceases to be a serious risk if a delayed-action accelerator is used, such as cyclohexyl benzthiazyl sulphenamide. Use of ISAF black is increasing. SAF black is at present less popular because of its higher cost and the hazards it adds to processing, but it is not unlikely that experience will overcome these difficulties and that it will then be more widely used.

Medium-reinforcing blacks

The highest reinforcement is not always needed. When abrasion resistance is not especially important but good tear strength is necessary and resilience must be kept high and heat build-up low, one of the following grades of black is used:

FEF	Fast-extrusion furnace black
FF	Fine furnace black
GPF	General-purpose furnace black
HMF	High-modulus furnace black
SRF	Semi-reinforcing furnace black
LB	Lampblack

Except for lampblack, these are made by the furnace process; both FEF and GPF can be made from oil and are now being manufactured in the United Kingdom. Lampblack is the oldest of the carbon blacks and has

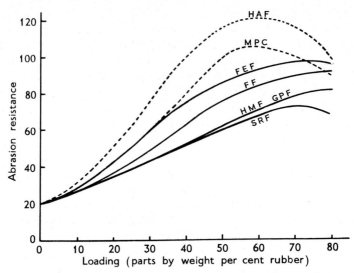

Fig. 7.48. Effect of carbon black loading on abrasion resistance of natural rubber.

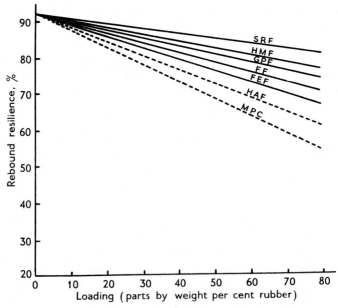

Fig. 7.49. Effect of carbon black loading on rebound resilience of natural rubber at 50° C.

been produced in the United Kingdom for a very long time; it was used as a pigment for rubber long before its reinforcing ability was recognised.

FEF and FF blacks provide the greatest reinforcement of this group and, indeed, at higher loadings (Fig. 7.48) they give abrasion resistance not far short of the channel blacks, with appreciably higher resilience (Fig. 7.49). FEF blacks have been described as medium-abrasion furnace (MAF) blacks. Both FF and FEF have been recommended for large-tyre treads and for other products in which a fair level of abrasion resistance is needed, but high resilience and low heat build-up are important; the alternative may be to use one of the more reinforcing blacks at a lower loading, and this is less economical, because, even on a volume basis, carbon black is cheaper than rubber, and the medium-reinforcing grades are cheaper still than those which are finer and more fully reinforcing.

SRF and HMF blacks and lampblack have been established for a long time, lampblack longest of all, for compounds which must withstand dynamic service. At moderate loadings, between 25 and 40 parts with 100 of rubber, they give stocks which, not being too stiff and having good resilience, do not build up too high a temperature in service and so retain good tear resistance and good fatigue resistance. GPF and FEF are both also finding favour for the same applications, GPF because it gives resilience almost as high as HMF or SRF, with somewhat better tear strength, while FEF gives better tear strength still, though with lower resilience.

Lampblack is used for solid tyres. Although the abrasion resistance it gives is little more than half that given by MPC black, resilience is higher and consequently heat build-up and the danger of blow-out are less, and it is from this that solid tyres are likely to fail before they are worn out.

Electrical conductivity

Carbon blacks with small particle size, high specific surface, permanent chain structure and low volatile content give the most conductive rubber compounds.

The finer furnace blacks made from oil are the best in these respects, and the reinforcing furnace blacks, SAF, ISAF and HAF, promote high conductivity—appreciably higher than the reinforcing channel grades, HPC, MPC and EPC.

HAF or ISAF black gives adequate anti-static protection for most motor-vehicle requirements, but not always enough for aircraft tyres or for other products, such as footwear, flooring, belting and hose, which may be used where there is a danger of explosion. For such purposes special conductive grades of black are used.

Chief among these are the conductive furnace (CF) and super-conductive furnace (SCF) blacks, which give resistivities in rubber of the order of

20–200 ohm-cm. in tread-type stocks, compared with 1,000–5,000 ohm-cm. given by HAF. Other physical properties of the compounds are similar.

Before these special furnace blacks were developed, conductive channel (CC) blacks and acetylene blacks were used.

Other carbon blacks

Fine thermal black makes compounds much less hard and stiff than lampblack but with slightly higher resilience, tear strength and abrasion resistance. It is used in inner tubes, curing bags, mechanical goods and in wire and cable covers.

Medium thermal black gives still softer stocks than fine thermal black and even higher resilience but much lower abrasion resistance and tear strength. It does not reinforce natural rubber appreciably, but it is quite widely used as a filler, because it is cheap and because, of all the carbon blacks and inorganic fillers, it alone can be incorporated at high loadings without much loss in resilience and without adverse effects on other properties.

The only other grades of carbon black that need be mentioned are the fine channel blacks with particle sizes between 5 and 20 mμ, which are ordinarily used as pigments in the paint and ink industries. Because of their fine particle size, they are difficult to disperse in rubber, and so their potential reinforcing ability cannot be realised. There is also some doubt whether, even if they could be well dispersed, they would provide better reinforcement than the present reinforcing carbon blacks.

Compounding of carbon black in natural rubber

The chief point to bear in mind is the difference between the channel and furnace grades in their influence on rate of cure and scorching.

The channel blacks tend to retard both scorching and vulcanisation because, it is generally thought, their pH is low (3–5). Scorching during processing of channel-black stocks is more likely to be a problem when their viscosity is high because they are highly loaded or because they contain the finer grades (HPC or CC).

Because their pH is high (8–10) the furnace blacks are inherently more prone to cause scorching. The first to be introduced (SRF and later, HMF), although giving more rapid vulcanisation than the channel types, give no serious scorching difficulties because the viscosity of their stocks is sufficiently low to make processing easy: the heat generated during processing is not enough to raise the temperatures of the stocks to dangerous levels for scorching.

Scorching became a serious problem with the introduction of HAF black as an alternative to the channel blacks. Straight replacement of channel by furnace black without changing the vulcanising system greatly reduced the scorching time. Accelerator levels have been reduced with some, but not enough, improvement and various retarders have been tried, but without marked success.

The problem has been largely overcome by using accelerators with more-delayed action. For instance, mercaptobenzthiazole (MBT), the accelerator most widely used with channel blacks, has been replaced to some extent by mercaptobenzthiazyl disulphide (MBTS) and even more, and with greater advantage, by cyclohexylbenzthiazylsulphenamide (CBS). In channel-black tread compounds it was customary to use 2·5–3 parts of sulphur (with 100 of natural rubber) and 0·8–1·0 part of MBT; for furnace-black treads it seems quite common to use about 2·5 of sulphur with 0·5 part of CBS.

Finer blacks, such as HPC, and, even more markedly, ISAF and SAF blacks, aggravate the problem, because they give increased viscosity. HPC could probably be used with safety with modern delayed-action accelerators, such as CBS, but is not used (widely, at any rate) because the finer furnace blacks give better reinforcement and are cheaper.

Whatever the vulcanising system, SAF-black stocks are much more difficult to process than those loaded with HAF black. It was because of this that the ISAF grade was introduced. ISAF gives less reinforcement than SAF, but, with care, its compounds can be processed with little more difficulty than HAF-black stocks.

Carbon black in SBR

The behaviour of carbon black in SBR (" hot " or " cold " or oil-extended) is broadly similar to that in natural rubber.

The most noticeable difference is in tensile strength. SBR gum stocks have very poor tensile strength, much lower than natural rubber; the addition of carbon black increases this property remarkably, though never to the values that could be attained by adding the same grade of black (in any quantity) to natural rubber. Even the coarser blacks, such as lamp-black and the thermal blacks, improve the tensile strength of SBR gum stocks, though they have the reverse effect on natural rubber.

It is generally accepted that SBR, particularly cold (LTP) or oil-extended (OEP), when reinforced with carbon black, is capable of better abrasion resistance than reinforced natural rubber.

When compounding OEP with carbon black it is necessary, to obtain more or less equivalent reinforcement, to use the same ratio of black to total OEP as the ratio of black to polymer alone that would be used with unextended polymer.

SBR compounded with furnace black tends to scorch more readily than with channel black.

Carbon-black structure, usually more marked in furnace than in channel blacks, has a pronounced effect in SBR on smoothness of extrusion and shrinkage after extrusion;[11,12] smoothness improves with increased black loading and shrinkage is less with structure blacks. These effects are very noticeable in SBR, but barely so in natural rubber.

Reinforcement of special-purpose elastomers

Generally speaking, the relative behaviour of different reinforcing agents is the same in other elastomers as it is in natural rubber and SBR, though the degree of reinforcement that any of them will then provide is not so high.

Neoprene, which has good gum-stock strength, responds to most reinforcing agents and fillers in much the same way as natural rubber does.[13,14,15] The tendency for the tear and tensile strengths of neoprene to fall off rapidly as its temperature is raised is markedly reduced by loading with reinforcing agents or fillers.

Gum stocks of Butyl rubber of low unsaturation have high tensile strength, which is not noticeably increased by reinforcing agents.[16] If unsaturation is high gum-stock tensile strength is lower but will respond to reinforcement. Whatever the degree of unsaturation of the raw polymer, tear strength and modulus can both be raised, especially by carbon black, but higher reinforcement can be realised when the unsaturation is high. The improved reinforcement of Butyl rubber which results from heat treatment is described in separate sections (p. 450).

Nitrile rubbers are best reinforced with carbon black, which greatly improves their very low gum-stock strength.[17] Silica made by the combustion process (see p. 497) will give tear resistance and tensile strength as high as ISAF black.[18]

Polysulphide elastomers are best reinforced by the furnace blacks. Channel blacks alone give less reinforcement, because their acidity affects vulcanisation,[19] but mixtures of channel blacks with SRF black give good results.[20]

Silicone rubbers are not capable of high reinforcement. Silica gives better properties than carbon black, which tends to interfere with vulcanisation.[19]

Dispersion

Particle size and surface area are important characteristics of reinforcing materials, and on them depends much of the reinforcement imparted to the vulcanisate. Thus, if the reinforcing ability of a filler is to be used fully its particles must be well dispersed so that their surfaces are in contact with the polymer.

In spite of this, it is sometimes doubted whether good dispersion is really necessary, because so little direct evidence is available to demonstrate it, and because attempts [21,22] to obtain such evidence can be criticised as inconclusive. Variation of dispersion has been achieved by changes in mixing procedure which might themselves have a direct influence on final properties.

Dispersion must not be confused with distribution. Filler particles may be well dispersed without being uniformly distributed throughout the rubber,[23] and it seems likely that non-uniformity of distribution is not necessarily detrimental to reinforcement, provided dispersion is good.

Routine examination of dispersion is useful for the control of mixing processes in both the laboratory and the factory. In the absence of such control poor dispersion may be the cause either of poor quality in factory production or of misleading results being accepted during a laboratory investigation.

Several methods of measuring dispersion have been proposed. Allen [24] developed a squeeze-out method for preparing specimens thin enough for microscope examination with transmitted light, and Adams, Messer and Howland [25] a pneumatic method. Tidmus and Parkinson [26] describe a technique for cutting thin sections with a microtome for light-microscope examination, and this can be used to give a quantitative measure of dispersion.[23] Chappuis, Polley and Schulz [27] have shown how the electron microscope can be used with specimens prepared either by a transfer technique or by microtome sectioning.

The electron microscope will record the ultimate dispersion in detail, but the procedure is too long and cumbersome for any but special use. The gross dispersion shown by the light microscope is sufficient for control purposes either in the factory or the laboratory.

It is widely held that furnace blacks are easier to disperse and less likely to be poorly dispersed in natural rubber and SBR than are the rubber-grade channel blacks.[7,22,28,29,30] It is certainly easier to produce poor dispersions of MPC black than of HAF black in natural rubber, and although maturing and remilling are still practised, they have a less-important effect on the dispersion of HAF blacks than of channel blacks.[7,30]

Dispersion becomes progressively more difficult with finer-particle-size carbon blacks.[29] This is one of the factors that limits the use of SAF blacks and the suitability in the rubber industry of the very fine colour and ink blacks.

Pelletising carbon black to make its handling easier and cleaner affects dispersion in natural rubber, SBR and Butyl rubber hardly at all, though it does influence dispersion in polyethylene and nitrile rubber.[29] The nerve or elastic properties of the elastomer rather than its viscosity seem to be responsible for breaking down the pellets.

Effects of milling and processing

The level of reinforcement reached in practice does not depend only on the types of polymer and reinforcing materials and the proportions in which they are combined.   Although these factors have a greater effect than any others, the process by which they are combined also has its effect. Mastication, the order in which ingredients are added during mixing, time and temperature of mixing or after-treatment, maturing periods and amount of reworking, each has its influence on the properties of the vulcanisate and on the ease of handling of the unvulcanised material during processing.   It is difficult to assess each of these influences separately and unambiguously, because the extent of any one of them will be affected by those that have preceded it and by the equipment that is used.   Appreciation of their relative importance will be coloured by opinions of what is necessary, expedient or economical.

Changes in the level of reinforcement are usually supposed to occur because of changes brought about in the dispersion or in the uniformity of distribution of the reinforcing particles in the polymer matrix.   Although this explanation is probably at least partly correct, it is founded largely on indirect evidence, and its implications are not straightforward.   Thus it is not possible to say beforehand what results a particular mixing process will lead to, and the best process for each purpose and for each set of circumstances will have to be reached by experiment.

Mastication

Breakdown of the polymer alone, before mixing is begun, can have direct consequences on properties such as tear strength,[30] or it can have the indirect consequence that increased plasticity of the polymer may prevent the reinforcing particles being adequately dispersed.   It is misleading [30] to consider these effects in terms only of the plasticity of the polymer after mastication, however it is measured, because varying the time or temperature of mastication can cause changes in vulcanisate properties even when the plasticity of the raw polymer is not affected.

Order of addition of ingredients

If all the compounding ingredients, except, perhaps, sulphur and accelerators, are added during an unbroken mixing cycle at usual mixing temperatures, reinforcement is not affected by the order in which the different materials are added to the rubber.   But, it has been said that the reinforcement of a black-loaded compound can be improved if a highly-loaded masterbatch containing the black, the softener and some of the rubber is mixed first at a higher temperature than usual, and if the rest of the rubber is added later with the other compounding ingredients.   Martin and Parkinson [30] found that tear strength fell with increasing concentration of black in the masterbatch. Diluting highly-loaded masterbatches with more rubber can easily lead to inhomogeneity or uneven distribution of the black in the final stock;[32] opinions differ how far this should be avoided or how or to what extent it should be controlled.

Mixing time and remilling

Mixing time should be sufficiently long to ensure adequate dispersion of the ingredients. If it is prolonged much beyond this or if the stock or any part of it is excessively reworked the polymer may be broken down too much, and tear strength [30] and tensile strength [33] will suffer.

Maturing periods

Intervals between different stages of the mixing process are often allowed for the stock to mature while it stands without being worked. When channel black is used, maturing periods followed by remilling are thought essential for good dispersion,[30] and hence for good reinforcement. When furnace blacks are used the need is much less apparent and may not exist at all, but the custom is still widely practised.

Mixing temperature and heat treatment

High-temperature mixing of all the ingredients of a black-loaded stock except sulphur and accelerators considerably lowers tear resistance and to a lesser extent [7] tensile strength. Abrasion resistance is not improved and may even be reduced.

On the other hand, high-temperature mixing of rubber and black alone or heat treatment of such a masterbatch, followed by milling at a lower temperature to add the other ingredients, can be expected to increase resilience, and some improvement in reinforcement has been claimed. The rubber and black are either mixed together,[34] then heated for from 10 to 60 minutes at between $150°$ and $190°$ C, allowed to cool and milled for 2 or 3 minutes at between $40°$ and $100°$ C; or such a masterbatch is mixed hot for from 10 to 60 minutes between $150°$ and $190°$ C.

Gerke et al.[34] claim that such heat treatment improves abrasion resistance by 30% and reduces hardness and hysteresis. Parkinson [32, 35] has confirmed these conclusions in general, though he contends that laboratory and road testing have shown abrasion resistance to be improved only by about 4%. Promoters such as benzidine, urea, and thiourea do not improve reinforcement but allow resilience to be increased after shorter times or lower temperatures of heat treatment or both. The effect of heat treatment, with or without benzidine, on SBR stocks containing channel black is similar to that on natural rubber.[36]

Heat treatment of black-Butyl stocks

The mechanical properties of black-loaded Butyl-rubber stocks can be appreciably improved by mixing and heating a masterbatch of the polymer and black as a preliminary step in the mixing process.[37,38,39,40]

The heat treatment can be applied in either of three ways.[37]   In the first of these, *cyclic heat treatment*, the masterbatch is alternately heated for $\frac{1}{2}$ hour in open steam at 160° C and milled for 5 minutes.   These two steps may be repeated with advantage as many as twelve times.   In the second, *static heat treatment*, the heating is maintained for a single unbroken period of several hours without alternate milling, but the masterbatch is milled afterwards.   The third and more practicable method, *dynamic heat treatment*, combines the milling and heating of the cyclic method simultaneously into the single process of masticating the masterbatch in a Banbury for between 10 and 30 minutes at a temperature between 180° and 235° C.

Heat treatment by any one of these three methods of a masterbatch comprising Butyl rubber, channel black and stearic acid, before the remaining compounding ingredients are added, improves the tensile strength, resilience, abrasion resistance and modulus.   Milling without heating has none of these effects.

Furnace blacks, unlike channel blacks, do not respond to this treatment [38] because they have less oxygen on their particle surfaces.   If a channel black is heated to 900° C beforehand to remove its surface oxygen, heat treatment of a Butyl-rubber masterbatch containing it will have no effect on vulcanisate properties; if a furnace black is oxidised by heating it in oxygen between 250° and 300° C it will then respond to masterbatch heat treatment.

Oxidation of furnace blacks is necessary only to demonstrate the part oxygen plays in this heat-treatment process.   In practice, masterbatches of Butyl rubber and furnace black can be made to benefit by heat treatment if a promoting agent is added to the masterbatch when it is first mixed.[39] Effective promotors include sulphur, *p*-dinitrosobenzene and *p*-quinone dioxime; selenium has much less effect than sulphur, and tellurium almost none.   About 0·2 part of sulphur or 0·6 of Polyac (30% *p*-dinitrosobenzene, 70% inert filler) to each 100 parts of Butyl rubber will give the best effect.

Heat treatment of Butyl-rubber masterbatches containing FT black gives little improvement in reinforcement unless a plasticiser is included in the masterbatch.[41]   Plasticisers usually have a mere diluent effect, but in this case the addition of 20 parts of plasticiser before heat treatment will double the tensile strength.

A promoter, Elastopar,[62] has recently been announced which is claimed to provide equivalent results without heat treatment.

Inorganic reinforcing agents

No other material has yet been produced which has the same reinforcing power as the best of the carbon blacks. Efforts to develop such materials have been intensified in recent years, and will no doubt continue because of the attraction of coloured reinforced-rubber products, the hope of producing a reinforcing material cheaper than carbon and cleanliness in the factory.

Before the Second World War the available non-black materials were mostly merely fillers, in the original meaning of the word. Clay, whiting and magnesium carbonate, for example, stiffen natural rubber but give no real reinforcement; zinc oxide, iron oxide and precipitated calcium carbonate provide some reinforcement but much less than the channel blacks. During the War finely-divided calcium silicate came to be used, first in synthetic rubber and later in combinations of rubber and resin. Since the War small-particle silicas and silicates have been developed which surpass the reinforcement given by any other non-black material but which still fall short of the finer carbon blacks.

Polymers such as SBR, which have very poor gum-stock properties, are useless unless they are reinforced. They cannot successfully be compounded with inert fillers, and before the development of silicas and silicates had to be reinforced with carbon black; hence coloured stocks were impracticable.

Inert fillers

There is a variety of non-black materials which are used only as diluents because they cannot properly be said to exert any reinforcing effect. Among these are whiting, china clay, barytes, diatomaceous earth, talc, lithopone, blanc fixe and many more. Tear strength of compounds containing them is not greatly better than that of a gumstock; abrasion resistance is no better and is sometimes worse. Even their stiffening effect is not great, and high loadings are required to equal the stiffness of HAF-black stocks; other physical properties, including resilience, are then very much inferior.

Magnesium carbonate behaves a little differently from most of the inert fillers: it stiffens natural rubber considerably and has the advantage that tear resistance does not become noticeably poorer at higher temperatures.

Older inorganic reinforcing materials

Zinc oxide, iron oxide and precipitated calcium carbonate, unlike the inert fillers, do give some reinforcement, and were the only non-black materials known to do so before the advent of the fine-particle silicas and silicates.

Zinc oxide, as well as being used as a white pigment and for activating most of the organic accelerators, can be compounded with natural rubber at loadings between about 30 and 150 parts by weight to improve tear strength.   Such compounds have good resilience—higher than with SRF black and almost as high as with MT black—and are somewhat softer than SRF-black stocks.   Tear strength at high temperatures is poor—no better than when fillers are used—and there is no improvement of abrasion resistance.   Thermal conductivity is good, and this virtue, combined with high resilience, keeps down the heat generated in dynamic service and lessens the danger of tear strength being reduced by high temperatures; this allows zinc oxide to be used, at loadings, usually of 50–60 parts by weight, in tyre-carcass compounds, though this use is no longer as common as it was 25 years or more ago, because furnace blacks are now more popular.   Furnace blacks give lower resilience and greater heat build-up than zinc oxide, but, in compensation, provide much superior tear strength at high temperatures and, because zinc oxide has such high specific gravity (5·5 compared with 1·8 for carbon black), they give much lighter compounds.

Iron oxide (ferric oxide, Fe_2O_3) can be used either as a red pigment or, at loadings up to about 150 parts by weight, as a mild reinforcing agent for natural rubber.   The tear strength of such compounds at room temperature is similar to that given by zinc oxide; at higher temperatures it is better.   Hardness is similar to zinc-oxide stocks; resilience is lower and is more nearly comparable with SRF black.   Abrasion resistance is slightly better than that of a gum stock.   Like zinc oxide, iron oxide has the disadvantage of a high specific gravity, 5·0.

Precipitated calcium carbonate has particles much finer and rounder than those of ground whiting, and has usually been treated with a fatty acid, such as stearic acid.   The principal result is improved tear strength; this is much better than that given by whiting and almost as good as zinc oxide, though it falls off at high temperatures to much the same extent as with zinc oxide.   At the same volume loading precipitated-calcium-carbonate stocks are a little softer than those of zinc oxide with about the same resilience.   Abrasion resistance is even poorer than that of the gum stock. Specific gravity, 2·5, is much lower than that of either zinc or iron oxide.

These three materials, zinc oxide, iron oxide and precipitated calcium carbonate have another advantage not possessed by most other non-black fillers: the permanent set of their compounds is lower and increases less with loading.   But, in common with the inert fillers, they do not increase the tensile strength of the natural-rubber gum stock.

Modern inorganic reinforcing materials

In recent years silica, calcium silicate and aluminium silicate have each been produced with particle size comparable with the reinforcing carbon blacks.   The silicates are prepared by precipitation and the silicas either by precipitation or by a combustion method similar to the impingement process used for the manufacture of channel black, but in which the raw material is silicon tetrachloride.

All these materials are widely used—either one at a time, as combinations of two or more of them or one of them in conjunction with clay or whiting to reduce cost. This applies to compounds based on either natural rubber or SBR or a mixture of both, and to resin-and-rubber compounds, since they reinforce each of these elastomer systems.

Silica

The silicas are often credited with reinforcing ability comparable with carbon black.[42,43,44] This is to some extent true; silicas with particle sizes between 15 and 25 mμ will give about 90% of the tear resistance of HAF black, either at room or at higher temperatures, and tensile strength as high, if not higher. But abrasion resistance is only about 60% of that given by HAF or about 70% of MPC black,[7] though much higher levels have been claimed.

Although abrasion resistance is definitely poorer than that obtained with the reinforcing carbon blacks or with FEF and FF blacks, and it is doubtful whether it is better than that provided by blacks such as SRF, HMF or GPF, it is greatly superior to that imparted by any other known non-black material.

Stocks loaded with silica differ from black-loaded compounds chiefly in hardness, modulus and elongation at break, especially at high loadings. At 50-part loadings modulus at 300% can be as low as 55 kg./cm.^{2}, compared with about 120 kg./cm.^{2} for HAF black, elongation at break 700%, compared with 500%, and hardness 75° B.S., compared with 65° B.S.

It has been claimed [45] that as much as two-fifths of the carbon black in a tyre-tread compound can be replaced by an equal volume of silica with a loss in abrasion resistance of only 5% or less. This loss is much less than the 12–16% that would have been expected from the amount of black replaced and from the relative abrasion resistances of silica and reinforcing carbon blacks. Resilience and heat build-up are improved by this substitution and tearing is made more knotty. The knotty tearing of these compounds led Wolf [45] to suggest that mixtures of black and silica might reduce cutting and chipping in off-the-road tyres, but this has yet to be confirmed.

High loadings of fine-particle silicas are difficult to incorporate in rubber because the mix becomes dry and hard. The heat generated during mixing is nearly as high as with reinforcing furnace blacks, but scorching is not a problem because of the slow-curing characteristics of silica stocks. Dispersion is usually good. Small quantities of silica, less than 10 parts, added to stocks which are difficult to extrude are said to remove this difficulty and to improve dispersion of other fillers present without affecting the properties of the vulcanisate.

The principal problem when compounding with silica is its tendency to adsorb accelerators and so retard vulcanisation. This can be overcome by increasing the accelerator content to about 3% on the polymer, or by increasing it to about 2·0–2·5% and also adding 1–2% of a glycol (ethylene or propylene glycol) or an amine (triethanolamine). Unfortunately, increases in accelerator loading have a noticeable effect on cost. Lower levels of acceleration than these may still give an optimum level of properties after an acceptable time of cure, but compression set is likely to be high and hardness low.

Mercaptobenzthiazyl disulphide (MBTS) and cyclohexylbenzthiazyl sulphenamide (CBS) seem to be the accelerators most often used with silica; mercaptobenzthiazole (MBT) is not suitable [44] because it gives poorer physical properties. CBS can be used alone (up to 3%) or in conjunction with about 0·2% tetramethyl thiuram disulphide (TMT); MBTS is used more often in conjunction with diorthotolyl guanidine (DOTG) and triethanolamine, about 1% of each, or with some combination of DPG or TMT, hexamethyl tetramine (HMT) and triethanolamine or one of the glycols. The quantities suggested here are intended only as a guide, because they will need to be varied according to the different adsorbent activities of silicas from different sources. The inclusion of a glycol or triethanolamine also improves mixing and processing: incorporation of the silica becomes easier, less heat is generated and viscosity is reduced.

Silicates

Precipitated aluminium and calcium silicates each reinforce to a lower degree than silica, but are still superior to all other non-black materials. Aluminium silicate reinforces more than calcium silicate.

Aluminium silicate will give about 80%, calcium silicate about 60% of the tear strength of HAF black; and each gives tensile strength very nearly as high as HAF black or silica. Their abrasion resistance is only about 30–40% of that expected of an HAF-black stock.

Aluminium-silicate stocks are usually about 5° B.S. and calcium-silicate stocks about 10° B.S. less hard than HAF-black stocks.

The mixing and processing of compounds loaded with silicates is not as difficult as of those containing silica, nor do the silicates adsorb accelerators to a sufficient extent to make higher accelerator loadings necessary.

Heat treatment of silica stocks

The properties of silica-loaded Butyl-rubber stocks, like those black-loaded (p. 494), can be improved by heat treatment.[42] Silica-loaded SBR compounds also benefit. Tensile strength and resilience are both increased if, as a first step in the mixing process, a masterbatch of the polymer and a hydrated silica such as Hi-Sil is heat treated. Gessler and Rehner [42] claim also that this process leads to abrasion resistance comparable to that obtained with channel blacks.

For Butyl rubber a masterbatch of polymer 100, stearic acid 2 and glycol 3, together with the silica and a promoter, is mixed on a hot mill for 20 minutes at between 150° and 155° C or in a Banbury mixer for 8–12 minutes at between 210° and 220° C. Heat treatment in open steam as used in the static and cyclic methods developed for carbon-black stocks (p. 494) cannot be applied to silica stocks because the silica absorbs water rapidly and the batch breaks up.

If p-quinonedioxime or p-dinitrosobenzene is used as the promoter the stock scorches easily, but this risk is much reduced by p-quinonedioxime-dibenzoate (Dibenzo GMF). Unlike carbon black, silica needs a promoter concentration depending on the silica loading—40 parts of silica and 100 of Butyl rubber need 0·6 parts Dibenzo GMF, 50 parts need 1·0 part promoter and 70 parts, 2·0 parts.[42]

Masterbatches of LTP SBR and silica respond to heat treatment even without a promoter, though the presence of Dibenzo GMF improves the response. Tensile strength and modulus are both increased and hardness is reduced. As for Butyl rubber, heat treatment consists of milling, on an open mill, for 20 minutes at between 150° and 155° C. If the work is done in a Banbury mixer the temperature must be kept down to 150° C; if it is allowed to rise, which it can do rapidly, there is danger that the stock will burn.[42]

Modification of the silica-particle surfaces with an organohalosilane, such as cyclopentadienyltrichlorosilane,[46] improves the resilience of Butyl–silica stocks without heat treatment, and with heat treatment tensile strength and modulus are increased without using a promoter. But in neither natural rubber nor SBR does this modification of silica influence the effects of heat treatment.

Organic reinforcing agents

The organic reinforcing agents include materials such as the phenolic, amino and high-styrene resins, cyclised rubber and lignin. Their particles are less rigid and more rubberlike than those of carbon black or the inorganic materials; at processing temperatures two or more particles that come together can merge into a single particle. Such different behaviour helps to provide a different balance of physical properties in the compounded rubber.

Rubber will take much higher loadings of organic than of inorganic materials or of carbon black, and at high-enough loadings the phases are reversed and discrete fragments of the rubber become dispersed in the organic reinforcing material.   However hard the vulcanisate, the uncured stock is usually soft and easily processed.   Tear strength and tensile strength may be nearly as high as in a good black-loaded stock, but abrasion resistance does not reach such levels.   Compounds with the same stiffness and strength as those loaded with black or inorganic fillers have the advantage of being much lighter in weight.

Styrene–butadiene resins with a high styrene component are now widely used in shoe manufacture.   Such rubber-and-resin compounds can be made with the same feel and stress–strain characteristics as leather and with wear resistance better.

Hardenable resins

Hardenable or polycondensation resins, of which there are many varieties, act in many polymers, both as thermosetting or vulcanising plasticisers and as reinforcing agents.   The two most important groups of these are the phenolic and the amino resins.   The phenolic resins are condensation products of phenols and aldehydes.   The amino resins are obtained by condensing urea, thiourea, aniline or melamine with an aldehyde.

In rubber compounding phenolic resins were first used with nitrile rubber, such as Buna-N,[47] with which they are more compatible than with natural rubber or SBR.   They increase tensile strength and hardness, reduce elongation at break and ease processing of the unvulcanised stock.

The fully-condensed phenolic resins cannot be mixed satisfactorily with natural rubber or SBR, but it has been shown [48] that this difficulty can be overcome if the resin is incorporated in the elastomer in an unhardened state at a temperature, between 70° and 90° C, which is too low for the resin to harden quickly if at all, to add hexamethylenetetramine (HMT) if necessary and then to raise the temperature to one at which hardening will proceed, 120°–180°, while continuing working the mixture in the mill or Banbury.   It is necessary to add HMT to provide more formaldehyde when the temperature is raised if novolak resins are used, but not for resol resins.

Emulsions or alkaline solutions of partly-condensed resins can be mixed with latex and the mixture coagulated and dried.   Most of the techniques developed for this give good reinforcement to products prepared directly from latex, but the reinforcement is destroyed if the dried, coagulated mixture is milled.

An exception to this is the method van Alphen [49] developed, in which condensation resins are formed in aqueous acid solution and added to latex (natural or SBR) which has been stabilised against acid by a cationic or non-ionic stabiliser.   The rubber and resin coagulate as soon as the resin is fully condensed. The mixture is leached with ammonia, washed and dried and can then be mixed on a mill with vulcanising and any other compounding ingredients without destroying the reinforcement given by the resin.

Resins can be added to elastomers in proportions up to about equal parts of each. Below about 50 parts by weight of resin to each 100 of elastomer the product is rubberlike, with good tear and tensile strengths; these properties are lower than a black-reinforced compound of the same hardness, but resilience is higher. As loading is increased beyond 50 parts of resin the compound becomes tougher and more leatherlike and at 90–100 parts it resembles a rigid plastic, though it has better impact resistance than many of these. Processing is easy, and conventional rubber equipment can be used with mixtures of up to about equal parts of each; beyond that the compounds are powdery and can sometimes be used as moulding powders.

Mixtures of rubber and resin can be reinforced or filled with carbon black or inorganic materials. If carbon black is added the same levels of abrasion resistance and tear strength cannot be reached as with optimum loadings of black in the rubber alone, but good levels of these properties can be obtained together with higher resilience and easier processing than would be achieved if black alone were used to reinforce the elastomer.

Coloured products with quite good reinforcement can be made, especially if silica, aluminium silicate or calcium silicate is added. Most of the phenolic resins give products tinged with yellow or brown; if this is likely to have an objectionable effect on the desired final colour, as it can if a pastel shade is required, it is best to use a urea–formaldehyde resin which will give a more nearly white base stock.

High-styrene resins

Copolymers of styrene and butadiene containing more than 50% styrene (SBR normally contains about 25%) or polystyrene (100% styrene) can be blended with natural rubber or SBR to give hard, tough, leatherlike stocks with good tear strength and wear resistance for footwear. Products can be made whose properties and appearance resemble leather closely but whose wear resistance is even better; these have successfully competed with leather in the U.S.A. and are likely to do so more than before in the United Kingdom now that high-styrene resins are becoming more available.

Cyclised rubber

Natural rubber can be cyclised to form a resin which behaves in natural rubber very much as high-styrene resins do but with the added advantage that the stocks soften less readily on heating.[50] The cyclised rubber can be prepared from natural latex as a masterbatch with uncyclised rubber;[50, 51] sheet rubber can be cyclised during milling;[51] or solutions of rubber can be heated with suitable catalysts.[52]

Coumarone resins

Coumarone resins added to stocks loaded with fillers such as clay or calcium carbonate will improve tear and tensile strength as well as easing processing.

Lignin

Lignin will reinforce natural rubber or SBR to a moderate extent, but the amount of reinforcement depends very much on the way the rubber and the lignin are brought together.

Lignin, which can be regarded as a kind of natural phenolic resin, is obtained in two forms as a by-product of wood-pulp in paper manufacture;[53] lignin–sulphonic acid from the sulphite process for newsprint and lignin from the alkali process. The second of these is more useful in rubber.

Rubber is not reinforced by lignin if the two are milled together dry.[54] Reinforcement has been obtained by milling rubber with lignin which has been soaked either in water, in a solvent for lignin or in an aqueous alkali,[55, 56] but there seems to be some doubt whether such a method is sufficiently reproducible.

The most satisfactory results have been obtained by co-precipitating the polymer and lignin together from a mixture of latex and an alkaline solution of the lignin. Even then, different methods of precipitation will give different combinations of final properties. Tibenham and Grace [57] used a cold-precipitation method, after which the lignin merely acted as an extender, and a hot-precipitation method which led to a moderate amount of reinforcement.

When reinforcement is obtained from lignin, tear and tensile strengths are below the levels given by MPC or HAF black, though not greatly so, and resilience is much higher; but the vulcanisate is only a little harder than a gum stock. Abrasion resistance is much lower than MPC or HAF will give.

Because lignin is a kind of phenolic resin it will respond to hot milling with HMT.[48] If the masterbatch of natural rubber and lignin is mixed with HMT and milled for 20 minutes at $150°-155°$ C the vulcanisate is harder and has resilience as high as a gum stock.[57]

Combinations of carbon black and lignin coprecipitated with the rubber [54, 57] give higher tear strength and abrasion resistance than lignin alone, though abrasion resistance is still appreciably lower than without the lignin, but resilience is higher than for a black stock of the same hardness.

Graft polymers

Graft polymers can be prepared by polymerising a monomer in the presence of another polymer, either in the form of latex or during cold mastication. The cold-mastication technique has not yet progressed beyond the laboratory stage. The latex method has already been developed further than this, and methyl methacrylate or styrene can be grafted in quantity on to natural rubber.[58, 59, 60, 61]

A natural-rubber graft containing 23% methyl methacrylate (Heveaplus MG23) will, when vulcanised, give stock harder than an HAF-black tread stock, with similar tensile strength, but higher resilience and elongation at break. Tear strength is good at room temperature but falls off as the temperature is raised because the grafted constituent softens. Flex-cracking resistance and crack-growth resistance are both exceptionally good. The unvulcanised graft stock is much softer than a tread stock and much less likely to scorch.

A graft containing 50% methyl methacrylate (Heveaplus MG50) can be used as a reinforcing resin. When diluted with ungrafted natural rubber the properties of the mixture are similar to those of an undiluted grafted rubber which has an equivalent proportion of methyl methacrylate. The undiluted 50% graft gives rigid shock-proof vulcanisates with hardness 95° B.S. or more.

Natural rubber grafted with styrene at equal parts of rubber and styrene (Heveaplus SG50) has properties similar to the corresponding methacrylate graft (MG50), but with lower proportions of styrene is softer, and less well reinforced, and has poorer cracking properties than the equivalent methyl methacrylate graft.

REFERENCES

1. Wiegand, W. B. (1920) *Canad. Chem. J.*, **4**, 160.
2. Wiegand, W. B. (1920) *India Rubb. J.*, **60**, 379, 423, 453.
3. Shepard, N. A., Street, J. N. and Park, C. R. (1937) *Chemistry and Technology of Rubber*, ed. Davis C. C. and Blake J. T. (New York: Reinhold Publishing Corporation), 392.
4. Mullins, L. (1950) *J. phys. Chem.*, **54**, 239; (1950) *Rubb. Chem. Technol.*, **23**, 733.
5. Smith, W. R. (1949) *Encyclopedia of Chemical Technology*, **3**, 34 (New York: Interscience Encyclopedia Inc.).
6. Parkinson, D. (1951) *British J. app. Phys.*, **2**, 273.
7. Parkinson, D. (1957) *Reinforcement of Rubber* (London: Institution of the Rubber Industry).
8. Parkinson, D. (1949) *I.R.I. Trans.*, **24**, 267.

9. Powell, E. F. and Gough, S. W. (1954) *Proc. Third Rubb. Technol. Conf.* (Cambridge: W. Heffer, 1955), 460; (1955) *Rubb. World*, **132**, 201.
10. Watson, J. W. (1956) *I.R.I. Trans.*, **32**, 204.
11. Stokes, C. A. and Dannenberg, E. M. (1949) *Ind. Eng. Chem.*, **41**, 381.
12. Dannenberg, E. M. and Stokes, C. A. (1949) *Ind. Eng. Chem.*, **41**, 812.
13. Neal, A. M. and Mayo, L. R. (1954) *Synthetic Rubber*, ed. Whitby, G. S. (New York: John Wiley and Sons, Inc.; London: Chapman and Hall, Ltd.), 767.
14. Buist, J. M. and Mottram, S. (1946) *I.R.I. Trans.*, **22**, 82.
15. Lanning, H. J. (1950) *I.R.I. Trans.*, **26**, 151.
16. Thomas, R. M. and Sparks, W. J. (1954) *Synthetic Rubber*, ed. Whitby, G. S. (New York: John Wiley and Sons, Inc.; London: Chapman and Hall, Ltd.), 838.
17. Semon, W. L. (1954) *Synthetic Rubber*, ed. Whitby, G. S. (New York: John Wiley and Sons, Inc.; London: Chapman and Hall, Ltd.), 794.
18. Boonstra, B. B. (1956) *Rubb. Age, N.Y.*, **80**, 284.
19. Fisher, C. H., Whitby, G. S. and Beavers, E. M. (1954) *Synthetic Rubber*, ed. Whitby, G. S. (New York: John Wiley and Sons, Inc.; London: Chapman and Hall), 892.
20. Laurence, A. E. and Perrine, V. H. (1943) *Rubb. Age, N.Y.*, **54**, 139.
21. Ford, F. P. and Mottlau, A. Y. (1952) *Rubb. Age, N.Y.*, **70**, 457.
22. Dannenberg, E. M. (1952) *Ind. Eng. Chem.*, **44**, 813.
23. Leigh-Dugmore, C. H. (1956) *Rubb. Chem. Technol.*, **29**, 1303.
24. Allen, R. P. (1930) *Ind. Eng. Chem., Anal. Ed.*, **2**, 311.
25. Adams, J. W., Messer, W. E. and Howland, L. H. (1951) *Ind. Eng. Chem.*, **43**, 754.
26. Tidmus, J. S. and Parkinson, D. (1937) *I.R.I. Trans.*, **13**, 52.
27. Chappuis, M. M., Polley, M. H. and Schulz, R. A. (1954) *Rubb. World*, **130**, 507.
28. Dannenberg, E. M. and Collyer, H. J. (1949) *Ind. Eng. Chem.*, **41**, 1607.
29. Dannenberg, E. M., Jordon, M. E. and Stokes, C. A. (1950) *India Rubb. World*, **122**, 663.
30. Martin, B. J. A. and Parkinson, D. (1955) *Rubb. Chem. and Technol.*, **28**, 261.
31. Braendle, H. A., Estelow, R. K. and Wiegand, W. B. (1950) *Rubb. Age, N.Y.*, **67**, 64.
32. Parkinson, D. (1940) *I.R.I. Trans.*, **16**, 87.
33. Wiegand, W. B. and Braendle, H. A. (1944) *Ind. Eng. Chem.*, **36**, 699.
34. Gerke, R. H., Ganzhorn, G. H., Howland, L. H. and Smallwood, H. M. U.S.P. 2,118,601.
35. Parkinson, D. (1946) *Advances in Colloid Science*, **2**, 411 (New York: Interscience Publishers Inc.).
36. Parkinson, D. and Blanchard, A. F. (1948) *I.R.I. Trans.*, **23**, 259.
37. Gessler, A. M. (1953) *Rubb. Age, N.Y.*, **74**, 59.
38. Zapp, R. L. and Gessler, A. M. (1953) *Rubb. Age, N.Y.*, **74**, 243.
39. Gessler, A. M. and Ford, F. P. (1953) *Rubb. Age, N.Y.*, **74**, 397.
40. Rehner, John, Jr. and Gessler, A. M. (1954) *Rubb. Age, N.Y.*, **74**, 561.
41. Shuart, S. R. and Gessler, A. M., Paper presented at the 69th meeting, Division of Rubber Chemistry, American Chemical Society, Cleveland, Ohio, May, 1956; Abstract (1956) *Rubb. Age, N.Y.*, **79**, 101).
42. Gessler, A. M. and Rehner, J., Jr. (1955) *Rubb. Age, N.Y.*, **77**, 875.
43. Harris, J. D. (1956) *Rubb. J.*, **130**, 101.
44. Harris, J. D. (1956) *Proc. Inst. Rubb. Ind.*, **3**, 145.
45. Wolf, R. F. (1955) *Rubb. World*, **132**, 64.
46. Gessler, A. M., Wiese, H. K. and Rehner, J., Jr. (1955) *Rubb. Age, N.Y.*, **78**, 73.
47. Searer, J. C. (1947) *Rubb. Age, N.Y.*, **62**, 191.

48. Simmons, D. N., B.P. 686,757, and Naunton, W. J. S. and Siddle, F. J. (1931) *Ind. Rubb. J.*, **82,** 535, 561.
49. van Alphen, J. (1954) *Proc. Third Rubb. Technol. Conf.* (Cambridge: W. Heffer) (1955), 670.
50. Bloomfield, G. F. and Stokes, S. C. (1956) *I.R.I. Trans.*, **32**, 172.
51. Davies, B. L. and Glazer, J. (1955) *Plastics Derived from Natural Rubber*, Plastics Monograph No. C8, The Plastics Institute, London, 61.
52. Janssen, H. J. J. (1956) *Rubb. Age, N.Y.*, **78**, 718; (1956) *Rubb. Chem. Technol.*, **29**, 1034.
53. Nicholls, R. V. V. (1944) *Canad. Chem. and Process Ind.*, **28**, 163.
54. Sagajllo, I. (1954) *Proc. Third Rubb. Technol. Conf.* (Cambridge: W. Heffer), (1955), 610.
55. Keiler, J. J. and Pollak, A. (1947) *Ind. Eng. Chem.*, **39**, 480.
56. West Virginia Pulp and Paper Co., B.P. 633,725.
57. Tibenham, F. J. and Grace, N. S. (1954) *Ind. Eng. Chem.*, **46**, 824.
58. B.R.P.R.A. Technical Bulletin No. 1, *Heveaplus M.* (London: British Rubber Development Board).
59. Bloomfield, G. F., Merrett, F. M., Popham, F. J. and Swift, P. McL. (1954) *Proc. Third Rubb. Technol. Conf.* (Cambridge: W. Heffer), (1955), 185.
60. Merrett, F. M. and Wood, R. I. (1956) *Proc. Instn. Rubb. Ind.*, **3**, 27.
61. British Rubber Producers' Research Association (1956) *Rubber Developments*, **9**, 2.
62. Monsanto Chemical Company (1956) Development Bulletin ODB–56–29, Nitro, West Virginia.

CHAPTER VIII

PART ONE

ELASTICITY AND DYNAMIC PROPERTIES OF RUBBER

by

A. C. EDWARDS and G. N. S. FARRAND

RUBBER differs from other materials in its capacity to undergo large deformations without rupture and its apparent ability to return to its original form. This latter property is generally referred to as elasticity. A more critical examination, however, of the properties of rubber-like materials reveals that only a negligible proportion of the deformation is recovered instantaneously and that the time factor is an important consideration. The response of rubber-like materials to time variable, or dynamic, forces has both theoretical and technical interest. Theoretically dynamic studies are of importance as a basis for the formulation of a consistent theory of the mechanism of the rubber-like state, while practically they are essential to enable some prediction to be made of the behaviour of rubber engineering components that experience cyclic deformation. The practical applications resulting from dynamic studies will be dealt with in Part Two of this chapter.

Gough in 1805 first noticed that rubber generates heat on fast stretching and that rubber extended by constant load contracts on heating. Lord Kelvin pointed out in 1855 that Gough's second observation follows thermodynamically from his first observation. As a result of Kelvin's theoretical conclusions, Joule in 1859 set out to repeat Gough's work more quantitatively and found that at low elongations most of the work applied in stretching rubber is transformed into heat, and therefore concluded that the " elastic force " of rubber is due to the motion of its constituent particles. Katz's discovery in 1925 of the crystallisation of rubber at high elongations offered a two-phase explanation of the heat developed during stretching. Between 1927 and 1933 a number of authors produced qualitative evidence for Joule's ideas and, as by this time much more was known about the structure of high-polymer molecules, were able to suggest the nature of the motion given in general terms by Joule. Haller called attention to the possibility of the coiling up of long-chain molecules by rotation about single bonds, and Karrer and Meyer applied Haller's suggestion to solid rubber. In 1934 Guth and Mark worked out a general quantitative theory of rubber elasticity. Since 1939 James and Guth have developed a comprehensive theory of rubber elasticity.

Characteristics of the rubber-like state

Normal engineering materials, other than rubber, are usually used so that the " limit of proportionality " is not passed. Up to this point the strain is proportional to the applied stress, or in other words Hooke's Law is, for practical purposes, obeyed over the whole working range of the material. Although in a typical material, e.g. steel, there is a difference between " limit of proportionality " and " elastic limit " (i.e. the stress above which the strain is not fully recoverable), the difference is small and can be neglected in favour of the more easily determined " limit of proportionality ". The normal elasticity exhibited by materials such as steel is defined as " true elasticity ", to distinguish it from the other forms to be discussed later.

Rubber-like materials are distinguished by a different form of elasticity known as " high elasticity ". These materials undergo much larger deformation without rupture, and the stress required to produce the deformation is of a much lower order. Unlike the " true elastic " materials, the stress–strain relationship is linear for only a small portion of the characteristic. The initial modulus of elasticity is of the order of 10 kg./cm.^{2}, but increase rapidly at large extensions to the order of 10^4 kg./cm.^{2} compared with a value for steel of the order of 10^6 kg./cm.^{2}. A further important distinction between true and high elasticity is the variation of high elastic deformation with time. Although the rubber-like property is normally confined to long-chain polymeric compounds, not all such compounds show any rubber-like properties at normal temperatures. An examination, however, of the elastic properties of a typical range of high polymers, over a wide range of temperature, in conjunction with some fundamental thermodynamic property, such as thermal expansion or specific heat, shows that the materials exhibit the rubber-like state in the temperature range above the apparent second-order transition in basic properties (i.e. a discontinuity in the first derivative of the property with respect to temperature). Thus it can be seen that polymeric materials which are glass-like at room temperature will pass through a second-order transition at some higher temperature, and over a range of somewhat higher temperatures exhibit rubber-like properties. The description of the material as a " rubber " or as a " plastic " depends only on whether its transition occurs below or above normal temperatures. A second-order phase transition is not so definite and characteristic as a first-order change, such as a melting point. Indeed, the observed temperature is modified by the experimental conditions, such as rate of heating, used by different observers. Boyer and Spencer [1] found that the apparent second-order transition temperature observed on polystyrene at about 80° C was entirely due to a rate effect. They gave volume–temperature relationships measured under equilibrium conditions which were linear from 20° to 140° C. In addition to the normal almost instantaneous expansion when the temperature was increased, they observed an additional slow increase in volume. Round about room temperature this latter process had a " half-time " of more than 10 hours, but the rate of attaining equilibrium increased rapidly with increasing temperature. Thus in the conventional experiment, with a fairly rapid heating rate, the second process would not make a measurable contribution to the observed expansion at low temperatures, but would add to the expansion measured at high temperatures. From the rates measured at different temperatures Boyer and Spencer deduced an activation energy of 12 kcal. for the retarded thermal expansion process, which corresponds with the value for the viscous flow of solid polystyrene extrapolated from the viscosities of solutions in xylene.[2] On this basis the apparent second-order transition point is simply the lowest temperature at which an observable viscous flow occurs, under the conditions used in a particular experiment. A value of 10^{12}–10^{13} poise has been quoted for the viscosity at which this limit is reached.[3]

This hypothesis has been strongly criticised by Buchdahl and Nielsen [4] and by Fox and Flory,[5] who both claimed that the previous work was not sufficiently precise to establish the absence of a discontinuity at the apparent second-order transition point. Fox and Flory presented detailed experimental evidence for the existence of the discontinuity, but on the other hand, Millane and McLaren [6] determined equilibrium volume–temperature relationships for commercial polystyrene, which showed a maximum deviation from linearity of 0·001 c.c./g. in the specific volume over a temperature range of 20–120° C.

It is generally agreed, however, that the temperature and degree of the discontinuity appear to change as the time scale of the experiment is changed. Polystyrene was taken as an example because it is a simple amorphous polymer that has been very widely studied, but the transition temperature is of general significance. In relation to polymers which are used for their rubber-like properties the transition temperature, which may be described as the "glass" temperature (T_g), is an indication of the low-temperature limit of the rubber-like range. For technical purposes many mechanical tests are in use which establish an arbitrary measure of the stiffening of the material with decreasing temperature. The temperature determined is sometimes called the " brittle " temperature (T_b).[7] The test usually involves the deformation of a specimen by a standard amount in a specified time. The limit is specified as the temperature for fracture (or in some cases for an increase in stiffness by a certain ratio). T_b is much more affected by the conditions of the experiment than is T_g. With a slow deformation T_b may be within a few degrees of T_g, but with rapid deformation T_b will be at a higher temperature. It is clear that when the transition point is obtained from volume or heat-capacity changes the force on the sample will be very small, whereas in the brittle-point type of test the force involved will be large and will vary with the amount and rate of deformation to be imposed. It will be seen later than many of the " dynamic " methods of measuring mechanical properties can be used to investigate the change in properties with temperature, and this is a much more reproducible way of characterising the transition region between rubber-like and glass-like behaviour. The apparent transition temperature is still affected by a change in the time scale, that is the frequency, of the dynamic measurement, but it can be deduced theoretically that there should be a definite connection between the effect of change in frequency and a change in temperature, such that an increase in the frequency is equivalent to a decrease in the temperature. In general, for any given frequency the transition temperature is that temperature at which the log modulus changes most rapidly with temperature, and this is coincident with the temperature of maximum damping, see Payne and Scott.[119]

We have already referred, in the introduction, to Joule's deduction that the elastic restoring force in an extended rubber-like material arises from the " motion of its constituent particles ". Little attention was paid to this early work until Meyer, von Susich and Valko [8] put forward a kinetic theory of rubber elasticity in 1932. Before considering the kinetic theory we will briefly examine the thermodynamic aspects. Since the ordinary laws of thermodynamics apply only to reversible phenomena, it is necessary when investigating their application to rubber to eliminate as far as practicable the irreversible changes occurring in an extended rubber specimen. Meyer and Ferri [9] did this by carrying out an initial relaxation of the specimen at the highest temperature and extension to be used in the experiment. More recently Gee [10] ensured complete attainment of equilibrium by swelling the specimen with solvent.

The relationship derived from the first and second laws of thermodynamics, which is usually applied to gases, is modified as follows. As a first approximation the volume change on extension is assumed to be zero, so that work done is $F \cdot dl$ (where F = tension force and l = length) and $-PdV$ vanishes. In this way the following two relations can be obtained, a detailed treatment is given by Treloar:[11]

$$F = \left(\frac{\partial U}{\partial l}\right)_T - T\left(\frac{\partial S}{\partial l}\right)_T$$

and

$$\left(\frac{\partial S}{\partial l}\right)_T = -\left(\frac{\partial F}{\partial T}\right)_l$$

Where U = internal energy; T = absolute temperature; S = entropy.

The second equation means that the entropy change per unit extension can be obtained as the temperature coefficient of tension at constant length. The latter is a much easier quantity to determine. Substituting in the equation for F, we have

$$F = \left(\frac{\partial U}{\partial l}\right)_T + T\left(\frac{\partial F}{\partial T}\right)_l$$

Thus we can by observing equilibrium tension at various temperatures obtain both the entropy change and internal energy change associated with a deformation. Meyer and Ferri [9] found that the tension–temperature relation was linear over a wide range of temperature, and this confirmed that the tension in extended rubber was almost entirely due to the entropy term as predicted by the kinetic theory of elasticity. In a material showing " true elasticity ", such as steel, the opposite is the case, almost the whole of the work of extension goes to increase the internal energy by distorting the atomic arrangement away from its normal configuration. The much higher tension developed is the result of the strong tendency of the bonds to return to their normal length and valency angles. As will be seen below, the restoring tendency postulated by the kinetic theory is of a much weaker nature, and this provides an explanation for the low modulus of rubber-like materials.

The theory and experimental technique of the temperature coefficient of equilibrium tension method have been further developed by later workers. The volume change due to thermal expansion, which was neglected above, counterbalances the increase in tension with temperature when extensions less than about 7% are used. This thermo-elastic inversion was observed by Meyer and Ferri and confirmed by later workers. The more complete theoretical treatment also indicates that the tension–temperature characteristic will not be exactly linear. Baldwin, Ivory and Anthony [12] have shown fairly close agreement between theory and experiment, both in respect of this non-linearity and the thermoelastic inversion, an example of their experimental results is shown in Fig. 8.1.

Since it was first advocated by Meyer et al.,[8] the kinetic theory has developed through numerous stages and been approached from different view-points by various workers. It is now generally agreed that rubber-like properties are an indication of long-chain flexible molecules in a random arrangement. The chemical constitution of the chain is only significant in so far as it affects crystallisation and provides reactive points for the formation of inter-chain cross-links (vulcanisation). Although a few effective cross-links exist in the unvulcanised material due to physical entanglements, further cross-linking by chemical means is necessary to reduce flow effects to a minimum and enable the rubber-like properties to be utilised. Since the modulus increases with degree of cross-linking, this process must be limited if a compliant material is to be obtained, one cross-link for every thousand or more atoms in the chain is sufficient. Although the vulcanisation produces a random three-dimensional network throughout the material, the chains are still in continual thermal agitation and are able to assume a great many configurations all having about the same energy. In general, the ends of the chain will be considerably closer together than the length of the chain extended to its maximum. It has been shown statistically [13, 14] that, with a large number of links, the most

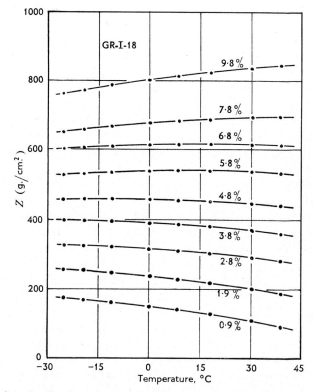

Fig. 8.1. Family of stress–temperature curves for GR-I-18 (Butyl Rubber).

probable end-to-end length is proportional to the square root of the number of links. This provides an explanation of one of the points that previously always presented difficulty, the enormous extension possible in a soft rubber without rupture, since a chain of 10,000 links can elongate 10,000/100 times in going from its probable to its maximum theoretical length.

The most detailed theoretical treatment, and the one more nearly representing the actual physical structure of rubber, has been the work of James and Guth.[15] They relate the elastic force to the change of entropy produced when the chain is extended from its more probable kinked state to a less probable extended state. Their model describes a complete molecular network extending throughout the material. James and Guth [16] have discussed the approach used by other workers and criticised the assumption often made that the junction points of the network are fixed in relation to the surface of the material. They show, however, that the stress–strain relationship derived is not upset by this assumption. The equation obtained is of the following form, after simplification from the generalised strain case to that for a simple extension or compression,

$$\sigma = G(\lambda - \lambda^{-2})$$

where σ = tension or compressive stress; G = shear modulus; λ = ratio deformed length (or height) to initial length (or height).

It will be seen from this that the conventional conception of a Young's modulus E = stress/strain is no longer applicable for a finite strain. If it is preferred, however, the shear modulus G may be replaced in the equation by $(E_0/3)$, where E_0 is the Young's modulus determined at infinitesimally small extension or compression, since it can be shown that in the limit $(\lambda \longrightarrow 1)$ $E_0 = 3G$.

The equation can be confirmed by practical experiment for extensions and compressions up to about 20–30% and holds with less precision for greater deformations. In the case of compression it is necessary to deform the rubber between well lubricated plates in order to eliminate friction. If this is done the deformation conforms to the requirements for a simple compression and the relationship is obeyed. In the majority of cases where practical rubber components in engineering applications are concerned the deformation is not simple. The rubber is either bonded to metal end-pieces or, if not bonded, restrained by friction from freely slipping over the metal. These cases can be covered by introducing another factor into the equation. Since this factor depends solely on the geometrical proportions of the rubber item, and not on the fundamental modulus, it is described as a " Shape Factor ". For cylinders it is $(1 + 0.413\delta^2)$ where δ = ratio (radius/height). Payne [17,18] of RABRM has published details of shape factor formulae for this and numerous other cases and also shown [17,19] how to apply the relationship to the calculation of modulus under dynamic conditions. Gent [20] of BRPRA has also published work on the load–deflection relations for various shaped rubber pads, using a rather different approach. For full details on this subject see Payne and Scott.[120]

As mentioned above, the simple one-constant formula given by the statistical theory of rubber elasticity is only a first approximation to the actual stress–strain relationship for rubber undergoing large deformations. The generalised stored-energy function derived by Mooney,[21] being a two-constant relation, does provide a better fit to the experimental data, but it does not offer any physical basis for the deviation from the statistical theory. Treloar [22] discusses the various theories covering large deformations.

Previous sections have attempted to set out the elastic behaviour of rubber-like materials and describe the theoretical relationships which have been put forward and which in some measure correspond with observed elastic properties. This treatment took no account of non-reversible deformation and flow, which is always exhibited to a greater or lesser extent by rubber-like materials.

An empirical relationship of the form

$$\tau = c - a \log t$$

where τ = tension; t = time; c and a are constants, was given many years ago for the force required to maintain a constant deformation in a rubber specimen. If the force is maintained constant the deformation will similarly increase with time

$$\alpha = d + b \log t$$

where α = extension ratio, t = time, d and b are constants. The process which occurs at constant deformation is usually described as " stress relaxation " while the change of deformation under constant force is referred to as " creep " or " flow ". The latter description should not be taken to indicate viscous flow. True viscous flow occurs in rubber only in the unvulcanised state. In vulcanised rubber it would appear that a continuous creep process must involve the rupture of primary chemical bonds. Tobolsky et al.[23] investigated the mechanism of the process by measuring the relaxation rate of natural rubber in an oxygen-free atmosphere and found a considerable reduction in relaxation rate. These experiments were carried out at elevated temperature (130° C) and indicated that both breaking and formation of chemical bonds takes place in the presence of oxygen. At lower temperatures rupture of secondary bonds may be of more importance. Mooney and others base a theory of the creep process on progressive longitudinal slippage of molecules by the breaking up of crystallites or other secondary bonds.

It has been observed that creep at ordinary temperatures is considerably increased by mechanical vibration of the specimen, but no systematic study of this effect appears to have been published. The subject, however, is of considerable practical importance in view of the increasing use of flexible mountings for prime movers of the internal-combustion type and the present limitations of flexible-shaft couplings which necessitate the maintenance of close alignment of the shafts.

Turning to practical consideration of the determination of the stress-strain characteristics of rubber compounds, there are various basic types of

S

loading cycle that can be applied. Because the non-reversible creep phenomenon is superimposed on the elastic behaviour, the type of loading cycle used in the measurements is of particular importance.

The conventional types of physical test apparatus can be utilised to make stress–strain measurements on rubber specimens, but they are quite severely limited in respect of the rate of loading. The condition commonly laid down for standardised measurements on rubber compounds is a rate of increase of strain of 20 in./min. While it would be a simple matter to modify the conventional equipment to give very much lower rates of loading if required, the achievement of any considerable increase in rate of loading on a conventional stress–strain apparatus will obviously be precluded by the limitations of the mechanical strength and inertia of the moving parts.

Attempts have been made to overcome this limitation, and Villars [24] has developed a very high rate of loading equipment.

In addition to the modulus, the stress–strain data for slow rates of loading and unloading provide a mechanical hysteresis curve for the material, showing ratio of energy returned to energy applied. For higher rates of loading it is more practicable to observe this directly by applying a known energy to the specimen in kinetic form, i.e. by impact of a free-falling weight or of a pendulum. Apparatus of this type is well known [25] and gives a measure of resilience, defined as the ratio energy returned/energy supplied, for certain rates of loading.

The impact types of resiliometer have times of loading ranging from about 10^{-3} to 10^{-1} second, i.e. of a much lower order than can be obtained with conventional stress–strain apparatus. Although this means that tests simulating service conditions in respect of loading time can be carried out, conditions cannot be made truly representative because it is not possible to adjust deformation independently of loading time. Furthermore, any one type of apparatus will provide only a very limited range of loading time. Because of these disadvantages, the use of resiliometers is mainly confined to quality control rather than fundamental measurements.

A type of method which gives some indication of energy dissipation in the material and does allow the amplitude of deformation to be adjusted over a range, independently of the time of loading, is represented by the so-called Flexometers (Goodrich, Firestone and St. Joe Flexometers). Although conceived as fatigue testing machines, a measure of energy dissipation in a sample under repeated deformation is given by the temperature rise in the sample. It is, of course, necessary to reduce loss of heat from the sample to a minimum if quantitative results are to be obtained. By incorporating a force-measuring transducer in one platen of a flexometer measurements of modulus as well as of damping have been made [26] on this

type of apparatus, but generally speaking, the flexometer, like the resiliometer, has been mainly applied to comparative evaluation of materials
under conditions simulating particular service applications. If we consider the requirements of a laboratory method designed primarily for the
measurement of fundamental properties under a wide range of loading
time and amplitude of deformation without attempting to reproduce the
conditions in service, the following general points can be set down:

(a) A method using repeated deformation does make for ease of
measurement, provided that the range of deformation for any particular
rate of loading does not extend to the point where a significant breakdown of the sample, or temperature build-up, occurs during the time
required to make the measurement.

(b) The rate of loading and amplitude of deformation should be
capable of being maintained constant at any required values within the
range of the apparatus.

Having adopted a system involving repeated loading and unloading of
the specimen, we must decide upon the form of the amplitude–time
function. Cycles of loading and unloading carried out on a conventional
stress–strain apparatus would give functions approximating either to (a)
or (b) of Fig. 8.2. Case (a) being obtained when the period for which the

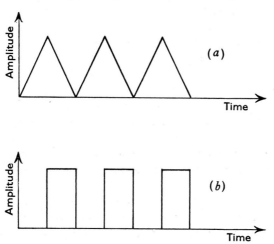

Fig. 8.2. Idealised loading/unloading cycles.

maximum amplitude and minimum amplitude are maintained is negligible
compared to the time required to build up the deformation, while (b)
represents the opposite case of negligible time of application or removal of
deformation. Both practical and theoretical considerations suggest that
neither of these forms is desirable. The square-wave motion would be

very difficult to generate at high rates of loading, and similarly accurate generation of the triangular form involves an instantaneous reversal of motion at the peaks. Theoretical analysis, using Fourier's method, shows that any repeating function, whether of the arbitrary forms quoted or any other, is a summation of a series of simple harmonic forms. The lowest-frequency component or fundamental is the main term, and it has the same frequency as the original function. The other components are harmonics (i.e. multiples) of the fundamental. In determining the characteristic properties of materials it is desirable to make each measurement at one single rate of loading, because of the possibility that the values of the various parameters will show a dispersion with frequency. This indicates the desirability of using a pure sinusoidal wave form without harmonics. Later, when the individual methods of dynamic measurement are studied, it will be found that the satisfaction of this requirement often presents practical difficulties.

The arguments in favour of a sinusoidal wave form are strongest where it is required to determine basic physical properties. In other cases where it is desired to simulate the loading experienced by a component in service, particularly if conditions are sufficiently severe to make fracture of the unit possible, it is necessary to apply impulsive loading. The response of a material to this type of loading is much more difficult to analyse. Methods using impulsive loading will be briefly touched on in a later section.

In preceding sections reference has been made, first, to the so-called " high elasticity " of rubbery materials, including variation in high elastic deformation with time, and second, to plastic flow phenomena, stress relaxation and creep, as if these effects were separate properties. In fact, these phenomena are exhibited at the same time in one material, and furthermore, the relative importance of elastic and plastic properties in any given material is profoundly affected by the temperature and time scale of the experiment.

Numerous attempts have been made to rationalise the diverse experimental findings on the properties of rubbery materials by describing the results in terms of mechanical analogues. The object of this method is to postulate a mechanical model, made up of a number of simple elements with stipulated parameters, whose behaviour over the whole range of dynamic conditions used will correspond with the experimental findings.

The simplest model is the " Maxwell body ", formed of a spring and dashpot in series, as shown in Fig. 8.3a. This model predicts a simple experimental law for stress decay at constant strain, while the " Kelvin body ", consisting of the same elements in parallel as in Fig. 8.3b, gives a simple experimental law at constant stress. A complex combination of these two forms has resulted in a number of models being formulated to explain the behaviour of various elastic polymers. Roscoe [27] has, how-

ever, recently pointed out that these complex models can all be represented in one of two canonic forms which are given in Fig. 8.4*a* and 8.4*b*.
Practical rubber compounds, particularly those containing appreciable

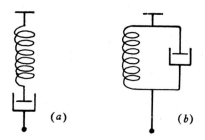

Fig. 8.3. (*a*) Maxwell; (*b*) Kelvin model.

quantities of reinforcing filler, show non-linear dynamic properties which
cannot be represented by simple models. An empirical relationship has
been given by Bulgin and Hubbard [122] which describes this effect but it

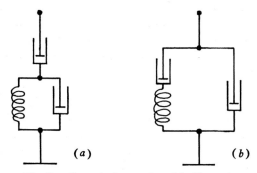

Fig. 8.4. Canonic forms of models (Roscoe).

will still be essential to make measurements at various amplitudes, covering
the whole range of conditions to be expected in service, when new types
of compound are investigated. Further details are given by Payne and
Scott.[121]

METHODS OF MEASUREMENT OF DYNAMIC CONSTANTS

The main purpose of Part One of this chapter is to describe the different
methods of measurement of dynamic constants, and the following sections
survey each of the main fundamental lines of approach, giving examples of
practical methods with the various limitations associated with the particular
method or apparatus.

1. Free vibration methods

Derivation of dynamic properties from observation of damped free vibrations

It would appear that one of the easiest methods of determining the dynamic properties of a rubber-like material is to set up a vibrating system in which a mass is supported by a test piece of the material under examination. The test piece may be deformed in extension, compression, simple shear or torsion. When we come to examine some actual examples of this type of method it will be found that there are many practical obstacles to the precise determination of properties in this way, but for the moment we will consider a simplified system as follows.

It is assumed that the elastic deformation is small and that Hooke's law is obeyed. Then if S is the stiffness (or spring constant) of the specimen and x is the deformation the elastic restoring force is $-Sx$. Secondly, it is assumed that the internal damping of the specimen produces a force which is directly proportional to the rate of deformation (this is called " viscous " damping by analogy with the Newtonian viscosity law that shear stress is directly proportional to rate of deformation).

This assumption is followed in the theoretical treatment throughout Part One of this chapter. In Part Two a form of damping more closely representative of actual rubber-like materials is described under the name of " rubber damping ", see page 588. The necessity for making an assumption as to the damping mechanism can be avoided when it is possible to define the damping in terms of energy loss per cycle. The relationships between the different methods of expressing damping are given by Payne and Scott.[118]

The constant of proportionality for the force due to internal damping is called R, the " Mechanical Resistance ", and the viscous damping force is therefore $-R(dx/dt)$. By Newton's second law of motion the total force acting on the mass m at any time is given by $F = m(d^2x/dt^2)$. We may now equate all the forces in the system as follows (using $\dot{x}$ and $\ddot{x}$ for the first and second derivatives of x with respect to time).

$$m\ddot{x} = -Sx - R\dot{x} \qquad . \quad . \quad . \quad . \quad (8.1)$$

Rearranging and dividing by m we have

$$\ddot{x} + \frac{R\dot{x}}{m} + \frac{Sx}{m} = 0 \qquad . \quad . \quad . \quad . \quad (8.2)$$

which is the standard form of differential equation for a damped free vibration, and is a linear differential equation of the second order with constant coefficients. A derivation of the general solution of equations of this type will be found in various standard works (for example, Lamb).[28]

Instead of attempting a comprehensive treatment, we will examine the solution for the range of conditions of practical interest and endeavour to show the physical significance of the different terms.

In practical vibration experiments the mechanical damping is never zero, but it is usually small compared with the degree of damping that is just sufficient to prevent oscillation. (This is later defined as " critical damping ".) First, then, consider the equation of motion (8.2) with zero damping, it then becomes

$$\ddot{x} = -\omega^2 x \qquad . \quad . \quad . \quad . \quad . \quad (8.3)$$

for convenience the ratio S/m has been replaced by ω^2. The physical significance of ω will be examined later.

To put eqn. 8.3 into a form suitable for integration use $v(dv/dx)$ in place of $\ddot{x}$ where $v = $ velocity.

If $\qquad \dfrac{dx}{dt} = v, \quad$ then $\quad \dfrac{d^2x}{dt^2} = \dfrac{dv}{dt} = \dfrac{dv}{dx}\cdot\dfrac{dx}{dt} = v\cdot\dfrac{dv}{dx}$

Hence eqn. 8.3 may be written $\quad v\cdot(dv/dx) = -\omega^2 x$

Integration then gives $v^2 = C - \omega^2 x^2$. Since C is arbitrary, we may let $x = a$ when $v = 0$, which makes $C = \omega^2 a^2$. Hence

$$v = \omega\sqrt{(a^2 - x^2)} \qquad . \quad . \quad . \quad . \quad . \quad (8.4)$$

Putting back (dx/dt) instead of v and collecting all terms in x on one side,

$$\frac{dx}{\sqrt{(a^2 - x^2)}} = \omega\,.\,dt$$

which is a standard form that gives the following on integration

$$x = a\sin(\omega t + B) \qquad . \quad . \quad . \quad . \quad (8.5)$$

This is the general solution of the equation of undamped free vibration. The maximum value of the displacement x for any time t is equal to a which is called the *amplitude*.

In the normal free-vibration experiment the system is held at the maximum deflection and then released. In this case at $t = 0$, $x = a$. Hence $\sin B = 1$ and $B = \pi/2$. Therefore

$$x = a\sin(\omega t + \pi/2) = a\cos\omega t \qquad . \quad . \quad (8.6)$$

The constant ω was introduced above in the place of $(S/m)^{\frac{1}{2}}$. In eqn. 8.6 ωt is an angle (measured in radians) and t is time (in seconds) so that the dimensions of ω are radians per second, and it is described as *angular frequency*.

Since $\cos(\omega t + 2\pi) = \cos \omega t$, it will be seen from eqn. 8.6 that the values of x will repeat periodically for each increase in ωt of 2π radians. Hence the *period* of a complete oscillation is given by

$$T = 2\pi/\omega \qquad . \quad . \quad . \quad . \quad . \quad . \quad (8.7)$$

while the frequency $\qquad f = 1/T = \omega/2\pi$

Since $\omega^2 = S/m$, the frequency of an undamped free vibration is therefore

$$f = \frac{\omega}{2\pi} = \frac{1}{2\pi}\sqrt{\frac{S}{m}} \qquad . \quad . \quad . \quad . \quad . \quad (8.8)$$

It will be seen later that the introduction of damping will modify this frequency, but in the majority of practical cases the effect may be neglected, and eqn. 8.8 used to give a close approximation to the natural frequency of the system. To obtain the frequency in cycles per second it is essential that stiffness (S) and mass (m) are given in one consistent set of absolute units. In the c.g.s. system the units will be the dyne/centimetre and gramme respectively. In the m.k.s. system the newton/metre and kilogramme, and in the f.p.s. system the poundal/foot and pound (mass). Since the rubber technologist or engineer will probably prefer kg./cm. and kg. or lb./in. and lb. as practical units, the following form of eqn. 8.8 is given

$$f = \frac{1}{2\pi}\sqrt{\frac{Sg}{m}} \qquad . \quad . \quad . \quad . \quad . \quad . \quad (8.9)$$

	International units	British units
S = stiffness	kg./cm.	lb./in.
m = mass	kg.	lb.
g = (gravitational constant)	981 (cm./sec.²)	386 (in./sec.²)
f = frequency, cycles/sec	$f = 4\cdot98\sqrt{S/m}$	$f = 3\cdot13\sqrt{S/m}$

In most standard engineering texts on vibration, for example,[29] eqn. 8.9 is converted to the form

$$f = \frac{1}{2\pi}\sqrt{\frac{g}{d}} \qquad . \quad . \quad . \quad . \quad . \quad (8.10)$$

The quantity d is the deflection of an elastic system of stiffness S when supporting a mass m, under stationary conditions, it is called the " static " deflection. Two important assumptions are made in deriving d, (*a*) that the stiffness S is constant with respect to frequency (*b*) that the elastic system has a linear stress–strain relationship. Now while these assumptions are usually valid at normal working deflections where the elastic materials is a metal, in work on rubber-like materials (*a*) is never true and (*b*) is approximated to only for small deflections. Consequently the relation (eqn. 8.10) should not be used in connection with rubber-like materials.

We now return to the consideration of the equation of free vibration with damping (eqn. 8.2).

In this equation, for ease of analysis, let $2r = (R/m)$ and as before $\omega^2 = (S/m)$, we then have

$$\ddot{x} + 2r\dot{x} + \omega^2 x = 0 \quad . \quad . \quad . \quad . \quad . \quad (8.11)$$

We will assume that the solution has the form

$$x = e^{-\alpha t} . y \quad . \quad . \quad . \quad . \quad . \quad (8.12)$$

where α is an unknown constant and y is some function of t also to be found. From eqn. 8.12 we can write $\dot{x} = (\dot{y} - \alpha y) \exp(-\alpha t)$ and $\ddot{x} = (\ddot{y} - 2\alpha\dot{y} + \alpha^2 y) \exp(-\alpha t)$.

Substituting in eqn. 8.11 dividing by $\exp(-\alpha t)$ and collecting coefficients we have

$$\ddot{y} + 2(r - \alpha)\dot{y} + (\alpha^2 - 2r\alpha + \omega^2)y = 0 \quad . \quad . \quad (8.13)$$

Since α has not yet been fixed we may let $\alpha = r$ then

$$\ddot{y} + (\omega^2 - r^2)y = 0 \quad . \quad . \quad . \quad . \quad . \quad (8.14)$$

Now as previously mentioned, we are interested in practical cases in which mechanical damping coefficient R is small in relation to stiffness S. Consequently ω^2 is larger than r^2 and $(\omega^2 - r^2)$ in eqn. 8.14 must be positive. Therefore we can write

$$\omega_d = \sqrt{(\omega^2 - r^2)} \quad . \quad . \quad . \quad . \quad . \quad (8.15)$$

and insert this in eqn. 8.14 which becomes

$$\ddot{y} = -\omega_d^2 y \quad . \quad . \quad . \quad . \quad . \quad (8.16)$$

now this is identical in form with eqn. 8.3, which we solved for the " free vibration without damping " equation.

Hence $\qquad\qquad y = a \sin(\omega_d t + C) \quad . \quad . \quad . \quad . \quad (8.17)$

and $\qquad\qquad x = a e^{-rt} \sin(\omega_d t + C) \quad . \quad . \quad . \quad (8.18)$

with the same initial conditions as before

$$x = a e^{-rt} \cos(\omega_d t) \quad . \quad . \quad . \quad . \quad (8.19)$$

This is the solution for the damped free vibration, and it represents an oscillation with amplitude diminishing exponentially to zero with increasing time. Since $\cos(\omega_d t)$ will vary between $+1$ and -1 with increasing time, the oscillatory curve will be bounded by the exponential curves $x = \pm a \exp(-rt)$, and the initial amplitude will be a. By the same reasoning as was used for the undamped vibration the period of the damped vibration is related to ω_d, which is defined by

$$T_d = \frac{2\pi}{\omega_d} = \frac{2\pi}{\sqrt{(\omega^2 - r^2)}} \quad \cdots \quad (8.20)$$

where $\omega^2 = S/m$ and $r = R/2m$.

We must now consider the definition of mechanical damping in relation to " critical damping ". In solving eqn. 8.14 it was stipulated that $(\omega^2 - r^2)$ must be positive. With increasing damping a point will be reached when the motion is no longer oscillatory. This occurs when $(\omega^2 - r^2) = 0$. It will be seen from eqn. 8.15 and 8.16 that the cosine term then disappears, and the motion will consist of an exponential decay from amplitude a to zero, with increasing time given by $x = a \exp(-rt)$.

It is often convenient to express R in terms of R_c, the value of R for critical damping, since, at critical damping,

$$r^2 = \omega^2 \quad \cdots \quad (8.21)$$

$$(R_c/2m)^2 = S/m \quad \cdots \quad (8.22)$$

and
$$R_c = 2\sqrt{(Sm)} \quad \cdots \quad (8.23)$$

R/R_c is a dimensionless ratio, called *damping factor* and is given by

$$b = \frac{R}{R_c} = \frac{R}{2\sqrt{(Sm)}} \quad \cdots \quad (8.24)$$

Since ω is usually the measured parameter, and $\omega = \sqrt{(S/m)}$, it is more convenient to use

$$b = R/(2m\omega) = r/\omega \quad \cdots \quad (8.25)$$

and
$$\omega b = R/2m = r \quad \cdots \quad (8.26)$$

Hence the frequency of free vibration of the damped system, given by $1/T_d$, which is called the *damped natural frequency*, can from 8.20 and 8.26 be given simply as

$$f_d = \frac{1}{T_d} = \frac{\omega_d}{2\pi} = \frac{\omega\sqrt{(1 - b^2)}}{2\pi} \quad \cdots \quad (8.27)$$

Since in most practical measurements on rubber-like materials R is small in relation to S, it will be seen that b will be a fractional quantity and $\sqrt{(1 - b^2)} \approx 1$. Consequently ω_d is normally little different from ω, and the original eqn. 8.8 can be used to relate stiffness (S), mass (m) and frequency (f).

Now consider how the value of the damping factor can be calculated from the experimental observation of a damped free vibration. We have seen that the effect of damping is to cause a progressive reduction of the amplitude of the cosinusoidal displacement curve in such a way that it touches the exponential curves $x = \pm a \exp(-rt)$.

We could observe the time during which the amplitude is decreased by a factor $1/e$. This time is called *modulus of decay* or *time constant* (t_c), it is related to r and damping factor (b) as follows:

$$t_c = 1/r = 2m/R \quad . \quad . \quad . \quad . \quad (8.28)$$

hence

$$b = 1/\omega t_c \quad . \quad . \quad . \quad . \quad . \quad (8.29)$$

A more convenient method of expressing decay rate is the *logarithmic Decrement* (Δ), which is defined as the " natural logarithm of the ratio of the amplitudes of two successive displacement maxima on the same side of the axis ".

We will assume that the maximum values of displacement occur when $\cos(\omega_d t) = \pm 1$. This is not strictly true, as, owing to the progressive decrease of the $a \exp(-rt)$ term, the maximum of x will occur slightly before $\cos(\omega_d t) = \pm 1$. (This will also be apparent on considering that the tangent at the maximum point must be parallel to the time axis, while the common tangent to the displacement curve and the exponential envelope curve must have a negative slope.) The discrepancy is small, and for practical purposes can be neglected.

Then the time interval between the two maxima will be T_d, and if $t = t'$ at the first maximum, then $t = (t' + T_d)$ at the second maximum

at t'

$$x' = a \exp(-rt') \quad . \quad . \quad . \quad . \quad (8.30)$$

and at $(t' + T_d)$

$$x'' = a \exp[-r(t' + T_d)] \quad . \quad . \quad . \quad (8.31)$$

hence

$$\frac{x'}{x''} = \exp[rT_d] = \exp[\Delta] \quad . \quad . \quad . \quad (8.32)$$

where Δ = logarithmic decrement.

Substituting for r and T_d from eqn. 8.26 and 8.20

$$\Delta = \frac{2\pi b}{\sqrt{(1 - b^2)}} \quad . \quad . \quad . \quad . \quad (8.33)$$

as before, we can take $\sqrt{(1 - b^2)} \approx 1$, and therefore

$$\Delta \approx 2\pi b \quad . \quad . \quad . \quad . \quad . \quad (8.34)$$

From the foregoing analysis it will be seen that it is theoretically possible to characterise the dynamic properties of a material by observation of the natural frequency and logarithmic decrement of a free vibrating system in which the material under investigation forms the restoring element. In practice, as will be seen later, the requirement for elastic properties to be independent of amplitude of deformation is often not met. Providing sufficiently sensitive methods of recording displacement are used, the observations can be taken in a small range of displacement where the properties are approximately linear. Instead of calculating the logarithmic decrement from one pair of amplitude measurements it is an advantage to plot the logarithm of a number of amplitude maxima against time. If the points lie near to a straight line a representative value of logarithmic decrement can be calculated from the slope of the line times the period. In some systems it is possible, by using a recorder with a logarithmic response characteristic, to obtain a straight-line decay record directly.

Up to this point we have used S (the stiffness of the specimen) and R (the mechanical resistance), which are properties of the test piece of material examined. For fundamental work it is obviously necessary to convert these quantities into specific parameters characteristic of the material and independent of the dimensions of the particular test piece used. From S we should derive the " dynamic elastic modulus ", and from R the " specific mechanical resistance ". The latter is usually described as a " viscosity coefficient ", although its definition is not exactly analogous to the usual fluid viscosity coefficient. In many practical experiments it is by no means easy to define precisely the geometrical factors connecting the fundamental quantities with the observed values of S and R. In the simple case, which is not often met in practice, we have a test-piece of undeformed length l, which undergoes an extension or compression x which is very small in relation to l. In addition, there is no pre-loading of the test-piece. Then if P' is the elastic component of the force developed in the test-piece, and P'' the resistive component we have simply

$$P' = E'(A/l)x . \qquad . \quad . \quad . \quad . \quad (8.35)$$

and
$$P'' = \gamma(A/l)\dot{x} \quad . \quad . \quad . \quad . \quad . \quad (8.36)$$

By comparison with the previous working in terms of S and R it will be seen that

$$E' = S(l/A) \quad . \quad . \quad . \quad . \quad . \quad (8.37)$$

and
$$\gamma = R(l/A) \quad . \quad . \quad . \quad . \quad . \quad (8.38)$$

Now in the dynamic experiments in which we are interested x will vary sinusoidally (e.g. in eqn. 8.6 derived previously $x = a \cos \omega t$), but instead of using a trigonometric expression we can let:

$$x = x_0 \exp{(j\omega t)} \quad . \quad . \quad . \quad . \quad (8.39)$$

and because
$$\exp{(j\omega t)} = \cos \omega t + j \sin \omega t. \quad . \quad . \quad (8.40)$$

it will be seen that the real part of x in eqn. 8.40 is of the required form. Then the velocity $\dot{x}$ is given by:

$$\dot{x} = (j\omega)x_0 \exp{(j\omega t)} . \quad . \quad . \quad . \quad (8.41)$$

i.e.
$$\dot{x} = j\omega x \quad . \quad . \quad . \quad . \quad . \quad . \quad (8.42)$$

Substituting this in eqn. 8.36 we have:

$$P'' = j\omega\gamma(A/l)x \quad . \quad . \quad . \quad . \quad . \quad (8.43)$$

Comparing this relationship with eqn. 8.35 it will be seen that P' and P'' now have similar forms and that E' in eqn. 8.35 corresponds to $(j\omega\gamma)$ in eqn. 8.43.

The total force P can therefore be expressed as:

$$P = P' + P'' = [E' + (j\omega\gamma)](A/l)x \quad . \quad . \quad (8.44)$$

It is on this type of relationship that the commonly used " complex modulus " is based. (It should be remembered that it was assumed initially that the resistive force is velocity dependent.)

$$E^* = (E' + jE'') \quad . \quad . \quad . \quad . \quad . \quad (8.45)$$

where $E^* =$ complex Young's modulus, $E' =$ elastic (real part) modulus, $E'' =$ resistive (imaginary part) modulus and $E'' = \omega\gamma$, so that eqn. 8.44 above becomes simply

$$P = E^*(A/l)x \quad . \quad . \quad . \quad . \quad . \quad (8.46)$$

The following more explicit definitions of the different dynamic moduli have been put forward,[30] and in them the term " storage " is synonymous with " elastic " used above, and the description " loss " with " resistive " above.

" *Storage modulus:* Amplitude of the part of the stress which is in phase with a sinusoidal strain, of angular frequency ω, and of unit amplitude."

The designations are $E'_{(\omega)}$, $G'_{(\omega)}$ and $K'_{(\omega)}$ for storage moduli of the tension, shear and bulk types, respectively.

" *Loss modulus:* Amplitude of the part of the stress which has a phase lag of $90°$ with a sinusoidal strain, of angular frequency ω, and of unit amplitude."

$E''_{(\omega)}$, $G''_{(\omega)}$ and $K''_{(\omega)}$ represent the loss moduli of tension, shear and bulk types respectively.

Decay of free vibration—Types of apparatus

(*a*) *The rocking beam oscillator.* A number of methods depending on the observation of decay of free vibrations have been described. Yerzley [31] and Nolle [32] have both designed apparatus of the rocking-beam type, of which the Yerzley mechanical oscillograph is the better known, having been adopted as an ASTM Standard Method of Test.[33] It consists of a balanced beam supported at its centre and designed so that its motion is controlled by a rubber sample strained in compression or shear. A pen mounted at one end of the beam draws a trace on a recorder drum rotating at a constant speed (Fig. 8.5). The natural frequency of the system can easily be obtained from the trace by taking the time for a convenient number of oscillations. This value can then be used to calculate the effective dynamic modulus K of the rubber from the formulae

$$K_c = 210 . If^2 \quad \text{(Compression)}$$
$$K_s = 105 . If^2 \quad \text{(Shear)}$$

where $f =$ frequency in cycles per second; $I =$ moment of inertia of the beam and weights used.

A number of other properties can be obtained from the trace. For example, the ratio of the heights of the first and second oscillations gives

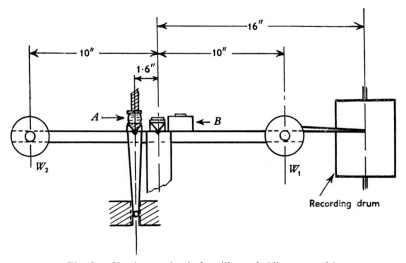

Fig. 8.5. Yerzley mechanical oscillograph (diagrammatic).

an arbitrary measure of the resilience of the rubber which, expressed as a percentage, is termed the " Yerzley " Resilience.

The apparatus can also be used for obtaining a static load compression curve, the slope of which at any point will give a value of the so-called " static " modulus at the selected deformation. The apparatus is, how-ever, only suitable for comparative measurements, as the amplitude of the oscillation must change over a considerable range and the specimen will show a non-linear stress–strain characteristic, particularly when de-formed in compression. This is the reason for referring to the " Effective Dynamic Modulus " in expressing the results from this apparatus. The measurements can normally be made only over a very limited frequency range, which is of the order of a few cycles per second. The range is dictated by the constants of the apparatus combined with the size and the stiffness of the sample.

Nolle's apparatus [32] is essentially similar, except that the restoring force is provided by rubber in extension. After imparting an initial displacement the free oscillations of the apparatus are observed by watching, through a low-power microscope, a pointer fastened to one end of the beam (Fig. 8.6). The period of oscillation is measured by means of a manually operated high-speed stop-clock, and the damping by noting the fractional reduction of amplitude over a convenient number of swings. The methods are satisfactory over a frequency range of 0·1–3 c/sec. For higher frequencies forced vibrations of the beam can be arranged by means of a coil fastened to one end of the beam, operating in a magnetic field, and

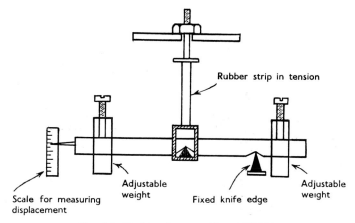

Rubber strip in tension

Adjustable weight

Scale for measuring displacement

Fixed knife edge

Adjustable weight

Fig. 8.6. Rocking beam oscillator (Nolle).

observations made of the frequency for maximum amplitude and the band-width. This modified apparatus is effective up to 25 c/sec.

(b) *The vibrating reed.* Sack et al.[34] determined the damping properties of high-polymer materials in the form of reeds (2 mm. thick, 4–15 mm. wide and of various lengths) by three different methods, one of which utilises the decay of free vibration of the reed. A small metal shutter attached to the reed partially interrupts a beam of light falling on a photo-cell, the output of which is amplified and displayed on an oscilloscope. When the reed is deflected from its rest position and released it executes a damped free vibration, and the amplitude–time relationship is recorded photographically from the oscilloscope. The mathematical analysis of the vibration of a reed of viscoelastic material is very involved and will not be considered here. The other method using reeds, described by Sack and by Nolle,[35] is a forced-vibration method and is referred to later in the section. Sack was mainly interested in measuring loss factor rather than the elastic modulus and, provided that the loss factor is small ($E''/E' \ll 1$), a simple relation connects the logarithmic decrement and the loss factor thus

$$\frac{E''}{E'} = \frac{\Delta}{\pi}$$

The definitions of E' and E'' were given previously (see p. 525).

(c) *Torsion pendulum.* In its simplest form the torsional pendulum is made up of a torsion element, a vertical wire or rod, supporting an inertia element, consisting of a rigid bar or disc, and it is named the Coulomb torsion pendulum after its originator. If the inertia element is given a small rotation and released it will execute a simple harmonic rotational vibration with an exponential decrease in amplitude. The theory will not be worked in detail here, but the equation of motion is analogous to the one previously shown for the linear motion, eqn. 8.2, and may be derived from the latter by making the following substitutions:

Angular deflection	(θ)	in place of	Displacement	(x)
Moment of inertia	(I)	,, ,,	Mass	(m)
Restoring couple per unit twist	(C)	,, ,,	Stiffness	(S)
Rotational resistance	(R_R)	,, ,,	Mechanical Resistance	(R)

(Thus we now have $\omega^2 = C/I$ and $2r = R_R/I$)

From the equation it can be shown, in the same way as before, that the damped natural (angular) frequency is as follows (cf. with eqn. 8.15)

$$\omega_R = \sqrt{(C/I) - (R_R/2I)^2} \quad . \quad . \quad . \quad . \quad (8.47)$$

From which, the period T is:

$$T_R = 2\pi \sqrt{\frac{I}{C - (R_R^2/4I)}} \quad . \quad . \quad . \quad (8.48)$$

Similarly from eqn. 8.32 $\Delta = rT$, and therefore in the rotational case the logarithmic decrement Δ is given by:

$$\Delta = (R_R/2I) . T_R \quad . \quad . \quad . \quad . \quad (8.49)$$

The form of apparatus described above is adequate for the determination of the properties of metals, in wire or rod form, since the specimen can be made the torsion element of the apparatus and the properties calculated directly from observations of the oscillations of the pendulum. This procedure is not practicable with a readily extensible material, since the specimen bears the weight of the inertia element. Two types of method have been adopted to avoid this difficulty. The inertia element may be supported other than by the torsion system, or alternatively, the torsion system may be in two parts, one serving to support the mass and the other being the specimen under investigation. A method of the first type was described in 1936 by Cassie, Maldwyn Jones and Naunton,[36] who included a torsional oscillation method for determining rigidity modulus and internal friction in a paper on " Fatigue in Rubber ". The apparatus consisted of an inertia bar with two weights which could be clamped at any position on it, to give the required moment of inertia. The bar was free to swing in a horizontal plane, being supported on a short vertical shaft freely mounted in ball bearings. The lower end of this shaft carried a clamp for a rubber specimen (7 in. long by 1 in. by $\frac{1}{2}$ in.). The lower end of the specimen was held by a stationary clamp attached to the base of the apparatus. A temperature-controlled box surrounded the test piece, and measurements were made over a range of 20–100° C. The above-mentioned workers measured modulus and internal friction on rubbers containing various compounding ingredients and correlated internal friction and fatigue life. A simple falling-weight drive was used to convert the free-vibration torsional system to a maintained one, and the minimum force required to maintain oscillation taken as a measure of internal friction. Experimental agreement in the slope of the modulus–friction ratio versus elongation by the two methods was shown. The rotational inertia bar was also adapted for measurement of Young's modulus and the associated internal friction by coupling an extended dumb-bell specimen to it. The decrements of free vibrations of this system were measured, but the oscillation of this type of system is not pure sinusoidal.

The importance of making measurements on specimens at zero strain was recognised and the suggestion made that methods based on acoustic propagation and attenuation should be developed. (This type of method is treated later.)

The use of any type of bearing to support the inertia element of a torsion pendulum is open to objection. A constant frictional loss in the bearing is not important, but erratic changes are liable to occur, particularly when measurements are made on specimens cooled below room temperature. Even though the bearing is not directly in the cold chamber, it is usually impossible to isolate it completely.

The second type of method, the two-part torsion system, has been more frequently used, particularly for measurements of modulus and loss factor of polymeric materials over a wide temperature range, −100° C to +100° C or more.[37–42, 53] The usual practice is to employ a fine wire (of steel or other spring material of the order of $\frac{1}{2}$ mm. diam.) as the main torsion element and suspend the inertia bar or disc from it. One end of the specimen is held in a clamp connected to the underside of the inertia element and the other end is gripped in a stationary clamp. This method avoids the possible troubles with the bearings or other supports used in the first method, but there is still a problem to be overcome in connection with the fixed specimen clamp. Owing to differential thermal contraction, the specimen will be strained in tension as its temperature is lowered.

The effect will be of the order of 1% for a fall in temperature of 50° C. Two methods of avoiding this difficulty have been described. Nielsen [39] observes the period and damping of the torsional pendulum system under several known tensile loads and extrapolates the results to zero loading. His apparatus had the lower clamp attached to a pivoted bar in such a way that it was free to move vertically but prevented from rotating or moving laterally. Small weights were suspended from the clamp to give the required loading. In a later development of Nielsen's [40] the torsion wire passes over a pulley and the load is applied at the upper end of the suspension. This apparatus has a torque recording system attached to the lower clamp. The other method of compensating for thermal contraction, due to Fletcher, Gent and Wood, [42] avoids the multiple observations and extrapolation of Nielsen's method. The lower grip is attached to a thin metal plate, clamped along opposite edges, which is fairly flexible in a vertical direction, but not in other directions. A development of this idea, which does not seem to have been put forward, would be to attach the lower grip to the centre of a thin circular metal diaphragm which has deep annular corrugations and is fastened around its outer edge. In this way it would probably be possible to combine improved vertical compliance with maximum torsional stiffness.

Apart from the thermal effect, longitudinal displacement occurs in the specimen due to the twisting. The definition of a pure torsion is that every small element in the specimen is displaced along a circle which has its centre in the axis of the specimen and lies in a plane at right angles to this axis. Rivlin [43] has shown that compressive forces on the ends of the cylinder, in addition to the twisting couple, are required to maintain a pure torsion. He also confirmed this finding experimentally [44] on a rubber cylinder of 4·12 in. diam. $\times$ 1 in. high bonded between two brass discs. The bonded cylinder was mounted in a rigid frame designed to keep the height of the cylinder constant while one disc was rotated. The upper bonded disc had a series of $\frac{1}{2}$-in.-diam. holes at varying distances from the centre, and it was observed that the rubber bulged up into these holes when the cylinder was in torsion. It was assumed that the amount of the bulge was proportional to the force required at that point to maintain a pure torsion. The forces deduced in this way varied with the amount of the torsion and the distance from the axis of the cylinder, according to the relationships which had been derived using Mooney's [45] two-constant stored-energy function to represent the elastic properties of rubber. The experiment therefore supports the validity of Mooney's function.

In the torsional pendulum method a pure torsion cannot be applied to the specimen, even if it is cylindrical, because the length of the cylinder is much greater than the diameter, and a compressive force on the ends would therefore cause buckling. As mentioned above, the specimen is, in the ideal case, completely free to elongate or contract in the axial direction, that is the force normal to the end of the cylinder should be zero. Rivlin [46] also examined the case of torsion combined with extension or compression of a cylinder [47] and showed that the torque is not changed by extension of the cylinder (provided that G is constant). An expression relating the tensile force to the extension ratio and twist is also given. This work was based on the single-constant stored-energy function (the one derived from the statistical theory of elasticity of rubber), but it is reasonable to assume that the order of the solution would be the same with the two-constant function due to Mooney. If we put the tensile force equal to zero in this expression the relation between twist and extension ratio under the condition we hope to achieve in the torsion pendulum is obtained. Substitution of numerical values in the formula, as an arbitrary example, shows that a cylinder 8 mm. in diameter undergoing a torsional deflection of 0·5 radians/cm. would only extend by $\frac{1}{3}\%$. It is clear from this analysis that the torsional pendulum results on a cylindrical specimen will not be in error due to allowing free longitudinal extension, since the measured torque is theoretically unchanged by the extension, and in addition a torsional loading much larger than is normally used produces a negligible extension.

If the specimen is not of circular section the longitudinal displacement of the cross-sections is such as to produce an overall contraction when it is twisted. In this case, if the specimen is not completely free longitudinally, an increase in measured torsional stiffness with increasing angular deflection of the pendulum will be observed. Timoshenko [48] gives a relationship for a rectangular sectioned specimen in torsion and tension which shows that the extra torque is directly proportional to tension but increases rapidly with increasing specimen width/thickness ratio. Even if the pendulum deflection used is kept small to avoid non-linearity, the use of specimens of rectangular section is not to be recommended, because the device adopted to provide for free longitudinal contraction is unlikely to be infinitely compliant, and particularly at extremely low temperatures the specimen may be subjected to a small static extension due to differential contraction. Gent [49] drew attention to this problem and made an approximation of Green and Shield's [50] relationship for the torsional stiffness of an extended prism as follows. In this equation the rigidity modulus has been given a value of unity and S is used for " torsional rigidity ". (In our notation $S = C . l$, where $l =$ length.)

$$S_e \approx S_o + 3_e(I_o - S_o) \quad . \quad . \quad . \quad . \quad (8.50)$$

where $S_e =$ torsional rigidity of extended prism; $S_o =$ torsional rigidity of unextended prism; $e =$ fractional extension; $I_o =$ second moment of area of original cross-section (i.e. geometrical moment of inertia).

In Coulomb's original theory of torsion the torsional rigidity was thought to be proportional to the moment of inertia of the cross-section, and on this basis $S_o = I_o$ and the effect of extension in the above vanishes. In fact, as shown by Saint-Venant,[51] this is true only if the section is circular. The values of the geometrical constant $(k = (S_o/l))$ are given later (see p. 532), and comparing these with the geometrical moment of inertia for a rectangular section (for a section of $(2a \times 2b)$, $I_o = (4ab/3)(a^2 + b^2))$ shows that the ratio I_o/S_o increases with the ratio of the sides of the rectangle. These considerations suggest that wherever possible precise determinations of modulus by the torsional method should be carried out on specimens of circular section. When it is necessary to cut a specimen from a sheet sample a square section is the best alternative. For a section $(a \times a)$, $I_o = a^4/6$ and $S_o = a^4/7 \cdot 11$, so that $I_o/S_o = 1 \cdot 19$. Using Gent's formula (eqn. 8.50), extension of a square-sectioned specimen by 1% causes an increase in torsional stiffness of approximately $0 \cdot 5\%$, whereas the rectangular sectioned test-pieces used in many standard torsional stiffness tests of a routine nature would show a torsional stiffness increase of a much higher order for the same extension.[49]

We will now examine the way in which the shear modulus is calculated from the observations of the torsional pendulum. From the mathematical theory of elasticity for small strains, the twisting couple required to apply a pure torsion to a right cylinder is given by: [52]

$$M = \frac{\pi}{2} G \phi a^4$$

where $G =$ rigidity (shear modulus); $\phi =$ twist per unit length of cylinder; $a =$ radius of cylinder; $M =$ total couple about the axis, applied to end of cylinder. Hence the couple per unit twist is $M/\phi = (\pi/2)Ga^4$ and in the notation used previously and putting $\theta = \phi \cdot l$ we have:

$$C = M/\theta = \left(\frac{\pi}{32} \cdot \frac{d^4}{l}\right)G \quad . \quad . \quad . \quad . \quad (8.51)$$

where $l =$ length of cylinder twisted; $\theta =$ total twist; $d =$ diameter of cylinder. Hence $C = k \cdot G$ where k is a geometrical constant. The values of k for different shaped sections are as follows:

Circular section:

Diameter $= d$ $\qquad\qquad k = \dfrac{\pi d^4}{32l}$

Square section:

Side $= a$ $\qquad\qquad k = \dfrac{a^4}{7 \cdot 11l}$

Rectangular section:

Width $= 2a$

$$k \approx \frac{ab^3}{l}\left[\frac{16}{3} - \frac{b}{a}\,(3{\cdot}361)\right]$$

Thickness $= 2b$

$(a > 3b)$

The analysis for a rectangular section was first carried out by Saint-Venant.[51] Exact values of k may be calculated by reference to his complete formula, which is quoted in Love.[52] The relationship is often quoted in the form $k = (ab^3/l)\mu$, with tabulated values given for μ at various ratios.[53, 54] For the reasons which were discussed above, the use of a rectangular-sectioned specimen should be avoided if there is any possibility of obtaining the material in suitable form to prepare circular or square-sectioned specimens.

If the damping is so small that $(R_R^2/4I)$ may be neglected in eqn. 8.48 the period is simply given by $T^2 = 4\pi^2(I/C)$ and, letting T_o be the period with wire only as the torsion element and T_R the period with specimen added, we have

$$G = \frac{C}{k} = \frac{4\pi^2 I}{k}\left(\frac{1}{T_R^2} - \frac{1}{T_o^2}\right) \qquad . \quad . \quad . \quad (8.52)$$

As an alternative approach which brings in the effect of damping and the calculation of the " Loss Modulus " we will make use of the complex modulus described previously (see p. 525), but as we are now evaluating shear modulus instead of tension modulus, the complex form will be

$$G^* = G' + jG'' \qquad . \quad . \quad . \quad . \quad . \quad (8.53)$$

where $G^* =$ complex shear modulus; $G' =$ elastic (real part) modulus; $G'' =$ resistive (imaginary part) modulus.

To write the equation of motion bringing in the complex modulus substitute rotational terms in eqn. 8.2, as before, but use kG^* to replace S. Since the resistive part is incorporated in G^*, the resistive term is omitted and the equation of motion is as follows:

$$\ddot{\theta} + \left(\frac{kG^*}{I}\right)\theta = 0 \qquad . \quad . \quad . \quad . \quad . \quad (8.54)$$

This procedure may be justified thus, $E'' = \omega\gamma$ from equ. 8.45 and similarly $G'' = \omega\eta$ ($\eta =$ viscosity) also $\dot{\theta} = j\omega\theta$ (compare equ. 8.42). Hence $kG^*\theta = kG'\theta + k\eta\dot{\theta}$. Thus R_R has been replaced by $k\eta$, i.e. the same geometrical constant is used to relate viscosity to rotational resistance as is used to relate shear modulus to rotational stiffness.

Assume a solution for eqn. 8.54 of the same form as before, eqn. 8.6, but replace cos ωt by the corresponding complex term exp $(j\omega t)$ (see eqn. 8.39). This gives:

$$\theta = \theta_0 \exp (j\omega - r)t \quad . \quad . \quad . \quad . \quad (8.55)$$

hence

$$\ddot{\theta} = (j\omega - r)^2\theta \quad . \quad . \quad . \quad . \quad . \quad (8.56)$$

Substitute in eqn. 8.54, divide by θ and rearrange, giving:

$$\frac{kG^*}{I} = \omega^2 + 2j\omega r - r^2 \quad . \quad . \quad . \quad (8.57)$$

Equate real and imaginary parts separately thus:

$$G' = (\omega^2 - r^2)(I/k) \quad \text{and} \quad G'' = (2\omega r)(I/k)$$

Since $\omega = 2\pi/T$ (from eqn. 8.7) and $rT = \Delta$ (from eqn. 8.32) we can substitute for ω and r, giving:

$$G' = (4\pi^2 - \Delta^2)(I/kT^2) \quad . \quad . \quad . \quad (8.58)$$
$$G'' = (4\pi . \Delta)(I/kT^2) \quad . \quad . \quad . \quad (8.59)$$

Eqn. 8.58 does not take account of the stiffness of the torsion wire suspension of the usual system. To include this, we will make the assumption that the damping due to the wire is an insignificant proportion of the observed damping and that the wire only contributes to the real part of the observed stiffness. The rotational stiffness of the specimen, allowing for the suspension wire is then:

$$C = kG' = (4\pi^2 - \Delta^2)(I/T^2) - C_o . \quad . \quad . \quad (8.60)$$

Hence G' is given by the following:

$$G' = (4\pi^2 - \Delta^2)(I/kT^2) - (C_o/k) \quad . \quad . \quad (8.61)$$

where I = moment of inertia of pendulum; T = period of pendulum with specimen; Δ = logarithmic decrement of pendulum swings; k = a geometrical constant (see p. 532); C_o = rotational stiffness of suspension wire; while G'' is still given by eqn. 8.59, as before.

The ratio (loss modulus/elastic modulus) is called the " damping " or the " loss factor ". From eqn. 8.58 and 8.59 it will be seen that the damping in shear is given by:

$$\frac{G''}{G'} = \frac{4\pi\Delta}{4\pi^2 - \Delta^2} \quad . \quad . \quad . \quad . \quad (8.62)$$

When Δ is small enough to enable Δ^2 to be neglected then

$$(G''/G') = (\Delta/\pi) \quad . \quad . \quad . \quad . \quad (8.63)$$

This corresponds to the value for damping in tension (E''/E') which was quoted previously (see p. 528).

In order to be able to calculate G' and G'' we need to know the apparatus constants, namely the moment of inertia (I) and the stiffness of the suspension wire (C_o). The inertia element may be of a complicated shape so that the calculation of its I is difficult, also it is not advisable to use a calculated value for the torsional stiffness of the wire suspension because of end effects and possible variations in the material. The required constants can be obtained by observing the period of the pendulum with no specimen attached under two conditions. First, with the inertia element in the condition used for the specimen measurement (T_o), and second, with the complete inertia system replaced by a bar or disc of simple shape whose I has been calculated. Let the latter value be I_c and the period with it in position be T_c then:

$$T_o = 2\pi\sqrt{(I/C_o)} \quad \text{and} \quad T_c = 2\pi\sqrt{(I_c/C_o)}$$

and hence the required constants are:

$$C_o = I(2\pi/T_o)^2 \quad \text{and} \quad I = I_c(T_o/T_c)^2$$

If it is not practicable to replace the complete inertia element for calibration the same result can be achieved by adding two known masses to the original, at a measured distance from the axis, and calculating the resulting increase in I. Observation of T in this condition and appropriate substitution in the $T = 2\pi\sqrt{(I/C)}$ equation will give the required constants.

2. Forced-vibration methods

Previously we considered methods of dynamic measurement which utilised " free " vibration, i.e. those in which no energy is supplied from outside the vibrating system, after the initial impulse which sets it in motion. As mentioned then, the exponential decrease in amplitude of vibration, due to damping, makes it difficult to carry out absolute measurements when, because of the nature of the material or the shape of the test-piece, the properties to be measured vary with amplitude. If an oscillating force is applied to the system it will come to a steady state and vibrate with the same frequency as that of the applied force. This motion is said to be a *forced vibration*.

To obtain the equation of motion, equate the forces as we did before (eqn. 8.1) but add an extra term representing the applied oscillating force, giving:

$$m\ddot{x} = P\cos\omega t - Sx - R\dot{x} \quad . \quad . \quad . \quad (8.67)$$

rearranging this will give a linear differential equation of the second order

$$m\ddot{x} + R\dot{x} + Sx = P\cos\omega t \quad . \quad . \quad . \quad (8.68)$$

The solution of the free vibration (eqn. 8.19) which we have already obtained is also a part of the solution (the complementary function) of the above equation. This part is of little physical significance in dealing with forced vibration because it represents a transient which soon dies away owing to damping. We are interested in the solution of eqn. 8.68 (the "particular" integral), which describes the steady-state vibration set up by the applied oscillating force. To ease the solution let $P \cos \omega t$ be replaced by a complex term $P \exp (j\omega t)$. Since

$$\exp (j\omega t) = \cos \omega t + j \sin \omega t . \quad . \quad . \quad (8.69)$$

the real part of the complex term represents the actual driving force. Using this convention, the solution x will also be complex, but the actual value of the displacement will be obtained from it. The equation of motion will now be

$$m\ddot{x} + R\dot{x} + Sx = P \exp (j\omega t) \quad . \quad . \quad (8.70)$$

It can be assumed that the resulting displacement will have the same frequency as the driving force, but in general will not be in phase with it. Let x have the form:

$$x = A \exp [j(\omega t + \phi)] \quad . \quad . \quad . \quad (8.71)$$

where $\phi = $ a constant indicating the phase difference between force and displacement; $A = $ the maximum amplitude of displacement. Since $\exp (j\phi)$ is constant, it may be combined with A to give a complex constant A, then

$$x = A \exp (j\omega t) \quad . \quad . \quad . \quad . \quad (8.72)$$

From this $\dot{x} = j\omega A \exp (j\omega t)$ and $\ddot{x} = -\omega^2 A \exp (j\omega t)$, substitute these values in eqn. 8.70

$$(-\omega^2 Am + j\omega AR + AS) \exp (j\omega t) = P \exp (j\omega t) \quad (8.73)$$

for this to hold for any value of t, A must be given by:

$$A = \frac{P}{(S - \omega^2 m) + j\omega R} \quad . \quad . \quad . \quad (8.74)$$

The absolute value of A, the maximum displacement, may now be found, bearing in mind that the absolute value of a complex number is $\sqrt{(a^2 + b^2)}$ where a is the real part and b the imaginary part, and hence:

$$A = \frac{P}{\sqrt{(S - \omega^2 m)^2 + \omega^2 R^2}} \quad . \quad . \quad (8.75)$$

The exp $(j\phi)$ factor contained in A has been neglected since exp $(j\phi) =$ cos $\phi + j$ sin ϕ, its absolute value is unity, but now return to eqn. 8.71 to evaluate ϕ

$$A = A \exp(j\phi) = \frac{P}{(S - \omega^2 m) + j\omega R} = A (\cos \phi + j \sin \phi) \quad (8.76)$$

To eliminate the complex term, multiply numerator and denominator by $(S - \omega^2 m) - j\omega R$, and the equate the real and imaginary parts separately

$$\cos \phi = \frac{(S - \omega^2 m)(P/A)}{(S - \omega^2 m)^2 + \omega^2 R^2} \quad \sin \phi = \frac{-\omega R(P/A)}{(S - \omega^2 m)^2 + \omega^2 R^2}$$

Hence ϕ is given by:

$$\tan \phi = \frac{-\omega R}{(S - \omega^2 m)} \quad . \quad . \quad . \quad . \quad (8.77)$$

We have then evaluated A and ϕ in the solution (eqn. 8.71) of eqn. 8.70.

However, the solution can be put into a more convenient form for general use by the substitution of the following terms:

$$\omega_R = \omega/\omega_o \quad \text{where} \quad \omega_o{}^2 = S/m$$

ω_o is the same as ω in the free vibration case, that is the " natural frequency (angular) " of the vibrating system. Hence ω_R is a dimensionless ratio relating the applied driving frequency to the natural frequency of the system.

Also from eqn. 8.24

$$b = \frac{R}{R_C} = \frac{R}{2m\omega_o}$$

Lastly, let $$D = P/S \quad . \quad . \quad . \quad . \quad . \quad (8.78)$$

D represents the deflection that would be caused by a force equal to the force amplitude P acting upon the stiffness S in the absence of inertia or damping forces, i.e. at zero frequency. This quantity has no physical significance because S is a function of ω. If the stiffness is measured under conditions approximating to zero frequency (pseudo static) it will not, in general, equal S. Hence D is a hypothetical quantity.

Now to simplify eqn. 8.75 divide numerator and denominator by S, giving:

$$A = \frac{P/S}{\sqrt{(1 - \omega^2 m/S)^2 + (\omega R/S)^2}} \quad . \quad . \quad (8.79)$$

Since $1/\omega_0^2 = m/S$, then $\omega^2 m/S = \omega^2/\omega_0^2 = \omega_R^2$, and since $2b = R/\omega_0 m$, then $2\omega_R b = \omega R/\omega_0^2 m = \omega R/S$. Hence eqn. 8.79 can be rewritten:

$$A = \frac{D}{\sqrt{(1 - \omega_R^2)^2 + (2\omega_R b)^2}} \qquad . \quad . \quad . \quad (8.80)$$

where A = displacement amplitude; $D = (P/S)$ = force amplitude/dynamic stiffness; ω_R = driving frequency/natural frequency; b = actual mechanical resistance/critical mechanical resistance.

Similarly divide numerator and denominator of eqn. 8.77 by S giving

$$\tan \phi = \frac{-\omega R/S}{(1 - \omega^2 m/S)} \qquad . \quad . \quad . \quad . \quad (8.81)$$

and hence:

$$\tan \phi = \frac{-2\omega_R b}{1 - \omega_R^2} \qquad . \quad . \quad . \quad . \quad (8.82)$$

The physical significance of the negative sign is that the displacement (of amplitude A) lags behind the force (of amplitude P) by the phase angle ϕ.

Resonant vibrators

Methods utilising electromagnetic vibrators driving resonant systems have been described by Naunton and Waring [55, 64] for rubber in compression, Fletcher and Gent [56] and Oberto and Palandri [58] for rubber in shear, and by Kuhl and Meyer [57] for rubber in extension.

(a) *With rubber in compression.* Naunton and Waring's apparatus (Fig. 8.7) consists of a source of alternating current, of variable frequency, connected to a moving-coil driver unit. A moving platen connected to

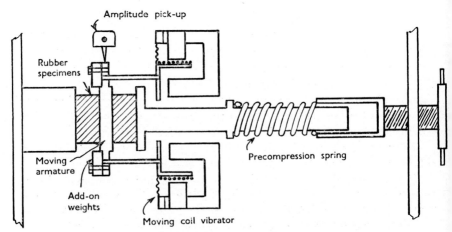

Fig. 8.7. Resonant vibrator—compression (Naunton & Waring).

the driver unit applies alternating stresses to two rubber samples mounted on either side of it. The system is tuned mechanically and electrically to resonance, and the amplitude of vibration at resonance is measured electrically. A means of applying a static load to the rubber samples is incorporated in the apparatus.

(*b*) *With rubber in shear.* Fletcher and Gent's apparatus makes use of four rubber cylinders bonded to metal end pieces and mounted in a carriage as shown in Fig. 8.8.

The mountings are subjected to a simple harmonic vibration in shear by imparting a horizontal motion to the carriage by means of vibrators attached to each end of the carriage rods. The whole system is suspended by flat steel strips that constrain it to motion in a horizontal direction only. The force is determined from the current through the electro-magnetic

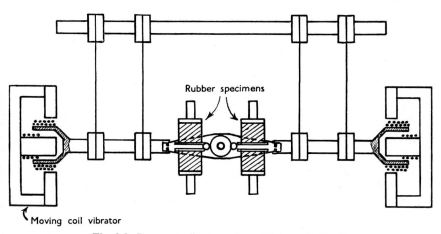

Fig. 8.8. Resonant vibrator—shear (Fletcher & Gent).

vibrators, which have previously been calibrated against a force by a system of hanging weights. The amplitude is determined either by observing the apparent broadening of an illuminated slit attached to one of the vibrating rods or by a photo-electric device.

The apparatus is suitable for measurements of dynamic modulus and viscosity of rubber test pieces in shear over a frequency range 20–120 c/sec. at amplitudes of approximately 0·01–5% shear strain.

Oberto and Palandri [58] have described a forced-resonance type of apparatus developed in the Pirelli Research Laboratories utilising rubber in shear. The rubber test piece is in the form of a circular ring of special section, similar to that which would be obtained by sectioning a hollow cone. There are triangular-shaped teeth on both edges, the outer ones fit into corresponding teeth in a static ring and the inner ones into a tooth cone connected to a coil which can be oscillated electro-magnetically. By the addition of weights suspended from the tooth cone it is possible to obtain resonance at various frequencies within a range of about 20–200 c/sec.

(c) *With rubber in extension.* For measurements of rubber in extension Kuhl and Meyer describe an apparatus developed by Berthold Wurbs in

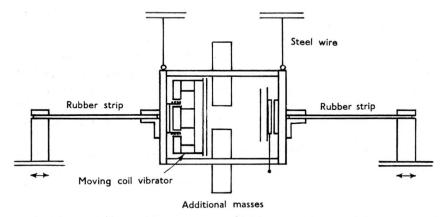

Fig. 8.9. Apparatus for extensional vibration (Kuhl & Meyer).

which two rubber strips mounted horizontally are clamped to a suspended cage connected to an electro-magnetic vibrator and incorporating an electrostatic system for measuring the vibration amplitude (Fig. 8.9). By suitably choosing the dimensions of the rubber strips, and loading the suspended cage, a range of resonant frequencies can be obtained. The apparatus was suitable for a frequency range of 20–200 c/sec.

Non-resonant vibrators

(d) *Out-of-balance mechanical exciter type.* The unwanted vibration forces that commonly arise in all kinds of machinery are usually due to incomplete balancing of reciprocating or rotating masses. Consequently it is not surprising that one of the earliest types of vibrator exciter developed for experimental purposes consisted of a rotating mass with a large amount of unbalance with respect to the axis of rotation. In order to develop the periodic force in the required direction it is necessary to restrain the movement of the exciter in all other directions. One simple way of doing this is to mount the exciter on a platform fitted with rollers which run freely between vertical guides. The force developed by the exciter can then be applied to a specimen mounted between the platform and a fixed baseplate. If a variable-speed motor is used to drive the rotating mass the frequency of the exciter may be adjusted within the available speed range of the motor. It is also desirable to be able to vary the degree of unbalance of the rotating mass.

The system described above is a mechanically simple one that has been applied for production control, but for scientific investigation it has several disadvantages. The minimum static load that can be applied to the specimen is the total weight of the exciter and platform, which may be undesirably large. The roller and guide system cannot be made completely friction free, and this may introduce significant losses at low force amplitudes.

The force amplitude is given by $Mk\omega^2$, where M = rotating mass; k = radius of gyration; ω = angular velocity. The value k can be adjusted only over a limited range, and though it is possible to arrange that this can be done while the apparatus is running, the force cannot be kept constant over a wide frequency range. With further complication it may also be possible to vary M, but not while the exciter is running, and again only over a limited range.

The necessity for the constraints to lateral motion can be largely avoided by contra-rotating two unbalanced masses so that the resultant out-of-balance force is developed only in a vertical direction, although it will still not be possible to apply this exciter to a single small specimen, unless the set-up is arranged so that the centre of gravity of the exciter is below the specimen.

Roelig hysteresis apparatus. A further development of this type of exciter was produced by Roelig [59, 60] to measure the dynamic modulus and mechanical hysteresis of rubber specimens. Roelig's apparatus, or modifications of it, have been used by several workers. [61-65]

The unbalanced mass consists of a D-shaped flywheel mounted on a driving shaft in a light alloy housing, which is supported on four steel leaf springs in such a way that it can move only along one horizontal axis. At one side the rubber test-piece is supported between two cylindrical anvils, one of which is mounted on the flywheel housing and the other on a steel dynamometer ring which is rigidly supported. At the other side of the housing is fastened one end of a helical steel spring, the other end being attached to a rigid bracket. The flywheel housing, complete with one anvil and precompression spring, is mounted on a sliding platform which can be advanced or withdrawn from the other anvil and dynamometer by a hand-wheel and lead-screw. By this means a rubber specimen can first be clamped between the two anvils with any required pre-compression (static-loading), the slide then locked to the base-plate and the exciter started up (Fig. 8.10).

A stress–strain oscillogram is produced optically and viewed on a ground-glass screen, by means of the optical system shown in Fig. 8.11. An intense point source of light is provided by a carbon-arc lamp or a compact-source high-pressure mercury-vapour discharge lamp. The steel dynamometer ring contains a mechanical–optical strain gauge and is arranged so that a small deformation of the dynamometer, due to the force exerted by the rubber specimen, relaxes the tension in a steel strip connected to another strip maintained in torsion. A tiny plane mirror mounted on the torsion strip rotates through an angle (in a horizontal

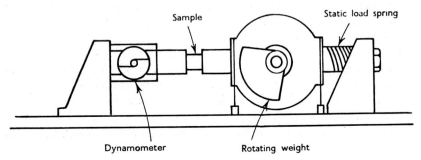

Fig. 8.10. Roelig apparatus.

plane) which is directly proportional to the force exerted on the dynamometer.

Light passes through a small aperture in front of the light source, falls first on the dynamometer mirror M_1, is reflected on to a second fixed

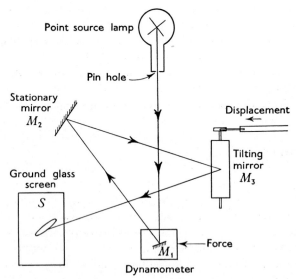

Fig. 8.11. Roelig apparatus optical system (schematic—not to scale—lens omitted).

mirror M_2 and then on to a third mirror M_3, which is mounted so that it turns through an angle in a vertical plane which is proportional to the deformation of the rubber specimen. The beam from M_3 falls finally on the ground-glass screen S. It will be seen from this description of the mirror system that the path of the light spot on the screen will be the resultant of the motion of mirror M_1 in a horizontal plane and mirror M_3 in a vertical plane. If the position of the light spot, referred to horizontal and vertical axes on the ground-glass screen, is at a given instant represented by $(x_1 : y_1)$, then x_1 is directly proportional to the force applied to the specimen at that instant and y_1 is directly proportional to the deformation of the specimen at that instant.

If the mechanical hysteresis of the specimen is sufficient to be detectable by this apparatus the figure described by the spot on the screen will approximate to an ellipse. The method of calibrating the trace and deriving the properties of the specimen will be described below, but first consider the procedure for setting up the apparatus and making a measurement. First the bracket forming the fixed end of the static load spring must be adjusted to the position on the sliding platform which will give the required static loading with the specimen compressed between the platens and the leaf springs, which support the flywheel housing vertical. The spring bracket is then bolted solidly to the platform. Secondly, the eccentricity adjustment on the flywheel housing is set to a fairly small value for starting up the machine. The specimen is clamped in place between the anvils and the desired pre-loading applied by traversing the platform with the hand-wheel and lead-screw. When in position the platform is clamped solidly to the bed-plate. The light spot will now have taken up a position on the screen representing the static loading and deformation of the specimen. The driving motor is now started and its speed set to give the required frequency of vibration. In order to monitor this accurately a more precise method than the ordinary mechanical tachometer is required. Suitable methods that have been used are:

(*a*) Stroboscope lamp and a divided disc mounted on the driving shaft.

(*b*) Photo-electric pick-up and frequency counter using a disc with a number of apertures near the periphery.

Once the apparatus is vibrating at the required frequency, which, subject to several limitations which will be discussed later, may be anywhere in the range from 2–3 to 40 c/sec., the eccentricity may be increased by means of the adjusting sleeve on the flywheel housing until the required dynamic force is produced. A reading may be taken immediately, if required, by photographing the screen or by copying the figure manually on tracing paper. Since the indicated dynamic stiffness and mechanical damping decrease steeply in the first few minutes, it is desirable either to take a series of records at various running times or to allow a sufficient period to elapse before taking the record, to enable fairly stable conditions to be reached (10–20 minutes depending on type of specimen).

If it is desired to take an instantaneous record of the initial cycles this may be done photographically by setting the eccentricity, speed control and camera before switching on the motor. Care should be taken with this procedure at high dynamic forces, and at frequencies above one-half the machine's own resonance because of the damagingly large amplitudes that may be developed during the run up to speed. The serious effects due to the inherent resonance of the apparatus will be discussed later.

Unless the specimen is rigidly attached to the platens, by using rubber-to-metal bonded end plates and fastening these to the anvils, it is necessary to ensure that the dynamic force is not increased to the point where the algebraic sum of static and instantaneous dynamic force can fall to zero. In this event the platens will separate from the specimen, which will fall out, and damage will possibly result, due to the machine running free at large dynamic force.

The Roelig apparatus may be used to observe heat build-up in the specimen over an extended running period. The most reliable method of measuring temperature rise in the rubber specimen is to insert a needle thermocouple into the centre of it, but if this is done with the machine running a temperature higher than the true temperature is observed, due to friction at the point of the thermocouple. It is therefore necessary to stop the machine before taking a temperature reading. An alternative method is to use a layered specimen with a thin metal plate between each layer. The metal plates have thermocouples embedded in them so that the temperature near the centre of the specimens can be observed.

An insulated container is available with apertures for the anvils of the apparatus to enable the specimen to be enclosed in a temperature-controlled chamber. The temperature is maintained above or below room temperature by passing thermostated air into the box. Since this apparatus is often used at fairly large amplitudes, the temperature rise in the specimen may be considerable, and it is almost impossible to make measurements with both a uniform temperature throughout the specimen and stable dynamic conditions. The method known as the " jab technique " described by McCallion and Davies [66] minimises internal temperature rise. The specimen is first brought to the required temperature with the exciter stationary, the machine turned on for just a few cycles and the record taken. Although this method avoids a large temperature gradient in the test-piece and is most useful for the determination of the fundamental properties, it does not serve to predict the behaviour of many rubber compounds which exhibit progressive change in dynamic properties, due to mechanical degradation of the rubber structure, in addition to heat build-up. It is often necessary to make measurements of dynamic properties under conditions approximating to those experienced by a rubber component in service under continuous vibration. For this purpose the technique originally described of running until fairly stable conditions have been established would be preferable. The temperature difference between the centre of the test piece and ambient can be determined at the end of the run and the air flow or size of specimen (keeping geometrical proportions constant) altered to give a heat build-up representative of practical conditions.

Advantages and disadvantages of the Roelig hysteresis apparatus. Following development in Germany during the War, this apparatus came into use in its original or modified forms by a number of laboratories in Britain and the U.S.A. It has the advantage that large dynamic forces can be generated by a relatively simple mechanical system and, provided a suitable electric motor and speed controller is fitted, various frequencies can be generated over a range of a decade in a region which is of practical interest in engineering. The original design also had the merit of a simple design of mechanical–optical force and deformation-measuring system and a display screen from which a steady-state hysteresis loop could be copied, if desired, without resorting to photography.

Unfortunately these apparently substantial advantages are overshadowed by the fundamental drawbacks of the system of dynamic force generation used in the Roelig apparatus, while the optical system of recording has insufficient sensitivity to enable measurements to be taken with low dynamic force. The latter disadvantage has been overcome by fitting electrical displacement pick-ups of the differential transformer type. A sensitive pick-up fitted in the existing steel dynamometer ring gives a much greater force sensitivity than the optical system. A second pick-up with a linear range of about 0·5 in. connected alongside the anvils, converts the deformation into an electrical signal of similar type to that given by the force system. These two signals, after amplification, can either be displayed on a cathode-ray oscilloscope to give the conventional hysteresis loop or for greater accuracy the amplitude ratio of force and displacement signals can be measured on a valve volt-meter to give dynamic stiffness directly. Similarly, the phase difference between the signals can be measured directly on a phase-shift network calibrated in damping factor.

The fundamental disadvantages of the force-generating system have been extensively studied by Payne [67] and co-workers at the Research Association of British Rubber Manufacturers. Their investigation using a piezo-electric force pick-up revealed that the force generated by the Roelig apparatus is far from sinusoidal. Measurements made on the force signal with a wave-analyser showed significant harmonic distortion, with the second harmonic content approaching 100% of the fundamental under some conditions. This excessive generation of second harmonic occurs because the natural frequency of the mass/spring system (made up of the exciter and the precompression spring plus the rubber sample) is

T

usually of such a value that a frequency equal to ($0·5 \times$ natural frequency) falls in the normal working range of the apparatus. This fact, together with non-linear properties inherent in the rubber sample and or the apparatus, produce the excessive harmonic distortion. In the paper quoted the author derives a theoretical curve for a lossy non-linear rubber sample which agrees quite well with the experimental curve of second-harmonic content versus frequency. When a steel spring was placed between the anvils, representing a sample of linear stress–strain characteristic, second harmonic rising to 100% was still found, but the curve fell away much more steeply on either side of the maximum.

Two sources of this non-linearity in the apparatus are known. Movement of the flywheel housing does not deform the pre-compression spring exactly along its axis, giving rise to a non-linear restoring force. At low eccentricity the effect of gravity on the flywheel rotating in a vertical plane also generates second harmonic. These apparatus sources of non-linearity are most significant with a sample such as a gum rubber which has little damping and requires only a small flywheel eccentricity for a given dynamic deformation. When measurements are made on filled rubber samples the non-linearity in the specimen is the most significant factor, but the fact that the apparatus contributes to it as well makes it difficult to utilise it for the precise measurements of the effect in the sample.

In conclusion it should be stated that it is possible by suitable choice of sample stiffness and test frequencies to reduce the disturbing effect of distortion. A wide range of force and amplitude sensitivity (much wider than available in the original apparatus) is necessary to do this successfully. In addition alterations to the weight of the moving system and stiffness of the pre-compression spring can be used, but these involve radical modifications of the apparatus.

(e) *Other mechanical vibration generators.* The fundamental limitations, described above, of the Roelig type of apparatus lead to the consideration of a means of generating a pure sinusoidal force, or a displacement, by a positive mechanical system which will be substantially independent of the stiffness or non-linearity of the specimen. An apparatus was described shortly after Roelig's publication which partially met this requirement. It was due to Aleksandrov and Lazurkin.[68] In their apparatus a cylindrical rubber specimen, held between horizontal platens, was subjected to an oscillatory force generated by compressing a steel spring. A sinusoidal displacement developed mechanically was applied to the upper end of the spring, the lower end of which rested on the back of the upper specimen platen. Aleksandrov and Lazurkin measured the relative deformation of the specimen under these conditions for a frequency range of approximately $0·002$–15 c/sec. and a temperature range of $-80°$ to $+20°$ C. The compliance of the specimen was chosen to be as small as possible to reduce the effect on the compression of the force-generating spring. The small deformation of the specimen which was produced was measured by means of an optical device which deflected a beam of light through an angle proportional to the deformation. Unlike the Roelig apparatus, the force was not displayed optically. Consequently it was only possible to measure the overall length of the band of light produced by the oscillating spot, and hence the peak deformation. From a calibration of the spring and the maximum displacement applied the corresponding peak force can be calculated, and from the ratio of the two, the absolute value of the dynamic stiffness, and hence the absolute modulus. The apparatus, however, provided no means of obtaining the phase angle between the force and deformation. The absolute modulus could not therefore be resolved into elastic (storage) modulus and loss modulus (p. 525), which are the quantities usually required.

Fletcher and Gent described [69] an apparatus utilising the same principle as the above. An eccentric cam imparts a reciprocating motion to a sliding cross-head. The motion of this is transmitted by a rigid rod to the upper half of an elliptical spring, and the lower side of this spring is coupled to the specimen carriage. The rubber specimen consists of two cylinders bonded to either side of a steel block which is fastened to the moving carriage, while metal plates bonded on the outer ends of the rubber cylinders are anchored to the base of the apparatus. The elliptical spring has a compliance in the direction of motion at least 100 times that of the rubber specimen. The deformation of this spring and the specimen are observed by means of photo-electric cells, the illumination of which is modulated by the movement to be measured. In another paper [70] Fletcher and Gent detailed their experimental determinations of shear modulus and damping factor for a number of natural and synthetic rubber compounds using the above apparatus.

The type of apparatus just described has a distinct advantage over the out-of-balance type of exciter in that, once the throw of the eccentric has been set, the force applied is constant irrespective of the frequency of measurement. It can be argued, however, that it is even more satisfactory to apply a constant-amplitude sinusoidal displacement to the specimen and measure the force developed, provided that a really stiff force-measuring system can be used. With a constant-deformation apparatus the large changes in the modulus of the test material, which normally occur when properties are measured over a wide temperature range, can be readily catered for, whereas a test at constant force would result in excessive strain and possibly failure of the specimen when the modulus is low. In addition to this practical advantage, it is obviously desirable to measure the properties at constant amplitude when dealing with materials which exhibit a large change in stiffness with change in amplitude.

For the above reasons the constant-deformation class of apparatus now to be dealt with is considered to be the preferred type of mechanical dynamic measuring apparatus.

Mullins [63] previously described an apparatus of this type, in which a sinusoidal displacement was produced by a rotating eccentric cam. The cylindrical rubber specimen was held between an upper platen in direct contact with the cam and a lower platen resting on a piezo-electric crystal slab. The voltage developed by the crystal was observed on a cathode-ray oscilloscope, so that a continuous record of the force transmitted through the specimen could be obtained. A commutator mounted on the shaft of the cam gave pulses which were also recorded on the oscilloscope and indicated the position of cam, and thereby the applied deformation, at 24 points in each cycle. Measurements were made over a frequency range of 8–150 c/sec. and a temperature range of $-25°$ to $+80°$ C.

The piezo-electric system satisfied the requirement for a very stiff force detector, but in other respects it could not be said to be ideal. This method of force measurement is difficult to calibrate, and its sensitivity may vary with frequency. Later developments of the constant-amplitude method are more satisfactory in this respect.

Davies [71, 72] has described a machine which is completely mechanical, including the force-measuring device. The latter consists of a flat spring steel strip rigidly clamped at each end, and its centre portion is in the form of a platen against which the specimen is compressed. The flat strip forms a beam encastré which deflects by an amount proportional to the force transmitted through the specimen. Consequently the angular rotation of the point of contraflexure of the beam is also proportional to the force to be measured. A fairly long light pointer attached to this point converts the angular movement to an approximately linear one on the record. The lower specimen platen is connected to a yoke driven by a rotating eccentric cam. The apparatus is shown in Fig. 8.12. For simplicity the guides which constrain the yoke so that movement can occur only in a vertical direction are not shown. The specimen thus undergoes a sinusoidal compression between the reciprocating yoke assembly and the horizontal beam. The recording plate, which consists of a smoked glass slide, is carried on an arm attached to the lower specimen platen. There is therefore a relative vertical movement between the slide and moving pointer equal to the vertical displacement between the lower platen and the part of the beam where the pointer is attached. The true compression of the specimen is actually less than the amount recorded. However, the discrepancy is directly proportional to force and is allowed for when the force axis (i.e. compression zero) and the compression axis (i.e. force zero) are recorded on a calibration slide. An auxiliary stationary pointer is used to make a reference line on this slide and all subsequent records so that the calibration lines are readily transferable to all the records. The main drive-shaft is eccentric by $\frac{1}{16}$ in. and has locked on it a collar with the same amount of eccentricity. By altering the position of the collar relative to the shaft the amplitude of deformation can be set at any value between zero and $\frac{1}{8}$ in. The recording slide is not normally in contact with the scribers, but since it is mounted on a leaf spring arm it may be pushed into position when it is required to take a record. In this way a miniature

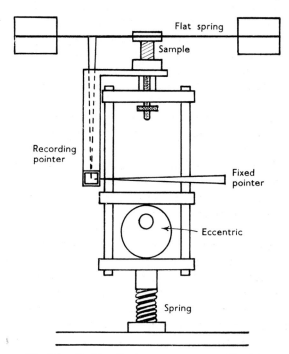

Fig. 8.12. Positive displacement apparatus (Davies).

hysteresis loop is recorded. This is enlarged approximately 60 times by projection and traced off together with the reference line.

McCallion and Davies [66] have carried out measurements on this apparatus over a frequency range of 0·2–20 c/sec. and a temperature range of —60° to +130° C. The test piece was a cylinder of 0·5 in. diam. by 0·5 in. high deformed in compression by various amplitudes up to 10% of its free height.

The Davies apparatus is attractive in principle, particularly to engineering designers, because it sets out to make direct measurements of stress in relation to strain throughout the cycle, without relying on any particular theory of the mechanism of the visco-elastic process in rubber. Some of the methods, described elsewhere, which utilise electro-mechanical transducers and ancillary electronic equipment, as an essential element in the technique, have met with criticism because the conversion of the experimental observations to fundamental quantities is based on the solution of a differential equation which assumes a particular energy loss mechanism, e.g. viscous loss, in the rubber. This view has been extended into a general prejudice against the use of transducers and electronic apparatus for dynamic measurements.

Davies' method may be said to represent the limit in this reversion to purely mechanical techniques; certain practical disadvantages inevitably follow. The compliance of the force-measuring spring must be large enough to provide a usable record with the ratio of mechanical magnification, followed by optical enlargement, that is available. Consequently it cannot be made negligible in relation to the compliance of the rubber specimen, also the range of force that can be measured in one series of experiments is limited, and correspondingly the range of deformations that may be used. McCallion and Davies [66] recognise in their discussion that the finite compliance of the measuring spring interferes with the observation of the non-linear behaviour of the rubber specimen. Although the total deformation imposed is truly sinusoidal, the stress developed in the rubber is not a linear function of strain, and the measuring spring deflects in proportion to this stress. Since this deflection diminishes the compression of the rubber specimen, the resultant strain imposed on it is distorted.

McCallion and Davies' method of taking the record after only a few cycles, called the " jab technique ", already referred to on p. 544, is suited to their experimental set-up. If it is required to follow progressive changes in the specimen, due to mechanical breakdown or heat build-up, the apparatus is not so convenient, since there is no way of visually monitoring the changes in the hysteresis loop so that a suitable moment to take the recording may be chosen.

The apparatus described by Payne [73] and known as the RABRM Sinusoidal Strain Machine overcomes most of the disadvantages of the mechanical methods described above. It utilises the flexibility and sensitivity of electro-mechanical pick-ups and electronic amplification and display without losing the basic advantages of the positive mechanical generation of a sinusoidal displacement.

In this apparatus an eccentric on the driving shaft rotates in a sliding block and thereby moves a cross-head. Horizontal rods are fixed to each side of the cross-head and pass through guide sleeves so that they can move only on the horizontal axis. The outer ends of the rods bear specimen platens, and opposite each moving platen is a stationary one which may be advanced towards it by rotating a hand-wheel on a tail-stock device. The mechanism thus imparts a sinusoidal motion in a horizontal direction to the moving platens. A specimen may be placed between the platens and the required amount of pre-compression applied by rotating the hand-wheel. Fittings are available to strain test pieces in tension, shear or torsion, in addition to compression. The throw of the eccentric is adjust-able by unlocking and rotating an eccentric sleeve around the mainshaft eccentric, similarly to the Davies apparatus. An extra bolt-on flywheel is used to provide sufficient momentum in the moving system at low speeds. The developed form of the apparatus uses only one pair of platens for a rubber specimen, while a steel coil spring, with effectively zero hysteresis, is placed between the other two platens. Two steel dynamometers are fitted between the stationary platens and the tail-stocks. In this way the system is balanced on the two sides, and the dynamometer on the side with the coil spring provides a signal proportional to and in phase with the displacement of the moving platens, while the dynamometer on the other side indicates the force developed in the rubber specimen.

The type of dynamometer used was described by Payne and Smith,[74] it consists of a proof ring formed from a rectangular steel block by drilling a hole at each end and connecting the holes with a narrow slit. The stiff-ness is adjusted to the required value by bevelling the corners of the block. The force–displacement characteristic is linear and is mainly a function of the ring thickness at its thinnest part. A Philips displacement pick-up of the differential transformer type is fitted so that it detects the deflection of the proof ring. When used in conjunction with the Philips measuring bridge the displacement of the proof ring may be indicated in various ranges, the most sensitive being $\pm 3 \mu$ full scale with $0 \cdot 1 \mu$ per division. In order to keep the dynamometer deflection to a low order compared with that of the specimen, the bridge is not normally used on a range higher than 100μ. Steel proof rings can be of any required maximum loading up to several tons. Two described by Payne and used for normal laboratory specimens covered force ranges of approximately 0–10 lb. up to 0–300 lb. for the lighter ring and 0–30 lb. up to 0–900 lb. for the heavier one.

The differential transformer pick-ups are energised from the measuring instrument at 4000 c/sec., and the output signal is in the form of a modula-tion on this carrier. The peak-to-peak force amplitude developed in the rubber specimen may be obtained from readings of the displacement bridge, or the signal may be fed to a cathode-ray oscilloscope and the amplitude measured on the calibrated scale of the oscilloscope. If re-quired, demodulated force and displacement signals may be fed to the oscilloscope to produce the conventional type of hysteresis ellipse for direct observation. The differential transformer type of pick-up has no lower frequency limit, so that force calibration of the dynamometers may be carried out under static conditions.

The apparatus covers a range of strain amplitudes of from 0·001 to 0·25 in. The drive is taken from a 3-h.p. electric motor through a hydraulic transmission giving an infinitely variable speed adjustment. The maximum measuring frequency is 30 c/sec., and by using auxiliary worm-reduction gear-boxes the lower frequency limit is extended to 0·0001 c/sec. Temperature-controlled chambers can be placed over the rubber specimen, enabling measurements to be carried out over a range of −70° to +200° C.

The method of obtaining the phase angle between stress and strain has been improved in the latest development of the apparatus.[75] Direct observation of the hysteresis loop is not a very accurate method of obtaining phase angle when the value is small, as it often is when making measurements on rubber compounds. Payne formerly used the " vector subtraction method " due to Painter.[76] This is only satisfactory if there is negligible harmonic distortion of the force and displacement signals, which in practice limits accurate measurements to shear specimens or compression test-pieces at very low static and dynamic amplitudes, Payne's present method utilises a direct mechanical phase-measuring device. It consists of an insulating disc fastened to the shaft of the machine and having two small metal inserts fastened in its periphery 180° apart. A capacity pick-up is mounted on an arm swinging on the same axis as the shaft. As each metal insert passes under the pick-up the change of capacity is detected by a proximity meter which gives an output pulse on the oscilloscope, twice every revolution of the machine, which is superimposed on the force or displacement signal being viewed on the oscilloscope. By putting the oscilloscope time-base out of action the two pulses appear as horizontal marks on a vertical trace, the position of the pick-up arm is adjusted manually until the two marks coincide, when a reading of its angular position can be taken on a graduated scale behind the arm. Phase readings are taken on the displacement and force signals in turn, and the difference between the two scale readings gives the phase angle directly in degrees.

The advantages, in principle, of making dynamic measurements at constant strain amplitude have already been indicated above (p. 547). The RABRM sinusoidal strain machine, in its present state of development, combines these advantages with a comparatively straight-forward technique of measurement. The object of RABRM has been to develop an apparatus suitable both for scientific work and for general use as a control test and for obtaining engineering design data on samples of rubber compounds, actual whole components or scale models of very large components. It is considered that a further simplification of the measuring technique would help towards this end. No doubt this could be achieved only with purpose-built electronic equipment and consequent increased costs. If this could be accepted, a peak-reading voltmeter could be arranged to read directly the absolute value of specimen stiffness in lb./in., by setting up the applied peak deformation on a calibrated sensitivity control. The method of phase-angle measurement, already considerably simplified compared with the original " Vector " method, could possibly be made even more direct so that the phase-difference reading is taken in one operation instead of two. A sensitive and direct-reading electronic phasemeter, unaffected by harmonic distortion, can be built, but the cost would probably be prohibitive.

The limitations of the apparatus are mainly those inherent in any mechanical system. Inertia and excessive wear on the moving parts will limit the maximum driving frequency. Measurements were made up to 30 c/sec., but the designed upper limit was given as 50 c/sec. Provided that maximum frequencies of this order are acceptable, an apparatus of the type represented by the RABRM sinusoidal strain machine and also by that of Philippoff,[77] not described here, is the most suitable general-purpose dynamic measuring apparatus. Although it is possible to extend the low-frequency observations to higher frequencies by reducing modulus–frequency data obtained at various temperatures, using the very effective temperature–frequency relationship due to Ferry,[78, 79, 80, 119] it is often desirable to make direct observations at higher frequencies, and then one of the electromagnetic, or other electromechanical drive, types of apparatus described in the following sections is to be preferred.

(*f*) *Electro-magnetic type.* The use of moving-coil electro-magnetic vibration generators in systems designed for the measurement of dynamic properties has been reported on numerous occasions, but almost invariably in connection with resonating systems. These have been discussed previously (pp. 538–540), and the severe limitations applying to resonance methods have been commented on. Some years ago this situation could have been explained by the low dynamic force given by the vibration generators then available, and the consequent necessity to operate at resonance in order to develop vibration amplitudes that could be measured with reasonable facility. In recent years vibration generators have reached a high state of development due to their use for full-scale investigation of structural resonances and fatigue in aircraft and other highly stressed structures. As a result, all sizes of generator and associated driving gear are available for this purpose, but the design of electro-mechanical systems for making fundamental measurements of the properties of materials has been investigated by a few workers only.

King, who had already published details of a dynamic measuring apparatus of the resonant type with a moving-iron exciter, discussed a design for an improved type of moving-coil drive resonant apparatus with Erwin Meyer. The latter recommended the double moving-coil method originated by Costadoni,[81] which enables the mechanical impedance of the specimen to be determined without bringing the vibrator to resonance. The Costadoni circuit formed the basis for subsequent developments of King's apparatus.   The details of the large version of this apparatus were published in 1946,[82] and an improved smaller version in 1953.[83]   The final form of this apparatus is well adapted for determinations of dynamic mechanical properties on small rubber test pieces, and will be described in detail.   The most important features of King's apparatus which distinguishes it from ordinary permanent-magnet moving-coil vibration generators, are:

(i) The magnet and moving-coil system is in two parts identical with each other.

(ii) The two moving-coil systems are locked together axially by a bar or tube chosen for maximum stiffness–weight ratio (a thick-wall glass tube or a rod of phenolic resin–cloth laminate have been used).

(iii) The rubber test piece is also duplicated.   One piece being held in contact with each end of the moving system.

A schematic diagram of the apparatus is shown in Fig. 8.13.   As mentioned above, the electrical circuit follows the method of Costadoni.   An oscillator (electronic or electro-mechanical depending on the required frequency) feeds moving coil A (the driving coil), and also connected in series with this coil are the primary of a variable mutual-inductance and

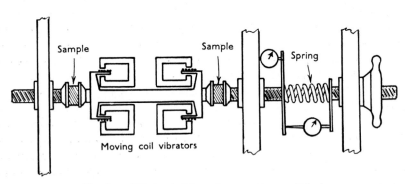

Fig. 8.13. Mechanical impedance apparatus (King).

the input side of a variable resistance network.   The second moving coil B, being rigidly connected to the driving coil through the central armature, undergoes the same vibratory motion.   An output voltage is therefore generated by coil B which is directly proportional to the velocity of the moving system.   This coil is connected in series opposition with the secondary of the mutual inductance and the output of the resistance network. The resulting difference voltage is fed to a selective amplifier-detector, which is tuned to the frequency of the driving oscillator. The variable mutual inductance and the resistance network are successively adjusted until a minimum voltage is indicated by the detector. At this minimum point the output of moving coil B is balanced both in amplitude and phase by the co-ordinate potentiometer. The readings of mutual inductance and resistance at the balance point, when inserted in the equations which are derived below, enable the dynamic stiffness and mechanical damping of the test pieces to be calculated.

The measuring system described is not usable for frequencies below about 1 c/sec., because the design of a tuned detector for frequencies much lower than this is rather impracticable. In addition, since the output voltage for a given amplitude of the moving coil is proportional to the square of the frequency, the voltage to be balanced by the co-ordinate potentiometer will be inconveniently small at very low frequencies. Nevertheless, with suitable alternative driving and measuring systems there is no lower limit to the frequency at which measurements may be made with this apparatus. King makes use of a low-frequency electro-mechanical oscillator consisting of a D.C. generator modified so that the output is taken from brushes which can be rotated around the commutator at the required frequency. The brush drive is servo-controlled, so that a stable output frequency is obtainable over a wide range of frequencies. Other methods of generating very-low-frequency alternating current are available, such as motor-driven potentiometer systems or the mixing of the output of two alternators having a difference in frequency equal to the required frequency. Generally speaking, none of these methods will give an absolutely pure output at the required frequency, but a low-pass filter system can be used to reduce harmonics, or brush noise, or the unwanted components from the mixed-frequency system.

The alternative measuring system for low frequencies must be one which responds to amplitude of the vibrator motion, rather than velocity, for the reason given above. The method used by King consists of a small tilting mirror connected by a lever to the armature of the vibrator so that the mirror rotates through an angle proportional to the vibrator amplitude. The tilting mirror is used in conjunction with a multiple-channel photo-graphic recorder from which one of the mirror galvanometers normally used has been removed. A beam of light from a galvanometer lamp is reflected from the tilting mirror back on to the recording camera. One of the remaining galvanometer channels is used to record the current through the driving coil. In this way a simultaneous recording can be taken of driving current and armature motion, and in addition to the amplitude of the vibrator the phase relationship with the drive current can be directly assessed.

The equations relating dynamic stiffness and damping and the co-ordinate potentiometer readings are derived as follows.

It is assumed that the two test pieces on which measurements are made have identical properties. Since the dynamic stiffness (S) determined with the apparatus is the sum of the stiffness of the two samples, then $S = 2s'$, where $s' =$ stiffness of one test piece. Secondly, it is assumed that mechanical damping may be calculated in terms of viscous damping, i.e. the damping force $= F \cdot \dfrac{dx}{dt}$, where $\dfrac{dx}{dt} =$ velocity of armature; $F =$ damping coefficient. As noted for S, $F = 2f'$, where $f' =$ damping coefficient for one test piece. The apparatus constants, which are determined by the methods described later, are:

$W =$ Total mass of moving parts;
$P =$ Force developed by driving coil per unit current;
$V =$ Voltage output of pick-up coil per unit velocity.

The standard equation of motion for forced vibration with viscous damping is of the form

$$m(d^2x/dt^2) + c(dx/dt) + kx = p \cos \omega t$$

where $m =$ mass; $x =$ displacement; $c =$ damping coefficient; $k =$ stiffness; $p =$ force amplitude. This may be rewritten in terms of the quantities given above, thus

$$\frac{W}{g}\left(\frac{d^2x}{dt^2}\right) + F\left(\frac{dx}{dt}\right) + Sx = PI \cos \omega t \quad . \quad . \quad (8.83)$$

The physical significance of this relationship is that the vector addition of the forces due to inertia, damping and elasticity is balanced by the driving force produced by a sinusoidal current $I \cos \omega t$.

A second equation representing the null balance of the vibrator output voltage against the co-ordinate potentiometer may be written as follows:

$$V(dx/dt) = RI + M(dI/dt) \quad . \quad . \quad . \quad (8.84)$$

In the vector system single differentiation is equivalent to multiplication by $j\omega$, and double differentiation is equivalent to multiplication by $-\omega^2$, eqn. 8.83 and 8.84 may be written vectorially as follows:

$$-(W/g)\omega^2 x + j\omega Fx + Sx = PI \quad . \quad . \quad (8.85)$$
$$RI + j\omega MI = j\omega Vx \quad . \quad . \quad . \quad (8.86)$$

Hence
$$I = \frac{j\omega Vx}{R + j\omega M} = \frac{j\omega Vx(R - j\omega M)}{R^2 + \omega^2 M^2} \quad . \quad . \quad (8.87)$$

Substitute eqn. 8.87 in eqn. 8.85 to eliminate I and x giving

$$-\omega^2(W/g) + j\omega F + S = VP(j\omega R + \omega^2 M)/(R^2 + \omega^2 M^2) \quad (8.88)$$

By taking out the real terms and imaginary terms and equating them separately we get:

$$S - \omega^2\left(\frac{W}{g}\right) = \frac{VP}{M}\left(\frac{\omega^2 M^2}{R^2 + \omega^2 M^2}\right) \quad . \quad . \quad . \quad (8.89)$$

and

$$F = \frac{VPR}{R^2 + \omega^2 M^2} \quad . \quad . \quad . \quad . \quad (8.90)$$

Thus it will be seen that if the apparatus constants W and VP are known the values of S and F can be calculated from the readings of M and R on the co-ordinate potentiometer.

To obtain the calibration constants it is possible to remove the double moving-coil and magnet assembly, mount it with the axis vertical instead of horizontal and determine a relationship between direct current through one coil and force developed. The latter can be determined by placing weights on the upper platen until the armature is just restored to its un-deflected position. The value of the constant P is then given directly by the slope of the force v current graph. Since the relationship between P and VP can be derived theoretically, it is not essential to determine V separately. The remaining apparatus constant W can be determined by weighing all the moving parts before assembly, but there is a slightly indeterminate factor in that the mass of the leaf-spring suspensions contributes to some extent to the total mass in motion.

There is an alternative method of arriving at both VP and W which is preferable in some respects to the direct approach. Under normal operating conditions the first term in eqn. 8.89 (S = the stiffness of the two test pieces) is larger than the second term ($\omega^2(W/g)$ = the inertia of the moving system). In other words, the apparatus is normally operated well below the resonant frequency of the test piece and armature system, and the movement of the armature is said to be " stiffness controlled ". If the apparatus is operated without test pieces between the platens the inertia term becomes very much larger than the residual stiffness due to the leaf-spring suspension. Under these conditions the resonant frequency of the system is brought down to a much lower value than normal, and it is therefore possible to operate above the resonance in the " mass-controlled " frequency range. The residual damping in the apparatus without test pieces is also negligible, and eqn. 8.89 can therefore be reduced to

$$-\omega^2\frac{W}{g} = \frac{VP}{M} \quad . \quad . \quad . \quad . \quad (8.91)$$

The method of calibrating the apparatus making use of this relationship is as follows. In place of the normal sample platens, two alternative platens, to which can be bolted a series of additional masses, are fitted on the vibrator.   The armature is driven at a small amplitude, and balance readings taken as when making measurements on rubber specimens, but as the inertia term $(-\omega^2 W/g)$ is negative, a negative value of M will be required to obtain a balance.   This is obtained by reversing the connections to one winding of the mutual inductance.   From eqn. 8.91 it will be seen that

$$(W + \Delta W) = (VPg)(-1/\omega^2 M) \quad . \quad . \quad . \quad (8.92)$$

and that if the values of $(-1/\omega^2 M)$ are plotted against known values of ΔW the points will fall about a straight line.   The slope of the straight line gives the value of the constant (VPg) in eqn. 8.92, and consequently the value of the required constant VP.   If the straight line is extrapolated downwards, to the point where $(1/\omega^2 M) = 0$, it will give an intercept on the negative part of the x-axis (the ΔW axis), equal to the dynamic value of W, which, as mentioned previously, may be slightly higher than the mass of the armature only, due to the inertia of the suspension.

Range and limitations of King's apparatus.   As mentioned in the description of the apparatus, there is no fundamental lower-frequency limit to the use of the apparatus itself, but the driving supply and detector system used at normal frequencies are not suitable for very low frequencies. For very-low-frequency work the mechanical displacement types of apparatus have the advantage of simplicity of driving system.   One form of the latter (see p. 551) also has a detector system which has no low-frequency limit (a differential transformer type of pick-up).   There is no reason why a similar system could not be adapted for very-low-frequency measurements of displacement on the King Apparatus so that the optical method could be dispensed with.

The measurement of properties of rubbery materials in the very-low-frequency range is mainly of interest in completing the survey of these properties over several decades of frequency as part of the effort to correlate the fundamental relaxation properties with polymer structure.   From the practical design of rubber components standpoint measurements in a frequency range from about 10 c/sec. upwards are normally required, and for this range the King apparatus with the co-ordinate potentiometer measuring system is convenient in use and capable of measuring dynamic stiffness to an accuracy of about 2%.   Known static loading is applied to the rubber specimens by means of calibrated steel springs, and loads up to 225 kg. may be applied without damage to the central rod which connects the moving coils and transmits the loading from one specimen to the other. The platens are designed to apply compression loading to the specimens, but provided that the rubber is bonded to suitable metal pieces, measurements may be made using simple shear deformation instead of compression. Within the limits of space and loading available the properties of small sizes of rubber mounting units may be determined in this apparatus. The upper sample stiffness to which the apparatus will function without loss of accuracy is about 1,800 kg./cm. for the combined stiffness of the specimens. The highest measurable mechanical Q at the upper stiffness limit is 20, and for lower stiffness samples higher Q's may be accurately determined. The axial stiffness of the suspension system supporting the armature is of the order of 6 kg./cm. If measurements are required on specimens whose order of stiffness is not much higher than this, the value of the suspension stiffness should be subtracted from the calculated values of S. Measurements must be made at frequencies which do not approach the resonance of the armature system combined with the specimens in question. With this proviso, frequencies up to 500 c/sec. may be used without exciting any self-resonances in the mechanical structure of the apparatus.

The apparatus is not suitable for making measurements on semi-rubbery materials which exhibit a large amount of plastic flow under static loading. To some extent this problem can be overcome by applying a known deformation to the specimens instead of a known load. The stress decay under constant deformation may then be determined in a separate experiment. This is required because the outer platens are necessarily clamped in position during dynamic measurements so that the properties are effectively observed under constant deformation.

Another disadvantage of King's apparatus, in its normal form, is the difficulty of making measurements at temperatures much removed from ambient, owing to the large heat conducting paths presented by the structure of the apparatus connected to the fixed platens. A considerably modified version of the method has been developed by Fitzgerald and Ferry [79] who describe a double moving coil apparatus immersed in a thermostat bath, so that measurements can be made over a temperature range of $-50°$ to $+150°$ C. The specimens are deformed in shear against a suspended mass and measurements can be made on materials ranging from soft gels to rigid solids, over a frequency range from 25 to 5000 c/sec. A precision better than $\pm 2\%$ is claimed but not, of course, over the whole range of temperature and frequency mentioned.

3. Resonance of specimens without added mass

(a) *As a long cord.* If one end of a long rubber strip is vibrated at fairly low frequencies (below about 1 kc/sec.) the attenuation along the strip may be sufficiently small for resonance of the whole strip to be observed at certain frequencies. This will occur when the length of the strip is an integral number of half-wavelengths. This effect may be described as a " mechanical transmission line " resonance, and it is possible to derive the complex dynamic modulus from observations of the centre frequency and band-width of the resonance. Nolle [32] describes an apparatus, shown diagrammatically in Fig. 8.14. The exciting and receiving transducers are gramophone-record cutting heads, of the piezo-electric or electro-magnetic type, connected mechanically to the strip so that they generate

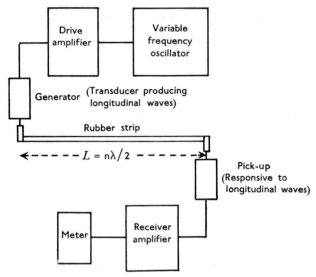

Fig. 8.14. Schematic diagram of strip resonance apparatus (Nolle).

or respond to longitudinal waves. Nolle used this technique to investigate temperature dependence of dynamic properties in a temperature range of $15°–70°$ and a frequency range of 60–300 c/sec.

Nolle [84] gives a theoretical analysis of the method, and by making various simplifying assumptions derives some useful approximations as follows:

$$E_1 = \rho(2lf/n)^2 \quad . \quad . \quad . \quad . \quad (8.93)$$
$$E_2/E_1 = 1 \cdot 55 \Delta f/f \quad . \quad . \quad . \quad . \quad (8.94)$$

where ρ = density; n = mode of vibration (1, or 3, or 5, etc.); f = frequency of maximum response; Δf = band-width c/sec. (i.e. difference between frequencies at which amplitude is $(1/\sqrt{2})$ of maximum); l = length of strip.

(b) *As a diaphragm.* Meyer has made attempts to utilise the bending of circular plates of rubber by clamping on two aluminium foil electrodes and using electrostatic applied forces and electrostatic methods of picking up the amplitude of vibration, but little useful information has been obtained, because of the limitations of the present theory of the bending of plates.

(c) *As a cantilever.* A method using the flexural wave resonance of an elastic cantilever has been described by Nolle.[35] The method involves observing the frequency of resonance and the band-width for forced vibrations of a rubber reed. The method can be used in the frequency range of 10–500 c/sec., but above a 100 c/sec. it is difficult to see the resonance with materials having a Q of less than about 5.

4. Double electromechanical transducer

The transmission of mechanical vibrations in the lower audio-frequency range through a variety of rubbers has been measured by Morris and co-workers.[85, 86] The method used consisted basically of clamping a rubber specimen in the form of a right cylinder ($\frac{1}{2}$ in. thick × $\frac{3}{4}$ in. diam.) between two metal plates, causing one of the plates to vibrate through a small amplitude, and measuring the vibrational force transmitted through the rubber to the other plate. A piezo-electric transducer was used to generate the vibrations, and an identical transducer was used as a detector. The whole assembly was mounted in a heavy steel block suspended on rubber. With rubbers of about 50° B.S. hardness and with a static load of about 60 lb. on the sample the apparatus could be used from 25 up to 2,000 c/sec. Above this frequency mechanical resonances in the apparatus made the results unreliable at various frequencies.

The apparatus was chiefly used for comparison of the transmissibility, but the force transmitted can be used as a relative measure of the dynamic modulus.

$$\text{Dynamic modulus } E = \frac{\Delta F/A}{\Delta H/H}$$

where ΔF = Max. value of sinusoidal force applied; A = cross-sectional area; ΔH = amplitude of vibration; H = height of compressed sample.

Measurements of the internal viscosity can also be obtained from the phase change between the voltage in the generating transducer and in the detecting transducer.

Most of the disadvantages of the above method are avoided in the modification due to Harrison, Sykes and Martin,[123] who measure transmissibility as the ratio of the accelerations of two masses separated by the rubber specimen. A separate vibration generator is used, and since the driven mass is freely suspended, the excessively massive framework is no longer needed. Snowden[124] has used this technique to determine the transmissibility of various rubber compounds at frequencies ranging up to 10 kc/s.

5. The magnetostriction method
(Loading effect on an independent transducer)

Measurements of the dynamic moduli of rubbers in the higher-frequency ranges (about 10–100 kc/sec.) can be made by observation of the change of resonant frequency of a metal rod excited longitudinally by magneto-striction when a rubber sample is forced into contact with the end of the rod.   The change of resonance frequency is proportional to the real part of the modulus of the rubber, while the accompanying change in band-width is proportional to the imaginary part of the modulus.   An apparatus using this method has been described by Nolle,[87] and is shown schematically in Fig. 8.15.   A small disc sample of rubber is held under compression

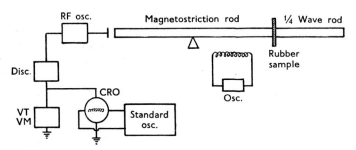

Fig. 8.15. Magnetostriction apparatus (Nolle).

between a resonant magnetostrictive rod and an anti-resonant rod having half the length of the resonant rod.   The resonant rod is driven magneto-strictively and the relative amplitude of vibration of the rod measured by means of an electrostatic pick-up plate located near the free end of the rod. A number of rods are necessary to cover a frequency range, but as the second and third modes of vibration of each rod can be used, a small number of suitably chosen rods will cover a wide frequency range.

Though the method is simple in outline, the apparatus tends to be complex and the operation tedious, but the method gives reliable results in frequency ranges that have proved difficult to cover by other methods. A number of thicknesses of rubber are necessary, as the sample must be thin enough to load the rod sufficiently to cause a detectable frequency shift, but the loading must not decrease the amplitude of the vibration below detectable limits.   The thickness of the sample must also be small compared with a wavelength in the rubber at the measuring frequency. A maximum ratio of 1 : 12 is suggested by Nolle in order that the specimen can be considered as a simple damped spring.

6. Impulse loading systems

Volterra [88,89] and co-workers have worked out a theory and described a method for deriving the dynamic properties of rubbery materials from the stress–strain curves obtained when materials are subject to impact loads of very short duration.

The apparatus used consisted essentially of two long bars, between which the sample is clamped. An impact load is applied to the first bar by means of a blow from a falling hammer bar, and the shock transmitted to the second bar is measured by means of strain gauges clamped to it. The apparatus has been used for rubbers of hardness 20°–50° shore and for impact velocities of 20–80 cm./sec.

7. Acoustic transmission methods

(a) *Longitudinal waves in strips.* Measurements of the propagation of longitudinal acoustic waves can be used to determine the visco-elastic properties of a rubber-like material. The cross-sectional dimensions of the specimen must be small in relation to the wavelength of sound in the material at the frequency in question, and care must be taken to avoid the occurrence of flexural waves in addition to the longitudinal. The quantities to be determined experimentally are the density of the specimen, the attenuation of the transmitted wave and either the velocity or the wavelength of sound in the material. Nolle outlined this method [90] and derived the relationship between the experimentally measured quantities and the dynamic Young's modulus and loss factor. In a second paper [91] the method is described in detail, and the following simplified equations are given:

$$E'/\rho c^2 = (1 - r^2)/(1 + r^2)^2 \quad . \quad . \quad . \quad (8.95)$$
$$E''/E' = 2r/(1 - r^2) \quad . \quad . \quad . \quad . \quad (8.96)$$

Where E' is the real part of the dynamic Young's modulus, and E'' the imaginary part, so that E''/E' is the " loss factor ", ρ is the density of the sample and c the velocity of sound in the sample. The attenuation in the sample is measured in dB/cm. and is represented by β. Hence the attenuation in dB per wavelength is given by $\beta\lambda$. In the above equations r is a dimensionless ratio relating the observed attenuation per wavelength to the attenuation in a purely viscous wave, and is equal to $\beta\lambda/54\cdot6$. Nolle also gives [91] a nomograph to facilitate conversion of observations of wavelength and attenuation at a certain frequency into values of E' and E''.

The longitudinal wave method was first used by Meyer. The apparatus described by Kuhl and Meyer [57] uses an electro-magnetic vibration generator for the lower frequencies, or a piezo-electric or magnetostriction generator for the higher frequencies, to excite one end of the sample strip. Originally the receiver consisted simply of a gramophone pick-up with a stylus resting lightly on the sample strip. The pick-up system was arranged so that it could be mechanically traversed along the strip. This system has disadvantages which become more critical at higher frequencies. The contact of the stylus has a slight damping effect on the vibration in the strip, reflection of the transmitted wave may take place at the point of contact, and above about 5 kc/sec. the amplitude in the strip is usually too small in relation to the sensitivity of the pick-up and the method breaks down. Meyer developed an alternative system in which the sample strip hangs down into a column of liquid contained in a thermostated metal pot. Provided that precautions are taken to avoid transmission of sound from the projector, other than through the sample strip, and also to avoid picking up extraneous noise, a very sensitive hydrophone immersed in the liquid gives a signal proportional to the vibration level in the sample strip. With this set-up a plot of the variation of vibration level along the strip can readily be obtained by arranging for the projector, and sample strip suspended from it, to be moved upwards on a carriage running along a vertical lead-screw. The lead-screw and the chart of an automatic level recorder are both driven by synchronous motors, and the drive gearing is arranged to give various simple ratios between the movement of the sample and the movement of the recorder chart. The vibration level recorded on the chart at any instant represents the level in the sample strip in the plane of the liquid surface, so that as the strip is drawn upwards the required plot is made automatically. It should be noted that if the liquid in the pot had a free surface, open to the air, the level obtained from the hydrophone would not strictly represent sample vibration in the plane of the liquid surface, but over a range extending down from this place for a distance of approximately a quarter of a wavelength in the strip. To avoid this uncertainty Meyer closed the liquid surface with a rigid metal lid, with a slot in it just large enough for the sample strip to pass freely through. By this means the strip enters the liquid at a " sound-hard " interface (instead of a " sound-soft " one), and the transfer of energy to the liquid is effectively at the surface place.

Meyer's apparatus is shown schematically in Fig. 8.16, which includes a block diagram of the recording gear referred to above. The phase-difference recorder produces a chart of phase angle between the driving voltage and the amplified signal from the receiver versus the distance along the sample strip. The wavelength of sound in the sample strip (λ) can be read directly from the phase-difference chart. The other record is an automatic plot of signal (in decibels above a reference level) versus distance along the strip. This record, apart from short-term fluctuations, should approximate to a straight line. The slope of this line gives the attenuation in the sample strip in dB/cm. (β). Wavelength may be converted to velocity by the usual simple relationship, as follows, and the values inserted in eqn. 8.95 and 8.96 above.

$$c = f\lambda \qquad . \qquad . \qquad . \qquad . \qquad . \qquad (8.97)$$

where $c =$ velocity of sound in the sample; $f =$ frequency; $\lambda =$ wavelength of sound in the sample. Alternatively, the uncorrected relationship between velocity and modulus in a long thin elastic rod may be used, as follows, and a correction applied for the effect of damping. The correc-

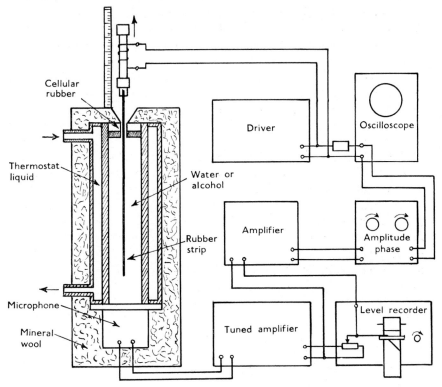

Fig. 8.16. Longitudinal wave apparatus (Meyer).

tion is given in Fig. 8.16a together with the relationship between $\beta\lambda$ and the loss factor η, both taken from Meyer's paper.[42]

$$c = \sqrt{\frac{E}{\rho}} \qquad \ldots \quad \ldots \quad \ldots \quad (8.98)$$

Hence
$$E = \rho f^2 \lambda_c^2 \qquad \ldots \quad \ldots \quad \ldots \quad (8.99)$$

where E = dynamic Young's modulus, ρ = density, λ_c = (observed wavelength) $\times$ (correction factor from Fig. 8.16a).

The apparatus described by Nolle [91] differs from Meyer's in two main respects. The sample strip is held horizontally, one end being connected to the vibration generator (a record-cutting head) and the other end passes over a pulley to a small weight which keeps the strip in tension. Nolle also uses a direct contact pick-up, a method which was rejected by Meyer, the pick-up being either a normal gramophone type with a light stylus or, alternatively, a thin piezo-electric bimorph, similar to those used in gramo-phone pick-ups, may be placed directly in contact with the sample strip. Nolle's apparatus is built up on a small lathe bed, and the pick-up is mounted on the tool post and can be continuously traversed along the sample strip by the normal lathe lead-screw. A heating or cooling thermostat surrounds the specimen so that measurements can be made over a range of $-60°$ to $+100°$ C, provided that the sample properties

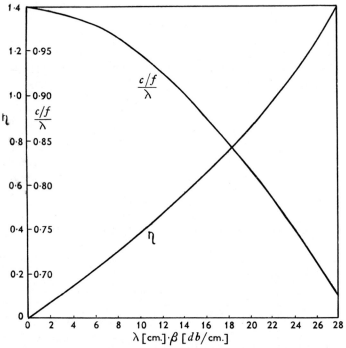

Fig. 8.16a. Ratio of wavelengths in undamped and damped medium ($c/f\lambda$) and loss factor ($\eta = E''/E'$) as functions of the measured quantities λ and for β extensional and torsional waves. (Kuhl and Meyer [42]).

have not changed to such an extent that they are outside the measurable range. The recording equipment used by Nolle is similar in principle to Meyer's, which is described above. Hillier and Kolsky [92, 93, 94] have used a method similar to Nolle's but without the continuous traverse for the pick-up or the automatic recording gear. Instead, the pick-up was moved by fixed amounts along the rubber strip and readings of phase difference (on a double-beam oscilloscope) and amplitude taken at each point.

A similar technique has been described by Witte, Mrowca and Guth,[95] who made measurements on thin strips (cross-section 2–3 mm. × 0·45 mm.) of butyl and butadiene–styrene (SBR) synthetic rubbers.

Limitations of the strip transmission method

In order that the method described above may be used for the accurate determination of the elastic and dissipative constants it is necessary to use a specimen in the form of a strip or cord with cross-sectional dimensions which are small compared with the wavelength of sound in the material. As the measuring frequency is raised it eventually becomes impracticable to meet this requirement. Even if the problem of fabricating the thin-sectioned specimen is overcome, the energy transferred to it by the generator and transmitted through it to the water vessel will fall below the limit of sensitivity of the hydrophone system.

For a given specimen dimension the upper limit of measuring frequency will occur approximately at the value where

$$b/\lambda_0 = 1/6 \quad . \quad . \quad . \quad . \quad . \quad . \quad (8.100)$$

where b = width of specimen; λ_0 = wavelength in specimen as $b \longrightarrow 0$. Above this frequency wave propagation becomes critically dependent on the geometry of the specimen and the method is no longer a practicable one for the determination of the constants of the material.

If the thickness of the specimen is kept below the limit and the width increased to several wavelengths ($b/\lambda_0 > 4$), valid measurements can again be made. Instead of observing longitudinal waves in the thin rod, and deriving the dynamic Young's modulus (E), we are now dealing with longitudinal waves in a thin plate, and it can be shown theoretically that the modulus for this condition is given by:

$$E_{\text{Plate}} = E/ (1 - \nu^2) \quad . \quad . \quad . \quad . \quad (8.101)$$

where ν = Poisson's ratio (i.e. ratio lateral contraction/longitudinal extension, in a uniaxial extension). To a first approximation $\nu = 0.5$ for rubber-like materials, so that

$$E_{\text{Plate}} \approx 4E/3 \quad . \quad . \quad . \quad . \quad . \quad (8.102)$$

This value can be substituted for E in the equations given previously (eqn. 8.95 and 8.96), leaving the expression for attenuation unchanged. The excitation of a wide strip presents practical difficulties, since it is necessary that the vibration should be in phase across the width of the strip. A condition approximating to this has been achieved by Meyer, who suspended the specimen from one edge of a U-sectioned steel channel. The latter is excited in a simple mode in which the arms of the U vibrate transversely in antiphase, like an extended tuning fork. The uniform amplitude of the channel is not maintained in the rubber strip, but the phase of the longitudinal vibration is constant across the majority of the width of the strip.

In general, the narrow-strip transmission method can be applied almost to the upper limit of the audio range, that is to about 15,000 c/sec. The wide-strip method does not appear to have been used to extend the frequency range, presumably because of the difficulty of designing a suitable section and resonating it for such a frequency, coupled with the fact that a reliable value of the Poisson's ratio (v) is required to derive E with any precision. At rather lower frequencies, where both methods can be applied, it would seem that the comparison of moduli obtained by the narrow- and wide-strip methods could be used to derive the value of v at these frequencies, using the eqn. 8.101 above.

The lower limit of measurement of the strip transmission method is governed by the velocity and attenuation in the specimen. It is necessary that there should be a sufficient phase change in the specimen to enable the wavelength to be determined and also enough attenuation to avoid a significant reflection of energy from the free end of the strip. In practice, this means that the lower limit comes at about 100 c/sec. or a few times higher than this.

(*b*) *Bulk wave propagation.* We have seen in the previous section that measurements by methods using thin strips or sheets are limited to the audio-frequency range. At ultrasonic frequencies, that is above about 20 kc/sec., specimens with minimum dimensions several times the wavelength of sound in the material, at the frequency of measurement, are normally used. Consequently, the specimen may be considered to approximate to an infinitely extending medium for the propagation of acoustic waves. If the medium is a true fluid only the longitudinal type of wave can be propagated, but in the elastic or viscoelastic materials that we are concerned with, shear forces as well as compressional can be supported, and consequently transverse (shear) waves as well as longitudinal (compressional) waves can be propagated. Ignoring, for the moment the dissipative, i.e., viscous properties, the velocity of propagation may be shown by the classical theory of elasticity to be given by:

$$c = \sqrt{(\text{Elastic wave constant})/(\text{Density})} \quad . \quad . \quad (8.103)$$

This is the same form as was quoted above for longitudinal waves in thin rods (eqn. 8.98), but whereas in the latter case the elastic constant was the Young's modulus, a different constant applies for each type of bulk wave propagation and, in terms of Lamé's constants λ and μ, they are as follows:

Elastic wave constants

Longitudinal bulk wave	$\lambda + 2\mu$	. .	(8.104)
Transverse wave	μ	. .	(8.105)

The value of the common elastic moduli in terms of Lamé's constants are as follows (see, for example, Love [96]).

Young's modulus (E) $\qquad = \dfrac{3\mu(\lambda + \frac{2}{3}\mu)}{\lambda + \mu}$. (8.106)

Shear modulus (G) $\qquad = \mu$ . . . (8.107)

Compression (bulk) modulus $(K) = (\lambda + \frac{2}{3}\mu)$ . . (8.108)

The longitudinal bulk wave is for convenience called a compression or a dilational wave, while the transverse wave is called a shear or distortional wave. Since the constant for the latter is the ordinary shear modulus, it may seem anomalous that the dilational wave constant is not equal to the bulk modulus. In fact, the longitudinal bulk wave involves both dilation, that is alteration of density, and distortion. Imagine a small cube of material in the path of a plane dilational wave. A cross-section of the cube at right angles to the direction of propagation will be unchanged by the passage of the wave, but along the line of the wave the dimensions of the cube will undergo a disturbance, hence the description " longitudinal wave ". Thus the small element not only changes in volume but is also distorted from its cubical shape and the dilational wave constant is not simply the bulk modulus. From eqn. 8.104, 8.107 and 8.108 the dilational wave constant can be expressed in terms of ordinary moduli as follows:

$$\lambda + 2\mu = K + \tfrac{4}{3}G . \qquad \qquad (8.109)$$

Similarly, from eqn. 8.106, 8.107 and 8.108, Young's modulus can be expressed in terms of the two other common moduli:

$$E = \frac{3KG}{K + G/3} \qquad \cdot \quad \cdot \quad \cdot \quad \cdot \quad (8.110)$$

It will be seen that it is not possible to derive the ordinary moduli solely from observations of dilational waves, but if measurements are also made with distortional waves over the same frequency range it is possible to calculate equivalent values of Young's modulus, or bulk modulus, from the two wave constants. The discussion above has been confined to the simple case of plane waves in an elastic medium without boundaries, and the various constants have not been derived from first principles. For a detailed treatment the reader is referred to the monograph by Kolsky,[97] which covers both the classical theory of elastic waves and its extension to imperfectly elastic materials.

The simplest way to define wave constants for an imperfectly elastic material is to assume that the dissipative mechanism is viscous and replace the ordinary elastic moduli with the complex moduli defined on p. 525. In these definitions a " loss bulk modulus " K'' was included without comment. In fact, there has in the past been considerable discussion on whether a " *bulk viscosity* " η_B exists at all ($K'' = \omega\eta_B$). The classical hypothesis, due to Stokes, was that there is no viscous loss associated with a bulk compression. This has been disproved for a number of liquids, but data on the complex bulk modulus of rubber-like materials is difficult to obtain. Apart from the experimental problems, the relationship between the various fundamental constants, and their relative values in the case of rubber, make an accurate determination difficult. If each type of elastic modulus has associated with it a corresponding loss modulus the observations of the attenuation of dilational waves will lead to an estimate of $(K'' + 4G''/3)$. Independent observations with shear waves will provide a value of G'' so that K'' may be obtained by subtraction of $(4G''/3)$. The estimate of K'' is necessarily less precise than either of the quantities from which it is derived, and since the values obtained for many rubber polymers have been small compared with G'', the error involved in retaining Stokes's hypothesis has in these cases been less than the experimental error of the determination. The adoption of this expedient leads to a " three-constant " system, in which two elastic moduli and one loss modulus are sufficient to define the properties of the material at any one frequency. In the general case two elastic and two loss moduli are required. Theoretically K' can be calculated if any other two elastic constants are known, but because of the large difference in order between K' and G', this is not a practical possibility for rubber-like materials. There is no way in which K'' can be derived other than by observations of bulk waves or by direct bulk compressibility measurements at the required frequency. The relationships for calculating the constants from the experimental observations are given later (see p. 582).

Experimental methods using bulk-wave propagation

Numerous workers have made measurements of the propagation of bulk waves in rubber-like materials. Such investigations are valuable in connection with the fundamental study of viscoelastic behaviour and the structure of polymers, and are also of practical importance because these materials find many applications in ultrasonic devices.

Piezoelectric transducers provide the most convenient means of generating and detecting ultrasonic waves, and the development of the newer ceramic electrostrictive materials has overcome many of the limitations of the crystals originally used for this purpose.

(*i*) *Continuous wave methods, single frequency.* If a continuous wave is passed between a transmitter and receiver several wavelengths apart and facing one another in a fluid medium, a standing wave will in general be set up. This can be shown by moving one of the transducers towards or away from the other, when cyclic changes in the amplitude of the signal received will be observed. This is the basis of the " acoustic interferometer ", which has been widely used for making precision measurements of velocity and attenuation in gases and liquids. For this purpose one of the transducers may be supported on a carriage traversed by an accurately cut lead-screw, but for the interferometer method it is often more convenient to use only a single fixed transducer and oppose it with a rigid metal reflector connected to the micrometer. As the acoustic path length is changed the load presented to the transducer will vary between maxima, which occur when the path is an integral number of half wavelengths, and the minima at the quarter wavelengths. This can be observed as a variation in transducer driving current. When making measurements on a liquid, the current maxima (i.e. quarter-wave points) will be the sharper points, and the velocity is simply derived as

$$c = \left(\frac{2 \times \text{Distance traversed}}{\text{Number of intervals between current maxima}} \right) \cdot f \quad (8.111)$$

where f = frequency; c = velocity in medium.

The interferometer method is not so convenient or precise for measurements on solids. Obviously the path length cannot be continuously variable. The alternative of the fixed-path interferometer, in which the number of wavelengths in the path is varied by altering the frequency, is not satisfactory for rubber-like materials because of their large change in properties with frequency. The method that has been adopted is to introduce a sheet of the solid material into the acoustic path in a liquid-filled interferometer. Thus over a portion of the path equal to the thickness of the specimen the liquid has been replaced by the material whose properties are to be measured. The following requirements must be met before this method can yield satisfactory results:

(a) The acoustic impedance (ρc) of the specimen must be approximately the same as that of the liquid medium, in order to minimise reflections at the solid–liquid interfaces.

(b) The material must be homogeneous and free from voids or particles of a size which is a significant fraction of the wavelength in the material.

(c) The liquid must thoroughly wet the specimen to ensure acoustic contact.

The last point can be met by soaking the specimen in the liquid for a long period prior to the measurement or by using a wetting agent, i.e. a surface-active compound. Fortunately the requirement for impedance matching is already approximately satisfied for many soft rubber compounds in a water medium. In cases where water presents too great a mismatch, or is not suitable because of the required temperature of measurement, alternatives, such as glycerol or ethylene glycol, which have higher acoustic impedances, or methyl or ethyl alcohol, which have lower impedances, may be more suitable (see table of properties in Mason [99]). Combinations of miscible liquids may be used to obtain a required impedance, but the properties of mixtures often cannot be simply predicted from the properties of the components.   For example the sound velocity in 30% ethyl alcohol in water is appreciably higher than in either alcohol or water alone, presumably due to a reduction in the degree of association (see Hueter and Bolt [101]).

On introducing the solid specimen into the interferometer there will be a change in the standing-wave pattern, unless it so happens that the velocity in the specimen is exactly the same as in the liquid medium.   If the interferometer is adjusted to resonance (i.e. a current maximum) and then readjusted after inserting the sample, the required velocity can be obtained from the displacement (x) and the velocity in the liquid medium (c_0).   If the velocity in the sample is higher than in the liquid the adjustment will be to increase the path length, and the sign of x will be negative, while for a lower velocity in the sample a decrease in path length will be required and x will be positive.   The velocity is given by:

$$c_r = c_0 t/(t \pm x) \quad . \quad . \quad . \quad . \quad . \quad (8.112)$$

where c_r = velocity in sample; c_0 = velocity in medium; t = thickness of sample; x = displacement.

It is possible that doubt will arise with some specimens as to the direction of displacement required to adjust the path to the original number of wavelengths.   This ambiguity can be resolved by examining two or three samples of differing thicknesses.   A full analysis of the acoustic interferometer is given by Mason,[98] who also derives the relationships for obtaining the attenuation from the curves connecting the points of maximum and minimum current (see also Hueter and Bolt [100]), but this is not easily applicable to the case where the acoustic path is a composite of two materials.

It is necessary that the transducer used in the acoustic interferometer should transmit a non-diverging beam (i.e. a plane wave) to avoid interference from the walls of the container.   This is even more important when a solid specimen is introduced, because there could be an appreciable velocity difference between the specimen and the medium, even though it is approximately matched in respect of acoustic impedance (ρc), and refraction of a diverging beam passing through the specimen may lead to spurious results.   In order to ensure a small beam angle, the diameter of the transducer face should be several times the wavelength in the medium at the frequency of measurement.   For a circular source of diameter d, the theoretical half-beam width is given by:

$$\sin \theta = 1 \cdot 2 \, \lambda/d \quad . \quad . \quad . \quad . \quad (8.113)$$

This relationship gives the half angle at which, theoretically, the intensity first drops to zero.   This cannot be observed experimentally so that an arbitrary practical limit, often -3 dB, -6 dB or -10 dB, has to be adopted. The half angle for a 10-dB reduction (0·1 ratio) can be calculated approximately as θ' given by $\sin\theta' = 2\lambda/9d$. If we consider as an example a transducer of 1·5 cm. diameter operating at 1 Mc/sec. into water, then the transducer face is approximately 10 λ in diameter, giving a theoretical half-beam width of only about 7°. It is clearly not possible to reproduce these conditions at frequencies of the order of 50 kc/sec. or less, at least not in a conveniently small apparatus. However, there are other means of reducing the beam width to some extent, and it is possible to reduce tank reflections with sound-absorbent coatings. Mason [98] describes these techniques and reports interferometer measurements on various rubber compounds at a frequency of about 25 kc/sec. Details of the design of underwater sound absorbers are given by Tamm.[102]

If the total attenuation in the liquid and solid path exceeds about 15 dB the standing-wave system becomes too poorly defined, and the interferometer method of measurement cannot be used. Under these conditions the double-transducer system can be applied to advantage. If the phase of the transmitted and received signals is compared, by connecting them to the X and Y plates of an oscilloscope, the half-wavelength points can be observed as the collapsing of the Lissajous ellipse to a straight line on altering the path length by traversing one of the transducers. Hatfield [103] used this method to obtain measurements of the velocity in various rubber compounds at a frequency of 50 kc/sec. and temperatures from 5° to 50° C, and absorption at frequencies of 50, 150 and 350 kc/sec. and a temperature of 17° C (see also ref. 104). The transducers were only 2·5 cm. in diameter and, as would be expected from the details given above, the divergent beam produced tank-wall reflections at the receiver which precluded measurements on very thick or very absorptive samples. In addition, the focusing effect, due to refraction of the diverging beam through iron-oxide-filled rubbers, which have a velocity appreciably lower than the water medium, was observed as an anomalous increase in signal on inserting these specimens. The side reflections could, of course, be reduced by an absorbing lining, but some form of beam collimation would be needed to eliminate the latter effect.

If the experimental conditions can be chosen to avoid the occurrence of the various disturbing effects mentioned, it is then a straightforward matter to observe the absorption in the specimen by measuring the signal voltage before and after inserting it in the path. A more precise estimate, and a confirmation that no spurious effects are present, can be obtained by relating the absorption in a series of samples of differing thicknesses. The results are usually expressed as attenuation in dB/cm. (β) given by:

$$\beta t = 20 \log_{10} (V_r/V_o) \quad . \quad . \quad . \quad (8.114)$$

where t = thickness of sample cm.; V_o = signal voltage before insertion of sample; V_r = ditto after insertion. Usually the loss in the liquid medium is negligible compared with that in the sample, otherwise the loss in the liquid path equal to the thickness of the sample would have to be included in the above.

Several workers have made use of the fact that light passed through a medium at right angles to the path of an ultrasonic wave is diffracted.[105,106] This is due to the alternate regions of higher and lower density acting as an optical diffraction grating. These methods have been used to measure velocities and, by means of a colour effect associated with intensity, attenuations were also obtained.[107] Measurements can be made on solid specimens even if they are not optically transparent by inserting them in the acoustic path in a cell filled with a transparent medium. Where the velocity in the specimen differs appreciably from that in the liquid medium the refraction effect can be used to determine the velocity in the solid in terms of the known velocity in the liquid. For example, the sample may be prepared in the shape of a lens of known radius of curvature (r) (plano-concave for a high velocity in the solid and planoconvex for a low velocity). The focusing action in the liquid can be observed by the optical method and the focal length (d) measured. The velocity is given by:

$$c_r = c_0/(1 \mp r/d) \quad . \quad . \quad . \quad . \quad (8.115)$$

(*ii*) *Continuous wave methods, multiple frequencies.* It will be seen from the above that transmission measurements with a single-frequency continuous wave are very liable to error. After steps have been taken to eliminate other reflections there will, in general, still be a standing-wave system set up between the two faces of the transducers. The introduction of extra absorption into the acoustic path, for example by the use of a very lossy medium, while being helpful in one respect, will lead to inaccuracy due to the low signal level to be measured, and cause matching difficulties.

Several expedients intended to overcome the standing-wave problem have been described. Carlin[108] used transducers with several crystal elements with their faces in different parallel planes spaced a fraction of a wavelength apart. In this way the elements integrate the standing wave over a distance sufficient to indicate the mean level. While this method is satisfactory for measurement of transmission loss, it is complicated and not applicable to velocity measurement. The method of Shraiber[109] achieved a similar result by mixing the outputs of several oscillators operating at different frequencies. By this means the effect of a number of standing-wave patterns of different wavelengths will average out at the transducer face. Again this method will not be suitable for making velocity measurements. The logical extension of this principle is to use a selected band derived from a continuous spectrum of random signals known as " white noise ". This method has been used for ultrasonic inspection by transmission loss, but again it does not afford any possibility of making velocity measurements.

The method which appears to combine the advantage of minimising the Standing-wave Ratio, without sacrificing the measurement of velocity, is the use of a " Frequency Modulated Wave ". The frequency of the driving oscillator is swept up and down over a band centred about the nominal frequency of measurement. This modulation can be achieved by electronic means or more simply by a motor-driven tuning capacitor. For any given set of experimental conditions the Standing-wave Ratio will approach more closely to unity (i.e. no standing wave) as the frequency deviation is increased, but for reasons to be mentioned later it is desirable not to use a wider frequency sweep than is necessary to provide the required reduction in Standing-wave Ratio. It will be apparent that if the received signal is compared with the frequency being transmitted, owing to the fact that the former has been delayed by the time required to travel the acoustic path, a difference frequency will be observed. This will be proportional to the number of wavelengths in the acoustic path, and it will also be a function of the frequency deviation and the modulation frequency.

The frequency modulation method of eliminating standing waves was mentioned by Shraiber [109] in connection with the ultrasonic examination of metals. Apart from its use by Sack and Aldrich [110] for the measurement of the loss in various elastomers over a frequency range of 0·5–6 Mc/sec., and by Marvin, Aldrich and Sack [111] on polyisobutylene, the method appears to have received very little attention. This is to be regretted, because it does appear to overcome many of the limitations inherent either in the use of fixed-frequency continuous waves or in the pulsed-wave methods described later (see p. 577). Possibly the complication involved in measuring the difference frequency accurately is responsible for this neglect. The following scheme, which has not yet been investigated experimentally, is suggested by the writers to enable the velocity in the specimen, relative to that in the liquid medium, to be determined using a null method, thus avoiding the necessity to measure a difference frequency. Two similar test tanks are used, each with a transmitting and receiving transducer. The electrical and acoustic paths are identical in the two channels except that the first pair of transducers, between which the specimen is normally immersed, are fixed while one of the second pair can be traversed by a micrometer arrangement, as in the double transducer interferometer previously described. In addition, an accurately calibrated high-frequency attenuator is connected in the receiver circuit of the second bath. The relative amplitudes and phase of the two output signals can be compared on an oscilloscope. A block diagram of the arrangement is shown in Fig. 8.17. The measurement is carried out by first balancing the two channels for both amplitude and phase, then inserting the specimen in the fixed path, rebalancing the amplitude of the two channels by means of the attenuator and rebalancing the phase by adjusting the path length, in the second bath. The velocity in the specimen is related to the displacement

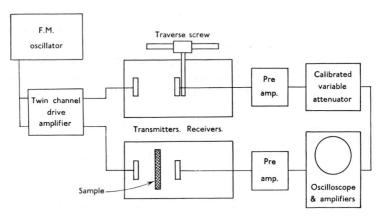

Fig. 8.17. Measurement of velocity and attenuation of bulk waves—using the double-path F.M. method-block diagram.

and the velocity in the liquid medium by the relationship given previously, equation (8.112). Where the specimen and the liquid medium are not well matched in acoustic impedance the additional loss due to reflection at the interfaces can be eliminated by comparing two samples of different thicknesses, one in each bath.

Obviously the transducers must have a certain band-width in order to pass the frequency-modulated signal. The mathematical description of the frequency spectra of frequency-modulated or phase-modulated waves is complicated and will not be gone into here. However, it can be stated that, although there is a theoretically infinite number of sidebands spaced $\pm nf_m$ from the carrier, where f_m is the modulating frequency, the outer sidebands rapidly diminish in amplitude. If the modulation index (deviation frequency/modulation frequency) is kept small all sidebands except those nearest to the carrier can be neglected. If outer sidebands with any significant contribution to the signal are cut due to restricted transducer response the effect will be seen as an amplitude modulation of the received signal, and will probably not be of any importance. In view of this, special mechanical loading of the transducers, such as is mentioned in the next section in connection with pulsed-wave methods, will probably not be necessary, and a suitable inductance and resistance shunted across the transducer should provide the required band-width.

(*iii*) *Pulsed wave methods.* Methods involving the use of pulse-modulated waves have been the ones most commonly adopted for the measurement of velocity and absorption at ultrasonic frequencies. The electronic instrumentation required for the generation and measurement of pulsed waves is more complicated than for unmodulated waves, but because of the extensive development of radar and sonar devices which utilise similar techniques there is ample published design data available, for example that published by the M.I.T.[112] While there are several practical advantages, detailed below, in the use of these methods, there are also fundamental drawbacks to making measurements with short pulses on rubber-like materials which are usually dispersive, i.e. their properties vary with frequency (see p. 582). The chief advantages are:

(*a*) The required received pulse is usually separated in time from unwanted pulses which have travelled by other paths or by other modes of vibration, and it can therefore be displayed and measured without interference on an oscilloscope, using a time-base sweep synchronised to the pulse-repetition rate. Consequently, reflections from the wall of the test tank, or solid wave-guide, are not so significant and, as well as unwanted acoustic signals, direct electromagnetic coupling between the transmitting and receiving circuits can be ignored.

(*b*) The peak power of the transmitted pulse can be fairly high without exceeding a low level of average power dissipation. This would normally be a limiting factor when using continuous waves because of the necessity to avoid undue heating up of the transducer or acoustic medium. Consequently, when making measurements on absorptive samples the signal-to-noise ratio of the received pulse can be kept at a high enough level for accurate measurement.

The duration of the pulses used for the measurement must be carefully considered. The number of wavelengths in the pulse must be less than the distance between any two reflecting surfaces. This requirement can easily be met in relation to the path through the acoustic medium, since the transducer-to-sample distance can be increased when necessary, but in general reflection will also occur at the sample–medium interfaces, and it will not always be practicable to increase the sample thickness by the required amount. If the specimen is sufficiently absorptive interference will not occur, but otherwise it will be essential to investigate a series of sample thicknesses to avoid misleading results. The use of too short a pulse is to be avoided, since the extent of the high-frequency spectrum of the modulating signal is inversely proportional to pulse duration. Hence the shorter the pulse, the greater the band-width required from the transducers to pass the signal undistorted. In any case it will be necessary

U

to damp the transducers, for example by loading with a quarter-wave face-plate, in order to provide sufficient band-width to handle the pulses required. An example will help to clarify this point. An air-backed barium titanate transducer transmitting directly into water may have a band-width of only about 2% of the resonant frequency, whereas by loading it with a quarter-wave face-plate having four times the characteristic impedance of water, together with suitable electrical matching, the band-width could be increased to the order of 50% of the centre band frequency. Suppose that the latter frequency is 3 Mc/sec., then the band-width $B \approx 1\frac{1}{2}$ Mc/sec. and the pass band will cover the range from approximately 2·25 to 3·75 Mc/sec. If now we assume that frequencies up to the 7th harmonic are sufficient to form the pulse shape, then a pulse duration (τ) of 5 microseconds will be about the minimum acceptable, since this has a square wave equivalent frequency $(1/2\tau = f_p)$ of 0·1 Mc/sec. with a seventh harmonic of 0·7 Mc/sec. If a carrier of 3 Mc/sec. is modulated with a series of such pulses the required amount of the sidebands will just be included within the band-width. If the other conditions of the experiment permit, increasing the above pulse length by two to three times will usefully improve the pulse shape. Each 5-microsecond pulse will consist of 15 cycles, and after the first 2–3 cycles the pulse will rise to nearly its full amplitude. In water the train of waves will cover a distance of approximately $7\frac{1}{2}$ mm.

The choice of the pulse-repetition frequency is not critical, since it is only necessary to ensure that the interval between pulses is much larger than the time taken for the pulse to cover the acoustic path. This usually means a repetition time of between 100 and 1,000 times the pulse duration. The average power dissipation can be kept fairly low, and at the same time the repetition frequency is large enough to enable a persistent display of pulse signals to be examined visually on an oscilloscope.

Pulse methods of measuring velocity and attenuation for both longitudinal bulk waves and shear waves in solid materials were first applied by Mason and McSkimin [113] for measurements on metals and glasses. In the following year, 1948, Nolle and Mowry [114] reported pulsed bulk wave measurements on synthetic rubber compounds at frequencies of 10 and 30 Mc/sec. using a liquid transmission medium. Ivey, Mrowca and Guth [115] made more extensive measurements covering five frequencies from 44 kc/sec. to 10 Mc/sec. and temperatures from $-40°$ to $+60°$ C. They gave bulk wave velocity and attenuation curves for natural rubber, butadiene–styrene and Butyl rubber over these ranges, and calculated bulk modulus and loss factor using the three-constant theory. The method used to obtain the velocity and attenuation is a simple one. Synchronising pulses initiate the oscilloscope sweep and the generation of the modulating pulses simultaneously. The velocity in the sample is obtained by noting the position of the received pulse on the time axis before and after inserting the sample, giving a time shift $\pm t$. The velocity is given by:

$$c_r = c_0/(1 \pm c_0\, t/d) \quad . \quad . \quad . \quad . \quad (8.116)$$

where $d =$ sample thickness; $t =$ time shift; $c_0 =$ velocity in liquid medium; $c_r =$ velocity in sample. The attenuation is obtained by measuring the amplitude of the received signal before and after inserting the sample, using a peak-reading voltmeter. Eqn. 8.114 will apply in this case as before.

It is clear that the accuracy of the velocity measurements is dependent on the precision of the oscilloscope time calibration and also on the linearity and stability of the sweep. These points will normally be checked by applying either a sinusoidal or pulsed timing signal, derived from a frequency sub-standard, to the oscilloscope. Ivey et al.[115] claimed an accuracy in velocity measurement within 2% at higher frequencies and 5% lower frequencies. Accuracy of attenuation measurements was not better than about 10%, even though measurements were made on samples of various thicknesses to confirm that errors were not introduced either by reflection at the liquid–sample interface or by standing waves between the interfaces. These workers made certain assumptions in order to calculate the shear modulus from the bulk wave results and hence the dynamic Young's modulus and loss factor. These results were extrapolated to lower frequencies and compared with measurements made by other methods. The modulus versus frequency curves show remarkable correlation considering the tentative nature of the assumptions made. However, they recognised that further progress could be made only by measuring shear-wave as well as bulk-wave propagation at high frequencies.

Since liquids in general will not support shear waves, they cannot be used as transmission media for making measurements of the propagation of shear waves. Very viscous liquids, particularly liquid polymers, for example low-molecular-weight polyisobutylene, show a shear elasticity, but they can only be used for transmitting shear waves in extremely thin films because of the very high attenuation. Such materials are useful as a shear-wave coupling layer between two solids, provided that the surfaces are flat and pressed closely together. Consequently, a solid transmission medium must be adopted for measurements with shear waves. The most satisfactory material for the transmission of ultrasonic waves is clear fused silica, but glass is a more readily available alternative, and for short lines the higher loss is not important. Metal rods have been used for this purpose, magnesium and aluminium being most suitable from the transmission point of view, but metals have the disadvantage for shear wave work that the longitudinal-wave velocity is approximately double the shear-wave velocity. Although the shear-wave pulse can be excited by a crystal cut for the shear mode, for example Y-cut quartz, a secondary longitudinal wave is unavoidably propagated at the same time. With two approximately equal transmission rods with the specimen held between them, a part of the longitudinal pulse will be reflected from the first sample surface return to the beginning of the rod and then travel forward to arrive at the receiving crystal almost simultaneously with the direct-path shear wave. Under some conditions it can even be stronger than the latter, owing to the higher attenuation of the shear wave in the specimen. Nolle and Sieck [116] used two Pyrex glass transmission blocks for shear-wave measurements and found that the longitudinal and shear pulses could be separated. They arrived at the pulse transit time for the specimen by measuring the pulse reflection time in each block separately and subtracting the mean value from the total transmission time for a pulse travelling the whole path including the specimen. They also obtained the attenuation in the specimen in a similar way after allowing for the partial reflection at the mismatched line-sample interfaces. Owing to a change in the electrical circuit conditions when transferring from the pulse-reflection measurement to the pulse-transmission set-up a small timing error was introduced. They endeavoured to correct for this by observing a standing-wave effect in the specimen under conditions when the attenuation was low. These workers also made longitudinal-wave measurements using aluminium transmission blocks. Comparison of these results with others made in a liquid transmission medium showed agreement within 5% except for certain measurements at 5 Mc/sec., where the timing error mentioned above was serious. There was no independent way of arriving at the error for the shear-wave measurements, but it was estimated to be between 10 and 20%. Nolle and Sieck carried out the above measurements on a butadiene–acrylonitrile rubber compound at frequencies of 2, 5 and 10 Mc/sec. and temperatures from $-65°$ to $+15°$ C. Values of bulk modulus, shear modulus and shear loss factor were deduced from the velocity and attenuation results. They concluded that within experimental error the whole of the longitudinal bulk-wave attenuation could be accounted for by the observed loss in the shear-wave experiments, that is a " Bulk Loss Modulus (K'') " was not observed. However, it was recognised that more precise evaluation might show the existence of a K'' small in relation to G''. The work of Marvin, Aldrich and Sack [111] on the N.B.S. sample of high-molecular-weight polyisobutylene indicated a definite energy dissipation associated with volume deformation. In fact, taking the imaginary part of the bulk-wave constant as $(K'' + 4\,G''/3)$, the bulk loss modulus K'' and the shear loss contribution $4\,G''/3$ appear to be approximately equal for this material.

The elimination of the spurious effect due to longitudinal waves in a shear-wave experiment under all conditions is difficult. In addition to the simple effect mentioned previously the cylindrical surface of the transmission rod is also involved in producing secondary echoes unless the diameter of the rod is very large in relation to the wavelength in the material. Consequently, the subsidiary echoes may still cause trouble even if the material and lengths of the rods are chosen to separate the main longitudinal reflections. Partial mode conversion between shear and longitudinal types of wave will occur on reflection. The material used to couple the specimen to the transmission bar also has more effect in a shear-wave measurement. Owing to the high attenuation for the shear mode in rubbers, extremely thin samples are necessary under some conditions, so that the coupling layers amount to an appreciable proportion of the specimen thickness. The method described by Cunningham and Ivey [117] makes a considerable contribution towards overcoming these problems. The acoustic path is in duplicate. In each path a 1-in.-diameter Y-cut quartz crystal transmits a shear wave through an aluminium rod 5 in. in diam. and 1·75 in. long. Rubber specimens of two different thicknesses are cemented to the aluminium rods, and receiving crystals identical to the transmitters are attached directly on to the other side of the samples. To a first approximation the double-path technique eliminates the effect of the cement layers, although it is not possible to ensure absolutely uniform pairs. Interference from longitudinal waves was still experienced under some conditions and also multiple internal reflections in the sample. To minimise the effect of the latter several different thickness combinations for the sample pairs were investigated. The electronic instrumentation for the double-path apparatus is so arranged that the signals from the two receiving channels are displayed on the oscilloscope alternately on successive pulses by a form of electronic switch, and the same pulses that actuate the switch also initiate the oscilloscope sweep. These pulses are derived from the original modulating pulse generator through a scale-of-two circuit which feeds alternate pulses through different delay circuits. In this way the sweep is not initiated until shortly before the transmitted pulses arrive, and it is possible to display them on an expanded time scale. If both delays were identical the received pulses would appear at different positions on the sweep because of the difference in the acoustic paths. However, the delay associated with the shorter path is increased until the alternate pulses coincide on the oscilloscope display. Similarly, the attenuation in the shorter path is increased until the alternate pulses also match in amplitude. Because of the repetition rate the two signals appear as one when the adjustments for delay and amplitude are complete. The extra delay inserted to achieve this coincidence represents the transit time for a thickness of rubber equal to the difference between the two samples and, similarly, the extra attenuation inserted is the loss in this thickness.

As mentioned earlier, the dispersive properties of most rubber-like materials present a fundamental limitation to the precision of pulsed-wave measurements. Over some frequency ranges with certain materials a 2 : 1 linear increase in frequency will correspond to an increase in attenuation of more than 2 : 1 measured on a logarithmic scale. Thus it will be seen that, even with a more limited frequency spectrum, components at the upper end may be appreciably reduced in relation to centre band signals, and this will result in degradation of the sharply rising front of the pulse. Under these conditions accurate measurement of pulse delay time will not be possible. In addition to the change in attenuation there will also be velocity dispersion. The object of the measurement is to obtain the phase velocity (c_p) at the carrier frequency, but the energy of the pulse will be transferred at the group velocity (c_g), which differs from the phase velocity by ($dc_p/d\lambda$)λ. This effect can be counteracted by using as long a pulse as possible so as to reduce the relative importance of the high-frequency components in the spectrum of the pulse, but this will not overcome the loss of the sharply rising front. Because the higher-frequency components travel at higher velocity the base length of the received pulse will be greater than is transmitted. It will be seen that the significance of pulse measurements made under dispersive conditions needs careful consideration.

Derivation of the fundamental properties from wave observations

In the methods discussed we have been concerned with plane, that is non-diverging, waves. The characteristic of a plane wave is that the disturbance of the medium has the same phase and amplitude throughout any plane at right angles to the direction of propagation. The equation for such a wave in an elastic medium has the usual form, as follows, in which y = particle displacement, x = distance in direction of propagation and c = velocity:

$$\frac{\partial^2 y}{\partial t^2} = \frac{c^2 \partial^2 y}{\partial x^2} \qquad \cdot \quad \cdot \quad \cdot \quad \cdot \quad \cdot \quad \cdot \quad (8.117)$$

Putting M for the elastic wave constant derived from the velocity c and density ρ by eqn. 8.103 gives:

$$\rho \frac{\partial^2 y}{\partial t^2} = \frac{M \partial^2 y}{\partial x^2} \qquad \cdot \quad \cdot \quad \cdot \quad \cdot \quad \cdot \quad \cdot \quad (8.118)$$

For a visco-elastic medium, that is one in which the dissipative forces are assumed to be proportional to the particle velocity, another term M'' ($\partial^3 y/\partial t \partial x^2$) has to be added to the right-hand side of this equation. The usual way of solving such an equation is to assume a solution such as $y = A \exp [-i(\omega t + kx)]$ and substitute. However, the modulus and dissipation coefficient cannot be taken as constants, since, as mentioned previously, both the elastic and loss properties of the material vary widely with frequency. Marvin, Aldrich and Sack [111] give a treatment of this problem in which the elastic and loss moduli are dealt with as functions of frequency. The complex longitudinal bulk wave modulus M^* is related to the complex bulk compression modulus K^* and the complex shear modulus G^* by:

$$M^* = K^* + \tfrac{4}{3}G^* \qquad (8.119)$$

which is simply equation 8.109 in complex form. These complex moduli are related to the elastic and loss moduli defined on p. 525 as follows:

$$K^* = K' + iK'' \qquad (8.120)$$
$$G^* = G' + iG'' \qquad (8.121)$$

Strictly suffixes, e.g. $K'_{(\omega)}$, should be included as on p. 525 to indicate that the elastic and loss moduli are functions of frequency. In Marvin's solution the displacement is taken as:

$$y = y_0 \exp\left[i\omega t - (\alpha + i\omega/c)x\right]$$

and the following relationship between the frequency dependent complex modulus and the observed quantities α and c is derived:

$$-\omega^2\rho = M^*(\alpha + i\omega/c)^2 \qquad (8.122)$$

This when separated into real and imaginary parts and solved for M' and M'' gives:

$$M' = \rho c^2(1 - r^2)/(1 + r^2)^2 \qquad (8.123)$$
$$M'' = 2\rho c^2 r/(1 + r^2)^2 \qquad (8.124)$$

in which $r = \alpha c/\omega$, where α is attenuation in nepers per centimetre, c the phase velocity and ω the angular frequency.

The neper is a natural logarithmic attenuation ratio such that an attenuation of 1 neper corresponds to a reduction in particle displacement or in acoustic pressure to $1/e$ of the original value, and it is equal to 8·69 dB.

The relationships for obtaining the real and imaginary distortional wave constants, that is the shear elastic modulus G' and the shear loss modulus G'', are derived in the same way as the above, and G' and G'' may be substituted for M' and M'' in eqn. 8.123 and 8.124. Reference to p. 563 will show that the eqn. 8.95 and 8.96 for deriving E' and E'' from the propagation of longitudinal waves in narrow specimens are also in the same form and that $\beta\lambda/54\cdot6$ is identical with $\alpha c/\omega$. Consequently, the curves shown in Fig. 8.16a may also be used to approximate the modulus and loss factor in the present cases.

When the attenuation per wavelength ($\beta\lambda$) is small compared with 54·6, then r^2 can, to a first approximation, be neglected in the above equations, the elastic moduli taken simply as ρc^2 and the loss modulus as $2\rho c^3\alpha/\omega$. If Stokes's assumption is adopted, then this latter quantity is equal to $4G''/3$ in the case of the longitudinal bulk-wave measurements.

REFERENCES

1. Spencer, R. S. and Boyer, R. F. (1946) *J. appl. Phys.*, **17**, 398.
2. Ferry, J. D. (1942) *J. Amer. chem. Soc.*, **64**, 1330.
3. Wiley, F. E. (1943) *Ind. Eng. Chem.*, **34**, 1052.
4. Buchdahl, R. and Nielsen, L. E. (1950) *J. appl. Phys.*, **21**, 482.
5. Fox, T. G. and Flory, P. J. (1950) *J. appl. Phys.*, **21**, 581.
6. Millane, J. J. and McLaren, S. M. (1952) *J. appl. Chem.*, **2**, 554.
7. (1946) *Advances in Colloid Science*, II, *Rubber* (Interscience, New York), p. 31.
8. Meyer, von Susich and Valko (1932) *Kolloidzschr.*, **59**, 208.
9. Meyer, K. H. and Ferri, C. (1935) *Helv. Chim. Acta.*, **18**, 570; (1935) Translated in *Rubber Chem. Tech.*, **8**, 319.
10. Gee, G. (1946) *Trans. Faraday Soc.*, **42**, 585.
11. Treloar, L. R. G. (1958) *Physics of Rubber Elasticity*, 2nd Ed. (Oxford: Clarendon), Chapter II.
12. Baldwin, F. P., Ivory, J. E. and Anthony, R. L. (1955) *J. appl. Phys.*, **26**, 750.
13. Kuhn, W. (1934) *Kolloidzschr.*, **68**, 2 and (1936) **76**, 258.
14. Guth, E. and Mark, H. (1934) *Monatsch.*, **65**, 93.
15. James, H. M. and Guth, E. (1943) *J. Chem. Phys.*, **11**, 455.
16. —— —— (1949) *J. Polym. Sci.*, **4**, 153.
17. Payne, A. R. (1956) *Nature*, **177**, 1174.
18. Payne, A. R. *RABRM* (1955) *I.B. Circ.* 427; (1955) *Res. Mem. R.*404; (1956) *Res. Rep. RR*77; and (1957) *Res. Rep. RR*84.
19. Payne, A. R. *RABRM* (1955) *Res. Mem. R.*404.
20. Gent, A. N. (1956) *Proc. Rubber in Engineering Conf.* Nat. Rubb. Dev. Board.
21. Mooney, M. (1940) *J. appl. Phys.*, **11**, 582.
22. Treloar, L. R. G. (1958) *Rheology of Elastomers* (London: Pergamon).
23. Tobolsky, A. V., Prettyman, I. B. and Dillon, J. H. (1944) *J. appl. Phys.*, **15**, 324.
24. Villars, D. S. (1950) *J. appl. Phys.*, **21**, 565.
25. Jones, F. B. and Pearce, W. H. (1940) *India Rubb. J.*, **100**, 167.
26. Payne, A. R. (1954) *Proc. Third Rubber Technology Conference*, 422.
27. Roscoe, R. (1950) *Brit. J. appl. Phys.*, **1**, 171.
28. Lamb, H. (1938) *Infinitesimal Calculus* (Cambridge).
29. Timoshenko, S. (1937) *Vibration Problems in Engineering* (New York: Van Nostrand).
30. (1956) *Proposals on Rheological Nomenclature and Definitions*, Netherlands Rheological Soc.
31. Yerzley, F. L. (1939) *Proc. Amer. Soc. Testing Materials*, **39**, 1180.
32. Nolle, A. W. (1948) *J. appl. Phys.*, **19**, 753.
33. ASTM D945–55.
34. Sack, H. S., Motz, J., Raub, H. L. and Work, R. N. (1947) *J. appl. Phys.*, **18**, 450.
35. Nolle, A. W. (1948) *J. appl. Phys.*, **19**, 761.
36. Cassie, A. B. D., Jones, Maldwyn and Naunton, W. J. S. (1936) *I.R.I. Trans.*, **12**, 49.
37. Bartoe, W. F. (1942) *India Rubb. World*, **105**, 570.
38. Kuhn, W. and Kunzle, O. (1947) *Helv. Chim. Acta.*, **30**, 839.
39. Nielsen, L. E., Buchdahl, R. and Levreault, R. (1950) *J. appl. Phys.*, **21**, 607.
40. Nielsen, L. E. (1951) *Rev. Sci. Inst.*, **22**, 690.
41. —— (1953) *J. Amer. chem. Soc.*, **75**, 1435.

42. Fletcher, W. P., Gent, A. N. and Wood, R. I. (1954) *Proc. Third Rubber Technology Conference*, 382.
43. Rivlin, R. S. (1948) *Phil. Trans.*, **241**A, 379.
44. —— (1947) *J. appl. Phys.*, **18**, 444.
45. Mooney, M. (1940) *J. appl. Phys.*, **11**, 582.
46. Rivlin, R. S. (1948) *Phil. Trans.*, **240**A, 509.
47. Treloar, L. R. G. (1958) *Physics of Rubber Elasticity*, 2nd Edition (Oxford: Clarendon), 177.
48. Timoshenko, S. (1941) *Strength of Materials Pt. II* (New York: Van Nostrand).
49. Gent, A. N. (1953) *I.R.I. Trans.*, **29**, 173.
50. Green, A. E. and Shield, R. T. (1951) *Trans. Roy. Soc.*, **244**A, 47, eqn. 3.26.
51. Saint-Venant (1855) De la torsion des prisms, *Mém. des Savants étrangers*.
52. Love, A. E. H. (1952) *Mathematical Theory of Elasticity* (Cambridge), p. 323.
53. Nielsen, L. E. (1950) *ASTM Bull.*, 165, 48.
54. Trayer, G. W. and March, H. W. (1929) Nat. Adv. Committee for Aeronautics, *Rep. No.* 334.
55. Naunton, W. J. S. and Waring, J. R. S. (1938) *Proc. Rubber Technology Conference*, 805.
56. Fletcher, W. P. and Gent, A. N. (1950) *I.R.I. Trans.*, **26**, 45.
57. Kuhl, W. and Meyer, E., 1948 Summer Symposium of the Acoustics Group, Physical Society, Report, 181.
58. Oberto, S. and Palandri, G. (1948) *Rubb. Age, N.Y.*, **63**, 725.
59. Roelig, H. (1938) *Proc. Rubber Technology Conference*, 821.
60. —— (1943) *Kautschuk*, **19**, 47; (1945) *Rubb. Chem. Tech.*, **18**, 62.
61. Aston, A. J. (1952) *I.R.I. Trans.*, **28**, 129.
62. Gehman, S. D. and Wilkinson, C. S. (1950) *Analyt. Chem.*, **22**, 283.
63. Mullins, L. (1950) *I.R.I. Trans.*, **26**, 27.
64. Waring, J. R. S. (1950) *I.R.I. Trans.*, **26**, 4.
65. —— (1951) *Ind. Eng. Chem.*, **43**, 352.
66. McCallion, H. and Davies, D. M. (1955) *Proc. Institution of Mechanical Engineers*, **169**, 1125.
67. Payne, A. R. (1954) *Proc. Third Rubber Technology Conference*, 413.
68. Aleksandrov, A. P. and Lazurkin, Y. S. (1939) *J. Tech. Phys. U.S.S.R.*, **9**, 1249; (1940) *Rubb. Chem. Technol.*, **13**, 886.
69. Fletcher, W. P. and Gent, A. N. (1957) *Brit. J.A.P.*, **8**, 194.
70. —— —— (1952) *J. Sci. Inst.*, **29**, 186.
71. Davies, D. M. (1952) *Brit. J.A.P.*, **3**, 285.
72. —— (1953) *Engineering*, **176**, 196.
73. Payne, A. R. (1955) *RABRM Research Report No.* 76; (1956) *Rev. gén. Caoutch.*, **33**, 885.
74. Payne, A. R. and Smith, J. F. (1956) *J. Sci. Inst.*, **33**, 432.
75. Payne, A. R. (1958) *RABRM Res. Mem. No. R411*.
76. Painter, G. W. (1951) *ASTM Bull.*, No. 177, 45.
77. Philippoff, W. (1953) *J. appl. Phys.*, **24**, 685.
78. Ferry, J. D., Fitzgerald, E. R., Grandine, L. D. and Williams, M. L. (1952) *Ind. Eng. Chem.*, **44**, 703.
79. Fitzgerald, E. R. and Ferry, J. D. (1953) *J. Colloid Sci.*, **8**, 1.
80. Williams, M. L., Landel, R. F. and Ferry, J. D. (1955) *J. Amer. Chem. Soc.*, **77**, 370.
81. Costadoni, C. (1936) *Z. tech. Phys.*, **17**, 108.
82. King, A. J. (1946) *J. Instn. Elect. Engrs.*, **93**, Part II, 198.
83. Jackson, R. S., King, A. J. and Maguire, C. R. (1954) *Proc. Instn. Elect. Engrs*, Part II, **101**, 512.
84. Nolle, A. W. (1948) *J. appl. Phys.*, **19**, 766.
85. Morris, R. E., James, R. R. and Snyder, H. L. (1951) *Ind. Eng. Chem.*, **43**, 2540.

86. Morris, R. E., James, R. R. and Cuyton, C. W. (1956) *Rubb. Age, N.Y.*, **78**, 125.
87. Nolle, A. W. (1948) *J. appl. Phys.*, **19**, 768.
88. Voltera, E., Eubanks, R. A. and Munster, D. (1955) *J. Amer. Soc. for Experimental Stress Analysis*, **13**, 85.
89. Volterra, E. (1953) *Proc. Second Int. Congress on Rheology* (London: Butterworths), p. 73.
90. Nolle, A. W. (1947) *J. acoust. Soc. Amer.*, **19**, 194.
91. —— (1948) *J. appl. Phys.*, **19**, 763.
92. Hillier, K. W. (1950) *I.R.I. Trans.*, **26**, 64.
93. Hillier, K. W. and Kolsky, H. (1949) *Proc. Phys. Soc. Lond.*, B**62**, 111.
94. Hillier, K. W. (1949) *Proc. phys. Soc. Lond.*, B**62**, 701.
95. Witte, R. S., Mrowca, B. A. and Guth, E. (1949) *J. appl. Phys.*, **20**, 481.
96. Love, A. E. H. (1952) *Mathematical Theory of Elasticity* (Cambridge).
97. Kolsky, H. (1953) *Stress Waves in Solids* (Oxford: Clarendon).
98. Mason, W. P. (1950) *Piezoelectric Crystals and their Application to Ultrasonics* (London: Macmillan).
99. *Ibid.*, Table XXII, p. 335.
100. Hueter, T. F. and Bolt, R. M. (1955) *Sonics* (London: Chapman and Hall).
101. *Ibid.*, Appendix A6, p. 436.
102. Tamm, K. (1957) *Broad Band Absorbers for Water-Borne Sound* (Technical Aspects of Sound, E. G. Richardson, Editor, Vol. II, Chapter 6) (Elsevier) (London: Cleaver-Hume).
103. Hatfield, P. (1950) *Brit. J. appl. Phys.*, **1**, 252.
104. —— (1956) *J. appl. Phys.*, **27**, 192 (letter).
105. Debye, P. and Sears, F. W. (1932) *Proc. Wash. Acad. Sci.*, **18**, 410.
106. Lucas, R. and Biquard, P. (1932) *Comptes Rendus, Acad. Sci. Paris*, **194**, 2132.
107. Willard, G. W. (1941) *J. acoust. Soc. Amer.*, **12**, 438.
108. Carlin, B. (Dec. 2, 1947) U.S.P. 2,431,862 (see also Carlin, B. (1949) *Ultrasonics*, McGraw-Hill, p. 133).
109. Shraiber, D. S. (1940) " Testing of Metals by the Use of Ultrasonics," *Z. Lab.*, **9**, 1001.
110. Sack, H. S. and Aldrich, R. (1949) *Phys. Rev.*, **75**, 1285.
111. Marvin, R. S., Aldrich, R. and Sack, H. S. (1954) *J. appl. Phys.*, **25**, 1213.
112. (1949) Massachusetts Institute of Technology, Radiation Lab. Series (New York: McGraw-Hill) (**1**, *Radar System Engineering*; **5**, *Pulse Generators*; **19**, *Waveforms*; **20**, *Electronic Time Measurement*).
113. Mason, W. P. and McSkimin, H. J. (1947) *J. acoust. Soc. Amer.*, **19**, (No. 2).
114. Nolle, A. W. and Mowry, S. C. (1948) *J. acoust. Soc. Amer.*, **20**, 432.
115. Ivey, D. G., Mrowca, B. A. and Guth, E. (1949) *J. appl. Phys.*, **20**, 486.
116. Nolle, A. W. and Sieck, P. W. (1952) *J. appl. Phys.*, **23**, 888.
117. Cunningham, J. R. and Ivey, D. G. (1956) *J. appl. Phys.*, **27**, 967.
118. Payne, A. R. and Scott, J. R. (1960) " Engineering Design with Rubber " (London: Maclaren), p. 20, p. 72, p. 162.
119. *Ibid.*, p. 22, p. 109.
120. *Ibid.*, Chap. 6.
121. *Ibid.*, p. 43.
122. Bulgin, D. and Hubbard, G. D. (1958) *I.R.I. Trans.*, **34**, 201.
123. Harrison, M., Sykes, A. O., and Martin, M. (1952) *J. Acoust. Soc. Amer.*, **24**, 62.
124. Snowdon, J. C. (1958) *Brit. J. appl. Phys.*, **9**, 461.

CHAPTER VIII

PART TWO

PRACTICAL APPLICATIONS OF THE DYNAMIC
PROPERTIES OF RUBBER

by

A. J. HIRST

1. Principles of vibration transmission and insulation

DURING the past 30 years almost the whole of the development of theory and practice of the dynamics of rubber has been associated with vibration-reducing devices. The manufacture of these has developed into an important industry, and a great amount of specialised knowledge has been accumulated. The mechanics of rubber anti-vibration mountings and bearings is growing into a new branch of engineering science with its own methods of calculation and design, which have not yet been described adequately in any text-book. In this chapter an attempt will be made to give the fundamental principles and a few typical applications to different branches of engineering.

Vibration is well known in many forms in which the cyclic change is due to an electrical, mechanical, hydraulic or other driving force and the range of frequencies is extremely wide. A frequency of 1 cycle in $12\frac{1}{2}$ hours, which is of particular interest as a vibration of which the movement can be plotted easily without special equipment, is provided by the tides, of which the very large range in some places, such as the Bristol Channel, is due to resonance. Radio waves may have a frequency of the order of 100 million c/sec., and amplification by resonance is the means by which they are received. Both in radio and in electrical technology vibration principles have become so important that many of the earlier experts on mechanical vibration used electrical analogies which proved helpful up to a point, but can be also misleading. Frequencies lower and higher than the examples given above can be found quite easily, but rubber is used mainly for a much narrower range, varying from suspension movements, or the oscillation of vehicles on their springs, up to impulses in machinery in the upper part of the audible range. The problems concerned with vibrations of less than $\frac{1}{2}$, or more than 1,000 c/sec. are extremely few.

This chapter deals also with the absorption of single impulses, or shocks, which must be considered at the same time as vibrations because they are analysed mathematically in the same way and defined by the same equations, moreover, some of the forms of anti-vibration mountings in use today are based upon those developed many years ago for shock absorption, which has been an important application of rubber ever since the development of effective means of vulcanisation.

In the first part of this chapter Farrand and Edwards have discussed the present state of development of the theory of the elasticity and damping of rubber, on which the work of Fletcher and Gent,[1] Davies [2] and others has given a much more accurate picture than is obtainable from the classical equation of forced and damped oscillation. The effect of amplitude and frequency and of pre-loading and other mechanical factors, as well as that of damping changes, is explained much better by these theories, but they cannot be used to give the engineer a simple picture of the way in which an anti-vibration mounting of rubber works in practice. An approximation is needed which separates the various elements of a vibration and expresses them by formulae that can be used easily in calculation and by straight-forward diagrams. Fortunately the properties of rubber make such a theory accurate enough for most practical purposes.

Rubber damping is still confused with the standard form of viscous damping, proportional to velocity, assumed in ordinary mechanical vibration and electrical theory, although the viscosity of rubber is nearly proportional inversely to the frequency, but this difficulty can be overcome without departure from orthodox methods by a small alteration in the standard equation of forced and damped oscillation.[3] This is of the form:

$$\frac{W}{g}\ddot{x} + c\dot{x} + Kx = P \sin \omega t$$

which is re-written for convenience in manipulation:

$$\ddot{x} + 2n\dot{x} + p^2x = \frac{Pg}{W} \sin \omega t$$

where $p^2 = \frac{kg}{W}$ and $2n = \frac{cg}{W}$. In this equation the damping force is the product of a constant $2n$, and the velocity $\dot{x}$ and is therefore not that due to rubber damping, so that the equation should be re-written as follows:

$$\ddot{x} + \frac{2r\dot{x}}{\omega} + p^2x = \frac{Pg}{W} \sin \omega t$$

The damping constant $2r$ is a characteristic of the rubber. There is no great advantage in expressing it in terms of viscosity, but substitution in the original equation gives:

$$2r = \frac{cg\omega}{W}.$$

The differential equation [4] can be solved in the ordinary way, and the particular integral leads to the following results:

Amplitude:
$$x_0 = \frac{Pg}{W} \cdot \frac{1}{\sqrt{(p^2 - \omega^2) + 4r^2}} \qquad \cdots \quad (8.125)$$

Phase angle:
$$\tan \alpha = \frac{2}{p^2 - \omega^2} \cdot \qquad \cdots \cdots \quad (8.126)$$

The maximum value of x_0 occurs when $\omega = p$, and the magnification $M = \dfrac{p^2}{2r}$ and $\alpha = 90°$. This result is remarkably simple; the resonant frequency is exactly the same as the natural undamped frequency, and the phase angle at resonance exactly 90°. This theory is only approximate, because the viscosity is not exactly in proportion to the inverse of the frequency and the stiffness of the rubber spring varies with the amplitude. There are many other factors which must be considered in attempting an exact solution, but the very simple result given above is much more accurate than that given by the classical theory. Eqn. 8.125 and 8.126 can be taken as the basis for an elementary theory of anti-vibration mounting in which the effect of the damping properties of rubber upon vibration transmission can be demonstrated without the use of mathematics.

Most vibrations encountered by the engineer are of a complex nature, but the only reasonable way of developing the theory is to start, not only with the simplified properties of rubber, given above, but also with the simplest case of vibration, namely a piston moving up and down with a simple harmonic motion. All the figures in these sketches illustrate an imaginary machine in which a piston of mass m is moved up and down by the mechanism best known as that producing simple harmonic motion. The mass of the complete machine is given as M and the problem simplified further by supposing that M is so much larger than m that the difference between M and $M + m$ can be neglected; this is not an important point, but simplifies the reasoning.

The theory is developed as follows:

(a) Distinction between rigid and flexible mounting

In Fig. 8.18a the machine is supposed to be supported from a base of infinite rigidity. It is therefore free from visible vibration, because the variations in loading, due to the movement of the piston, can cause no movement. The acceleration load on the piston is balanced by a change in load on the foundation, as shown in Fig. 8.18a. The machine can simply rest on a rigid surface, and need not be bolted down, provided that the maximum value of the acceleration load, $m\omega^2 a$ is not greater than the weight of the machine Mg. Fig. 8.18b shows the other limiting case of the infinitely flexible mounting.   It is assumed that the device which holds the machine in place is so flexible that there is no reaction if it is displaced. Like all limiting conditions, it is not attainable in practice, but helps in the understanding of the problem.   In theoretical mechanics the rigid body, which is free to move without resistance, is generally said to rest, " on a smooth plane ".   This convention could be applied to the machine in Fig. 8.18b if it were horizontal instead of vertical, when the effect would be exactly the same as that of an infinitely flexible mounting.

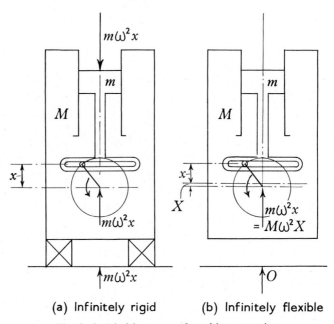

(a) Infinitely rigid   (b) Infinitely flexible

Fig. 8.18. Limiting cases of machine mounting.

The mass m moving up and down gives inertia loads similar to those on the rigid mounting, and to the inertia load there must always be an equal, opposite reaction.   This reaction can be given only by simple harmonic motion of the complete machine, which moves upwards while the piston moves downwards; equilibrium demands that the displacement X of the machine from its mid-position, is less than the displacement x of the piston in the ratio $\dfrac{m}{M}$, in other words, the amplitude and movement of the perfect flexible mounting is less than the throw of the crank in the ratio $\dfrac{m}{M}$, and the movement is always in the reverse direction, or " 180° out of phase ". Flexible mounting of machinery having unbalanced parts is acceptable only when the total mass supported is large compared with the unbalance, and for this reason engines and air compressors and other types of machine with heavy reciprocating parts are bolted to heavy foundation blocks which are themselves resiliently mounted from the floor or pit. Fig. 8.18b gives the fundamental principle, whether the flexible medium is rubber, steel, compressed air, cork, felt or any of the other materials used; it is the inertia of the machine, not the mounting material, which absorbs the vibration. If the cause of the vibration is not in fact a relatively small mass moving up and down with simple harmonic motion it is still equivalent to one or more such masses, not necessarily all moving in the same direction, or with the same frequency. The principle still applies of the small mass moving through a large distance, balanced by a large mass moving through a small distance.

(b) The effect of practical conditions

Many engineers still hope to obtain a little of the advantage of flexible mounting by making the spring supports of a machine only slightly flexible, but generally speaking, the real effect is by no means intermediate between the two extremes given in Fig. 8.18. A resilient mounting need not be in resonance or nearly in resonance with the impulses applied to give a result which must be considered worse than a completely rigid mounting. Resonance, critical speed or synchronous vibration need not be discussed here, though something is said below of the limitation of amplitude by damping without effect on the natural frequency.

If the mounting does not approximate closely either to the perfectly rigid, or to the perfectly flexible, or to the synchronous it can be represented in a simplified form, either by Fig. 8.19 or by Fig. 8.20. In both cases damping is neglected so that the effect of spring stiffness and inertia may be shown more clearly. Both these diagrams show a piston of mass m moving with simple harmonic motion and a mass of the machine M represented as a heavy cylinder. The supporting spring may be of any material, and the assumption that its reaction is proportional to its displacement is sufficiently correct in nearly all cases.

In Fig. 8.19 the spring supporting the machine is not stiff enough to give resonance at the frequency of the unbalance, but has a considerable stiffness, as is generally necessary to retain the machine in its correct position. This is the normal, practical form of resilient mounting. Its action can be explained by an extension of the method used by Manley [4] in connection with torsional vibrational problems. The mass M can be split into two parts. The first, shown shaded in Fig. 8.19b, is sufficient to have a natural frequency, when supported by the whole of the spring equal to the frequency of movement of the unbalanced mass m. This system of part of the mass and the whole of the spring, being in resonance, can vibrate at the frequency of the unbalance (though at no other frequency) with any amplitude without the application of any force from the piston.   This part of the mass M is therefore ineffective for limiting the movement of the whole mass, so that the acceleration forces on the piston are balanced, not against acceleration of the whole of M, but against that of the part shown shaded in Fig. 8.19c.   The amplitude of M is further increased in proportion as this part is reduced.   The advantage of making the supporting spring extremely flexible is clear enough; not only is there a reduction

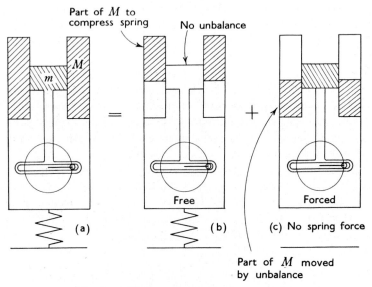

Fig. 8.19. Undamped anti-vibration mounting.

in the part of the inertia wasted in maintaining the spring in a state of oscillation but the reduced amplitude resulting from the greater effective inertia acts on a spring which transmits a smaller range of loading to the base, even for the same amplitude.

Fig. 8.20 shows a mounting in which the spring is too stiff to give the critical speed, even with the whole of the mass M; it is rigid rather than resilient and cannot be considered as an anti-vibration mounting for the movement of m.   It represents a condition which in itself has no merit, but often occurs when the conditions of mounting are determined by factors other than one particular source of vibration.   In this case the spring, not the mass M, must be divided into two parts.   One part maintains the whole of M in resonance without inertia force from m, while the other part is available to be compressed and released by the alternating loads from the acceleration of m.   In this case it is clearly better that the stiffness of the spring should be increased so that a greater part is available to limit the movement due to the inertia force on *m*. Although this movement is controlled entirely by the effective part of the spring, it is unfortunately not true that the inertia of M has no effect at all; not only does it render a part of the spring ineffective, but the alternating loads transmitted to the base are those due to the whole stiffness and not only to the effective stiffness of the spring.

In this sort of analysis it is permissible to divide either the spring stiffness or the inertia, but simpler to do it in such a way that there is no need to

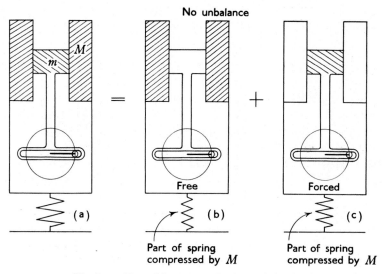

Fig. 8.20. Natural frequency above running speed.

assume negative inertia or negative stiffness. Frequency or speed of rotation cannot be divided, but often the vibration conditions are improved by deliberate change of frequency. One obvious example is the idling speed of a vehicle engine. If for any practical reason it is impossible to reduce the engine mounting stiffness and too much of the inertia of the power unit is wasted in the manner shown in Fig. 8.19*b*, then the idling speed may be increased slightly. A small change in speed, not enough to have much influence either on fuel consumption or on gear changing, may make enough of the inertia effective as in Fig. 8.19*c* to avoid excessive transmission to the vehicle.

If the diagrams in Figs. 8.19 and 8.20 are compared with the standard text-book results it will be seen also that they agree in giving a sharp change of phase angle by 180° at resonance. No force is required to maintain the synchronous or resonant part of the vibration, so that the position of the piston in Fig. 8.19*b* or Fig. 8.20*b* is meaningless.

(c) The effect of damping on resonance

So far it has been assumed that a resonant vibration of any amplitude maintains itself without applied force, but in practice the amplitude is limited, of course, by damping, of which the effect is explained simply by dividing the spring into separate elements of elastic force and damping. Fig. 8.21*a* shows the revised mounting system, in which the direction of rotation must be considered for reasons which follow.   It will be assumed throughout to be counter clock-wise.

Fig. 8.21*b* shows the mass M vibrating freely against the spring, which it can do without force from the piston and with any amplitude.   Fig. 8.21*c*

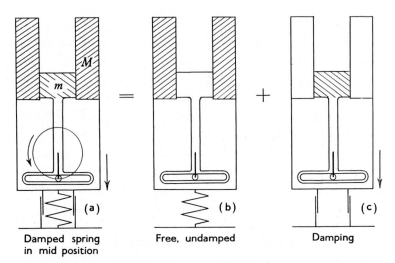

Fig. 8.21. Resonance with damping.

shows the damping force in equilibrium with the inertia force on m.   The inertia force is a maximum when the piston is at its top or bottom centre, and the damping force is a maximum when the velocity of movement of the flexibly mounted machine is a maximum, that is when the spring is in its mean or static position.   In Fig. 8.21*c* the inertia force from the piston is applied downwards and the spring is changing from the condition in which compression has been partly released to that in which extra compression is added.   It becomes fully compressed when the piston has risen again to its mid-position, so that the movement of the machine on its mounting upwards lags a quarter of a cycle, or 90°, behind the movement of the unbalanced piston.   That is in accordance with the theory given on p. 588; the $\dfrac{Pg}{W}$ sin ωt on the piston balances the $\dfrac{2r\dot{x}}{\omega}$ on the mounting, while in Fig. 8.21*b* the $\ddot{x}$ on the complete machine balances the P^2x on the spring.

The cycle of movement of the machine in resonance on a damped

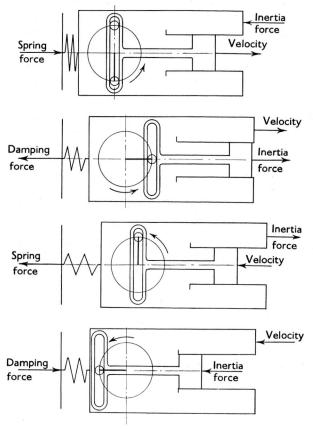

Fig. 8.22. Resonance (movement of base exaggerated)

mounting is illustrated further by the diagrams drawn for intervals of 90° in Fig. 8.22.

(d) Anti-vibration mounting with damping

The method used in Figs. 8.19, 8.20 and 8.21 is applicable equally with the damped mounting which is not in resonance. Fig. 8.23 refers to such a mounting, in which the spring stiffness is less than that required to give resonance, that is normal anti-vibration mounting. Both the reciprocating mass *m* and the machine mass *M* must be divided; the first into a larger part, acting against the effective inertia, and a smaller part acting against the damping force. The spring stiffness is supposed to be such that only a small part of M is wasted in maintaining the synchronous part of the vibration, as is the case in properly designed anti-vibration mountings. Fig. 8.23 gives the parts of m used on overcoming effective inertia and damping with the crank in positions at right angles to one another. As explained in connection with Figs. 8.21 and 8.22, the damping force has a maximum value at the same time as the inertia force on M is zero, and the

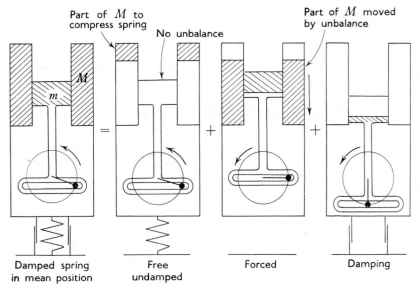

Fig. 8.23. Anti-vibration mounting with damping.

division of the applied force into components of 90° difference in phase is familiar to all engineers acquainted with alternating-current technology. The identity of these two parts of the force at right angles, with a single one at an intermediate angle, is merely a straightforward composition of forces.

Fig. 8.23, like Figs. 8.21 and 8.22, refers equally to normal viscous damping and to rubber damping, but the two forms of damping differ considerably in the distribution of m between its two parts. In rubber, maximum damping force remains practically the same proportion of maximum elastic force, however much the frequency is increased above that for resonance. A greater difference between the operating and resonant frequencies can be achieved either by higher rotational speed or by a more flexible mounting. As the proportion of M wasted in maintaining the free vibration is reduced so is the alternating force in the spring and in the same proportion, or very nearly the same proportion, the part of m needed to overcome the damping force. A limiting condition is approached in which all of m is used in overcoming the inertia, while in true viscous damping the limiting condition is one in which a finite proportion of m is used in damping work. That is an important property of rubber which is not yet appreciated generally; its damping prevents the build-up of excessive amplitudes at resonance, with far less influence upon the transmission at high frequencies than is given by the type of viscous damping generally assumed in vibration study and in electrical technology.

The elementary analysis of vibration insulation, given above, can be applied directly to a large proportion of the problems found in practice, but there may be many other considerations, most of which are discussed in the appropriate sections dealing with practical design of rubber components. At this stage it may be helpful, however, to consider the effect of several vibrations of different frequency superimposed upon one another. For instance, an internal combustion engine may have a primary unbalance giving one, a secondary unbalance giving two and firing impulses giving six vibrations per revolution. The speed of rotation may vary from 500 to 5,000 r.p.m. A fully efficient anti-vibration mounting must be flexible enough to use up very little of the engine's inertia in maintaining a free vibration of frequency 500 per minute, but it may not be practical to make the mounting so flexible, especially if the engine is mounted in a vehicle. It may be best to sacrifice some of the mounting's efficiency by leaving only a small equivalent inertia for the lowest frequency of vibration at the lowest speed, or even to allow a resonance of the lower frequencies somewhere between the idling and the normal running speed. The resonance is prevented from being too severe by the small amount of the unbalance and the damping of the rubber.

In applying the principle of equivalent inertia to several frequencies it must be understood that when much of the inertia is lost by the approach of resonance for one vibration this has no effect upon vibrations of other frequencies, for which the value of the equivalent inertia must be considered quite separately.

It is important also to distinguish between two sources of vibration, both of which may be regarded as of constant amplitude. Firstly, there is the constant unbalanced mass, such as m of Figs. 8.19–8.23, and secondly, there is the unbalanced force which remains independent of frequency while the constant mass gives a force proportional to the square of frequency. The first of these alternatives has been chosen because it is encountered much more widely in vibration insulation problems and because it leads to a simpler and clearer explanation of the properties of the mounting. The second alternative is used much more often, however, in the plotting of theoretical resonance curves, and does not show up in the same manner the adverse effect of normal viscous damping on transmission of high frequencies.

2. Some further considerations in vibration insulation by rubber

Fig. 8.19 showed that at resonance the applied vibration is used entirely in overcoming the damping forces of the rubber, which alone limit the amplitude of movement. Some of the damping may be derived from air resistance or other external causes, but in most cases it is reasonable to assume that damping other than that due to the rubber is unimportant. The value of the damping resistance for a given amplitude is almost independent of the frequency, so that the same applies to the resonance amplitude for a given vibratory force and mass. A single value of the dynamic magnifier M may be given for any rubber spring, while the standard case of viscous damping leads to a dynamic magnifier falling off with the resonant frequency.

Turning now to Fig. 8.23, the ratio of the viscous resistance to the elastic restoring force of the spring is still substantially constant, and the same as in Fig. 8.21. As the frequency increases the proportion of the inertia which is ineffective in controlling the amplitude falls off, so that the change in spring force becomes less, and so does the viscous resistance. The text-book resonance diagrams show the force transmitted due to damping as greater than the force transmitted by elasticity at very high frequencies, but that does not occur with rubber, where the force remains less in proportion to the dynamic magnifier M. The comparison is illustrated in Fig. 8.24, and it is remarkable that so little has been made of the important property of rubber, which has exactly the right sort of damping for vibration insulation. Fig. 8.24 refers to a vibration due to an unbalanced mass in which the force, the $\frac{Pg}{W}$, is proportional to the square of the frequency, so that the forces transmitted at high frequency, both elastic and viscous, are greater than in the case of a constant force. This applies, of course, to both forms of damping and the relative elastic force transmitted has a limiting value of one in both cases. The value of the elastic force is in fact practically the same, but there is a very marked contrast in the damping force. In the one case it begins to rise to a significant extent when the frequency exceeds twice that of resonance, and in the other case it falls off to a limiting value still equal to $\frac{1}{M}$ times the elastic force. These diagrams are based upon a dynamic magnifier $M = \frac{20}{3}$, which is about that of an average rubber, though less than that of high-resilience, low-creep rubbers, which are often favoured for anti-vibration mountings.

Occasionally even the most resilient rubbers have more damping than is desirable, and very often sufficient of the rubber damping, which is of the correct quality, can be obtained only by compounding in such a way that other undesirable properties are introduced.

Forms of separate damper which are dependent wholly or partially upon turbulent flow make for a characteristic even further from the ideal than true viscosity, but in the practical designs used mainly in vehicles a compromise is reached by the use of an additional mechanical device, such as a blow-off valve. The prospects of a satisfactory rubber being developed with a much increased damping are discussed in more detail in Section 12.

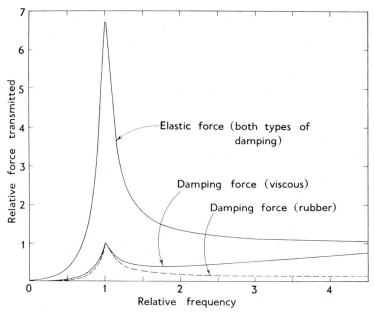

Fig. 8.24. Comparison of " viscous " and rubber damping.

Resonance amplitude can be limited only by the absorption of energy, that is by damping. This damping may be either in the rubber or other elastic material, in separate damping devices, or in relative movement of the machine and its surroundings. The truth of this statement should be made clear enough by the many works published on non-linear vibration, but still there is a very general belief that synchronous vibration can be avoided by ingenious manipulation of stiffness. The two false principles generally used are these:

(*a*) The use side by side of two or more springs having different " periodicities ". In fact, the two springs act as a single unit, and at resonance each is in equilibrium with the appropriate part of the mass supported.

(*b*) Non-linearity, that is stiffness changing with deflection. The plausible argument is that as fast as the amplitude changes, so does the natural frequency, so that there can be no one frequency at which the mounting is in resonance. It is true that the maximum resonance amplitude may be avoided, either as the speed increases or as the speed decreases, but it is always possible to obtain a resonance condition in normal operation. Many rubber springs have a stiffness which increases with the deflection, so that there is a tendency for a large amplitude to be retained for a longer time while the frequency increases, and for the

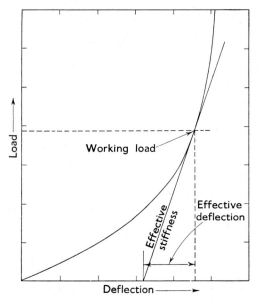

Fig. 8.25. Typical loading curve rubber " in compression ".

resonance to be avoided as the speed decreases. The reverse is true of a spring of which the stiffness falls off with the amplitude. More often the largest amplitude is small compared with the initial deflection, so that the non-linearity is of little effect upon the vibration characteristics. The effective stiffness is the tangent of the load-deflection curve at the point of continuous loading as shown, for instance, in Fig. 8.25.

There are advantages and disadvantages in many cases in the use of stiffness of a spring support variable with load. Some of these are discussed also in Section 12.

3. Shock absorption

The types of rubber spring used generally from the middle of the last century until the commercial development of bonding had the rising stiffness curve shown in Fig. 8.25. This, and the particular fatigue characteristic of rubber, which enables it to be stressed far more highly for occasional impacts than for continuous vibration, made rubber seem a very attractive material for shock absorption. A dynamic stiffness higher than the static, if it were understood, would have been considered an advantage, and a tendency to creep or permanent set of little importance. Absorption by damping of a part of the energy was also an advantage claimed by the rubber manufacturers, though contested by the Sheffield steel industry, who alleged that any dissipation of work in rubber hastens fatigue failure, which occurs after far fewer impacts with rubber than with steel springs.[5] To a large extent the right answer is that most shock-absorbing buffers have only a few impacts approaching the maximum design value, and that if the rubber spring withstands more than the possible service number of such impacts the much larger number at far lower stresses will do it no harm. On the other hand, the validity of the argument for rising stiffness characteristic is extremely doubtful. Small shocks are probably of no disadvantage in equipment which is designed to absorb the larger ones, and a shock absorber with a falling, rather than a rising, characteristic, absorbs more energy for specified values of maximum travel and maximum acceleration.

Nevertheless, the properties of rubber have been considered good enough for its use on a large scale in shock-absorbing elements ever since the invention of vulcanisation. The most important applications have been the buffing and drawgear of railway vehicles, of which the development of the spring is given in some detail by Macbeth.[6] The greatest energy is absorbed in a given travel by a shock absorber if the resistance is constant, but it is not possible always to make a shock-absorbing system to give this result, nor is it necessarily desirable when all practical conditions are considered. Fig. 8.26 compares the travel of springs of various characteristics in absorbing the same energy with the same maximum reaction. If the shock absorber is a spring of constant stiffness, then the travel is obviously twice that of a spring or other device of constant resistance, so that the area of the triangle is equal to that of the rectangle. The typical rubber spring having a stiffness increasing with deflection requires an even greater travel, so its characteristic could be considered better only when the reaction to relatively small shocks should be reduced relative to the reaction of the greatest shocks. The obvious disadvantage of the constant-resistance spring is that it gives the same maximum reaction whatever the energy absorbed. Methods of improving the efficiency of the shock absorber, without the disadvantage of the constant load devices, include these:

(a) The falling-rate spring, which is often the best compromise.
(b) The pre-loaded constant-rate spring, which gives a finite reaction

even to the smallest shock, but can be arranged to make this reaction small enough to be acceptable in practice.

(c) The damped spring, in which the damping may be in the rubber or external in the form either of friction plates, or of a hydraulic shock absorber, or of a viscous fluid. The dotted lines show how the characteristics of the constant-load spring and of the pre-loaded spring can be reproduced by adding damping to a constant-rate spring.

An approximation is sometimes possible to the ideal case in which the damping force at the beginning of the travel is equal to the elastic force at the end of the travel, but only for one particular magnitude of shock.

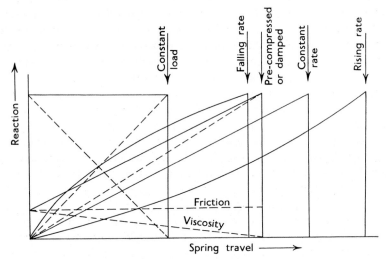

Fig. 8.26. Spring characteristics for a given energy absorption.

Generally speaking, the energy absorbed is that of a heavy body of which the velocity may vary, and in that case true viscous damping would maintain constant resistance. On the other hand, the velocity may be the same and the mass change as with an empty or laden railway wagon, in which case rubber damping would be correct, if indeed rubber damping is similar in nature for the single shock and for vibration, which does not seem at all probable. In any case, rubber damping must be considerably less than is needed for constant resistance, and very little has been published regarding its value during an impact.

The equivalent of the pre-compressed spring can be obtained by adding either viscous damping or rubber damping, or friction to an un-pre-compressed spring of straight-line characteristic. Friction or Coulomb damping has the advantage that it reduces the maximum load on the spring, but in some cases the minimum load required to give any movement may be a disadvantage, and the position of rest is not determined accurately.

It must be emphasised, however, that graphs for the effect of damping upon the characteristic of a rubber shock absorber are to a large extent conjectural. Accurate information may be in the hands of rubber manufacturers who have developed high damping compounds of Butyl and other synthetic rubbers, for railway buffers and similar duties, but no such information seems to have been published, and further research is required. The difficulties of judging the shock-absorbing properties of rubber are increased further by uncertainty regarding the dynamic stiffness.

If the constant-load property shown as one of the alternatives in Fig. 8.26 is obtained by combining a constant spring stiffness with a suitable damping characteristic, then the areas contained by the curves of the two types of reaction against spring travel are the same. The elastic or spring energy is returned but the damping energy is not, so that one-half of the total energy is dissipated in the first half cycle. If the damping characteristic is still the same for the second half cycle three-quarters is dissipated in the first complete cycle.

The energy which is not returned after the first half cycle is that which is dissipated in friction, viscosity or other form of damping and converted into heat. In shock absorption, as in vibration insulation, non-linearity is not damping, and with a constant, rising or falling rate, a spring made of material with no internal damping would contribute nothing to the reduction in amplitude with successive cycles of the transient vibration. In practice, rubber shock-absorbing springs always damp out the vibration in a fairly small number of cycles, and if the rate rises with the deflection the frequency becomes less as the amplitude becomes smaller. Similarly, a falling rate gives a rising frequency.

4. Rubber as a spring material

It has been shown already that rubber depends for its vibration-insulating properties mainly upon its elasticity, though also, to some extent upon its internal damping. Although it is about one hundred times weaker than a good grade of spring steel, it is one hundred thousand times more flexible in shear, the property which attracted the interest of spring designers as early as 1845.[7] The early rubber compounds seem to have been reinforced with lead sulphide, and talc, but over the comparatively narrow range of modulus which was practicable, the properties seem to have been good. A comparison of drawings and stated stiffness rates from this early period usually gives a modulus of rigidity of 90–100 lb./sq. in., which is still considered often to be the optimum as regards spring efficiency, low creep and other desirable properties. Craig describes his experience with rubber spring gear on the locomotives of the Monmouth-shire lines in a paper [8] read in Birmingham in 1853, and asserts that there is no trouble from creep or from oil contamination, or ageing. At that time there was undoubtedly great enthusiasm for rubber springing for locomotives and railway carriages, and at least a considerable interest in similar springs for the heavier horse-drawn road vehicles, but the enthusi-asm began to decline about 1855, and not many years later rubber was used for bearing springs only when nothing else would stand up to the job. An article in *Engineering* of January 12th, 1866, explains that rubber's "gradu-ally increasing resistance renders it badly adapted for use as a bearing spring in rolling stock ", though by that time rubber auxiliaries had come into general use in conjunction with laminated springs greatly improved by developments in steel making. Unfortunately, this half-column article in a technical magazine of nearly a century ago is not known to all engineers designing rubber springs today. The mistake which led to the return to steel about 1855 is repeated again and again when the estimated flexibility is based upon the total deflection from the free to the laden condition, and not upon the change in deflection for a small change of load above or below the fully laden. One of the worst examples was a design of axle-box springs for tramcars worked out within the last 20 years, in which an approximation to constant periodicity was obtained by a series of concentric rubber springs which came into contact successively with rigid stops.[9] The lightest of these springs was solid at a pressure less than the tare load of the vehicle, and was, therefore, totally ineffective under all working conditions. It could be freed from its overload stop only by excessive rolling of the vehicle, in which case its effect was to increase, quite un-necessarily, the angle of roll.

Patent specifications of the middle of the last century show also many devices for using rubber in small deflection springs for anti-vibration mounting of engines and machinery,[10] and include an ingenious device for tensioning the shrouds of sailing ships.[11] No evidence has been found yet of the systematic study in such early days of the application of rubber springs otherwise than to rail vehicles.

The renewed interest in rubber for high-deflection, continuously-loaded springs, including those for road and rail vehicles, results from the recent development of designs giving much more flexibility under normal work-ing conditions. At intervals attempts are made to improve the perform-ance further still by making a spring which almost collapses at its normal load and has a flexibility considerably greater than that at lighter loads. These attempts at controlled instability, in the direction in which the main load is applied, have not been successful because this condition, which appears in principle to be so desirable, is always accompanied by an unduly rapid rate of creep, and its achievement at the correct load and initial deflection requires impossibly close control of the quality of the rubber. Any further developments on the same lines must be viewed with suspicion, but it may be sound practice at times to design a spring so that its stiffness is reduced by the approach of instability in directions perpendicular to that in which the load is applied.

Rubber compression springs of the orthodox type have an effective deflection as defined in Fig. 8.25 of the order of $\frac{1}{7}$ of the rubber thickness, or even less. It is not surprising, therefore, that effective deflections of several inches were obtained generally by the use of leverage to impose a mechanical advantage upon the rubber. This is still done in many cases on modern designs of rubber springing, both in compression and in shear, especially where the load is small relative to the deflection. The springing of the new B.M.C. light car is a well-known example.[12]

Stressing in shear makes possible a greater deflection of the rubber spring itself for a given load, with a characteristic deviating very little from the straight line and a normal working deflection of the order of $\frac{1}{2}$–$\frac{2}{3}$ of the rubber thickness. Earlier attempts to use rubber in shear, without bonding to metal plates and without relying upon friction due to pre-compression, include an ingenious form of aircraft under-carriage by F. W. Lanchester. In this, cylinders of rubber were strained by layers of cord stretched alternately in opposite directions. Torsion springs have been formed also from discs of rubber compressed axially, but the load capacity, for a given size and weight of spring assembly, has not been enough for the method to develop beyond the experimental stage. One well-known type of cylindrical bush relies upon the compression of the rubber between the two sleeves, and although it is important mostly as an oscillating bearing, it is used as a spring, both axially and torsionally, in shear.

Most modern designs of rubber spring rely, to a considerable extent, both on the shearing of the rubber and on its bonding to metal. The simplest form is a single-shear sandwich consisting of two metal plates and a rectangular block of rubber, as shown in Fig. 8.27a. This construction is marketed commercially with the two bonded surfaces formed on adapter blocks of many different shapes, and with simple sheet-metal plates arranged for bolting to other components. Details of design are discussed later. But such a mounting is still popular for the vibration insulation of machines where the working deflection is often from $\frac{1}{10}$ to 1 in., and has been used in larger sizes, even for the springing of motor vehicles.[13]

The double-shear mounting, Fig. 8.27b, is applied even more widely for the anti-vibration mounting of machinery[14] and has the advantage of carrying its load symmetrically and of being adaptable easily to pre-compression at right angles to the direction of loading. The general recommendation of pre-compression by rubber manufacturers may seem to cast doubt upon the reliability of bonding, but in fact it is effective in a design on the lines of Fig. 8.27*b*, only because the bonding prevents the surface of contact with the metal from spreading over a larger area.   Its advantage is that it gives a much greater effective life to the rubber, which generally fails before the bond, and reduces the tendency to surface deterioration through oxidation.

Strictly speaking, resilient components of rubber always deflect in shear, because the bulk modulus is so high that other forms of deflection are negligible.   In practice, the term is used of any serious attempt to obtain

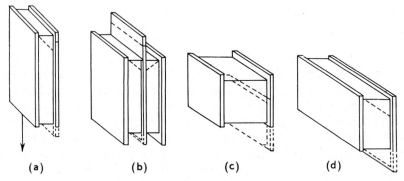

(a)   (b)   (c)   (d)

Fig. 8.27. Rubber bonded and in shear.

an approximation to uniform shear, as in the examples given already. There must be always some tension and compression and stress concentrations at the top and bottom surfaces, but they are confined to a small part of the rubber volume.   A mounting of the shape shown in Fig. 8.27*c*, on the other hand, may be described much more accurately as being in bending, and the stiffness for relative displacement, of the type shown, is far less than that calculated from the modulus of rigidity.   Fig. 8.27*d* is about the limit of the proportions of mounting which can be regarded as being in shear, though there is no doubt at all, of course, about the form of loading in the perpendicular direction.

The torsion bush, having a relatively small difference between the inside and outside diameters of the sleeves and a considerable axial length, as shown, for instance, in Fig. 8.28*a*, is a most efficient rubber spring in normal use, if efficiency is measured solely by strain energy stored in unit volume or weight of elastic material.   Shear stressing is continuous round the periphery, and the difference between the loading on inner and outer bonded surface is not too great, but the theoretical advantage does not compensate often for the cost and weight of the fastenings of the torsion arm and housing.   At one time it was considered reasonable to use a shear stress in a torsion bush three times as great as that in a flat shear mounting, so that the volume of rubber need be only one-ninth as great.

Further experience has shown that it is more reasonable to make the stress only about $1\frac{1}{2}$ times greater, mainly because the theoretical elimination of stress concentrations demands complete bonding of the surfaces; even the smallest area unbonded can be a source of some stress concentration, while the design of flat shear mountings has been improved greatly.   More is said on this subject in Section 7.

In spite of the theoretical loss of efficiency, many torsion bushes are

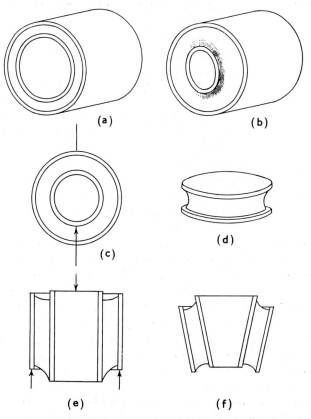

Fig. 8.28. Cylindrical bush and alternatives.

made with the centre sleeves of comparatively small diameter, as in Fig. 8.28b.   The convenience of the shorter torque arm for a given travel and the lighter associated metal parts often compensate for the greater volume of rubber.   The circular bonded bush is also popular as a form of direct-loaded rubber spring, in addition to being the usual form of oscillating bearing, and may be loaded either radially or axially.   Radial loading, as in Fig. 8.28c, allows a load several times greater than that which can be applied axially as in Fig. 8.28e, but the deflection is normally only one-tenth of the rubber thickness, whereas continuous shear up to half or even two-thirds of the thickness may be allowed under favourable conditions. If the load is always in one direction the cylindrical bush seems to be inefficient in compression compared with the simple bonded disc in Fig. 8.28d, and in shear compared with the conical bonded bush in Fig. 8.28f. If the bush is loaded axially and is cylindrical its capacity is increased by pre-compression, which may be carried out either by stretching the inner sleeve or by contracting the outer sleeve, or by making one or other in two or more sectors drawn together after moulding and bonding. In the conical bush the deflection which shears the rubber also compresses it, so that the pre-compression is made to carry a useful part, in some cases more than half, of the load. This comparison is shown by experience to be valid with reference to comparatively steady loading, but that does not mean that the cylindrical bush, used otherwise than in torsion, is necessarily an inefficient form of spring. For radial loading as in Fig. 8.28e it is the equivalent of two straight compression mountings, such as Fig. 8.28d, pre-compressed against one another so that the initial deformation is about one-eighth of the rubber thickness, and the maximum strain on the "compression side" is rather over one-fifth of the thickness. With the load reversing continually, this is a simple way of avoiding actual tension, and the rubber at the sides of the bush, which carries only a relatively small alternating shear strain, may be justified by the simple construction in which the pre-compression loads are retained within the spring itself or a housing into which it is pressed and the attachment to the machine is by turned parts only. Similarly, the cylindrical bush is preferred to the conical for continually reversing axial load, and is used even in aircraft engine mountings, where the reduction of space and weight to a minimum is of the greatest importance. Fatigue limits are discussed in Section 5, in which something is said of the reduction in stress range if the stress passes through zero at any time during the cycle. Generally speaking, it is advisable to pre-stress radially a cylindrical bush loaded in compression, so that the initial radial strain is greater than that subsequently applied, but not advisable to pre-stress an axially loaded bush, for instance, by making it in two sections loaded against one another, either in cylindrical or in conical form.

Since the majority of rubber springs are used in anti-vibration mountings in which the range of alternating load is small compared with the mean, it is not surprising that so many load the rubber partly in shear and partly in compression. Fig. 8.28f can be taken equally as a cross-section of a mounting made from two flat bonded sandwiches of rubber and metal, and this principle is in fact very usual. Some of the constructions which appear quite different are really similar in principle, obtaining the effect of the inclined or V mountings by trapping a part of the rubber in order that it cannot distort to any significant extent, leaving an effective section, not much different from the inclined rectangle or conical sleeve. It may seem bad design to put in dead rubber, but sometimes it is justified by the simpler form of the metal parts.

5. Rubber as a bearing material

Although rubber is regarded popularly as a material to give a high coefficient of friction, it is used, properly lubricated, as a sliding bearing, and more recently unlubricated with special compounding to reduce friction. The stern-tube glands of motor boats [15] are a well-known example of rubber lubricated with water, but this section is concerned rather with the application of the elastic properties of rubber to oscillating bearings, in which the relative movement between two members is accommodated by distortion in shear and not by sliding. Either oscillation or movement in a straight line or any direction in a plane can be accommodated in this way, and the rubber may be bonded either to both supporting members, or to one only, or to neither. Occasionally when an unbonded surface is used the design is proportioned so that relative movement up to a limit is allowed by shearing, after which sliding moves the bearing to a new position of rest, about which elastic distortion gives a range of frictionless movement as before. This principle may be used, for instance, in the erection of the suspension linkage of a car, which is put together with the spring unloaded, though the fully laden attitude represents too large an angular movement of the hinge bushes to be accommodated by shearing of rubber alone.

A rubber bearing may be identical in principle with the rubber spring, and the same component may be used for the two different purposes at different times, but that does not mean that the design requirements are similar. They are, in fact, quite the reverse: the object of a rubber spring is to store a certain amount of strain energy with a steady deflection, while a bearing should allow a certain deflection with the minimum storage of strain energy. It must be as flexible as possible in the direction in which it has to move, and relatively stiff in the direction in which it carries load. A spring may have negligible resistance, or even in fact negative resistance to deflection perpendicular to the direction in which it carries load, but a bearing must have very considerable stiffness in at least one such direction. That does not mean, of course, that rubber can perform only one of the two functions at the same time. One of its great advantages indeed is that it can act simultaneously as a spring and as an unlubricated oscillating or sliding bearing with no working parts. The conical bush in Fig. 8.28f, for instance, is a spring vertically and a bearing for a limited torsional movement, providing resistance to horizontal displacement which renders

x

unnecessary any separate supporting means.   In the sections dealing with practical applications reference is made repeatedly to this dual function of the rubber mounting, but a very great quantity of rubber components, mostly bonded to metal, is used under conditions where any restoring force in the direction of oscillation of the bearing is undesirable.   This class of component may be illustrated by the example of the independent front suspension of motor vehicles, of which a lay-out is shown diagrammatically in Fig. 8.29.   The loading of the wheel is supported entirely by the helical

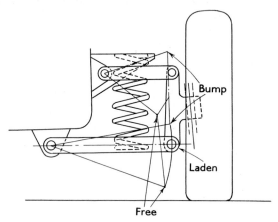

Fig. 8.29. Typical IFS of vehicle.

spring of which part of the reaction is carried at the outer end and part at the inner end of the lower transverse link.   The bearings of both links are loaded horizontally by the cornering force and the correct setting of the wheel to give accurate steering can be preserved only if the bushes give very little deflection under this force.   On the other hand, the softness of riding of the vehicle depends upon the low reaction of the spring and of the linkage to a small displacement from its mean position.   Fig. 8.30 shows how this is affected by the bushes which are assumed to be set so that they carry no load with the vehicle at rest in its normal position.   The effective deflection of the spring is reduced by the resistance of the rubber which gives the whole suspension the same characteristic as the helical spring alone with fewer coils.   The rubber carries only a very small part of the maximum load, so that it does not allow any substantial reduction in the capacity of the spring and the greater the reaction of the bearings, the larger must be the spring.   An increase in weight of spring steel by something like 20% is considered to be quite justifiable to secure the advantages of freedom from periodical lubrication and of complete reliability and occasionally some reduction in noise transmission, but sometimes it is difficult to avoid a greater stiffness.   The problem gets more difficult as vehicle springing becomes softer and accurate maintenance of steering geometry more important with higher speeds.

A solution of the problem, which appears attractive in theory, is to set the hinge bearings so that they are free in the same attitude as the spring and resist angular movement up to the maximum possible without slipping. The deflection rates for the spring alone and for the complete suspension would then be as shown by the dotted lines in Fig. 8.30, but unfortunately the angular movement, especially in the top transverse link, is nearly always far too much and is acceptable only if it is divided fairly equally on either side of the mean position.

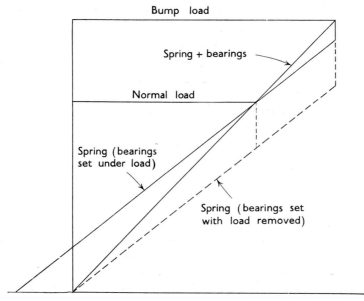

Fig. 8.30. Parasitic spring rate.

The torsional stiffness of a cylindrical bush, which is the form of bearing generally used, rises rapidly with the diameter, while if the rubber thickness remains in the same ratio to the inner sleeve diameter the reliable angle of oscillation remains the same and the load capacity increases very little. On the other hand, the load capacity increases almost as the square of the length, while the torsional stiffness, and consequently the addition to the spring-rate, rises only in proportion to the length.

Hence the best design bearing is one with the smallest diameter, and greatest length which is allowed by the stressing of the centre shaft. This should really be supported at both ends, but in practice over-hanging shafts of high-tensile material are used quite often because they lead to a more economical construction. Motor-vehicle springing is discussed in this section only as an illustration of the design principle in rubber bearings. Practical forms of construction are given in Section 12. For many years some of the leading motor-vehicle builders were inclined to pay insufficient attention to the effect of the bearing stiffness upon the spring characteristic, but the question came into prominence with the development of pneumatic suspension of very low periodicity in which the total working spring stiffness is little greater than the stiffness of some orthodox pivot bushes alone. Some designers consider that the best solution is the non-lubricated sliding bearing, made either from natural or from synthetic rubber, or backed by a rubber sleeve, but the extra complication may be avoided in most cases by correct proportioning of elastic bushes.

A large bearing is not necessarily lightly loaded, but the extra rubber may be used, if the design is not correct, in storing unwanted strain energy to such an extent as to overstress the rubber. A large angular movement demands a large thickness of the rubber relative to the pin diameter, and a small resistance demands the small diameter with length sufficient to carry the load.

When movement is needed or is allowable in a plane rather than a single direction the natural choice is a flat mounting in compression in the direction of the load. The design methods used in this sort of mounting, alike for springs and for bearings and for components working at the same time in both ways, are discussed in detail in Section 8. If the component is required solely or mainly as a sliding bearing the amount of compression under load may be unimportant and may have to be kept to a minimum, and in many cases it is well worthwhile to use the form of construction shown in Fig. 8.31a in which the rubber is divided into a number of layers by intermediate plates and, frequently, bonded to them. It is important to distinguish between the flexible bearing made in this way and the orthodox form of shock-absorbing spring, used, for instance, in railway buffers, in which the construction is rather similar, but the properties are such that the rubber slides over the metal while the thickness is reduced.[16] If bonding is used, as it must be for maximum load capacity, change in thickness by sliding is automatically avoided, but there are many cases in which the variation of load is small compared with the mean load, so that free slabs of rubber, once they have taken up their position of rest, are retained in practice by friction. The compression stiffness is increased in proportion to the number of intermediate steel plates, while the shear stiffness depends mainly upon the area and the total rubber thickness. Compression may have the effect, indeed, of reducing the shear stiffness even to the extent of making it negative, and in some cases an unstable bearing may be the best. The ratio of compression stiffness to shear stiffness is often greater than 50 : 1, and occasionally greater than 100 : 1. Intermediate metal plates, or occasionally plies of canvas re-inforcement, can be used both to increase the stiffness ratio and the load capacity for a given size, while a greater compression stiffness can be achieved without affecting the shear by using a greater size of rubber of lower modulus of rigidity.   Quite often the size of the bearing unit is determined rather by the stiffness ratio than by the safe, working pressure of the rubber.

An even higher ratio of stiffness between two perpendicular directions may be achieved by the use of links with rubber bearings at the two ends. Fig. 8.31*b* shows the most usual arrangement, in which the bushes may be

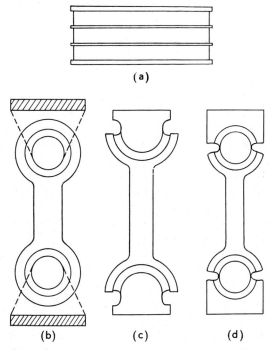

Fig. 8.31. Bearings for transverse movement.

either of the bonded or of the unbonded type, while Fig. 8.31*c* shows a variation in which only that part of the rubber of the bush which is compressed is used, and Fig. 8.31*d* a further variation in which the resistance to transverse movement is made even less.   The last two diagrams could refer either to cylindrical or to spherical bearings, but if the movement is in one direction only the lower resistance is given by the cylindrical bush of proper proportions.   The stiffness can be made, if necessary, to balance or to be less than the unstable effect of an inverted strut.   Both the use of intermediate plates and the replacement of the flat mounting by the radius arm or link with bushes are discussed in connection with a number of practical designs.   An application of rubber bearings which illustrates their advantages very well is the bridge mounting to allow for expansion of the concrete. The form of construction is that shown in Fig. 8.31a because it leads to simple design and replacement if necessary after many years and occupies the minimum amount of space. An expansion joint of this type moves to the maximum extent at a load far less than that needed to overcome friction between sliding surfaces. It may not seem superior in theory to a metal roller, but when it has been in service for some time the roller does not give the low resistance that might be expected.

6. Practical limits of stress and strain

With rubber, as with other engineering materials, it is usual to design to conventional limits of stress and strain based upon the maximum value of the loading. The conventional stress limit, which is the same as the strength of the material divided by the safety factor, is usually selected after long experience to allow for the range of stressing rather than the maximum value, but this method does not work as well with rubber as with steel. The main reason is that rubber has a more sloping curve of fatigue-range against loading cycles, so that the fatigue limit continues to fall off to a marked extent with a number of cycles at which the safe range for steel has become almost constant. Metal components may be designed, and in fact often are designed, so that the fatigue limit is never exceeded, but that cannot be done economically with rubber, which is used as a structural or spring material somewhere on the slope of its fatigue curve. An accurate knowledge of fatigue limits is therefore very important, and in many cases the only substitute for prolonged experience with similar designs working in similar conditions, but unfortunately there are very few publications giving useful information on the subject. Moulton and Turner [17] prepared a series of fatigue curves, taking into consideration both the mean stress and the range of stress in any number of cycles from 10^4 up to 10^{10}, but quite a lot of extrapolation was needed, and it was not claimed that these curves are applied accurately to any type of spring, except that described in the same paper. If these curves are compared with the specimen fatigue results quoted by McPherson and Klemin,[18] or any other published result, it will be seen that no definite conclusions can be reached regarding either the approximate stress limits or the extent to which they fall off with the number of cycles. The comparison of steel and rubber is something of the sort shown in Fig. 8.32, but this must be taken only as a general indication, not as a guide to practical design. The various rubber manufacturers of the world undoubtedly have much more information, especially with regard to particular classes of mechanical component in which they have specialised, but this information either has not been put into a form suitable for publishing or is regarded as too valuable a trade secret. The United States Rubber Company [19] have published a set of alignment charts (nomograms), but these may be based upon research carried out before the War and are more interesting for their method of presentation than for their value as design data.

This section must start therefore by pointing out that conventional stress limits are unsatisfactory and fatigue should be the basis of most designs and, secondly, that published information on dynamic fatigue is scanty and the little available cannot be considered reliable, except with reference to particular designs. It may be added that many of the earlier works on the subject made the fundamental mistake of trying to correlate fatigue with internal heat generation; that is indeed still a very usual belief and seems to be supported by the inferior fatigue properties of most high-damping rubbers. It explains also, in the general manner, the lower

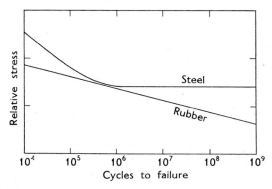

Fig. 8.32. Comparative fatigue properties of rubber and steel.

fatigue range at high temperatures and has been used by the manufacturers of steel springs as an argument against rubber. Other supporting evidence was obtained from the condition of a fatigue test specimen. A fatigue crack is often shown up first by a blister formed on the surface of the rubber, which might be considered to be due to an internal bubble of gas, while the crack which forms close to the blister usually emits a certain amount of semi-molten rubber, such as would be expected round a hot gas bubble. Actually the appearance of a blister is often given by relative slipping on two sides of a crack formed close to the surface, and the local over-heating and melting of the rubber is due to friction between the broken surfaces. Failures due to excessive heat generation do occur and are discussed in the next section, but true fatigue is much more frequent.

Although the nature of the property, which should form the main basis of good design and correct proportion, is understood so little and would form such a useful subject for further systematic research, it would be a great mistake to assume that the design in rubber is mainly a matter either of secret information or of guess-work. The experience which is available regarding many of the important classes of component does give already some approach to a logical design basis, but it is necessary first to forget all about conventional limits of stress and strain given in earlier publications. Such statements as that the normal shear stress should not be greater than 50 lb./in.², or the shear strain greater than 80%, or the compression strain 10%, were an advance upon previous knowledge in the time of Keys [20] and other pioneer workers on rubber mechanics, but cannot be accepted today. Ker Wilson [21] gives 50 lb./in.², or 75% in shear and

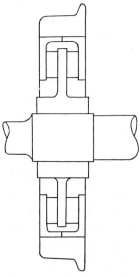

Fig. 8.33. Resilient wheel of tramcar.

500 lb./in.², or 15% in compression, and although these loadings may not be far from the average of anti-vibration mountings, they must be regarded, like the shape of the fatigue curve in Fig. 8.32, rather as a general indication than as working data.

The lowest stresses are used, of course, on components subjected to a very large number of reversals of loading, of which a typical example is the resilient wheel used commonly in the tramcars of European and American cities and to some extent in main-line railway vehicles and even in road and tracked vehicles. The principle is shown in Fig. 8.33, which shows that the wheel disc is separated from the rim by rubber in shear in the plane of rotation and in compression in the direction parallel to the axle. This rubber goes through a complete cycle of loading for every revolution, and as the average circumference is of the order of 9 ft., there are about 600 cycles per mile or two times 2×10^7 cycles per year. Quite obviously, the life of the rubber inserts in the wheel must be equal at least to the mileage between re-turning and should be preferably several times as great. When the rubber is in the form of two complete discs bonded to metal plates it is not generally practicable to test the bond, and the range of stress in a soft grade of rubber of shear modulus about 60 lb./in.² is made quite often as small as ± 15 lb./in.². Slightly higher stresses are used in European designs, both with parts bonded to metal and with cylinders of rubber held in place by compression only, but still ± 20 lb./in.² is about the maximum with a considerably harder rubber. The designers of resilient wheels, or at least some of them, appear to have started developing with considerably higher stresses, but even at the present low stress replacement is necessarily periodical, and the limited life is one of the main objections to the extension of these wheels to railways as well as tramways, but the maintenance cost in tramways is considered to be well worthwhile for the reduction in street noise. The resilient wheel is perhaps an extreme case, but there are many others in which allowance must be made for a large number of cycles, including crankshaft dampers or vibration absorbers on internal-combustion engines, which may be subject to vibration of frequency 300 to 500 c/sec. Here heat generation is important, and special steps must be taken to dissipate as efficiently as possible the heat generated by damping of the rubber. The stress range may be something like ± 30 lb./in.[2] at resonance, but the engine does not run continuously at the resonant speed.

A cylindrical bush of average proportions, subject to rapidly alternating radial loading, can be recommended for a service amounting to tens of millions of cycles only if the range of movement is within $\pm 3\%$ of the radial thickness, and a much greater size for a given loading is needed, for instance, on a vibratory screen [22] than on the spring gear of a motor vehicle. The highest stresses are used in anti-shock mountings for military equipment, in which the maximum stress need not be resisted more than a few times. The shock may be due to explosion or to parachute drop, when resistance to a single loading might be considered sufficient, or due to dropping or shunting of the packaged equipment in transport, when the number of severe impacts might be of the order of one hundred. In all cases the continuous load is extremely small compared with the maximum and the initial shock loading is followed by a transient oscillation which dies away more or less rapidly according to the damping. Official specifications often call for testing of the bond in shear or in tension up to 400 or 500 lb./in.[2], and the maximum load in practice is similar. Stress concentration in the rubber tends to be much more serious than in the bond, so that in such cases a bond strength of 1,000 lb./in.[2] is generally adequate, but the rubber may need a tensile strength of 2,500 lb./in.[2] to avoid failure during the bond test.

The resilient wheel is designed to meet operating conditions which are known accurately and the shock mounting to meet a definite test specification of number and intensity of impacts, but such well-defined requirements are unfortunately the exception rather than the rule, and good judgement in stressing becomes largely a matter of experience. Some of the considerations are these:

(*a*) the probable number of cycles at a stress approaching the maximum;

(*b*) the ambient temperature;

(*c*) the probable rise in temperature of the rubber within the time that it operates through a certain stress range;

(d) the constant stress which is superimposed, whether as supported loading or as preloading;

(e) the probable deterioration due to extraneous conditions such as ozone cracking and oil contamination.

Occasional stress ranges many times greater than the normal are found, for instance, in shaft-transmission couplings which pass through one or more critical speeds every time that the machinery is started or stopped.[23] There must be some cycles of oscillation in which the amplitude is limited only by the damping properties of the rubber and of the machines themselves, but it is not always possible or economical to design the coupling so that it would run continuously on the worst critical speed; that applies particularly to drives in which one of the machines is a Diesel engine or a compressor subject to much fluctuation of torque. The correct design leaves a reasonable safety factor in the fatigue life at maximum torque range, which may mean a normal working stress very small compared with the capacity of the rubber. Flexible couplings fail far more frequently due to the resonance stress range than due to overloading in the orthodox sense, and most of the makers have tried to simplify the problem by issuing charts of service factors, giving the reduction in capacity according to the class of driving or driven machine. No practical alternative to such charts has been found yet for general engineering, but these cannot take into account all the factors which control the resonance stresses. Similarly, road-vehicle springs of rubber, like those of metal, cannot be designed to operate continuously through their full range, and it is not easy to estimate how many cycles of the full range must be allowed during the life of a spring. Most other applications of rubber springs and bearings are found by careful analysis to be very little easier to define.

Fatigue life is influenced by the actual working temperature within the rubber, which depends in turn upon the ambient temperature and the internal heat generation. An attempt was made by Cadwell [24] and others as long ago as 1940 to analyse the influence both of temperature and of ageing, and the graph included in their paper is still quoted frequently. It shows a maximum fatigue range at atmospheric temperature and a very rapid drop in either direction. The second curve, taking into account ageing, suggests that natural rubber cannot be used at a temperature above 135° F (57° C), and even without allowance for ageing rubber becomes quite unsuitable as a spring material above 70° C. There is no reason to doubt that the results were measured accurately under certain specialised conditions, but the fact remains that natural rubber is operating reliably over a considerable fatigue range with temperatures up to 110° C intermittently and 80° C for considerable periods. At high temperatures, in fact, increase of permanent set or creep, rather than loss of fatigue properties, is the usual limitation. No practical evidence has been found of more rapid fatigue of rubber springs when operating in cold conditions, but the probable explanation is that the damping of rubber increases at low temperatures sufficiently for the heat generation to raise the working temperature to the range where fatigue characteristics are good.

The same paper by Cadwell and others is often quoted also for the effect on dynamic fatigue of pre-loading in compression and shear, but again the results apply to a very specialised condition, and generally speaking it is not true that simultaneous pre-loading in compression and shear reduces fatigue life; it is, in fact, generally the best condition, and the text of the article makes it clear that the anomalous result was due to shear on the particular shape, effectively removing compression. Unfortunately, the better the diagram, the more likely is it to be quoted without adequate explanation. Many rubber components must continue to give an adequate fatigue life when they are damaged to some extent by oxidation cracks which lead to greater effective stress and stress concentration, and by fluid contamination, which affects adversely the properties of the material and spoils the good proportions of the original design. Again some allowance is necessary in stressing, but it is quite impossible to give any definite rule.

No synthetic rubber is available on the large-scale with fatigue properties approaching those of natural rubber at any temperature up to 120° C, and it is difficult enough to try to lay down rules for the stressing of natural rubber which forms the subject of the remainder of this section. Of the available synthetics, neoprene seems to be the best in this respect, and Butyl would be considered more if its properties did not vary so much with temperature. Nitrile rubbers, although valued for their heat and fluid resistance, are not suitable for large stress ranges, while silicone cannot be regarded yet as satisfactory structural material, on account of its rapid change in properties, with stressing, and low tensile strength and fatigue limit. SBR is used occasionally in a blend with natural rubber, but even when its price becomes relatively favourable by market fluctuations, it is doubtful whether its use is a real economy, unless the component is much larger than it need be for natural rubber and can suffer the less satisfactory properties without serious loss of performance.

Some general rules are attempted below for the stressing of an average first-grade natural rubber compound of modulus of rigidity 100 lb./in.^{2} static:

(a) The safe stress range to either side of the unloaded position, and with a reasonable amount of pre-loading in shear, is shown in Fig. 8.34. This graph refers to ranges over which reliability can be expected with properly designed flat shear mountings precompressed, but subject to alternating load in shear only.   The degree of precompression depends so much upon the shape that it cannot be stated here.

(*b*) In torsional shear a stress 1·5 times greater may be allowed, provided that the proportions of the rubber are such that stress distribution over the bonded surface is reasonably uniform.

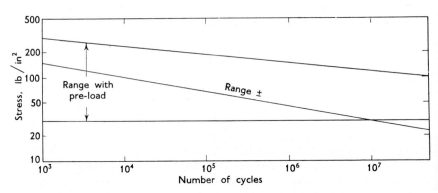

Fig. 8.34. Stress range in shear (note logarithmic scale).

(*c*) Stress ranges up to 50% greater may be allowed when reliability is not so important, while there should be a reduction by about 25% where the standard of reliability is so high that a single failure might condemn the use of rubber.

(*d*) Elevated temperature always reduces the stress range allowable,

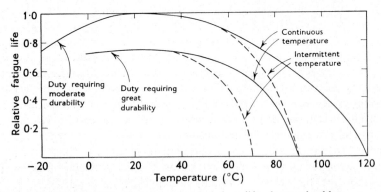

Fig. 8.35. Effect of temperature on fatigue life of natural rubber.

but widens also the gap between the limits for comparatively short or very long service.   Fig. 8.35 gives some idea of the allowance that should be made, assuming that the compounding of the rubber is the best for the particular temperature range.

If the rubber has a modulus of rigidity different from 100 lb./in.² the stress range should be varied in the manner shown in Fig. 8.36. The limits of modulus are given as 40–300 lb./in.², and it can be seen that any rubber outside these limits has comparatively poor properties. Recommended limits of 60–250 lb./in.² are shown also. There would be no difficulty in expressing these results in a single diagram, but this cannot be justified until knowledge of the subject is more advanced.

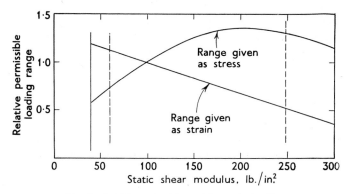

Fig. 8.36. Effect of rubber stiffness on loading.

It is even more difficult to state limits for stress and strain range, on rubber springs subject to compression, or a combination of compression and shear; most authorities give a limit for compression stress, but fail to justify it by reference either to systematic fatigue tests or to service experience. Many rubber bushes used as bearings in vehicle spring gear operate statically with loading of about 1,000 lb./in.², while the range on bad roads is from zero to twice the static, and on special test tracks up to three times. It is recognised, of course, that there is a limited life in these extreme conditions.

Rubber springs in " pure compression ", that is loaded perpendicular to flat plates, are frequently preloaded up to 300 lb./in.² and subjected to alternating stress of the order of ±200, but such figures mean very little when the range of deflection is not stated. Similarly, ranges of strain also are no indication of the real conditions of loading, and it is much more reasonable to give the limit in the form of a maximum absorption of strain energy per unit volume of elastic material. Examination of a number of successful rubber springs shows that when shear and compression are used together a range of ±25 in.-lb./in.³ is quite reasonable, with a mean loading of 50 in.-lb./in.³. On the other hand, the volume of rubber may have to be increased for reasons other than energy absorption, and a spring with a range of only ±10 in.-lb./in.³ is not necessarily designed inefficiently, and a shape of spring favourable enough to make proper use of all the rubber is not always practical.   A rubber compression spring cannot be unloaded entirely unless it is bonded, and the fatigue life falls off much more rapidly as the stress range approaches zero in a compression than in a shear spring. Sometimes it is better to avoid bonding to one at least of the contact surfaces, so that there cannot be load reversal, but still the highest energy reached is obtained from fully bonded springs.   The general shape of the fatigue curve is that shown in Fig. 8.34, with the possible limit of ± 25 in.-lb./in.^{3}, corresponding to 10^6 cycles and a much greater slope.   Actual drawing of a curve is scarcely justified.

Creep and permanent set are given often as reasons for stress limitation, but there is little evidence that within the range allowed by fatigue characteristics, creep changes relative to the initial deflection.   If it is given as the limitation on the loading of a given rubber spring the reason is probably the limited over-travel allowed by the design.   One particular type of creep, namely work-softening, does occur only in comparatively stiff grades of rubber and with a considerable range of compression strain. Work-softening may be defined as permanent reduction in static shear modulus resulting from the application of repeated stress cycles.   It occurs in rubber springs loaded either in compression or in compression and shear, and must be distinguished clearly from the temporary softening due to high stress, known as the Mullins effect.[25]   If a very small reduction in stiffness were enough to impede the working of the rubber, then work-softening might be regarded as a reason, either for limiting the range or maximum value of the compression stress in the harder mixes or for using direct shear, but the stiffness of rubber varies slightly with so many factors that this is scarcely a practical consideration.   In well-designed rubber springs, stressed even to the maximum permissible for fatigue, the amount of softening is seldom more than 10%; this subject is considered further in Section 6, as it is regarded more properly as a form of deterioration due to incorrect design or compounding.

Much has been written on static fatigue,[26] that is failure resulting from application over a long period of a stress, well below the breaking point, but the conditions leading to static fatigue are seldom found in rubber springs or bearings of modern design.   In rubber, as in metals, the loading of a structural component may be limited by stability, rather than stress, but the conditions leading to buckling, or negative stiffness, are a problem of design and considered in detail in Section 8.   The problem becomes very important in connection with vehicle springs.

The conclusions from this section are necessarily less than a complete guide to the stressing of mechanical rubber components, but if the few data given are found from general experience to be accurate they are an advance on anything published previously.

7. Types of failure

Fatigue is discussed already in Section 6 as the principal limitation on the load-carrying capacity of rubber, and is distinguished from failure due to internal heating. A component may be considered to have failed, however, when for any reason it is no longer fit for further service, and in the case of rubber one of the most usual causes of rejection is excessive creep or permanent set. It is not necessary to discuss here the exact technical meaning of the various terms relating to deflection beyond that corresponding to the elastic properties of the material, but the creep or settlement, when of such magnitude as to cause rejection after a period of use, is generally in the form of permanent set, and work softening. Work softening is discussed in Section 6 as a possible limitation on stress, but it occurs to some extent in most rubber compounds of modulus of rigidity above 150 lb./in.^{2} static. There is not yet sufficient information available from systematic tests to say at what stress it appears, but in most practical designs allowance must be made for its occurrence, and it must be kept to a minimum by good compounding and correct processing. Excessive work softening, involving a reduction of the static stiffness by as much as 30%, may occur in the stiffer mixes, and result either in loss of working clearance or of changed shape, such as to spoil the mechanical properties or to give stress concentration. Work softening is not always recognised because it leads to no permanent deformation. An anti-vibration mounting, for instance, may settle down so much that the working clearance is lost, but appear on removal from installation to be in perfect condition and show a dynamic stiffness very little different from the original. The design must allow for this property to a reasonable extent, and if the creep is unreasonable the cause may be excessive stress range, but is much more likely to be faulty compounding or faulty design leading to the use of an excessively stiff mix, say 75 Shore hardness, giving a static shear modulus of 250 lb./in.^{2} in a component where no mix of modulus more than 150 lb./in.^{2} should be considered. In a component which has been in service for a long time work softening and permanent set are often found together; the permanent set changes the shape of the rubber in such a manner as to increase the stiffness. Allowance must be made for this in estimating the degree of softening. Another factor is that the stiffness may have changed due to ageing, especially at an elevated temperature. Neoprene is particularly liable to hardening, and natural rubber to softening with over-cure, and in many cases compounding is at fault.

Hardening or softening, according to the grade of rubber, at high temperatures is generally recognised fairly easily, but in the case of natural rubber a distinction can be drawn between the cracked and brittle surface condition due to a temperature of the order of 120° C in dry air and the more gradual change in properties from longer periods at temperatures in the range of 70°–100° C. In connection with anti-vibration mountings the main thing to remember is that in nearly all cases a greater improvement is possible by modern compounding in natural rubber than by change to synthetics.

Failures due to fatigue and to internal heating are of several forms, of which the recognition is extremely important to the systematic development of mechanical rubber components. A complete breakage due to a single application of a load beyond the rubber or bond strength is extremely rare, but when it does occur it can be distinguished sometimes by the absence of signs of subsequent rubbing of the broken surface, and by the relative smoothness of the torn surface by comparison with that due to a few cycles of vibration of large amplitude. The appearance should resemble, in fact, that obtained during a destruction test in the laboratory, but the extremely large stress recorded in destruction tests shows how rarely the same condition can be reproduced in practice. The general characteristic of fatigue failure is the clear evidence of relative rubbing of the broken surfaces during the growth of the cracks. This may appear in the following ways:

(*a*) polishing of the broken surface;

(*b*) stickiness due to over-heating accompanied by the working out of a quantity of tacky or semi-molten rubber;

(*c*) comparatively dry powdered rubber, working out or thrown out from the crack;

(*d*) in some cases an actual gap forming between the cracks, where contact is made only during a part of the vibration cycle.

Wear does not occur in parts subjected to tension, but this method of stressing is unusual. The appearance is much the same whether the loading is in compression or in shear or in a combination of the two, or in shear with precompression added. The greater the number of cycles in growth of the crack, the more the wear or polishing and the less the raggedness of the surfaces, but the method of manufacture has also some influence. Compression moulding from laminations of calendered sheet rubber, without proper precautions or with unsuitable compounds, make for a comparatively smooth break with a small number of cycles due to tearing between the laminations, but this is rather a case of defective manufacture than of fatigue failure. Transfer mouldings are generally filled from a number of injection holes, in which case the failure may follow the junction of the injection streams, but that does not necessarily mean that there was not any fault in manufacture. Even with long experience it is sometimes very difficult to say whether the appearance of the break gives any indication at all of defective quality. Sometimes the crack runs

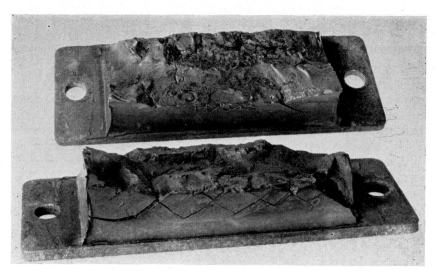

Fig. 8.37(*a*).

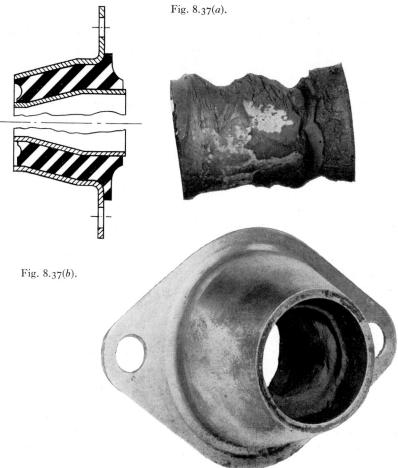

Fig. 8.37(*b*).

Fig. 8.37. Fatigue failure of mountings.

through a definite local defect, such as a small air pocket or a piece of foreign matter or a piece of rubber trimmed from the previous moulding which has found its way accidentally into the cavity. Such details can be misleading during the development of a component. The fault is not necessarily the cause of the trouble, and it is worthwhile looking for some indication whether the crack actually started from the defect or from a place where the defect could have given rise to stress concentration, or whether the only effect was to change slightly the direction of a crack, which would have started in any case. Similar difficulties are found in assessing the importance of a small patch of defective bonding which comes away cleanly when the failure over the rest of the cross-section is right through the rubber.

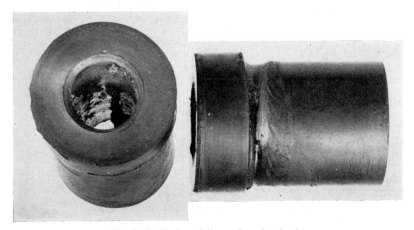

Fig. 8.38. Fatigue failure of torsion bush.

The general form of a fatigue failure is shown rather clearly in the two illustrations of components in Fig. 8.37, one is a flat mounting loaded in compression and the other a conical bush loaded axially, and in both cases the fatigue failure had proceeded part of the way through the rubber, starting very close to the edges, and the final fracture was on a test machine. It is easy to distinguish between the polished surfaces of the fatigue cracks and the rather rough, clean surfaces of the break due to a single load. Sometimes in practice the final break is caused by a single impact when the cross-sectional area is reduced by the fatigue cracks so much as to make the strength insufficient for the maximum force applied.

Components, subjected to alternating stresses, are not always bonded, and the surfaces in contact with metal may be held adequately as a whole by friction, but subject to a certain amount of local slipping. Rubber may be worn away, either in the tacky state or as powdered by actual friction against the metal surfaces, but damage attributed to this cause is often in fact fatigue cracking. There may be a considerable amount of stress concentration between the part of the rubber which is held by friction and that which has slipped, in which case a crack starts and may wear to such an extent that it opens up after release of the load. Fig. 8.38 is a typical example in which the crack is between the cylindrical part and the flange of a bush used in the springing of a car. Such a crack is quite usual, and provided that it does not spread too rapidly, amounts only to the separation of the thrust flange and the journal of the oscillating bearing, when they could have been made separate in the first place.

Generally speaking, in a bonded mounting the crack starts just under the

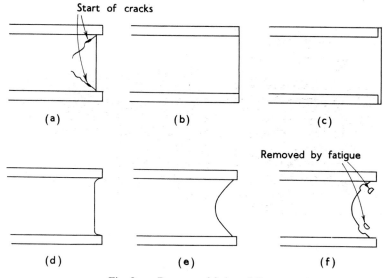

Fig. 8.39. Progress of fatigue failure.

surface, close to the junction of the free rubber surface, and spreads diagonally, as shown in Fig. 8.39a. Such a crack may start with too small a stress range and progress much too rapidly if the rubber surface ends at a sharp metallic edge, as in Fig. 8.39b or over-laps the edge as in Fig. 8.39c. The claim has been made that an exact fit in the mould leading to the precise condition shown in Fig. 8.39b is an advantage, but this, like so many theories of rubber fatigue, cannot be accepted on the evidence available. It is quite certain, however, that whether the form of stressing is alternating compression or alternating shear a sharp edge does considerably more damage than a blunt one. Even the difference between the two sides of a plate blanked in a press may have a large effect. Quite often the plate can be moulded either way up, and there have been cases where, after a certain period of service, all the top edges of blanks and none of the bottom edges started fatigue cracks sufficient to cause rejection of the components. The obvious solutions are to remove the sharp edges or to bond always to the bottom of the blank or to step the rubber back from the edge, as in Fig. 8.39*d*. In bonded compression or shear-and-compression mountings subjected to severe stresses, it is easy to make the external rubber surface concave, as in Fig. 8.39*e*. Photo-elasticity shows that such an arrangement does not eliminate stress concentration, but practical results show a very great advantage; this is due in part to the fact that the initial fatigue cracks do not proceed into the rubber but almost parallel to the surface and result in the breaking off of a small strip, rather as shown in Fig. 8.39*f*. The loss, or partial loss, of this small quantity of rubber cannot be regarded as a failure at all, and may occur at a very small fraction of the useful life

(*a*)   (*b*)   (*c*)

Fig. 8.40. (*a*) New, (*b*) Permanent set, (*c*) Internal over-heating.

of the component. In connection with the concave end profiles, it may be mentioned also that the formation of surface creases, or wrinkles, is not necessarily any evidence either of defective design or of over-stressing. If the rubber close to the surface is put into compression, then it must have a tendency to buckle into folds, and fatigue testing, photo-elasticity and actual service experience show that in most cases these folds have no tendency to cause failure or significant wear, or local over-heating.

   Failure due to internal over-heating, rather than to fatigue of the rubber at a temperature high enough to reduce its resistance to fatigue, is marked by the formation in the centre of the mass of rubber of a number of gas bubbles or a single cavity surrounded by tacky material. There may be blisters on the surface which can be distinguished from the external evidence of fatigue cracks, because they are larger and form in the middle, not close to the bonded surface, Fig. 8.40 shows a conical over-load buffer which has failed in this manner on a fatigue test. It is compared with a new part, and one that failed due to excessive permanent set. Not only has a large gas cavity formed through over-heating of the rubber but the external size has been increased. Such failures show that the work done on the material is too great relative to the capacity to carry away the resultant heat. In such cases the total number of stress cycles is irrelevant; the range of stress might be quite acceptable if there were a resting period between periods of vibration of a limited number of cycles of any frequency, or if the continuous vibration were at a much lower frequency. As explained in Section 1, the amount of work done per cycle in damping is almost independent of the frequency, so that the number of cycles to over-heating, if it takes place at all, depends upon the heat which is removed in the time taken to build up these cycles. The solution may lie either in the provision by design of a better conductivity path or the use of material with better heat conductivity, or of one with less damping. Porosity is found also in new components which have not been cured adequately, but it is distinguished easily from that due to internal heat generation. The blow-holes are usually small and are always smooth and surrounded by clean rubber, which often takes on a whitish bloom when exposed to the atmosphere. These blow-holes are formed after the component is removed from its mould, so they also give an increase in overall dimensions; the bloom that forms on the surface, cut through the middle of the specimen may extend beyond the region of the blow-holes, but not necessarily to the outside. The surface may be cured adequately, and rubber compounds have not all the same tendency to bloom. Under-cure does result sometimes in excessive heat generation, so that it may be a contributory cause of the sort of failure described above. Surface bulging due to internal over-heating may be confused with swelling due to fluid absorption, especially when the two are found on the same specimen. They are distinguished easily enough when the specimen is cut right through, as the fluid reaches the centre last. Rubber compounds, both natural and synthetic, vary widely in their resistance to different fluids, but by far the commonest examples are natural rubber damaged by petrol, diesel oil and by lubricating oil; even a small quantity of the fluid eventually diffuses uniformly, fuel much more quickly than lubricating oil. The typical fuel contamination is uniform swelling and weakening through the mass of rubber, while lubricating oil leaves the outside surface slimy, but generally speaking, the smell is sufficient guide when only one type of fluid is concerned. High temperature and fluids act together, because the high temperature reduces the fatigue resistance, and the rate of absorption doubles with about 8° C temperature rise. Most complete failures which are attributed rightly to fluid contamination are due to the reduction in the mechanical strength or fatigue resistance of the material, which results from the weakening. Bonding reduces the free area over which the fluid may be absorbed, but on the other hand, the swelling can result in a large bond stress which increases the tendency for fatigue cracks to form on the free edge.   A typical form of defect, due to lubricating oil and fatigue, is that shown in Fig. 8.41, after which the rubber may be still serviceable for a limited period, though it should be replaced as soon as possible.   Bond failure due to fuel and lubricating oil is not usual except when extra stress is imposed due to swelling on a bond which is already inadequate.   On the other hand, some chemicals with which rubber is used do attack most forms of bond, and in such cases a different process is the usual solution.   In avoiding the ill effects of oil contamination consideration should be given carefully to means of keeping the oil away before accepting the inferior mechanical properties of oil-resisting synthetics.   Surface damage due to contamination may give a bad appearance long before it has any adverse effect upon reliability.

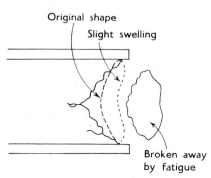

Fig. 8.41. Failure of overload buffer combined oil damage and fatigue.

In motor vehicles and in equipment mounted in exposed places on ships one of the most usual causes of bond failure is corrosion due to a solution of common salt.   There seems to be a definite correlation between the incidence of failure of certain bonded rubber components on motor buses and the extent to which salt is used to clear the roads of snow.   Brass-plate bonding, which has very little resistance to electrolyte solutions, is still popular because of its suitability for mass production, but this difficulty is overcome by other processes in which the bond is formed by a coating of a rubber derivative.   Salt contamination is detected by chemical tests for chloride in the material collected from the crack.   The cracks caused by fatigue and by bond failure are not difficult to distinguish from those due to oxidation, which, being a characteristic rather of the material than of the mechanical component, is discussed elsewhere in this book.   The tendency for surface cracks to grow is much greater when the free surface of the rubber is in tension and greatest close to the bond edge where there is a stress concentration.   Tension along the surface is sometimes severe in bonded mountings which are deflected in shear, especially if the rubber is not pre-compressed and is not properly profiled.   The effect is given of tearing away from the bond, but quite often the oxidation crack spreads only for a limited distance from the edge then ceases when it reaches a region where there is no severe tension.

A reasonable amount of general cracking and hardening of the surface has usually very little effect upon performance, except when the rubber section is comparatively thin. The life of a component of rubber section $\frac{1}{4}$-in. thick is often limited by oxidation cracking, even when the exposure to sunlight, etc., is not unusually severe: on the other hand, this form of deterioration is seldom important when the rubber thickness is 3 in. or more and compression is applied for the greater part of the time. Surface cracks increase the initial rate of absorption of fluids. Again a warning must be given against unnecessary acceptance of the inferior mechanical properties of synthetics when the amount of cracking is not really detrimental or when adequate protection can be given, either by a shield against direct heat or sunlight or by coating with flexible paint.

8. General design principles

The design of mechanical rubber components must often link closely with that of the rest of the equipment in which they are used, so that the mechanical designer rather than the rubber manufacturer may choose the form of construction that he considers most appropriate. In the majority of cases standard products are adequate, and there is certainly too much special design, but often requirements are such that a better result or greater economy is achieved by making the rubber component to suit the rest of the equipment than by adapting the design to suit a rubber manufacturer's standard. The basis of new design must be the limitations of fatigue life and methods of loading given in Section 5 and an appreciation of the moulding process. Nearly all mechanical rubber components, whether bonded to metal, or reinforced with fabric, or of solid rubber are made by vulcanisation in the cavity of a high-pressure steel mould. For mass-production some manufacturers insist that the moulds should be hardened. Typical designs for producing bonded and unbonded components in moderate quantities are shown in Fig. 8.42, from which it will be observed that transfer moulding is used in the bonded component. The mould is maintained all the time at a temperature of about 150° C, and the pressure, sometimes of the order of 2 tons/in.^{2}, forces the rubber into the spaces between the piston and the mould body and round the various cores and other pieces close to the moulding cavity. Even the best-designed mould requires a certain amount of force to break it down for removal of the work-piece, and it is handled mainly with levers very like large tyre levers and the hot metal picked up with asbestos gloves or an asbestos cloth. The lighter bonded plates and the weighed blank of uncured rubber can be put into place cold in most cases, but during breakdown after the vulcanising period, which averages about $\frac{1}{2}$ hour in the press, everything is hot. Sometimes for very large quantities of simple components, such as motor-vehicle suspension bearings or engine mountings, the process is more mechanised and the moulds with many cavities are made in one with the platens of the press,[27] but the ordinary designs are those in Fig. 8.42. It is easy to see that the design limitations are much more than

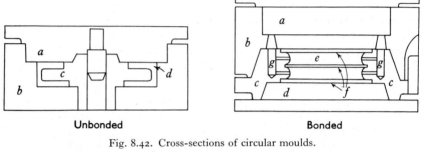

Unbonded   Bonded

Fig. 8.42. Cross-sections of circular moulds.

a Piston.	*a* Piston.
b Cylinder.	*b* Cylinder.
c Core.	*c* Split cores.
d Rubber.	*d* Base.
	e Rubber.
	f Bonded plates.
	g Injection galleries.

those, for instance, of sand casting. Although cores split in four or more pieces can be used, they are not easy to handle, and wherever possible the construction should be such that the only core is one in three or more pieces round the outside. The simplest possible moulding formed only

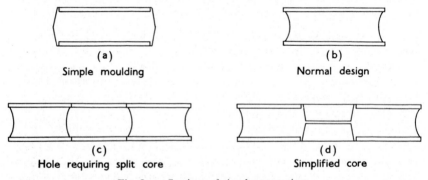

(a)   (b)
Simple moulding   Normal design

(c)   (d)
Hole requiring split core   Simplified core

Fig. 8.43. Sections of circular mountings.

between the top and bottom plates is usually practicable only for a limited range of designs, but is still much easier for economical mass-production, when it may be preferable, even when it leads to a greater volume of rubber to correct for less efficient features of detail design. The shape shown in Fig. 8.43*a*, for instance, is considerably less correct than that in Fig. 8.43*b*, but may be preferred because it can be formed between the top and bottom plates, while Fig. 8.43*b* requires split cores of the type shown in Fig. 8.42. A circular mounting with a hole in the middle, Fig. 8.43*c*, can be made either with a split core or with an expendable core of synthetic rubber that withstands the moulding temperature, or with a core which can be dissolved subsequently in water.[28] All these procedures are expensive, so that a central hole is usually made with the rubber extending slightly beyond the middle and core, tapered from one side or from both. A thin film of rubber, as in Fig. 8.43*d*, is often left and has negligible influence upon the properties. It is cut away easily enough if anything has to pass through the centre hole in the final assembly. The more complicated forms of moulding are justified more often in the larger than in the smaller sizes. Further examples of the deliberate waste of rubber to secure easy manufacture are the forms of small conical bush shown in Fig. 8.44. In Fig.

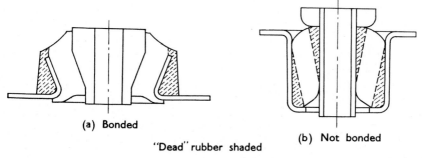

(a) Bonded

(b) Not bonded

"Dead" rubber shaded

Fig. 8.44. Simplified conical bushes.

8.44*a* the rubber round the outside of the pressing plays no part in the resilience of the mounting, but is included simply to facilitate the simultaneous manufacture of a number of these mountings in cavities between the top and bottom plates. The extra material costs less than the operation of fitting split cores which would otherwise be necessary. In Fig. 8.44*b* there is no bonding but pre-compression between the sleeves, which are flanged to form wedges of " dead " rubber to give the equivalent of a conical bush, with a cylindrical sleeve easily fitted in a bored-out housing.

After the fatigue limits and manufacturing methods the next principle is the limitation imposed by scale effect, especially in the case of rubber springs. Something is said of this already in Section 4 and illustrated in Figs. 8.27 and 8.28, but approximate numerical data are needed. Deflection in shear is generally of the order of half of the thickness, so that it is useless to start on the design of a continuously loaded spring in shear or in shear and compression unless there is space to include a thickness of rubber between the plates greater than normal deflection. The position is different, of course, with regard to anti-shock mountings, where the maximum deflection applied occasionally may be several times the thickness. In Fig. 8.34 the mean stress of an average spring is shown to vary between 50 and 100 lb./in.^{2}, and as the linear dimension of the bonded plate must be somewhat greater than the rubber thickness, it follows that 1 in. in shear is difficult to obtain in a satisfactory manner with less loading than 300 lb. The deflection increases as the linear dimension, and the load capacity as the square of the linear dimension, so that the lower limit of loading could be as follows: $P = 300\, x^2$, where P is the load in pounds and x is the deflection in inches. This applies to a single shear unit and the double side unit, as in Fig. 8.27b, must have twice the load.

By the rule given above, a rubber spring with only $\frac{1}{10}$ in. normal deflection may be used for a load of 3 lb. and with $\frac{1}{16}$ in. for 1 lb. These are by no means the lower limits used in practice, as aircraft instrument mountings for $\frac{1}{16}$ in. deflection in the form of cylindrical bushes in shear have been made for many years with ratings down to $\frac{1}{4}$ lb.; moreover the cylinder-bush form, like the double-sided shear, should have twice the load, that is 2 lb., but the smallest aircraft instrument mountings are made in rubber with a shear modulus of the order of 40 lb./in.^{2}, and in sections so thin as to be impracticable in general engineering.

A rubber spring for a vehicle, or for any other purpose, having a normal deflection of the order of 5 in. should carry a load of about 7,500 lb., that is $3\frac{1}{2}$ tons. It will be seen, therefore, that the block of rubber, loaded directly in shear, could be used on railway rolling stock or on the heavier commercial vehicles, but not on private cars, where the load per wheel is from 5 to 10 cwt. The same applies to rubber using both shear and compression, while the minimum load is, in fact, rather higher, so that rubber springing on cars must use leverage to increase the load and decrease the deflection. No single rule could be given for shear and compression together, but it is difficult to work below $P = 500\, x^2$. For a given deflection the upper limit of the load that can be carried is determined rather by manufacturing problems and economics than by the properties of rubber. If the maximum modulus of rubber for springs is given as 250 lb./in.^{2} and the minimum economic stress with this modulus 50 lb./in.^{2}, the thickness of the rubber must be not greater than 5 times the deflection. Production difficulties are often encountered with bonded rubber having a width of bond surface greater than 20 times the rubber thickness, while the plates may become unreasonably heavy and bulky relative to the very thin section. No definite rules can be given, but if the rubber seems out of proportion the alternatives of partial compression or pure compression with separate guiding elements should be considered carefully. If there is any absolute limit to the minimum size of rubber spring that is acceptable irrespective of shape it is fixed by the relative size of ageing cracks formed by surface oxidation. The size and the rate of growth of these does not change with the dimensions of the component, and any attempt to get back a reasonable thickness of rubber by lower shear modulus is made less effective by the inferior ageing characteristics of the soft rubbers. Generally speaking, thickness less than $\frac{1}{4}$ in. should be avoided. The problem of durability in thin sections is overcome with silicone rubber, but only at the expense of mechanical properties in which silicone is far inferior to natural rubber. If silicone rubber can be developed with the present temperature range and durability, but a better tear resistance and far less work softening, rubber would become once more the best material for very small instrument mountings, in which steel is used at present.

Scale effect is equally important and a more complicated matter when rubber is used in compression rather than shear. Deflection of the order

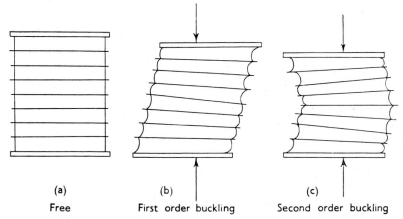

| (a) | (b) | (c) |
| Free | First order buckling | Second order buckling |

Fig. 8.45. Buckling of compression springs.

of one-fifth the initial thickness is quite normal, and the size for a given deflection is limited largely by stability. The great flexibility and extremely high bulk modulus, which are the distinctive properties of rubber, result in a spring becoming a buckling strut, when it has proportions which in most materials would be regarded as those of a compression block. This applies whether or not the rubber is bonded to metal plates, and in either case most compression springs are of the general form shown in Fig. 8.45, that is a series of discs or rings of rubber separated by metal plates. Such a spring has two main limiting or crippling loads. In the first the transverse, or shear stiffness, becomes zero when the two ends keep parallel but are free to float in the transverse direction. The second is the load at which the strut buckles when the two ends are constrained to move relative to one another along the axis. There are also cases, of course, in which one or other end is free to rock, with or without transverse restraint, but such cases are less usual in practice.   Unfortunately there is no theory of the stability of rubber compression springs available for publication, but the following points may be noted:

(a) The first-order instability, illustrated by Fig. 8.45b, does not necessarily limit the load capacity and may assist in the spring's correct working, especially if the action of a frictionless bearing is needed in the direction perpendicular to that in which the load is carried.

(b) The spring with a hole in the middle is intrinsically more stable than the solid spring because the resistance to buckling is determined mainly by rubber near the outer edge, while extra bulge surface in the centre gives more compression flexibility.

(c) For a given size the deflection, though not the load, to give instability, is reduced inversely in proportion to the number of intermediate plates.

(d) In some springs the shape may change, with the increase of load, to such an extent that instability is not reached at all.   That is the case particularly in unbonded mountings where the rubber is free to slide over the metal.

(e) The deflection at which instability occurs is changed very little, if at all, by the stiffness of the rubber mix.

(f) When a spring is made of two mountings in a V, as in Fig. 8.46, the reduction in the shear stiffness due to the approach of the first-order instability may be offset against the increase in compression stiffness, so that the resultant load-deflection curve may be a straight line.   Negative stiffness of such a pair of mountings in the direction in which they are in shear may be avoided by making them with a width greater than the height.

In the absence of a fully developed theory, the following rules may be taken as a guide to the design of the circular compression mounting:

(a) For 1 in. deflection with rubber of modulus of rigidity 100 lb./in.^{2} first-order instability is approached if the load is less than 5,500 lb. per layer.

(b) The minimum load per in. deflection increases in proportion to the number of layers.

(c) The minimum load is proportional, as in the case of shear mountings, to the square root of the deflection.

(d) It is proportional also to the modulus of rigidity of the rubber.

(e) If the design allows first-order instability, but not second-order the load may be doubled.   For example, a solid circular compression mounting, to deflect $\frac{1}{2}$ in. under 1 ton, would have to be made as a single cylinder of rubber to avoid instability, unless the mix had a modulus considerably less than 100 lb./in., when a single intermediate plate could be used. If the end surfaces were constrained to move axially relative to one another by external means, one intermediate plate could be used with the moderately stiff rubber and three with a very flexible rubber.

In practice, it is doubtful whether rubber need be rejected ever as a material for a resilient mounting or other spring on account of excessive load, provided that the space is available.

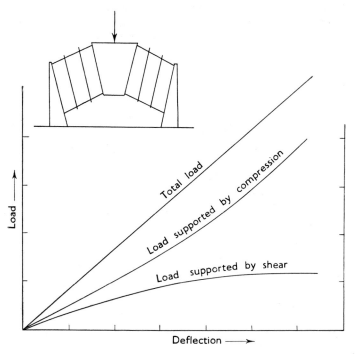

Fig. 8.46. Combined compression and shear.

When the simple form of compression spring is inadequate owing to the combined load and deflection being outside the stability limits, even with a soft grade of rubber, the problem may be overcome either by the use of pure shear or combined compression and shear or by some mechanical device. The most usual device is a construction which gives the effect of two or more separate springs in series. This method is used for shear, for compression and for other forms of loading. Two examples are shown in Fig. 8.47. In the first is a shear mounting of a design which is used widely by reason of its simplicity, but proves unreliable when the load for a given deflection is so small that the rubber is in bending rather than shear. The two ways of correcting the design are to introduce a floating intermediate plate constrained to remain parallel to the end-bonded plates and to arrange the two sections in series, with identical end channels.   The second alternative is the lighter, and appears simpler, but the first alternative may be preferred because it retains a high stiffness due to compression of the rubber in one direction perpendicular to that of loading.   The second example is a stack of compression mountings, divided by a floating stabilising plate. This plate is subject to no bending moment due to the direct compression, but there is a bending moment when loading in a perpendicular direction applies shear to the rubber.   Stabilisation in this way requires a minimum of three circular mountings, but it may be used for two only when the cross-section is elliptical or rectangular, so that there would be otherwise

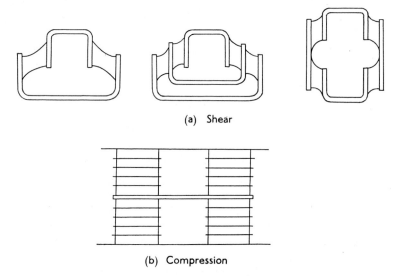

(a)   Shear

(b)   Compression

Fig. 8.47.   Stabilisation of rubber springs.

instability in one direction only.   It is effective against first-order buckling (Fig. 8.45) but not against the second order, in which the slope of the centre plate does not change.

Quite apart from the limitations imposed by the relative values of loading and normal deflection, there are many cases in which the total range of movement must be considered relative to the overall size of the rubber. This problem is encountered most frequently in mountings loaded in compression but subjected to shearing movement so that they act as springs in compression and sliding bearings in shear.   Lateral displacement always causes distortion of the type shown in Fig. 8.48a, whether the rubber is bonded to the metal plates or not, and whatever the number of layers of rubber.   Intermediate plates show up bending clearly, but much the same effect will be seen on a solid block of rubber if lines are painted where the plates would be otherwise. From considerations of symmetry and equilibrium of force in the various layers, it follows that the centres of pressure P_1, P_2, P_3 in the layers must lie on a line inclined as shown. If the compression load is such that the shear stiffness is reduced to zero this line is upright, and if the shear stiffness is negative the direction of inclination is

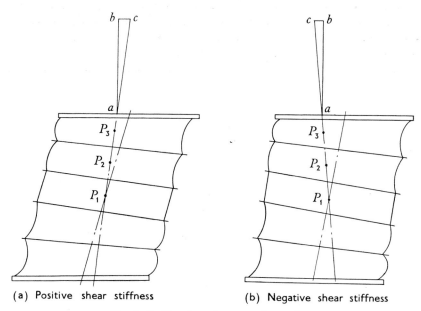

(a) Positive shear stiffness   (b) Negative shear stiffness

Fig. 8.48. Shearing of compression springs.

Compression load $\propto ab$
Shear load $\propto bc$
Centres of pressure P_1, P_2, P_3

reversed and becomes opposite to that of shear displacement Fig. 8.48b. Owing to the high ratio of compression stiffness to shear stiffness the inclination of the line of resultant force seldom approaches that of the distortion of the rubber, so that the shape in various cross-sections must change to keep the centre of pressure on the line of resultant force. Some important points follow from this principle:

(a) If compression in the rubber due to symmetrical loading were uniform over the cross-section, tension would be avoided by keeping the line of resultant pressure within the " middle third " or its equivalent for its particular section. In practice, the pressure increases with the distance from the free edge, so that tension begins with rather a smaller relative displacement, of which the precise value cannot be given.

(b) The range of strain near the edges of the rubber is from zero to twice the mean, if the range of shear movement is such as to remove compression entirely from two sides alternatively. Generally speaking, such a strain range comes well down on the fatigue curve, so that the range of compression may determine the safe alternating travel in shear.

(c) If the rubber has intermediate metal plates and is bonded it is permissible on rare occasions to give a transverse deflection sufficient to produce considerable tension. The load capacity may be considerably more than is suggested by the areas of the plates which remain over-lapping. With a component such as shown in Fig. 8.48 the occasional maximum displacement may be as much as two-thirds of the diameter, though the range applied frequently should not be more than one-eighth of the diameter in either direction, and in some cases considerably less. The large change in shape relative to the initial size may result in con-siderable bending stresses in intermediate metal plates; these may not be made always of very small thickness.

(d) The bending moment in the intermediate plates explained above does make it possible for a compression spring, with a number of such plates to support its load with greater shear displacement than should be allowed in one without intermediate plates, while the value of the tension in the rubber in applying a restoring moment is lost if the plates are not bonded.

(e) There is some reduction in the height of the compression spring as the result of shear displacement; otherwise there can be no reduction in shear stiffness from compression loading. The rate of loss of height with shear deflection increases with the approach of instability.

(f) The range of permissible shear displacement is increased by the same means as tend to make the spring more stable.

A rather similar condition is obtained in the loading of springs in com-bined compression and shear where the relative increase of the two types of deflection is constant. Using the intermediate metal plates rather as indicators of the loading condition than as an essential design feature, Fig. 8.49 shows that they remain parallel to the end plates only if the shape in the loaded position is correct. The centres of pressure of the various layers always lie on the line of resultant force, but the stressing remains uniform only if the centres of pressure correspond to the geometrical centres of the layers of rubber. In determining this condition for a statically loaded mounting allowance should be made for creep and work softening which influences the unladen shape. When the load varies over a considerable range the increments of compression and shear deflections are in a fixed ratio, but as shown by Fig. 8.46 the compression and shear loads do not necessarily increase by corresponding amounts. The com-pression Pd may increase considerably, while the shear load de may remain almost the same or even fall off, so that the inclination of the resultant force Oc may become less as the load supporting aO increases. To some extent the change in the direction of Oc compensates for the change in shape of the rubber spring with increasing load, but it is very doubtful whether a practical design could ever be worked out in which the plates remain parallel when the deflection has removed the whole of the initial

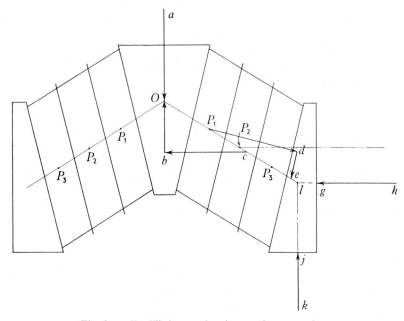

Fig. 8.49. Equilibrium under shear and compression.

P_1, P_2, P_3, centres of pressure. cb = horizontal component (balanced).
aO = applied load. P_1d = compression : de = shear.
cO = reaction from one side. jk = vertical load from abutment.
bO = vertical component = $\dfrac{aO}{2}$. gh = horizontal load from abutment.

offset in the spring, making its cross-section rectangular. The points P_1, P_2 and P_3 must lie always on the line of the resultant force in the spring, of which the plates remain parallel only if the resultant force passes through the geometrical centre of each layer. If the spring is rectangular in the view shown in Fig. 8.49, then the plates are parallel only if $de = $ o, which means that the shear resistance, not the shear stiffness, is zero. That is the case only when the loading has been carried well beyond the first-order buckling (Fig. 8.45b) and reaches almost to the second-order buckling, Fig. 8.45c.

The spring in Fig. 8.49 is drawn as if provided with separate abutment wedges to fit in a housing with vertical and horizontal surfaces only. The

Y

position of the resultant vertical reaction jk varies according to the structure, but in any case it determines the intersection i, and thus the position of the horizontal reaction gh.

This simple example of the methods of securing uniform shear and compression strain in an angular rubber spring shows also the value of setting out the stress diagrams on the principle of three forces meeting at a point. Any attempt to represent these forces in arbitrary positions and to correct them by the addition of moments adds a lot of unnecessary complication and confusion. The theories of the resultant vertical and horizontal force jk, gh should be used in designing the supporting structure, but care must be taken to allow for the positions of the resultant force under all conditions of loading, not under maximum load only.

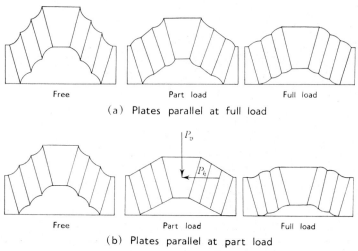

Fig. 8.50. Uniform loading of inclined mountings.

Although the change in direction of Oc with loading may help in reducing the change in slope of intermediate stages, a large range of deflection must involve some change of slope, and it is better to achieve uniform stressing at the maximum normal load than at a smaller load. The arrangement shown in Fig. 8.50a, in which the plates become parallel at full load, is better than that in Fig. 8.50b, provided that the symmetrical load Pv is the only one to be considered. If, on the other hand, transverse loading Ph is an important factor the best overall result may be achieved when the normal attitude of the spring is more suitable for direct compression; the alternative in Fig. 8.50b, for instance, may be the better. The stress range in pure shear due to loading in the other transverse direction is seldom important in itself, but may affect the compression in the manner shown in Fig. 8.48. With all these forms of loading the safe limit may be determined by the slope of the intermediate surfaces which places the rubber locally in tension instead of compression.

The importance of selecting the correct initial offset results, like many of the other problems of design in rubber, from the large value of the

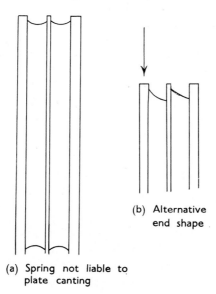

(b) Alternative
end shape

(a) Spring not liable to
plate canting

Fig. 8.51. Relatively thin rubber.

deflection relative to the initial size. If the spring has a large area and small rubber thickness, as shown, for instance, in Fig. 8.51, absence of offset is detrimental only as an end condition tending to cause fatigue cracking, as explained in Section 7. With such proportions it would be admissible even to construct the end surfaces, as shown in Fig. 8.51*b*.

When the component cannot be designed so that the moments on intermediate sections are either absorbed in the rubber without overstrain or balanced by correct proportioning, the alternative is some device as is used in stabilising compression springs, namely resistance to the moment by external means or balancing against an offset moment

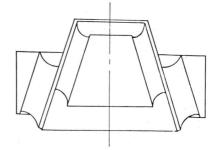

Fig. 8.52. Two-stage conical bush.

from another similar, opposed spring. A two-stage conical bush-type spring can be made in the form shown in Fig. 8.52, provided that the intermediate sleeve is strong enough to take the outward bursting force.

A pair of inclined springs may have their intermediate stages tied together in the manner shown in Fig. 8.53, but this way of resisting the bending moment on the intermediate plate does not necessarily prevent the development of negative stiffness in the transverse or shearing direction.

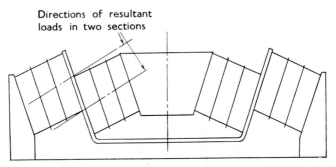

Fig. 8.53. Two-stage inclined spring.

The rubber torsion spring, whether in the form of a cylindrical bush or of a disc which may be flat or designed for uniform torsion stress as in Fig. 8.54, is comparatively free from the difficulties of scale-effect and of distortion discussed above, because the shape remains substantially the

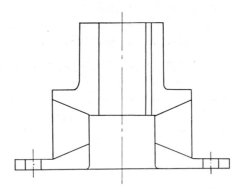

Fig. 8.54. Simple torsion spring (Vee-coupling).

same after deformation of the rubber. It is also capable of giving a very high ratio of stiffness in the various directions because the shear deformation is magnified by the lever arm, and in many cases the compression is applied directly. The main limitation of the bush is the angle through which it can move for a reasonable rate of shear stress. If the rubber is of constant length for all radii, as in Fig, 8.55a, it can be shown easily that the strain is given by the following formula:

$$\theta = \frac{e}{2}\left\{ 1 - \left(\frac{r}{R}\right)^{2}\right\}$$

The angular deformation θ is given, of course, in radians, and the strain e is the tangent of the angular strain at the inner periphery. If the outer radius R is increased the torsion angle approaches the limiting value of half the strain of which the permissible value is given approximately in Section 6, where it is explained why the range is rather larger than given in Fig. 8.34. A normal strain of 1·5 corresponds therefore to the limiting angle of 43°. Many publications dealing with the bonded rubber bush [29] give the theory of constant torsional stress, which results in a section such as that shown in Fig. 8.55b. In practice, an approximation is obtained to

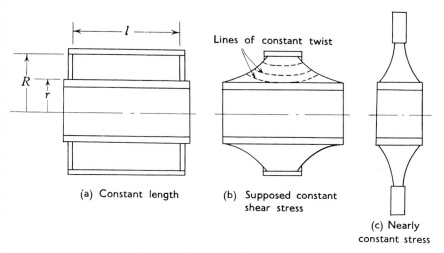

(a) Constant length   (b) Supposed constant shear stress   (c) Nearly constant stress

Fig. 8.55. Types of cylindrical bush.

the theory only in bushes which are of small length relative to the diameter and not too great a ratio $\dfrac{R}{r}$; that is to components more like diaphragms than bushes, such as that in Fig. 8.55c. The lines of constant angular deformation are shown roughly in Fig. 8.55b so that the shear strain is much greater in the middle of the inner sleeve than towards the ends, where the rubber becomes almost dead. The tapering ends may serve a useful purpose in protecting the more highly stressed inner sleeve from damage due to corrosion, oxidation and other causes, but the claim of constant shear stress is quite false, and it is difficult to see why it remains in so many text-books and manufacturers' catalogues. Most calculations of the torsional-shear properties of cylindrical bushes are sufficiently accurate when based upon the theoretical result for constant rubber length, though some allowance based on experience is often given for the shaped end surfaces, which do give a really important improvement by reducing stress concentrations. Fig. 8.56a shows a well-proportioned bonded bush for combined torsional shear and radial loading, but if the rubber is long axially by comparison with its radial thickness, as in Fig. 8.56b, it is quite impossible to maintain an elegant end profile after the pre-compression has been applied either by distortion of one sleeve or by making the outer

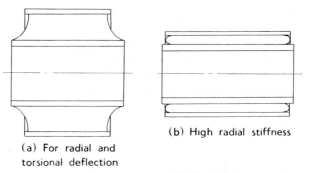

(a) For radial and torsional deflection

(b) High radial stiffness

Fig. 8.56. Shapes of cylindrical bush.

sleeve in sectors.   The formula above is sufficient to estimate the torsion of such bushes, as the torque carried is obviously given by $T = 2\pi r^2 leN$, where l is the axial length of the bush and N the shear modulus.

More energy can be stored per unit volume of rubber in torsional shear in a bush in which the difference between the inner and outer diameters is relatively small,[30] and such a bush is often described as being " more efficient ".   That does not mean necessarily that it leads to the more economical construction because the longer torque arm to give a given deflection is itself heavier, and a greater moment is applied to the housing of the outer sleeve.   The greater the length relative to the radial thickness, the greater the tension due to shrinkage after moulding.   If the bush is fully bonded there must be a limit beyond which tension or " negative hydro-static pressure " is built up sufficiently either to split the rubber or to break the bond, but this limit has not yet been determined.   In practice, if the length is more than ten times the thickness it is advisable to bond only to the inner sleeve and to rely for resistance to all kinds of loading on the outer sleeve, on pre-compression which, with such proportions, gives an adequate friction in nearly all cases.   Bonding to the inner sleeve is still useful to resist the greater intensity of stressing on the smaller area, but in many cases the bush relying entirely upon compression is adequate.

The resistance to radial as to torsional loading is influenced very little by making the inner sleeve longer than the outer, but axial loading always in the same direction demands a relative offset, as shown in Fig. 8.57.   Here there is often a real advantage in making the inner sleeve the longer.

Bushes, like other rubber components, can be used in series in conditions which are beyond the capacity of the single unit.   A link with a bush at either end has twice the working radial deflection of a single bush, while the most popular way of increasing the torsional movement is to connect the relatively moving parts to the outer sleeves of bushes having a common floating pin.

Calculation of the simpler forms of bonded rubber component is explained adequately by text-books and manufacturers' publications. Ker Wilson [31] gives formulae for shear and compression. Some very convenient nomograms, in addition to much useful information, are included in the publication of the United States Rubber Company,[32] which is unfortunately not always available in Britain. The simple empirical formulae for calculation of compression based largely on the work of Keys [33] are not always sufficiently accurate for practical design,

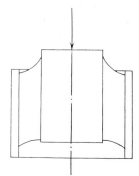

Fig. 8.57. Bush for axial load.

and the improvement worked out by Gent and Lindley [34] is of considerable importance. The various earlier theories are discussed in some detail by Payne, Gent and Lindley, and the extremes of shape for which earlier methods give large errors are dealt with particularly well, but there is one further consideration in the design of cylindrical bushes. The standard formula for compression or radial loading assumes that the deformation is allowed only by bulging of the rubber at the end surfaces. Designs are often prepared, as in Fig. 8.58, with great restriction of the free surfaces in

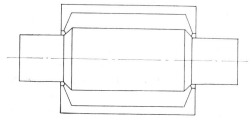

Fig. 8.58. Constricted bush, supposed to have very high radial stiffness.

the hope of an extremely high radial stiffness and low torsional stiffness; in fact, the bush of such proportions deflects by flow of the rubber circumferentially from the compression to the tension side. A long bush should be considered as a pair of separate semicircular units, as shown in Fig. 8.59, the amount of rubber which bulges outwards from the one part is the same as that which is driven back into the other part, so that no additional stiffness is obtained by joining them together.

The points of detail design which are favourable to manufacture and to uniform stressing are discussed in manufacturers' handbooks, but many of them, such as the avoidance of screws projecting into the rubber, are little more than matters of common sense. Allowance must be made in all designs for the probable creep of the rubber in service. Various forms of creep are discussed in Section 7, and the general rule for a component operating under average conditions for a number of years is that the creep is of the order of one-third of the initial deflection. There is considerable variation, of course, according to the grade of compound and temperature and other conditions. The various published results do not agree, but those quoted by the United States Rubber Company [34] are typical. Many designs which seem theoretically to be attractive fail because the properties

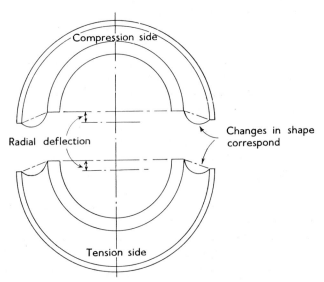

Fig. 8.59. Deformation of long radial bush.
Two halves of bush fit together accurately, strained or unstrained.

change too much as a result of the additional deformation resulting from creep. That applies particularly to those in which a high rate of flexibility is obtained over a limited load range by an approach to instability and those in which rapid stiffening with over-load is obtained by built-in abutments. Limitation stops are often a very useful feature of a design, but where their range of movement is small compared with the initial deflection of the rubber their position relative to the main rubber spring must be adjustable. A further consideration is that most rubber manufacturers require a toler-ance of $\pm 15\%$ on the stiffness rate, and this is reduced to $\pm 10\%$ or less only in exceptional cases where special precautions in manufacture are considered to be worthwhile. In synthetic rubbers variation of stiffness with temperature and even in natural rubber the stiffening at low temperature and the dimensional change due to crystallisation and the so-called Joule effect [35] may be important. The Joule effect is a reversible creep, not a change in stiffness, but it can have a considerable effect upon the dimensions of the rubber. Its average value is about $\frac{1}{2}\%$ of the initial deflection per ° C. The other design principles are considered best in connection with the typical rubber components described in the following sections.

9. Examples of anti-vibration mounting

In Section 1 it was shown that the anti-vibration mounting of a machine subjected to alternating forces is fundamentally a question of balancing the large movement of one or more small masses by the correspondingly smaller movement of a much larger mass. The forces causing vibration are not absorbed by the flexible mounting but by the inertia of the machine. Resilient mounting is not always used, however, to insulate the surroundings from the impulses applied to a particular machine; very often the object is to insulate a particular machine, or a particular group of machines, or even a whole floor from the vibration which would other-wise reach it from outside. Consider, for instance, the case of a workshop containing both a reciprocating air compressor and a precision jig borer. The air compressor may be prevented from vibrating the floor of the workshop excessively if it is flexibly mounted, but it may be more con-venient to allow a transmission to the floor which is generally acceptable, but too much for the particular precision machine, which can be itself mounted resiliently from the floor. A clear distinction must be drawn therefore between the two purposes of resilient mounting, known re-spectively as vibration isolation and vibration insulation. In the first the vibration is generated within the machine itself, so that it must have an amplitude of movement corresponding to the relative values of the forces and of the inertia, in the second the limiting value of the amplitude, as the stiffness of the mountings approaches zero, is also zero, and there is no need to achieve a certain minimum inertia for a stated minimum amplitude. That does not mean that the inertia of the machine insulated is always sufficient. The amplitude transmitted is proportional to the natural frequency, so that the stiffness of the mounting may be increased for a given result in proportion to the inertia. Increased stiffness may be an advantage as the means of avoiding undue change in levelling or align-ment with change or redistribution of weight or in reducing movement due to operation of controls or many other incidental sources of occasional load. A jig borer, for instance, is often mounted with a fairly large concrete block, and in a laboratory the flexibly mounted bench is generally preferred to the flexible mounting of the individual instrument. A heavy bench slab may retain its alignment accurately enough for the mounting of chemical balances.

Generally speaking, the same type of construction is used for vibration insulators and for vibration isolators, though the former are seldom subject to wide ranges of stress. Both are known generally as anti-vibration mountings and can be classified in the following ways:

(a) Those designed to have a constant stiffness over the whole range of loading for which they operate, and those designed for a stiffness varying according to the conditions either by some property of the main mass of rubber or by the use of separate limiting devices. In America the second class is sometimes illustrated in catalogues as snubber-mountings. It is pointed out in Section 8 that the setting of stops, whether rigid or gradual, must take account of the creep or other dimensional change in normal service, and the range of flexibility must be enough to allow the amplitude which the mounting is designed to insulate. If the amplitude is excessive, due, for instance, to insufficient inertia relative to the disturbing force, then no good result can follow from an attempt to reduce it by stiffening the mounting beyond a certain travel. Snubber-mountings are used when it is better to allow sufficient flexibility under normal conditions and to sacrifice vibration insulation during the small part of the time that loads are applied which would cause impracticable movement or excessive strain in the main rubber spring. An obvious example is the mounting of equipment in aircraft which may have to withstand accelerations up to 10g, but operate for almost the whole of the time with very little loading beyond that due to gravity.

(b) Those with equal flexibility or flexibility of the same order in all directions and those in which flexibility enough to be effective for anti-vibration purpose is provided in some directions only. Mountings of the first type are generally selected for ordinary anti-vibration machinery installations, largely because they can be fitted without consideration being given to the directions in which the vibration acts. The second type can be subdivided again into those which are merely ineffective in one or other direction and those which are designed deliberately to be of greatly different stiffness in another direction. For example, an internal-combustion engine often has practically no vibration in the direction of its crankshaft, so that if it is mounted statically, it does not matter if there is very little flexibility in this direction. If the same engine is mounted in a vehicle the stiffness is extremely useful in preventing excessive movement due to longitudinal forces which might interfere with the action of controls or allow the fan to come into contact with the radiator.

(c) Self-contained mounting assemblies for bolting on to machinery of existing design and units for building in as part of an original design. Self-contained units are generally preferred for small quantities, but as an integral part of mass-produced equipment may be unnecessarily heavy and expensive. The motor-car manufacturer, for instance, finds it better to work out an anti-vibration mounting to suit the needs of his particular engine in the way in which it is installed in the vehicle. Commercial motor vehicles use more often the standard forms of mounting assembly for fitting into brackets to suit the chassis, while the installation of the same engine in a motor boat may be made with a set of self-contained assemblies designed to fit between the engine and its bearer-beams without any special brackets.

The vibration insulating mounting in which stiffening for over-load is unnecessary, and substantially uniform stiffness in all directions allowable,

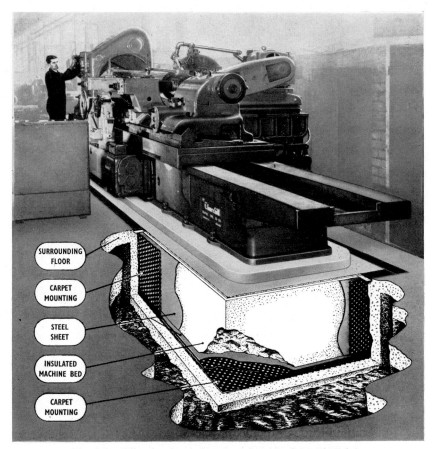

Fig. 8.60. Vibration-insulating mounting (*Steel Co. of Wales*).

is illustrated by Fig. 8.60. This grinding machine operates in a steel works, where it can maintain the necessary standard of accuracy and finish only if it is insulated from vibration due to a rolling mill. A concrete foundation may be necessary to give the machine bed sufficient rigidity, and is always desirable to reduce the change in level as the slides are moved and the work-piece changed. Such an installation can be made alternatively with a small number of self-contained mounting units between the foundation block and the floor, and the mounting units may be used also to lift the block after it has been cast in place. It is quite

Fig. 8.61. Vibration-isolation of generating set (*Anglo-Belgian Co., Ghent*).

usual, however, to fit some flexible material in sheet form, and the particular variety shown uses a large number of cylinders of rubber staggered to either side of a continuous web which deflects in shear and bending. The pit is completed first, then lined with the number of layers of mounting material required to give the flexibility specified, then with steel plates, into which the foundation block can be cast. In this case the flexible material round the side walls of the pit is used mainly to support the steel plates, which act as a mould for the foundation. The horizontal forces applied to the grinding machine are so small that a very low transverse natural frequency would be acceptable. The natural frequency of vibration transmitted through the floor varies, but is usually between 12 and 25 c/sec., so that an equivalent deflection of 0·2–0·23 in. is quite sufficient.

Vibration isolation is illustrated by the generating set in Fig. 8.61, but examples can be found in which a generating set is put on a concrete foundation block over a carpet of resilient material and a grinding machine mounted directly on self-contained mounting units. The engine shown in Fig. 8.61 is of the six-cylinder four-stroke type, having no inherent primary or secondary unbalance, so that the amplitude can be kept very small without any extra weight, provided that there is no other equipment on the same bed-plate having a greater unbalance; actually there is a single-cylinder air compressor driven from the tail end of the generator through a clutch. When this compressor is disconnected the amplitude is, in fact, extremely small, but when the compressor operates the partly unbalanced reciprocating weight does give quite a considerable amplitude which might not be acceptable for continuous running. The compressor is comparatively light, and a large part of the weight of the complete installation is at the opposite end of the bed-plate, so that the movement is mainly in the form of a pitching and yawing, with a node towards the engine end. Calculation of the natural frequencies and form of pitching vibrations is quite an easy matter, and is explained in many text-books, including Ker Wilson. Resonant vibrations, consisting substantially of the so-called " decoupled modes ", that is of vertical movement or of pitching about the axis through the centre of gravity, are comparatively rare. Although they simplify calculation, design of the mounting to achieve them does not generally give any improvement in performance. In a case like the generating set in Fig. 8.61 the positions of the axis of oscillation or " nodal axis " may be somewhat as shown in Fig. 8.62. An unbalance cannot excite a vibration whose node is on its line of action for the simple reason that an alternating force without displacement cannot do work to overcome damping, hence the first of the two critical conditions given in Fig. 8.62 cannot be excited by the compressor and the second only very slightly by the engine unbalance. As the second frequency is the higher, this property does not help in vibration insulation. The principles described above are sometimes used to avoid resonant vibration, but the advantage is limited; a node on the line of the force does not prevent the transmission of vibration at frequencies other than that of resonance. The mounting unit used is typical of self-contained units having the same stiffness over the whole range of deflection but different rates for the three mutually perpendicular directions. The rubber is seen from Fig. 8.61 to be partly in shear and partly in compression vertically, mainly in compression in one horizontal direction, and purely in shear in the other horizontal direction. The standard cast-iron housing, with interchangeable rubber-bonded inserts, is designed so that it can fit, in most cases, directly between the machine foot or bed-plate and the floor and give some protection from oil contamination and accidental damage. The stiffness ratio is 1 : 4 : 10, so that the best vibration insulation is given if the stiff direction is that in which there is very little vibration; in this case fore and aft.

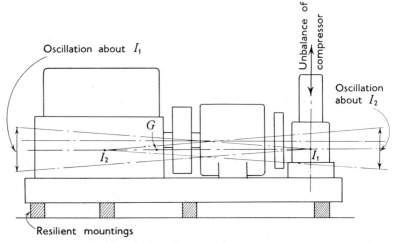

Fig. 8.62. Centres of pitching vibration.

G = centre of gravity, including bedplate.
I_1 = centre of oscillation, lower resonance.
I_2 = centre of oscillation, higher resonance.
Force through I_1 cannot excite resonant vibration about I_1.

Self-contained mounting units with adjustable over-load stops include the type shown in Fig. 8.63. This differs from that in Fig. 8.61 in having four rubber inserts disposed symmetrically in such a way as to give equal

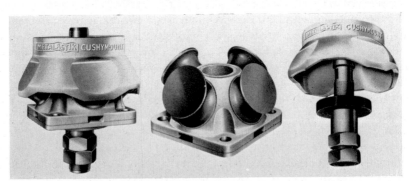

Fig. 8.63. Self-contained resilient mounting with built-in stops.

stiffness in all directions. The central spindle carries the limiting buffer in the form of a disc which is adjustable, so that in the normal position there is equal clearance in all directions. The same rubber spring can be used without the limiting buffer for mounting machinery not subject to inertia loading or excessive amplitude in passing through a critical speed, and may be regarded as an alternative to an arrangement of three or more mountings of the type shown in Fig. 8.61 symmetrical in plan view, which gives also equal stiffness in all directions. An assembly 9×5 in. in plan and about $4\frac{1}{2}$ in. high may be used for loads up to $1\frac{1}{2}$ tons and static deflection up to $\frac{5}{8}$ in. for normal stationary engine installations, while one 12 in. diameter is suitable up to 5 tons and $\frac{3}{4}$ in. deflection. Both the types of industrial anti-vibration mounting described above are made from separate simple bonded mouldings assembled in castings. A bolted attachment is used for the moulded plates of the smaller type, but as the rubber springs of the larger are prevented by stops from carrying a reverse load, it is sufficient for the inserts to rest in recesses. The range of loading in service is not large enough relative to the mean compression to give any tendency towards metal-to-metal fretting. Smaller mountings are often made as single mouldings, complete with flanges and screw sockets, typical examples being the two shown in Fig. 8.64. The second is

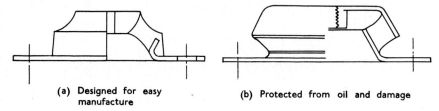

(a) **Designed for easy manufacture**

(b) **Protected from oil and damage**

Fig. 8.64. Self-contained mountings with similar stiffness in all directions.

interesting because it requires split cores, both in the centre and round the outside, for its moulding and must have free rubber profiles of a shape not conducive to good fatigue life. The low overall height, convenient form of fixing, and protection from oil and accidental damage are regarded as sufficient reason to introduce extra complications in the manufacturing processes.

Approximate calculation of the natural frequencies is carried out by the methods given by Ker Wilson [36] and others, but difficulties are experienced with less symmetrical bed-plate lay-outs, such as the compressor shown in Fig. 8.65. The natural frequencies must be calculated with reference to the minimum moment of inertia, which is often about an axis inclined to that of the crankshaft. More is stated on this subject in Section 12 in connection with the mounting of internal-combustion engines in vehicles. The machinery suspended may have vibration also in the form of an un- balanced couple, when the amount transmitted to the floor depends upon the resistance of the whole group of mounting units to the angular vibration about the vertical axis for a yawing couple, or the horizontal axis for a pitching couple.   A force acting along a line some distance from the centre of gravity is equivalent to the sum of a force through the centre of gravity and a couple, but it is better to calculate the axis of oscillation, and design the mounting accordingly, than to design separately for the force and

Fig. 8.65. Mounting of belt-driven compressor (*Lightfoot Refrigeration Ltd.*).

couple.   The unbalance force at one end of the installation is illustrated by the compressor in Fig. 8.61 and by the unbalanced scavenge pump often fitted to the front of two-cycle stationary engines, and its effect is to give a form of vibration on the flexible mounting similar to that illustrated in Fig. 8.66.   The axis of oscillation in this case is determined by the un-balance force and the inertia, and must not be confused with the nodal axis of free or resonant vibration shown in Fig. 8.62.   The two are not necessarily in anything like the same position but the vertical and horizontal axes of forced vibration may intersect or nearly intersect, in which case a completely rigid mounting situated at the point of intersection would transmit no vibration of the particular form.   The mounting point would then obviously become also the nodal point for one mode of free vibration.

In most cases this point is either inaccessible or requires an inconvenient structure to carry the load from the foundation, so that the mounting must be quite flexible in directions tangential to an axis passing through it. Fig. 8.66 shows mountings in the transverse plane of this point, stiff in compression vertically, but flexible in shear horizontally.   The front mountings could be inclined to the vertical as shown and still give good vibration insulation, but the most practical and convenient arrangement is to make them flexible, or even equally flexible, in all directions. A single mounting inclined to the direction of loading is not necessarily equivalent to one-half of the pair in a V. If the supported mass is constrained horizontally only by the single mounting the reaction in this mounting must be in the direction directly opposite to the load, so that the condition

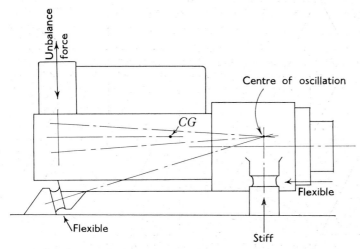

Fig. 8.66. Forced vibration due to unbalance at one end of installation.

of deformation is that shown in Fig. 8.67a. The stiffness in compression many times greater than that in shear constrains the movement to a direction almost parallel to the metal plates, so that the mounting is really in shear rather than in shear and compression. If the mounting is one-half of a pair arranged symmetrically to the load the deflection must be in the direction of the load, as shown in Fig. 8.67b. The shear and compression components of the reaction are no longer in proportion to the inclination of the plates, but the compression component is increased in proportion to the stiffness ratio, which is explained above to be often of the order of 10 : 1, and may be as high as 50 : 1. As the ratio becomes high the pairing of mountings becomes more like a wedge and the individual rubber unit more like a bearing than a spring. The behaviour of inclined mountings of relatively large stiffness ratio is considered in more detail in Section 11. For a resilient mounting to behave as an inclined spring it must have a stiffness ratio. The limitation of the rubber spring having the same stiffness in all directions, and one of the features which makes it convenient for most ordinary installations, is that it always gives a deflection in the direction of the load.

Recommendations for maximum loading of standard anti-vibration mountings are given in manufacturers' catalogues, although the limitation should be theoretically the stress range not the static loading.   Catalogue figures are based upon the more severe type of condition likely to be encountered in practice, and it is easy enough to find instances in which good performance is given at a load higher than that recommended and

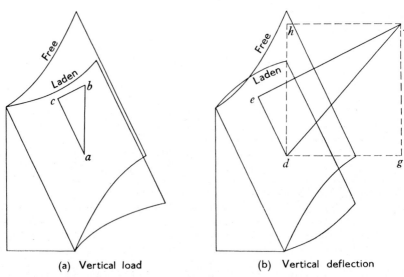

(a) Vertical load   (b)   Vertical deflection

Fig. 8.67. Mountings focused for forced vibration.

ab = total load. dh = vertical load.
ac = shearing load. dg = horizontal load.
cb = compressive load. de = shearing load.
                                       ef = compressive load.

premature failure occurs at the recommended load owing to the nature of the super-imposed vibration.   In most types of self-contained machine mountings over-load is prevented by the clearances available in the casings, and in many cases would not increase the equivalent deflection to any considerable extent, because the stiffness begins to rise nearly as rapidly as the total deflection.   The rubber may be designed also so that it is suitable geometrically only for a certain deflection and begins to develop stress concentration with overstrain.

Attempts are made sometimes to design mountings of stiffness in one or more directions proportional to the load over a wide range.   The object is to give the equipment suspended constant natural frequency, irrespective of its weight, and the principle used most widely is the gradual rolling of the end surfaces of a cylindrical or conical bush against a flat or special formed abutment, in the manner shown in Fig. 8.68.   Such a design may be favoured on the false assumption that it prevents resonance, but it appears attractive as a standard unit for use on a wide variety of equipment.   The advantages are not as great as they appear to be, because the frequency changes both with creep and with the Joule effect, which acts in the wrong direction on a rubber liable to stiffening at low temperatures. The natural frequency increases also with the amplitude of oscillation.

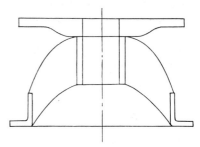

The number of mounting points and individual loading may be determined by the construction of the machine, while differences in loading may be accommodated by the use of different grades of rubber. When there is some freedom in selecting the lay-out as well as the mounting

Fig. 8.68. Mounting with stiffness proportional to load.

unit the three-point support may be preferred, because it determines the load distribution geometrically without reference to relative stiffness and deflection. When one of the points is more heavily loaded than the other two it is often made with a pair of the same standard mounting units close together. The carpet-type mounting, shown in Fig. 8.60, requires flat surfaces, but variations in loading can be balanced by cutting away the mounting locally. If there are more than three mounting points and the surfaces are not prepared carefully individual adjustment is usually necessary, and is often carried out by placing packing pieces under one or

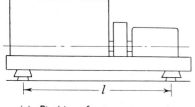

(a) Pitching frequency approx. proportional to 'l'

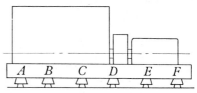

(b) Pitching frequency reduced by making 'A' and 'F' more flexible, 'C' and 'D' more rigid

Fig. 8.69. Effect of longitudinal spacing of mounting points.

more mounting units, so that as the levelling is corrected each mounting has the proper deflection. Distribution of loading over many points on the machine base or foundation is needed occasionally to avoid concentrated loading and, when separate mounting units are used, allows more scope in selecting the natural frequencies about various axes. It is explained above that the angular, as well as the vertical or horizontal frequency, may be important, and to give a single example the frequency about the transverse axis of the mounting shown in Fig. 8.69a might be low enough relative to the vertical natural frequency only if the longitudinal spacing of the mountings were below a certain value: on the other hand, the arrangement shown in Fig. 8.69*b* offers two methods of changing the frequency about the transverse axis; either the mounting points may be placed closely together or those in the centre may be made stiffer and those towards the end more flexible. The second alternative can be useful in correcting the installation found in practice to give unsatisfactory results, and may be preferred by an engineer who objects to the unstable appearance of a bed-plate or foundation block over-hanging at both ends.

10. Examples of anti-shock mounting

The distinction between shock absorption and vibration insulation is quite clear, but it is not always so easy to say what is an anti-shock mounting and what is an anti-vibration mounting. Sometimes the same installation performs both functions, and sometimes the absorption of the higher harmonics of a vibration having a definite frequency with magnification of the fundamental component may be regarded as either. A piece of workshop plant, such as a press, for instance, can complete its cycle, including an impact, once or twice per second and be mounted with a natural frequency of 10 c/sec. Although the cyclical fluctuation of load in the foundation has one sharp peak, it may be resolved into a whole series of harmonics, of which some have a frequency below and some above the natural frequency, and there may be one in resonance. The mounting is successful because the high-frequency harmonic components are the more important ones, but this is usually only a point of theoretical interest. If the vibration due to one impact dies out mainly before the next impact occurs it is a case of shock absorption. Fig. 8.70 shows a department in a factory in which wrapping machines are supported on the simple type of mounting shown in Fig. 8.64*a*. The primary object is to absorb the shocks due to closing of the mechanism, but the same mountings can absorb vibration due to faster-running parts of the machinery. Similarly, blanking and piercing presses, such as that in Fig. 8.71, are often mounted to absorb the impact due to the actual cutting of the material, and resilient mounting often allows the installation of machinery on a suspended floor in the right position for the flow of production, where otherwise the work would have to be taken to the ground floor and back again. It can also be more economical than a heavy foundation block. Objections raised at the first operation, to the tremor of the machine under the impact, are found usually to be associated only with the unusual appearance, and interference with the speed or accuracy of the operation is comparatively rare. After an hour or two of experience the tremor is usually ignored.

As explained in Section 3, shock absorption, without the support of

Fig. 8.70. Anti-shock mounting of wrapping machines
(*Fox's Glacier Mints, Leicester*).

continuous load, was among the earliest applications of vulcanised rubber, and in the form of the buffers of railway rolling stock has been in general use ever since. There has been much argument regarding the relative merits of rubber and of steel springs [37] as regards both the reliability and load-deflection characteristics, and recently there has been some tendency for hydraulic dashpots to be preferred on account of the much greater maximum energy absorption,[38] but rubber is still used extremely widely. Many designs, both for side buffers and for couplers, are still similar in

Fig. 8.71. Resilient mounting of mechanical press.

principle to those used more than a century ago. One of the rail-car buffers shown by McPherson and Klemin,[39] for instance, might have been produced as long ago as 1847, while the multiple concentric form came into use not much later. Many of the earlier, and some of the recent, designs of rubber buffer and draw-bar have hollow cylindrical springs of unbonded rubber built up in stages, separated by metal plates to a length which gives them a first- and second-order buckling deflection less than the maximum used in service. Some of the intermediate metal plates must be guided on a central spindle or in a housing. A plate fitting loosely in a housing has the advantage that it cannot jam due to a tendency to buckle, but a central spindle with a generous clearance over the draw-bar is usual for couplings. Many examples of pre-war designs are given by Macbeth,[40] and the unbonded compression buffer is still a British Railways standard; the nature of the load/deflection curve and its advantages and disadvantages are discussed in Section 3. More recent designs, especially those of American origin, use rubber bonded to metal plates, usually in compression but sometimes in a V arrangement loaded partly in compression and partly in shear. The bonded compression units vary greatly in shape; some are of the general form shown in Fig. 8.72a, in which the concave rubber surface is included partly to give better fatigue resistance under the small number of cycles of very large amplitude and partly to fill the space available as completely as possible at maximum deflection. Others use a stack of simple units, each consisting of rubber bonded to both sides of a single disc, as shown in Fig. 8.72b. The shape of the rubber depends upon the characteristic which the particular designer considers to be best, but it may be noted that any straight compression mounting can be split in the plane, mid-way between the bonded surfaces, without change in performance, provided that the two halves are the same and the loading is axial. There is no shearing across the central plane, and whether the halves are

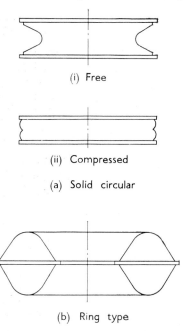

(i) Free

(ii) Compressed

(a) Solid circular

(b) Ring type

Fig. 8.72. Shock mountings used in compression.

divided or not, there can be no tendency to relative sliding, but this applies only to compression springs, not to those loaded wholly or partly in shear. The surface of contact of the metal and rubber, on the other hand, has the maximum shear, and in the unbonded unit relative sliding over this surface gives valuable extra damping, even without significant wear. Nevertheless, the present demand for increased strain-energy storage, combined with low resilience or dissipation of the maximum possible percentage energy during the first cycle, has led to designs of special synthetic rubbers bonded to steel plates. Since the shock-absorbing spring generally carries very little static load, permanent set and creep are unimportant, and it is claimed that butyl rubber is extremely satisfactory, in spite of the great variation in its properties according to temperature. Sufficient information on service results does not seem to be available to show whether these claims are justified. Automatic couplers, other than the experimental types now running on British Railways' freight stock, are usually designed to take both traction and buffing loads, and it is not uncommon for a single spring to be used for both sorts of load and to apply suitable pressure to friction blocks which give additional damping beyond that due to the viscosity of the rubber. Fig. 8.73 illustrates the principle used. If the draw-bar (*a*) is in tension

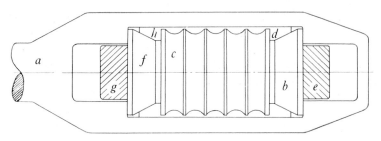

Fig. 8.73. Combined rubber and friction draw-bar for railways.

it loads the block (*b*), which compresses the bonded spring (*c*) through the wedge (*d*). The wedges bear against the eye of the draw-bar, but have no relative movement as the block (*b*) is drawn away from the stop (*e*). The load on the bonded spring is resisted by a similar block (*f*) at the other end, which remains in contact with the other stop (*g*), both (*e*) and (*g*) being fastened to the wagon under-frame. The second set of wedges (*h*) slides inside the draw-bar, giving friction damping proportional to the load on the spring (*c*). If the draw-bar is in compression the action is identical, but the load is carried by the opposite stop (*e*) and (*f*) moves away from (*g*). The spring (*c*) may fit freely in place, or it may be pre-compressed so that a finite loading, equal to any desired proportion of the maximum, must be applied before either of the blocks leaves its abutment. The pre-loaded spring, shown by Fig. 8.26, absorbs more strain energy in the manner illustrated, but does not absorb shocks which are insufficient to overcome the pre-compression force. This method of pre-loading is obviously economical in rubber, because the single spring is used for deformation in both directions from the mean position, and has a cycle of loading kept always on the same side of zero stress. One difficulty in its practical application is that mechanical accuracy is needed to make the blocks sit simultaneously on the stops and on the draw-bar, but without the extra friction this principle is used widely on locomotives. It is applied to bogie centring springs, which are rather a part of the spring gear than shock absorbers. On military equipment it is sometimes known as the " rigid-resilient mounting ". It may be used, for instance, between the fire-control tower and the hull of a ship. Vibration insulation is unnecessary, and the pre-loading may be sufficient to avoid deflection under the normal rolling and other movement, thus maintaining the exact position relative to the armament, except where there is excessive shock loading.

The buffer or draw-bar is effective along one axis only, and the rigid resilient mounting of ship's equipment is made to resist shocks in various directions by inclination of the individual units in the manner described in Section 11, but there are many types of anti-shock mounting in which it is better to use individual units capable of resisting loads in all directions. Fig. 8.74 is a good example of a packing-case designed for the shocks due both to shunting in the railway yard and to handling by the crane at the docks. The valuable piece of equipment, in this case a jet pipe for an aircraft turbine engine, is supported on an inner framework which is separated from the outer casing by resilient mounting units. The packing-case, except for the base, has been removed, but its large size relative to its contents can be seen, and is due to the relative travel required to absorb the test shocks with the specified acceleration. Recording instruments are mounted on the end timbers of the inner frame, which is subject to the same shock as the jet pipe during test. The test illustrated consists of the packing-case, mounted on a trolley, being run down a gradient from a standard height directly into a rigid buffer stop. Other tests include lifting at one end to a specified height and dropping on to a hard surface. The hollow conical shock mountings are designed to give an unusually large deflection relative to the load and stiffnesses in the various directions, including tension, not much different from one another. The radial stiffness falls off with axial compression, but the specification does not require the most efficient possible use of the space between the inner and outer frames with simultaneous vertical and longitudinal shock. Typical load–deflection curves are included, and that for compression has the characteristic shape for mountings which buckle before they are loaded fully. Such a shape of curve is difficult to avoid in a mounting of the relative load and deflection used in this case and has, for a limited range of shocks, the advantage of a greater energy absorption for a given maximum load.

Development of mountings of the type shown in Fig. 8.74 requires great care in the proportioning of the rubber, but the requirements are laid down definitely and accurately by the official test specification, so that after completion of the test the mountings' ability to give the right results may be considered to be established. Unfortunately in many cases ambiguous specifications are used; one of the commonest is that the mounting shall resist a shock of 10g, 100g or some similar value;

[Fig. 8.74(a).

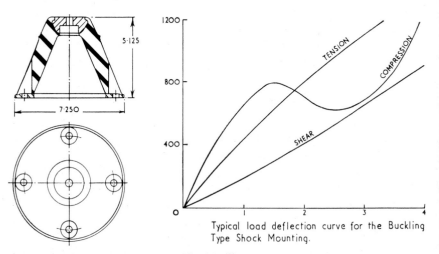

Typical load deflection curve for the Buckling Type Shock Mounting.

Fig. 8.74(b).

Fig. 8.74. Buckling type shock mountings for jet pipe transit stands. A shunt test being carried out with the mountings under a Bristol-Siddeley Sapphire 7 Extended Cold Pipe. (*Bristol-Siddeley*.)

sometimes the shocks in several directions are given in this way, but do not offer any basis for design. The ordinary drop and shunting tests consist of the sudden change in velocity of the supporting frame-work with an extremely high acceleration, while the maximum acceleration of the object supported depends upon the amount of over-travel before it follows the movement of the support and the type of resistance provided during this over-travel. The object of the anti-shock mounting is to reduce the acceleration imposed upon the object mounted, not to resist the full acceleration of the supporting frame or case. If the object mounted has a lower acceleration load, so have the mountings.

The jet pipe and its supporting frame-work are carried permanently on the mountings, so that the energy stored during a shock must be either dissipated as damping or returned to the supported mass as the next half-cycle of transient vibration. Where rubber is used alone there are several cycles following the initial impact, so that the shock absorption is important equally for recoil. An ordinary railway side buffer, on the other hand, does not absorb the energy imparted to the wagon during recoil; this may be transferred to the centre coupler or to the next wagon in the train, or it may be used to give the wagon velocity to be absorbed later, for instance, in brake friction. The side buffer may be designed, therefore, so that it is permanently pre-loaded and cannot extend beyond its set position. The only energy which is absorbed in its recoil stops is the kinetic energy of the buffer head itself and a part of the spring. The central automatic coupler, on the other hand, has to absorb the recoil and subsequent transient oscillation as well as the initial shock, but along a single axis this can be done by the method shown in Fig. 8.73.

11. Theory of mounting in V formation

Section 8 referred to rubber loaded in shear, in compression and simultaneously in the two forms of stressing by inclination in the direction of the load; it was shown also, in Section 9, that a shear and compression mounting makes use of both forms of stressing to provide energy storage only if the compression is balanced against the resistance of another mounting unit and that the special advantage of combining shear and compression and of inclining the surfaces of contact of rubber and metal to the direction of the load can be achieved only if the stiffness in one direction is much higher than that in another direction. In Section 4 it was shown that under some conditions a link with a resilient bush or equivalent device at either end can be regarded as a replacement for a mounting having a high ratio of compression stiffness to shear stiffness. All these principles must be considered in connection with the use of mountings in V and conical formation which must be understood to appreciate fully many of the most important applications of rubber as a spring material, such as the engine mountings and spring gear of road and rail vehicles and aircraft-engine mountings. The simplest form of V-mounting is that shown in Fig. 8.75, in which a body is supported resiliently on a pair of rubber springs, each taking the form of a single circular or rectangular slab of rubber in contact with and often bonded to metal plates. The axes of maximum stiffness intersect at a point O, which is within the suspended body, and therefore inaccessible as a mounting point or accessible only by a special structure. This section includes a detailed discussion of resilient mounting arrangements of this general type with some reference to three-dimensional arrangements on the same principle

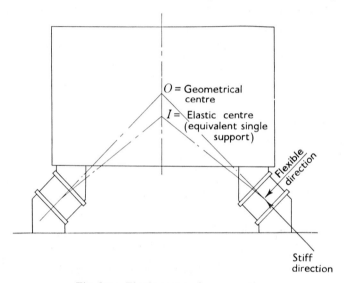

Fig. 8.75. Elastic centre of vee mounting.

using mounting points arranged with their axis of maximum stiffness converging conically on a single point. Until recently there was a great shortage of published technical information on such mountings, but this has been remedied by Ker Wilson,[41] who gives both the theoretical analysis and diagrams, which save much time in calculation and show what results are obtainable from a given ratio of shear and compression stiffness. It is difficult to say where the idea of using rubber springs in a V originated. The application of the conical lay-out to aircraft engines seems to have been worked out first by Carter of the Royal Aircraft Establishment, Farnborough, and published shortly afterwards, as a result of the independent work of Taylor of the Massachusetts Institute of Technology and Browne of the Wright Aeronautical Corporation, whose paper [42] was for a long time the classical work on the subject.

Some of the patents and publications by automobile engineers before and during the War show that their authors believed the pair of mountings, as in Fig. 8.75, to be equivalent exactly to a single support at the point O, but it is surprising that so elementary a mistake persisted so long. If O were the equivalent centre, then a small angular displacement about the axis through this point perpendicular to the plane of the diagram would leave the suspended body in equilibrium under the applied couple and the reaction in the mountings. In Fig. 8.76a it is seen that the displacement of either mounting consists of shearing, to which there must be a tangential reaction, together with tilting of the upper plate, to which the reaction is a couple which becomes extremely small if the mounting unit is small compared with its distance from the centre O. The body suspension

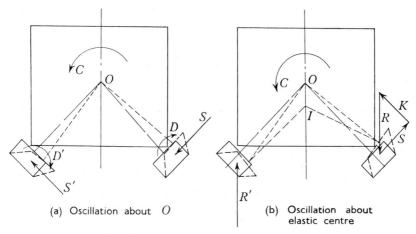

(a) Oscillation about O (b) Oscillation about elastic centre

Fig. 8.76. Vee mounting reaction to torque.

cannot be in equilibrium under an applied couple C, the two small re-action couples D, D'' and the two shearing forces S, S'. From the symmetry of the lay-out, it is obvious that the two reactions must be parallel, as R, R' in Fig. 8.76b. The reaction R is composed of a shearing load S and a compression load K, and the centre of oscillation must be displaced from O to I, so that the shear and compression deflections are such as give reactions in the ratio S and K. The higher the stiffness ratio of the rubber spring, the smaller the deflection in compression necessary to give the reaction K and the closer I comes to O. The couple applied to the body about a direction perpendicular to the plane of the diagram gives a rotation about an axis in the same direction through I; it follows logically, and can be proved mathematically, that a force in any direction in the plane of the diagram through point I gives a displacement of the suspended body without angular movement, though not necessarily in the direction of the force. The displacement is in the direction of the force, in fact, only in three particular standard cases:

(a) the force is along the axis of symmetry;
(b) it is perpendicular to this axis;
(c) the mounting has the same stiffness in these two and in all other directions in the same plane.

The points O and I coincide only if the compression stiffness is infinite, that is if the springs are equipped with rigid sliding bearings instead of being loaded in compression, while equal stiffness in the shear and compression directions would result in a position of I on the straight line joining the two mountings; that is they no longer act as if set in a V.

The theory given in this section does not imply that it is necessarily wrong or inefficient to provide brackets to put a resilient support actually on the axis of oscillation: that is done with excellent results on some small electric motors in which the bearing housings are surrounded by rubber sleeves carried on a frame separated from the casing. The V-mounting, however, gives greater scope for controlling the relative stiffness and natural frequencies in the various directions, and in many cases, even where support points on or in any desired relation to the theoretically correct point I are accessible, it gives the best result. The point I is described variously as the equivalent centre, elastic centre, meta-centre and centre of rotation, while a line through two or more such points may be the axis of oscillation, natural axis, rocking axis, etc. Quite often the term used refers rather to the properties of the centre or axis with regard to the suspended body than to the properties of the mounting system. In Section 13, for instance, examples are given in which the mounting points are arranged relative to the axis of minimum inertia.

The discussion above shows how the V arrangement works and what are, generally speaking, its limitations, but mathematical formulae are needed for practical application. For the full analysis it is best to refer to Ker Wilson, but a few simple formulae help in setting out designs. Consider a simple V-mounting as shown in Fig. 8.77.

The formula which is most worthwhile for the designer is that for the relative position of O and I, which is

$$\tan \beta \tan (\alpha - \beta) = 1/k$$

From the stiffness ratio of the rubber spring it is possible therefore to determine whether the elastic centre can be achieved, and if so what are the two alternative angular settings. In Fig. 8.78 the angle α is plotted against $\alpha - \beta$ and β for the two values of k 5 and 20 which are typical of the ratios obtained with small symmetrical bonded instrument mountings

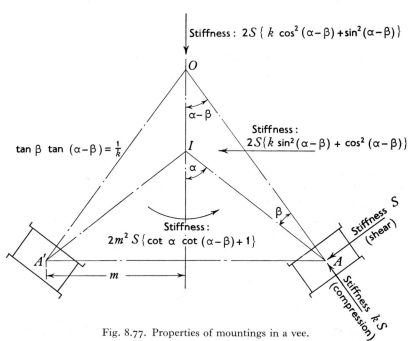

Fig. 8.77. Properties of mountings in a vee.

Shear stiffness of each mounting S; Compression stiffness of each mounting kS; Intersection of compression axes O; Position of elastic centre I; Normal centre of rubber spring A; Angle of AI of the vertical α; Angle IAO or "correction angle" β. Angle of compression axis to the vertical $\alpha - \beta$. Distance $A.A' = 2m$.

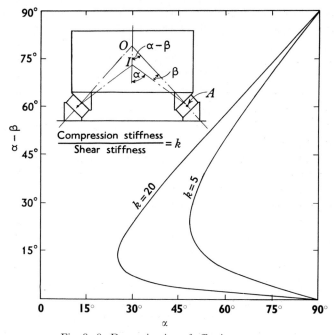

Fig. 8.78. Determination of effective centre.

and larger mountings with intermediate plates, respectively.   Of the two
values of $\alpha - \beta$, the larger is that used generally because it gives the lower
value of the angular flexibility relative to that along the axis OI and more
particularly relative to that perpendicular to the axis OI, but the smaller
value of $\alpha + \beta$ has a particular importance in connection with the railway vehicle spring gear, which is explained in Section 13.   The various
stiffnesses for movement in the plane of the diagram may be given as
follows:

Along OI— $2S\{k \cos^2 (\alpha - \beta) + \sin^2 (\alpha - \beta)\}$

Perpendicular to OI for a force passing through I—

$$2S\{k \sin^2 (\alpha - \beta) + \cos^2 (\alpha - \beta)\}$$

Rotation about the axis through I due to a couple—

$$2m^2S\{\cot \alpha \cot (\alpha - \beta) + 1\}$$

A special case of some importance mentioned already is that in which
the stiffness in all directions in the plane is the same.   This occurs when
the angle $\alpha - \beta$ not α is 45° and the position of I is determined by the
formula:

$$\cot \alpha = \frac{k-1}{k+1} \quad \text{or} \quad \tan \beta = \frac{1}{k}$$

The equal stiffness condition cannot be obtained from a V-mounting in
which the angle α is less than 45°, and that angle can be approached only
with a high value of k.   The three natural frequencies of vibration in the
plane are the same only if I corresponds to the centre of gravity, which
is often the intention of the design, and the value of m is chosen according to the radius of gyration and the ratio k; such terms as " equi-
frequency " are often used loosely to denote rubber springs having a
stiffness the same in two or more directions, but none can make two or
more frequencies the same unless they are placed correctly relative to the
centre of gravity.

The term m^2 occurs in the formula for the angular stiffness, but m does
not occur at all in those for the stiffnesses in the linear directions, hence
the angular stiffness increases as the square of the spacing of the mounting
points, while the translational stiffness remains the same, but a relatively
low angular stiffness can be obtained with a large spacing m by using a
rubber spring with a high stiffness ratio k.   See also Section 12 in connection with the design of vehicle engine mountings.

One of the objections raised most frequently against the use of rubber
springs in a V is that they magnify forces by means of their wedge effect.

Sometimes the belief that supporting structures must be made heavy is based upon a common mistake in stressing in which the load is assumed to be carried entirely by the component of the compression without allowance for the part carried by shear. This error may be avoided by reference to the analysis given in Section 8, but there are undoubtedly cases in which the inclined reaction to a vertical load makes modification in the structure necessary. Generally speaking, this means redesign rather than a simple increase in strength. The direction of the resultant force in the rubber spring must not be confused with the direction of the radius from the elastic centre I. These two directions are inclined oppositely to the compression axis, as shown in Fig. 8.79, which illustrates

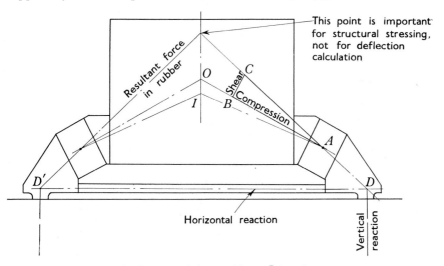

Fig. 8.79. Loads imposed by vee mounting.

also some of the points regarding the design of supports. AB represents the compression in the spring support A; BC the shear; and AC the resultant force. A direct tie is set between the points D and D', which are on the intersection of CA and the corresponding line of resultant on the other side, and the respective vertical reactions from the ground. The foundation loads are then vertical and the extra stressing avoided by the member DD', which takes a direct load without bending. The difficulty arises when some part of the equipment supported extends downwards below this level, say into a pit in the foundation, but that is not usual, because the purpose of the V-mounting is largely to fit the rubber springs at a convenient mounting plane to one side of, or below, the equipment supported. The inclined resultant force AC is larger than this vertical component, but not necessarily liable to cause a more severe stress in the equipment supported. In some cases indeed the line AC passes nearly

z

through the centre of gravity, thus balancing the bending moment which would occur otherwise in the frame-work of the machine.

The relative value of AB and BC depends not only upon the stiffness ratio but also upon the initial setting; it is possible, for instance, to arrange the design so that in the final assembly the rubber spring at A has compression but no shear, in which case the reaction is in the direction AB; on the other hand, it could carry all the load by means of shear in the direction BC, or most of it in shear, so that AC was perpendicular to DD. In none of these cases would the stiffness ratio k be altered to any considerable extent, but that in which the spring assembly is in its un-distorted form when completely unloaded is by far the most usual, and often approximates to that giving the best results from a given volume of rubber, but the amount of shear may be increased with advantage when that is necessary to prevent reversal in stress direction under angular oscillation. Failure of the V-type mounting to perform in the manner predicted is due often to insufficient rigidity of supporting structures, especially to flexibility in the compression direction of the structure supporting the rubber spring, comparable with that of the spring itself. This applies particularly to springs having a high value of k. In many cases the flexibility of the structure is inevitable, and can be used effectively as part of the resilient mounting system; that is true particularly of air-craft-engine mountings.

The theory of the pair of mountings in a V may be extended quite easily to a conical arrangement having similar properties in all planes, but a larger ratio k is needed for a given value of α, and the condition of equal stiffness in all directions is given by $\alpha - \beta = 54°$ 42 min. Most practical mountings designed for approximately equal stiffness in all directions use an angle of 60°, though it is not really any cheaper to produce than 55°. A simple V-mounting requires flexibility in one direction and stiffness in the perpendicular direction in a particular plane; the rubber spring may be either of low or of high stiffness in the direction perpendicular to the plane. Satisfactory working of the conical arrangement, on the other hand, demands a single axis only of comparatively high stiffness, so that the possible form of construction is much more restricted. This section discusses only the simple form of rubber spring, consisting of a slab of rubber between two plates, but many other constructions giving the necessary stiffness ratio are used in practice. Some are discussed in Sections 12 and 13.

12. Engine suspension of road and rail vehicles

The resilient mounting of internal-combustion engines in vehicles has been used at times since the earliest days of motoring, and became usual in private cars during the ten years preceding the War. As long ago as 1896 some Daimler two-cylinder engines, having both pistons moving up and down together, as in modern motor cycles, were mounted on helical springs. Farman [43] said that this was done to avoid the transmission of vibration caused by the unbalance, and this resilient mounting may well have been a straightforward application of the principle described in Section I of this chapter. The Rolls-Royce Silver Ghost used a linkage to allow relative torsional movement of the front and rear ends of the crankcase, but it appears that the object was rather to avoid unnecessary stresses in a light-alloy crankcase than to reduce vibration transmission, which was at all times at a very low level.

The modern science of engine mounting, starting with the work carried out by Chrysler about 1929 [44] leading to the development of the " floating power " system, had a great influence upon the trend of automobile-engine design. For some years previously the tendency was towards increase in the number of cylinders, but the proper absorption of the torsional impulses of the simpler and more compact four-cylinder engine by its own inertia reversed this trend, so that the straight 8, V12 and V16 forms are no longer used.

There is no indication from such records as are available that the dynamic basis of design was appreciated when " floating power " was developed. The axis of the engine running from the front cylinder-head through the centre of gravity to the region of the gear-box output coupling, about which the mounting is given the maximum rotational flexibility, is determined in fact by the principal axis of minimum inertia of the engine. The direction of the torsional impulse is inclined to the principal axis, so that the axis of oscillation of the engine, if suspended freely in space, is not the same as the principal axis, but in most practical cases the difference is comparatively small.

Since either the axis of minimum inertia or that found in practice to be best passes in the normal engine–gear-box unit close to the output coupling, many automobile engineers believed that the secret of good engine mounting was the prevention of displacement of the front universal joint in the transverse plane. Various modifications to, and alleged improvements upon, the " floating power " principle, were worked out on this assumption, which is quite unfounded. Vibration transmission to the vehicle is by alternating load at the mounting points, not by movements of the propeller shaft coupling or of any other component not in contact with the vehicle structure. If the mounting points constrain the power unit to oscillate about an axis different from that on an infinitely flexible mounting, then they must achieve that result by transmitting alternating forces additional to those required to give a reasonable resistance to the torque reaction. The basic form of engine mounting is therefore that shown in

Fig. 8.80, in which there are two bearings on an axis through the centre of gravity to the power unit, approximating closely to the principal axis of minimum inertia. The torsional resistance of these bearings is such that the oscillation due to torque impulses is absorbed mainly by the inertia of the engine. The same principles may be applied whatever the number of cylinders and whether the engine is petrol or diesel. The diesel engine, being governed by the amount of fuel injected and not by the weight of charge admitted, has relatively much larger torsional impulses at low power and particularly when idling, but shows much smaller differences between the powers from the various cylinders. In a petrol engine it does not seem to be practicable at low powers to obtain similar indicator diagrams from all cylinders, so that the frequency of impulses is

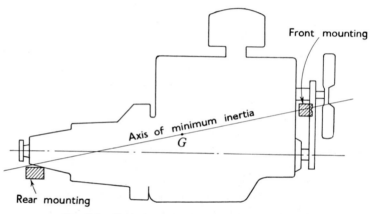

Fig. 8.80. Basic form of resilient engine mounting.

not always only what would be expected from simple theory. On a six-cylinder engine, running at low power, for instance, it is quite usual, even with a well-designed carburation system, to find considerable torsional impulses of frequency a half to one and a half times the speed of rotation comparable in size with the firing impulse at three times the speed of rotation. The frequency one and a half times the rotation is found also in commercial-vehicle six-cylinder diesel engines, but rather as a defect termed eight-stroking than as a feature of the design. The principle of engine mounting given above refers only to torsional impulses, which are in many cases the most important, but the higher standards demanded today require careful consideration of other forms of vibration. Secondary forces, vertical in the four-cylinder and horizontal in the 90° V8 are well known, but simple unbalance of rotating parts within practical limits is by no means an unimportant factor, and is often the main cause of vibration in the structure of diesel rail cars. Vibration of the frequency of engine rotation is not necessarily due either to unbalance or to torsional impulses, but is often due to structional bending of the power unit. This occurs in a number of ways, but the average engine–gear-box unit is not as rigid as is commonly supposed, and the bending couple on the crank-shaft of a six-cylinder engine, for instance, may result in quite a large amplitude at the back of the gear-box. This form of vibration is generally more important in petrol-engined cars than in diesel-engined vehicles, and was well known also on the larger in-line-type aircraft engines.

As a construction for the mounting of private car engines, the cylindrical rubber bush or equivalent mounting unit placed actually in front of the cylinder block is now practically obsolete. It occupies valuable space and adds unnecessary weight and cost, and is well replaced by the alternative of two mountings in a V, of which the principle is explained in Section 11. The precise form of mounting unit used depends upon many factors, but generally speaking, the greater the distance from the axis of minimum inertia, the greater must be the ratio of shearing stiffness to compression stiffness. The alternative lies generally between the mounting unit of moderate size with a single intermediate plate, such as that shown in the typical lay-out in Fig. 8.81, and a much larger unit in which the stiffness ratio remains about the same and the absolute values of the compression and shear stiffnesses are reduced sufficiently by the use of a very soft grade of rubber. The first alternative seems in principle to be the better, because rubbers of moderate stiffness, having a shear modulus of the order of 120 lb./in.^{2}, are more durable when subjected to the conditions under a car bonnet and in particular are attacked more slowly by fuel and oil. The cost of the intermediate metal plate is small compared with that of the extra rubber and larger end plates, but the manufacture of simple rectangular mounting units has been developed highly with very economical production methods and, as explained in Section 8, it may be economical to use rubber inefficiently. In some recent cars a much higher ratio of compression stiffness to shear stiffness has been used to raise the vertical and transverse frequencies. In other cases a lower frequency in a direction other than the torsional has been found desirable to correct the tendency to vibration of the front end of the vehicle structure. Experiments on the specially constructed tracks of the Motor Industry Research Association show that engine-mounting units may be subject to shock loadings of the order of 2g vertically in either direction, so that the range is from −1g to +3g. That means that although, for nearly all the time, a mounting, like that shown in Fig. 8.81, carries a load very little different from 1g with the addition of a little shear and compression due to torque reaction, it may have an occasional load for which the fatigue range is extremely limited. The probable number of cycles of large range is many more on the very bad roads in some overseas countries than in Europe, and the manufacturer generally judges the durability by the number of circuits of a special track before failure.   The range of shear loading due to torque, even allowing for the lowest gear, seldom controls the proportions of the rubber.

Front engine mountings similar to that shown in Fig. 8.81 are used widely on the heavier passenger and goods vehicles and on diesel-engined rail cars, as well as on private cars.   They are preferred because they are

Fig. 8.81. Front engine mounting of private car (*Rover Co.*).

economical and simple to instal and generally give very reliable service. Their main limitation is the small number of cycles that they will resist of the large load reversals which occur on some vehicles, especially those with comparatively hard springing and a short wheel-base.   The natural frequency of pitching of an engine on its mountings is always much higher than the frequency of pitching of the vehicle on its spring gear, but not necessarily higher than the frequency of vibration of the unsprung masses of the axles of a road vehicle.   A pitching resonance of the engine is obtained easily enough on special tracks by selection of speed, and although such vibrations are seldom predicted or analysed mathematically, they do cause mounting failures similar to those reported from overseas. Failure is most usual when the front mountings carry very little load under normal conditions, that is, when the rear mountings are forward of the gear-box, so that the complete unit is almost balanced about them and the frequency of pitching resonance is low.

When this simple form of mounting gives inadequate fatigue range the alternatives are:

(*a*) Addition of separate rebound devices to limit the tension strain. These may be either in the form of further mountings of the same or

Fig. 8.82. Front engine mounting of heavy vehicle (*E.R.F. Ltd.*).

of different size permanently precompressed against those carrying the normal load, or rubber-faced buffers, or similar devices making contact only when the range of load due to pitching of the engine is greater than usual. The second alternative is usually more economical and has the advantage of not increasing the stiffness under normal conditions.

(*b*) Replacement of the mountings by inclined links, which are another means of giving the ratio of stiffness in the two perpendicular directions. A typical link mounting for a heavy vehicle is shown in Fig. 8.82. In most cases the links are arranged so that gravity load puts them in tension and the pendulum effect adds a little to the resistance, due to the bonded or unbonded rubber bushes at the ends, but there is really no reason why the links should not be in compression if that simplifies the construction of the brackets. This alternative is particularly attractive when the engine is supported below a structure, as in the under-floor-engined bus and rail car. The link may be loaded either way, but the flat mounting with or without intermediate plates must be loaded normally in compression, so that the brackets for the under-floor installation may become rather complicated. The disadvantages of links are that they tend to give too low a resistance for torsional movement and too high a resistance for vertical and transverse movement, so that they insulate torsional impulses better than the other forms of engine vibration and are too dependent upon the accurate estimation of the position of the axis of oscillation.

(c) Return to the single mounting point, as in the original form of " floating power ". This method, using a cylindrical bush, also requires accurate estimation of the axis, but it is still very popular with the under-floor installation of horizontal engines. A modification is the single vertical link or hanger, with a bush at either end giving considerable radial deflection. The function of the front mounting is then only to support vertical load, and movement in directions other than the vertical must be controlled by entirely the other mountings.

It is more difficult to give a systematic account of the rear mountings, as the positions of support and the forms of construction vary enormously. Many are illustrated by Horovitz,[45] but the main classes are:

(a) mountings to either side of the flywheel;
(b) the single point under the gear-box.

The principle of two mountings in a V, including links, is used extensively for the flywheel support on the larger engines, whether or not a gear-box is mounted integral with the engine, and sometimes an auxiliary gear-box support is used as well. Adequate longitudinal stiffness is usually given by the mountings themselves, but occasionally a separate longitudinal link with some kind of flexible rubber bearing at the ends is included. Many mountings from the flywheel housing, however, do not make use of the principle of the elastic centre, but give stiffness of the same order vertically and transversely. Fig. 8.83 is a typical example in which the use of rubber in shear for vertical and transverse loading and torque reaction, and in compression longitudinally, provides insulation against all the main forms of vibration. If the engine is mounted upright the plane of maximum flexibility, that is the plane in which the rubber is purely in shear, should be perpendicular to the axis of oscillation, but this feature is important only when the rear mounting assembly has a compression stiffness many times that in shear. The usual form of conical bush mounting has a stiffness ratio only of the order of 4 : 1, so that it performs almost as well placed upright. It has been found from experience

Fig. 8.83(a).

Fig. 8.83. Rear engine mounting of heavy vehicle (*Dodge,
Britain, Ltd.*).

Fig. 8.83(b).

that the most successful mountings of six-cylinder oil engines in vehicle chassis have a total torsional resistance of the order of 10^7 lb. in./ radian for each litre of engine capacity. The minimum moment of inertia of this class of engine does not seem to vary very much from one make to another, and such empirical rules are useful when the value of the moment of inertia and the direction of the axis are seldom known. Similar rules might well be made with regard to other classes of engines, though difficulties would be introduced by private cars with the great variations in ratio of bore to stroke and valve mechanism. When it is not possible to obtain sufficiently low torsional flexibility from the type of rear mounting shown in Fig. 8.83 the same general construction is sometimes maintained, with an additional support for part of the load either over the flywheel housing or under the gear-box. Such a support gives negligible increase in torsional resistance.

When a gear-box integral with the engine has a high ratio it is generally necessary to add some additional stiffness for torques greater than the top-gear maximum. A combination of mounting units with torque reaction buffers is shown in Fig. 8.83. The effective stiffness of the mounting is increased in the indirect gears, but the occasions on which high torques are used at engine speeds low enough to require the maximum flexibility are usually very few. Torque reaction buffers may be used to avoid excessive stress range or engine movement which cannot be accommodated in the installation space available. Large amplitudes may be due either to indirect gear reaction or the few cycles of resonant torsional vibration in starting up or shutting down. Flywheel housing mountings of the general type shown in Fig. 8.83 have the further advantage that they require, to complete the support of the engine, stiffness only in one direction at the front end. They can be used therefore with the single link described above or with the single compression mounting at the front, such as that shown in Fig. 8.84, giving a high ratio of compression stiffness to shear stiffness, say of the order of $15:1$. The mounting point may be displaced from the axis of oscillation, but the resistance to oscillation is so small as to be negligible. This principle is used, for instance, in the front engine support on the latest Rolls-Royce car. The majority of private-car engine mountings use a single support point under the gear-box or its rearward extension, though such an arrangement is not favoured on heavy vehicles, on which an arrangement is generally made for gear-box removal without disturbing the engine. Many different constructions using bonded and unbonded rubber are used, but it does not seem to be a good practice to mount from the end of the gear-box extension, where there may be a considerable amplitude of movement due to bending of the power unit, and in the four-cylinder engine it is necessary to use a high flexibility to insulate effectively the vertical secondary force.

The mounting of high-speed oil engines under rail cars has proved more difficult than was supposed when large-scale development started with British Railways modernisation. It may be reasonable to assume that the much more massive structure of a railway carriage makes mount-

Fig. 8.84. Single compression-type front mounting.

ing an easier problem than in a road vehicle, but unfortunately a rail car of normal construction has a well-marked resonance of frequency about 25 per second. The form of vibration in this resonance consists of bending of the floor and of the sides rather in the manner shown exaggerated in Fig. 8.85. This resonant vibration is excited both by the firing impulses of a six-cylinder oil engine idling and by unbalance of the rotating parts at normal running speed, so that in both cases unpleasant vibration can be transmitted to the passenger. Unless the natural frequency of the carriage can be changed considerably, the only solution is to make the mountings flexible enough not to transmit sufficient vibration to cause discomfort. This is a typical example of the danger of assuming that an apparently massive structure behaves as a rigid body at the frequency of a particular vibration. Structural resonance rather than the general principle of vibration insulation may control the design also of engine mounting in cars, especially in those without a separate chassis, in which the annoyance caused by the movement of panels can be magnified by the formation of a standing wave in the air inside the car. The passengers in the rear seat, whose ears are in the region of large pressure fluctuation, are troubled more by this effect than those in the front seat, who suffer mainly a velocity change.

On the Continent the larger diesel engines used in locomotives, and especially those running over speed ranges of 600–1,500 r.p.m., are sometimes equipped with resilient mountings much like those used in motor vehicles, which are built in as an integral part of the structure. In Britain, on the other hand, it is more usual to fit standardised self-contained mounting units which can be placed directly between an under-frame and the locomotive platform plate. The range of acceleration applied otherwise than longitudinally to the locomotive structure is much less than that applied to road vehicles, and seldom approaches $\pm \frac{1}{2}$ g either vertically or transversely. If the engine drives a generator the two

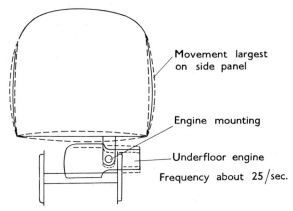

Fig. 8.85. Form of vibration of railcar body excited by unbalance at running speed and firing impulses of six-cylinder engine idling.

are nearly always mounted together so that there is no torque reaction loading, and if it drives through a shaft to a mechanical or hydraulic transmission unit the torque reaction is still small compared with the static loading, so that a flexibility giving static deflection of an order of $\frac{1}{4}$ in. involves no practical problems beyond the usual flexible pipe and electrical connections. Stops to limit the travel are essential, both to keep the engine in place in a derailment and to absorb the longitudinal buffing shocks. These stops are still often provided separately on the structure, but mounting units are now available, such as that shown in Fig. 8.63, providing the necessary resistance in self-contained unit. It is commonly specified that all the equipment in a locomotive should withstand a longitudinal acceleration of 5g without damage, though the velocity of impact giving rise to this acceleration varies greatly according to the design of the buffers.

13. Vehicle suspension systems

This section deals with vehicle suspension, in which rubber is the spring material supporting the whole or the greater part of the strain energy. Until recently such suspension systems were used only to a very limited extent, the most important being the torsion bushes used in conjunction with orthodox axles on certain American coaches.[46] The development, accompanied by an enormous amount of publicity, of air suspension gave the impression that rubber as a vehicle spring material might not be established permanently. There is no doubt that air suspension has important advantages and has performed well under specialised conditions, but at the time of writing there is a renewed interest in rubber suspension, which has been standardised both in Britain and in other countries by important operators of road and rail vehicles and is used by the largest firm in the British Motor Industry for two popular models. Even where the spring medium is still steel, there is an increasing tendency for rubber to be used to accommodate angular movement and small displacements in linkages, thus eliminating wear and maintenance. Rubber springs are often used also to modify the characteristics provided by steel and to reduce the weight of steel by absorbing occasional over-load impacts, and there are some cases in which the cost of the components of rubber and of rubber bonded to metal, used to improve steel springing, is greater than that of most systems of all-rubber springing. Such designs should be regarded rather as special cases of bearings and shock absorbers than as rubber spring gear.

Development has been more rapid with railway carriages than with road vehicles for a number of reasons:

(*a*) The load is greater relative to the deflection, so that loading may be direct, not through leverage. The limitation of deflection of rubber springs for a given load is explained in Section 8.

(*b*) The orthodox type of bogie suspension on railways contains far more sliding bearings than the orthodox road vehicle suspension.

(*c*) The pneumatic tyre can absorb transverse shocks by lateral drift, and has also a certain amount of lateral flexibility. The flanged wheel, on the other hand, is constrained to follow the rail, so that the provision of transverse flexibility greater than the vertical is regarded almost universally as necessary for good riding. Rubber simplifies construction much more in springing flexible in two directions than in springing flexible in one direction only.

(*d*) The pneumatic tyre provides already a certain amount of non-metallic springing free from damping. The advantages of " breaking up the sound path " by the use of rubber may be exaggerated by many engineers, but undoubtedly this effect is considered often to be important.

In theory rubber offers the greatest advantages on electric and diesel–electric locomotives, where the loading is greatest relative to deflection, but most railway engineers consider that development should be carried out first on normal trailer carriages and self-propelled rail cars. Rubber springing of locomotives is at present mainly experimental.

Direct compression springs, such as were popular over one hundred years ago and are still applied extensively to railway vehicles as shock-absorbing buffers, are in use today mainly as auxiliaries to laminated springs, but are used also as side bearers in locomotive and rail-car bogies, in which they accommodate vertical loading in compression and horizontal movement, including that due to pivoting of the bogie round curves, in shear.[47] The earlier compression springs are mentioned in Section 4, and more recent examples include the rear axles of a heavy road vehicle,[48] and the under-carriage springs of aircraft. In Italy a modification has been introduced recently of the helical spring embedded in rubber, in which the greater part of the load is taken by compression of rubber, of which the stiffness is made to increase fairly rapidly for over-load by convoluted external and internal surfaces which roll over one another to give the effect of a change of shape.[49] These springs have been used both for buses and for railway vehicles, mostly as direct replacements for simple or double concentric helical springs. In buses they have been used also with variable internal air pressure, so that the tare load is carried by rubber and steel and the same level maintained for additional load by compressed air. There are obvious advantages in a spring gear which allows the vehicle to operate properly sprung in the unladen state when the air supply fails, yet maintains a constant level in service. This principle can be achieved with air, metal and rubber, air and rubber or air and metal springing. The helical spring embedded in rubber may be used like the more usual forms of rubber compression spring to allow horizontal as well as vertical movement.

The cylindrical rubber bush in torsion has been used in vehicles of all sizes from the pedal cycle to the main-line railway carriage, though on the latter it has been so far only experimental. Its advantages for this, as well as for other forms of springing, are discussed in Section 8, but the two reasons why it seems to be in favour less than it was a few years ago are probably that it does not give in itself a stiffness characteristic increasing with the load, and that its simple construction as a spring unit does not compensate for the extra cost and weight of the associated metal parts. The first small British motor car in mass production with rubber springing uses a conical bush operating through a leverage to increase the load on the

(*a*) Front.

(*b*) Rear.

Fig. 8.86. Independent suspension of wheels of small car (*B.M.C.*).

rubber and reduce its deflection; the arrangement is shown in Fig. 8.86.
The rising stiffness for over-load is achieved by rolling of the rubber

surface against its abutments, and the swinging arms supporting the wheels separately do
not, in this case, add to the weight or complexity of the vehicle. They replace other
structural members in carrying the wheel hubs
from the rigid part of the car body, and the
reactions in the pivots and rubber springs,
although magnified by the leverage balance,
pass only through a small and simple part
of the structure, which can remain extremely
light. At the front of the car the spring gear
leaves space clear for the engine and transmission, and at the back it leaves the maximum space for the rear passengers and luggage
compatible with the small overall dimensions.

The springing of heavier road vehicles may
be represented by that used for some years
now by a large Midland operator of buses
and long-distance coaches which builds its
own vehicles and has standardised rubber

(c) Detail of rubber spring.

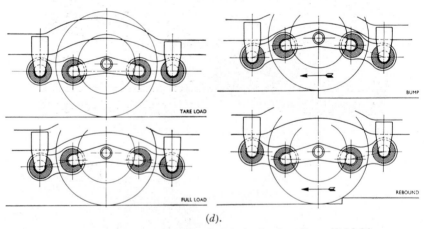

(d).

Fig. 8.86. Independent suspension of wheels of small car (B.M.C.)

both for single deckers and for double deckers. The axle loading of the
typical single-deck bus is practically at the lower limit for direct-loaded
rubber springs, and in this case direct loading was chosen for the independently sprung front wheels and torsion bushes for the rear axle.
The loading with the vehicle unladen is in fact less on the rear axle than

the front, but the main reason for the choice of two different systems in the same vehicle is that the independently sprung front wheels must be controlled in any case by separate links to maintain accurate steering geometry, while on the rear axles the links with torsion springs at the ends are sufficient also to maintain the axle in its correct position relative to the vehicle. The rubber suspension units act at the same time in fact as springs and as bearings for a limited amount of oscillating movement. The front-wheel suspension linkage, shown in Fig. 8.87, is designed in the usual way, so that the point of contact between the tyre and the ground moves almost in a vertical line when the springs are deflected.

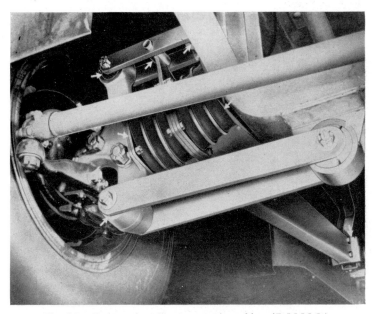

Fig. 8.87. Independent front suspension of bus (*B.M.M.O.*).

This geometrical feature is usual on modern motor vehicles, but it is doubtful whether the precise relative length of links is important, and the upper transverse link has to be made shorter than the lower to fit conveniently in most vehicle structures. The spring is made in two stages, each of which has almost the smallest diameter permissible for the loading and deflection. The size is controlled rather by the approach of negative shear stiffness and the relative value of the linear dimensions and the deflection than by stressing of the rubber either in shear or in compression. The intermediate stabilising plate is hinged from the centre of the top link so that it has always half the deflection of the king pin standard relative to the vehicle body. It carries quite a considerable bending moment, as explained in Fig. 8.53. The alternative method of stabilisation shown in that diagram may not be practicable, as it would involve some rigid member passing through from one side of the vehicle to the other, where there would be great difficulty in avoiding the various parts of the control mechanisms. All the bearings of the transverse links and the forward bearing of the torque reaction arm are formed with rubber bushes, and all except that on the bottom of the king-pin standard are of a type with a spherical rubber sleeve, which accommodates in shear angular movement about all axes. The stiffness of the bushes in the radial direction is made as high as possible, without adding a significant parasitic spring rate (see Fig. 8.30). It is important that accurate geometry should be maintained, especially in a type of coach which is used on the motorway at

Fig. 8.88. Rear-axle springing of bus (*B.M.M.O.*).

speeds up to 80 m.p.h., while little advantage can be gained from trying to derive useful strain energy from the radial deflection of the bearings.

Both the construction of the rear-axle suspension and the principle by which the stiffness is made variable according to the load are shown in Fig. 8.88. The usual setting is that in which the links are horizontal when the vehicle rests under its tare load only. The rubber is then stressed mainly in torsional shear, though there is also a direct vertical loading due to the weight carried, this vertical loading providing only a small part of the deflection. Travel of the axle, either upwards or downwards, inclines the links, so that the bushes must become eccentric and the vertical component of the radial loading provide extra resistance. The load carried by the springing can be made to follow approximately the law:

$$P = A + By + Cy^3$$

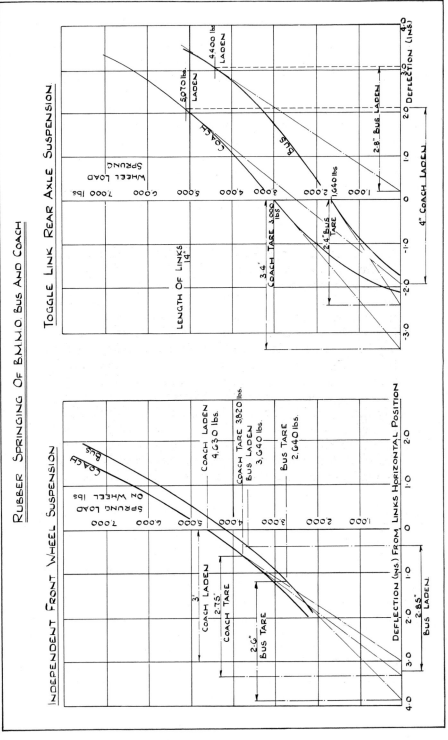

Fig. 8.89. Rubber springing of B.M.M.O. bus and coach.

where y is the deflection from the position in which the links are horizontal and A, B and C are constants. B and C depend upon the proportions of the bushes and the length of the links, while A depends also upon the amount of torsional strain in the unladen position. The inclination of the links in plan view gives transverse stiffness, so that no separate transverse link is necessary, while the lengthwise spacing of the bushes, fore and aft of the axle, is made sufficient for torque reaction to be absorbed without excessive wind-up of the final-drive unit.

When this kind of springing is used on the double decker these links are set transversely and a separate longitudinal link with bushes acting only as bearings provided to take the traction and braking forces. The modification is made to fit in better with the structure of the double decker and the low floor level.

The load–deflection curves for front and rear springing are shown in Fig. 8.89, from which it is seen that the front springs, of which the variation of loading is moderate, are a compromise between constant stiffness and the so-called constant periodicity, or stiffness proportional to load. The back springs, on the other hand, approximate very closely to constant periodicity over the range from unladen to fully laden, with additional stiffening for large deflections in either direction. Stiffening for over-travel is not in theory a good thing, because it increases transmitted forces when the spring is most needed, that is, when a large shock is applied to the wheel. It is necessary in practice, however, because the travel for a uniformly flexible spring is not available, and it makes possible better absorption of the type of shock which occurs frequently on the normal load. Rubber springs have been shown already to have an average life much greater than that of steel springs, but accurate statistics will not be available until a considerable fleet has completed vehicle mileages of the order of half a million.

Most railway vehicles made today for running in passenger traffic have two four-wheel bogies, each with springing between the axles and bogie frames and between the bogie frames and the bolsters on which the bogies are pivoted from the vehicle body. It is generally considered better to put the greater part of the spring flexibility in the secondary stage, that is between the bogie and the body.[50] The secondary suspension also provides nearly the whole of the transverse flexibility, which some authorities say should amount to 40 in. deflection for a loading of 1g. Such a flexibility has been provided in some passenger bogies of orthodox design in which the body is suspended on two sets of pendulum links in series in which the lengths are respectively about 24 in. and 16 in.[51] The vertical deflection of the primary and secondary springing together from the free to the fully laden position may vary from 3 in. for moderate-speed passenger carriages and locomotives up to 8 in., or even more, for

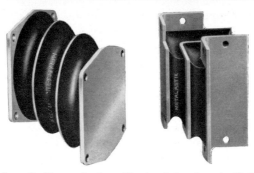

Fig. 8.90. Rubber springing of bogie of electric train (*L.T.E.*).

high-speed carriages. Any vertical or transverse deflection within these ranges can be provided by rubber springing, but the example illustrated in Fig. 8.90 is that used for new tube railway stock,[52] of which the maximum speed is about 50 m.p.h. Small tunnel clearances and the extreme compactness of the bogie and very high over-load demand a limited deflection of about $3\frac{1}{2}$ in. vertically from the free to the fully laden.

The primary springing consists of chevron-shaped springs, of which the assembly with the retaining frame may be considered to be equivalent to a single conical bush, of which the two halves, separated in an axial plane, are put one to either side of the axle box. Longitudinal stiffness is improved, so that the two axles of the bogie remain parallel. It is considered that for high speeds the longitudinal stiffness should be of the order of 15 × the vertical to avoid a self-excited oscillation of the bogie about its vertical axis, resulting from the conical form of the wheels. Such an oscillation causes a snaking movement of the bogie, known also as hunting, but at the time of writing no reports have been received of this trouble on rubber-spring bogies, even when attempts have been made to produce it with tyres deliberately turned to an unfavourable profile. The secondary suspension gives vertical flexibility in shear and compression, and a considerably greater flexibility in pure shear in a direction inclined slightly to the transverse. This inclination serves the purpose of reducing the tendency of the carriage to roll and correcting to some extent increase in shear flexibility of the spring with load. Sufficient flexibility to give results equivalent to those of pendulum swing links is achieved only by making use to some extent of the approach of unstable conditions in the manner illustrated in Fig. 8.45. Obviously the compression component of the load in the secondary spring with the carriage fully laden must not be as great as that for first-order buckling, but one factor in settling surface profile of the rubber is to secure a more gradual approach to this condition. Longitudinal loads due to traction and braking do not influence lateral stiffness to any marked extent, because the reduction in stiffness to one side of the bolster is balanced by increasing stiffness to the other side. In the primary springing about one-half of the load is carried by compression and the other half by shear: in the secondary springing the ratio is about 2 : 1. Deflection sufficient for main-line stock, running up to 100 m.p.h., can be provided by using a two-stage bolster spring. The relative simplicity of the rubber springing is shown by the comparison in Fig. 8.91 of the spring units and the parts which they replace; this is a good example of the results obtainable by using rubber at the same time as a spring and as a bearing which is free from friction and needs no lubricating. The first few years' experience in the large-scale operation on vehicles have shown a very considerable economy, resulting both from the elimination of maintenance and reduction of the weight to be accelerated and braked.

Noise reduction is also important, and the vehicle riding characteristics can be made at least as good as those with other forms of suspension, provided that the flexibility is sufficient. External shock absorbers are generally needed, and are usually of the hydraulic telescopic type, but in this respect rubber springing does not differ from modern forms of metal springing. The orthodox railway bogie springing is sufficient without shock absorbers only because of the greater amount of friction and wear.

Many vehicle engineers, especially on the railways, hope that a rubber compound may be developed with sufficient inherent damping to make

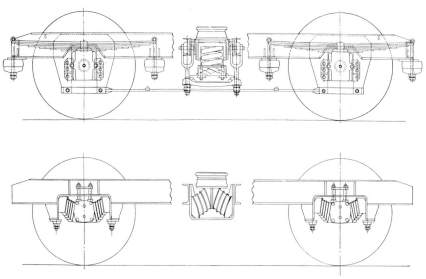

Fig. 8.91. Comparison of steel and rubber springing of main-line bogie.

shock absorbers unnecessary. The characteristics of rubber damping are correct, but at present the compounds with sufficiently low creep and low ratio of dynamic stiffness to static give only about one-third of the total damping that is absorbed, while those being developed for even less creep tend to give rather less damping. There is no difficulty in providing the right amount of damping with a synthetic rubber, but all the compounds tried so far seem to have one or more of the following faults:

(*a*) too much static creep;
(*b*) too much work softening;
(*c*) too high a ratio of dynamic stiffness to static;
(*d*) too great a change in mechanical properties with temperature;
(*e*) a poor fatigue range;
(*f*) change in properties with time, even at normal temperatures.

There is no sign yet that the perfect spring material will become available, but the various properties needed are not fundamentally as incompatable as was thought until recently, and the enormous potential demand makes the evolution of such a material an extremely important matter.

14. Rubber as a vibration absorber

Most of the examples of the use of rubber in engineering components described in this chapter are concerned with the suppression, isolation or insulation of vibration, but there are others in which the rubber supports a mass which is intended to work in resonance or nearly in resonance. The properties of elasticity and damping are used as in anti-vibration devices, but some unit of the machine is given deliberately, by dynamic magnification, a larger amplitude than the remainder. One of the most obvious examples is the vibratory screen or trough, which is given movement, sufficient to traverse or sift the material handled, by supporting it from the base on springs of such stiffness in the proper direction of motion as to reduce greatly the external force which must be applied. The weight to be vibrated generally varies according to the amount of loose material actually on the vibrating surface, and it is impossible therefore to work exactly at the critical speed. The general practice is to make the actual speed of oscillation a little less than the critical speed, in which case the hydraulic or mechanical device applying alternating load may act in one direction only. This type of drive does not reduce the power dissipated in maintaining the vibration, and may indeed increase it somewhat, by reason of the hysteresis work done in the rubber, but it does reduce the loads on the driving device, in addition to the possibility of making it single-acting. The rapid increase in power consumption with the approach of resonance stabilises the speed, while any attempt to run just above the critical speed would introduce great difficulties in making the input fall off for a small increment of speed as rapidly as the power absorbed. Any engineer or student who has carried out experiments with mechanically-driven vibrators is familiar with the way in which the speed of rotation runs away as soon as resonance is passed. Most vibrating screens and conveyor troughs are made to run continuously for very long periods with the maximum amplitude, so that the range of stress in the rubber should be low, sometimes even lower than on resilient wheels.

This chapter is concerned mainly with one type of application of rubber in resonance which, having a special technical interest and commercial importance, has been the subject of extensive study, namely the tuned vibration absorber.

Most of the practical applications of vibration absorbers are to resonant or nearly resonant systems, of which the properties are modified to avoid resonance or to reduce greatly its amplitude, but the simplest form is that in which the vibration absorber is attached to a freely suspended mass. Fig. 8.92 uses the same example of simple harmonic motion and the same notation as Fig. 8.18. A small mass m moving up and down harmonically is controlled by a large mass M, of which the mounting is supposed to be so flexible that the cyclical change of force which it imposes upon M may be negligible. The vibration absorber attached to M has a mass A, and its supporting spring has both stiffness and damping.

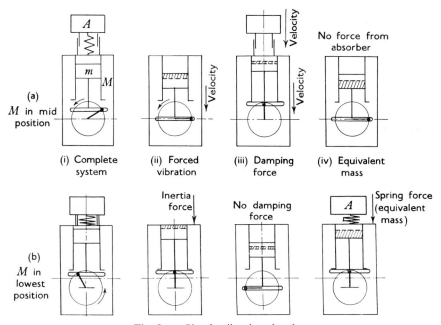

Fig. 8.92. Simple vibration absorber.

The principle upon which this device works is generally explained mathematically, and it is easy to see that at resonance the mass A vibrates in such a way that the force transmitted through its supporting spring is equivalent to a mass many times larger than A, added to M. A physical rather than a mathematical explanation is seldom admitted, but appears to be as follows: Two stages in the cycle of vibration are considered; the first in Fig. 8.92a, in which the mass M is in its mean position travelling downwards, and the second in Fig. 8.92b, where the mass M has moved through a quarter of a cycle and is at its lowest position.

If there were no vibration absorber the acceleration forces on m and M would balance, so that the movement would be as in $a(ii)$ and $b(ii)$, and in fact a part of m is still available to cause this sort of movement, depending upon the amplitude of M that remains with the vibration absorber fitted. The amplitude of A at resonance is limited by the damping of its supporting spring, so that there must be a component of the movement of m as shown in $a(iii)$ and $b(iii)$, which gives the maximum force at a time when the velocity of M is the maximum in $a(iii)$, the force on m and the velocity of M are a maximum downwards and A must be moving downwards or upwards substantially in its middle position so its relative movement to M is also at maximum velocity. In this case the movement is downwards; otherwise the force would not balance.

Turning now to $b(iv)$, the mass A has moved to its lowest position, so that the spring applies a force downwards at the same time as the mass M, and its effect upon the vibration is therefore the same as that of an additional mass. A part of the unbalance m is used therefore in overcoming this spring force. The proportion of m which can be balanced in this way, and therefore prevented from increasing the amplitude of M, depends upon the relative mass of A and upon the damping, but the relative movement of A and M is limited by the dynamic magnifier of the rubber, so that the extremely large reduction amplitude, which appears possible from calculation that does not take account of damping, is unobtainable in practice. The advantage of the vibration absorber in this elementary form is that it gives the effect upon vibration of a mass many times its own value. In stationary plant it may be easier to install than a suspended foundation slab, and in many types of machinery the saving of weight is important.

The analysis given above may be considered over-simplified because it takes no account of the phase difference between M and A, but it does illustrate the manner in which the force in the vibration absorber spring can be made equivalent to additional mass on M, not to a spring support. If A moved in the opposite direction from M it would give negative equivalent mass and A and M might act together with the spring so that the whole of M was used in maintaining the state of free vibration and the amplitude therefore made larger than without the absorber. Such a condition is often found in practice, but the correctly designed vibration absorber, either in the simple system of Fig. 8.91 or in a more complicated system, is designed so that it gives at the working frequency a large equivalent mass.

An interesting practical example of the tuned vibration absorber used very much in the way given above is given by Den Hartog,[53] who explains also the theory in the mathematical form which is most useful for solving design problems.

It cannot be recommended that the argument used above should be extended to the application of the absorber to a combination of free and forced vibration such as that shown in Fig. 8.23. The analysis becomes altogether too complicated, and a mathematical method is essential. In systems where there would be resonance otherwise with very little damping, equivalent mass is provided when it is most needed. But there must be always two other frequencies at which the complete system, including the vibration absorber, is still in resonance. In the case of equipment working over wide speed range the substitution of two critical speeds for one is justified by the reduced amplitude resulting from the damping of the rubber. This damping is proportional to the stiffness of the vibration absorber spring and its amplitude of movement; it is the magnification of relative movement in the rubber by the resonance of the vibration absorber

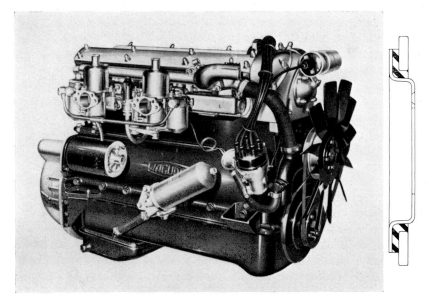

Fig. 8.93. Automobile engine with crankshaft vibration absorber
(*Jaguar Cars, Ltd.*).

which leads to the efficient reduction in maximum amplitude. By far the most important individual use of the vibration absorber is to reduce the torsional amplitude of internal-combustion engines; an absorber with a rubber spring is in fact the type of vibration damper fitted to most six-cylinder and some four-cylinder and V8 car engines and to quite a number of oil engines for vehicles and other types of drive. A typical example is that shown in Fig. 8.93, in which is seen that the vibration absorber takes the form of a small flywheel mounted through a torsional spring from the front end of the crankshaft. The natural frequency of a modern car crankshaft may be of the order of 400 c/sec., so that the rubber spring, to give a similar frequency to the small floating inertia, must be comparatively stiff; hence the large area and small thickness of rubber. There is no continuous torque and a negligible weight relative to the radial stiffness of the spring, so that the problems of creep and ratio of dynamic stiffness to static stiffness become unimportant, except that in some recent designs the manufacturing cost is reduced by pre-compressing the rubber in place without bonding, so that sufficient frictional grip to avoid slipping must be maintained over the life of the engine. The torsional vibration, which the crankshaft damper reduces, consists of twist of the crankshaft relative to the flywheel, which has a polar inertia many times greater than that of the cylinder, so that the free end moves in the opposite direction from the flywheel in its oscillation, though the maximum velocity of oscillatory movement is generally small compared with the velocity of rotation. As the inertia of the damper, though far less than that of the flywheel, is often greater than that of one cylinder line (piston, connecting-rod, crank-pin, etc.), the relative amplitude is controlled rather by inertia than by damping, and the best results are obtained from a high damping rubber which would not be acceptable as a spring material. Both synthetics and special natural rubber mixes are used, and the dissipation of the heat generated by internal work is considered both in the mechanical design and in the conductivity of the rubber.

The crankshaft damper may be used in the following ways:

(*a*) To reduce the amplitude of the engine in passing through its critical speeds when these are important, as a source of noise and vibration inside the car which might be objectionable to passengers, or of wear in the valve mechanism of the engine.

(*b*) To reduce the alternating stress in the crankshaft in passing through a severe critical speed which might lead to fatigue failure eventually in the metal; the two resultant resonances have an amplitude within the fatigue limit.

(*c*) To enable an engine to run continuously at a speed which would be otherwise too close to the critical speed of the crankshaft. The damped critical speeds are placed above and below the normal running speed; the engine passes through one quickly as it starts and stops and does not reach the other. For instance, the engine may be designed so that it runs below a major critical speed when generating 50-cycle alternating current, but a crankshaft damper may be needed to enable it to generate at 60 cycles without major modification either to engine or to alternator.

(*d*) To raise the maximum speed of a variable-speed engine, such as one for a car. The splitting of the critical speeds may make them all acceptable, though within the range, or the higher of the two formed from the most severe of the original critical speeds may be still outside the extended range.

The tuned vibration absorber of natural or synthetic rubber seems to be an established feature of the smaller high-speed engines, and has replaced types dependent upon sliding friction. On larger machines the viscous damper is used extensively: it is not a vibration absorber but uses a small flywheel floating in a film of viscous fluid, so that the damping is derived from the relative angular velocity of the front end of the crankshaft and of a member which rotates more nearly at a constant angular velocity.[55] One reason why this type is preferred in spite of its greater cost and weight is that its properties do not have to be modified with changes of natural frequency of the engine resulting from different flywheel sizes, types of drive and front-end auxiliaries. Vibration absorbers are used on large marine engines, where they are known as De-tuners. The springs are generally of metal, but rubber can be used.

Uses of the vibration absorber, otherwise than for engine crankshafts, have seldom met with any permanent success. At one time some cars were provided with front bumper bars having tuned masses at their ends, and the complete power unit has been given resilient mountings which, in addition to insulating the engine vibration, have made it act to some extent as an absorber for the unsprung masses between the springs and the tyres.[57] Comparatively small masses, supported by rubber springs, may give a greater attenuation of vibration of aircraft cabin walls than is obtainable from the same weight of sound-deadening material, but in all these cases the vibration absorber is rather a device to overcome a specific fault encountered in development than a normal design feature. The metal spring device fitted commonly to overhead power-transmission cables, on the other hand, deals with self-excited vibration of a type which is inherent in the use of long stretched cables in a high wind, but the alternatives using rubber do not rely for their efficiency upon de-tuning, but upon the impact of the loose metal discs upon rubber washers.

It is difficult to see why vibration absorbers are not used more extensively, especially in the simple form of a mass of concrete or other material supported on rubber springs, which can achieve the effect of the alternative devices used at present at a small fraction of the cost and weight. In mounting an engine or compressor running at a constant speed, for instance, it might replace a large foundation block or a system of counterbalanced weights driven from the crankshaft; there would be no maintenance problem, and if replacement of the rubber springs were necessary eventually it would be only a few minutes' work. Perhaps one of the difficulties is that the advocates of the vibration absorber are inclined to make exaggerated claims to degrees of amplitude reduction which ignore the limitations imposed by the dynamic magnifier and relative equivalent masses, but the advantages obtainable in practice are enough to establish this device as a normal part of engineering design.

15. Principles of flexible couplings

Of the practical applications discussed so far in this chapter only the crankshaft vibration absorber deals with the fluctuations in the angular velocity of rotating shafts, but there is no difficulty in applying, to flexible couplings for power transmission, the principles used in resilient mountings and spring gear.   Flexible couplings are made in so many different types [56] that it is pointless to give examples of practical construction, so the more important design factors will be considered with reference to the use of rubber.   Broadly speaking, the two purposes of a coupling are the allowance for misalignment in the two shafts joined and the absorption of cyclic irregularity or torsional vibration.   Naturally enough manufacturers are more inclined to claim that their couplings perform both these functions than to give the limitations.   The chart of torque capacities, maximum speeds and service factors by which the torque is reduced, according to the type of drive, are generally sufficient to avoid torsional stress range which might cause premature failure, but they do not guarantee adequate allowance for misalignment without overloading the bearings on either side, or a cyclic fluctuation less on the side of the coupling opposite from the machine causing the vibration.   Misalignment may be parallel, angular (conical) or axial, or more than one of these at the same time, and it may be either continuous, as in machines not set in the same axis on a rigid bed-plate, or intermittent, as in the rear axle of a car rising and falling relative to the gear-box.   Large amounts of relative parallel misalignment of shafts are usually absorbed by an intermediate floating or cardan shaft having a coupling at either end, when the coupling may allow only a very small radial displacement, but single rubber couplings are now available which run continuously with a relative parallel displacement of the order of $\frac{1}{8}$ in. in a small size, such as 100 lb.ft. normal torque up to $\frac{1}{2}$ in. in a large size running at low speeds of 150 r.p.m. or less.   Many designs are available in which the misalignment in any form is accommodated by deflection of rubber in shear without any relative sliding of friction surfaces, and in some cases small relative displacements are accommodated by rubber in compression.   It is inevitable that the rubber should pass through a cycle of stressing every revolution of the shaft, and permanent misalignment means continuous cyclic fluctuation in the rubber.   Even in a shaft rotating fairly slowly, a large number of cycles is soon built up, and in most cases a life running into tens of millions of cycles is essential.   Reference to the fatigue curves on Fig. 8.32 shows that the stress range must be small, and for that reason it has proved very difficult to make the rubber flexible coupling of reasonable torque capacity for its size to run continuously at more than about 4° relative angularity of the two shafts.   The occasional large angular movement is quite another matter, as the normal alignment may be restored after a few cycles which use up only a very small part of the fatigue life.   In a vehicle propeller shaft, for instance, it is the cardan angle with the vehicle laden and unladen, not the maximum angle due to road shocks, which determines the reliability. Loading of the shaft bearings due to the resistance of the coupling is seldom large when the intermediate cardan shaft is used, but is a serious consideration, of course, when there is only a single coupling, especially if this is of the type in which relative displacement gives rise to compression rather than shear.   The direction of loading of the rubber in the coupling goes through a cycle with every revolution, but the reaction in the bearings has a constant direction, so that there is a danger of power loss and over-heating, but not of vibration.   On the other hand, there are cases in which the rubber coupling itself is made with insufficient accuracy, so that in its free position it does not place one shaft true relative to the other: such an error, whether in the parallel or angular direction, has the reverse effect from misalignment of the machines coupled; it gives a steady load in the rubber and a load in the bearings which goes through a cycle with every revolution.   The resilient coupling can act, then, as a generator of vibration.   This trouble has been experienced, for instance, in the simple type of coupling in which the torque is transmitted in shear through a flat circular disc or cylinder of rubber.   Relative angularity of the shafts is resisted by compression, so that a small deviation from the parallel of the axes on the two sides of the coupling can give quite a large rotating couple. The solution is simply more accurate manufacture.

In allowing for misalignment it is the continuous, not the intermittent, condition which generally limits the life of the coupling, but in transmitting torque it is the intermittent condition which is important.   Failure due to continuous torsional over-load is found only when the size of coupling is absurdly small relative to the torque transmitted, but it is often difficult to insulate torsional vibration at the running speed without going through resonance in starting and stopping.   A machine liable to large torque fluctuations, such as a single-cylinder internal-combustion engine or compressor, seems to call for a flexible-drive coupling, but the larger the torque fluctuation, the more difficult is it to maintain reasonable stresses. Methods of calculation of torque range are complicated, but one simple formula illustrating the problem very well is:

$$\theta = \frac{TM}{I\omega^2}$$

where θ is the angle of twist of the coupling at resonance in radians; T is the forcing torque, that is the range of applied torque to either side of the mean; M is the dynamic magnifier of the rubber; I is the moment of inertia of the machine causing the vibration; ω is the angular velocity of rotation in radians per second.

The units of T and I do not matter so long as they correspond, for instance, T may be given in lb.in. and I in lb.in.–sec.²; this formula applies only to the simple case of two machines with comparatively rigid shafts or armatures joined by a single coupling, but the general principles apply equally to more complicated systems.

The amplitude varies inversely with the inertia of the machine causing the vibration. The formula is independent of the inertia of the other machine, but if this increases, ω becomes less, so that the amplitude is greater, hence the resonance amplitude may become impossibly large if a flywheel is not provided on the machine giving the torque fluctuation, particularly if the other machine has a large inertia. To give an extreme example, attempts have been made to put a flexible coupling, using rubber in shear, between a six-cylinder diesel engine with no flywheel and a direct-current generator. Application of the formula above shows that although the shearing stress in the rubber due to full torque may be only of the order of 20 lb./in.², the torque range at resonance is of the order of ± 500 lb./in.². The coupling inevitably fails before the engine has got up to speed for the first time. A similar problem occurs in driving an air compressor or similar small machine from a large engine, but in this case the engine, although the driving unit, is on the opposite side from the source of torsional vibration and has a large inertia.

Another problem which occurs in the driving of auxiliary machines is the effect of gear ratio upon the torsional amplitude. Increase in the speed of rotation due to gearing reduces the mean torque transmitted, but it increases the amplitude of torsional oscillation in the same ratio; hence the difficulty in making a satisfactory resilient coupling for a super-charger drive. Conversely, a reduction gear puts the coupling in a much more favourable condition for a given torque. Of the coupling-design features used in overcoming excessive resonance amplitudes, by far the most usual is the provision of over-load buffers which are simply a means of increasing the stiffness for amplitude beyond a certain limit. These buffers do not prevent resonance, but they provide additional rubber spring material to reduce the stress and limit the amplitude by increasing the value of ω. Not being subject to continuous loading, they may be made of high-damping rubber which reduces the value of M.

As in other applications of over-load buffers for rubber springs, it is important to allow for creep in the continuously loaded rubber, except when the drive takes the load equally in both directions. There are also some cases in which it is sufficient to make the flexible coupling itself adequate only for the torque of the engine or other machine when it is idling and to use the over-load buffers to carry the greater part of the normal power.

Where over-load buffers do not suffice the resilient coupling is sometimes placed in series with a slipping clutch, while a form of centrifugal clutch is now on the market [58] which is used to engage the driven member when the driving member has exceeded the critical speed, after which it acts as a flexible coupling providing sufficient absorption of torque fluctuations and some allowance for misalignment.

This section is concerned largely with the possible cause of trouble with flexible couplings, but most of the applications to industrial machinery are made in conditions in which allowance for a little misalignment is the main consideration and large cyclic torque fluctuations are not encountered. Under these conditions there is seldom any difficulty in obtaining complete reliability with a suitably chosen design without any special calculation or development.

16. Some publications

To those readers who are commencing their study of this field it is recommended to read " Rubber Properties of Special Interest to the Engineer ", by W. J. S. Naunton (*I.R.I. Trans.*, 1946, **22**, 111), " The Engineer's Approach to Rubber ", by A. H. Willis (*I.R.I. Trans.*, 1951, **27**, 264) and *What Every Engineer Should Know about Rubber*, by W. J. S. Naunton (Natural Rubber Development Board publication). The textbooks by W. E. Burton (*Engineering with Rubber*), by A. T. McPherson and A. Klemin (*Engineering Uses of Rubber*) and by the Andre Rubber Company (*Elastomeric Engineering*) should be studied. For a complete bibliography of the field the reader is referred to *Some Mechanical Properties of Rubber and Rubber Units*, by A. J. Carmichael.

For the advanced reader there are several specialised text-books, for example, Timoshenko's *Vibration Problems of Engineering* covers all the theory that any practical engineer dealing with vibration is likely to use and avoids imaginary numbers, while Den Hartog makes the subject simpler for those who like imaginary numbers. To judge by the references given in specialised papers, these are the text-books used most often, but there are many others. In all cases it is important that in reading the orthodox theory the difference between viscous damping, coulomb damping and rubber damping should be remembered clearly, but specialised papers on the dynamic properties of rubber deal specifically with the case of rubber damping, though sometimes the method of mathematical analysis does not make this clear to the average engineering reader.

General text-books usually show in their method of treating the subject their origin in university lecture notes, so Ker Wilson's latest work *Vibration Engineering* is particularly important as a guide to the practical solution of vibration problems. It is based on a very long and varied

A A

experience, probably unique in this country at least, in the marine-engine and aircraft industries and as a consulting engineer for the vibration problems of other industries as well.

There is unfortunately very little good published information on the design of rubber components or on properties affecting the design, such as stress and temperature limitations and creep. Most text-books seem to be content to quote the works of American authors of the period 1935–42, which were indeed thorough and very good in their day, but are no longer adequate for systematic and economical design. Sometimes extracts from the works of Cadwell, Merrill, Sloman and Yost and of Keys, Downie-Smith and E. H. Hull seem to have been taken from manufacturers' catalogues in which they were incorporated, and therefore published without acknowledgement of their authors. Where original papers are quoted, the sources are usually given. Particulars of actual designs of rubber components are best studied in catalogues, but many important types are illustrated and the makers named in *Encylopédie Technologique de l'Industrie du Caoutchouc*, published by Dunod in Paris. *Automobile Engineer* gives excellent descriptions of application of rubber components to various types of motor vehicle, while important special articles on the subject include " Rubber in Automobile Design ", December 1955 and " Body Mounting ", March 1958. The designs shown in the second article may be applied also to other applications of rubber as a spring and sliding or oscillating bearing. The prototype of a rubber suspension was described in detail in March 1950, and all these three articles have been reprinted for Metalastik Ltd., Leicester. Information on the design of mounting units for engines in vehicles is given in a paper by M. Horovitz to the Institution of Mechanical Engineers, 1958, and in one by T. H. Pierce and J. B. Robinson to the American Society of Automotive Engineers, 1951. The second paper deals also with the various types of tuned rubber and viscous vibration absorbers for crankshafts. Much general information with calculation methods and many examples of practical application of rubber as a spring and as a bearing are included in E. F. Göbel's *Berechrung und Gestaltung von Gummifedern*; the illustrations, especially those of machinery mounting, are worthy of study even without the text. Many types of flexible shaft-coupling, both in rubber and in other materials, are summarised very well in a special survey included with the *Engineer's Digest* of July 1957. Lastly, a bibliography of *Devices for Damping Mechanical Vibrations* was published by the United States Naval Research Laboratory in December 1956 and is available without restriction.

REFERENCES

1. Fletcher, W. P. and Gent, A. N. (1950) *I.R.I. Trans.*
2. McCallion, H. and Davies, D. M. (1956) *Proc. Instn. mech. Engrs., Lond.*
3. Timoshenko, S. *Vibration Problems in Engineering* (London: Constable), Chapter 1.
4. Manley, A. (1948) *Fundamentals or Vibration Theory* (London: Chapman and Hall).
5. Anon. (1932) *Rubber Springs or Steel Springs?*, published by Sheffield Steel Spring Makers.
6. Macbeth, C. (1939) *Rubber and Railways* (Natural Rubber Development Board).
7. Goodyear (1853) *Gum-Elastic*, Facsimile 1937—*India Rubb. J.*
8. Craig, W. G. (1853) *Proc. Instn. mech. Engrs., Lond.*
9. McPherson, A. T. and Klemin, A. (1956) *Engineering Uses of Rubber* (Reinhold), p. 136. (This diagram does not show an incorrect use of the Bush.)
10. Coleman (1852), B.P. 14,193.
11. De Bergue (1847), B.P. 11,649.
12. (1959) *Automobile Engineering*, p. 304.
13. *Auto-Union*, Germany.
14. McPherson, A. T. and Klemin, A., *Engineering Uses of Rubber*, p. 135.
15. Burton, W. E. (1949) *Engineering with Rubber* (McGraw-Hill), p. 409, also (1959) *Pumping*.
16. Macbeth, C. *Rubber and Railways*, p. 25.
17. Moulton, A. E. and Turner, P. W. (1957) *Proc. Instn. mech. Engrs., Lond.*
18. McPherson, A. T. and Klemin, A. *Engineering Uses of Rubber*, p. 134.
19. Anon. (1950) *Engineering Properties of Rubber* (United States Rubber Co.).
20. Keys, W. C. (1937) *Mech. Eng. (U.S.)*.
21. Ker Wilson, W. (1959) *Vibration Engineering* (Charles Griffin), p. 128.
22. Göbel, E. F. (1955) *Berechnung und Gestaltung von Gummifedern* (Springer), p. 50.
23. Ker Wilson, W. *Vibration Engineering*, Chapter 5.
24. Cadwell, S. M. and others (1940) " Dynamic Fatigue Life of Rubber ", *Ind. Eng. Chem.*, pp. 22–23.
25. Mullins, L. *I.R.I. Trans.*, **23**, 280.
26. Anon. *Engineering Properties of Rubber*, p. 25.
27. McPherson, A. T. and Klemin, A. *Engineering Uses of Rubber*, pp. 35–41.
28. B.P. 632,972.
29. McPherson, A. T. and Klemin, A. *Engineering Uses of Rubber*, pp. 118–119; Downie-Smith, J. F. (1939) *J. appl. Mech.*, p. A.165.
30. Moulton, A. E. and Turner, P. W. *Proc. Instn. mech. Engrs., Lond.*
31. Ker Wilson, W. *Vibration Engineering*, pp. 128–143.
32. Anon. *Engineering Properties of Rubber*, pp. 3–19.
33. Keys, W. C. (1937) *Mech. Engr.*
34. Anon. *Engineering Properties of Rubber*, pp. 19–20.
35. *Rubber in Engineering*, Government Publication, Edited by W. J. S. Naunton, p. 57.
36. Ker Wilson, W. *Vibration Engineering*, Chapter 9, p. 70.
37. *Steel Springs or Rubber Springs?* (Sheffield Steel Spring Makers).
38. (1956) *Engineering*.
39. McPherson, A. T. and Klemin, A. *Engineering Uses of Rubber*, p. 138.
40. Macbeth, C. *Rubber and Railways*, pp. 15–97.
41. Ker Wilson, W. *Vibration Engineering*, Chapter 10, pp. 93–117.
42. Taylor, E. S. and Browne, K. A. (1938) " Vibration Isolation of Aircraft Power Plants ", *Journal of Aeronautic Sciences*. (Taylor and Browne papers were reprinted extensively by Wright Aircraft Corporation Licencees.)

43. Farman, Autocars, Cars, Tramcars & Small Cars. Tr. Seraillier (Whittaker, 1896).
44. B.P. 399,161.
45. Horovitz, M. (1958) " The Suspension of Internal Combustion Engines in Vehicles ", *Proc. Instn. mech. Engrs., Lond.*
46. Fageol, F. R. (1948) " Rubber Torsilastic Suspension System ", *SAE Quarterly Trans.*, **2**, No. 2, 345.
47. Sanders, T. H. (1940) *Springs—A Miscellany* (Locomotive Publishing Company), p. 287.
48. Anon. (1956) *Oil Engine and Gas Turbine.*
49. Génin, G. and Mousson, B. *Encyc.*, Tech. de l'Industrie de caoutchouc (Dunod) p. 557.
50. Koffman, J. (1957) *Proc. Inst. Loco. E.*
51. Sanders, T. H. *Springs and Suspensions.*
52. Manser, A. W. *Proc. Instn. mech. Engrs., Lond.*
53. Ker Wilson, W. *Vibration Engineering*, p. 213.
54. Den Hartog, J. P. (1934) *Mechanical Vibration* (McGraw-Hill), p. 102.
55. Pierce, T. H. and Robinson, J. B. (1952) *SAE Quarterly Trans.*
56. (1957) *Engineers' Digest.*
57. Carlson, J. A. (1959) *The Automobile Engine as a Dynamic Vibration Absorber*, Amer. Soc. Mech. Eng. Paper No. 59-SA-10.

CHAPTER IX

PART ONE

PHYSICAL TESTING OF RUBBER

by

J. M. BUIST

By the end of the eighteenth century some work had been done on the mechanical testing of rubber; about the middle of the nineteenth century natural rubber was being used as a railway shock absorber, and several workers were testing the material comprehensively in both extension and compression. These early experiments established that rubber did not fit into any of the accepted categories, e.g. solid or liquid, elastic or plastic, amorphous or crystalline. Further, they led to an appreciation that by changing environment, history or conditions of test the balance of properties due to the " dual state " (elastic/plastic) was altered. For example, the classical work of F. Kohlrausch (1876), using rubber thread, demonstrated that the Superposition Principle could explain the behaviour of rubber under repeated stressing and provided conclusive evidence that the properties of rubber depended to a very great extent on the previous history of the specimen.

The fact that the modulus of rubber is influenced by the " elastic after-effect " or the memory effect is only one complicating factor. The term " modulus " has never been satisfactory in the case of rubbers. Owing to the large strains involved, the early departure from linearity of the stress–strain curve, the presence of " creep ", the development of crystallinity in certain polymers when stressed, the breakdown of certain bonds between fillers and the rubber molecules when stressed, and the " shape factor " and dimensions of the rubber specimen, it is extremely difficult to quote " modulus " figures which can be readily appreciated by engineers and other rubber users.

With rubber, stresses are frequently referred to the initial cross-section, and due to the very great change in area on stretching the usual terms of theory of elasticity and engineering practice can be misleading. For example, a soft rubber breaking at $1,000\%$ elongation under a stress of $1,925$ lb./in.^{2} based on the initial cross-section actually breaks at a stress of $16,350$ lb./in.^{2} on the breaking cross-section. If stress–strain curves are plotted using real stresses instead of nominal stresses the curves become much steeper as the strain increases, the shape of the stress–strain curve and the relative positions of different stress–strain curves being altered.

The fact that the properties of rubber depend on the form of test pieces used is clearly demonstrated by the factors which must be considered when ring and dumb-bell test pieces are being compared in a tensile-strength test.

When a ring is stretched the percentage elongation is greater at the internal circumference than at the outer circumference; the tensile stress in the rubber decreases from the inside to the outside circumference, and the total force on the ring, as indicated by the test machine, is equal to the cross-section of the ring multiplied by the average stress. In studying the stress–strain relation of the rubber it is necessary to compare this average stress with the corresponding average elongation; this average elongation being obtained by expressing the actual extension (in centimetres or inches) as a percentage of the mean circumference of the ring. For this reason, in all measurements of modulus or of elongation at constant load the elongation should be calculated on the mean circumference. Experiments [1] have shown that when this is done the results agree with those obtained on dumb-bell test pieces in which the stress is uniform over the cross-section; if the elongation were calculated on the internal circumference, which is 9% smaller (in the usual Schopper ring), the results would all be 9% too large.

The above considerations do not apply to the measurement of the elongation at break which must be calculated as a percentage of the internal circumference, because the inside of the ring is the most highly stressed part, and the ring must therefore break when the internal circumference reaches the breaking elongation of the rubber.   It has been shown [1] that breaking elongations calculated in this way agree with those obtained on dumb-bell test pieces.

The aim of rubber testing is, in general, to obtain results that are independent of the kind of test piece used and are a true measure of the property being studied. When such a true measure is required, the methods described above must be used. The common practice of using elongations calculated on the internal circumference to obtain the stress–strain curve, and of calculating tensile strength of rings simply by dividing breaking load by cross-section, is only valid in making comparisons between similar rubbers.

Comparison with other materials

In *Rubber in Engineering* [2] the position was summarised as follows:

" Rubberlike materials are unique in their ability to undergo large reversible elastic deformations under the application of comparatively small stresses. Compared with metals, rubber shows a very large difference in extensibility: its breaking elongation may be of the order of 1,000% as compared with 1–40%. A further characteristic is the ' S ' shape of the stress–strain curve. Rubber does not obey Hookes' law except for small deformations (i.e. up to 50% extension), and unlike metals it does not show a yield-point at which plastic flow begins.''

Since the above summary was written it has been shown [3] that frozen rubbers exhibit a yield stress on stretching, and similar effects have been found [4] with filled vulcanisates containing 40–60% mineral filler by volume. As more research is done it appears that rubber-like materials obey the same basic laws of elastic behaviour as do metals, but with rubber-like materials some characteristics predominate at the expense of others and give the impression that high polymers belong to a different physical category from that of metals. However, when a great deal of further research is completed one conclusion may be that the elasticity of metals is a special case of rubber-like elasticity.

Tensile stress–strain properties

Tension tests are almost invariably used either to give an indication of the quality of rubber vulcanisates or for purposes of quality control in production, and are seldom, if ever, used to assist in the design of components.

In measuring the quality of rubber vulcanisates the tests may be used for a variety of purposes: assessing the state of cure, following the effects of changes in composition or the effects of changes in processing conditions of a known compound.

When used as production-control tests the performance of the compounds in tension is already known and the results provide a check that the correct quality and quantity of materials have been used and that the processes of production have been followed satisfactorily. Control charts [5] are frequently employed in such cases.

Type of test piece

Of the testing problems which have concerned the rubber industry the form of the tensile test piece,[6] the methods of preparation and the method of clamping the test piece in the test machine have received continuous study over the last 50 years.

In 1909 Memmler and Schob [7] were the first to describe systematic work on the shape and dimensions of the dumb-bell test piece. Many countries developed their own particular dimensions, and it was in 1950 that the dumb-bell test piece of the dimensions given in Fig. 9.1 was adopted internationally. This test piece was compared with 7 others [8] and was chosen because it gave more uniform results.[9] The test piece is the same as type C in ASTM D412–51T and as type D in BS903 Part A2: 1956. The width of the narrow portion is closely specified, and in view of the difficulty of working to close tolerances of $\pm$0·001 in. with different compounds, the design of the cutting die is important.[6] American practice [10]

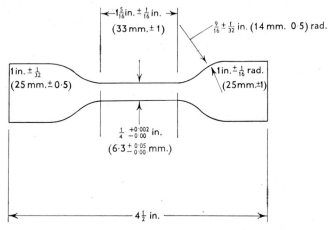

Fig. 9.1. Dimensions of I.S.O. tensile strength test-piece.

suggests that the die design given in Fig. 9.2 gives better control of the spacing of the cutting edges. Sled-type grips, eccentric rollers, toggles and self-tightening wedges are all employed, but gum compounds, in particular, sometimes cause difficulty by breaking in the grips. A recent design of grip, it is claimed,[11] does not suffer from this defect.

Ring test pieces were used by early workers, such as Stevart [12] and Breuil,[13] and the development of the Schopper testing machine in 1908 popularised this test piece, which is widely used on the Continent and in Britain. Rings can be prepared by moulding, stamping out with a die or by cutting a tube. Rotary knife cutters were developed in order to obtain a truly rectangular cross-section, and a simplified method employing razor blades [14] gives greater accuracy, enabling the tolerance of 0·2 mm. on the width specified in BS903 to be met.

The Schob attachment [15] to the Schopper machine was one of the most useful advances in technique, as it meant the stress–strain curve for ring test pieces could be recorded autographically. In the writer's opinion this advance was the main reason for the wide use of ring test pieces, in spite of the fact that they gave lower tensile strength values than dumb-bells (values up to 20% lower have been quoted [2]). In 1931 Albertoni [16] described an autographic device for dumb-bell test pieces, and an optical system for following the extension of dumb-bells was patented by Callenders Cables [17] in 1945. A simpler device, which can be used for dumb-bell test pieces in conjunction with the Schob attachment, has been patented [18] and manu-

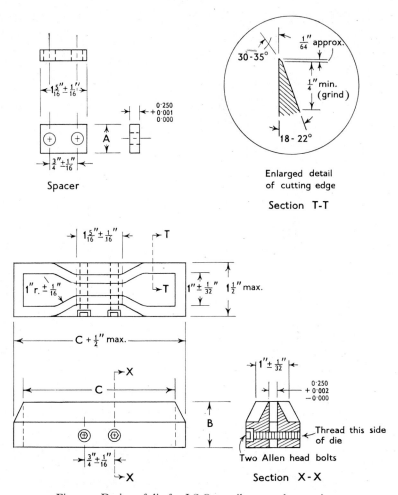

Fig. 9.2. Design of die for I.S.O. tensile strength test-piece.

factured.[19] This device, and the Schob attachment, is illustrated in Fig. 9.3.

The extensometer consists of a pen carriage, chart drum, two levers, cams and followers with telescopic arms to which are attached light spring clips for attaching to the test piece at the gauge marks. The mechanism is simple, robust and purely mechanical. The angular movements of the cam followers are directly proportional to the linear movements of the

gauge marks, and the difference in the movements is used to give a measure
of the extension. A cord system is employed for the transference of the

Fig. 9.3. I.C.I. stress–strain recorder.

difference in the movements of the cam followers to the recording attachment, as a result of which the chart drum is revolved, giving a horizontal
line. The load is registered by employing the normal parts of the Schob
attachment.

Calibration

As tensile testing equipment is normally in regular use, the necessity to calibrate the machines has in the past been too often ignored. Dead-load calibration was a cumbersome technique that appealed to no one and did not correspond to actual testing conditions, where the load is increased progressively and continuously. The use of suitable springs [20] having a spring constant comparable with the stiffness of rubber compounds overcomes these objections, and this method is recommended in BS903 Part A2: 1956. Where machines are in regular use it has been found useful to calibrate the equipment once each month.

New equipment

Most of the equipment used for tensile testing employs a pendulum for applying the load. Such equipment has the defect that inertia effects are always present, and this is an additional reason for frequent calibration. Machines have been developed recently [21, 22] which replace the pendulum by strain gauges and electronic circuits to measure and record the load. The Research Association of British Rubber Manufacturers have developed this type of equipment and have extensive experience comparing it with the older conventional equipment. Electrical systems for following strains are also being developed.

The strain test, in which the elongation at some fixed stress is measured, was developed by the National Bureau of Standards [23, 24] for studying the state of cure of rubber compounds. A simplified model operating on the same principles was recommended by the BRPRA [25] for

Fig. 9.4. BRPRA strain test.

work on technically classified natural rubber, and is illustrated in Fig. 9.4. The test piece is 6 in. long and $\frac{1}{4}$ in. wide and is held very simply in the machine.   Sixty seconds after the chosen load is applied the extension is measured.

Another method of studying the state of cure of rubber compounds has been developed in Germany.[253] The progress of cure, and hence the optimum cure time, is assessed by measuring the dynamic properties of a rubber while it is being cured.   Original work was done on the Roelig machine, and later a " Vulkameter " was built specially for this purpose. A constant force is applied cyclically to a pair of test pieces held between oil-heated platens.   The corresponding displacements are recorded against

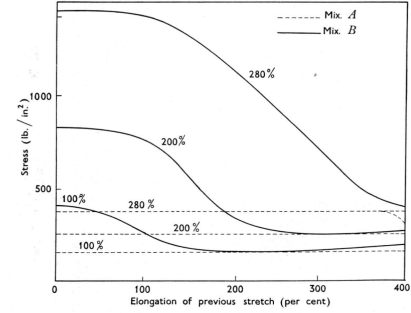

Fig. 9.5.   Effect of pre-stressing.

time on a moving chart;   the displacement is large when the rubber is uncured, and decreases up to the optimum cure for " modulus ".   The advantages claimed for the method are that it uses small amounts of stock, can be operated by unskilled personnel and gives a continuous picture of the cure of the stock, completely replacing the separate range of cures with tensile stress–strain tests on each.   A simplified version of the apparatus has been developed and described by the Research Association of British Rubber Manufacturers.[254,255]

Effect of pre-stressing

Tension tests are often criticised because they are little guide to product performance, but Juve [6] considers that " the enormous background of data on the stress strain properties of various compositions and its value in rubber technology cannot be minimised. The reported poor correlation with service may be a hasty conclusion resulting from the sparseness of adequate data, particularly on service performance." In support of this view it is well known that the stress–strain curve determined during the first extension is unique and will not be repeated during subsequent extensions. Pre-stretching results in a softening of the rubber, and Mullins [26] found

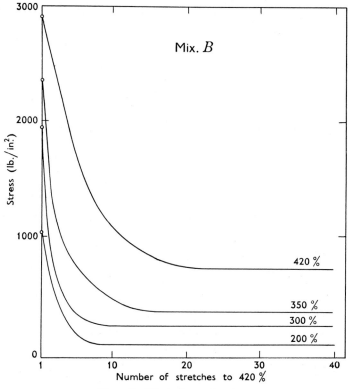

Fig. 9.6. Effect of pre-stressing.

that the greater the stiffening effect of the filler used in the compound, the greater the degree of softening. This softening is apparent only at elongations below that reached in pre-stretching, and beyond this point the stress–strain curve is practically identical with that of the original un-stressed material. These effects are illustrated in Figs. 9.5 and 9.6.

It has been argued that the correlation with service performance would be improved if test pieces for tension tests were mechanically conditioned, but an investigation carried out on mechanical conditioning indicated that there was no greater discrimination in tests carried out after various mechanical conditioning treatments than in tests carried out without previous conditioning.

In an attempt to resolve various points the United Kingdom delegation to Committee ISO/TC/45 undertook in 1951 a programme of work in six different laboratories to determine

(1) The effect of pre-stressing on tension strength and breaking elongation.

(2) The number of pre-stresses necessary to produce complete structure breakdown.

(3) The dependence of the number of pre-stresses required to cause structure breakdown on the pre-stress elongation.

(4) Whether uniformity of results for modulus measurement is affected by pre-stressing.

The conclusions of this work can be summarised as follows:

Tensile Strength. Table 9.1. When a specimen is pre-stressed to an elongation practically equal to the ultimate it will exhibit lower tensile

TABLE 9.1

EFFECT OF PRE-STRESSING ON TENSILE STRENGTH (kg./cm.^{2})

Number of pre-stresses	Pre-stress elongation as % of ultimate						
	Die B					Die C *	
	0	20	40	60	80	0	Approx. 100
0	288	—	—	—	—	282	—
1	—	298	298	304	296	—	255
2	—	302	304	283	286	—	—
3	—	295	298	298	291	—	—
5	—	304	298	294	285	—	—
7	—	298	286	295	288	—	—
10	—	288	284	292	280	—	—

* A suitable dumb-bell for this type of work has been described by R. G. Newton.[242]

strength than if it has not been pre-stressed. For lower pre-stress elongations, even when repeated up to 10 times, it appears that, for all practical purposes, the tensile strength is not affected.

Percentage elongation at break. Table 9.2. Elongation at break increases with increases in pre-stress elongation. The number of pre-stresses after the first do not greatly affect the results.

Modulus. Pre-stressing elongations between 20 and approximately 100% of ultimate cause some loss of modulus irrespective of the elongation at which the modulus is measured. The effect is greater, however, when the pre-stress elongation equals or exceeds the elongation at which modulus is measured.

For any given pre-stress elongation, modulus falls with successive pre-

TABLE 9.2

EFFECT OF PRE-STRESSING ON PERCENTAGE ELONGATION AT BREAK

Number of pre-stresses	Pre-stress elongation as % of ultimate						
	Die B					Die C	
	0	20	40	60	80	0	Approx. 100
0	572	—	—	—	—	628	—
1	—	595	614	629	664	—	719
2	—	595	602	625	657	—	—
3	—	588	605	645	664	—	—
5	—	603	615	632	672	—	—
7	—	594	605	644	672	—	—
10	—	572	621	636	688	—	—

stresses, and would continue to do so for further pre-stresses beyond the number given in the present experiment.

Uniformity of results. The coefficient of variation is not reduced by pre-stressing.

As a result of this work it was decided not to standardise a method of conditioning until delegations had collected more precise information on the utility of the mechanical conditioning.

Study of test conditions

The effects of test-piece shape and dimensions, pre-stressing of the test piece, test temperature and speed of extension all have an important bearing on the result obtained. For routine tests each test variable is rigidly specified, and the fact that in the standard test it is essential to ensure that there are no variations in the conditions often obscures the fact that it is only when the conditions are deliberately varied that differences in behaviour of polymers become apparent. If the problem concerns the characterisation of a new polymer it is often more informative to study the polymer under a variety of conditions, e.g. temperatures, than to build up a mass of data obtained under standard conditions.

Various authors [27–32] have published data on the variation of tensile strength and elongation over a wide range of test temperatures for both gum- and tread-type vulcanisates of natural and synthetic rubbers. In Fig. 9.7 it will be seen [31] that the tensile strength increases and elongation at break decreases with a decrease in temperature. The time of exposure to the temperature of test is important, and when studying times of conditioning at $-40°$ C before testing at $-40°$ C it was found [3] that neoprene GN, Perbunan, Thiokol FA and Vulcaprene A had a definite yield stress on stretching and exhibited cold drawing.

The above studies give information on the broad changes that take place in polymers when the environment is changed and show that in the temperature region $20°-23°$ C the tensile properties of some polymers are more

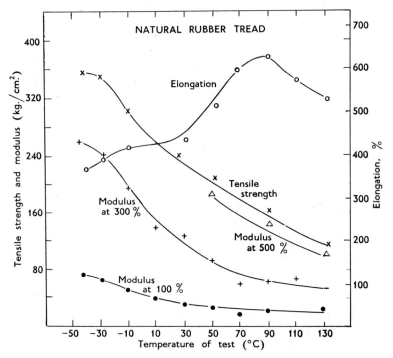

Fig. 9.7. Effect of temperature on physical properties.

susceptible to temperature changes than others. Ideally the test should be carried out under controlled temperature, but this is not always possible. Correction values have been published [33,34] which illustrate how stress–strain results of production lots of synthetic rubbers (GR-S, GR-I, GR-M) prepared for the test-specification compounds can be corrected to a constant test temperature. The warning is given that these corrections do not necessarily apply to other compounds.

In BS903 Part A2: 1956 the standard rate of jaw separation is 20 $\pm$ 1 in./min., and this speed is accepted internationally. Roth and Holt [35] studied the effect of speed on tensile tests and found, with rates of elongation up to 100%/sec., only small changes in stress values, resulting in slightly greater stiffness in the early part of the stress–strain curves, but the effect on the ultimate tensile and elongation varied with the type of compound used. Casual comments that tensile strength increases and elongation at break decreases as the speed of stretching is increased are therefore suspect until more specific information is obtained. The above statements are probably correct at very high rates of stretching [36] (above 10,000%/sec.), but the effect of small variations in the rate of jaw separations in the region of 20 in./min. is probably negligible for most commercial compounds.

Compression and shear tests

In engineering applications rubber is used in compression or shear and seldom in tension. Published data on compression and shear are sparse, but useful information is given in *Rubber in Engineering* [2] and in the Users' Memoranda.[37]

For simple shear deformation over small distortions the stress–strain curve is much more linear than is the case with either extension or com-

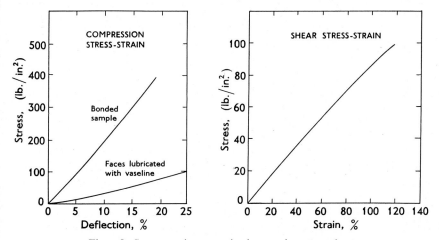

Fig. 9.8. Stress–strain curves in shear and compression.

pression. Shear modulus is not as sensitive to change in test-piece dimensions and other test conditions as compression modulus. In compression different results are obtained, depending on whether the faces of the test piece are tightly gripped or lubricated, and in an attempt to standardise test conditions ASTM D575–46 recommends the use of a standard test piece with sand-paper to prevent face slippage. Fig. 9.8 shows the effect of these variations on compression modulus [38] along with a typical stress–strain curve in shear.[39]

" Set " and " creep " tests

The evaluation of " set " in a rubber compound is usually carried out by applying a specified elongation for a standard time and measuring the recovery after a given period. Although the method is widely practised and is well established, the results obtained are often inaccurate and of limited value.

Compression set is measured either by imposing a fixed stress or strain for a given time and measuring the residual strain on removal of the load and expressing the residual strain as a percentage of the original height. The normal test is carried out at $70°$ C. This test is widely used, and there is a need to have a detailed method accepted internationally. Test-piece dimensions common to ASTM D395–55 and BS903 Part A6: 1957 are illustrated in Fig. 9.9, and work was recently carried out to investigate the following features of the test: the method of gripping the test piece, the

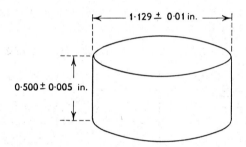

Fig. 9.9. Dimensions of compression set test-piece.

effect of lubrication, the shape factor of the test piece, the method of measuring the thickness, the effect of temperature variations and the methods of allowing the test piece to recover when the stress is removed. Interlaboratory comparisons showed unfortunately that the errors of test were extremely high, and it was difficult, due to the high errors, to decide whether the differences noted were significant.

After the 1957 meeting of ISO/TC/45 further inter-laboratory comparisons were carried out and at the New York meeting of ISO/TC/45 in 1959 the following points were agreed:

(1) Size of test piece. The meeting agreed that two sizes of test piece should be adopted of the following sizes and tolerances:

(a) Large. 13·0 ± 0·5 mm. thickness, 29·0 ± 0·5 mm. diameter.

(b) Small. 6·0 ± 0·2 mm. thickness, 13 ± 0·5 mm. diameter.

(2) A uniform degree of compression of 25% was accepted for all rubbers of hardness between 30 and 94 International Rubber Hardness Degrees.

(3) The use of a lubricant on the clamping surfaces should be left optional, but where a lubricant was used it should be a silicone fluid.

(4) The following times and temperatures of test were adopted:

22 ± 2 hours at 70° C;
22 ± 2 hours at 100° C;
3 days at 20° C.

Fig. 9.10. I.C.I. shear creep test apparatus.

(5) The tolerances on the spacers were important, and the spacer heights for the large and small test pieces would be 9·75 ± 0·01 mm. and 4·5 ± 0·01 mm. respectively.

(6) Delegates were unanimous that recovery should be allowed to take place at room temperature rather than at the test temperature.

During the Second World War the increased use of rubber (natural and synthetic) in gaskets and engineering applications necessitated the development of tests for studying the creep of rubbers in shear. Systematic data have been published,[2,3,37,39] and a suitable apparatus [3] using the double-sandwich test piece is illustrated in Fig. 9.10. Normally 10% nominal compression is applied to the test piece and shear loads in the range 20–80 lb. applied. The shear deformation can be followed continuously on the dial micrometer.

The importance of studying creep phenomena over sufficiently long periods has been stressed,[37] and data on SBR and Perbunan show greater rates of creep than natural rubber in the early stages, but this order is reversed with time. Reference should also be made to a series of papers [40–42] from the U.S. Navy Yard, where several specialised jigs for studying creep in extension and compression are described, and it is claimed that some of these tests correlate with certain service applications.

A phenomenon complementary to " creep " is a decrease of stress due to internal relaxation under strain, e.g. loss of interference in oil seals. The term " stress decay " has been used.[2] In the case of oil seals semi-service tests are often employed, since the problem of creep under constant deformation is complicated by the amount of swelling, which affects the loss of interference. A simple test [37] which gave informative results consisted of fitting rings into circumferential grooves on a mandrel with the rubber projecting slightly and forcing a metal collar over the rubber rings to compress them. The overall diameters of the rings was measured periodically, within 10 minutes of removing the collar.

Stress-relaxation methods have also been developed by Tobolsky et al.,[43] and other designs of apparatus [44–47] all follow basically the same principle as the original. A simple design of apparatus is shown in Fig. 9.11. The above workers have all used the method for obtaining results which are used to assess the ageing of rubber compounds. This is a complex chemical field in which there are several difficulties associated with the interpretation of results.[47] The writer [48] has said: " Stress relaxation techniques are undoubtedly useful research tools which may yet play an important role in establishing both the nature and the site of the type of bond involved in oxidative scission. The method should not be used in a routine manner to compare results from widely different compounded rubbers until the complex chemical reactions involved are understood more exactly."

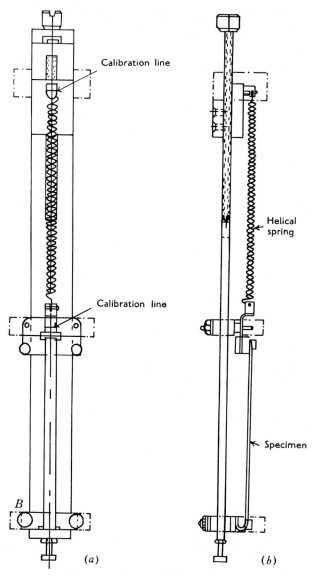

Calibration line

Calibration line

Helical spring

Specimen

(a)   (b)

Fig. 9.11. Stress-relaxation apparatus.

Tear testing

Hand tearing tests were probably among the earliest crude tests to be carried out on vulcanised rubber.   Certain technologists feel instinctively that a hand tear test gives them more information than a test carried out on a machine, whereas it would be truer to say that the hand test gives different information. This is because the forces involved in tearing rubber are very susceptible to the shape and dimensions of the test piece, the direction in which the separating forces are applied, the temperature of test, the speed of loading, the nature of the test material (isotropic or aniso-tropic) and the type of compound being studied. Many methods of test have been suggested, and a summary of the early history of tear testing is available.[49] Most of the published methods fit into the Patrikeev and Melnikov classification:[50]

> *Group I.   Direct tearing methods* (Fig. 9.12a).   In this group the con-centration of force at the point of tearing is a maximum, and therefore the force required to produce rupture is a minimum.

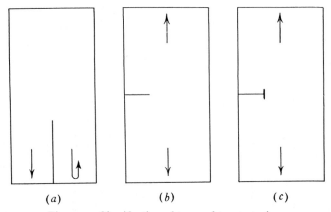

$$(a) \qquad\qquad (b) \qquad\qquad (c)$$

Fig. 9.12. Classification of types of tear test-piece.

> *Group II.   Tearing perpendicular to the direction of stretching* (Fig. 9.12b).   In this group the concentration of force at the point of tearing is intermediate and hence it is the force required to produce rupture.
> *Group III.   Tearing a test piece cut in the direction of stretching* (Fig. 9.12c).   In this group the concentration of force at the point of tearing is a minimum, and therefore the force required to produce rupture is a maximum.

The methods proposed by Zimmermann,[51] Evans,[52] Lefcaditis and Cotton [53] are Group I tests. Tests in this group are very sensitive to changes in tear direction, and if there is any departure from " straight " tearing the test almost invariably changes to a Group II test.

The methods proposed by Tuttle,[54] Winkelman,[55] Carpenter and Sargisson,[56] Poules,[57] Buist,[58] Graves [59, 60] and Nijveld [61] are all Group II tests. Tests in this group are also sensitive to changes in tear direction, and when there is pronounced departure from " straight " tearing (such a departure has been referred to as " knotty " tearing) the test changes to a

Group III test, were it will be noted the force is applied only to one side of the tear.

The method proposed by Patrikeev and Melnikov [50] is a Group III test, but little work appears to have been done by other workers with this or similar methods.

The present writer has made another important distinction between these groups of tests.[49]   Referring to Figs. 9.13 and 9.14, it will be seen that the stress–strain relationship shown in Fig. 9.13 is typical of a normal ply separation test (ASTM D413–39) and is also typical of the stress–strain relationship found with Group I tear test pieces.   The property measured is therefore tear resistance, since after the stress has reached its

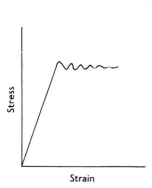

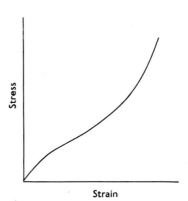

Fig. 9.13. Stress–strain curve for ply separation.

Fig. 9.14. Stress–strain curve for tear strength.

maximum the time of test is the factor governing the length of strip separated or torn.

In Fig. 9.14 the stress is increasing throughout the whole of the test in Group II tests in a similar manner to that found in tensile-strength testing. This means that the property being measured is dependent not only on the thickness but also on the width of rubber to be torn.   In Group II tests therefore it is more correct to define the property measured as tear strength and express it in appropriate units.   This view has received support [61] and is now recognised in the international method.[62]

Further reference must be made to the method of expressing results, however.   Graves [63] is able to accept the principle that the width of the test piece influences the values obtained, but feels that it is " not so important as thickness, and completely overwhelmed in importance by the influence of changes in stress gradient ".   He feels that the property should be expressed in units of stress only if the stress is distributed uniformly across the area of the test piece.   By their nature the stresses in tear specimens are not distributed uniformly throughout, but to a lesser

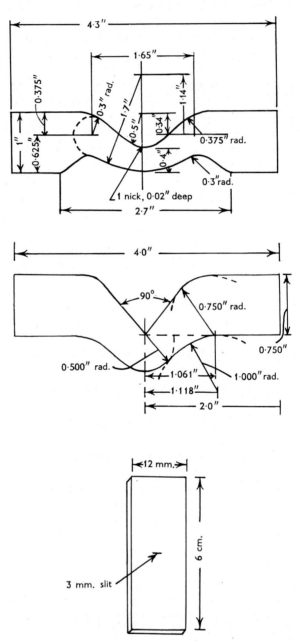

Fig. 9.15. Dimensions of crescent, angle and Delft test-piece.

extent non-uniform stressing is also present in tensile strength test pieces. It is difficult to accept the logic of the argument against expressing the results as a stress. The fact that stress gradients complicate all tear tests must be accepted, but recognition of this should not mean that other facts are ignored. These differences in view-point led to the following compromise agreement in the international discussions of Committee ISO/TC/ 45: " that a comparison between test results obtained with test pieces of different stress gradients should not be made; that the results of any one type of test piece should be expressed as the load necessary to tear a test piece of standard width and thickness ". The simpler method of expressing the results as kg./cm.^{2} or lb./in.^{2} has much to commend it.

The rubber industry generally employs Group II tear tests, and the crescent method is most widely used and has been standardised internationally.[61] Two other methods, the angle method [64] and the Delft method,[61, 65] are of interest. The details of the three test pieces are shown in Fig. 9.15.

With the crescent test piece a nick 0·020 in. in depth is made in the centre of the crescent and the force required to tear across the unnicked

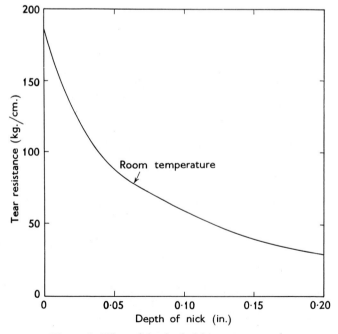

Fig. 9.16. Effect of depth of nick on tear strength.

portion measured. The tear strength of vulcanised rubbers is very susceptible to the depth of the initial nick,[49] see Fig. 9.16 and in the ISO/TC/

45 method and BS903 Part A3: 1956 tolerances of $\pm 0 \cdot 003$ in. are specified on the 0·020-in. depth of nick. The I.C.I. Tear Cutter [66, 67] was designed specifically to control the depth of cut within these limits. The instrument is easy to operate, and a measure of its accuracy is that a nicked test piece can be replaced in the holder and when renicked only one slit is obtained.

Newman and Taylor [68] found that, when test pieces are died out from a flat slab, the cut edges are not normal to the surfaces, and their work emphasises that it is essential to use a good die that will give a good vertical cut as shown in Fig. 5 of their paper. The writer recommends that the Newman–Taylor method of checking the state of the die should be employed to check tensile, crescent tear, angle tear and Delft tear dies, and if the profile departs from linearity by more than x thous (e.g. say 6 thous) the die should not be used.

The angle test piece has the advantage that after dieing out the test piece no additional operation, such as inserting a nick, is required, and a similar advantage is claimed in the case of the Delft test piece in the sense that the initial cut is inserted during the dieing-out operation. The angle test is slightly more reproducible than either the crescent or the Delft method.[58, 65, 69]

The angle method gives different tear values from those obtained with either the crescent or Delft methods; the latter methods, using the dimensions of test piece in Fig. 9.15, give the same values when expressed as kg./cm.^{2} or lb./in.^{2}. The reasons for the differences between the angle test and the other two are interesting, and have been the cause of some useful controversy.[49, 58, 63, 70, 71] A review and discussion of the more important points follows:

Busse [72] demonstrated the relation between tear and tensile tests, and his view was that tear, by the nature of the test, was analogous to a tensile test under high rates of strain, since the strain is concentrated on the rubber just behind the cut. One of the main differences between tensile and tear tests therefore is the higher stress gradients introduced in tear test pieces. It will be seen in Fig. 9.17 that the unnicked crescent has greater stress gradients than the tensile dumb-bell; the introduction of a nick in the crescent further increases the stress gradients; the form of the angle test piece is such that the stress gradients are higher than with the nicked crescent. In other words, each of these test pieces, in the order discussed above, is a step farther away from the conditions of " uniform stressing " that are desirable in a tensile test. This has been a deliberate development, since it was realised that in the measurement of tear strength the load recorded is a composite one made up of stresses at the apex of the tear and of other stresses not involved in the process of tearing. Naturally it was thought desirable to increase the former stresses and diminish the latter, but the ideal balance is difficult to attain. If the stresses at the apex are concentrated to too great an extent there will be a danger that most compounds will tear at apparently low loads, leading to poor discrimination between different compounds, particularly for non-black-filled rubbers.

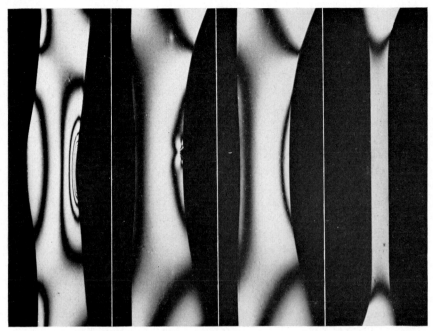

Fig. 9.17. Stress gradients in angle, nicked crescent, unnicked crescent tear pieces and tensile test-piece.

The results given in Table 9.3 have been published [58] where tensile-strength, unnicked-crescent, crescent-tear and angle-tear measurements were compared.

TABLE 9.3

Compound	1	2	3	4	5	6	7	8	9	10	11	12	13	14	15
Tensile strength, kg./cm.^{2}	253	244	184	157	191	255	264	239	169	171	150	135	118	84	79
Unnicked crescent tear, kg./cm.^{2}	218	220	180	149	136	223	219	214	127	132	117	109	94	76	68
Crescent tear, 0·02 in. nick kg./cm.^{2}	160	111	72	100	50	172	153	162	74	77	72	70	63	54	44
Angle tear, kg./cm.^{2}	110	62	35	65	30	107	100	101	37	39	39	41	36	36	37

Compound 1 = natural rubber tread.
Compound 2 = Neoprene GN tread.
Compound 3 = SBR tread.
Compound 4 = Butyl tread.
Compounds 5, 6, 7, 8 = increasing loadings of Kosmobile HM in natural rubber.
Compounds 9, 10, 11, 12, 13, 14, 15 = increasing loadings of treated calcium carbonate in natural rubber.

In discussing the above results the author drew attention to the fact that the angle-tear results were always lower than the crescent-tear results.

There was a wide difference in tensile strength, unnicked crescent tear and crescent tear of the treated calcium carbonate compounds, and yet the angle tests gave a more or less constant value.   It has also been reported [8] that data obtained on the effect of cure on the crescent tear and angle tear of natural rubber compounds showed that the crescent tear passed through a maximum, whereas the angle tear was practically constant for under, optimum and over cures.

To sum up, therefore, it can be said that although the angle test piece is excellent in principle, in practice the stress concentration appears to be too high and too many compounds are assessed as having low tear strength.

In the above papers there is a considerable discussion of tear initiation and tear propagation, terms which I have avoided using in the present summary.   The point at issue has been that the forces required to start a tear differ in value from those required to continue tearing.   In the different test pieces (crescent and angle) the balance of these forces is different and the arguments [58] suggesting that the angle test favoured initiation at the expense of propagation and the counter arguments [6] are perhaps of limited interest now that more refined methods of measuring the forces involved in initiation and propagation are being developed.[73, 74]

An interesting method of assessing tear initiation in the direction of strain [74] uses the " trousers " test piece pulled flat between clamps to given fixed strain or elongation, and the tearing load applied at right angles by two thin metal strips wrapped around the legs of the test piece as near the end of the slit as possible.   This is observed by a hand-lens and the stress required to initiate tear recorded.   For natural rubber reinforced with either channel or furnace blacks, two distinct types of tear were found; one occurred below about 80% strain, and corresponded to a high tear strength being associated with a special orientated structure giving the " stick–slip " behaviour;   the other above about 140% characterised by lower tear strengths and giving the knotty type of tear.   This work, when carried further with a comprehensive set of compounds, may well resolve some of the difficulties surrounding tear testing.   For example, it was suggested [49] that the effect of an increase in the speed of testing was the same as a decrease in testing temperature.   Is this so for both initiation and propagation forces?

Mention should also be made of other new tear tests, which are either attempts to study the tearing of thick slabs of rubber [75, 76] or wire-cutting tests [77] or stitch-tear tests [78] for shoe-soleing compounds.   Truly comparative and comprehensive data obtained with these methods have still to be published, and therefore it is difficult to assess their value.

Hardness testing

Hardness tests are probably the methods most frequently employed by the rubber industry, and due to their apparent simplicity there is a real danger that frequent use encourages rather casual disregard of the many simple but nevertheless stringent precautions that must be observed. Hardness methods have been used with many varied materials, e.g. minerals, metals, rubbers, wood, etc., and the term hardness is a vague one, the range of expressions such as " scratch hardness ", " indentation hardness ", " cutting hardness ", " abrasion hardness ", etc., illustrating that different concepts of hardness exist.

The difficulties associated with defining hardness have been summarised;[79] briefly Mohs [80] did not define hardness when he developed his scale of hardness ranging from talc to diamond with "the state of liquidity " as the zero of the scale, whereas Osmond [81] defined hardness as " that property possessed by solid bodies, in a variable degree, to defend the integrity of their form against causes of permanent deformation, and the integrity of their substance against causes of division ". The latter definition includes the idea of wear and is more applicable to metals than to rubbers, since, with the latter, permanent changes or disintegration are not involved. In rubber testing the elastic structure is not damaged and the original shape is restored, since the deforming forces are lower than the recovery forces which can be exerted by the elastic structure. In this respect rubber test methods differ from those applied to metals, bitumens, waxes, greases and ceramics, where measurements are made of the permanent deformation. As rubber hardness is a measurement of almost completely elastic deformation, it could be expected that attempts would be made to relate hardness measurements to elastic modulus.

Most rubber hardness tests measure the depth of penetration of an indentor under either a fixed weight or a spring load, and when rubber is assumed to be an ideal elastic isotropic medium the indentation obtained at small deformations depends on the elastic modulus, the load applied and the dimensions of the indentor. Scott [82] showed that with a spherical ball indentor the relation between the indenting force D and the Young's modulus E was given by

$$D = ER^2 f (H/R)$$

where R = radius of ball, H = the depth of indentation and $f(H/R)$ is a function of the " shape factor " H/R, which is characteristic of the shape of the indentation. Experimentally it was found that for natural rubber $D = KER^{0.65} H^{1.35}$ provided H is less than about $1.6R$, the value of the constant K being 2.1 if c.g.s. units were used.

The important factors concerned when using an indentation method have been discussed and listed [79] as follows:

(1) Type and form of indentor.
(2) Amount of friction between indentor and material being tested.
(3) Constant initial load or constant deflection.
(4) Duration of load.
(5) Stress–strain characteristics of material being tested.

The three main types of indentor are: (a) sphere; (b) a cone fitted with a sharp point; and (c) a frustum of a cone. Each of these types of indentor produces different stress–strain distributions in the rubber being deformed. It has been suggested [83] that by using a cone of large angle, e.g. 120°, puncturing of the surface can be avoided and one advantage of the cone over other forms of indentor is that the shape of the indentation is independent of its depth, so that it is much easier to deduce mathematically the relation between indenting force, dimensions of the indentor, modulus of the rubber and depth of indentation. Scott [84] has calculated that the penetration of a perfectly elastic material at a constant force would be inversely proportional to the square root of the modulus. Further, apparently with large cone angles in the region of 136° the effects of friction can be neglected.[85] Conical indentors are not widely employed, however, and the majority of national specifications and the International Rubber Hardness Method [86] specify the use of spherical indentors.

Experiments have shown that lubricating the rubber surfaces has little effect if the rubber is 1 cm. thick, but when the rubber thickness is 1 mm. or less lubrication of the bottom surface eases lateral displacement of the rubber immediately under the indentor, and therefore the indentation is increased. The thickness of the rubber test piece affects the hardness measurement, and this is why a definite thickness is specified in standard tests. It has been found [79] that the shallower the indentation the less effect the variations in the thickness of the rubber test piece have on the hardness measurement. The effect is also less, the smaller the diameter of the indentor. With the conventional tests [92] the dependence of indentation on thickness is illustrated in Fig. 9.18. The reasons [87] for this dependence are clear if the applied force is considered to be divided into two components, one for the local deformation in the region of the indentor and the second a compressive force which compresses the material between the indentor and the bottom plate of the test piece. Using an instrument [88] which measures the force required to produce a given indentation, it has been found [79] that with small indentations it is possible to obtain readings independent of thickness at much lower thicknesses than with the conventional tests. The so-called micro-hardness tests, BS903: Part A20: 1959, based on the work of Oberto,[89] use the other principle of reducing

the ball diameter to achieve the same effect.   These developments mean
that a wider range of rubber products can be tested for hardness and results
can be obtained in interpretable terms.

With all the conventional tests the duration of the load is important,
since the rubber under the indentor will flow with time, and increased

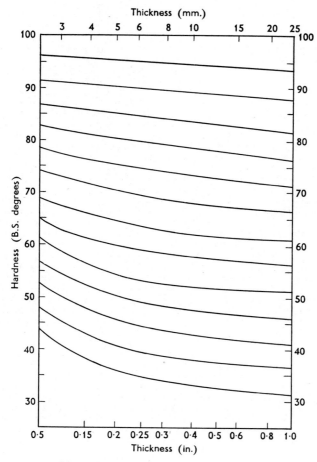

Fig. 9.18. Effect of thickness on hardness.

indentations will result.   Naturally the amount of flow which occurs will
depend on the load, type of indentor and the other factors affecting the
stresses applied to the rubber.   The fact that flow or creep occurs to
varying degrees under the conditions of test applicable to the different
methods makes it impossible to obtain exact correlations between the
different methods.   The one exception to this lack of correlation is the
new International Rubber Hardness Method,[86] based on the British

Fig. 9.19. B.S. hardness test.

Standard Method,[90-92] in which the scale of measurement has been mathematically adjusted and chosen to correspond to the popular Shore scale, which has a value of 0 for an infinitely soft material and 100 for an infinitely hard one.

The wide range of instruments used by the rubber industry can be listed as follows:

Portable instruments: Shore A durometer,[93] Rex hardness gauge,[94] RABRM hardness meter,[95] Wallace pocket meter.[96]

Constant dead load instruments: Pusey and Jones plastometer,[97]

ASTM hardness tester,[99] DVM hardness tester,[99] British Standard hardness tester.[92]

Constant indentation instruments: I.C.I. hardness tester.[88]

Portable instruments have popular appeal, and until recent years the Shore durometer was probably the most widely used. It was found that it was difficult to obtain good agreement between durometers either in the same or different laboratories,[37] and the instrument requires frequent calibration [37, 96, 100] and inspection of the indentor for wear. Portable instruments are now described in a separate British Standard (BS2719–1956) covering the Shore A durometer and the Wallace Pocket Meter. This section was removed from BS903 in recognition of the fact that these methods are not sufficiently accurate for reference work but are still of practical value in the factory. The Rex gauge appears to be widely used in America. The above three instruments employ the same hardness scale.

The constant-dead-load instruments in general give accurate results, but formerly the scale of readings employed a softness scale rather than a hardness scale (larger number, softer rubber). A new method of expressing results with the British Standard Hardness Tester was developed [90, 91] whereby the scale was reversed, and by relating the indentations to Young's modulus and by using a Probit curve it was possible to make the scale correspond to the Shore scale over the range of hardnesses of interest. This method has been adopted both nationally [92] and internationally.[86] The type of instrument designed to operate under the internationally agreed conditions is illustrated in Fig. 9.19, and the main conditions of test are summarised in Table 9.4.

TABLE 9.4

Diameters of Indentors, mm.:		Loads		
		Minor, g.	*Major,* g.	*Total,* g.
Either Ball	2·38 ± 0·01			
Foot	20 approx.	30 ± 1	534 ± 1	564 ± 2
Hole	5 approx.			
Or Ball	2·50 ± 0·01			
Foot	20 approx.	30 ± 1	550 ± 1	580 ± 2
Hole	5 approx.			

Thickness of standard test piece	Between 8 and 10 mm.
Distance of indentor ball from edge of test piece	9 mm. for 8-mm.-thick test piece
	10 mm. for 10-mm.-thick test piece
Dimensions of foot	20 mm. diameter with central hole
	5 mm. diameter
Pressure of foot on test piece	200–300 g./cm.²

A most useful review of the use, adjustment and calibration of most of the commonly used hardness testers published by Soden [96] and another

B B

paper,[101] which summarises the work done by Committee ISO/TC/45 on improving the accuracy of hardness testing deserve close attention by all concerned with this subject.

Resilience tests

The coefficient of restitution is defined as a number expressing the ratio of the velocity with which two bodies separate after a collision to the velocity with which the same two bodies approach each other before a collision. The term coefficient of restitution is analogous to the term resilience, which is widely used in the rubber industry. Rubber compounds have a high resilience, above 90% with certain pure gum compounds, and in Table 9.5 the resilience values for different materials when dropped on a steel plate are given for comparison.

TABLE 9.5

	Resilience, %
Glass	95
Steel	90
Natural rubber	90
Ivory	80
Wood	60

Resilience, defined as the percentage ratio of energy output to the energy input, is frequently measured on a pendulum-type machine, in which a ball indentor is dropped on to the test piece and the energy of fall and rebound noted. Various instruments [102-112] have been proposed for measuring resilience, and the following three pendulum-type instruments are probably the most widely known: Dunlop Pendulum,[103] Dunlop tripsometer,[2,113] Lupke Pendulum.[104] The results obtained with these three instruments have been published,[2] and in general the correlation is good, provided attention is paid to several factors which can be sources of error.[109] Factors which have been listed [2,6,109] are: size of indentor, pre-working, magnitude of stress, friction losses between striker and the surface of the test piece, air drag, " shuffle " or movement of the test piece in the holder, and vibration.

Falling-ball impact tests, where the ball is either dropped on to a horizontal test piece [105,110] and the rebound height measured or dropped on to an inclined test piece [111] and the horizontal component of the rebound measured, have also been used. The writer's experience supports the view that it is difficult to attain the same degree of accuracy with falling-ball methods as with pendulum methods.

Due to the fact that rubbers never have 100% resilience, they heat up when subjected to a single impact or to continuous high-speed deformations, and if resilience is expressed as a percentage, then hysteresis is the difference between 100 and the resilience. It has been found with filled rubbers that resilience increases with repeated stressing [2,103] reaching a maximum value at about six impacts, and synthetic rubbers have a tendency to reach their maximum after a smaller number of impacts than does natural rubber. For this reason test pieces are preconditioned in the standard methods quoted in national specifications.[113,114] With these methods it is also important to maintain adequate temperature control, because resilience is particularly sensitive to temperature. Resilience–temperature curves for natural rubber, SBR and Butyl rubber carbon-

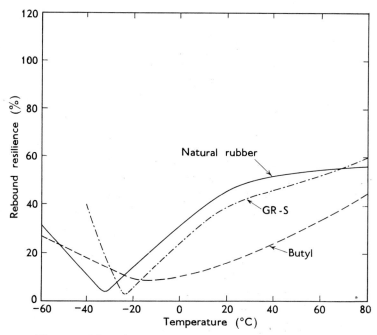

Fig. 9.20. Effect of temperature on resistance of various rubbers.

black compounds are shown in Fig. 9.20. As the temperature is reduced the rubber becomes stiffer and less resilient in each case until a leathery stage is reached, when the resilience passes through a minimum value and begins to increase as the temperature is lowered further. It will be seen that these three rubbers have different resilience–temperature characteristics, and any assessment of their possible performance in a selected application should be made at a temperature near that of service.

Although the above tests give useful results, it has been pointed out [115] that their value is limited by the fact that resilience is a function not only of the internal friction or hysteresis but also of the dynamic modulus. For more scientific work many workers prefer to use more complicated methods to measure dynamic modulus and dynamic resilience, and reference is made to these tests in Chapter VIII (p. 517).

Low-temperature tests

During the last War intensive work was done to devise suitable test methods for studying the physical properties of polymers at low temperatures. A multitude of test methods has been used; many were simple extensions of existing rubber test methods operated at low temperatures, e.g. stress–strain tests, hardness and permanent set; others were specifically designed to investigate low-temperature behaviour, e.g. flexibility, brittleness. As data became available from all these tests it was clear that the low-temperature characteristics of a given polymer could not be classified simply by a single figure or property. Further, the position was complicated by the fact that conditioning and previous history of the sample and the method of cooling the sample influenced the results obtained.

It may be useful to summarise the general picture of what changes occur in rubber-like polymers when the temperature is lowered. When subjected to low temperatures natural and synthetic rubbers undergo a progressive change in properties which is dependent upon both time and temperature.[3,37] As the temperature decreases they steadily become harder, less flexible and less elastic, passing through a leather-like stage, finally becoming brittle and less capable of resisting shock. This general picture might suffice if the rate of change of one physical property corresponded to the rates of change of several other physical properties, but unfortunately this is not so, and therefore the mechanism of the changes involved must be studied more closely.

The three fundamental changes which take place on lowering the temperature are:

(a) stiffening due to an increase of cohesive forces brought about by restricted molecular movement at the lower temperature;[116]

(b) crystallisation, which is accompanied by a volume change and which requires time for its development, depending on the polymer structure and on the temperature of storage;

(c) a second-order transition,[37,117] evidenced by a rapid change in physical properties within a narrow temperature range.

Since both the transition temperature and the temperature for maximum rate of development of crystallisation vary widely for different polymers, each polymer must be studied over a wide range of temperature. The results of storage tests at one temperature cannot be used to predict the behaviour at any other temperature.

Crystallisation in unstretched rubber is thought to be a slow process, and is said to be most rapid at temperatures between $-35°$ and $-15°$ C; at $-50°$ C it has been reported that no crystallisation occurs.[118] The latter statement must be accepted with some reserve, however, as at $-50°$ C the size of the crystallites formed may be so small as to make their detection difficult. Previously it has been thought that for most practical purposes crystallisation is a secondary effect, but this does not mean that the effects of rate of cooling and of the temperature range favouring crystallisation can be overlooked. At the present time little systematic work has been carried out on the effects of prolonged storage at low temperatures, but the data

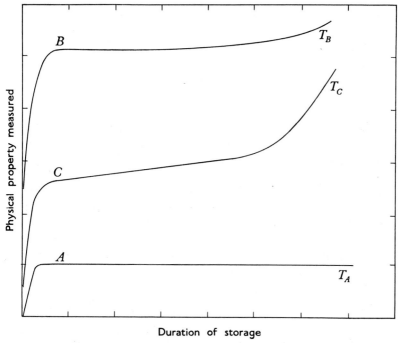

Fig. 9.21. Effect of time and temperature on crystallisation.

available [3,37,119,120,125] emphasises the importance of carrying out low-temperature tests over a prolonged period. The effects of prolonged storage at $-20°$ C and $-40°$ C on a wide range of physical properties and over a wide range of natural and synthetic rubber compounds has been reported,[3,37,121] and it is quite clear that effects of storage at one temperature cannot be used in predicting behaviour at a different temperature, since the time-dependent effects of crystallisation vary so markedly with temperature. The effects of the variation of crystallisation with both time and temperature have been summarised as follows [3] (see Fig. 9.21):

T_c is the temperature at which crystallisation is most rapid. T_a is well above and T_b well below T_c. The points, A, C and B represent the effects of temperature alone on the physical property measured, and are largely explained in terms of the increase of cohesive forces with decreasing temperature common to all polymers. In the case of T_a no crystallisation is assumed to develop, and the magnitude of the physical property remains constant $(= A)$ in time. In the case of T_b only a very slow development of crystallisation occurs, while at T_c a very marked and rapid change of physical properties can occur with time. It is obvious that short-period tests, which determine only the points A, C and B, could be quite useless in estimating behaviour in service when prolonged exposure to low temperatures is involved. For these reasons it is often necessary to employ

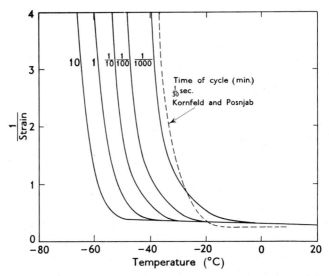

Fig. 9.22. Effect of temperature and frequency on dynamic modulus.

special tests for specific applications such as sealing gaskets,[121] but no attempt can be made to discuss these tests in the present section.

Equally it is not possible to discuss in any detail studies that have been made with the measurement of dynamic properties over a temperature and frequency range, but attention is drawn to the discussion in *Rubber in Engineering* [2] on this point, and Fig. 9.22 shows how the dynamic modulus data of Alexandrov and Lazurkin [122] compare with torsional rigidity measurements made on the I.C.I. torsional flexibility test.[37] It appears therefore a tenfold increase in frequency is equivalent in its effect on properties, to a reduction of approximately 8° C. As most rubbers are stressed dynamically in service, it is clear that if any attempt is being made to assess service performance it will be necessary to employ the same temperature and frequency ranges and periods of storage that would apply in the actual application.

The tests which will now be described have been developed as short-term tests which will give some indication of the low-temperature characteristics of rubbers, but because of the complications discussed above, they can only give the roughest guide to even simple service applications. The tests normally used by a laboratory to assess low-temperature characteristics fall into one of two categories—(a) flexibility tests, and (b) brittleness tests—and a useful review of both categories has been published.[123]

Flexibility tests

The tests in this category are concerned with determining the rate at which hardening or stiffening develops as the temperature is lowered. Conventional modulus or hardness tests can be determined over a temperature range [31] to obtain data, as was shown earlier in Fig. 9.7, and several workers [124-126] have calculated Young's modulus from beam-bending formula. More popular, however, have been tests where torsion modulus has been determined at low temperatures by measuring angular displacements when a torque is applied to one end of a strip of rubber. In the I.C.I. torsion flexibility apparatus, which is specified in BS903 Part A 13: 1960, the force required to twist the test piece through 90° is measured at each temperature and the modulus is calculated from the following formula:

$$\text{Rigidity modulus} = \frac{L}{WT^3K} \cdot \frac{180}{\pi} \cdot \frac{\text{torque}}{\theta}$$

where L is the distance between clamps, W and T the width and thickness of the test piece respectively, θ the angle of twist in degrees and K a function of $\frac{W}{T}$, which is given in Table 9.6.

TABLE 9.6

VALUES FOR CALCULATION OF RIGIDITY MODULUS

Ratio $\frac{W}{T}$:	1·5	2·0	2·5	3·0	4·0	10·0
K:	0·196	0·229	0·249	0·263	0·281	0·312

The above BS method specifies that the temperatures at which the rubber attains moduli which are 2, 5 and 10 times the room-temperature modulus should be determined.

The apparatus developed by Clash and Berg [127,128] is very similar in principle to the I.C.I. apparatus, the only essential differences being the use of a fixed torque and measuring the angle of twist.

The torsion test, most favoured in America, is the Gehman test,[129] which has been adopted as an ASTM method.[130] A rectangular strip of rubber is connected in series with a calibrated torsion wire so that when twisted through 180° the twist is distributed to a measurable extent between the wire and the test piece. As the modulus is calculated by the relation

$$\text{Modulus} = \frac{\text{Stress}}{\text{Strain}} \propto \frac{180° - \text{Twist}}{\text{Twist}}$$

the torsion-wire constant and the geometry of the test piece can be omitted, since only relative modulus values at different temperatures are used. Normally the temperatures at which the rubber attains moduli which are 2, 5, 10 and 100 times the room-temperature modulus are quoted.

Committee ISO/TC/45 decided in 1959 that the Gehman test should be adopted as the international standard.[256]

Brittleness tests

Many tests have been devised for testing the brittleness of rubbers, varying from slow hand-bend tests [37,131-135] to high-speed bend tests.[136-138] Unfortunately the results obtained are extremely variable, due to the fact that the results depend very largely on the speed of impact and degree of bending. Hand-operated instruments are only adequate with very small, thin test pieces where the energy absorbed in the deformation is a small fraction of the energy applied.

The effects of speed and degree of bend have been shown with the Kemp apparatus,[138] which has been adopted as ASTM D746–57T. By doubling the speed of the striker from 75 to 150 r.p.m. the brittle temperature was raised by 6° C, whereas changing from a right-angle bend to one of 3·8 in. radius lowered the brittle temperature by more than 20° C with a natural rubber gum stock. Such variations indicate clearly the difficulties of obtaining reproducible results between laboratories, and explain the initial reluctance of certain delegations to Committee ISO/TC/45 to adopt this method internationally. Nevertheless, the present ASTM method, where the striker's speed, edge radius and clearance are specified, appears to be as good as any other brittleness test which has been developed. Useful amendments have been made to the method in the last few years; in 1959 it was adopted by Committee ISO/TC/45 as a draft ISO Recommendation.[256]

Electrical properties

There are three electrical properties which are of interest to the rubber industry: resistivity, power factor and dielectric constant. Published values [139] for volume resistivity, power factor and dielectric constant of natural rubber, SBR, neoprene GN, Perbunan, Butyl and Vulcaprene are reproduced in Table 9.7.

TABLE 9.7

ELECTRICAL PROPERTIES OF INSULATING COMPOUNDS, NATURAL AND SYNTHETIC RUBBER

Insulating compounds	Natural rubber	SBR	Butyl rubber	Neoprene GN	Vulca-prene A	Per-bunan
Resistivity, ohm-cm.	10^{17}	10^{15}	10^{16}	10^{10}	10^{8}	10^{10}
Dielectric constant, 50 cycles, 20° C, 75% R.H.	2·8	2·85	2·6	8·0	—	13·4
Power loss, 50 cycles, 20° C, 75% R.H.	0·0096	0·0022	0·0026	0·04	—	0·454

It will be seen that the values obtained for these properties depend on the polymer being used: other technological studies [140,141] indicate that natural rubber and other polymers can be compounded so that they can be either insulators or conductors. Originally rubbers were used primarily as insulators, but in order to dissipate static electricity many applications are known where electrically conducting rubbers are used.

Electrical properties of filled rubbers are very susceptible to the previous history of the compound, and the application of external stress or the presence of internal stresses in the rubber both change the effective electrical properties. Great care has to be exercised in the preparation of test rubbers for electrical properties, and in production it is often difficult to reproduce conducting rubbers due to these factors (see BS 2050: 1953).

In the standard tests BS 903 [142] and ASTM [143] for volume resistivity the procedure is to measure the current passing under an applied D.C. potential between electrodes in intimate contact with opposite faces of a uniform sheet of material. The measuring circuit is guarded from leakage over the surface of the material. Different sizes of electrodes are employed in the two specifications. Errors due to measuring current,[143,144] type of electrode,[145,146] flexing the testpiece,[146] contact resistance [6,147] have been noted in the literature. Temperature variations are more important with polyvinyl chloride than with natural rubber, but it is increasingly obvious that more reproducible results are obtained when electrical properties are determined under conditions where both temperature and humidity are controlled.

Methods for determining dielectric constant and power factor are given in BS 903.[142] As these properties change considerably with frequency and temperature, the results of the test are valid for prediction and performance only for a narrow band of frequencies and temperatures in the vicinity of those adopted in the test. For audio-frequencies a Schering bridge with Wagner earth attachment is recommended and the Hartshorn–Ward [148] apparatus for tests at radio frequencies.

Abrasion

Abrasion resistance is not a specific property of rubber, but depends both on the method of measurement and the machine used :[149] it is pointed out in BS 903 " the abrasion resistance is commonly represented by its inverse, the abrasion loss, which, in the absence of absolute or standard methods of measurement, can be defined only as the volume of rubber abraded from a specified test-piece when subjected to abrasive wear under specified conditions ". Because of this dependence on the method of measurement and the machine used, it is essential to review the laboratory abrasion tests which have been developed, and in 1950 the writer [149] listed and classified 21 machines of interest to the rubber industry.

The four categories are:

Category A.   Use of loose abrasive.
Category B.   Tests for fabrics, proofed fabrics, thin films.
Category C.   Tests for solid rubber where the abrasion is essentially continuous.
Category D.   Tests for solid rubber where the abrasion is discontinuous and the test piece is allowed to recover between the abrasion cycles.

Discussing the important tests in turn there are a few observations worth noting.

Category B.   Abrasion tests for coated fabrics are still in the development stage, and an excellent review of this field has been provided by Dawson.[179]   The use of the Martindale wear test with coated fabrics has been described,[154] and this test method has also been used with success to evaluate flooring materials.[180]

The Schiefer test [157] has many attractive features; probably the most important being the continuous measurement of the abrasion during the test by means of a condenser " thickness gauge ".   The Martindale and the Schiefer are the most useful tests in this category.

Categories C and D.   It is apparent from Table 9.8 that a wide variety of test methods and machines have been designed.   For a detailed comparison of machines 8, 13, 9, 7, 19, 15, 16, 2 the reader is referred to Cosler's paper;[181]   Klaman [182] has compared numbers 15, 19, 13 and 9; Depew [183] has described the following machines—13, 15, 16, 7, 9, 19, 8, 1; Dawson [173] has classified different types of abrasion machines and describes numbers 18 and 16; finally, attention is drawn to the detailed work on the Goodyear, Akron, Akron/Croydon and du Pont machines carried out by the RABRM.[174,185,186,187,188]

The main distinction between categories C and D lies in the fact that in Category D the test piece is normally circular and there is a period of relaxation between successive impacts, so that the abrasion is discontinuous.   In the main the abrasion in tests in Category C is normally continuous.   Although it cannot be stated as a general rule, there is a tendency for the tests in Category D to be run at faster speeds under higher energy inputs than is the case with tests in Category C.   In Category D therefore the rate of abrasion is higher.   The tests in Category D are normally used for development work by firms making tyres.

If good correlation with service is the criterion for choosing a particular abrasion machine no one of the above methods can be considered as satisfactory for a wide range of compounds and service applications.   The choice appears to be either between having different machines for each compound and particular application or choosing a simple method where the test variables can be changed for different compounds or applications. Committee ISO/TC/45 considered this problem and decided to standardise the du Pont method as being a simple method which was widely used.[189] This is a useful step, in that users of this method can now follow an internationally agreed procedure, but it leaves many questions concerning abrasion testing unanswered.

It has been argued [190] that the general dissatisfaction with the present laboratory and service tests for abrasion is due to expecting too much of the laboratory test, which, while indicating broad differences between compounds, cannot be used to discriminate closely between similar compounds.   In the service testing of tyres it is known that the type of road surface, changes with atmospheric conditions (temperature, wetness or dryness), speed of running, acceleration and braking, alignment of wheels are some of the more important conditions which affect the life of a tyre tread.   Even this restricted list of variables emphasises that it is extremely optimistic to imagine that any laboratory abrasion test, carried out under one set of fixed conditions, can correlate with the service life, which is obtained by the integration of the wear under varied (and constantly varying) conditions.   Another complicating factor is due to the laboratory tests being carried out under too severe conditions (e.g. type of abrasive, load, speed, temperature at abrading surface) in order to employ an accelerated test.[190]   These arguments raise the question—what use are laboratory abrasion tests?   Laboratory tests are used because they are simpler to carry out, are less expensive and give a result in a shorter time than the service test.   Although such tests are often quoted in specifications, there is always the proviso that the results cannot be used to estimate the service life of the rubber product.   This is certainly true,

TABLE 9.8
TYPES OF ABRASION MACHINES

Category	Name	Mechanical features	Nature of stress	Type of material tested	Comments
A	1. Falling carborundum [150, 151]	Stream of carborundum impinging on surface	Complex	Rubbers or plastics	Simple method. Seldom used for rubber work. Used with some success to evaluate surface abrasion of plastics
	2. Sproul-Evans [152]	Rubber rotated in cylinder containing carborundum powder	Complex	Rubbers for sand-blast hose and certain types of conveyor belting	Claimed to be the only abrasion test correlating with service wear of sand-blast hose
B	3. Martindale [153, 154]	4 test pieces. Abrasive normally stationary. Test piece describes Lissajou figure during abrasion	Continuous	Textiles. Rubber or plastic coated fabrics. Thin polymer films. Packaging materials. Rubber flooring	The testing condition in methods 3 and 4, e.g. type of abradant, load on test piece, can be varied. Methods of assessing the results have not been standardised, but in many cases the normal weight-loss–wear curve gives the required information
	4. Wyzenbeek [155]	4 test pieces. Test piece stationary under tension. Abrasive held on drum which oscillates by means of cam	Continuous	Textiles. Rubber or plastic coated fabrics. Thin polymer films	,,
	5. Schiefer [156, 157]	Test piece and abradant both rotate. Movement designed to produce uniform abrasion over test-piece surface	Continuous	Felt, textiles. Rubber or plastic coated fabrics	

B	6. Du Pont Scrub [158]	Single test piece, folded, held by two oscillating clamps moving in opposite directions	Continuous	Felt, textiles. Rubber or plastic coated fabrics	The property measured is a combination of adhesion, flex-resistance and abrasion
C	7. du Pont-Graselli-Williams	Test piece stationary, abrasive disk moves in a vertical plane. Power loss controlled by Prony brake	Continuous	General rubber compounds, e.g. tyre treads, soles and heels	Machine most widely referred to in national specifications throughout the world
	8. National Bureau of Standards [161,162]	Test piece stationary, abrasive revolves on drum. Simple design	Continuous	General rubber compounds. Soles and heels	Results are expressed in terms of the number of revolutions per 0.1 in. thickness worn. Good correlation with sole and heel compounds is claimed
	9. New Jersey Zinc Co. [163]	Test piece normally stationary, abrasive is a moving circular track	Continuous	General rubber compounds	Results are expressed as volume loss. In one modification of the apparatus the test piece can be alternately raised and lowered from contact with the abrasive by means of cams. Claimed that original model over-emphasised hardness of test piece
	10. A.P. Conti Abrasion [164]	Test piece bonded to metal is stationary. Abrasive fitted and moves on eccentrically mounted roller	Continuous	Tread stocks. Conveyor belting	Results expressed as volume loss. Load on test piece can be varied. Test relatively short. End point after travel of 40 metres

Table 9.8 (contd.)

Category	Name	Mechanical features	Nature of stress	Type of material tested	Comments
C	11. DVM–Schopper Abrasion [164]	Test piece moves across the abrasive which is rotated on drum. Once in each revolution the test piece is lifted over clamp holding abrasive	Continuous (apart from lifting over clamp)	Tread stocks. Soling compounds. General rubber compounds	This method is widely used in Germany. The results are expressed as volume loss. As in (10) end point after travel of 40 metres
	12. Rotating disc [164]	Test piece is rotated in opposite directions at a higher speed than the revolving disk holding abrasive	Continuous	General rubber compounds	Results expressed as volume loss or as loss in height or thickness. As in (10) and (11) end point after travel of 40 metres
	13. U.S. Rubber Co. [165]	Both test piece and abrasive move. Similar to DVM (11)	Continuous	General rubber compounds	Similar in principle and method of operation to the DVM (11)
	14. B.B.S.A.T.R.A. [166,167]	Two test pieces move backwards and forwards across abrasive cloth, which is moved slowly forward	Continuous	Leather. Rubber sole and heel compounds	Decrease in thickness of test piece is indicated continuously. Correlation with service wear is difficult,[168] and method is used mainly for development work
D	15. Dunlop (Lambourn) [169]	Both test piece and abrasive are driven. The % slip between test piece and abrasive can be controlled by Eddy current brake	Discontinuous	Tyre treads	Working at 16%, slip good correlation with service is claimed for limited range of tyre-tread compounds. Useful for development work. Referred to in BS 903 Part A9: 1957. An improved model, operating under conditions of constant

	Either the test piece or the abrasive (or both) are driven with the test piece at an angle to abrasive	Discontinuous	Tyre treads	Similar in principle to Dunlop (15) and the Goodyear model is used quite widely in the U.S.A. In America it is the next most popular method to the du Pont
16. Goodyear ... (Vogt) (Angle)				
17. Akron [173]	Similar in principle to Goodyear. Employs smaller test piece. Abrasive moves at approx. $\frac{1}{4}$ speed of Goodyear	Discontinuous	Tyre treads	Similar in principle to Goodyear (16)
18. Akron/Croydon [174]	Similar to Akron. Modified test-piece holder and provision for cleaning abrasive	Discontinuous	Tyre treads	The variables associated with this method, which is included in BS 903 Part A9 : 1957, have been studied in detail by the R.A.B.R.M.
19. Kelley [175]	Both test piece and abrasive move. Test piece is strip clamped to periphery of wheel	Discontinuous	Tyre treads	This method is crude, and many factors are uncontrolled
20. Goodrich [176]	Full details not known. Test piece is miniature pneumatic tyre	Discontinuous	Tyre treads	Sufficient information on the method is not yet available. May be similar to Dunlop (15) and Goodyear (16) in essential principles
21. Armstrong Cork [177,178]	Both test piece and abrasive move. 8 test pieces. Abrasive is in form of long roll of sandpaper moving in opposite direction to test piece	Discontinuous	Wide range of general rubber compounds	The great advantage claimed for this method is non-clogging of the abrasive, as a new abrasive surface is continuously presented, and each of the eight test pieces is abraded in turn

but, nevertheless, they are useful quality-control tests for product specifications as long as it is realised that the test is merely assessing the level of abrasion resistance of the compound under one set of conditions rather than denoting any definite value for the " wear life ".

Effect of laboratory test variables

As abrasive papers or bonded abrasive wheels provide the means of producing wear, it is natural that many workers [149,187,188] have studied the variability of different abrasives. It has been shown [149,187] how the variations in the power of the abrasive can affect the abrasive indices relative to a standard compound. There is about 3–5% coefficient of variation between new replicate abrasive wheels made to the same specification,[149] and the French system [191] of checking the abrasive power and discarding those wheels or papers having an abrasion index outside specified limits is a sound procedure. Having obtained a consistent supply of abrasives, the problem remains of assessing the useful life of the abrasive, and in the international method and BS 903 Part A9 : 1957 it is suggested that 180-grit silicon carbide abrasive has about 6 hours useful life and " generally need only be discarded when the weight loss from the standard compound has fallen to about 75% of the original. The rate of loss of cutting power is dependent on the compound being tested, high grade carbon black compounds causing much less loss of cut than lower grade compounds containing whiting ".

The abrasive can become contaminated with use, and it is specified that it shall be continuously cleaned by means of air jets, and this procedure may be supplemented by the use of stiff-bristle brushes. Softeners in a compound can contaminate the abrasive [192] and provide lubrication, and Griffiths et al.[193] suggested an extraction procedure which claimed to remove materials which led to fictitiously low abrasion losses in the laboratory. Their claims to improved correlation with service tests using this procedure were substantiated with a range of tyre and sole and heel compounds.[149] Unfortunately the procedure is a cumbersome addition for routine work.

The effects of varying the load on the du Pont machine have been studied [149,190] and the suggestion made that since the rate of wear on the du Pont test is highly correlated with the hardness or stiffness of the compound, this dependence on hardness can be reduced only by operating the test under extremely low loads.

There is lack of information on the effect of changes in temperature on laboratory tests, primarily due to the difficulty of measuring the important temperature at the rubber interface being abraded (not the ambient temperature). Information from road-wear tests suggests, however, that as the temperature is raised so the rate of abrasion increases.[169,194] Juve [6] has given an excellent summary of the difficulties associated with establishing the exact effects of temperature.

Information on the effects of speed of testing [171,195] shows that the rate of abrasion loss increases with speed, but in the case of the du Pont method as long as a uniform speed within the range 34–40 r.p.m. is employed reproducible results will be obtained.

New developments

Two new machines have been described since the 21 machines given earlier were listed. The first of these is a modification to the du Pont so that it can be operated under conditions of constant torque.[171,189,196] Only minor mechanical changes are made to the machine, the normal dead weight of 8 lb. (3·62 kg.) being replaced by a spring system which can give an adjustable pressure. Using this Dunlop Rubber Co. modification, results have been reported suggesting that the method gives better correlation with service. The compounds used have been described,[149] and using compound 8759 as the standard 100 index, the following comparisons were obtained by the two methods of test.

TABLE 9.9

COMPARISON OF CONSTANT LOAD AND CONSTANT TORQUE DU PONT TESTS

Compound reference	Constant load		Constant torque		Road test	
	Abrasion index	Ranking	Abrasion index	Ranking	Abrasion index	Ranking
8759	100	3–4	100	1	100	1
8760	145	2	92	2	92	2
8761	159	1	85	3	80	3
8762	100	3–4	73	4	74	} 4–5
8763	54	5	63	5	76	
8764	50	6	38	6	59	6

Herzog and Burton [197] have described an abrasion test where the abrasive disk is mounted horizontally on a type of turntable. This test would fall in Category C, and the authors consider the method of applying the load to be important and draw attention to the necessity of adjusting the height of the test piece (outside the holder) during the test. The latter point may merit consideration and study with other abrasion machines.

Analysis of wear curves

Another view of how to tackle the problem of abrasion testing can be postulated. Briefly it can be stated as follows: the rate at which materials wear will depend on the severity of the imposed conditions as, of course, occurs with tyres in service, e.g. tread life in Switzerland is less than in Great Britain, due to severer conditions of cornering, speed, etc. By studying the wear curves, using the power law relationship $y = ax^n$,[190,198,199] produced under a variety of conditions on any one machine it is possible to relate log y with log a, and curves of the general form shown in Fig. 9.23 are obtained. It will be seen that the curve passes through a minimum, and under the conditions of test or service which apply at that

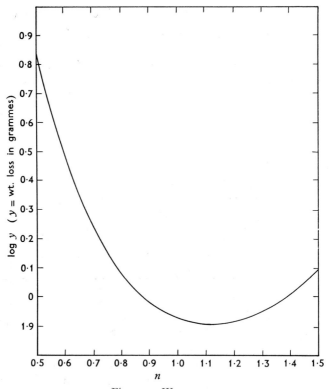

Fig. 9.23. Wear curve.

minimum the compound will have its highest resistance to abrasion. As the conditions become more severe, so the curve on the right-hand side of the minimum rises. The slower this rate of rise, the more resistant will be the compound to severe conditions, e.g. racing conditions, braking and cornering, etc. This type of analysis [200] is an extension of the earlier work using the power law relationship which showed that road-wear curves could be calculated and extrapolated from early measurements in the wear curve. Good agreement between the calculated and actual values [190,201] meant that savings in time and money could be made with road tests, and the technique also helped to establish when some abnormality had occurred in the road test.[190, 202] The type of analysis referred to above can be employed with any abrasion test in which the test conditions can be changed in a known manner, and it appears to be a most useful procedure for assessing the full potentialities of new polymers and compounding ingredients. This approach to wear testing was discussed in the 12th Foundation Lecture.[200]

Flexcracking and crack growth

Flexcracking ranks equal in importance to abrasion resistance as a problem of concern to the rubber industry. The subject is extremely diffuse and complex, but a large amount of the published information on this subject has been reviewed [203] under the following headings:

(*a*) Definition of terms.
(*b*) Mechanism of crack-initiation and crack-growth.
(*c*) Service conditions and methods of test.
(*d*) Methods of rating and errors of test.
(*e*) Effect of modification of the test environment, test conditions, and method of sample preparation.
(*f*) Relation with other tests.
(*g*) Discussion of du Pont, De Mattia, Flipper and Vogt machines.

Flexcracking has been defined as the occurrence and growth of cracks in the surface of rubber when repeatedly submitted to a cycle of deformation. This phenomenon occurs in the sidewalls of tyres and in the base of grooves in the tread.

Flexcracking tests must be distinguished from fatigue flexing tests, in which the breakdown is of a different type, as in detrition machines and the Goodrich and Firestone flexometers. These so-called " flexometers " are really compression-fatigue machines.

In the process of flexcracking, two stages are recognised:

(1) *Crack initiation.* The period up to the point where cracks are first apparent.

(2) *Crack growth.* The stage where cracks, already initiated, become larger until ultimately the sample may fail by breaking.

As with abrasion, a great variety of machines have been devised for flexcracking, and they have been classified [203] into three groups according to the type of strain:

(*a*) repeated linear extension;
(*b*) repeated bending without tension;
(*c*) combination of extension and bending.

The De Mattia test (group (b)) and the du Pont test (group (c)) are specified in ASTM D430–57 and BS 903 Parts A. 10 and A. 11: 1956, and the De Mattia machine is now specified internationally for flexcracking and crack-growth tests.

The du Pont machine employs a specially moulded test piece with a fabric backing and with 8 transverse V-shaped grooves on the surface. Test pieces are joined together to form an endless belt, which is driven over pulleys, and in order to eliminate variations in the tension in the belt a special balance arm, shown in Fig. 9.24, was designed.[31] It can be shown

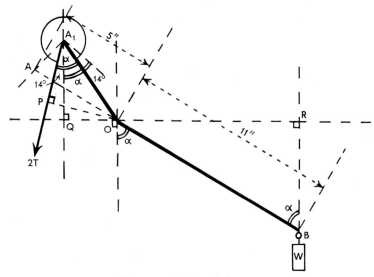

Fig. 9.24. Du Pont belt arm.

that the tension in the belt $T = \dfrac{11W}{10 \cos 14}$ and therefore is independent of the angle α of the balance arm, and with a balance weight of 15 lb. a tension of 17 lb. is produced irrespective of the angle of the arm.

The De Mattia test is more widely used, and consists of bending a standard test piece with a moulded groove. Many investigators [204–209] appreciated the importance of fatigue in flexcracking tests, since if the test piece returned to zero strain during a cycle the rate of cracking was a maximum. It has been argued [210] that it may be preferable to choose the conditions of strain such that the maximum fatigue, rather than an unknown amount, occurs. Certainly a given flexing test should operate under conditions where there is a definite extension, return to zero strain and, where possible, a definite compression; the testing conditions should never be such that small variations in the specified conditions can lead to the test piece either returning to or passing through zero strain in cases where it is intended that the test piece should always be under a positive strain.

In the De Mattia test the mean strain and the dynamic strain are determined by:

(1) the relative setting of the fixed and movable clamps;
(2) the amplitude of movement of the moving clamp; and
(3) the free length of test piece between the clamps.

It was found that when items (1) and (2) were kept constant and item (3) altered so that the free length of test piece was reduced from $3\frac{1}{4}$ to 3 in. the following crack growth results were obtained:

TABLE 9.10

EFFECT OF FREE LENGTH OF TEST PIECE

Compound	Free length			
	3 in.		$3\frac{1}{4}$ in.	
	Kilocycles for crack to reach 8 mm.	Kilocycles for crack to reach 15 mm.	Kilocycles for crack to reach 8 mm.	Kilocycles for crack to reach 15 mm.
Natural rubber tread, channel black + antioxidant	32·8	>170	2,177	>6,000
Natural rubber tread, furnace black + antioxidant	6·0	53·3	1,305	>6,000
SBR tread 30 minutes cure	7·4	21·5	11·7	40·0
SBR tread 60 minutes cure	4·2	14·7	8·5	25·7

Further, it was suggested that when the free length of the test piece was a nominal 3 in. a variation of less than 0·1 in. in the distance between the clamps (which simultaneously gives a variation in free length of the same magnitude) caused an obvious change in rate of crack growth. Similarly, when a double-sided machine was adjusted as accurately as possible significantly different results could be obtained on the two sides.

These results led to consideration of the following essential requirements which an agreed test for crack-growth measurement should possess:[210]

(a) It should be possible to complete the test with a " normal " rubber compound in a " reasonable " time, e.g. in less than 100 kilocycles.

(b) The rate of crack growth should be sufficiently great for the test to be completed before the appearance of subsidiary cracks which alter the stress distribution and confuse the appearance of the test piece. In an extreme case cracks starting from the edge of the test piece could join with the principal crack before it has attained the maximum specified length.

(c) The initial crack should be propagated as a unique crack.

Rainier and Gerke [204] reported a linear breakdown of the test piece provided the degree of deterioration does not exceed 60%, and the writer suggested that crack initiation should be measured by the kilocycles required for an initial crack of 2 mm. to reach 4 mm. and crack growth by the kilocycles required for the 4-mm. crack to grow to 8 mm.

The above suggestions for flexcracking and crack-growth tests using the De Mattia machine were assessed by means of two co-operative experiments,[211] and the results confirmed the validity of the proposals, and a 3-in. free length of rubber is now specified in the international and British methods for flexcracking [212] and crack growth.[213]

Early work on crack-growth tests [204,214,215,216] gave poor reproducibility, and one important source of error was found to be the shape of the puncturing tool.[217] In the latter work considerable improvement in reproducibility was obtained by using a spear-shaped tool in place of a round cross-section needle. The co-operative work on crack growth was carried out with a special tool (Fig. 9.25) which is readily manufactured from an American No. 6 chisel-point round awl.[218] This tool makes an incision in the form of a slit 2 mm. long, cut completely through the thickness of the test piece. It is essential to ensure that the cutting tool is inserted normal to the surface of the test piece and that each incision is made to the same depth in each; special probe locators [219] of the type shown in Fig. 9.26 are recommended.

Effect of temperature of test

Reports [6,203] on the effect of temperature are conflicting; for example, Somerville found that the rate of cracking decreased with rise of temperature with natural rubber gum compounds, whereas Rainier and Gerke [204] reported that the rate of cracking of natural rubber tread compounds increased with temperature. A De Mattia type machine was used in both cases. Similarly conflicting evidence has been published on crack growth by Carlton and Reinbold [215] and by Breckley.[214]

Buist [210] obtained additional information, and crack growth was determined on a Flipper machine similar to that described in BS 903, Section 26.3, 1950 operated over a temperature range of 40°–100° C. The results provide information on the behaviour of different polymers over a range of temperature; Butyl rubber being outstanding in resistance to crack growth and not greatly affected by temperature; neoprene GN and natural rubber crack at a similar rate at 40° C but neoprene GN is

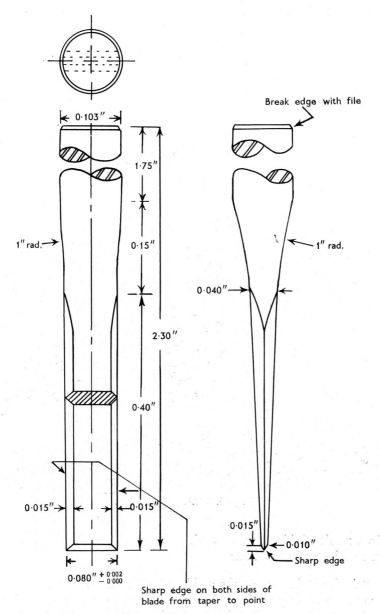

Break edge with file

0·103″

1·75″

1″ rad,

0·15″

1″ rad.

0·040″

2·30″

0·40″

0·015″

0·015″   0·015″

0·015″

0·010″

Sharp edge

0·080″ + 0·002 − 0·000

Sharp edge on both sides of
blade from taper to point

Fig. 9.25. I.S.O. tool for crack-growth test. ×7.

definitely inferior at higher temperatures; both SBR and Perbunan show rapid crack growth, which is accelerated by a rise in temperature.

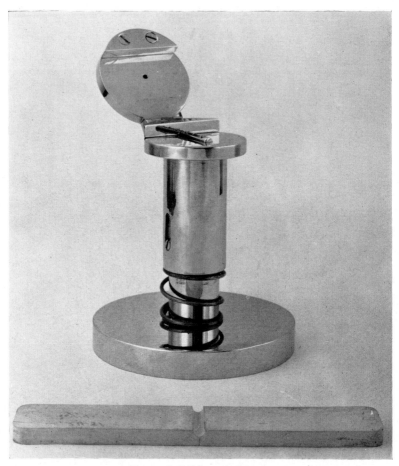

Fig. 9.26. I.C.I. probe locator.

As a result of this work, Committee ISO/TC/45 recommended at the 1951 meeting at Oxford that:

" A close tolerance on the ambient temperature is not specified and tests are normally performed at room temperature although elevated temperatures may often be used with advantage. There is some evidence that the rates of cracking of neoprene GN and of GR-S are particularly sensitive to the test temperatures, and in these cases it is suggested that the tolerance in temperature should be ±2° C."

Methods of interpreting flexcracking and crack-growth results

In the treatment of flexcracking results it is accepted [210, 220] that two quantities must be measured, one being the period of flexing or number of flexures and the other " the degree of flexcracking ". The degree of cracking is normally defined by certain specific stages of breakdown illustrated by means of standard samples or photographs. It is possible to construct a series of samples covering a range of cracking so that the samples are equally and regularly spaced as judged by visual assessment. Under these conditions Newton [221] claims that the number of flexures to produce each successive grade of cracking increases in an exponential fashion, and there is therefore a linear relationship between the grade number and the logarithm of the number of flexures when the grades are numbered consecutively. Buist and Williams [220] pointed out cases where Newton's logarithmic method was not always satisfactory, and suggested a graphical method of treating the results. With the graphical method random variations in results are ignored and average flexcracking results obtained.

These authors compared the two methods of treating results using data from a paper published by Newton and Scott,[222] and the results of this comparison are summarised in Table 9.11.

TABLE 9.11

COMPARISON OF GRAPHICAL AND LOGARITHMIC METHODS FLEXCRACKING RESISTANCE (STAGE C)

Lot	Graphical kc.	Logarithmic	
		kc.	log kc.
A	30·8	30·9	1·49
B	34·5	36·3	1·56
C	30·0	30·9	1·49
D	31·9	33·9	1·53
E	40·0	39·8	1·60

The agreement between the two methods of interpretation is excellent and in addition it was claimed [210] that the graphical method also gave information on crack initiation and crack-propagation characteristics which could not be obtained by means of the logarithmic method. The graphical method has been adopted in BS 903 Part A. 10: 1956 and is included in the draft I.S.O. methods. Its successful application has also been confirmed by Blackwell.[223]

Adhesion to metals and textiles

The development of suitable testing methods for adhesion to metals and textiles was retarded for many years due to unsatisfactory production techniques giving rise to wide variability in the strength of bond. Over the years the efficiency of chemical systems for rubber–metal bonding has improved steadily; partly due to the improvement of the chemical agents themselves, but also due to their wider use leading to greater experience

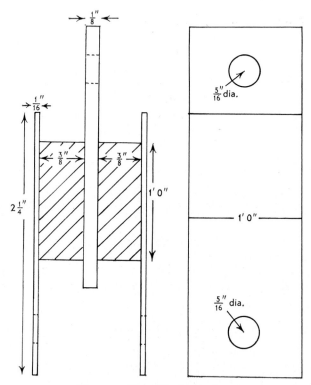

Fig. 9.27. Shear bond test piece.

and the development of improved bonding techniques. Before 1939 bond strengths of 300–500 lb./in.² were published, by 1950 values of 800 lb./in.² were quoted,[224] and a recent paper [225] which evaluates various testing methods quotes values of 1,250 lb./in.² In the latter publication the authors report that the variability of the conventional straight-pull test should not exceed that given by a coefficient of variation of about 8–12% of the mean value. Progress of this kind means that testing techniques can now be properly evaluated.

Tests which have been used are tensile break in straight pull,[226] shear strength,[225] 90° peeling test,[225, 227] compression fatigue,[224, 225] shear fatigue,[225] impact strength and impact fatigue.[76, 224, 225]

In the normal straight-pull test [226] the break often occurs in the rubber under conditions of non-uniform stressing. The thickness of rubber specified is $\frac{1}{2}$ in., but published data [224] supports the view that when the

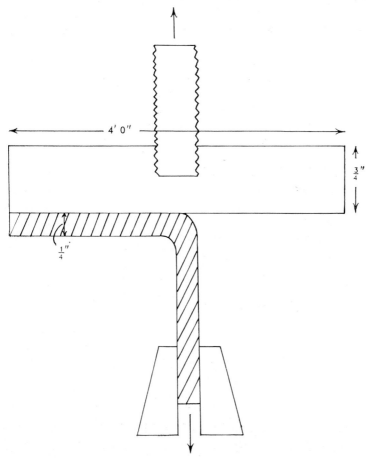

Fig. 9.28. 90° peeling test.

test is designed to evaluate bonding agents the thickness of rubber should be reduced to $\frac{1}{4}$ in. This has been accepted by Committee ISO/TC/45 and by the BS committee preparing a standard method for this type of test.

Test pieces for testing shear strength are not standardised, but the dimensions given in Fig. 9.27 have been used successfully, and the results reported [225] suggest that this type of test deserves more attention by industry. It is important to design the mould for the shear test pieces so that " wiping " of the bonding agent by the injected rubber is reduced to a minimum.

The 90° peeling test has been used in various forms, but the latest version, developed by the Lord Manufacturing Co., is now being considered as a revision of ASTM D429–56T. Fig. 9.28 shows a dimensioned sketch of a test piece of this type.[225] The 2-in.-wide bonded rubber of thickness $\frac{1}{4}$ in. is stripped to within $\frac{1}{2}$ in. of the centre, and then peeling is carried out over an inch length.

The arguments in favour of carrying out dynamic tests on bonded units are fairly self-evident, and many rubber companies have been employing special rig tests for many years. Three publications,[76,224,225] however, have advocated and shown the value of dynamic tests for evaluating bonding agents. Compression fatigue tests were carried out on the Goodrich Flexometer. A special falling-weight impact machine[224] was developed, and interesting results on the effect of " shape factor " were published.[76] The importance of the volume of rubber in a given unit of various shapes being stressed, and when the volume of rubber was kept constant experimental confirmation that the same maximum stress was developed in units of different shape was obtained. In an improved design of this equipment,[225] see Fig. 9.29, a simple mechanical switch has been incorporated whereby the falling weight is arrested after the first rebound.

The writer and his colleagues are convinced from data obtained under a variety of dynamic conditions that it is difficult to distinguish clearly between fatigue of the rubber and fatigue of the bond. Since different dynamic tests, e.g. impact and shear flexing, discriminate differently between bonding agents, classified as equally good by simple tensile break tests, it is clear that in laboratory comparisons of bonding systems a variety of tests is essential.

Testing of textile bonding agents

In ply-separation (stripping) tests for rubber fabric articles international standardisation has been confined to the " machine " method, based on ASTM D413–39, where the test piece is stripped at a constant rate, within the range 2–10 in./min. (50–250 mm./min.) and the load recorded. Test pieces are 1 ± 0.02 in. wide, and in the case of both strip and ring test pieces the thickness of the ply or layer being separated should be not greater than the thickness of the remaining portion of the test piece, and should in no case be greater than $\frac{1}{4}$ in. (6 mm.). The temperature of test is 20° C, and test pieces should be preconditioned for 24 hours at this temperature. Many authors have argued that the above type of test is not sensitive enough to discriminate adequately between different types of

Fig. 9.29. Falling-weight impact test.

bonding agent. Other tests involving a measurement of the adhesion of single cords have been developed, and these include the Goodrich compression-cylinder method [229] and the Goodyear H test.[229]

Dynamic fatigue tests have also been developed. Roelig [230] designed a cord-adhesion test for tyre cords where 24 cords were spaced at $\frac{5}{8}$-in. intervals in a rubber strip which is held in a slotted holder. Each cord is attached to a 1-kg. weight and the sample holder oscillates through 1·9 mm. at a speed of 250 cycles/min. Buist and Naunton [224] modified this test so that the cords could be grouped 25 to the inch. Pittman and Thornley [231] fatigued single cords by compressing rubber rods containing the cord and gave useful examples of laboratory failures, which it was claimed correlated with service failures.

None of the above fatigue tests appears to be satisfactory, and the writer's experience of two of them [224, 230] has been that the reproducibility of results is extremely poor and much more work remains to be done in this field before the position can be regarded as being satisfactory.

Dynamic properties

These properties are dealt with in detail in Chapter VIII.

Swelling of rubbers

Swelling tests have been used for many purposes, ranging from evaluation of new polymers, assessment of state of cure, calculations of number of cross-links in a rubber, characterisation of synthetic rubbers, to providing semi-service data for the selection of materials for chemical-plant linings.

The most commonly used methods for determining swelling are the conventional volumetric and gravimetric methods. The linear swelling method developed by Garvey [232] has been adopted in ASTM D471–57, and is useful for studying dimensional changes when grain effects are present. If grain effects are not present volume swelling can be calculated, and convenient tables are provided in the above specification. The method has the advantage that the test pieces are not withdrawn from the swelling medium during the test, and it has been adopted in BS 1673 Part 4: 1953 as a convenient test for studying the development of cure after heating unvulcanised compounds for specified periods at elevated temperatures. For this purpose benzene is a suitable swelling liquid, since it produces rapid swelling at room temperature. The maximum swelling decreases with degree of vulcanisation until it reaches a minimum, thereafter remaining practically constant. The time of vulcanisation to reach this minimum tends to correspond to the time for optimum modulus rather than optimum tensile strength.

Swelling tests consist essentially of immersing a rubber test piece in a liquid for a given time, at a constant temperature, and determining the change in volume or linear dimensions. With some compounds the swelling liquid may extract a proportion of the plasticiser, or other soluble ingredient of the compound, and when the amount of material dissolved out of the compound is thought to be significant it should be determined. Attempts [37, 233] have been made to standardise test fuels, and specifications for certain test fuels have been issued.[234] In BS 903 [235] attention is drawn to the fact that light mineral lubricating oils and fuels vary in aromatic content even when supplied to a specification. The aniline point of a mineral oil gives an indication of its aromatic content, and in general the lower the aniline point, the more severe is the swelling action.

In addition to questions of dimensional stability it is important in most applications to ensure that the physical properties of rubbers, after any change due to swelling, be maintained for long periods.[48] There are several difficulties associated with testing swollen rubbers, and the methods which are specified by the ASTM [233] test the immediate deterioration in properties and also the change in properties after evaporation of the test liquid. In no case, however, is the test piece tested during immersion, and there is scope here for improved testing techniques.

Statistics

As statistical methods derive the maximum amount of information from the results of an investigation and at the same time supply a means of assessing the reliability and value of the information extracted, the scope for their application to the field of testing rubber-like materials described in this chapter is extensive. Many authors [236-252] have used statistical methods to evaluate accurately the experimental errors inherent in test methods. The methods used to assess the errors have been either by a process of replication, or from the interaction terms in an analysis of variance, or from the residual term in a regression analysis. Calculation of the size of the errors is not enough, however, and it is important to

TABLE 9.12

VALUES OF ERROR DUE TO DIFFERENT SOURCES

	Testing, $\pm 2\sigma\%$	Curing, $\pm 2\sigma\%$	Mixing, $\pm 2\sigma\%$	Processing, $\pm 2\sigma\%$	Total laboratory error, $\pm 2\sigma\%$
Tensile strength	$\pm 2\cdot9$	$\pm 3\cdot5$	$\pm 6\cdot6$	$\pm 7\cdot6$	$\pm 8\cdot1$
Elongation at break	$\pm 1\cdot9$	$\pm 6\cdot6$	$\pm 3\cdot7$	$\pm 7\cdot6$	$\pm 8\cdot0$
Resilience	$\pm 1\cdot1$	Not significant	$\pm 2\cdot2$	$\pm 2\cdot6$	$\pm 2\cdot8$
Shore hardness	$\pm 2\cdot2$	$\pm 3\cdot1$	$\pm 4\cdot1$	$\pm 5\cdot5$	$\pm 6\cdot1$
Swelling	$\pm 4\cdot2$	Not significant	$\pm 2\cdot8$	$\pm 3\cdot0$	$\pm 5\cdot1$
du Pont abrasion	$\pm 2\cdot1$	$\pm 8\cdot6$	$\pm 12\cdot0$	$\pm 13\cdot2$	$\pm 13\cdot4$

trace the source of the errors and take steps to improve processes and tests. The main sources of error in laboratory processes and tests have been listed, [236,242,249,250] and it is now accepted that the variation between repeat mixings is greater than the simple error of test. From a study of repeat mixings the total laboratory error has been separated into errors due to testing, curing and mixing for many properties by Buist and Davies,[236] and a selection of their data is given in Table 9.12.

The same authors [236] found that various tests had different degrees of discriminating power between different grades of filler. Discriminating power was defined as the ratio of the variance between the fillers to the total error variance. Estimations of discriminating power enable one to decide whether a test method has a small amount of variability because it is an effective test or because it is so insensitive that measurements always tend to be the same.

TABLE 9.13

ERRORS OF TEST

Test	Standard deviation	Coefficient of variation, %
Tension stress strain:		
Tension strength		5 approx.
Elongation at break		3 approx.
Modulus		$2\frac{1}{2}$
Tension set:		
Rings		3
Dumb-bells		4
Compression stress–strain	4·2 lb./in.²	
Compression set:		
Constant stress	0·5% set	
Constant deflection	0·5–2·0% comp. set	
Hardness:		
British Standard hardness test	Same operator	1·2 (hard value)
	Mean results of test by different operator	1
Durometer indentation test	Same operator	1·4
	Mean results of test by different operator	3
Rebound resilience:		
Dunlop pendulum	0·06 unit of % resilience	
Dunlop tripsometer	1·7 units of % resilience	
Lupke pendulum	0·1 unit of % resilience	
Resistance to low temperature	1–2° C of the measurements of the temperature corresponding to a given change in modulus	
Abrasion:		
Akron machine		3–4% on single test measurement
du Pont machine		5 approx.
Dunlop (Lambourn)	0·0095 (log. of abrasive index)	

TABLE 9.13 (*contd.*)

Test	Standard deviation	Coefficient of variation, %
Tear strength		Less than 8
Swelling in liquids:		
Volumetric and Linear Method		4–12
Permeability to hydrogen		10 approx.
Power factor		5 approx.
Permittivity		3 approx.
Oven ageing—based on co-efficient of deterioration	8–15 units	
Oxygen pressure method—based on coefficient of deterioration:		
Tension strength	5–10 units	
Elongation at break	2–5 units	
du Pont belt flexing—based on variability between 6 re-plicate test pieces cut from a single slab:		
Stage of cracking—		
Pin holes		35–40
Small cracks		20–25
Medium cracks		20–25
Deep cracks		15–20
Adhesion:		
Rubber to metal straight-pull test		8–12

Another way in which statistical methods can help is by establishing correlation coefficients between tests, and as would be expected, it has been shown [236] that the degree of correlation between each property is not the same for all rubbers. Correlation coefficients for a range of properties of both natural rubber and neoprene GN are given in the above paper, and the relation between different properties of SBR has been summarised by Juve [6] and others.[243,244] There is also a general discussion of the relationship between different properties in *Rubber in Engineering*,[2] where it is suggested that properties are either directly compatible when an improvement in one property is accompanied by an improvement in another, or directly incompatible when an improvement in one property is accompanied by a worsening in another, or there is an unpredictable relationship between pairs of properties.

So far this discussion has been concerned with the application of statistical methods within a single laboratory, but just as the variation between

c c

repeat mixings is greater than the error of test, so the variations between different laboratories are normally greater than the variations within a laboratory.[211,237,245,246,251] Newton [242] summarised work done before 1948 very effectively and emphasised that correlations between service behaviour and laboratory tests would not be attainable " until the excessive inter-laboratory variation has been greatly reduced ". A welcome feature of the work carried out on behalf of Committee ISO/TC/45 has been the large

TABLE 9.14

ERRORS OF TEST " BETWEEN " AND " WITHIN " LABORATORIES

	Coefficient of variation between laboratories, %	Error of a single test result, %
Gum stock, combined mixing, curing and vulcanising errors:		
Tension strength	9	—
Elongation	16	—
Modulus 700%	4	—
Tension stress–strain test:		
Thickness of test piece	1·8 *	2·5
Thickness (corrected for gauge pressure)	0·28	—
Load at break	2·7 *	4·3
Tension strength	2·85	3·25
Elongation at break	3·4 *	2·2
Elongation (corrected for rate of stretch)	1·65 *	—
Load at 400% elongation	8·3	4·7
Load at 400% elongation (corrected)	3·4 *	—
Modulus at 400%	8·7	4·2
Tests of GR-S compounds:		
Tension strength	4·6 *	—
Breaking elongation	12·8 *	—
Hardness (indentation $\frac{1}{100}$ mm.)	3·7 *	—
Abrasion (Akron)	About 5 *	4
Tear strength—		
Gum stock	12·7 *	5·9
Tread stock	14·4 *	10·5
Plasticity (Williams) 1 c.c. pellet, 100° C, and 10 minutes compression	6·5 *	1·5
Mooney viscosity—		
Uncorrected data	S.D. 3·1	—
Corrected data	S.D. 1·9	—
Ageing (Oven at 70° C oxygen bomb)	Large inter-action between laboratories and compounds	—
Crack growth (De Mattia)		
stage of growth: 2–4 mm.	24	—
4–8 mm.	12	—

* Significantly greater than error within laboratories.

number of co-operative programmes of work which have been planned statistically so that both the " between " and " within " laboratory error could be established for many properties.[101,189,200,210,211,251] This work has enabled many errors, hitherto unsuspected by the laboratories concerned, to be traced and eradicated. A table of errors of test associated with many of the tests discussed in this chapter has been published [247] and is now amplified in Tables 9.13 and 9.14 with information which has become available from the ISO/TC/45 co-operative programmes.

Reference has been made to the problem of relating laboratory tests to service tests, and correct statistical planning of the service test [202,248] has often revealed that the lack of correlation is due in part at least to the large errors associated with service tests. Statistical methods have already been used successfully to improve service tests, and as further progress is made along the lines discussed in the next part of this chapter improved correlation between laboratory tests and service behaviour can be expected.

REFERENCES

1. Scott, J. R. (1949) *J. Rubb. Res.*, **18**, 30.
2. *Rubber in Engineering* (1946) (H.M.S.O.).
3. Buist, J. M. and Stafford, R. L. (1953) *I.R.I. Trans.*, **29**, 238.
4. Bryant, K. C. and Bisset, D. C. (1954) *Third Rubb. Tech. Conf.*, 655.
5. Davies, O. L. (1954) *Design and Analysis of Industrial Experiments* (Oliver and Boyd).
6. Juve, A. E. (1954) Chapter in *Synthetic Rubber*, Whitby (John Wiley and Sons).
7. Memmler, K. and Schob, A. (1909) *Mitt Materialprüfungsamt. Berlin-Dahlem*, **27**, 173.
8. Buist, J. M. (1951) *India Rubb. J.*, **120**, 451.
9. Herzog, R. and Burton, R. H. (1952) *Schweizer Archiv. füs Augewandte Wissenschaft and Technik*, **18**, 6, 178.
10. *Specs. for Gov. Syn. Rubbers* (1949), Fig. 2, R.F.C., O.R.R., Washington, D.C.
11. Stubbs, A. J. (1953) *I.R.I. Trans.*, **29**, 215.
12. Stevart, A. (1870) *Bull. Musee ind. Belg.*, **57**, 5.
13. Breuil, P. (1904) *Caoutchouc and Gutta Percha*, **1**, 54, 76.
14. Buist, J. M. and Kennedy, R. L., B.P. 618,008.
15. Schob, A. (1923) *Gummi-Ztg.*, **37**, 235.
16. Albertoni, G. J. (1931) *Ind. Eng. Chem., Anal. Ed.*, **3**, 236.
17. *Callenders Cables*, U.S.P. 2,363,964.
18. Buist, J. M. and Jamin, G. W., B.P. 677,391.
19. Messrs. Goodbrand & Co., Britannia Foundry, Stalybridge, Cheshire, England.
20. Stafford, R. L. (1953) *India Rubb. J.*, **125**, 8.
21. Burr, G. S. (1949) *Electronics*, **22**, 5, 101.
22. Wilson, B. J. (1956) *Rubb. J.*, **99**, 273.
23. Holt, W. L., Knox, E. O. and Roth, F. L. (1948) *India Rubb. W.*, **118**, 513, 578.
24. Roth, F. L. and Stiehler, R. D. (1948) *India Rubb. W.*, **118**, 367.
25. B.R.P.R.A. Strain Test, BS 1673 Part IV.
26. Mullins, L. (1947) *J. Rubb. Res.*, **16**, 275.
27. Somerville, A. A. and Russell, W. F. (1933) *Ind. Eng. Chem.*, **25**, 1096.
28. Tener, F., Kingsbury, S. S. and Holt, W. L. (1928) *Amer. Bur. of Stands. Paper 364.*

29. Naunton, W. J. S. (1948) *I.R.I. Trans.*, **24**, 10.
30. Boonstra, B. (1949) *India Rubb. W.*, **121**, 299.
31. Buist, J. M. (1947) *Fundamentals of Rubber Technology* (I.C.I. Ltd.).
32. Morron, J. D., Knapp, R. C., Linhorst, E. F. and Viohl, P. (1944) *India Rubb. W.*, **110**, 521.
33. *Specs. for Gov. Syn. Rubbers* (1949), Tables I and II, R.F.C., O.R.R. (Washington, D.C.).
34. *Specs. for Gov. Syn. Rubbers* (1947), Table II, R.F.C., O.R.R. (Washington, D.C.).
35. Roth, F. L. and Holt, W. L. (1939) *J. Res. Nat. Bur. Stand.*, **23**, 603.
36. Villars, D. S. (1950) *J. app. Phys.*, **21**, 565.
37. *The Services Rubber Investigations* (1954) (H.M.S.O.).
38. Kimmich, E. S. (1940) *India Rubb. W.*, **103**, 45.
39. Hahn, S. H. and Gazdik, I. (1941) *India Rubb. W.*, **103**, 51.
40. Werkenthin, T. A. (1946) *Rubb. Age, N.Y.*, **59**, 173.
41. Werkenthin, T. A. (1946) *Rubb. Age, N.Y.*, **60**, 196.
42. Morris, R. E., James, R. R. and Seegman, I. P. (1949) *India Rubb. W.*, **119**, 466.
43. Tobolsky, A. V., Prettyman, I. B. and Dillon, J. H. (1944) *J. app. Phys.*, **15**, 380.
44. Mooney, M., Wolstenholme, W. E. and Villars, D. S. (1944) *J. app. Phys.*, **15**, 324.
45. Pedersen, H. L. and Nielsen, B. (1951) *J. Polymer Sci.*, **7**, 97.
46. Berry, D. S., R.A.B.R.M., Research Memorandum No. R.394.
47. Berry, J. P. and Watson, W. F. (1955) *J. Polymer Sci.*, **18**, 201.
48. Buist, J. M. (1956) *Ageing and Weathering of Rubber* (W. Heffer).
49. Buist, J. M. (1945) *I.R.I. Trans.*, **20**, 155.
50. Patrikeev, G. A. and Melnikov, I. A. (1940) *Caoutchouc and Rubber, U.S.S.R.*, **14**, 12.
51. Zimmerman, E. C. (1922) *Rubb. Age, N.Y.*, **12**, 130.
52. Evans, B. B. (1922) *India Rubb. J.*, **64**, 815.
53. Lefcaditis, G. and Cotton, F. H. (1932) *I.R.I. Trans.*, **8**, 364.
54. Tuttle, J. B. (1922) *India Rubb. W.*, **67**, 150.
55. Winkelmann, H. A., see Memmler (1934) *Science of Rubber* (Reinhold Publishing Corp.), 603.
56. Carpenter, A. W. and Sargisson, Z. E. (1931) *Proc. Amer. Soc. Test. Mat.*, **31**, II, 897.
57. Poules, I. C. (1941) *India Rubb. W.*, **103**, 41.
58. Buist, J. M. (1948) *Proc. Second Rubber Tech. Conf. London*, 269; (1949) *India Rubb. W.*, **120**, 328.
59. Graves, F. L. (1944) *India Rubb. W.*, **111**, 305, 317.
60. Graves, F. L. (1946) *India Rubb. W.*, **113**, 521.
61. Nijveld, H. A. W. (1948) *Proc. Second Rubber Tech. Conf. London*, 256.
62. Committee ISO/TC/45. I.S.O. Recommendation R49.
63. Graves, F. L., see Buist, J. M. (1951) *India Rubb. J.*, **120**, 451.
64. ASTM D624–54 Die C.
65. Buist, J. M. and Geldof, H. (1950) *India Rubb. W.*, **122**, 291.
66. Buist, J. M. and Kennedy, R. L. (1946) *India Rubb. J.*, **110**, 809.
67. Buist, J. M. and Kennedy, R. L. (1946) *J. Sci. Inst.*, **23**, 242.
68. Newman, S. B. and Taylor, R. H. (1948) *India Rubb. W.*, **119**, 345.
69. Morris, R. E. and Bonnar, R. U. (1947) *Anal. Chem.*, **19**, 436.
70. Buist, J. M. (1945) *Annual Report on the Progress of Rubber Technology*, **9**, 37.
71. Graves, F. L. (1950) *India Rubb. W.*, **122**, 534.
72. Busse, W. F. (1934) *Ind. Eng. Chem.*, **26**, 1194.
73. Greensmith, H. W. and Thomas, A. G. (1955) *J. Polymer Sci.*, **18**, 189
74. Chasset, R. and Thirion, P. (1958) *Rev. gen. Caout.*, **35**, 481.
75. Cooper, L. V. (1944) *Symposium on the Applications of Synthetic Rubber* (Philadelphia: ASTM), 17.

76. Buist, J. M., Lindsey, C. H., Naunton, W. J. S., Stafford, R. L. and Williams, G. E. (1951) *Ind. Eng. Chem.*, **43**, 373.
77. Werkenthin, T. A. (1946) *Rubb. Age, N.Y.*, **60**, 197.
78. S.A.T.R.A., Specification for Resin Rubber Soling Materials 9/56.
79. Buist, J. M. (1946) Report of the General Conference of the British Rheologists' Club, Bedford College, University of London, 92.
80. Mohs, F. (1922) *Grundiss der Mineralogie* (Dresden).
81. Osmond, F. (1892) *Sur la dureté: sa définition et sa mesure* (Paris).
82. Scott, J. R. (1934) *I.R.I. Trans.*, **11**, 224.
83. Scott, J. R., Discussion on reference 79.
84. Scott, J. R. (1948) *J. Rubb. Res.*, **17**, 7.
85. Kunze, W. (1938) *Kunstoffe*, **28**, 225.
86. Committee ISO/TC/45, I.S.O., Recommendation R48.
87. Scott, J. R. (1948) *J. Rubb. Res.*, **17**, 9.
88. Buist, J. M. and Kennedy, R. L., B.P. 617,465.
89. Oberto, S. and Pirelli, S. A. (1954) *Ricerca e Sviluppo*, N2.
90. Scott, J. R. (1948) *J. Rubb. Res.*, **17**, 145.
91. Scott, J. R. (1949) *J. Rubb. Res.*, **18**, 12.
92. BS 903 Part A20:(1959.)
93. ASTM D676–58T.
94. Naugatuck Chemical Co. Distributors.
95. Newton, R. G. and Scott, J. R. (1940) *J. Rubb. Res.*, **9**, 91.
96. Soden, A. L. (1950) *India Rubb. J.*, **119**, 1143; (1951), **120**, 13, 55, 92, 137, 173, 212, 254, 292, 332.
97. ASTM D531–56.
98. ASTM D314–52T.
99. D.V.M. D.I.N. 3503.
100. Larrick, L. (1940) *Proc. Am. Test. Mat.*, **40**, 1239.
101. Scott, J. R. (1951) *I.R.I. Trans.*, **27**, 249.
102. Fielding, J. H. (1937) *Ind. Eng. Chem.*, **29**, 880.
103. Jones, F. B. and Pearce, W. H. (1938) *Proc. Rubb. Tech. Conf. London*, 830.
104. Lupke, P. (1934) *R.C.T.*, **7**, 591.
105. Memmler, K. (1934) *Science of Rubber* (New York: Reinhold Publishing Co.).
106. Albertoni, G. J. (1937) *Ind. Eng. Chem. Anal. Ed.*, **9**, 30.
107. Bashore, H. H. (1937) *R.C.T.*, **10**, 820.
108. Church, H. F. and Daynes, H. A. (1937) *I.R.I. Trans.*, **13**, 96.
109. Bulgin, D. (1944) *I.R.I. Trans.*, **20**, 24.
110. Dillon, J. H., Prettyman, I. B. and Hall, G. L. (1944) *J. app. Phys.*, **15**, 309.
111. Hock, L. (1925) *Z. tech. Phys.*, **6**, 50.
112. Schob, A. (1919) *Mitt. Kgl. Materialprüfungsamt.*, **37**, 227.
113. BS 903 Part 22: 1950.
114. ASTM D1054–55.
115. Dillon, J. H. and Gehman, S. D. (1946) *India Rubb. W.*, **115**, 217.
116. The Services Rubber Investigations Users' Memorandum, No. U7.
117. Boyer, R. F. and Spencer, R. S. (1946) " Scientific Progress in the Field of Rubber and Synthetic Elastomers " (*Advances in Colloid Science*, Vol. II, edited by Mark A. and Whitby G. S. (New York and London)).
118. Bekkedahl, N. and Wood, L. A. (1943) *J. Res. Nat. Bur. Stands.*, **13**, 411.
119. Norman, D. B. (1944) *Ind. Eng. Chem.*, **36**, 738.
120. Ritter, F. J. (1956) Rubber-Stichting Communication No. 324.
121. The Services Rubber Investigations Users' Memorandum No. U15.
122. Aleksandrov, A. P. and Lazurkin, J. S. (1940) *Acta Physiochim. U.S.S.R.*, **12**, 648.
123. Conant, F. S. (1954) *ASTM Bull.*, No. 199, 67.
124. Koch, E. A. (1940) *Kautschuk*, **16**, 151.
125. Liska, J. W. (1944) *Ind. Eng. Chem.*, **36**, 40.

126. Conant, F. S. and Liska, J. W. (1944) *J. app. Phys.*, **15**, 767.
127. Clash, R. F. and Berg, R. M. (1942) *Ind. Eng. Chem.*, **34**, 1218.
128. Clash, R. F. and Berg, R. M. (1944) Symposium on Plastics (Philadelphia: ASTM), 54.
129. Gehman, S. D., Woodford, D. E. and Wilkinson, C. S. (1947) *Ind. Eng. Chem.*, **39**, 1108.
130. ASTM D1053–58T.
131. Graves, F. L. and Davis, A. R. (1943) *India Rubb. W.*, **109**, 41.
132. Martin, S. M. (1942) *Rubb. Age, N.Y.*, **52**, 227.
133. Selker, M. L., Winspear, G. G. and Kemp, A. R. (1942) *Ind. Eng. Chem.*, **34**, 157.
134. ASTM D736–54T.
135. Chalten, C. K., Eller, S. A. and Werkenthin, T. A. (1944) *Rubb. Age, N.Y.*, **54**, 429.
136. Bimmerman, H. G. and Keen, W. N. (1944) *Ind. Eng. Chem., Anal. Ed.*, **16**, 588.
137. Graves, F. L. (1946) *India Rubb. W.*, **113**, 521.
138. Kemp, A. R., Malm, F. S. and Winspear, G. G. (1943) *Ind. Eng. Chem.*, **35**, 488.
139. Buist, J. M. (1955) *Application of the Sciences in Rubber Technology* (I.C.I. Ltd.).
140. Habgood, B. J. and Waring, J. R. S. (1941) *I.R.I. Trans.*, **17**, 50.
141. U.S. Rubber Products, U.S.P. 2,118,601.
142. BS 903 Parts C1, C2, C3: 1956.
143. ASTM D991–48T.
144. Newton, R. G. (1946) *J. Rubb. Res.*, **15**, 35.
145. Miller, R. F. (1948) *ASTM Bull.*, **151**, 98.
146. Waring, J. R. S. (1940) *I.R.I. Trans.*, **16**, 23.
147. Norman, R. H. (1951) *I.R.I. Trans.*, **27**, 276.
148. Hartshorn, L. and Ward, W. H. (1936) *J. Inst. Elec. Eng.*, **79**, 597.
149. Buist, J. M. (1950) *I.R.I. Trans.*, **26**, 192.
150. Schuh, A. E. and Kern, E. W. (1931) *Ind. Eng. Chem., Anal. Ed.*, **3**, 72.
151. Starkie, D. (1942) *Trans. Soc. Glass Tech.*, **26**, 130.
152. Evans, W. W. (1923) *Proc. Amer. Soc. Test. Mat.*, **23**, II, 517.
153. Martindale, J. G. (1942) *J. Text. Inst.*, **33**, T.151.
154. Buist, J. M. (1947) *Fundamentals of Rubber Technology*, 160.
155. Tanenhaus, S. J. and Winston, G. (1948) *ASTM Bull.*, **154**, 74.
156. (1948) *Rubb. Age, N.Y.*, **62**, 567.
157. Schiefer, H. F., Crean, L. E. and Krasny, J. F. (1949) *ASTM Bull.*, **159**, 73.
158. (1948) *Vanderbilt Handbook*, 433.
159. Williams, I. (1927) *Ind. Eng. Chem.*, **19**, 674.
160. Ookita, Y. (1935) *J. Soc. Rubb. Ind. Japan*, **8**, 534; (1936) *R.C.T.*, **9**, 502.
161. Sigler, P. A. and Holt, W. A. (1930) *India Rubb. W.*, **82**, 63.
162. Glancy, W. E. (1931) *Proc. Amer. Soc. Test. Mat.*, **31**, II, 930.
163. Depew, H. A. (1928) *Proc. Amer. Soc. Test. Mat.*, **28**, II, 871.
164. Naunton, W. J. S., Staudinger, J. P., Buist, J. M., Jones, F. A., Alton, M. D. L. and Downing, J., B.I.O.S., 1779, Item, No. 22.
165. Henry L. Scott Co., Providence, R.I.
166. Lewis, T. R. G. (1946) *I.R.I. Trans.*, **21**, 375.
167. Mitton, R. G. and Lewis, T. R. G. (1946) *J. Int. Soc. Leath. Chem.*, 74.
168. Hobbs, Kronstadt (1945) *J. Amer. Leath. Chem. Ass.*, **40**, 12.
169. Lambourn, L. J. (1928) *I.R.I. Trans.*, **4**, 210.
170. Parkinson, D. (1943) *I.R.I. Trans.*, **19**, 131.
171. Powell, E. F. and Gough, S. W. (1954) *Proc. Rubber Tech. Conf. London*, 460.
172. Tronson, J. L. and Carpenter, A. W. (1931) *Proc. Amer. Soc. Test. Mat.*, **31**, II, 908.
173. Dawson, T. R. (1926), R.A.B.R.M. Lab. Circ. No. 9.

174. Daynes, H. A. (1940) *J. Rubb. Res.*, **9**, 15.
175. Hardman, A. F., Mackinnon, W. L. and Jones, S. M. (1931) *Rubb. Age*, *N.Y.*, **28**, 463.
176. Juve, A. E., Fielding, J. H. and Graves, F. L. (1947) *ASTM Bull.*, **146**, 77.
177. (1949) *Rubb. Age, N.Y.*, **29**, 438.
178. Gavan, F. M., Eby, S. W. and Schrader, C. C. (1946) *ASTM Bull.*, **143**, 23.
179. Dawson, T. R. (1946) *J. Rubb. Res.*, **15**, 65.
180. Buist, J. M., Unpublished Work.
181. Cosler, V. A. (1932) *India Rubb. J.*, **84**, 231; (1933) *R.C.T.*, **6**, 345.
182. Klaman, C. A. (1931) *Proc. Amer. Soc. Test. Mat.*, **83**, 44.
183. Depew, H. A. (1932) *Rubb. Age, N.Y.*, **30**, 397.
184. Daynes, H. A. (1943) *J. Rubb. Res.*, **12**, 90.
185. Daynes, H. A. and Scott, J. R. (1947) *J. Rubb. Res.*, **16**, 123.
186. Scott, J. R. (1947) *J. Rubb. Res.*, **16**, 125.
187. Morley, J. F. and Scott, J. R. (1947) *J. Rubb. Res.*, **16**, 129, 130.
188. Newton, R. G., Scott, J. R. and Willott, W. H. (1948) *J. Rubb. Res.*, **17**, 69.
189. Buist, J. M. (1955) *Rubb. J.*, **129**, 520.
190. Buist, J. M. (1952) *Engineering*, **73**, No. 4489.
191. AFNOR T46-012.
192. Morley, J. F. (1948) *J. Rubb. Res.*, **17**, 61.
193. Griffith, T. R., Storey, E. B., Barkley, J. W. D. and McGilvray, F. M. (1948) *Ind. Eng. Chem., Anal. Ed.*, **20**, 837.
194. Evans, R. D. (Dec. 1942) *Proc. Twenty-Second Annual Meeting Highway Research Board.*
195. Shallamach, A. (1952) *J. Polymer Sci.*, **9**, 385.
196. Powell, E. F. (1954) *Lab. Pract.*, **3**, 67.
197. Herzog, R. and Burton, R. H. (1953) *Schweizer Archiv.*, **19**, 1, 1.
198. Buist, J. M. (1951) *India Rubb. J.*, **121**, 180.
199. Buist, J. M. (1951) *India Rubb. J.*, **121**, 629.
200. Buist, J. M. (1957), *I.R.I. Trans.*, **33**, 102.
201. Stechert, D. G. and Bolt, T. D. (1951) *India Rubb. W.*, **123**, 578.
202. Buist, J. M., Newton, R. G. and Thornley, E. R. (1950) *I.R.I. Trans.*, **26**, 288.
203. Buist, J. M. and Williams, G. E. (1951) *India Rubb. W.*, **124**, 320, 447, 567.
204. Rainier, E. T. and Gerke, R. H. (1935) *Ind. Eng. Chem., Anal. Ed.*, **7**, 368.
205. Cooper, L. V. (1930) *Ind. Eng. Chem., Anal. Ed.*, **2**, 391.
206. Busse, W. F. (1934) *Ind. Eng. Chem.*, **26**, 1194.
207. Cassie, A. B. D., Jones, M. and Naunton, W. J. S. (1936) *I.R.I. Trans.*, **12**, 49.
208. Cadwell, S. M., Merrill, R. A., Sleman, C. M. and Yost, F. L. (1940) *Ind. Eng. Chem., Anal. Ed.*, **12**, 19.
209. Prettyman, I. B. (1944) *Ind. Eng. Chem.*, **36**, 29.
210. Buist, J. M. (1953) *I.R.I. Trans.*, **29**, 72.
211. Buist, J. M. and Williams, G. E. (1955) *ASTM Bull.*, **205**, 35.
212. BS 903 Part A10: 1956.
213. BS 903 Part A11: 1956.
214. Breckley, J. (1943) *Rubb. Age, N.Y.*, **53**, 257.
215. Carlton, O. H. and Reinbold, H. B. (1943) *India Rubb. W.*, **108**, 141.
216. Swartz, H. F. (1944) *India Rubb. W.*, **110**, 412.
217. Buist, J. M. and Powell, E. F. (1951) *I.R.I. Trans.*, **27**, 49.
218. ASTM D813-57T.
219. Buist, J. M. and Kennedy, R. L., B.P. 622,325.
220. Buist, J. M. and Williams, G. E. (1951) *I.R.I. Trans.*, **27**, 209.
221. Newton, R. G. (1939) *I.R.I. Trans.*, **15**, 358.
222. Newton, R. G. and Scott, J. R. (1947) *J. Rubb. Res.*, **16**, 245.
223. Blackwell, R. F. (1955) *Rubber J.*, **129**, 260.
224. Buist, J. M. and Naunton, W. J. S. (1950) *I.R.I. Trans.*, **25**, 378.

225. Buist, J. M., Meyrick, T. J. and Stafford, R. L. (1956) *I.R.I. Trans.*, **32**, 149.
226. ASTM D429-56T.
227. Lord Manufacturing Co.
228. Busse, W. F., Lessig, E. T., Loughborough, D. L. and Larrick, L. (1945) *J. app. Phys.*, **16**, 120.
229. Lyons, W. J., Nelson, M. L. and Conrad, C. M. (1946) *India Rubb. W.*, **114**, 213.
230. Combined Intelligence Objectives Sub-Committee Report XXXIII-19.
231. Pittman, G. A. and Thornley, E. R. (1949) *I.R.I. Trans.*, **25**, 116.
232. Garvey, B. S., Jr. (1941) *ASTM Bull.*, **109**, 19.
233. ASTM D471-57T.
234. Specifications for fuels for use in aircraft engines are issued by the Ministry of Supply.
235. BS 903 Part A16: 1956.
236. Buist, J. M. and Davies, O. L. (1946) *I.R.I. Trans.*, **22**, 68.
237. Meuser, L., Stiehler, R. D. and Hackett, R. W. (1947) *India Rubb. W.*, **117**, 57.
238. Schade, J. W. and Roth, F. L. (1947) *India Rubb. W.*, **116**, 777, 788.
239. Vila, G. R. and Gross, M. D. (1945) *Rubb. Age, N.Y.*, **57**, 551.
240. Morley, J. F., Porritt, B. D. and Scott, J. R. (1946) *J. Rubb. Res.*, **15**, 215.
241. Newton, R. G. (1948) *J. Rubb. Res.*, **17**, 178.
242. Newton, R. G. (1948) *Proc. Second Rubb. Tech. Conf. London*, 233.
243. Juve, A. E. (1947) *Ind. Eng. Chem.*, **39**, 1494.
244. Borders, A. M. and Juve, R. D. (1946) *Ind. Eng. Chem.*, **38**, 1066.
245. Morris, H. B. and Gerwels, C. H. (1947) *Rubb. Age, N.Y.*, **61**, 323.
246. Taylor, R. H., Fielding, H. H. and Mooney, M. (1947) *Rubb. Age, N.Y.*, **61**, 567, 705, 738.
247. Buist, J. M. (1953) *Kautsch. u. Gummi*, **1** WT 1, **2** WT 27.
248. Stiehler, R. D., Steel, M. N. and Mandel, J. (1951) *I.R.I. Trans.*, **27**, 298.
249. Williams, G. E. (1958) *Rubb. J. Inst. Plast.*, **134**, 728.
250. Thornley, E. R. (1958) *Rubb. J. Int. Plast.*, **134**, 827, 903.
251. Buist, J. M. (1958) *Rubb. J. Int. Plast.*, **134**, 979, **135**, 5.
252. Coutie, G. A. (1958) *Rubb. J. Int. Plast.*, **134**, 328, 439, 599.
253. Peter, J. and Heidemann, W. (1958) *R.C.T.*, **31**, 105.
254. Payne, A. R. (1958) *Rubb. J. Int. Plast.*, **134**, 915.
255. R.A.B.R.M., H. W. Wallace & Co. inv. Payne, A. R. and More, A. R. Patent applied for.
256. Buist, J. M. (1960) *Rubb. J. Int. Plast.*, **138**, 386.

CHAPTER IX

PART TWO

THE TESTING OF FINISHED PRODUCTS

by

R. N. THOMSON and W. A. GURNEY

THE subject of testing finished products falls naturally into two fields. One, the narrowest, is concerned with routine testing applied to a manufactured article to ensure a standard of quality, and by extension, to examination in the laboratory of parts or sections cut from an article, to the same end. A second, wider field, includes all tests carried out on completed products, and hence by implication the whole extent of experiment and research on composite articles, but this, of course, is impossibly broad. It must suffice therefore to consider generally only those methods and principles of product testing which have a wide applicability, or are of fundamental importance to the product and to ignore as far as possible the often fascinating trials that have been made in individual cases.

When we consider the range of experimental and standard tests available in the laboratory, it might be thought that tests on the product, apart from control tests, were obsolescent. Unfortunately this is not so; our knowledge of rubber physics is not sufficiently complete either to measure all the fundamental properties involved or to predict from these properties the complete performance of a complex structure such as a tyre. Many treasured tests of the laboratory, such as tensile strength, are often singularly uninformative on the things that matter in a product. The low tensile properties of the early butadiene–styrene rubbers did not help the technologist to foresee how well they would perform in tyre treads; but laboratory measurements of resilience accurately foretold that synthetic rubbers would have a higher power loss and heat build-up.

Even laboratory tests, such as flex testing and abrasion measurements, which attempt to simulate service conditions give answers far from the truth. This is not necessarily a fault of the test procedure. It is rather that the factors operating in service are much more complex than a superficial study would suggest and many of the laboratory tests that have been proposed seem to have been based on superficial studies. It is becoming more and more necessary to design and operate laboratory tests in conjunction with a close investigation into the factors operating in service.

There are sound economic arguments encouraging the development of laboratory tests and discouraging " field trials ", however necessary the latter may be as a final judgement. As an example, to test four tyres for road wear will require the salary of a driver for many weeks, in addition to petrol, oil, car maintenance and depreciation and the cost of the tyres themselves; it has been estimated that the cost of road testing is of the order of £50 per tyre. Similar conditions will hold for other products. Service testing will involve the destruction of some valuable articles, in addition to the cost of labour involved, so that the technician rarely gets support or facilities for all the desirable tests, and careful use of statistical methods and experimental planning are essential to obtain the best value for the money expended.[1-11, 80]

The objects of tests on finished products may be summarised as follows:

(*a*) To ensure that the product is free from manufacturing defects— e.g. blisters, bad bonding.

(*b*) To ensure that the physical properties of the manufactured product lie in the required range, e.g. hardness, compression modulus.

(*c*) To provide data on materials or design which will result in a better product and/or a cheaper one.

(*d*) To develop products to satisfy a specific set of operating conditions, e.g. low temperatures.

(*e*) To obtain a satisfactory balance of components, as premature failure of one component is not only wasteful but bad for business.

Product tests themselves are often, for various reasons, exaggerated versions of service conditions, and like all accelerated tests are liable to the dangers of either introducing new and unsuspected factors into the situation or of upsetting the balance of operating conditions to give a false assessment. As with laboratory testing, it is here that the skill and experience of the technician, supported by evidence from normal service, are employed to make a proper evaluation.

Pneumatic tyres

The pneumatic tyre is still the article with the largest and most important production in the rubber industry, and more thought and care have been devoted to its testing than to that of any other product. The major subjects for investigation are tread wear, which is usually carried out on the road, tread cracking and carcass durability, usually tested on special machines, and tyre behaviour in relation to the vehicle, such as steering properties, the effect on, ride and skidding. These latter, although fundamentally related to the vehicle, are also conveniently examined by specially designed machines.

The laboratory testing of resistance to abrasion is discussed in Part One of this chapter.

Tread wear testing

Tread wear tests represent the bulk of road testing on tyres, and this seems at present the only method of obtaining reliable data for tread compounding, although claims have been made for a machine test [12] in which a tyre runs at a slight angle on a drum with a specially prepared rough surface.

Although almost every car driver and vehicle operator has opinions on the relative tread wear of various brands of tyres, the tyre manufacturer finds it much more difficult to arrive at an opinion. There are, of course, differences to be expected between different types of vehicle and driving conditions, but wide variations are also produced by the position on the vehicle, by the nature of the road and by the weather.

In comparing road wear between individual tyres, the most important factor is the position of the tyre on the vehicle, and the effect of this in turn is modified by the nature of the road. For example, in Britain the winding roads with few long straight portions result in the greatest wear occurring, in private cars, on the front wheels, whereas in the United States, where on average these conditions do not obtain, wear may be greater on the rear wheels,[6,13] being chiefly affected by acceleration and braking. Abrasion in cornering is considerably greater than in straight running,[11,12,14] so that comparable tyres may give 50% better service in the U.S.A. than in Britain. It has also been shown by Gough and Shearer [14] that the design of the steering linkages themselves can considerably modify the abrasion of the tyres on the front wheels. For these reasons, it is important, especially when whole tyres are being compared, that the tyres should be periodically transferred to each wheel in turn, preferably in some non-systematic arrangement such as the statistical " Latin Square ". Amerongen,[8] for example, used this arrangement:

Period	Right front	Left front	Right rear	Left rear
1	A	B	C	D
2	C	A	D	B
3	D	C	B	A
4	B	D	A	C

where A, B, C and D represent four different test tyres. A more complicated " Latin Square " arrangement by Stiehler *et al.* is described later.

The arrangement of tyre test programmes can be classified as controlled or uncontrolled.[6] Controlled tests are those where vehicles are reserved for testing and are used in a systematic manner, running over a definite route. This enables the technician to have a much clearer picture of what is happening and of the effect of such factors as weather.

Uncontrolled tests are those where tyres are fitted to vehicles not running on fixed test schedules, but which carry on with their normal duties. The accuracy of repetition and the discrimination of these tests are much lower, particularly if whole tyres are used, but generally many more vehicles are available for test, and the cost of running them is absorbed in other ways, so this form of testing must always be attractive to management. In practice, most laboratories use both methods concurrently. Amerongen, for example,[8] used taxicabs in conjunction with controlled runs along a motor road.

Test tyres for tread wear comparisons may be made either with only one compound in the tread (" whole tyre ") or with two or more sections of different compounds round the circumference (" half and half ", " two-way ", etc.). The latter is an attractive arrangement, as one section of the tyre can be a standard of comparison, and thus the effects of wheel position can be largely overcome. It is still desirable, however, to change the wheels around the vehicle.[15] In a most interesting statistical study, Amon and Dannenberg[7] analysed the various factors operating in two road tests and showed that 12,000 miles of testing with " half and half " (" two-way ") tyres would give results equivalent to 48,000 miles with whole tyres. As an indication of the amount of testing required, their results show that 39,000 miles of whole tyre testing is required to discriminate at the 0·05 probability level between compounds having a difference of 5% in wear.

Although from these results the advantage seems to lie with multi-tread tyres, there are arguments on the other side. With modern cars and high speeds it is most important to obtain an accurate balance around the tyre, which means careful preparation and calculation if the compounds vary in density. Even when the tyres are prepared correctly, effects may be produced by a difference in hardness, and in one case it was found that a difference in tread wear between two halves of the order of 10% produced so much vibration at the front of the test cars that the test had to be discontinued.

It has also been claimed by Gough[16] that mechanical unbalance between tread segments may produce a modified rate of tread wear according to whether the frequency of rotation is above or below the natural frequency of the suspension system, an effect which will intensify as the out of balance increases.

It is common practice nowadays for tyre manufacturers to use " half and half " tyres, probably running on uncontrolled test vehicles for preliminary sorting, while using the more refined whole-tyre techniques with a carefully controlled programme for more important tests.

A method which avoids the disadvantage of " half and half " tyres while maintaining the close similarity of running conditions is the " twin-car " technique for directly comparing two tread compounds. Two cars of the same make, and as closely alike as possible, are used, with tyres of one tread compound fitted to all four wheels of one car, and the other tyres to the other car. The cars are then run together, with only a short distance between them. It is necessary to exchange drivers and the order of running periodically, and to change the tyres over from one vehicle to another every day. It is found that even " twin " cars which are very similar in the beginning rapidly develop noticeable differences, but nevertheless it is claimed that this method gives a discrimination between compounds as good as with " half and half " tyres.

If whole tyres are used, the method of assessing tread wear is important. The most common method in use today is to measure the depth of one or more of the grooves of the tread, at up to ten selected positions, during the life of the tyre. An alternative method is to weigh the tyre and thus obtain directly the weight of rubber worn away. Both methods have strong advocates. It was claimed by Roth and Holt [17] that results could be obtained more quickly by the weighing method, and it has also been claimed that weighing is more sensitive to small differences than the depth method. This view has been challenged by Sperberg,[6] and other investigators have taken the opposite view, that depth was more accurate than weight.[13] The statistical analysis of Amon and Dannenberg [7] showed little difference in discriminating power between the two methods. The weight method has the additional disadvantage that the tyre has to be stripped from the vehicle whenever a measurement is taken, and it cannot be used, of course, for tyres with multiple treads.

It has been found that results obtained by the two methods are not linearly related. The rate of depth loss decreases with mileage, while it is claimed that the rate of weight loss is constant.[4] It has been asserted that in general the rate of wear decreases with the progress of abrasion,[18] and this produces interesting results, as demonstrated by Sperberg [6] (Fig. 9.30). From this figure due to the changing gradient of the curves, Sperberg deduces that an assessment of relative tread wear for two compounds would differ if judged as " miles to baldness " than if rated by the relative " inches per mile ", due to the treads being compared at different stages of their life.

With so many variables having an important effect on the final result, a planned statistical approach is the only possible method of carrying out accurate wear tests. These include the use of the statistical techniques of Latin Squares [9] already described, Greco-Latin Squares, randomised incomplete blocks [10] and so on. The use of multiple-tread tyres allows quite complicated experimental designs to be used, and all this care is necessary if accurate comparisons are to be made at a reasonable cost. Examples of these techniques and their analysis are described by Buist, Newton and Thornley,[3] Amon and Dannenberg,[7] Stiehler and others,[1, 2, 4, 5] and interesting comments on the subject have been made by Sperberg.[6]

A complicated Latin Square arrangement is described by Stiehler, Steel and Mandel.[1,4] Four vehicles were used, and 16 tyres were tested

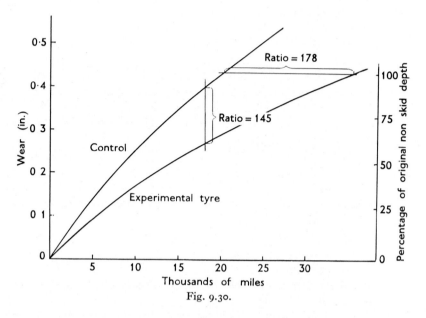

Fig. 9.30.

simultaneously. In the course of 16 test periods, each of 800 miles, each tyre was tested on each of the 16 wheels. The total number of assessments of tyre wear was 16 × 16 = 256.

From another such test valid comparisons were made between:

four " rubbers "; seven blacks; vehicles; wheel position; test periods; climatic conditions; and ageing.

This scheme, using 7 blacks in combination with 4 polymers, is not, of course, statistically balanced.

In any statistical analysis some differences will arise according to whether tread wear is judged as " miles per thousandth of an inch " or " inches per mile ". Since the two expressions are reciprocally related, if one satisfies the condition of normality the other cannot. Stiehler overcomes this by using the logarithm of tread wear as his variable, and this has a further justification in that test errors are found to increase numerically with the amount of wear, but an error term expressed as a logarithm remains approximately constant. On the Continent wear is rather more logically measured as a volume loss.[11]

The effect of test route and running conditions

For obvious reasons, the tyre technician would like his road tests to be as short as possible, and this determines to some degree the routes on which testing is done and the conditions with which the tyres are faced. Whitley [19] has pointed out that an area of sparse traffic is desirable, as is freedom from ice and snow, and that these conditions have largely concentrated road testing in the U.S.A. in the south-western states. Sperberg [6] mentions also that there is an economic advantage in testing in a dry climate, since wear on wet roads is only half that on dry. In Britain, in the past, roads did not exist where prolonged high speeds could be maintained, [20] and hence British high-speed testing had to be carried out on the Continent, using autoroutes. The south of France also has its attractions. [20] The Dutch autoroutes have been extensively used for tyre testing, particularly between The Hague and Arnhem. [11,20] German technicians often use the Nurburgring, [21] a road circuit designed for car racing. This circuit, which is exceedingly winding, offers an interesting contrast in high-speed testing to the straight autoroutes otherwise used. Both in Britain and France high-speed testing is often carried out on the runways of closed aerodromes, [20,11] and very severe cornering effects can be produced.

The question then arises as to how far testing in special climatic regions and at sustained high speeds is representative of normal running. Certainly if the condition of the road surface affects the ranking of tread compounds, tests in a dry climate will not be applicable to Britain or Western Europe generally. This point has been raised in connection with the alleged superiority of SBR over natural rubber: a claim which has not always been accepted in Britain. It has been argued by Prat [11,22] that different assessments have arisen from differences in climate, particularly ambient temperatures. From an analysis of existing data, he claimed that natural rubber is superior below $16°$ C, the advantage lying with SBR above that temperature. This was supported by evidence gathered in Sweden and France. Deaken, Houwink and van Amerongen have also suggested that the difference in average temperature between the U.S.A. and Europe may alter the relative economic advantages of natural rubber and SBR. [8]

It has also to be borne in mind when considering how accelerated road testing compares with normal wear that the relation of two compounds may be altered by the severity of abrasion, as shown by Biard and Svetlik [23] (Fig. 9.31). In addition to increased severity, the actual time taken is considerably shortened. A test vehicle will wear out a set of tyres in 3 months which would normally last from 18 months to 3 years, and thus any chemical effects due to ageing will not operate to the same extent. It has been shown that shelf ageing alone will produce a surface layer of reduced abrasion resistance.

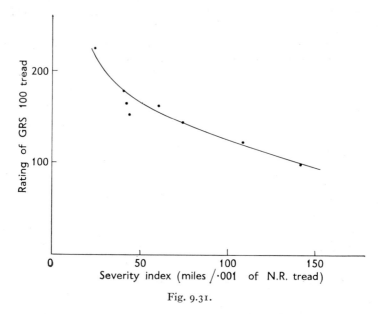

Fig. 9.31.

Geesink and Prat [11] have considered a number of factors influencing the rate of wear, including the choice of route and the methods of the driver. They compare test severity under various conditions with conditions of laboratory testing, which generally wear rubber away much faster. This has also been done by Kern,[24] who gives an interesting table of the normal speeds and intensity of wear under various conditions. Wear is expressed in the useful units of microns per minute:

	Average speed, m.p.h.	Intensity, μ/min.
Normal travel	40	0·27
Road test travel:		
Truck (*a*) 8·25–20	31	0·6
,, (*b*) 8·25–20	39	0·63
Private car	52	0·95
Nurburgring circuit:		
Truck 8·25–20	39	7·6
Private car	53	9·5
Laboratory tests:		
DVM-DIN 53516	—	240
Lambourn	—	26

The Nurburgring is seen to have over 10 times the severity of testing on normal roads.

Moyer and Tesdall [13] have given vivid illustrations of the wide range of surfaces and conditions upon which tyres may have to be used.

It seems to be now well established, and must be borne in mind when evaluating new polymers or tread recipes, that the relative rating of compounds may well alter with the conditions under which they will have to operate. These may be finally summarised as:

Load.
Speed.
Tyre pressure and pattern.
Wheel position.
Type of vehicle.
Driver.
Acceleration and braking.
Sinuosity of route.
Surface of route.
Wetness or dryness of surface.
Ambient temperature.

Temperature testing and fuel consumption

The imperfect elasticity of rubber and fabrics inevitably results in a considerable proportion of the energy used to deform a tyre being retained within it as heat, so that the temperature of the tyre rises. With the normal running of passenger-car tyres the effect is small, but quite high temperatures can be attained with high-speed running and large tyres. 100° C is not uncommon, and Powell [20] has recorded temperatures up to 145° C after 9 minutes running at 102 m.p.h.

The study of temperature rise is an important one, particularly with large-section tyres in hot climates. The inherent power loss of the basic polymer plays a large part in this heat development. The usual method of measurement is to push a needle-shaped thermocouple into the tyre at the shoulder or through to the base of the tread.[25,45] Moyer and Tesdall, however, used thermocouples built into the tyres and connected to slip-rings on the wheel,[13] but this method might interfere with the normal behaviour of the tyre and the measurements be affected by conditions at the slip-rings. The needle thermocouple is prepared by pushing a wire or wires through a large hypodermic needle and hard soldering the tip.[25] The couple is connected to the cold junction and a galvanometer or recorder in the usual way (Fig. 9.32).

Closely connected with temperature rise is fuel consumption. The normal tyre is responsible for only about 12% of the power consumption of the average car, so that large changes in resilience of the compounds used produce only small changes in the power used.[26] It can, however, be easily measured by running under standard conditions with a special calibrated fuel container.[8, 26]

Fig. 9.32. Thermocouple set for measuring tyre temperatures.

The power consumption of tyres may also be conveniently measured with a dynamometer.[12]

Tread cracking

Tread cracking is usually tested on the machine (p. 788), preferably out of doors,[12] but Sjothun, Green and Rhodes[15] have described a method wherein pre-cuts are made in the tread groove before the tyre is run, exactly as in a laboratory flexing test (p. 755).

It is more usual for tread and sidewall cracking to be carried out by fitting special tyres to private cars or on bus fleets, since these phenomena are essentially a function of time, and unduly accelerated tests may give misleading effects.

Machine testing of tyres

Endurance Tests. One of the earliest forms of indoor testing machines for tyres was a circular track around which a tyre runs, the tyre being attached to an arm pivoted at the centre of the track.[27,28] The driving motor is also on the arm, current being supplied by slip-rings. With the track filled with sharp stones or iron tetrahedra, and the arm revolving at a high speed, this apparatus can be quite spectacular, but from a technical point of view it was found to have definite limitations, and has been generally superseded by drum-type machines.[12,27,28,29] An early form of this machine took the tyre over cement, sand, mud and a " mountain " section, where the tyre was said to climb a 45% slope, " all day and every day " until it failed.[28]

The earliest drum machines were used for cycle tyres, and appear to pre-date the circular track.[28] From the beginning, ridges or slats were affixed to the surface of the drum to increase the punishment given to the tyre; in fact, when one considers the relatively frail construction of the early tyres, the treatment appears to have been drastic.

A diagram of a typical drum machine is given in Fig. 9.33. The loading weight W can be moved along the lever arms by a screw and handwheel S,

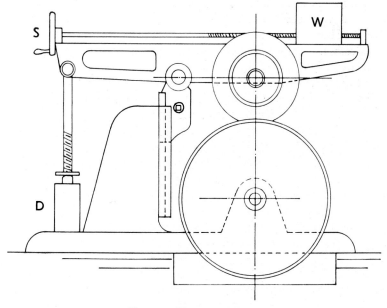

Fig. 9.33. Drum tyre tester.

and a dashpot D is provided to eliminate excessive vibration.   A machine of this type with 1 ton load on the tyre can run at drum surface speeds of 80 m.p.h., and a larger type, with a load of 3 tons, up to 40 m.p.h.   Much larger machines have, however, been constructed.   One has been described [30] in which two tyres can be applied on opposite sides of a drum with loads up to 10 tons and surface speeds up to 75 m.p.h.

The principle use of drum machines is to produce failure of the structure of the tyre.   A suggestion has been put forward for using a drum as an abrasive surface,[12] but it is probable that this would give results similar to the laboratory Lambourn machine, and hence not be completely comparable with the road.   By using slats from $\frac{1}{2}$ to 1 in. high on the drum and under-inflation of the tyre, the effect of impact on the tyre can be studied and casing break-up initiated.[12, 27]

For the study of sidewall and tread cracking, exposure to weather is important, and a description has been given of a drum machine operating out of doors.[12]   Half and half treads are used and sidewalls in three or four parts.   The results are found to be strongly influenced by the time of year, April and May giving the most severe conditions in the British Isles, due no doubt to seasonal changes in atmospheric ozone concentration.

Aircraft operation imposes some of the most severe service conditions on tyres.[20]   Apart from taxi-ing, normal running service is not often obtained, but during landing the tyres may be subjected to severe concussion, the wheels often have to be accelerated from rest to a high rotational speed and the kinetic energy of the aircraft has to be dissipated in the brakes in a very short time.   The rate of energy dissipation may be thousands of horse-power.   All this subjects the whole tyre construction to severe stresses.   Take-off and landing conditions are simulated in a machine described by Williams and Clifton,[12] in which two tyres are pressed together, one driving, the other being free.   In the take-off test the full working load is applied to the tyres at rest, and the driven tyre is speeded up.   For the landing test, the tyres are separated, the driven wheel brought up to speed and the idle tyre bumped against it at a predetermined rate.   A total power of 1,700 h.p. is available at surface speeds up to 300 m.p.h.   The sequence of operations is controlled automatically to follow the process of an actual landing.   It is not unknown for tyres to burst under extreme conditions on this machine.[20]

Larger machines for the same purpose employ flywheels 16 ft. diameter weighing up to 185 tons, with a surface speed of 200 m.p.h.[31]

Williams and Clifton [12, 27] have also described a cambered drum machine (Fig. 9.34), which, by producing lateral distortion of the tyre, applies high stresses to the beads of the tyre and to the wheel.

Impact test.   An impact test, in which a heavy weight with a conical tool on its lower face, was dropped on the tyre, was written into the SAE

Specification for aeroplane tyres in 1918,[28] and almost exactly the same test is used today.[12, 27]   The falling weight produces a fracture of the cords

Fig. 9.34. Cambered-drum tyre test machine.

similar to that occasionally occurring in service, and the severity of the test can be increased to cause the tyre to burst.

Rolling resistance and power consumption

Although the energy consumed by a tyre may be measured fairly easily on the road (p. 786), it is more readily determined on a drum machine. The drum is usually driven, the tyre running freely, and the driving motor is suspended in such a way that the torque may be measured.[12]   An early machine of this type was developed by Firestone [18] which measured both the power input and the power transmitted by the tyre, the difference giving the power lost in the tyre.   This principle is essentially the same as that of the belt dynamometer (p. 798).   Evans [26] used the deceleration of a large flywheel as a measure of power loss, and discussed the factors influencing this property.

High-speed testing

High-speed testing machines were first developed in preparation for the attempt on the Land Speed Record, and one such apparatus is capable of surface speeds up to 420 m.p.h.,[27] both drum and tyre being driven.

Under high-speed conditions " ripple " often appears [12, 32] and the power consumption increases, with increased fatigue, which may lead to more rapid casing breakdown.[33] The effect has been analysed by Turner, and is shown to be due to stationary waves developed in the tyre above a critical speed, which varies with the tyre construction, load and inflation pressure among other factors. As pointed out by Powell,[20] this pheno-menon results in a definite speed " ceiling " for a given tyre design.

Noise measurement

With the reduction of mechanical noise in the modern motor car, the noise and vibration produced by the tyre itself come into prominence. The tread pattern itself can produce " hum ", which is an airborne noise. This can be conveniently measured on a suitable testing drum, using standard acoustic measuring and analysing equipment.[34] The tyre can also generate coarser vibrations, such as " thumps ",[35] which are trans-mitted to the axle, and which may be measured by strain gauges mounted on the axle, and wheel bearings.[43] " Squeal " on cornering or braking is best observed on the road and recorded on tape for subsequent examina-tion.[43] Finally, the tyre may excite vibrations inherent in the car con-struction or, more happily,[35] minimise road noise. These effects can only be recorded inside the moving car by using a suitable noise meter.

Load deflection and contact area tests

These unspectacular but important tests should be briefly mentioned. The tyre, mounted on a rim and suitably inflated, is supported in a standard compression testing machine and the deflection of the tyre measured under varying loads.[37]

To obtain a picture of the contact area, a piece of smoked paper is placed between the tyre tread and the platen of the machine. The imprint is fixed by a solution of wax or shellac. Photographs of tread patterns under load have also been obtained by using platens of thick plate glass.

The tyre in relation to the vehicle

In the discussion so far the tyre has been considered in isolation, as an individual article. In practice, the tyre is always used as part of another complex structure, the vehicle, and tyre and vehicle mutually influence one another and modify each other's behaviour in service. For example, we know that the wear of a tyre is affected by its position on the vehicle, and

Gough has shown, by a detailed analysis,[14] that the design of the front suspension and steering can have a large effect on the type and amount of wear produced. The study of such factors in conjunction with the car designer is an important part of the work of the tyre technician.

The tyre has two principle functions on a vehicle; first, to act as a spring and thus absorb the minor inequalities of the road, and secondly, to control the direction in which the vehicle moves. The importance of the latter is not so readily appreciated until such control disappears, as in skidding on icy roads. Both front and rear wheels are involved in this action, but the deliberate steering of the car depends, of course, on the front wheels.

The tyre as a spring was dealt with in a classic paper by Healey,[38] wherein the interaction of the tyre characteristics and those of the vehicle springing were considered theoretically. It was shown how modifications in the tyre section, in inflation pressure and in the internal friction of the tyre, could reduce or intensify the vertical motion of the car due to inequalities in the road.

The joint action of the tyre as a spring and as a directing mechanism can, in appropriate circumstances, set up undesirable oscillations and lack of response. Such features are well known in automatic control mechanisms,

Fig. 9.35. Vibration testing of tyre and vehicle.

and their application to the motor vehicle is now receiving considerable attention.[36]

Although the practical study of the relation of tyre and vehicle must often be carried out on the road, laboratory apparatus has been designed in which each wheel of the car is mounted on a drum. An early example is described by Pearson,[28] and similar, though more complex and refined, types of equipment are in use today. The car must of necessity be anchored, and the development of undesirable resonant vibrations of the car (Fig. 9.35) or wobble in the front wheels can be observed as the drums

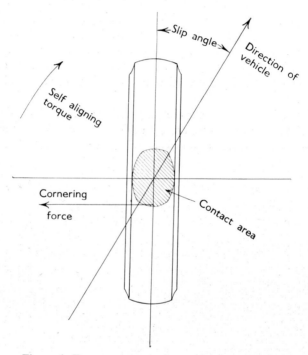

Fig. 9.36. Forces acting on a front tyre when cornering.

are speeded up. By turning the steering-wheel the steering behaviour of the car can be seen, and the increase in " drag " measured. One or more of the drums may be fitted with slats so that the whole car may be set in violent oscillation, thus providing a test not only of the tyre but also of the whole suspension and steering linkage.

The steering of a car is performed by turning the plane of the front wheels away from the direction in which they and the car are travelling at the moment, the angle of turn being known technically as the " slip angle ". As a result of this angle, a sideways force is produced, the " cornering force " [44] (Fig. 9.36), acting along the axle, and this pushes the front of the car round; at the same time the reaction of the tyre produces a " self-aligning torque ", tending to return the tyre to the direction of motion.[39,44] The cornering force produced by a given slip angle is dependent on the size of the tyre, the load it carries, the inflation pressure and the tyre construction.[42] It is also modified by the angle that the plane of the tyre makes

Fig. 9.37. Machine for measuring cornering forces on a tyre.

with the vertical—the " camber angle ". Gough and Roberts [39] have given a very clear explanation of the operation of these factors.

Individual tyres can be studied on the road by dragging them behind a vehicle, but in order to control accurately the aspect of the tyre and measure its reactions elaborate and heavy machinery is necessary.[36]

By contrast, the problem is comparatively simple in the laboratory, and several cornering-force machines have been described.[12, 39, 40] These are all on the same principle, a modification of the drum tester so that the angle of the plane of the tyre can be adjusted and the consequent changes in " drag ", " cornering force " and " self-aligning torque " are measured with appropriate equipment (Fig. 9.37).

Typical results are shown in Fig. 9.38, where cornering force and self-aligning torque are plotted against slip angle. It will be noticed that the self-aligning torque, which is felt by the driver at the steering-wheel, first increases and then decreases. At the point X the tyre commences to skid,

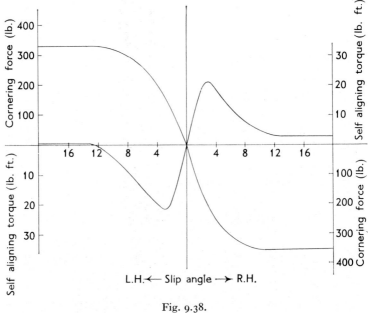

Fig. 9.38.

the cornering force being now constant and the self-aligning torque falling to zero.

The point at which skidding occurs depends on the coefficient of friction of the tyre against the road surface. This may be measured on drums if the surface can be modified. Clifton describes how thick ice is formed on a tyre-testing drum by packing the interior with dry ice.[12] A large part of skidding tests are, however, carried out on actual vehicles by intrepid drivers on specially designed skid tracks.[12, 41]

In addition to skidding tracks, special " proving grounds " are now often used for investigating the tyre in relation to the vehicle. Testing on the road is necessary to supplement that in the laboratory, but the amount and character of testing that can be done on the public highways is limited. The " proving ground " is an open-air laboratory in which a variety of road

Tyre Proving Ground

Plan of Sections

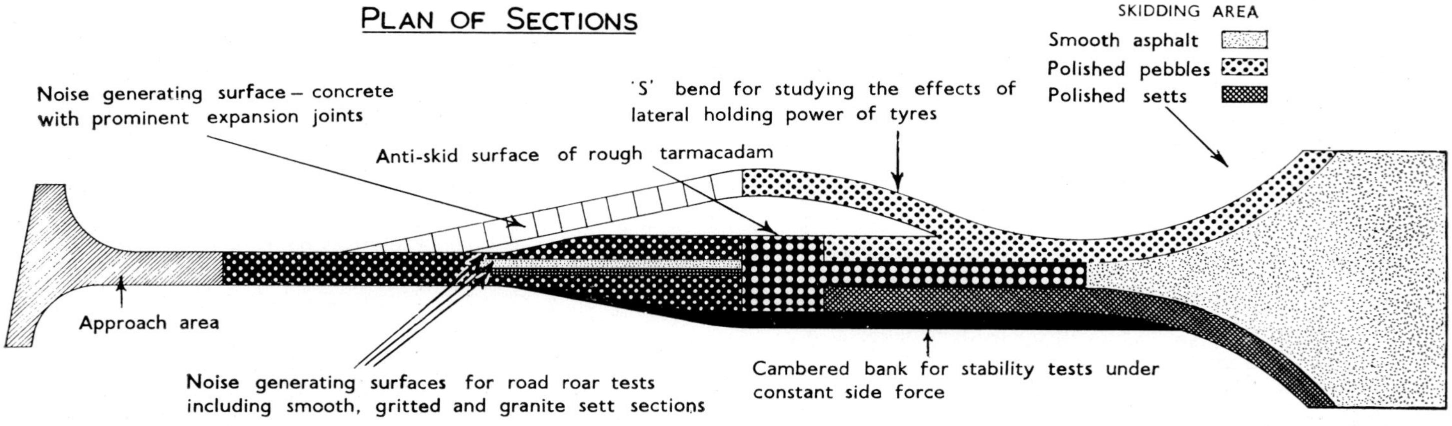

Noise generating surface – concrete with prominent expansion joints

'S' bend for studying the effects of lateral holding power of tyres

Anti-skid surface of rough tarmacadam

Noise generating surfaces for road roar tests including smooth, gritted and granite sett sections

Cambered bank for stability tests under constant side force

Approach area

SKIDDING AREA

Smooth asphalt

Polished pebbles

Polished setts

Fig. 9.39.

conditions are provided and where car manoeuvres can be carried out with complete freedom and privacy.[41] A range of road surfaces from smooth, slippery granite sets to rough tarmacadam are provided, on which noise measurement and road-holding tests can be performed. An interesting feature of this particular arrangement is the provision of a track with a 1 in 5 slope from side to side. This exerts a constant side force on the vehicle, so that steering stability can be studied (Fig. 9.39).

Belting

Many factors contribute to satisfactory performance of a conveyor belt. Since the large physical size and complexity of the associated mechanical components of a conveyor belt installation imposes economic limitations on the amount of testing that may be carried out on complete belts, the trend has been towards the development of specific tests for the examination of each factor separately under controlled conditions.

Such tests may be made on small samples cut from the belting on standard rubber laboratory testing apparatus, or may themselves require complicated test machines simulating some particular feature of a conveyor-belt system.

Conveyor belts must withstand driving and loading stresses, and longitudinal and transverse strengths, and elongations under loads are therefore important. These tests may be made on samples of full belt width, samples cut to given dimensions [46,47] or on test pieces taken from individual fabric plies of the belt.[48,49] It has, however, been shown [50] that the total belt strength is less than the sum of the strengths of the various plies, for if the plies are assembled under unequal tensions it follows that loads at a given extension will be unequally shared by the plies. Hence this loss of theoretically available strength may provide an index to the efficient use of the reinforcing fabric.

In practice, the strength of a conveyor belt is fixed by the fasteners between adjacent lengths, and it is only in belts spliced *in situ* to a fixed length that the potential belt strength is approached.

Although the rubber parts of fabric/rubber belts do not contribute significantly to the strength of the belt, tensile tests are made—and in fact specified [48]—as a means of determining quality of the rubber compound.[47] These tests may be made after accelerated ageing to determine heat resistance of the rubber cover, or in the case of oil-resisting belting, after immersion in the appropriate fluid.[46]

Ply adhesion tests on belting are usually of the type described as " dead weight ",[46,48,49] but the effect of rate of separation on the measured adhesion has also been investigated,[51] and a rate of 100 mm./min. is used in Germany.

Perhaps the most important aspect of conveyor-belt development in recent years has been the emphasis on non-inflammability, and many test methods have been devised to give qualitative and quantitative measures of fire resistance. These tests fall into two categories, generally described as drum-friction tests and flame tests, whose objects are respectively to determine the resistance of the belt to self-ignition by friction and the extent to which the belt will support combustion when ignited by this or other causes.

The Cresswell Colliery disaster of 1950 [47] made only too clear the advisability of using only non-inflammable belting in situations where the consequences of fire may be serious. It has been established that this fire was initiated by a damaged and stalled conveyor belt rubbing against a belt-driving drum until sufficient heat was generated to ignite the belt.

A number of drum-friction tests have since been described [53-56] and field trials reported.[57, 58]

The fundamental test work leading to the establishment of various national specifications for fire-resistant belting is described by Acres [59] in a comprehensive review, to which is appended an extensive bibliography.

The test specified by the National Coal Board is representative of drum-friction tests. Section 5 of the specification [53] covering fire-resistant conveyor belt is reproduced in full, by kind permission of the Board.

Drum friction test

A length of the belt 6 in. wide shall be passed through an arc of 180° around a horizontally disposed steel drum * 8 in. diameter. As shown in Fig. 9.40 the horizontal length shall be secured at one end and a 70 lb. weight shall be attached to the free end hanging vertically from a guide pulley. The drum shall be rotated at 190 ± 10 rev./min. away from the top secured portion (i.e., similar to the forward direction of a conveyor drive) until the belt is destroyed. The test shall be carried out in:

(*a*) still air;
(*b*) an air current having a velocity of 500 ft./min. at 8 in. from the drum surface.

The sample shall fail the test if in either (*a*) or (*b*) above:

(1) any sign of flame or glow appears on any part;
(2) the temperature of the surface of the drum exceeds 300° C.

The simplicity of both apparatus and test method, and absence of liability to subjective error in assessing the results, merit particular attention.

The U.S. Bureau of Mines,[54] in a somewhat similar test specification,

* Within wide limits the surface texture (i.e., the roughness) of the drum has little effect on the severity of the test although the test duration may be altered. Surface textures between the limits of very smooth and rough turned are permissible and the worn surface which develops naturally in the course of repeated testing is admissible. The surface should not, however, be treated artificially to reduce the duration of the test.

also requires that no flame or glow should appear, but in this case the temperature of the drum, as measured by thermocouples inserted between the plies of the belt, must not exceed 250° C.

Many other general tests have been applied to belting, among which may be mentioned surface friction and electrical conductivity.[60] The latter is of importance for the dissipation of static electrical charges as a potential fire hazard.

Power consumption in conveyor belts does not appear to have been extensively investigated, no doubt due to much greater losses occurring in

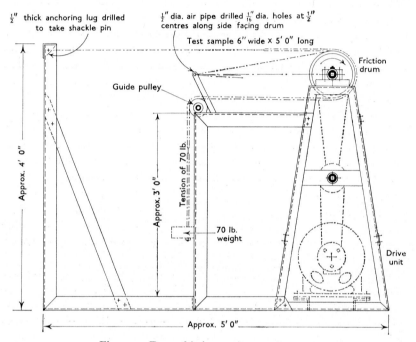

Fig. 9.40. Drum friction testing apparatus

practice due to uphill gradients and friction. The property, however, is of first importance in power-transmission belting, since any energy lost to the belt and pulleys may be regarded as equivalent to a direct reduction of power delivered by the prime mover. Swift [61] investigated this loss of transmitted power for canvas, rubber and other belts as early as 1928, and introduced a " coefficient of performance " or " pull efficiency " $\dfrac{T_1 - T_2}{T_1}$, where T_1 and T_2 are the tensions in the tight and slack sides of the belt respectively. This value was subsequently recorded for various types of belting, including V-belting, by Brazier and co-workers [62] in 1938. The effect of tension on slip was also investigated and the point made that coefficients of performance should be compared at safe working tensions, having due regard for the tensile properties of the belts. The unique ability of V-belts to transmit torque with zero tension in the slack side is also first noted in this paper.

In an early series of articles covering many aspects of transmission-belt testing Sturtevant [49] also relates power transmission to slip. His use of a dynamometer in life tests is also interesting; small pulleys were used in this test to give severe flexing, and the belts considered to have failed when ply separation occurred over a length of 5 in.

Flame tests for conveyor belting follow the usual pattern. Samples are ignited in a controlled flame under specified conditions, and the times of persistence of the flame and afterglow measured from the instant of removal of the burner. [47, 53, 54, 63] An attempt by Sardemann [64] to determine the dependence of inflammability upon temperature, using an electric muffle furnace, gave inconsistent results, due to the fumes and smoke evolved.

It has been found that simple tests of the kind often described as " static " are insufficient for the full evaluation of conveyor belts. In service, belts are subjected to abrasion, flexing, impact, cutting and other wearing processes, all of which may contribute to failure. Tests have been devised for the separate examination of each of these factors.

The various laboratory abrasion tests developed for tyre treads, shoe soleing, flooring, etc., are available and relevant to the testing of rubber covering compounds; abrasion is also sometimes assessed in conjunction with other properties, such as cutting, on a test installation in which the belt carries sharp rocks. [59]

In a survey of the development in Germany of tests for belts and hose for use in coal-mines, [47] distinction is made between the types of abrasion occurring under wet and dry conditions. For use under normal coal-mining conditions, Schlobach and Bursen developed in 1938 an abrasion machine in which samples punched from the belt are pressed against a drum covered with abrasive cloth. This appears to have become a standard test. [65] For the damp condition of brown coal-mining, where abrasion is largely due to the action of scrapers, a special test is described. The abrasive action of the cleaning scrapers is simulated by the machine, sand being the abrasive medium.

Impact tests are designed to simulate the destructive action that may occur at the loading point. Heavy stones or large pieces of coal dropping on to the belt may cause damage by crushing or bursting of the belt structure, according to whether the belt is supported or not at the point of impact. One such machine combining both concussion and flexing subjects a 6-in.-wide belt to a series of hammer blows while the belt is passing over a steel plate. [66] Although external examination may reveal little or no damage, subsequent tensile tests show that the textile reinforcement is substantially reduced in strength by such treatment.

An additional feature is the provision of bolt heads protruding from the driving drum to produce the type of stresses set up by trapped stones.

The Izod type of pendulum test has been extensively used to determine the resistance to impact of textile reinforcement.[67] Meiners [47] describes the application of this type of test to fatigue assessment, the growth of the belt under impact being recorded.

Flexing tests are conveniently made by running test belts over pulleys; severity is easily controlled by adjusting pulley diameter and belt speed. Work absorption has also been investigated in this way.[68, 69]

Hose

The function of most rubber hose is to convey liquids or gases between points liable to relative motion. The chief exception to this generalisation is the use of hose connections between fixed points on a rigid structure, such as an aircraft engine. Here the choice of a flexible hose rather than a rigid metal pipe is often governed by considerations of vibrations or thermal expansion.

The ability of hose to withstand repeated flexing is therefore fundamental, and many tests of this property are in use. These vary from " whip tests ",[70] in which one end of a pressurised hose is carried repeatedly at high speed around a circle of large radius (Fig. 9.41), to vibration tests of small amplitude.[71, 72, 73] In order to achieve maximum destructive effort, vibration tests are best made on hoses bent to their minimum specified radius, under extreme conditions of internal pressure and temperature (Fig. 9.42).

Flame tests for fire-resistant hose may be misleading if conducted on static samples, owing to the formation of a protection layer of adherent but brittle ash. It is therefore better to subject the sample to some form of flexing or vibration throughout the flame test.

Various standard flames have been used, the most satisfactory being those produced by burning gases of known composition in burners of strictly specified design and construction. A typical test consists of subjecting the pressurised hose, bent to its minimum radius and with one end fitting mechanically vibrated, to the flame for 5 minutes, during which time no leakage should result.

For hoses carrying oxygen or inflammable gases, an ignition test is required for British Standards approval.[74, 75] In this test a sample of the lining is placed in a stream of pure oxygen at 360° C, and must not ignite in a time of less than 2 minutes.

Pressure and bursting tests are largely self-explanatory. Pressure tests

Fig. 9.41. A typical hose fatigue test.

Fig. 9.42. Vibration tests on high-pressure aircraft hoses.

D D

may be made with the hose straight or bent to its minimum radius, and dimensional changes in diameter and length under the influence of internal pressure may also be informative. In the case of hose reinforced with an enbedded wire helix, change of length may be appreciable, and recovery of its original length on release of pressure is important. Determination of percentage set after given pressurisation and recovery periods gives a useful basis of comparison.[76]

Oil resistance of internal and external linings is best determined in the laboratory on the rubber compounds employed, or may be examined by means of swelling tests on samples cut from the hose itself,[77, 78] in cases where the effect of the fluid on ply adhesion and strength is to be determined. Such tests may be supplemented by flow tests, or checks of bore reduction by passing balls of slightly under nominal diameter through the hose after pressure and temperature tests. This method is also used to confirm that bore diameter has not been significantly decreased by the attachment of end fittings, and to examine the effect of suction, i.e. sub-atmospheric internal pressure, on bore.[71, 72] Alternatively, suction hose may be checked for collapse by external measurements when connected to a vacuum pump [70] or by measuring the load necessary to compress short sections of hose.[77]

Shoes and shoe soleing

The post-war development of high-styrene resins has greatly extended the use of rubber in the footwear industry. Rubber–resin composition soleing in various forms are now accepted soleing materials for a wide range of shoes; indeed, the manufacture of shoe soleing in sheet form is now an important part of rubber production, and as would be expected, special tests have been developed for this product.

Among the attractions of resin–rubbers in this application are hardness, low gravity, good wearing characteristics and flexibility, with adequate resistance to cracking. Hardness and specific gravity are ubiquitous tests which call for no special comment here.

Machine tests of abrasive wear of shoe-soleing materials in general present many of the problems encountered in the abrasion testing of tyre-tread compounds, notably poor correlation with service trials.[78, 79]

Buist [78] examined results obtained by Grimwade and Clapham [79] in which the pressure between the test pieces and the abrasive disk on a du Pont machine was varied, and suggests that test conditions could be derived to give improved correlation with wear for each type of soleing, but remarks that this has no practical value, since a prohibitive amount of work would be required to establish conditions appropriate to each type of material.

As with tyres, however, such tests are usually regarded as an initial assessment and are followed by service trials.   The use of children's shoes in wear trials has much to commend it, since, as all parents will agree, wear is extremely rapid, and the co-operation of a local school goes far to simplify administrative problems.   In a test of this nature [80] the British Boot, Shoe and Allied Trades Research Association (SATRA) calculate " durability ratios " between test and standard soleing from weight losses, but the relation between thickness and volume loss is also investigated.   This report on resin–rubbers is also interesting as an example of the statistical analysis of test data.

Both crack initiation and crack-growth tests are relevant to shoe soleing, and machines such as the De Mattia (p. 755) may be used.   Hall,[81] however, has developed a machine specifically for examining the cut growth of properties of resin–rubbers; in this test the sample is bent into a semicircle of constant radius, and the flexed configuration is independent of the stiffness of the test sample.   The cut is initiated by piercing with a chisel of specified dimensions.   In its Specifications [82, 83] for rubber–resin and micro-cellular soleing, SATRA requires that after 125 kc. the crack shall not have extended beyond 8 mm. in length.

Low compression set is very desirable in soleing, since a tendency to " spread " in wear causes the shoe to become generally misshapen, and in particular makes the toe turn up.   Compression set at constant load [84, 85] rather than constant deflection is to be preferred.

While the usual laboratory tear-test methods are applicable to shoe soleing, two other types of tearing tests have been developed for this product.   " Stitch tear ", for evaluating the ability of the material to resist tearing between adjacent stitches when this method of attachment is employed, appears to have been first measured in Germany.[86]   A needle of 1 mm. diameter is pushed through the test piece 5 mm. from one end. The force necessary to tear the needle sideways through the test piece is measured on a tensile testing machine.   A similar test has been employed for micro-cellular and solid soleing, in which a loop of piano wire is passed through two holes drilled in the test piece, and the load required to tear the loop through the intervening material measured in the same way. " Split tear " is also measured in the case of micro-cellular soleing.[83]   This test is designed to examine the resistance of the material to separation into layers by tearing in its own plane, the method being somewhat analogous to tear down adhesion tests.   The test piece is a strip 1 in. wide, which is prepared by cutting into two layers of equal thickness at one end.   The two tabs so formed are gripped in jaws and the load required to continue the separation by tearing down is recorded.   SATRA have developed an elegant test machine, utilising a cantilever beam, for this test.[87]

The importance of frictional properties of soles and heels can hardly be overrated.   Tests have been reported on a wide range of materials using laboratory friction measuring devices,[88, 89] and the British Boot, Shoe and Allied Trades Research Association have made subjective tests on complete shoes [90] in which a ramp of adjustable angle was employed to determine the slip of different soles and heels on snow and ice (Fig. 9.43).   The

Fig. 9.43. Adjustable ramp used by British Boot, Shoe and Allied Trades Research Association to examine slip of different types of soleing on various surfaces.
[*Central Office of Information Photograph.*

angle of the ramp is increased progressively until it is impossible to walk up, or down, without making use of hand-rails.   No difference was apparent on ice between cleated and plain rubber soles, but crêpe rubber and cellular soleing enabled high gradients to be negotiated safely.   In general, high resistance to slip on smooth surfaces is obtained with soft materials.

Other tests made on complete shoes are designed to examine the product from a structural point of view.   Repeated flexing or scuffing at the toes may cause separation of the sole or upper, or such faults as cracking in waterproof rubber boots.

Cellular rubber

The rapid post-war expansion of the foam-rubber industry has been accompanied by the development and use by each manufacturer of a number of special tests, often domestic and unpublished, for quality control purposes.

Apart from such simple concepts as ageing, the experimenter is faced with the problem of deciding what properties are desirable in foam rubber. Ideally for the majority of uses an objective measure of comfort is required; but personal tastes differ so widely in this respect that it is unlikely that the generalisation " comfort " will ever be reduced to a single physical index, even to cover such a limited field as, say, mattresses.

The trend has therefore been towards accelerated service type tests on products, although a number of tests of the more obvious physical properties have now been standardised. These are discussed briefly below.

The term " density ", where applied to foam rubber or cellular materials generally, is the weight in air per unit volume of the unstressed material. " Apparent density " is a better description, but this term has been reserved in some specifications [91] to cover " cored " products, i.e. products having large cavities in their construction.

Compression stress–strain relationships are used as a measure of hardness for cellular rubbers, although the term " hardness " is often used subjectively. Distinction must be made between the compression characteristics of cellular rubber *per se* and that of products incorporating moulded cavities. Existing nomenclature is not entirely unambiguous on the point, " indentation " or " indentation hardness " sometimes applying in both cases.

Talalay [92] discusses the factors affecting hardness of foam-rubber products in some detail. These fall into three groups: cellular, comprising density, cell size and air-to-polymer ratio; rubber properties, notably modulus; and structural considerations, including the size and shape of moulded cavities.

The British Standard method [93] for determining stress–strain relationship of cellular rubber slab or sheeting is interesting in that the shape, but not the size, of the test piece is specified; a square of side four times the sample thickness is required, giving a shape factor of unity. This allows direct comparisons to be made between sheets of different thickness, the moulded surfaces being left intact. Results are expressed as stress per unit area for various percentage compressions of the sample. In the corresponding ASTM tests test pieces of standard dimensions are used, and the load per unit area for a 25% compression is determined.[94]

Tensile tests are sometimes made, usually to determine loss of strength and elongation due to accelerated ageing. Large dumb-bell-shaped test

pieces are necessary in order to minimise the effect of the cellular structure.[91, 93, 95]

Compression set under constant deflection follows the normal practice
for rubbers.   Compressions of 50–75% are usual.[93, 94]

For testing complete products, such as cushions and mattresses, compression stress–strain measurements are replaced by various forms of
indentor tests.[95, 98]   A full description and illustration of a suitable tester
is given in various British Specifications;[93, 97] a circular indentor 12 in.
diameter with rounded edges is lowered on to the cushion with a load of
2 kg. to obtain the initial height, and then forced into the cushion.   The
hardness is expressed as the load required to produce 40% indentation.
This procedure is followed in Germany [95] but in the U.S.A. 25% compression is usual.[94, 98]

The use of hardness tests alone, whether for foams themselves or for
products, is far from satisfactory, as a single number is insufficient to
identify the character of the material.   Whereas natural latex foams have
a progressive increase in the slope of the stress–indentation curve (Fig.
9.44*a*), polyurethane foams, for example, show a curious and characteristic
flattening of the curve after an initial stiffness, as shown in Fig. 9.44*b*.

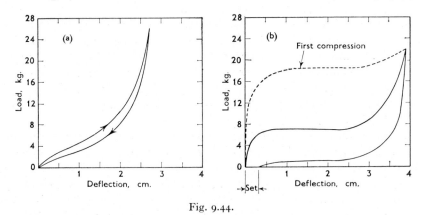

Fig. 9.44.

This gives the material a peculiar feel and a different behaviour as a
cushioning material.   As with solid rubber, the nature of the return curve
forming the hysteresis loop is also important.

Another feature of foams is their softening, temporary or permanent,
under repeated flexing, and various methods have been devised for studying
this.   Most specifications require the flat cushion or other article to be
repeatedly " pounded " by a circular indentor (12–18 in. diameter) for
about 250,000 cycles at 60–240 blows per minute, the loss in hardness and
set being recorded.[92, 94, 96, 98]

Another method of measuring fatigue resistance, particularly for mattresses, is to pass heavy rollers over the article—for example, rollers 42 in. long, 18 in. diameter, weighing 224 lb. at a rate of 42 " passes " per minute, until 150,000 passes have been made.[99] A more ingenious method, although not specific for foam mattresses, uses two " realistic " figures weighing 12 stone (168 lb.) and 9 stone (126 lb.), respectively, which roll from one " shoulder " over their " backs " to the other " shoulder " and back again, eight times per minute, so that 10 years normal wear can be simulated in 60–70 hours.[100]

For some purposes a flammability test is specified. In one case [101] the rubber is required to be held in a standard candle for 1 minute, while in another [91] the material is held in a wire-mesh trough over a standard bunsen burner for only 10 seconds. The duration of after-burning and loss in volume are measured.

Golf and tennis balls

Certain properties of finished golf and tennis balls are closely specified by the ruling authorities of the respective games. Size and weight suffice for golf balls, but tennis balls are controlled for size, weight, hardness and rebound.[102] The hardness of golf balls is, however, an important feature, and is always controlled by the manufacturer. In both tennis and golf balls the final hardness is measured by automatic machines which press a plunger on the ball, with a small initial load. The plunger is then clamped and a higher standard load applied to the ball. The resulting deflection is used as a basis for sorting. By virtue of their shape, golf and tennis balls can conveniently be moved from place to place by gravity, and automatic sorting for hardness, size and weight is easily achieved. The official hardness of tennis balls is determined by a standard machine designed by Stevens,[103] in which the compression caused by a load of 18 lb. is recorded. Bounce, or more correctly " bound " is determined by dropping the ball from a standard height of 100 in. on to a concrete base and noting the height to which the ball rebounds. With a little practice, a high degree of accuracy is possible with a simple vertical scale. A bound of between 53 and 58 in. is required for official approval. This test is also of assistance to the manufacturer in selecting balls suitable for use at different altitudes.

The behaviour of the golf ball in flight is of paramount importance, and machines have been designed to strike a ball with a club in a standard manner [103] (Fig. 9.45). Testing with this or similar apparatus is essential for development work, and can be very pleasant in summer weather. Flights of over 200 yards are usually obtained. The flight of the ball is governed by the pattern on the surface, that is the shape and depth of the recesses. In normal flight, due to the rotation of the ball imparted by the

Fig. 9.45. Golf-ball flight-testing machine.

club, the first part of the trajectory is concave upwards, and the additional
height can increase the length of flight.   Excessive lift will, however, lead
to a loss of length.
    Some typical values have been given by Ball.[102]

Depth of pattern, in.	Carry, yd. (horizontal distance in the air)
0·002	117
0·004	187
0·008	223
0·010	238
0·012	225

    Observations are made of height of flight, length of " carry ", length of
run and of any swerving that may occur in the air.   As the results are obviously greatly affected by weather, particularly wind, a statistical approach
is necessary, and tests should preferably be repeated on several days.
    Methods have also been devised to test the resistance of the cover to
cutting by " topping ".   The ball is hit a glancing blow by a hammer of
appropriate form, and subsequent examination of the resulting damage

facilitates the comparison of different compositions or thicknesses of cover.
A point of importance in the design of tennis balls is the durability of the cover. An endurance tester for obtaining information on this has been in use for many years, and consists of a racket attached to the end of a rotating arm driven by an electric motor. About six balls are placed in a reservoir above the racket and are released one at a time by an electric mechanism so as to fall exactly at the right instant in front of the racket. The struck ball rebounds from a base-plate, on to an end wall and thence is reflected back in to the reservoir, thus giving a continuous process. The same machine will also test the racket.

Bonded products

In the majority of bonded products the most important test is the strength of the bond between the rubber and metal or other base material, but often this is difficult to measure. For a first sorting, a crude pushing at the rubber at a bonded edge with a blunt tool is often used. Crude though it is, this will often reveal bad bonding, and particularly weaknesses due to excessive flow of rubber at the edge of a bonding surface. This may be followed by a distortion of the rubber of the product to several times its working deflection, either by a proper tool or by bars and levers. Such elementary methods, although common, need care, as an over-enthusiastic examiner may often ruin good products without adding greatly to the improvement of the standard of work.

More refined methods use specially designed jigs or tools to apply a known load or deflection to the product in a suitable testing machine.[104] Often special machines are designed for the purpose where a long run of production justifies it, but standard tensile, compression- or torsion-testing machines are satisfactory if proper ancilliary equipment is provided. Most bonded articles are designed to have a working stress at the bond from 50 to 150 lb./in.^{2}, and proof stresses up to 300–400 lb./in.^{2} may be applied. This is sometimes difficult, as the metal or base parts themselves may fail at this loading. Many bonded parts are made to a customer's own specification, and it is common in these cases for testing rigs to be provided in the same way that moulds are.[105]

Static tests often give insufficient information on the product, and dynamic tests may be used.[106] Here again, the testing equipment may need to be specially designed. Difficulty arises in dynamic tests owing to heat build-up in the sample, which may alter the test conditions completely by producing a very high temperature at the bond. In one series of tests the fatigue life of a bond was found to vary inversely as the eighth power of the applied load, but at the higher loads the sample became too hot to touch, and the results were quite unfair to the product.

The difficulty of bond testing on the product is illustrated by the fact that some factories find it necessary to test 5% of their products to destruction [105] to ensure consistent working of the bonding process.

A large proportion of bonded products have to function as springs, and their load–deflection characteristics must be determined using similar equipment to that used for bond testing.[106]

Solid tyres

Solid tyres are a special case of a bonded product. For many years the rubber was attached to the steel base by use of an intermediate layer of ebonite, but now " direct bonding " by brass-plating or by special agents is becoming more usual. The usual method of measuring the bond is to cut off surplus rubber, leaving a layer $\frac{1}{2}$ in. thick above the metal base.   In the centre of the surface of the rubber a cut is made down to the base all round the tyre, and two cuts 1 in. on each side of the centre, thus giving two strips of rubber 1 in. wide.   One end of each strip is cut free, and the load required to maintain tearing is determined either by dead weights or by a suitable loading mechanism.   Owing to the pronounced anistropy of most solid tyres, it is necessary to tear in two directions around the tyre,[107] hence the provision of two strips.   Good bonds require from 50 lb. upwards to maintain tearing.   Care has to be taken to cut back to the bond surface whenever the tear runs up into the thickness of the rubber.

Service tests on solid tyres are also carried out on suitable vehicles, as for pneumatic tyres.   Abrasion wear is relatively unimportant, since cutting and overloading leading to overheating and bond failure are the usual causes of failure.

Testing by ultrasonics and X-rays

Sound waves of very high frequency (ultrasonic) passing through a solid are reflected when they come to a solid–air boundary.   For this reason they can be used to detect cavities in nominally solid bodies, for example, between the plies of a pneumatic tyre.   The Research Association of British Rubber Manufacturers has prepared a comprehensive bibliography of the earlier application of this method to the testing of rubber products.[108]

The principles and apparatus used have been well described by Hatfield.[109]   The sound waves used have a frequency of about 50 kc./s.   They are generated by a piezo-electric crystal, and transmitted through water to the inside of the tyre immersed in water.   The ultrasonic waves pass without hindrance from the water to the tyre, but are stopped at any air cavity existing in the tyre structure.   A battery of receiving crystals on the outside of the tyre enables the position of the fault to be located (Fig. 9.46).

Cavities of $\frac{3}{8}$ in. diameter can be detected, thickness being unimportant, provided there is no contact between opposite faces.

It is customary for the tyre to be hung vertically from rollers, dipping into water in a trough so that the tyre may be rotated [109-111] during the test.

Ultrasonics have also been used to examine bonded articles, where blisters and patches of non-adhesion are of particular importance, and it has been shown that these defects can be detected if sufficiently large.[112] Even though an area of poor adhesion is present, it will not be detected

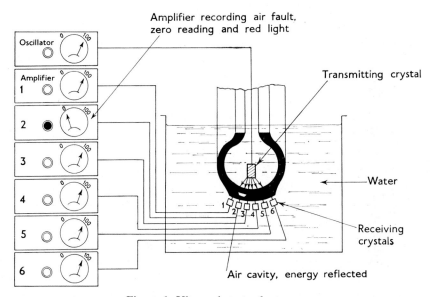

Fig. 9.46. Ultrasonic tester for tyres.

unless there is an actual void. For this reason it is necessary to apply a small strain to the article to cause separation. Flaw detection in bonded products is difficult with products which are not flat, and dangerous areas of low adhesion will not be discovered unless actual separation can be produced. The method does not seem to have been widely adopted.

The X-ray examination of pneumatic tyres has been standard for many years. The apparatus used is normal, and the process does not call for any particular comment.[113] The chief objects of the examination are bead-wire abnormalities, checking on the angles of the cords in the casing and detecting foreign matter. Occasionally metal wires, mercury or other opaque matter may be inserted or built into experimental tyres to elucidate specific problems.[113]

Conclusion

While the testing of pneumatic tyres is obviously of great importance and complexity, and has therefore been discussed at some length, it does not follow that other simpler products can be adequately evaluated by less exhaustive test procedures. A rubber O-ring or cup-section seal is superficially a very simple product, and it might be supposed that its performance could be judged from a few simple tests. Experience has shown, however, that extensive and complicated test equipment [115] is necessary to investigate fully all the factors relevant to the service behaviour of the seal—among which we may list minimum and maximum operating temperature, effect of hydraulic fluid, pressure, friction, dimensional tolerances, hardness, ageing characteristics and many others.

The rubber technician is therefore faced with a two-fold problem of devising test methods and programmes. The purely technical one of developing efficient and economical methods of examining specific properties, capable of significant and unambiguous conclusions, is often overshadowed by the uncertainty of the relative importance of these properties. Thus to the five objects of testing as defined on p. 778 could be added a sixth—to achieve objects (c), (d) and (e) with a minimum expenditure of time, energy and money.

While a careful study of the relevant literature is often invaluable, the danger of assuming a too wide validity of published test data should be emphasised. It is often wise to ensure that published data is directly applicable under the local—or national—conditions of product use by conducting abbreviated confirmatory test programmes. As an example, already cited, it has been found that relative tread wear assessment based on fleet tests on the long straight roads of the southern U.S.A. are not always valid under the driving conditions prevailing in the British Isles or continental Europe. With this cautionary reservation, a study of published data is to be recommended before any major test programme is undertaken.

REFERENCES

1. Stiehler, R. D., Steel, M. N. and Mandel, J. (1951) *I.R.I. Trans.*, **27**, 298.
2. Stiehler, R. D., Richey, G. G. and Mandel, J. (1953) *Rubb. Age, N.Y.*, **73**, 201.
3. Buist, J. M., Newton, R. G. and Thornley, E. R. (1950) *I.R.I. Trans.*, **26**, 288.
4. Mandel, J., Steel, M. N. and Stiehler, R. D. (1951) *I.E.C.*, **43**, 2901.
5. Stiehler, R. D., Steel, M. N. and Mandel, J. (1951) *International Symposium Abrasion and Wear* (Delft).
6. Sperberg, L. R. (Nov. 1955) A.C.S. Fall Meeting, Philadelphia.
7. Amon, F. H. and Dannenberg, E. M. (1955) *Rubb. World*, **131**, 627, 770.
8. de Decker, H. C. J., Houwinck, R. and van Amerongen, G. J. (1954) *Proc. Third Rubber Tech. Conf.*, 640.

9. Fisher, R. A. *Design of Experiments* (Edinburgh: Oliver and Boyd).
10. Fisher, R. A. and Yates, F. *Statistical Tables* (Edinburgh: Oliver and Boyd).
11. Geesink, H. A. O. W. and Prat, C. (1956) *Rev. gén. Caoutch.*, **33**, 973.
12. Williams, J. I. S. and Clifton, R. G. (1954) *Proc. Third Rubber Tech. Conf.*, 512.
13. Moyer, R. A. and Tesdall, G. L. (1945) *Iowa St. Coll. Bull.*, No. 161.
14. Gough, V. E. and Shearer, G. R. *Inst. Mech. Eng.* (In press.)
15. Sjothun, I. J., Green, P. S. and Rhodes, S. N. (1953) *Rubb. Age, N.Y.*, **74**, 231.
16. Gough, V. E. and Jones, P. W. B. (1952) *Auto Engineer*, **42**, 17.
17. Roth, F. L. and Holt, W. L. (1944) *M.B.S. Res. Paper No.* 1574.
18. Buist, J. M. (1951) *Int. Symposium Abrasion and Wear* (Delft).
19. Whitby, G. S. (1954) *Synthetic Rubber* (London: Chapman and Hall).
20. Powell, E. F. *S.A.E.* (In press.)
21. Fromandi, G. and Oetner, K. (1954) *Kautch. u. Gummi*, **7**, 212.
22. Prat, C. (1955) *Rev. Caoutch.*, **32**, 991.
23. Biard, C. C. and Svetlik, J. F. (1952) *Rubb. World*, **127**, 363.
24. Kern, W. (1956) *Rubb. Chem. Technol.*, **29**, 806.
25. Horning, V. J. (1953) *Rubb. Age, N.Y.*, **74**, 395.
26. Evans, R. D. (1948) *Proc. Second Rubber Tech. Conf.*, 438.
27. Patterson, P. D. (1951) *Motor*, **100**, 102, 133.
28. Pearson, H. C. (1922) *Pneumatic Tyres* (New York: India Rubber Publishing Co.).
29. Mountford, L. J. (1929) *I.R.I. Trans.*, **5**, 284.
30. Sjothun, I. J. and Cole, O. D. (1949) *Ind. Eng. Chem.*, **41**, 1564.
31. Adamson United Co. (1953) *India Rubb. W.*, **128**, 171.
32. Turner, D. M. (1954) *Proc. Third Rubber Tech. Conf.*, 735.
33. Gardner, E. R. and Worswick, T. (1951) *I.R.I. Trans.*, **27**, 127.
34. Avon India Rubber Co. (1955) *Comm. and Electronics*, **2**, 52.
35. Apps, D. and Vanator, G. M. (1956) *Rev. gén. Caoutch.*, **33**, 1029.
36. Milliken, W. F. (1956) A1. *Symposium on Automobile Stability* (London: Institute of Mech. Eng.).
37. Anon. (1955) *Rev. gén. Caoutch.*, **32**, 970.
38. Healey, A. (1924) *Proc. Inst. Auto. Eng.*
39. Gough, V. E. and Roberts, G. B. *I.R.I. Trans.* (In press.)
40. Wolff, H. (1956) *A.T.Z.*, **58**, 20.
41. Anon. (1957) *Autocar*, **106**, 622.
42. Gough, V. E. (1954) *Auto. Eng.*, **44**, 137.
43. Lippman, S. A. (1956) *Noise Control*, **2**, No. 3, 41.
44. Joy, T. J. P. and Hartley, D. C. (1954) *Autocar*, **100**, 554.
45. Sjothun, I. J. and Green, P. S. (1953) *Rubb. Age, N.Y.*, **74**, 77.
46. ASTM D378-51T.
47. Meiners, H. (1955) *Glückauf Bergmannische Zeitschrift*, **91**, 406–416.
48. BS 490: 1951.
49. Sturtevant, W. L. (1930) *India Rubb. W.*, **83**, 63.
50. (1952) *Annual Report of the Progress of Rubber Technology of I.R.I.*, 95.
51. Borroff, E., Elliot and Weeks (1952) *Rubb. Chem. Technol.*, **25**, 891.
52. Bryan, A. M. (1952) Ministry of Fuel and Power, Command 8574, HM. 80.
53. National Coal Board, Specification No. P.113/1954.
54. U.S. Bureau of Mines, Title 30, Chapter 1.
55. Mass, W. (1949) *Geologie on Mynbouw*, **11**, No. 11, 309–312.
56. Klinger, K. (1953) *Glückauf Bergmannische Zeitschrift*, **89**, 1048–1055.
57. Wilcox, Robertson, Tideswell and Jones, Ministry of Fuel and Power Res. Report 20, TS. 1951.
58. (1955) National Coal Board, File No. DN.203/7. Report SC.243.
59. Acres, J. (1955) R.A.B.R.M., Information Bureau Circular 428.
60. *National Coal Board Science Bull.* 1955.4.6.
61. Swift, H. W. (1928) Institute of Mech. Eng.

62. Brazier, S. A., Holland-Bowyer, W. and Mellers, C. E. (1938) *First Rubber Tech. Conf.*, 1035.
63. Titze, A. (1952) *Kautch. u. Gummi*, **5**, 204–6.
64. Sardemann, W. (1952) *Glückauf Bergmannische Zeitschrift*, **88**, 304–7.
65. German Spec. DIN53516.
66. Rubber Improvements Ltd. (1953) *Colliery Guardian*, 20.
67. German DIN Spec. (1950) *Kautch. u. Gummi*, **6**, 218.
68. Neis, G. (1954) *Kautch. u. Gummi*, **6**, 124.
69. Neis, G. (1954) *Kautch. u. Gummi*, **7**, 154.
70. ASTM D571–1955.
71. (1954) Ministry of Supply, Spec. DTD. (R.D.I.) 3951.
72. (1951) Ministry of Supply, Spec. DTD. (R.D.I.) 3954.
73. U.S.P. 2,412,523; (1954) *Kautsch. u. Gummi*, **7**, 156.
74. BS 796: 1955.
75. BS 924: 1955.
76. BS 1435: 1953.
77. ASTM 622-1955T.
78. Buist, J. M. (1950) *I.R.I. Trans.*, **26**, 192.
79. Grimwade, D. and Clapman, J. C. R. (1949) S.A.T.R.A. Res. Report No. 100.
80. Grimwade, D. and Manning, J. R., S.A.T.R.A. Report No. TM.1134.
81. Bunton, J., Hall, E. F. and Waters, N. E., S.A.T.R.A. Res. Report No. 133.
82. S.A.T.R.A. Specification for Resin Rubber Soling Materials, 9/56.
83. S.A.T.R.A. Spec. No. 8/55.
84. BS 903: 1950 Part 18, 3.
85. ASTM D395-1955.
86. BIOS Final Report No. 928, Item 22, Part II, 204, H.M. Stationery Office.
87. *S.A.T.R.A. Bulletin* (May 1956), **7**, No. 5, 47.
88. Barrett, G. F. C. (1956) *Rubb. J.*, **CXXXL**, No. 22, Dec., 685.
89. U.S. Dept. of Commerce Nat. Bureau of Standards Report, BMS.100, 1943.
90. *S.A.T.R.A. Bulletin*, April 1953, **5**, No. 16, 135.
91. (1956) *Rubb. Age, N.Y.*, 804.
92. Talalay, J. A. (1954) *Md. Eng. Chem.*, **46**, No. 7.
93. BS 903: F1–F9; (1956) *Testing Cellular Rubber*, 1530–1538.
94. ASTM D1056–1954T.
95. (1955) *Deutschen Normenauschutz*, DN.7790, *Latex Schaum*.
96. British Standards Institution CX (RUC) 34C.
97. British Latex Foam Manufacturing Assoc. (1951) *Accepted General Spec. for Latex Foam Rubber Articles*.
98. Federal Test Method, No. 601.
99. (1955) *Bedding and Upholstery*, 379.
100. (1955) *Bedding and Upholstery*, 377.
101. U.S. Military Spec. MIL-R-5001.
102. Ball, G. S. (1948) *I.R.I. Trans.*, 6, **23**, 288.
103. Stevens, P. H., B.P. 230,250.
104. Buchan, S. (1948) *Rubber to Metal Bonding* (London: Crosby Lockwood), 98–99.
105. Andre Rubber Co. (1945) *Elastomeric Engineering*.
106. Moulton, A. E. and Turner, P. W. (1950) *I.R.I. Trans.*, 1, **26**, 86.
107. Gurney, W. A. and Gough, V. E. (1946) *I.R.I. Trans.*, **22**, 153.
108. (1952) *R.A.B.R.M. Bibliography*, ID.5451.
109. Hatfield, P. (1951) *Auto. Engineer*, **41**, 385.
110. Lebfeldt, W. (1954) *A.T.Z.*, **56**, 134.
111. Merris Stambough and Gehman (1953) *Caoutchouc*, **30**, 715.
112. Heughan, D. M. and Sproule, D. O. (1953) *I.R.I. Trans.*, **29**, 255.
113. Anon. (1948) *Engineer*.
114. U.S. Military Spec. MIL-P-5516A.
115. S.A.E. Standard, S.A.E. 60R.

CHAPTER X

PART ONE

THE FUNDAMENTALS OF EBONITE

by

J. R. SCOTT

Formation and structure of ebonite

The rubber–sulphur reaction

It was long customary to write the formula of the "ideal" natural rubber ebonite as $(C_5H_8S)_x$, representing a compound with precisely one atom of sulphur per isoprene unit, and it was commonly believed that such a compound actually existed and represented the upper limit of combination of sulphur with rubber. It is now quite clear, however, that this view is untenable, and such evidence as has been put forward for the existence of $(C_5H_8S)_x$, or indeed any other definite compound, is not valid. Thus, the existence of $[(C_5H_8)_2S]_x$ postulated [1] on the basis of the sudden change in coefficient of expansion at about 19% combined sulphur, was shown [2] to be false, since the sulphur content at which this change occurs depends on the temperature at which the coefficient of expansion is measured (see p. 833).

There has long been evidence, moreover, that proportions of combined sulphur much in excess of the 32% corresponding to C_5H_8S can be reached.[3-7] Figures as high as 43% (or 77 parts sulphur per 100 rubber) have been recorded for ebonites containing organic accelerators.[7] It should be noted that these figures are based on sulphur estimations made on samples previously acetone-extracted in the usual way for 16 hours; it is possible, from what is now known about the modes of combination of sulphur in ebonite, that more prolonged extraction might remove further sulphur by gradual breakdown of groups in the molecule (observations [8] suggest the presence of such labile sulphur). This, however, would not affect the validity of the conclusion that definite compounds, i.e. with simple ratios of C_5H_8 to S, do not exist.

As regards the rate of the rubber–sulphur reaction in the "hard rubber" region there is little to be said beyond the fact that the initial approximately linear relation between cure time and combined sulphur gives place to a slowing down and finally an asymptotic approach to a limiting combined sulphur which, however, does *not* correspond to the total sulphur in the mix. It appears that however long the cure proceeds some sulphur always remains uncombined, and indeed the free sulphur seems to reach a steady limiting value [7, 9] (Fig. 10.1). The amount of this " ultimate " free sulphur depends on the original rubber–sulphur ratio, and on the nature of the

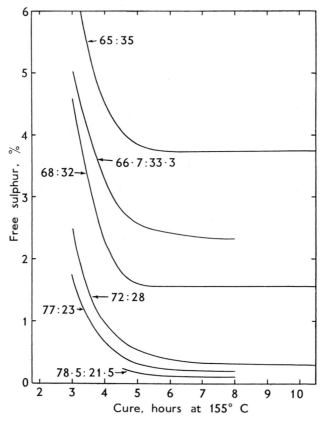

Fig. 10.1. Variation of free sulphur with cure; numbers denote ratios of natural rubber to sulphur.

polymer, being less with butadiene polymers and copolymers than with natural rubber [7, 9–11] (Fig. 10.2); it is also reduced by using an organic accelerator.

The flattening of the cure–free-sulphur curves in Fig. 10.1, and the effect of accelerators, have led to the suggestion that the rubber–sulphur combination is balanced by a reverse reaction $RS \rightarrow R + S$ (R being the rubber), so that the ultimate amount of free sulphur represents an equilibrium between the forward and reverse reactions.

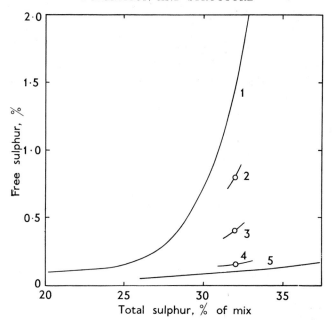

Fig. 10.2. Variation of " ultimate " free sulphur with total sulphur content. Curve 1: natural rubber (no accelerator); 2: natural rubber plus accelerator (DPG); 3: Buna N; 4: Buna S; 5: Buna 115.

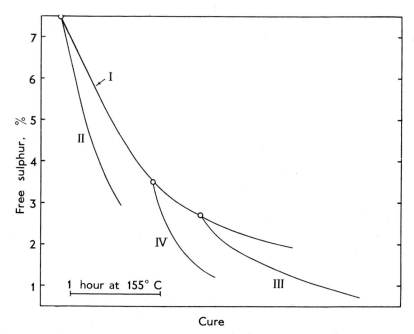

Fig. 10.3. Effect of organic accelerator (DPG) in accelerating combination of sulphur during the " hard rubber " reaction. Curve I: without DPG; Curves II, III, IV: with DPG.

Effect of organic accelerators

Contrary to a once widely held belief, organic accelerators do accelerate the combination of rubber with sulphur in the " hard rubber " region. Fig. 10.3 gives results of tests made to settle this point.[10]   Curve I shows the decrease in free sulphur with advancing cure (at $155°$ C) of an un-accelerated mix.   Curves II, III and IV relate to mixes with 1·0, 1·5 and 5·0 parts respectively of diphenylguanidine; these are plotted on the same time scale but have been moved horizontally so as to bring their upper ends on to Curve I.   In these accelerated mixes the free sulphur decreases more quickly than in the unaccelerated mix I, and since Curves II–IV relate to compounds containing between 26 and 32% combined sulphur, it is clearly the " hard rubber " reaction that is being accelerated.   A study of the corresponding changes of yield temperature with cure leads to the same conclusion.   These results confirm earlier statements [12,13] that organic accelerators do speed up the " hard rubber " reaction.

On the other hand, there is no evidence that accelerators change the course of the rubber–sulphur reaction and thus lead to a different type of molecular structure, as they do in soft vulcanisates.   Thus, addition of an accelerator does not noticeably alter the relationship between combined sulphur and yield temperature.   This is shown in Fig. 10.4, where yield temperature is plotted against free sulphur for three series of 68 : 32 natural rubber–sulphur mixes containing respectively no metallic oxide, 5 parts zinc oxide and 5 parts magnesium oxide, in each case with and without various accelerators and cured for various periods.   In any one series all the points, whether for mixes with or without accelerator, lie close to a single curve.[10]   Moreover, there is no evidence that accelerators make possible the production of an ebonite with less sulphur than is required in their absence.[12,14,15,16]

The fact that these various observations provide no evidence of ac-celerators altering the rubber–sulphur structure does not, of course, form conclusive evidence that they have no such effect; in soft vulcanisates accelerators alter the relative amounts of inter-molecular (cross-linking) sulphur and intramolecular sulphur, and as both these forms exist in ebonite (as noted below under " Molecular Structure "), there may be a similar effect of accelerators here also, but if so, it is not such as to affect noticeably the relation between total combined sulphur and mechanical properties.

Molecular structure

It is not at present possible to form any detailed picture of the molecular structure of ebonite.   It seems clear, however, that the combined sulphur is present partly as cross-links between neighbouring rubber chains (intermolecular sulphur) and partly as sulphur atoms linked to two carbon atoms in the same chain, forming a carbon–sulphur ring structure (intramolecular sulphur).

The presence of intramolecular sulphur was postulated by Midgley, Henne and Shepard [17] from a study of the products of pyrolysis of natural

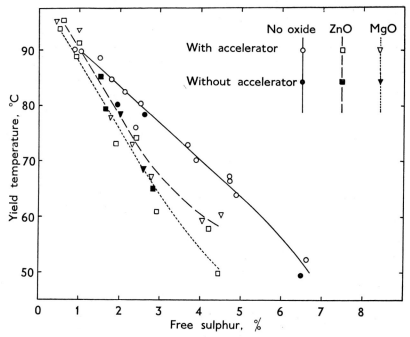

Fig. 10.4. Relation between free sulphur and yield temperature for three series of natural rubber mixes: without metallic oxide, with zinc oxide and with magnesium oxide.

rubber ebonite; they further showed that, of the various possible structures, the only one consistent with the facts was that having the sulphur attached to the tertiary carbon atom and forming a thiophene (thiocyclopentane) ring:

$$
\begin{array}{c}
\qquad\quad CH_3 \qquad\qquad CH_3 \\
-C-C-C-C-C-C-C-C- \\
-S-\quad\ \ \ L-S-\quad\ \ \ L-S-
\end{array}
$$

Their further conclusion that there is no intermolecularly bound sulphur linking together adjacent chains is, however, quite untenable in view of the known behaviour of ebonite towards swelling liquids (e.g. aromatic hydrocarbons, see p. 841) and the essentially elastic nature of its deformation (see p. 835).

The cyclic structure shown above was confirmed by more recent infra-red spectrographic studies.[18,19]   It was further demonstrated that cross-links containing one or more sulphur atoms (probably about two on the average) between the tertiary carbon atoms were present.   Just how much of the combined sulphur exists as cross-links and how much in intra-molecular cyclic structures is not known.   The statement by Salomon [20] that " thermoplastic properties and swelling show the number of cross-links in ebonite is not essentially different from that in soft vulcanised rubber " must be accepted with reserve, for in fact the elastic modulus of ebonite in its " high-elastic " state (i.e. at high temperature) is some 10 times that of a pure-gum soft vulcanisate,[21] while its swelling in active swelling liquids is only about one-eighth;[22] the known dependence of modulus and swelling on degree of cross-linking would therefore indicate that ebonite is much more densely cross-linked than a soft vulcanisate.

Even so, however, it seems likely that in a normal ebonite the cross-links comprise only a small proportion (perhaps one-tenth or one-fifth) of the total combined sulphur; this proportion cannot be stated more precisely, because it would be unsafe to assume that the quantitative relationships between cross-linking, modulus and swelling deduced for soft vulcanisates apply to the much more closely cross-linked structure of ebonite.

Moreover, it seems difficult to reconcile this conclusion as to the relative numbers of cross-links and intramolecular sulphur atoms with the very high combined sulphur contents recorded for some ebonites, as noted above, which represent as much as 1·6 atoms sulphur per C_5H_8 unit.   Even if it were assured that every isoprene unit had associated with it *either* 1 cross-link of 2 sulphur atoms *or* 1 intramolecular sulphur atom (and it is difficult to visualise more than this), this would represent not more than 1·1 sulphur atoms per isoprene; it is possible, of course, that ebonites made with very high proportions of sulphur may contain cross-links com-prising more than 2 sulphur atoms, but this is mere speculation.

Heat evolution during vulcanisation

The reactions involved in the formation of ebonite, or at least some of them, are strongly exothermic. Thus, the overall heat produced in forming a 68 : 32 natural-rubber–sulphur ebonite is about 300 cal./g.;[23] as the specific heat of the mix is 0·33, this heat would theoretically be sufficient to raise the temperature about 1,000° C. Clearly, unless the greater part of this heat is dissipated during the cure, e.g. conducted away to the press platens or to the steam in an open cure, serious over-heating will occur.

No complete theory of the evolution and dissipation of heat in a mass of rubber–sulphur stock during vulcanisation has yet been formulated. It would necessarily be very complex, as is evident from the formulae deduced by Takada,[24] and obviously based on simplifying assumptions, for " critical safe vulcanising temperature ". Even if the theoretical basis existed, it could not be used in practice, because there is still uncertainty as to how much heat is evolved in vulcanising a mix of given sulphur content,[23,25,26,27,28] and how the rate of heat evolution varies at different stages of the cure.

A useful approach, however, to the problem has been given by Daynes,[29] who, by considering a simplified case, shows qualitatively how the various

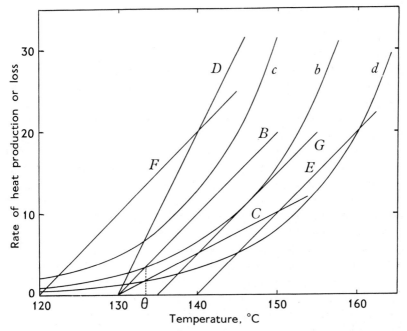

Fig. 10.5. Diagram illustrating heat generation and loss in curing of ebonite sheet.

factors involved (curing temperature, " reactivity " of the mix, thickness of the sheet being cured) influence the temperature rise at the centre of the sheet. Fig. 10.5, quoted from his paper, illustrates these effects. In this simplified case only a layer at the centre is considered as reactive, the remainder of the sheet on both sides being simply a medium resisting loss of heat, so that the temperature gradient is assumed uniform through these outer parts; the thickness of the central reactive layer is taken as proportional to the thickness of the sheet. This treatment also assumes that a steady state has been reached; it thus ignores variation of reactivity during the cure and also any effect of the heat capacity of the material on the form of the time–temperature curve. In a complete sheet of ebonite the heat-production and heat-loss conditions at any one time would vary with distance from the centre, and the curves relating these conditions to temperature would be more complex than those assumed in the figure. A fuller discussion of these complicating factors is given in Daynes' original paper.

The shape of curves b, c and d in Fig. 10.5 shows how the rate of heat *production* in the central reactive layer varies with the temperature at the centre. The three curves represent mixes of different reactivity; thus, b might be a rubber–sulphur mix, c an accelerated (more reactive) mix and d a mix diluted with filler and thus less reactive.

The straight lines B, C, D, E, F, G show how the heat *loss* (by conduction) varies with the temperature at the centre of the sheet. These lines all start from the external or vulcanising temperature; the slope depends on the thermal conductivity and the thickness of the sheet, the higher the conductivity or the thinner the sheet, the steeper the line.

Consider now curves b and B, relating to a curing temperature of $130°$ C; when the temperature has risen to $133·5°$ C (point θ) the heat loss B overtakes the heat generation b, so that the temperature will not rise further, and the system will remain stable with the temperature at the centre $3·5°$ C above curing temperature.

Curve c shows the heat generation in a more reactive mix; the rate of generation now always exceeds the rate of loss (B), and the system is thermally unstable, resulting in excessive—even explosive—overheating.

On the other hand, if the reactivity and heat generation are reduced by a diluent filler (curve d) the temperature rise will be reduced, say to $1·5°$ C, as shown by the intersection of d and B.

Changing the composition of the mix may also alter its thermal conductivity; reduced conductivity retards heat loss and may make the system unstable, e.g. if the loss is as shown by C and the heat generation by b; increased conductivity moves the loss curve from B towards D, and so reduces the temperature rise.

If the sheet is made thicker the central reactive layer is (by definition) thicker, and hence more heat is generated, giving (say) curve c instead of b, but heat loss is retarded (giving, say, curve C), so that generation greatly exceeds loss and the system is unstable. If the sheet is made thinner the increased loss (D) quickly overtakes the lessened heat generation (d), and the temperature rise is very small.

Fig. 10.5 shows also that curing temperature is very important. Thus, a reduction from $130°$ to $120°$ C moves the heat loss curve from B to F, and so (taking the b curve of heat generation) reduces the temperature rise from $3·5°$ to $1°$ C; if the curing temperature is raised we soon reach the limit of stability at G, which just touches b; at $140°$ C (curve E) conditions become unstable, because generation now exceeds loss.

These examples show that the margin between instability and a temperature rise of only a few degrees is small, especially for changes in the thickness of the sheet, because these act on two of the basic factors, the amount of heat generated and the rate of heat loss.

The following paragraphs summarise experimental work on heat evolution, which will be seen to confirm the above theoretical conclusions.

Influence of thickness and of curing temperature

Fig. 10.6 shows typical curves of internal temperature (at the centre of a sheet during press cure) against time, for various cure temperatures and thicknesses of sheet.[30] The outstanding feature is the high peak temperatures that develop in certain circumstances.   These results agree with the

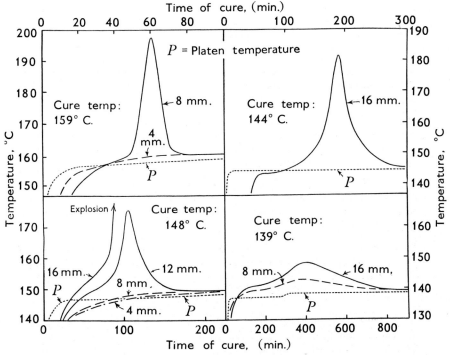

Fig. 10.6. Variation of temperature at centre of ebonite sheet during cure, compared with platen temperature; for sheets 4, 8, 12 and 16 mm. thick. (From Ref. 30.)

theoretical considerations in showing how critical is the choice of cure temperature, since a difference of $10°$ C can determine whether the internal temperature rise is negligible or dangerously high.   Also, if peak temperature is plotted against cure temperature, for a fixed thickness, the curve bends sharply upwards, in accordance with the theoretical prediction that

824 EBONITE

the temperature rise becomes extremely high at a critical curing temperature.

Variation of heat generation during cure

It is unfortunately not possible to predict with any certainty how the rate of heat evolution (at constant temperature) will vary during the cure, since the data are scanty and to some extent contradictory. The available evidence,[23,25,30,31,32,33,34,35] however, shows, firstly, that the strongly exothermic reaction does not start at the beginning of the cure (this is evident from Fig. 10.6), and secondly, that little if any heat is generated after the peak temperature is reached, whence it has been concluded[36] that the exothermic reaction is largely confined to a relatively short part of the cure, namely, between about 50 and 140 minutes at $153°$ C for a natural-rubber–sulphur mix which would need 240–300 minutes to reach a full cure.

Influence of composition of mix

Heat evolution appears to be greatest with a particular ratio of sulphur to rubber, though the actual ratio is open to some doubt, being about 27 (per 100 natural rubber) according to Perks[31] and 45–60 according to Hada and Nakajima.[28]

From the conclusion stated above that accelerators do not fundamentally alter the nature of the rubber–sulphur reaction, they would not be expected to alter greatly the total heat evolved. Nevertheless, they might alter the distribution of heat evolution over the cure period, and so increase or decrease the temperature rise. This point has been studied[37] by determining the highest cure temperature ("critical curing temperature") that would just avoid a blow-out, that is, would keep the exothermic temperature rise below some unknown but roughly constant figure; from data relating properties with cure time it was then possible to estimate the "critical curing time" needed to reach optimum properties when curing at the "critical" temperature; this time (given in Table 10.1) is, of course,

TABLE 10.1
CRITICAL CURING TIMES (RELATIVE)

All mixes contained natural rubber 68 and sulphur 32; with or without accelerator 1·5 and metallic oxide 5.

No accelerator	100
Tetraethylthiuram disulphide	75
Zinc pentamethylenedithiocarbamate	75
Zinc diethyldithiocarbamate	65–80
Diphenylguanidine (DPG)	70
Butyraldehyde–aniline (BA)	60
DPG + magnesium oxide	53
BA + magnesium oxide	40
DPG + zinc oxide	90
BA + zinc oxide	85

the shortest in which optimum properties can be attained without excessive overheating.

If accelerators merely accelerated, but did not change the nature of, the rubber–sulphur reaction they would not affect the "critical curing time ", although of course the cure could be made at a lower temperature. In fact, all the accelerators in Table 10.1 do shorten the critical time to some extent, and magnesium oxide, added to either DPG or BA, shortens it still further, but zinc oxide has the opposite effect, and almost destroys the advantage gained by using the accelerator.

It is not yet known by what mechanism accelerators and metallic oxides alter the " critical curing time ", but the fact that such alterations are possible is not surprising. Thus, if an accelerator acted only during the non-exothermic (initial and final) stages of the cure it would make possible a shorter cure without increased risk of over-heating. This example is doubtless an unattainable ideal, but accelerators may exist having at least a tendency in this direction.

Thermal decomposition

The rubber–sulphur compound that constitutes ebonite is by no means stable towards heat. It has been shown [38] that at temperatures even as low as 100° C a natural-rubber–sulphur ebonite in the form of powder shows a measurable rate of decomposition with evolution of hydrogen sulphide, although no volatile organic decomposition products were isolated in experiments up to 250° C. At higher temperatures more extensive breakdown occurs, forming a great variety of low-molecular organic sulphur compounds, the nature of which need not be discussed except to point out that it has given evidence about the molecular constitution of ebonite. The hydrogen sulphide was shown to arise from the decomposition of the caoutchouc–sulphur compound, not from the free sulphur or its reaction with acetone-extractable organic substances. Other workers [35] have shown that this evolution of hydrogen sulphide occurs also with ebonites made from butadiene–styrene and butadiene–acrylonitrile rubbers.

It has been demonstrated [39] that with natural-rubber ebonite the rate of evolution of hydrogen sulphide increases with temperature, but at any one temperature varies greatly with time, being relatively very rapid initially and then decreasing considerably to a rate that *appears* to be roughly constant (Fig. 10.7). It might be expected that the time–evolution curves for different temperatures would differ only in the time scale, and so would be superposable by varying this scale. It is difficult from the available data to decide whether this is so or not, and all that can be said is that the temperature coefficient of the process *appears* to be about 2·5 per 10° C.

The shape of the curves in Fig. 10.7 suggests that the initial rapid evolution and the final slow evolution represent two different processes, but any such conclusion must be accepted with reserve, since in heterogeneous reactions such as are here involved the slope of the curve does not necessarily represent the true reaction rate.   If, however, the difference is accepted as real it appears that the initial rapid reaction ends at 0·10– 0·12 g. hydrogen sulphide per 1 g. of ebonite, corresponding to about one-third of the combined sulphur in a 68 : 32 rubber–sulphur ebonite.   In

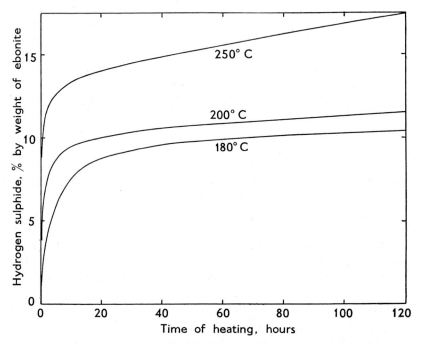

Fig. 10.7. Evolution of hydrogen sulphide from natural rubber ebonite heated at various temperatures.

any case it is obvious that more than one reaction must be involved, corresponding to different modes of combination of sulphur in the rubber–sulphur structure; this is entirely in keeping with what is known about this structure from other sources (see p. 819).

There is, indeed, an interesting resemblance between the curves of hydrogen sulphide evolution and those of high-temperature deformation plotted against time (so-called " plastic yield " curves), as shown in Fig. 10.11.   There cannot, of course, be any common immediate cause for these two phenomena, since the one depends on rupture of chemical bonds and the other on the breakdown of van der Waals forces between neighbouring molecular chains; the significance of the resemblance is that both phenomena indicate the marked heterogeneity of the bonds and forces that hold together the structure.

Virtually nothing is known as to the nature of the residual material after loss of hydrogen sulphide, except that it is chemically unsaturated, judging by bromine absorption tests.[39]

Action of light: surface deterioration

It has long been known that ebonite is liable to undergo what is generally termed " surface deterioration " when exposed to light in presence of moist air. The colour changes from the characteristic deep black to greenish-grey, and the ebonite loses its excellent electrical insulating power; in extreme cases drops or a film of acid liquid form on the surface. It was shown [38] that during light exposure sulphurous and sulphuric acids are formed on the surface; these absorb moisture and so form an electrically conducting film, which drastically reduces the surface resistance and can destroy the value of the ebonite as an insulating material.

Changes in surface resistance during exposure

The general nature of these changes is shown by the curves in Fig. 10.8, representing specific surface resistance or resistivity plotted against time of exposure, for a natural-rubber–sulphur ebonite [40] (exposure was to north daylight, with the specimens behind glass 1–2 mm. thick). These curves, especially when plotted on a logarithmic time scale, show three distinct portions:

(i) an " induction " period, during which resistivity changes little;

(ii) a rapid fall, which is a straight line when logarithmic scales of time and resistivity are used, as shown by the curves in broken lines;

(iii) a " saturation " period, in which resistivity falls more slowly, being here inversely proportional to the total exposure time; during this period the ebonite surface may become visibly wet.

The whole behaviour can be defined in terms of the points B and C in Fig. 10.9; B is the beginning of the rapid fall, phase (ii), and C the change from this phase to the " saturation " phase (iii). On a log/log plot, CD has unit slope, that is, doubling the time halves the resistivity, but BC is much steeper, having a slope usually between 10 and 20. The transitions between the three phases are not really sudden, as shown diagrammatically in the figure, and with some loaded ebonites the separate phases are less well defined than with unloaded rubber–sulphur ebonites.

The existence of three phases in the exposure–resistivity curve has been explained as follows: By the action of light plus oxygen and moisture a conducting solution of sulphuric and sulphurous acids is formed at first in minute droplets. So long as these remain isolated from one another they do not allow a current to pass along the surface of the ebonite, and so the resistivity remains high; this is the " induction " phase (i). As more droplets form they join up to form conducting paths over the surface; the number of such paths, and hence the current leakage, increases rapidly as the droplets multiply; this is phase (ii). Eventually the droplets join to

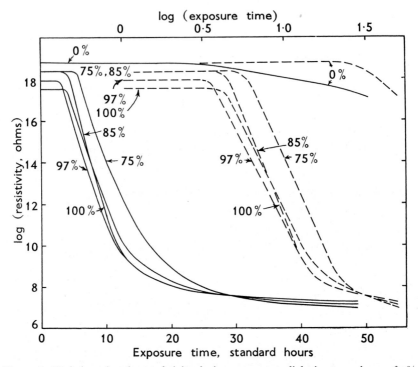

Fig. 10.8. Variation of surface resistivity during exposure to light in atmospheres of 0%, 75%, 85%, 97% and 100% relative humidity (continuous lines); same plotted on logarithmic time scale (broken lines). " Standard hours " represent approximately hours of north daylight.

form a continuous covering of acid liquid; in this phase (iii) further fall of resistivity is due to more acid being formed as exposure continues.

Effects of ambient humidity on resistivity changes

The effects of light exposure depend greatly on the humidity of the air, both during exposure and while resistivity is being measured, in the following way:[40]

(i) If ebonite specimens are exposed to light in air of various relative humidities, and surface resistivity thereafter measured in air of a *constant* relative humidity (R.H.) of 75%, the loss of resistivity is greatest for exposures at humidities between about 75 and 90% R.H. This is because the beginning of the rapid decrease (B in Fig. 10.9) occurs sooner the higher the humidity, while the decrease is most rapid (BC steepest) at about 75% R.H.

(ii) If resistivity is measured in air of the *same* humidity as the light exposure the loss of resistivity at low humidities is much lessened, and

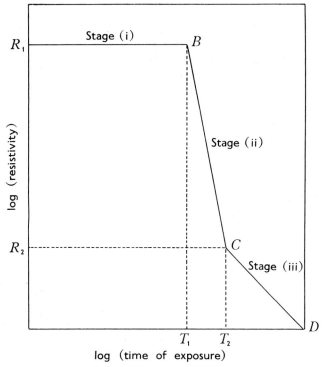

Fig. 10.9. Variation of surface resistivity during exposure to light (diagrammatic); log (time of exposure) and log (resistivity) are plotted on equal scales.

indeed becomes extremely slow in dry air, as shown by the " 0% " (R.H.) curves in Fig. 10.8. Deterioration is still quickest at about 90% R.H.

(iii) When exposure and measurement are made at the same relative humidity, as in case (ii), the resistivity decreases greatly over the range 60–90% R.H., because high humidity causes the acid droplets to absorb more water and so grow and coalesce to form more conducting paths.

Recovery of resistivity

The loss of resistivity caused by exposure to light is not all permanent; if the ebonite is subsequently kept in the dark the resistivity increases again to a greater or less extent. Complete recovery, however, to the value before exposure has never been observed, though the resistivity may increase 10- or 100-fold. The ultimate extent of recovery depends on the kind of ebonite and the conditions of light exposure and dark storage. Ebonites containing a filler, such as calcium carbonate, that converts sulphuric acid into an insoluble sulphate often recover more than unloaded ebonites.[41] With a given ebonite, recovery in the dark is quicker and ultimately greater, the more quickly the resistivity has fallen during light exposure, and recovery is quicker if the temperature is raised.

The causes of this recovery in the dark are not known definitely, but it seems likely that part of the acid formed during exposure is removed, perhaps by evaporation, which could happen with sulphurous acid, though not with sulphuric acid. There may, indeed, be two forms of surface deterioration: one due to sulphurous acid, which is temporary because this acid is volatile; and the other due to sulphuric acid, which is formed only slowly from sulphurous acid (and hence is more important in *prolonged* exposures to dull light), and is permanent because sulphuric acid is not volatile.

Influence of nature and intensity of light

Broadly speaking, surface deterioration is quicker the more intense the light. Changing the light source, however, does more than alter the overall rate of deterioration;[40] for example:

(1) With increase of light intensity the " induction " period, stage (i) of Fig. 10.9, becomes relatively shorter (indeed may almost disappear) until the intensity is so great that the temperature of the ebonite surface is markedly raised, when the induction period is again lengthened.

(2) For light intensities that raise the surface temperature the effect of a given quantity of light (intensity × time) depends on the intensity, in the sense that resistivity falls less if the intensity is high (and the time correspondingly shorter). With intensities that do not raise the surface temperature the fall in resistivity of unloaded ebonites appears to depend only on the quantity of light.

(3) The relative deterioration rates of unloaded and loaded ebonites may depend on the intensity; thus, using feeble light can make the loaded ebonite appear more stable relatively to the unloaded one, probably because the " recovery " effect noted above can assert itself more during the long period occupied by a test with feeble light.

The effects of light intensity described above can be ascribed partly to a difference in the process of acid formation according as the light is intense or weak, intense light acting rapidly and giving less time for oxidation of sulphurous to sulphuric acid, and partly to the " recovery " process involving loss of acid (e.g. by evaporation) from the surface film. This loss must be going on even during exposure, so that in weak light acid formation is slow and will be more or less counteracted by the loss of acid; coalescence of droplets to reach stage (ii) of Fig. 10.9 is thus delayed, and the induction stage (i) lengthened, as is observed. On the other hand, if the light is intense enough to heat the ebonite surface, acid will evaporate more quickly; thus the induction stage (i) will again be lengthened and the formation of conducting paths in stage (ii) retarded.

Loss of resistivity is caused only by light of wavelengths below about 5,700 Å, and chiefly by wavelengths below 5,200 Å, which is the region where ebonite absorbs radiation strongly.[42]

Chemical mechanism of surface deterioration

Early investigations [38,39] suggested that the sulphur acids responsible for surface deterioration were derived by oxidation of hydrogen sulphide, which is known to be formed during light exposure. Later work [43] disproved this, since it was found that uncured ebonite stock exposed to light in a mixture of air and hydrogen sulphide showed no loss of surface resistivity. The formation of acid and consequent electrical deterioration are not due to the free sulphur, but result from decomposition of the rubber–sulphur compound.

It was shown [44] that light activates the surface oxidation of soft vulcanised rubber by oxygen, and that this action is produced by the same wavelengths (below 5,700 Å) as act on ebonite. It is therefore likely that light also activates the oxidation of ebonite, giving a rubber–sulphur–oxygen compound. (It is known [45] that many organic sulphides are similarly oxidised, giving compounds in which oxygen is attached to the sulphur.) Such a compound would not be electrically conducting, but by the continued action of light plus air and moisture, could decompose to give sulphur dioxide and hence sulphurous acid, which would slowly oxidise to sulphuric acid; this mechanism agrees with the observed facts on loss and recovery of electrical surface resistance.

The action of light is confined to a very thin layer; estimates of the thickness of this layer, based on the amount of acid formed (either estimated directly or calculated from electrical conductivity) have varied widely, but the acid certainly could be produced from the sulphur in an ebonite layer not more than $1\ \mu$ thick.[36]

Avoidance of surface deterioration

Almost every compounding variable has been tried in the hope of stopping surface deterioration, but unfortunately without real success. As this aspect has less direct bearing on the fundamentals of the phenomenon, only the main conclusions will be summarised:

(i) None of the following modifications gave an ebonite free from surface deterioration, or indeed much better than a normal natural rubber–sulphur ebonite: varying the rubber–sulphur ratio, time or temperature of cure, or method of cure (i.e. whether in open steam, water or in moulds in a press); using deproteinised or other purified natural rubber; replacing natural rubber by purified gutta-percha or by butadiene, butadiene–styrene or butadiene–acrylonitrile synthetic rubbers; adding organic accelerators, softeners, fillers, ebonite dust or selenium (small amount in a rubber–sulphur mix). A low degree of vulcanisation, however, appears to help to a slight extent,[46] presumably by reducing the number of points in the molecule that can be attacked by oxygen to give the rubber–sulphur–oxygen compound postulated above.

(ii) Incorporation of light-absorbent pigments (e.g. carbon black) gives little improvement.[47]

(iii) Certain antioxidants have given definite improvements by reducing the rate of deterioration, as follows:[48]

Antioxidant	Rate of deterioration (relative)
Nil	100
Phenyl-α-naphthylamine	60
Phenyl-β-naphthylamine	50
Aldol-β-naphthylamine	50
p-Aminodiphenyl–acetone condensation product *	45
Quinol	40
p-Aminophenol	25
Sym. di-β-naphthyl-p-phenylenediamine †	17

* Santoflex.
† Age-Rite White.

The three most effective of these antioxidants are compounds that can form semi-quinones. This observation, and the fact that such compounds strongly influence oxidation–reduction reactions, suggest a possible line of approach to the problem of developing antioxidants for improving the light resistance of ebonite.

(iv) Acid-neutralising fillers, such as react with sulphuric acid to give insoluble or non-hygroscopic sulphates, have proved ineffective, except that whiting enhances the recovery of resistivity in the dark.[41] This negative result is surprising, because it would be expected that if the filler particles are actually at the surface, and so in contact with the acid film, diffusion of the acid should very rapidly lead to its reacting with these particles. The film, however, may well contain other water-soluble and ionisable substances besides the acids.

(v) Surface treatment with solutions of substances (e.g. benzidine) that form insoluble sulphates has given only little improvement.[41]

Effects of temperature: density and thermal expansion

Before discussing the effects of temperature on density it may be noted that the vulcanisation of a rubber–sulphur mix to the ebonite stage is accompanied by a marked decrease in volume, and hence an increase in density. Experimental data [1, 9] show that the densities, in g./c.c. at 15° C, of fully cured natural-rubber–sulphur ebonites containing between 20 and 35% sulphur agree to a sufficient approximation with values calculated from the composition of the mix by the mixture law, taking the following nominal values for the densities of rubber and sulphur: rubber 0·967; sulphur 2·18. These are, of course, greater than the actual densities, owing to the shrinkage during cure.

Ebonite differs from soft vulcanisates in having a much lower co-efficient of thermal expansion, viz. about 0·0002/° C as compared with 0·0006 for soft vulcanisates (these are *volume* coefficients). This low value, however, obtains only below a certain temperature; it was found [2] that when the temperature is gradually raised the coefficient of expansion increases suddenly to 0·0005–0·0006 at a critical temperature which is higher, the higher the combined sulphur, and is indeed closely related to the yield temperature.

In a series of fully cured ebonite mixes Curtis, McPherson and Scott [1] found that as the sulphur content of the mix is reduced the expansion co-efficient increases from about 0·0002 to 0·0006 in the region of 18–20% sulphur. As Kimura and Namikawa [2] showed, however, this "transition" sulphur content varies with the temperature at which the coefficient is measured, being greater, the higher this temperature.

Now 0·0006 is the coefficient of expansion of a soft vulcanisate, and this gives the clue to the explanation of these observations, as follows: At temperatures substantially *above* its yield temperature ebonite is in effect a " soft " vulcanisate (i.e. a high-elastic material, as explained on p. 835 below); hence it has the coefficient of expansion (about 0·0006) charac-teristic of the rubber-like state, as indeed was found by Kimura and Namikawa. *Below* the yield temperature, in its normal or " hard " condi-tion, ebonite is in a different (glass-like) physical state, and so has a low coefficient of expansion. At room temperature vulcanisates with less than 18% combined sulphur are not in this " hard " state, that is, are not true ebonites, while those with 20% or more combined sulphur are; the change from high to low coefficient of expansion when the combined sulphur is increased above 18–20% is thus due to the change from the " soft " to the " hard " or glass-like state.

The whole behaviour can be represented diagrammatically as in Fig. 10.10; each line shows how density varies with sulphur content at a fixed temperature; the break in the line is the transition from soft to hard. As

E E

the temperature is raised, this transition point moves to the right (higher sulphur), because increase of temperature lowers the left-hand (soft rubber) part of the line more than the right-hand (hard or ebonite) part. As pointed out by Kimura and Namikawa, the fact that the transition point varies with temperature disproves the view once held that this point

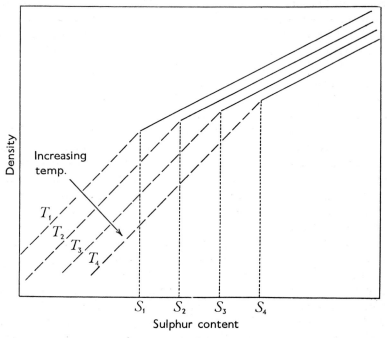

Fig. 10.10. Variation of density, measured at various temperatures, with sulphur content (diagrammatic). Broken lines: soft rubber state, high coefficient of expansion; continuous lines: hard state, low coefficient of expansion.

corresponds to a definite rubber–sulphur compound. Another characteristic of this point is its relationship with yield temperature, in the sense that T_1, T_2, T_3 and T_4 are (approximately) the yield temperatures of ebonites with combined sulphurs S_1, S_2, S_3 and S_4 respectively.

The difference in coefficient of expansion of ebonite above and below the yield temperature also explains the apparent cessation of volume shrinkage when the vulcanisation of ebonite is prolonged beyond a stage corresponding to about 19% combined sulphur.[1,49] It has been shown [36] that if all densities are measured *at vulcanising temperature*, i.e. with the vulcanisate in the " soft-rubber " condition at all states of cure, the curve of volume against time of cure decreases continuously and shows no discontinuity at 19% combined sulphur.

Effects of temperature: elastic and visco-elastic (" plastic ") deformations

It is well known that when the temperature of ebonite is raised to a certain point it becomes relatively soft and deformable; this deformation is commonly called " plastic yield " and the temperature at which it commences the " plastic yield temperature ". These terms are quite incorrect, because the deformation is entirely reversible and therefore elastic, not plastic,[50, 51] although the deformation may be strongly time-dependent (visco-elastic). Henceforward we shall refer simply to " yield " (or " high temperature yield ") and " yield temperature ".

It is possible to give the following rough picture of how the changes in properties in the region of the yield temperature arise from the chemical constitution of ebonite as outlined on p. 818 above.

Sulphur atoms are highly polar, and hence exert strong van der Waals forces of attraction. In ebonite there are so many intramolecular sulphur atoms attached along the rubber chain-molecules that at room temperature these forces hold neighbouring chains firmly together, making the material hard and rigid. The molecular chains are in a constant state of agitation owing to the vibrations of their constituent atoms, and when the temperature is raised this agitation becomes more vigorous and is able gradually to break down the van der Waals attractions, thus allowing neighbouring chains to move past each other more or less quickly.

At still higher temperatures (say $100°$ C) the chains are released yet more quickly from the attractions due to the intramolecular sulphur atoms, until finally these attractions cease to give any effective hold, and the material can deform instantaneously and elastically. The mechanical behaviour of the ebonite is now determined solely by the relatively heat-stable sulphur cross-links joining adjacent molecular chains. It is indeed in a similar state to a soft vulcanised rubber, the elastic properties of which are due to its consisting of flexible molecular chains held together here and there by cross-links. Ebonite, however, has many more cross-links, and therefore a higher elastic modulus than a soft vulcanisate. An unloaded ebonite at $100°$ C does indeed resemble a very stiff " soft " rubber; deformation is completely reversible, but the modulus is about 10 times that of a " pure gum " vulcanisate.[21]

The transition of ebonite from the rigid to the elastic state with rise of temperature is just the reverse of the " freezing " of a soft vulcanisate on rapid cooling. The difference lies in the temperature where a particular state occurs: ebonite at normal temperature has the hardness and rigidity that a " soft " vulcanisate possesses at (say) $-60°$ C; ebonite has to be heated to $80° - 100°$ C to acquire the high-elastic character that a soft vulcanisate possesses at room temperature.

The visco-elastic behaviour described above can be represented by the time–deformation curves in Fig. 10.11, where curves 1–8 relate to increasing temperatures. This diagram applies equally to ebonite and soft rubber, the differences being: (i) curves 1 and 8 represent the behaviour of ebonite at about 50° and 100° C respectively, whereas for a soft natural rubber vulcanisate the temperatures would be about −70° and −20° C; (ii) for a soft vulcanisate the vertical (deformation) scale would be about 10 times that for ebonite. If the deformation at a fixed time (from Fig. 10.11) is plotted against temperature, a " temperature–yield " curve of the

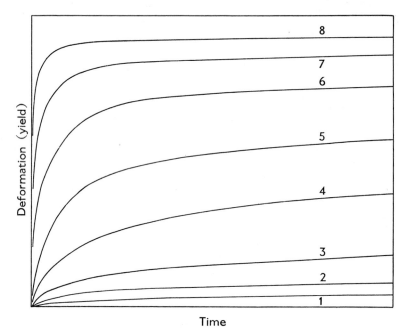

Fig. 10.11. Time/yield curves for ebonite at various temperatures; curves 1–8 relate to increasing temperatures.

shape shown by Fig. 10.12 is obtained. The middle part is practically straight and can be extrapolated backward to meet the temperature axis, so that the curve, and hence the yield characteristics of the ebonite, can be defined in terms of two quantities : [52] (i) *yield temperature*, i.e. the point A; (ii) *slope* of the straight part, i.e. the ratio CB/AB.

Strictly speaking, the yield temperature is not an invariable characteristic of any given ebonite, since it depends on the time (on the curves of Fig. 10.11) at which yield is measured; increasing the time moves the temperature–yield curve (Fig. 10.12) to the left, i.e. yield temperature is lowered. The effect, however, is small, since doubling the time lowers the yield temperature rather less than 1° C (or halving the time raises it the same amount).[52]

The yield temperature is higher the greater the proportion of sulphur used, except that in natural-rubber ebonites increasing the sulphur beyond 35% of the mix causes yield temperature to fall again.[7] The yield temperature also rises with advancing cure. However, it is not solely a function of the amount of combined sulphur, since a given amount of combined sulphur leads to a higher yield temperature (i) if attained by a

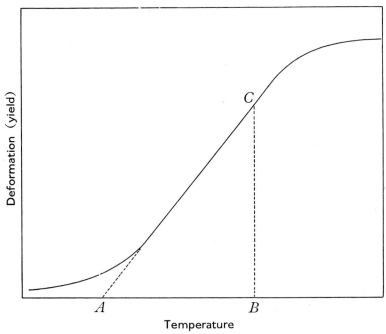

Fig. 10.12. Temperature/yield curve; A = yield temperature; ratio CB/AB = " slope ".

long cure on a low-sulphur mix than by a shorter cure on a high-sulphur mix, or (ii) if attained by using a low curing temperature and correspondingly longer cure; moreover, yield temperature can increase markedly during prolonged cure without any substantial increase in combined sulphur.[36] It is significant also that the Young's modulus of ebonite (at room temperature) is increased by these same factors that raise yield temperature.[7]

It seems reasonable to assume that these differences between ebonites having the same total amount of combined sulphur (and which are accompanied also by differences in resistance to swelling liquids, see p. 841) result from differences in the proportions of intermolecular (cross-link) sulphur and intramolecular sulphur, and/or in the number of sulphur atoms per cross-link. In soft vulcanisates these factors are known to vary with vulcanising conditions,[19] although there is as yet no corresponding evidence relating to ebonite.

" Set " after deformation

A consequence of the deformation mechanism outlined above is that the time-dependence of deformation should vary with temperature in the following way: At room temperature, where ebonite has a rigid structure bound together by strong van der Waals forces, deformation is due to the elastic straining of these bonds, and since the strain is elastic, both deformation and recovery are substantially instantaneous. At temperatures high enough to render these forces ineffective the deformations are high-elastic, and hence again substantially instantaneous. At intermediate temperatures, however, the van der Waals forces are overcome only at a finite (even slow) rate, so that deformation and recovery are time-dependent. This can be studied experimentally by measuring the " set " or residual deformation after a short recovery period following subjection to a fixed strain; this set, being a measure of the time-dependence of deformation, would be expected to show a maximum or peak at some intermediate temperature. This has been confirmed [50] by experiments which gave temperature–set curves very similar in shape to those predicted theoretically.[21] It was also found, in agreement with theory, that: (i) when the sulphur ratio or cure is altered, the " set peak temperature " changes in much the same way as the yield temperature; (ii) the set peak temperature corresponds to about the middle of the straight part of the temperature–yield curve (Fig. 10.12).

Visco-elastic behaviour of two-phase compounds

A further consequence of the deformation mechanism postulated above is illustrated by the behaviour of ebonites containing ebonite dust.[53] Such ebonites are two-phase structures comprising particles of the added dust embedded in a matrix of new ebonite. The dust phase is always more fully cured than the new matrix, and hence the ebonites show two yield temperatures, produced by the dust and matrix phases respectively, and two corresponding peaks on the temperature–set curve. Furthermore, with changes in the proportions of ebonite dust or of sulphur in the mix, or in the time of cure, the two yield temperatures and the two set peak temperatures change in precisely the way that would be expected from the equilibria set up in the three-component system rubber–sulphur–ebonite dust.

Electrical properties

Among the electrical characteristics of rubber vulcanisates the ones that have received most attention from the theoretical standpoint are the dielectric properties. Since ebonites are merely a part of the whole range of rubber–sulphur compounds, the study of the dielectric behaviour of ebonite is really part of the corresponding study of such compounds in general. It is therefore only necessary here to call attention to those features that result from the hard nature of ebonite, as contrasted with normal soft vulcanisates, and the consequences of the transition from hard to soft that occurs on raising the temperature.

Dielectric loss in rubber vulcanisates is due mainly to the alternating electric field causing movements of electrically unsymmetrical groups (dipoles) that result from the presence of sulphur atoms in the molecular structure. Although ebonite must contain many dipoles, it shows only small dielectric loss at room temperature. The explanation [54] is that the mechanical rigidity of the material prevents the dipoles from moving appreciably, or as Kitchin expresses it, " dielectric response is very slow "; in terms of the picture given above of the structure of ebonite, the dipoles are unable to move quickly, in response to the alternating field, by the strong van der Waals forces associated with the intramolecular sulphur atoms.

As the temperature is raised these forces are gradually relaxed and the dipole movements become greater, causing increased dielectric loss. At a sufficiently high temperature, however, the van der Waals forces exert virtually no control (the ebonite being then in the high-elastic or rubber-like state) and then, although the dipoles can move freely, there is little to oppose these movements, and hence little energy is absorbed. In short, therefore, the dielectric loss, which is due to absorption of energy from the electric field, passes through a maximum at some intermediate temperature where the ebonite is neither in the " hard " nor the " rubber-like " state. This maximum is clearly shown in the studies [54, 55] of the influence of test temperature and frequency on the dielectric loss (actually power factor) of ebonites with various sulphur contents.

Theory would indicate a relationship between dielectric constant and mechanical deformation, since both are controlled by the degree of mobility within the molecular structure. At room temperature (i.e. the condition represented by the bottom end of the temperature–yield curve, Fig. 10.12) both the deformation and the dielectric constant and loss are small, and for the same reason. At high temperature (top of the curve) the deformation and dielectric constant are large, but dielectric loss is again small. The maximum loss will thus correspond to the condition represented by the middle of the rising part of the curve, just as does the maximum set after constant strain (see p. 838).

It would therefore be expected that any factor, such as increasing the sulphur ratio or cure time, which moves the temperature–yield curve in the direction of higher temperature would also raise the temperature of maximum dielectric loss, just as it raises the " set peak temperature ". This was confirmed [54, 55] so far as sulphur ratio is concerned (effect of cure time was not studied); this is shown in Table 10.2, in which the temperature of maximum power factor is compared with the temperature corresponding to the middle of the temperature–yield curve (the difference between the results of Kitchin and of Scott *et al.* at 10^5 c/s. may be due to the latter having used purified rubber hydrocarbon for their stocks and given a much longer cure).

TABLE 10.2

Rubber–sulphur ratio	Temp.–yield curve mid-point, °C	Temperature, °C, of max. power factor at:			
		10^3 c/s (a)	10^4 c/s (b)	10^5 c/s (a)	10^5 c/s (b)
80 : 20	c. 30	70	48	95	65
76 : 24	67	95	70	125	92
72 : 28	80	123	—	150	—
68 : 32	88	c. 137	100	>150	>100

(a) Scott *et al.*[55]; (b) Kitchin.[54]

The fact that the power-factor maximum does not occur at the temperature corresponding to the mid-point of the temperature–yield curve is due to various causes, notably: (i) the molecular groups involved in dipole oscillations and in mechanical deformations are not the same; (ii) there is a big difference in the time scale of the movements involved, those in the electrical test being extremely rapid (10^3–10^5 oscillations per second) while the yield test uses a 30-minute stressing period.

This connection between the effects of temperature and time (i.e. rate or frequency of movement) implies that at any given temperature the dielectric loss should pass through a maximum as the test frequency is increased; this is confirmed by the results of Kitchin.

Although mechanical deformation (yield) and dielectric loss do not involve the same molecular movements, yet in respect to the effects of temperature and frequency (or deformation rate), and the interaction of these two effects, there is a striking similarity between mechanical and electrical phenomena.[56]

Swelling in organic liquids

Although ebonite is much more resistant than soft vulcanised rubber to the swelling action of organic liquids, it is by no means immune from attack, and some account is therefore necessary of the extensive investigations that have been made on the swelling action of liquids on natural and synthetic rubber ebonites.

Dependence on chemical nature of the liquid [22]

It will be convenient first to indicate how the swelling of natural rubber ebonite has been found to depend on the nature of the liquid (figures in brackets are the swelling, expressed as % by volume, of ebonites with 27·2% and 31·4% combined sulphur respectively):

(i) Liquids consisting of aliphatic hydrocarbons (petroleum ether, paraffin oil, transformer oil) have little or no swelling action (1–4; o).

(ii) Hydroaromatic hydrocarbons (cyclohexane, decahydronaphthalene) produce rather more swelling (6–9; < 1), while aromatic hydrocarbons (benzene, xylene) have a strong swelling action (90; 60).

(iii) Halogenated hydrocarbons (carbon tetrachloride, chlorobenzene) and carbon disulphide resemble aromatic hydrocarbons in producing considerable swelling (70–100; 75).

(iv) Among the polar liquids, aliphatic hydroxy-compounds (ethyl alcohol, glycerin, castor oil) have no swelling action, while those with oxygen present as $>CO$ or $—CO_2R$ (acetone, ethyl acetate) produce a small or moderate swelling (6–25; 1–20). In aromatic compounds the introduction of hydroxyl, amino- or nitro-groups (as in phenol, aniline, nitrobenzene), though it may reduce the swelling action, does not by any means destroy it.

The swelling action of a liquid on ebonite does not bear a constant ratio to its swelling action on a soft vulcanised rubber. Although, with increasing sulphur content over the range from soft to hard vulcanisates, swelling almost always decreases, the extent of the decrease depends on the nature of the liquid, being greatest with aliphatic hydrocarbons, slightly less with hydroaromatic hydrocarbons, markedly less with aromatic hydrocarbons and halogen and sulphur compounds, and least with polar liquids. Consequently, the relative swelling capacities of two liquids may be reversed on passing from soft rubber to ebonite; thus, petroleum ether swells soft rubber more than nitrobenzene, but with ebonite the latter produces the greater swelling. Another important example is the comparison of aliphatic and aromatic hydrocarbons; with soft vulcanised natural rubber the ratio of swellings in petroleum ether and benzene is about 2 : 3, but when the rubber is vulcanised to a stage approximating to C_5H_8S it is completely unaffected by aliphatic hydrocarbons, whereas benzene (and other aromatic hydrocarbons) still swell it strongly. This change in the relative affinities of the rubber vulcanisate for different types of liquid is evidently due to the change in its chemical nature caused by the introduction of large amounts of sulphur.

So far we have considered the *amount* of liquid absorbed at equilibrium (i.e. the " swelling maximum "). Another important parameter of the swelling process is the rate factor or " swelling time ", which is conveniently defined as the time to reach half the swelling maximum and is an *approximate* relative measure of the time required to reach the maximum or equilibrium swelling.

The swelling time of ebonite is usually greater than (10–50 times) that for soft rubber in the same liquid; carbon disulphide is an exception, since it swells ebonite almost as quickly as soft rubber. Moreover, with ebonite there are greater differences between the swelling times of different liquids than with soft rubber. With soft rubber the swelling time is generally shorter the less viscous the liquid, but this relationship does not apply with ebonite, indeed some of the least viscous of the liquids studied (acetone, ethyl acetate and petroleum ether) diffuse into ebonite most slowly. This can be explained by making the assumption, which is supported by other evidence, that swelling of ebonite makes it more readily permeable, that is, increases the diffusion coefficient. The three liquids named have only a small swelling action, so that diffusion occurs in substantially unswollen ebonite, and hence is very slow. Carbon disulphide, benzene, xylene, carbon tetrachloride and chlorobenzene are at least as viscous as these three liquids and yet diffuse much more quickly, because they produce more swelling, which greatly increases the permeability of the ebonite.

The conclusion therefore is that although the viscosity of a liquid must influence its rate of penetration into ebonite, the permeability of the ebonite is so greatly increased by absorption of liquid that the swelling capacity of the liquid has much more influence on this rate than has the viscosity.

Dependence of swelling on degree of vulcanisation

In all liquids that have been studied the swelling is less the more fully vulcanised the ebonite, i.e. the higher the proportion of sulphur and the longer the cure.[57] The only exception is that very long cures have sometimes shown a slight increase in swelling (" reversion "). The influence of these factors is illustrated in Fig. 10.13, which shows also that swelling time behaves in the opposite way to swelling maximum, that is, it increases with sulphur ratio or length of cure. It is clear, however, that ebonites of the same chemical state of cure, that is, equal vulcanisation coefficient, do not necessarily have the same swelling time. Indeed, these and other data [7] for natural-rubber ebonites swelling in petroleum ether show that for a given vulcanisation coefficient the swelling time is greater (i.e.

absorption of liquid takes longer) if this coefficient is attained by a long cure on a low-sulphur mix than by a shorter cure on a mix of higher sulphur content.

Some evidence of an analogous effect with swelling maximum is seen by comparing the curves for the 72 : 28 and 68 : 32 mixes in Fig. 10.13 (swelling maximum being *lower* with the long-cured low-sulphur ebonite),

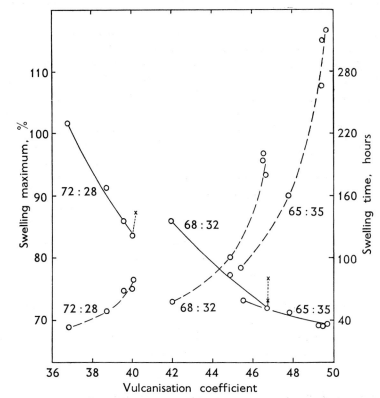

Fig. 10.13. Dependence of swelling maximum (continuous lines) and swelling time (broken lines) or vulcanisation coefficient, for 72 : 28, 68 : 32 and 65 : 35 natural rubber/sulphur mixes cured 3, 3¾, 5, 7, 10½ hr. at 155° C. Tests in benzene at room temperature. X = " reverted " samples. (Data from Ref. 57.)

and has been found more definitely in swelling tests with paraffin oil and petroleum ether.[7]

Since long swelling time and low swelling maximum both mean better resistance to the swelling action of the liquid, it appears that in general an ebonite of given vulcanisation coefficient resists swelling better if produced by a long cure on a low-sulphur mix. It is significant that this procedure also results in a higher elastic (Young's) modulus at room temperature and in higher yield temperature, that is, greater resistance to high-temperature deformation.[36] The effects on all three properties—modulus, yield temperature and swelling—imply that the long-cured low-sulphur ebonite has a more closely knit molecular structure.

Effect of temperature on swelling

So far the discussion has referred to the action of liquids at temperatures not far removed from room temperature. Raising the temperature somewhat increases the swelling, but does not alter its order of magnitude; thus, the swelling in xylene or nitrobenzene was found [36] to increase from 50–55% at 34° C to 95–100% at 100° C.

It is especially noteworthy that the latter temperature is well above the yield temperature of the ebonite, which is thus in the soft or high-elastic state (see p. 835). Thus, the transition from the hard or ebonite state to the soft or high-elastic state does not result in swelling characteristics like those of a soft vulcanisate; confirmation of this is furnished by the results in Table 10.3. The swelling after prolonged immersion in the hot paraffin oil is seen to be very small, and similar tests with transformer oil showed no measurable swelling; soft natural rubber vulcanisates would swell some 100–300% in these oils.

TABLE 10.3

SWELLING (% BY VOLUME) IN PARAFFIN OIL AFTER 29 DAYS AT 70° C FOLLOWED BY 38 DAYS AT 100° C (Scott [58])

Rubber–sulphur ratio and cure	Vulc. coeff.	Swelling
72 : 28; 3 hr. at 155° C	36·8	4·6
,,　　3¾ hr.　,,	38·7	3·9
68 : 32; 3 hr.　　,,	42·0	1·9
65 : 35; 3 hr.　　,,	45·4	0·8

This result is presumably due to the fact that swelling is strongly dependent on the chemical nature of the vulcanised polymer, and the high proportion of combined sulphur in ebonite gives it a much reduced affinity for aliphatic hydrocarbons.

On the other hand, it seems likely (though no data have been found) that at temperatures above the yield temperature the swelling *time* would be greatly reduced, since this property must depend on the van der Waals binding between adjacent molecular chains, which have to be separated to permit absorption of liquid, and this binding is very weak at temperatures above the yield temperature (see p. 835).

Swelling of synthetic rubber ebonites [11]

Ebonites made from butadiene polymers or butadiene–styrene copolymers do not differ fundamentally from natural-rubber ebonites in swelling behaviour; again, increasing the sulphur ratio or cure reduces the swelling maximum and increases the swelling time. Generally, however, in any given liquid the swelling maximum is less and the swelling time greater with the synthetic ebonites than with a comparable natural ebonite; this can be ascribed, in part at least, to the fact that the synthetic rubbers combine more nearly completely with the added sulphur. Butadiene–acrylonitrile rubbers are outstanding in giving ebonites almost unaffected even by liquids (e.g. benzene, carbon disulphide) that strongly swell natural, butadiene and butadiene–styrene rubber ebonites.

REFERENCES

1. Curtis, H. L., McPherson, A. T. and Scott, A. H. (1927) U.S. Bureau of Standards Scientific Paper 560.
2. Kimura, S. and Namikawa, N. (1929) *J. Soc. chem. Ind. Japan*, **32**, 196B.
3. Skellon, H. (1914) *Koll. Zeits.*, **14**, 96.
4. Skellon, H. *The Rubber Industry*, ed. Torrey, J. and Manders, A. S. (London), p. 172.
5. Stevens, H. P. and Stevens, W. H. (1929) *J. Soc. chem. Ind.*, **48**, 55.
6. Stevens, H. P. and Stevens, W. H. (1931) *J. Soc. chem. Ind.*, **50**, 397T.
7. Scott, J. R. (1948) *J. Rubb. Res.*, **17**, 170.
8. Blokh, G. A. and Chuprina, L. F. (1954) *Dokl. Akad. Nauk S.S.S.R.*, **99**, 757; (1955) *Chem. Abstr.*, **49**, 6639.
9. Church, H. F. and Daynes, H. A. (1945) *J. Rubb. Res.*, **14**, 165.
10. Fisher, D. G., Newton, R. G. and Scott, J. R. (1948) *J. Rubb. Res.*, **17**, 161.
11. Scott, J. R. (1944) *J. Rubb. Res.*, **13**, 27.
12. Glancy, W. E., Wright, D. D. and Oon, K. H. (1926) *Ind. Eng. Chem.*, **18**, 73.
13. Kashin, V. (1936) *J. Rubb. Ind., U.S.S.R.*, **10**, 521.
14. Stevens, H. P. (1927), B.P. 269,693.
15. Marchandise, R., *Encyclopédie du Caoutchouc et des Industries qui s'y rattachent* (Paris: Syndicat du Caoutchouc), p. 333.
16. J. M. Steel and Co., Ltd. (1937) *Vulkacit CT*, 2nd edn. (London).
17. Midgley, T., Henne, A. L. and Shepard, A. F. (1934) *J. Amer. chem. Soc.*, **56**, 1326.
18. Glazebrook, R. W. and Saville, R. W. (1954) *J. chem. Soc.*, 2094.
19. Bateman, L. C., Glazebrook, R. W., Moore, C. G. and Saville, R. W. (1954) *Proc. Third Rubber Tech. Conf.* (Cambridge: Heffer), p. 298.
20. Salomon, G. (1952) *Chem. Weekblad*, **48**, No. 16, 292.
21. Scott, J. R. (1942) *Trans. Faraday Soc.*, **38**, 284.
22. Parris, R. W. and Scott, J. R. (1941) *J. Rubb. Res.*, **10**, 123 (incorporated in Ref. 57).
23. Blake, J. T. (1930) *Ind. Eng. Chem.*, **22**, 737.
24. Takada, J. (1951) *J. Soc. Rubb. Ind. Japan*, **24**, 199.
25. Williams, I. and Beaver, D. J. (1923) *Ind. Eng. Chem.*, **15**, 255.
26. Blake, J. T. (1934) *Ind. Eng. Chem.*, **26**, 1283.
27. Hada, K., Fukaya, K. and Nakajima, T. (1931) *J. Rubb. Soc. Japan*, **2**, 389; (1931) *Rubb. Chem. Technol.*, **4**, 507.
28. Hada, K. and Nakajima, T. (1932) *J. Soc. Rubb. Ind. Japan*, **5**, 288; (1933) *Rubb. Chem. Technol.*, **6**, 56.
29. Daynes, H. A. (1935) *I.R.I. Trans.*, **11**, 336.
30. Church, H. F. and Daynes, H. A. (1944) *J. Rubb. Res.*, **13**, 55.
31. Perks, A. A. (1926) *J. Soc. chem. Ind.*, **45**, 142T.
32. Riding, H. (1930) *Trans. Inst. Rubb. Ind.*, **6**, 230.

33. Jessup, R. S. and Cummings, A. D. (1934) *Bureau of Standards J. Res.*, **13**, 357.
34. McPherson, A. T. and Bekkedahl, N. (1935) *Bureau of Standards J. Res.*, **14**, 601.
35. Winspear, G. G., Hermann, D. B., Malm, F. S. and Kemp, A. R. (1946) *Ind. Eng. Chem.*, **38**, 687.
36. Scott, J. R. (1958) *Ebonite, its Nature, Properties and Compounding* (London: Maclaren and Sons Ltd.).
37. Norman, R. H. and Scott, J. R. (1948) *J. Rubb. Res.*, **17**, 161.
38. Fry, J. D. and Porritt, B. D. (1929) *India Rubb. J.*, **78**, 307.
39. Webster, D. M. and Porritt, B. D. (1930) *India Rubb. J.*, **79**, 239.
40. Church, H. F. and Daynes, H. A. (1937) *J. Rubb. Res.*, **6**, 13.
41. Church, H. F., Cooper, L. H. N. and Daynes, H. A. (1945) *J. Rubb. Res.*, **14**, 155.
42. Dock, E. H., Porritt, B. D. and Willott, W. H. (1948) *J. Rubb. Res.*, **17**, 98.
43. Research Association of British Rubber Manufacturers, unpublished results.
44. Newton, R. G. and Wake, W. C. (1950) *J. Rubb. Res.*, **19**, 9, 17.
45. Bateman, L. and Cunneen, J. I. (1955), *J. chem. Soc.*, 1596; Bateman, L., Cunneen, J. I. and Ford, J. (1956) *ibid.*, 3056.
46. Church, H. F. and Daynes, H. A. (1938) *J. Rubb. Res.*, **7**, 19.
47. Fisher, D. G. and Scott, J. R. (1948) *J. Rubb. Res.*, **17**, 96.
48. Westbrook, M. K. and Whorlow, R. W. (1950) *J. Rubb. Res.*, **19**, 115.
49. Bunschoten, E. (1921) *Verslagen en Mededeelingen, Afdeeling Handel*, No. 6, p. 37.
50. Church, H. F. and Daynes, H. A. (1936) *RABRM J.*, **5**, 11.
51. Gurevich, G. and Kobeko, P. (1939) *J. Tech. Phys., U.S.S.R.*, **9**, 1267; (1940) *Rubb. Chem. Technol.*, **13**, 904.
52. Church, H. F. and Daynes, H. A. (1939) *J. Rubb. Res.*, **8**, 41; (1946), **15**, 127.
53. Scott, J. R. (1949) *J. Rubb. Res.*, **18**, 131.
54. Kitchin, D. W. (1932) *Ind. Eng. Chem.*, **24**, 549.
55. Scott, A. H., McPherson, A. T. and Curtis, H. L. (1933) *Bureau of Standards J. Res.*, **11**, 173.
56. Payne, A. R. *Rheology of Elastomers*, (London: Pergamon Press), p. 86.
57. Scott, J. R. (1937) *I.R.I. Trans.*, **13**, 109.
58. Scott, J. R. (1946) *J. Rubb. Res.*, **15**, 179 (incorporated in Ref. 57).

CHAPTER X

PART TWO

THE TECHNOLOGY OF EBONITE

by

H. A. DAYNES

S INCE ebonite was first manufactured in the middle of the last century there have been no revolutionary changes in its manufacture such as have taken place with soft rubber due to the introduction of accelerators of vulcanisation, antioxidants and reinforcing ingredients. Basic operations, such as mastication, mixing, calendering and extrusion, are so similar for ebonite and soft rubber that they require no detailed consideration here. In many other respects the problems which arise in the manufacture of ebonite are quite different from those with soft rubber, and different tests are used for the control of manufacture and for the assessment of the quality of the product.

Before considering the manufacture of ebonite in detail it is convenient to draw attention to some of the outstanding differences.

(*a*) Ebonite is so stable chemically that ageing presents no problem and ample life is normally achieved without the use of antioxidants.

(*b*) Reinforcement by the use of carbon black or mineral ingredients is not possible. These materials affect the mechanical strength adversely, or at least do not improve it.

(*c*) Owing to the dark colour of the basic material when vulcanised, the possibilities of pigmentation are very limited, and any departure from black involves sacrifice in some physical properties.

(*d*) Most properties of ebonite are comparatively insensitive to the quality of the rubber hydrocarbon used, provided that it is free from foreign matter.

(*e*) Times of vulcanisation are normally very long compared with those of soft rubbers.

(*f*) There is a large reduction of about 6% in volume on vulcanisation, which necessitates large allowances for shrinkage and special methods in moulding.

(*g*) The chemical combination of rubber and sulphur in the proportions used in ebonite is strongly exothermic. This is a very important factor in determining the methods of vulcanisation.

847

(h) Since all ebonite mixings contain a high proportion of sulphur and usually of ebonite dust, the consistency of the compound during processing prior to vulcanisation is never that of a " pure gum " stock.

(i) In spite of the high proportion of sulphur used, blooming does not occur.

Fields of use of ebonite

Since the early part of the century the use of ebonite has been seriously challenged by the development of a great variety of synthetic resins, and in some applications ebonite has been partly or completely replaced. The apparent decline of ebonite appears to be relative rather than absolute, since, as Davies has pointed out, the consumption of rubber in ebonite increased on the average by about 6% a year over a long period up to 1951.[1] The choice between materials for a particular use may be determined by a combination of technical, economic or aesthetic considerations.

Ebonite is often preferred on account of its good combination of physical and chemical properties, such as strength, rigidity and resistance to impact, dimensional stability in moist conditions, freedom from deterioration by oxidation and excellent resistance to most chemicals, even in hot solutions of high concentration.[2] On the other hand, the temperature of use is limited where the material is under mechanical load owing to its comparatively low softening point. This can be overcome to some extent by suitable compounding. A further weakness is the tendency to develop an acid surface and to lose its deep black colour when exposure to bright sunlight cannot be avoided.

Many synthetic materials are most suitable for rapid production in very large numbers. Ebonite is more difficult to produce in that way, but can be used where comparatively small numbers of articles are required in a variety of shapes and sizes.

Ebonite cannot be produced in the variety of brilliant colours which are obtainable with a number of synthetic resins. Some attractive colours are possible, but the range is very limited.

Ebonite products may be broadly classified according to their primary function as follows:

Mechanical, for example water-meter components, pipe stems, fountain pens, piston rings for hot-water pumps, textile machinery accessories, combs and surgical apparatus.

Chemical, for example battery boxes and separators, chemical pipe work and accessories, pumps for chemicals, tank linings, buckets and roller coverings.

Electrical, for example sheets, rods, tubes and mouldings for the machining of electrical insulating components, such as inductance coils, plugs and sockets, X-ray cable terminations and handle coverings for electricians' tools.

There are also various special products which do not fall into this classification, for example cellular ebonite for the thermal insulation of refrigerators, or for floats.

Although there is a variety of formulations, most ebonites fall into one or other of the following types:

(a) *Unloaded ebonite.* This may be of high grade containing nothing but rubber, sulphur and high-grade ebonite dust, or in cheaper grades many contain materials such as reclaim, factice and bitumen, but with no deliberate addition of mineral fillers.

(b) *Loaded ebonite.* In this class mineral fillers are added to produce a harder material or to reduce deformation at elevated temperature.

(c) *Flexible ebonites.* These are usually unloaded, but modified either by the use of a lower proportion of sulphur or by the inclusion of modifying ingredients, such as polychloroprene, polyisobutylene or Butyl rubber. The object may be either to make the material softer at normal temperatures or to increase the resistance to impact.

(d) *Special products.* For example cellular and microporous ebonites.

Properties and methods of assessment

Before considering how compounds are designed and processed for a particular product it is necessary to state briefly the chief properties which are of importance and the methods of test in terms of which these properties are expressed and by which the quality of ebonite is assessed.

Yield at elevated temperatures

Whether used for mechanical or electrical purposes, ebonite should not soften and yield under pressure at an unduly low temperature. The extent of deformation at a given elevated temperature is variously termed yield, plastic yield or cold flow, and the temperature at which a predetermined yield occurs under a standard condition of test is referred to as yield temperature, plastic yield temperature or softening point. The terms " yield " and " yield temperature " will be used here. The yield at a given temperature is usually measured by the deflection of a horizontal bar of the material firmly held at one end as a cantilever and loaded at the other end,[3,4] or resting on supports at the ends and loaded at the centre. Alternatively, it may be measured by the compression of a block of the material between parallel plates.[5]

Yield temperature may be determined by measuring the yield at a series of temperatures, constructing a curve and determining the temperature at which the yield reaches a predetermined value [6] or using the extrapolation method described on p. 837,[7, 8] (Part 1, Fig. 10.12). Alternatively, a sample may be stressed while the temperature is raised at a steady rate and the temperature determined at which the cumulative yield reaches a predetermined value.[9,10,11] Except in the extrapolation method, the values obtained for the yield temperature are dependent on the choice of load, dimensions of the specimen and the yield value selected as the criterion. In test specifications these are chosen to give an indication of the temperature under which yield would become intolerable in normal conditions of use, but such figures must be used with discretion when considering any particular application in which the mechanical stress may be unusually great or small.

The tests described above are useful as control tests for checking the formulation and cure of a particular material, but they have their limitations for investigation purposes and for comparing ebonite with other classes of material. As was explained in the first part of this chapter, ebonite is an elastic material, but over a certain range of temperature the deformation under a given load is very time-dependent, and it is just in the region of the yield temperature that it has the appearance in short-term tests of being plastic. It is in this same region that sub-permanent set after a period of constant strain is a maximum. At temperatures much above or much below the yield temperature the material is obviously elastic. To obtain a more complete description of the deformation properties it is necessary to measure the deformation over a wide range of loads and period of stress.

Mechanical strength

The second requirement in most applications is a definite degree of mechanical strength which is measured as tensile strength,[5,12] cross-breaking strength [5,13] or crushing strength.[14] There is no precise correlation between the values expressed in terms of breaking stress between these three types of test, nor would this be expected, since the distribution of stress and the element of shear stress vary from one test to another.[8] For comparative purposes and with a standard shape and dimension of test piece each test has its use as a guide in grading materials of the same class. When more precise data are required for design purposes it is best to select the type of test which most closely resembles the conditions of service.

The shape of the load–elongation curve for ebonite resembles that of metals in that after an initial stage of elastic extension it shows a fairly definite yield point, after which much of the elongation takes place rapidly and irreversibly with little further application of load.[15] Moreover, this irreversible extension takes place only in a portion of the test specimen, so that the tensile breaking elongation or its equivalent in the other types of test as judged by relative movements between the points of application of the load are of little significance.

Within the elastic range Young's modulus may be determined, but it is not a value which is often called for; in fact, it varies with composition and vulcanisation over a small range in comparison with the great variation which can be produced in the " modulus " of soft rubber.

Impact strength

The strength of a material when subjected to suddenly applied loads is very different from that under steady or slowly applied loads, and the former cannot be predicted from a knowledge of the latter. The most common type of apparatus for the determination of impact strength is a pendulum type of machine which is used to deliver a high-speed blow to a standard specimen and provides means for determining the kinetic energy lost by the pendulum during the fracture.[5,16] The most useful function of such a machine is for routine testing for quality control and specification purposes when applied to a narrow range of materials, but results of tests obtained by this method must be used with discretion in comparing materials of very different composition and physical structure. The method has the advantage that a useful mean value can be obtained from a comparatively small number of test pieces.

It is more significant in most cases to determine the energy of the smallest blow which will cause damage or rupture. For this reason there is an increasing use of simple falling-weight machines in which the test piece is struck by a freely falling striker of which the mass and height of fall can be varied so as to apply blows of a predetermined series of energy values. A number of test pieces are struck at each energy value. Each test piece is struck only once, and the blows applied are varied from one which breaks or damages a high proportion of specimens to one which breaks or damages only a small proportion. The blow which would break 50% of specimens is then estimated graphically or statistically.[5,17,18]

Impact strength expressed in terms of such tests is not a specific property of a material. For results of tests on different materials to be comparable it is necessary that the test pieces should be of the same form and dimensions.

Moreover, the blow which will break a specimen is very much affected by the presence of a notch at or near the point of maximum stress. It is customary, therefore, to test both unnotched and notched test pieces. This " notch sensitivity " may be illustrated by the results of notched and unnotched tests on a simple 68 : 32 ebonite in which the dimensions of the two types of specimen were so chosen that the cross-section at the point of fracture was the same in both cases. The impact strengths were found to be 2 and 56·5 kg.cm./cm.^{2} respectively.[19]

Volume and surface resistivity

A well-compounded ebonite free from carbon black and hygroscopic ingredients and with its surface in a clean condition has a very high resistivity, both through the mass of the material and over its surface. It is so far above what is required for most practical purposes that it is seldom required to measure these properties with a high degree of accuracy.

The method used when this is necessary is usually based on the use of the Curtis electrodes, a circular electrode system with guard ring by which the same electrical measuring system can be used for both volume and surface resistivity by connecting the measuring galvanometer or electrometer in different ways to the electrodes and guard ring.[20, 21, 22] It is not possible to make quite independent measurements of these two properties, since in any electrode system surface leakage is always accompanied by some volume leakage. Fortunately, when surface leakage is high enough to be of practical importance, e.g. at very high humidities or on a deteriorated surface, the error due to volume leakage becomes relatively very small, and much simpler electrode systems are possible, such as a conducting surface applied to the two long edges of a small rectangular strip and extending a short distance into the faces.[23]   In this case guard rings are unnecessary.   In the lower range of resistivity a simple D.C. galvanometer may be used to measure the leakage current; in the higher range electrometer methods become necessary.[24, 25]

Power factor and permittivity

In electrical engineering ebonite is used for components in alternating-current circuits over a wide range of frequency.   In such circuits, according to the application, the values of power factor and permittivity, or in some cases the product of the two, are important.

Methods of measuring these properties of insulating material are highly developed in connection with radio-frequency engineering. Bridge methods are used at the lower frequencies, from power frequency up to about 10^6 cycles/second, but for much higher frequencies substitution and resonance methods are available.[26, 27, 28, 29] The values obtained, especially for power factor, are frequency-dependent, so that where any accurate knowledge of these properties is critical, measurements must be made at the appropriate frequency. Audio-frequency tests in the range 800–1,600 cycles/second have been found useful and convenient as an approximate indication of quality for general applications.[30]

Sheets up to about $\frac{1}{16}$ in. thick are produced directly by calendering. Thicker sheets are usually made by plying up and rerolling by calender or a heavy hand roller. Tin foils are then applied to both sides and rolled on under pressure. Good adhesion is particularly important at the edges, since access of water under the foil during vulcanisation produces unsightly surface stains. The foiled sheets are usually stacked and cured in a steam-heated water tank. Groups of sheets may be spaced apart by metal plates to assist in dissipating the heat of the reaction. A long slow rise and a long cure, usually at a temperature of 140° C or less, are necessary for uniformity. After cure the tin foil is stripped off and the sheets are flattened while hot in a cool press. For most purposes, especially where the sheet is to be used as an insulator, the surface must be treated to remove any contamination by the foil. This may be done chemically, by sand-blasting or by scrubbing with wet abrasive powder. A fine polish may be produced by hot pressing between highly polished metal sheets, but the expense of this operation is seldom justified.

Small rods, tubes and specially shaped sections are normally extruded as for soft rubber, straightened on a hot table and packed in talc on trays for curing in open steam or inert gas. Larger rods and thick-wall tubes may be built up from calendered sheet about $\frac{1}{32}$ in. thick by wrapping under roller pressure and are then cloth wrapped for curing. Tubes are built up on a steel tube mandrel for support during cure.

With thick-walled tubes and rods, which may be up to about 4 in. in diameter, great care has to be taken in choice of curing temperature owing to the danger of internal heating. In extreme cases it is safer and more economical to cure in more than one operation, allowing time for cooling, or to use a stepped curing cycle. As an alternative, with large-diameter rods the outer portion may be wrapped on a core already partly cured to a stage at which it ceases to contribute to the exothermic heating.

Mouldings can be given complete accelerated cures in a short time at a high temperature only if small or thin-walled. In large mouldings, where the risk of internal heating exists, it is usually economical to use the mould only to produce a set cure to a stage where the cure can be completed in open steam or inert gas. Unless high proportions of ebonite dust are used, a good finish direct from the mould is difficult owing to the high shrinkage during vulcanisation. Progress has been made in recent years in adapting rapid production methods developed for curing thermosetting synthetic resins. Davies has given an account of the improvements affected with the smaller articles by the use of accelerators, fixed press tools, and better charging and discharging methods. As an example, small surgical sundries, which at the beginning of this century were given a 9 hours open-pan cure, can now be cured in a 6–8-minute cycle at a high temperature from preheated slugs in transfer moulds.[1]

Where complicated shapes have to be made in comparatively small numbers and a great variety of patterns and sizes, e.g. chemical-plant accessories, the finished article can be readily built up from the ebonite stock without expensive tools and finished by machining.

Ebonite is also widely used for roller covering and for protective coverings and linings of tanks for the prevention of corrosion of the metal by chemicals. The methods used vary with each particular case, and the application and cure frequently have to be carried out on site rather than in the factory. The general method is to prepare the metal by sand-blasting, coat it with an adhesive or in some cases an intermediate layer of soft rubber, and then apply unvulcanised sheets of ebonite stock by hand and press into contact by rolling. In closed tanks the vessel itself may be the container for the vulcanising steam; open tanks may be filled with hot water or brine and then gradually heated with steam. A more detailed account of such operations is given by Stevens and Donald.[2]

Vulcanisation in relation to properties

The composition of an ebonite mixing influences the processing before vulcanisation, the course of vulcanisation and the properties of the vulcanised product. These properties depend also on the degree and method of vulcanisation. Although vulcanisation is the last major factory operation, it is convenient to consider first the chemical and physical changes which take place during vulcanisation of simple rubber–sulphur mixings and the way in which they depend on the rubber–sulphur ratio and on the duration and method of cure. This leads to conclusions about the selection of optimum curing conditions. In later sections the effects of other ingredients will be considered, firstly, on processing operations, and secondly, on properties of the vulcanisate.

Much of the information to be quoted in these sections is based on the work of the Research Association of British Rubber Manufacturers, in which a large number of the possible variables were investigated using similar techniques and methods of test throughout. The results of this work have been arranged and critically discussed by Scott.[8]

Rubber–sulphur ratio and time of cure [19, 40, 42, 43, 44]

Consider first a 68 : 32 mixing (68 parts rubber, 32 parts sulphur by weight) vulcanised in a press in a sheet thin enough to avoid non-uniformity due to exothermic heating, for various periods up to 10 hours at 155° C. It has been seen from the first part of this chapter that under such conditions the uncombined sulphur decreases and the vulcanisation coefficient increases rapidly during the first 4 hours, reaching practically constant asymptotic values of approximately 1·5% and 47 respectively after about 5 hours, the vulcanisation coefficient being about the theoretical saturation value. This state may be called a full cure in the chemical sense. There is also a reduction of volume of about 6%.[39] It is known that after the combination of the first few per cent of sulphur the material passes through a leathery state, with low strength and poor resistance to oxidation, but we are concerned here only with the time after which a true ebonite is formed. This occurs when the vulcanisation coefficient is in the region of 25–30.[45,46]

Most of the properties of the ebonite show changes of approximately the same pattern as the changes in vulcanisation coefficient. The changes which take place between 5 and 10 hours are of little, if any, practical importance. At times up to 5 hours most properties are improving, with the exception of notched impact strength and radio-frequency power factor at temperatures above 60° C. The rate of approach to an asymptotic value varies from one property to another. If the time is reduced to 4 hours there is an appreciable reduction in yield temperature and in resistance to swelling in solvents, but a useful increase in notched impact strength. In other properties the time may be reduced to 3 or even 2 hours without any important change. This applies particularly to Young's modulus and indentation hardness.

Consider now the effects of increasing sulphur to a 65 : 35 ratio. At full cure the uncombined sulphur falls to about 4% while the vulcanisation coefficient rises to about 49, and neither value is changed by further curing. Tensile and cross breaking strength are increased at the optimum value by about 5%, but Young's modulus is negligibly higher. Both unnotched and notched impact strengths are reduced by about 10%. In the former case there is an appreciable reduction on extending the cure to 10 hours. The gain in yield temperature is no more than 2° C. Electrical properties are little changed, the radio-frequency power factor being about 5% lower both at room temperature and at 60° C. There is a distinct gain in resistance to swelling in aromatic solvents, the swelling in benzene being about 10% less and the swelling time greater by more than half. On the whole there is little to recommend the increase in sulphur, except for special purposes, to offset the possible disadvantage of the higher elemental sulphur.

The effects of reducing the sulphur from 68 : 32 to 72 : 28 are much more significant. The uncombined sulphur can be reduced to about 0·3%, the vulcanisation coefficient being about 40. Tensile strength, cross-breaking strength and Young's modulus are about 10% lower, and the former shows a further reduction on overcure. Unnotched impact strength is about 20% higher at the optimum, but the notched impact strength shows a different form of curve when plotted against time of cure, remaining constant from 3 to 5 hours and then falling to a much lower value at 10 hours. The 72 : 28 mixing always has the higher impact strength, and at 5 hours, when the difference is greatest, it has nearly twice the impact strength of the 68 : 32 mixing. Yield temperature remains about 7° C below that of the higher sulphur mixing. Radio-frequency power factor is greater both at room temperature and at 60° C, and in the latter case shows more sharply the effect of under cure, as would be expected from its lower yield temperature. Other electrical properties and water absorption are not significantly different. Swelling by solvents is about 20% higher, and the swelling time is reduced to about one-third. In general, an improved notched impact strength and a low uncombined sulphur have to be considered against an appreciably lower yield temperature and a much increased rate of swelling by solvents.

An ebonite can be made with a still lower sulphur content, but the outstanding physical properties of a fully cured ebonite are sacrificed to a large extent, and the material has only a limited use for special purposes. With 77 : 23 and 78·5 : 21·5 mixings the uncombined sulphur and vulcanisation coefficient become constant at about 5 hours cure, but Young's modulus continues to rise until about 7–8 hours, when it equals that of the higher-sulphur mixings. The yield temperatures reach values of about 55° and 40° C respectively, and swelling in organic liquid is very much increased both in the final absorption of liquid and in the rate at which this is absorbed.

To summarise, during the cure of a simple ebonite of a given rubber–sulphur ratio the best properties in most respects are obtained by giving a full cure. The most notable exception is notched impact strength, which is favoured by a lower vulcanisation coefficient. The correlation between properties and vulcanisation coefficient is not, however, complete, since some substantial physical changes can take place after chemical combination has ceased, particularly with low-sulphur mixings.

When the rubber–sulphur ratio is changed the properties attained at full cure other than notched impact strength are generally improved as the sulphur content is increased, but again the correlation between physical properties and vulcanisation coefficient is not close, since in some respects, notably yield temperature, Young's modulus and resistance to swelling in organic liquids, a given level of performance is reached at a lower vulcanisation coefficient as the sulphur content of the mixing is decreased.

For most purposes the useful range of rubber–sulphur ratio is from 68 : 32 to 72 : 28, and in fact a ratio of 70 : 30 is very commonly used as a satisfactory compromise for general application.

Temperature of cure [47]

If the temperature of cure is changed the rate of combination of sulphur increases with temperature by a factor of about 2·3 per 10° C. At the same time it appears that changes in physical properties depend on curing temperature in a way which cannot be accurately related to the chemical changes. This is most marked in yield at elevated temperatures. With a 65 : 35 mixing cured at 155° C the yield temperature becomes almost constant at a value of about 82° C after 5 hours. If the cure is carried out at 165° C the yield temperature becomes constant at the equivalent period (i.e. 5/2·3 hours), but at a value about 2° C lower. At a lower temperature of 135° C the yield continues to rise after combination of sulphur has ceased to a value of about 89° C after a time equivalent to 10 hours at 155° C. Similar effects are found with a 70 : 30 mixing, except that the continuous rise after " full cure " occurs at both 155° and 135° C, but not at 165° C. The yield values are also generally lower than for the 65 : 35 mixing. Although the gain in heat resistance by long cure at 135° C is considerable, it may not be economic, involving as it does a curing time of about 50 hours. There is also some indication that impact strength may be appreciably reduced under these conditions.

Method of cure [48]

Some of the technical properties of ebonite are appreciably affected by the method of cure, but it was seen on p. 855 that different methods have to be adopted according to the form of the finished article, so that it is not always possible to choose a particular method of cure, even if some advantage in technical properties is to be gained thereby. It follows that technical properties will also depend on the form of article and that this has to be taken into account in carrying out laboratory assessments of mixings.

Before discussing variations in properties with method of cure, consider the characteristic operating conditions of the various methods. In open steam the external pressure is limited to a few atmospheres steam pressure. The direct exposure to steam during cure causes a yellowish discoloration, which penetrates a short distance into the surface of the ebonite and is objectionable unless the surface layer is to be subsequently removed. The steam also causes chemical changes, at least in the outer layer, due to hydrolysis of non-hydrocarbon constituents of the rubber, and there is a noticeable loss of sulphur by volatilisation. Heat is easily transferred to the material in the early part of the cure, and temperature control by steam pressure is easy and precise. Steam, however, is not an ideal medium for conducting away the heat of the reaction.

The use of inert gas in place of steam avoids discoloration and chemical

changes, but the applied pressure is equally limited, and precise temperature control and dissipation of the heat of the reaction are more difficult.

In the water cure of foiled sheets the disadvantages of direct contact
with steam are avoided, except at the edges, and heat transfer is more
efficient than open steam in dissipating heat from the exothermic reaction.

In a platen press much higher external pressure can be applied and heat-
transfer conditions are good, but this method can be applied only to a
limited range of articles.

Variation of properties with method of cure can be associated with these
different operating conditions. The density of press-cured sheet and its
cross-breaking strength are slightly higher, which indicates absence of
porosity. There seems to be no effect of any technical importance in
yield temperature other than can be accounted for by a slight loss of
sulphur and a rather higher rate of cure in open steam. The most marked
effect is in dielectric properties, the power factor at normal temperature
of open-steam-cured ebonite being about 20% higher and the permittivity
slightly higher. This is probably associated with the chemical changes
due to contact with steam, since the equilibrium water absorption of
material taken from near the surface is found to be considerably greater
than material taken from the inside of the mass. One unexpected effect is
that the temperature–power-factor curve of open-steam-cured ebonite is
much less steep than those of press-cured or water-cured ebonite and
crosses the latter at about 60° C.

Comparison of synthetic rubbers with natural rubber

The changes during vulcanisation of synthetic rubbers are generally
similar to those of natural rubbers, but there are some notable differences.

Rubbers of the butadiene–styrene (SBR) type require less sulphur for
full development of their physical properties. Jackson recommends
35 parts sulphur per hundred of rubber (p.h.r.),[49] while Winspear and
co-workers found 40 parts, which is the theoretical quantity for saturation,
to be preferable on account of improved tensile and cross-breaking strength
and resistance to deformation at high temperatures. As with natural
rubber, the higher combined sulphur was accompanied by some loss in
impact strength. Increasing sulphur from 40 to 50 parts gave no important improvement. Good properties were obtained with 6 hours cure
at 153° C, but there was some slight improvement in properties other than
impact strength in extending this to 10 hours. Some technical formulations with sulphur as low as 37·5 parts p.h.r. were given.[50] Little increase
was found in tensile strength beyond 40 parts of sulphur p.h.r.[51]

The behaviour of SBR when vulcanised with quantities of sulphur
intermediate between those of the soft rubber and hard rubber range is

very different from that of natural rubber. Whereas the latter shows a maximum strength at about 6% combined sulphur, falling to a minimum at about 12% and a marked increase at about 25%, the strength of SBR increases continuously with combined sulphur.[52] SBR and natural rubber mixings of rubber–sulphur ratio 100 : 20 have been compared, and it was found that when vulcanised at 148° C tensile strengths of about 2,900 lb./in.[2] were obtained with both rubbers, but whereas with 36 hours cure the natural rubber was not noticeably changed, the SBR had increased to about 5,000 lb./in.[2]. Furthermore, the SBR cured for 16 hours was not noticeably changed after two days in the oxygen bomb, but the corresponding natural rubber was completely deteriorated.[50]

The curing conditions of butadiene–acrylonitrile rubbers with sulphur have been investigated, and it was found that the best impact strength was obtained with 35 parts of sulphur p.h.r. cured for 120 minutes at 350° F. With this proportion of sulphur tensile strength increased, breaking elongation decreased and yield temperature increased with time of cure. When sulphur was increased up to 40 and 45 parts p.h.r. there was some further gain in yield temperature, but tensile strength decreased and became sensitive to time of vulcanisation, showing a sharp peak.[53]

It was reported that the time curve for the combination of sulphur with SK rubber was similar in shape to that of natural rubber, but that the vulcanisation coefficient was lower.[54]

The effects of substituting reclaimed rubber for new natural rubber will be dealt with later, but it has been stated that reclaimed rubber resembles SBR in showing a continuous increase in strength throughout the range of combined sulphur.[55]

Compounding in relation to processing

In natural rubber ebonites, owing to the high proportion of sulphur and ebonite dust, the operations of mixing, calendering and extruding are very similar to those for a loaded soft-rubber mixing. For the same reason the proportion of mineral filler which can be absorbed is somewhat limited, and softeners, such as paraffin wax, mineral oil, petroleum aromatic extracts and drying oils, are freely used as processing aids.

Without processing aids butadiene–styrene rubbers are reported to be difficult to process, the unvulcanised material being nervy in calendering and lacking in tack for building up. Solutions of the polymer were found necessary in building up Buna S ebonite.[56] Substantial quantities of oil may be used as softeners, and Winspear and co-workers reported satisfactory tackiness by the use of a small quantity of magnesium oxide and 2% dodecyl mercaptan or Synpep N added at the end of mixing. Celite, a diatomaceous earth filler, and whiting used in conjunction with Naftolen

R-100 were also found useful for improving the working properties.[50] Rosin oil also has been recommended for producing tackiness.[51]

Butadiene–acrylonitrile rubbers were found to be more difficult to process, giving dry and leathery stocks which were, however, calenderable at 66° C. Sheeting and building up were made possible by using 10% Paraplex G-25 as softener. This was found to be better than the use of diatomaceous earth.[50] Garvey and Sarbach also studied the use of various softeners and advised the use of combinations of coal-tar, cumar, dibutyl metacresol and di-octyl phthalate. The experiments were made using 15% of softener, but it was pointed out that as much as 30% may be used in technical formulations. Of the fillers studied, clay, iron oxide, zinc oxide, whiting and dust (100 mesh) made from nitril rubber were all found to assist processing, but carbon blacks had little to recommend them.[53]

The use of softeners to overcome processing difficulties with synthetic rubbers tends partially to offset their advantages over natural rubber, such as their high yield temperature. The choice between these materials also depends on their various effects on the technical properties of the ebonite. (See p. 867.)

The processing problems characteristic of ebonite arise mainly in vulcanisation and are concerned: (a) with the reduction of curing time for economic reasons; (b) the control of the exothermic reaction; (c) the large volume shrinkage; and (d) the tendency of articles to change shape under their own weight in the early part of the cure.

Rate of cure

Vulcanisation of ebonite normally occupies some hours, and it is necessary for economic reasons to reduce this time as much as possible by the use of high temperatures and of accelerators.

Accelerators are useful both in causing a quick set up in the early stage of cure and also in completing the combination of sulphur in the later stage; but the range of activity is less than in soft rubber, and the order of activity of various types of accelerator is not the same. Zinc oxide is not effective in activating organic accelerators, but acts as a retardant under some conditions.[57]

The value of magnesium oxide and hydrated lime as accelerators has long been recognised, and there have been a number of publications on the value of various organic accelerators. DPG, ethylidene aniline and TMT have been used with little effect on tensile strength.[58] A number of accelerators were found to be effective in accelerating the formation of ebonite as judged by hardness during the intermediate part of the cure, and the concentrations (lying approximately in the range of 3 down to less than $\frac{3}{4}$ parts p.h.r.) in which they were most efficient were determined. It was found that tetraethylthiuram disulphide and zinc diethyldithiocarbamate needed great care in handling on account of scorching.[59] The rate of set-up, the acceleration of sulphur combination in the later stages of cure, the rate of attainment of good physical properties and the maximum safe rate of cure without damage by the exothermic reaction have been studied. Considering all these aspects butyraldehyde-amine or diphenylguanidine in combination with magnesium oxide were selected as the preferred accelerator systems. A number of other types of accelerator approached these in value.[57]

Although not acting chemically as accelerators, mineral rubber, ebonite dust and fillers also assisted in setting up quickly in moulds.[60]

An aldehyde amine accelerator has been recommended for GR-S ebonites [61] and DPG for ebonite based on SK rubber.[54]

The action of twelve accelerators in nitrile rubbers were investigated. It was found that some inorganic oxides other than zinc oxide, which retarded the cure, acted as accelerators. Selenium and tellurium also had some effect, but aldehyde amine and thiocarbamate types gave strong accelerating action with good physical properties in the vulcanisate.[53]

Vulcanisation of nitrile rubbers needed special care. At 148° C there was surface decomposition after 6 hours, long before the best yield temperature was reached, and for that reason a curing temperature of 142° C was adopted. In water curing under tin foil good contact was found essential, since any contact between steam and the ebonite caused hydrolysis and the formation of ammonia.[50]

The effect of ebonite dust on the course of vulcanisation is complicated. It absorbs and reacts with some of the elemental sulphur in the mixing, reduces the sulphur available for combination with the new rubber and so delays the attainment of a given state of vulcanisation. Unless additional sulphur is added, the development of the full physical properties may be prevented, however long the cure. The dust does, however, increase the rate at which the stock sets up to a hardness sufficient for removal from a mould.[62]

Exothermic reaction

It has already been explained that porosity or uneven vulcanisation due to internal heating limits the curing temperature, especially with thick articles, but the exothermic heating can be reduced and curing times shortened by suitable compounding, the most effective means being dilution by ingredients which take no part in the chemical reaction.

The best diluent in most respects is ebonite dust, since it can be added in a high proportion by volume, with little effect on most of the final properties. It is common for about half the volume of the mixing to consist of dust, but with such proportions attention must be paid to the effect on yield at high temperatures due to the effect just mentioned above. Dust cannot be regarded as a cheap filler, even where comparatively low-grade scrap can be used as the source of dust. In high-grade mixings, where the ebonite for the dust has to be produced from new raw materials or from high-grade soft rubber waste and subsequently ground, it costs considerably more than the new rubber and sulphur which it replaces.

The usual mineral fillers can also be used as diluents, provided that their effects on final properties are acceptable, but the volumes which can be added are more limited. Some fillers, such as zinc oxide, have an additional advantage that they increase the thermal conductivity of the stock and so assist in dissipating the heat of the reaction.

Although the use of an accelerator enables a lower temperature to be used for the same rate of vulcanisation, it does not follow that the time of vulcanisation at a given temperature can be reduced, for the rate of production of heat also is increased. This aspect of acceleration has already been discussed above. Fortunately it is found that with some accelerators the vulcanisation time can be approximately halved without increasing the danger of internal heating. Butyraldehyde-aniline and diphenylguanidine are effective in this respect, especially if used in combination with magnesium oxide. Zinc oxide, if present, largely offsets the gain in rapidity of cure.[57]

The internal rise of temperature in SBR containing 40, 45 and 50 parts of sulphur p.h.r. has been compared with that in natural rubber with 47 parts p.h.r. It was found that the temperature rise increased with sulphur content of the SBR and that the time required for the beginning of the exothermic heating was much longer than with natural rubber. At a curing temperature of 148° C under conditions such that the temperature rise in natural rubber was about 20° C, it appeared that the temperature rise in SBR with the same sulphur content would be nearly the same.[50] Since SBR can be satisfactorily cured with less sulphur than natural rubber, the former may show some advantage in control of exothermic heating.

Shrinkage during cure

During cure the compound shrinks by about 6% of the volume of new rubber and sulphur which it contains, and allowance for a change of dimensions has to be made for this in manufacture. The ebonite dust and mineral fillers added for controlling the exothermic reaction also serve to reduce this shrinkage in proportion to their volume.[62] Low shrinkage is particularly important in compression mouldings finished in the mould if " shrink marks " are to be avoided. SBR is to be preferred to natural rubber for moulding on the grounds that it is not susceptible to " shrink marks ".[49]

Retention of shape during cure

In open steam or gas curing of rods or tubes not cured on mandrels and of set-cured mouldings it is important that the articles should not flatten under their own weight during cure. It has been found that ebonite dust, mineral fillers, accelerators and reclaim all have the effect of hardening the stock at an early stage and reduce the tendency to loss of shape.[57, 62, 63]

Compounding in relation to properties

In the choice of ingredients for ebonite practice differs greatly from that of compounding for soft rubber. Some of the most important properties of ebonite fall into quite a different range of values or are irrelevant to soft rubber. Mineral fillers play quite a different role, and ebonite dust occupies a special position. Softeners, which are often used to modify the properties of soft rubber, are mainly a processing aid in ebonite. Synthetic rubbers are less necessary in ebonite for reducing the effects of organic liquids, but are used for enhancing other properties.

The properties of a given type of ebonite are closely related to the ratio of rubber–combined sulphur to rubber hydrocarbon (see p. 857). This may be varied either by using an excess of sulphur and stopping the cure at a suitable point or by varying the addition of sulphur and giving a full cure, i.e. to the point where the combined sulphur has become asymptotic. The latter method has technical merits and is easier for control in manufacture.

In the present section, where the influence of composition on properties is discussed, attention will be concentrated on ebonite which is fully cured in this sense.

Tensile strength, cross-breaking strength, impact strength and flexibility

It is fortunate that ebonite dust, which is such an important processing aid, can be incorporated in high proportions with little detrimental effect on tensile and cross-breaking strength or impact strength. There is evidence, however, that mechanical pressure is necessary to obtain the full strength. It is necessary also that the dust should be finely ground.[62]

There is no reinforcement of ebonite by finely divided fillers, such as occurs in soft rubber. These fillers either reduce tensile and impact strengths or at least do not improve them. The extent of the reduction in strength and the way in which it varies with the filler content depends on the particular filler. For example, it was found that with light magnesium carbonate cross-breaking strength fell sharply with the addition of

F F

the first 20 parts p.h.r., after which further additions up to 100 parts produced little further effect.[64]   It was also found that precipitated silica and kieselguhr gave a more uniform and ultimately a greater reduction. The effects on impact strength were more marked, particularly on the unnotched test piece.[8, 65]   These general conclusions are in agreement with the earlier work [66, 67] with talc and with clay and antimony sulphide respectively.

While strength is reduced, Young's modulus may be substantially increased.   With magnesium carbonate or precipitated silica it is increased by a factor of about two at 75 parts p.h.r., but the effect of the first 20 parts p.h.r. is small.[64]

As with soft rubber, a great variety of softeners may be used in ebonite, including paraffin wax, petroleum jelly, mineral oil, bitumen, petroleum aromatic extracts, factice, linseed oil and polyisobutylene.   It was found that when used in proportions of about 5% by volume the general effect of softeners was to reduce cross-breaking strength and unnotched impact strength appreciably (by about 20–30% and 50% respectively on the average).   Softened ebonites were, however, less notch sensitive and the notched impact strength was improved, in some cases by 100% or more. It was not possible to select individual softeners which gave favourable results in all directions, especially as high impact strength tends to be associated with low plastic yield temperature, but from the point of view of strength alone petroleum jelly, linseed oil and polyisobutylene were the most satisfactory.[68]

As would be expected, reclaim containing substantial proportions of mineral matter, carbon black and acetone-extractable material has a detrimental effect on cross-breaking strength and impact strength, particularly unnotched, but floating reclaims with a high proportion of rubber hydrocarbon can replace half of the new rubber or more without much effect.[63, 69]

It has already been mentioned (p. 860) that synthetic-rubber ebonites differ considerably from natural rubber in their vulcanising characteristics. They differ also in the effects produced by other additives than sulphur.

In the study of GR-S ebonites a striking similarity in strength properties between GR-S compounded with 40 or more parts of sulphur p.h.r. and natural rubber compounded with 47 parts sulphur p.h.r. was found, except that tensile and cross-breaking strengths were about 10–15% lower than with natural rubber.[50]   Even greater differences between natural rubber and various polybutadiene and butadiene–styrene rubbers[70] had been previously found.   GR-S with 50 parts of sulphur p.h.r. gave appreciably higher tensile strength but much lower impact strength than natural rubber.[51]

Although by most standard tests GR-S compared favourably with natural rubber, it appeared to be fundamentally less capable of with-standing a sharp bend.[50] A special test was developed to assess this property, but attempts to overcome this weakness by the use of various plasticisers or by the use of a lower sulphur content were unsuccessful. This is a feature which had become apparent in some applications, but which was not revealed by the tests normally applied to ebonite.

Natural rubber ebonite dust was found not to be a suitable ingredient in GR-S; and dust produced from GR-S ebonite, although it fulfilled useful functions in processing, could not be used in larger proportions than about 5% without considerable loss of strength.[50]

The use of whiting as a filler was found to reduce cross-breaking strength considerably, but one filler, a grade of diatomaceous earth, used in the proportion of 50 parts p.h.r. was found to give the same cross-breaking strength as unloaded ebonite, as well as being helpful in process-ing.   Young's modulus was also increased by about one-third.   It was also found necessary to use a higher proportion of softener (12–15% of Naftolen R.100) than is usually found necessary with natural rubber.[50] No filler was found to give the same physical properties as an unloaded mixing, but the effects of channel black and semi-reinforcing black on strength were comparatively small, while whiting and barytes gave more flexible products.[51]

The formation of ebonite from butadiene acrylonitrile rubber using a wide range of proportions of sulphur and a number of accelerators, fillers and softeners, has been studied.   It was found to be capable of vulcanis-ing to good-quality ebonite, comparable in strength with natural rubber ebonite, the optimum sulphur proportion being 35 parts p.h.r.[53]

A finely ground dust prepared from nitrile rubber could be used up to at least 50 parts p.h.r. without loss of tensile strength and with little loss in impact strength.   Accelerators varied considerably in activity, those which could be used with little or no loss of tensile strength being zinc oxide, aldehyde–aniline, MBT and ZDC.   There was some loss of impact strength with the last two.[53]

This rubber differed from natural rubber and resembled GR-S in that some mineral fillers could be added up to 50 parts p.h.r. without appre-ciable loss in strength.   Iron oxide and zinc oxide were outstanding in this respect.[53]

The effects of softeners in the proportion of 15 parts p.h.r. were deter-mined, although as much as 30 parts might be used in production.   Most softeners were found to reduce the tensile strength seriously, but two, dipolymer oil and dibutyl-m-cresol, gave strength as high as that of the unsoftened ebonite.   It was stated that in technical formulations these softeners were blended with others in order to combine tackiness during processing with a high yield temperature of the ebonite.[53]

Nitrile rubber ebonite is inferior to natural rubber ebonite in cross-breaking strength.[50, 70]

Yield at elevated temperatures

When measured by the extrapolation method described in Part I the yield temperature of a fully cured ebonite reaches a maximum of about 85° C at a rubber–sulphur ratio 65 : 35, but is only about 4° C lower for a ratio 70 : 30, which is very commonly used. As sulphur is reduced further the yield temperature falls steeply to about 68° C at a ratio 75 : 25. The yield temperature maximum is about 5° C higher in an accelerated mix, but occurs at the same rubber–sulphur ratio.[19, 43]

The effect of high proportions of ebonite dust is to depress the yield temperature. The slower vulcanisation and the lower yield temperature due to the addition of dust are less serious than would appear at first sight since: (a) the reduction in exothermic heating allows the use of a higher temperature or of faster acceleration, and (b) the increase in yield per ° C rise in temperature above the yield temperature is very much reduced by the inclusion of the dust.[62]

The depressing effect of dust on the yield temperature can be partly offset by a substantial increase of sulphur in the mixing.[62]

The value of accelerators is not confined to increasing the rate of cure; they have two important effects on properties. With a given proportion of sulphur they allow the free sulphur to be reduced to a lower level and, more important, they produce a higher yield temperature at full cure. In the case of the most active accelerators this improvement may be as much as 10° C.[57]

One of the main functions of mineral fillers in ebonite is to reduce the yield at high temperature; in many other respects they are detrimental. Mineral loading makes little, if any, difference to the yield temperature as defined by the extrapolation method, but causes the yield to be lower at any given temperature and to increase much less steeply with rise of temperature above the yield point. An addition, for example, of 100 parts of magnesium carbonate per hundred of rubber and sulphur raises the temperature at which a given small yield occurs under a fixed load by about 20° C.[8, 64]

Most softeners, if used in substantial proportions, depress the yield temperature, and in some cases to a serious extent, but there seems to be no clear relation between their effect on this property and their effects on other properties, such as strength, or on their value as processing aids, so there is scope for choice of a softener giving good all-round properties. Among the most favourable in this respect are polyisobutylene, bitumen, linseed oil and coumarone resin; compared with these, factice, mineral oil and paraffin wax are inferior.[68]

A good-quality reclaim may be included in proportions comparable with that of the new rubber without affecting the yield temperature by more than a few ° C. Any such effect is probably due to softeners in the reclaim rather than to any specific effect of the reclaimed rubber hydrocarbon.[63]

It is in yield temperature that some of the synthetic rubbers have a great advantage over natural rubber. There are a number of published investigations on this point, but it is difficult to give precise comparisons between the various rubbers in terms of suitable temperatures for use. The types of rubber differ considerably from one another, both in the changes in yield temperature with progressive cure and in the rate of change of yield with increase in temperature. With some rubbers yield temperature as determined by the extrapolation method continues to rise during curing long after the physical optimum, but the yield measured at 100° C becomes asymptotic after about 5 hours with most rubbers. Using this point as indicating an optimum cure, the determined yield temperatures with a 68 : 32 mixing were found to be as follows: [8, 71]

Natural rubber	80° C
Isoprene–styrene	84° C
Polybutadienes	85° C
Butadiene–styrene (styrene 25–29%)	90°–95° C
Butadiene–styrene (styrene 42–46%)	101°–110° C

Similar conclusions on SBR rubber were reached by other workers. Although below 60° C the yield of SBR ebonite was greater than that of natural rubber, it became much superior at higher temperatures, the temperature–yield curve being displaced by about 20° C.[50]

Butadiene–acrylonitrile rubbers give still higher yield temperature and show the same characteristic as some of the styrene copolymers of increasing yield temperature with continued cure and with increase of sulphur beyond the point at which other properties have reached their optimum.[53, 70] The yield temperature, with optimum sulphur content, is about 25° C above that of SBR.[50]

A heat-distortion temperature of about 132° C for a mixing with optimum sulphur content and cure was found. The effects of accelerators, fillers and softeners were also found to be dissimilar to their effects in natural rubber ebonites. Among accelerators tested some reduced the heat-distortion temperature, but lime, selenium and tellurium had practically no effect. No fillers increased the heat-distortion temperature; whiting had little effect up to 75 parts p.h.r., while iron oxide caused a reduction of about 28° C; both nitrile ebonite dust and natural rubber ebonite dust had a similar effect. Most softeners in the proportion 15 parts p.h.r. reduced the heat-distortion temperature considerably, but coal tar, K-gum resin and stabilite resin had no effect.[53]

Electrical properties

In many applications of ebonite electrical properties are of no importance. When the material is used as a high-frequency dielectric it is usually important that the power factor should be satisfactory at all temperatures at which the ebonite is satisfactory mechanically. There is a close connection between power factor and yield at elevated temperatures. Power factor increases to some extent with temperature, but at the yield temperature this increase becomes rapid. Provided that the material is compounded to be satisfactory at room temperature, any measures, such as the use of adequate sulphur and time of cure, of accelerators, of synthetic rubbers or of mineral fillers which raise the yield temperature, will also extend the range of temperature over which the dielectric properties are satisfactory, and the use of excessive dust or softeners, for example, will have the reverse effect (see Part One).

Dielectric loss depends on the product of power factor and permittivity, but the latter is much less sensitive to variations in compounding, except where mineral fillers are present.

In unloaded ebonites variations in power factor are comparatively small. There is some small advantage in using a high sulphur content,[19] or specially purified rubbers of low water absorption;[72] but at normal temperature high-grade ebonite dust,[62] high-grade reclaims [63] and some softeners,[68] when added in the usual small proportions, have comparatively little effect.

In loaded ebonites care must be taken in selecting a mineral filler. It has been shown that both power factor and permittivity rise continuously with increasing proportions of magnesium carbonate and rise to still higher values on long exposure to high humidity, especially at high temperatures.[68] Silica has been studied as an ingredient which by itself has good electrical properties. Permittivity is increased by its addition, but power factor is not seriously affected. The effect varies with the form of silica. Ground quartz, ground fused silica and washed and calcined kieselguhr all gave results at least as good as unloaded ebonite.[8, 65, 73]

When ebonite is used as an insulator at power or audio-frequencies or in direct-current equipment volume and surface resistivity are of importance, but the values are high, and there is generally no difficulty in meeting practical requirements, provided that obviously objectionable ingredients, such as carbon black or hygroscopic materials, are avoided. Considerable reductions, however, in electric strength (as measured with recessed sphere electrodes) have been observed with high proportions of both magnesium carbonate and ebonite dust.[8, 73]

Brief mention must be made of the serious deterioration in surface resistivity which can occur on exposure to bright light. This has been fully discussed in Part One of this chapter. No variation in compounding is known which will completely remedy this defect; it can only be limited to some extent in the rate or in the extent of the deterioration.

Of the synthetic rubbers the butadiene polymers and butadiene–styrene copolymers are the most interesting as high-grade radio-frequency dielectrics; the polar types, such as polychloroprene, ethylene polysulphide and butadiene–acrylonitrile, have too high a dielectric loss. There is little to choose between natural rubber and the normal SBR type at room temperature, but the power factor of the latter does not begin to increase rapidly below about 90° C. The higher styrene materials, such as Hycar EP and Buna SS, are not only superior to natural rubber at room temperature but also retain their good properties to a still higher temperature owing to their high yield temperature.[50, 70, 74]

Swelling in organic liquids

This subject has been fully discussed in Part One of this chapter. It is sufficient to draw attention to two facts: (a) high sulphur and adequate cure reduce both the final amount of swelling and the rate of swelling; (b) the synthetic rubbers generally are superior to natural rubber in resistance to swelling. Butadiene–acrylonitrile is outstanding in this respect.

Machining properties

In the industrial use of ebonite low tool wear and absence of chipping in drilling, sawing, tapping and turning are of considerable importance, and it is generally accepted that an unloaded ebonite is best in this respect. Such properties are difficult to express quantitatively, but it is widely held that a high combined sulphur is a disadvantage in this respect. No difference in machinability of unloaded ebonites is found over a wide range of combined sulphur contents, but difficulty in machining increases with mineral content in loaded ebonites.[8] The order of merit among silicas as filling materials varied with the machining operation and with the property concerned, i.e. tool wear or chipping. No silica-loaded ebonite is comparable in every respect with commercial loaded ebonites. The nearest approach is obtained with kieselguhr and one form of precipitated silica.[64, 73]

Colour

The dark-brown colour of the rubber–sulphur compound increases in depth with vulcanisation.[75] By the use of white pigment in sufficient quantities to mask the basic colour, some of the advantages of using an unloaded ebonite are lost. Some attractive colours can be produced by well-known inorganic pigments, such as yellow and red iron oxides, antimony sulphides, chromium oxide, vermilion and a range of cadmium pigments, but some of these are expensive. It has been stated that SBR rubber has an advantage in that the basic colour can be masked by a smaller proportion of pigment.[49]

REFERENCES

1. Davies, B. L. (1954) *Plastics*, p. 47.
2. Stevens, H. P. and Donald, M. B. (1951) *Rubber in Chemical Engineering* (London: British Rubber Development Board).
3. BS 903 Part D2 : 1957.
4. BS 2782 Part 2 : 1957, Method 102A.
5. ASTM D530–57T.
6. BS 903 Part D1 : 1957.
7. Church, H. F. and Daynes, H. A. (1939) *J. Rubb. Res.*, **8**, 41.
8. Scott, J. R. (1958) *Ebonite* (London: Maclaren).
9. ASTM D648–56.
10. BS 2782 Part 1 : 1956, Method 102D.
11. VDE 0302/III. 43, Verband Deutsche Techniker e.V.
12. BS 903 Part D5 : 1957.
13. BS 903 Part D4 : 1957.
14. BS 903 Part D3 : 1957.
15. Church, H. F. (1938) *J. Rubb. Res.*, **7**, 65.
16. BS 2782 Part 3 : 1957, Method 306A.
17. Church, H. F. and Daynes, H. A. (1937) *I.R.I. Trans.*, **13**, 96.
18. BS 2782 Part 3 : 1957, Method 306B.
19. Church, H. F. and Daynes, H. A. (1946) *J. Rubb. Res.*, **15**, 127.
20. Curtis, H. L. (1914) *U.S. Bureau of Standards Sci. Paper* 234.
21. BS 903 Parts C1 and C2 : 1956.
22. ASTM D257–57T.
23. Church, H. F. and Daynes, H. A. (1937) *J. Rubb. Res.*, **6**, 13.
24. Hartshorn, L. (1936) *J. Sci. Instrum.*, **3**, 1297.
25. Norman, R. H. (1950) *J. Sci. Instrum.*, **27**, 200.
26. Hartshorn, L. and Ward, W. H. (1936) *J.I.E.E.*, **79**, 597.
27. BS 903 Part C3 : 1956.
28. BS 2067 : 1953.
29. ASTM D150–54T.
30. BS 234 : 1957.
31. BS 903 : 1950, Section 32.4.
32. BS 2918 : 1957.
33. BS 903 Part C4 : 1957.
34. ASTM D149–55T.
35. BS 771 : 1954.
36. ASTM D48–54T.
37. BS 903 Part A18 : 1956.
38. Cooper, L. H. N. and Daynes, H. A. (1936) *J. Rubb. Res.*, **5**, 131.
39. Curtis, H. L., McPherson, A. T. and Scott, A. H. (1927) *U.S. Bureau of Standards Sci. Paper* 560, Washington, D.C.
40. Church, H. F. and Daynes, H. A. (1945) *J. Rubb. Res.*, **14**, 165.
41. BS 903 Part D6 : 1958.
42. Church, H. F. and Daynes, H. A. (1946) *J. Rubb. Res.*, **15**, 163.
43. Scott, J. R. (1948) *J. Rubb. Res.*, **17**, 170.
44. Dock, E. H. and Scott, J. R. (1937) *I.R.I. Trans.*, **13**, 109.
45. Gibbons, P. A. (1935) *I.R.I. Trans.*, **10**, 494.
46. Gibbons, P. A. and Cotton, F. H. (1935) *I.R.I. Trans.*, **11**, 354.

47. Church, H. F. and Daynes, H. A. (1947) *J. Rubb. Res.*, **16**, 93.
48. Dock, E. H., Scott, J. R. and Willott, W. H. (1947) *J. Rubb. Res.*, **16**, 266.
49. Jackson, E. D. (1952) *Chemistry in Canada*, 51.
50. Winspear, G. G., Hermann, D. B., Malm, F. S. and Kemp, A. R. (1946) *Ind. Eng. Chem.*, **38**, 687.
51. Morris, R. E., Mitton, P., Seegman, I. P. and Werkenthin, T. A. (1944) *Rubb. Chem. Technol.*, **17**, 704.
52. Cheyney, L. V. E. and Robinson, A. L. (1943) *Ind. Eng. Chem.*, **35**, 976.
53. Garvey, B. S., Jr. and Sarbach, D. V. (1942) *Ind. Eng. Chem.*, **34**, 1312.
54. Kashin, V. (1936) *J. Rubb. Ind.*, *U.S.S.R.*, **10**, 521.
55. Stafford, W. E. (1952) *Rubb. India*, **4**, No. 1, 23, 28. Correspondence.
56. Roelig, H. (1943) *India Rubb. J.*, **105**, 621.
57. Fisher, D. G., Newton, R. G., Norman, R. H. and Scott, J. R. (1948) *J. Rubb. Res.*, **17**, 161.
58. Glancy, W. E., Wright, D. D. and Oon, K. H. (1926) *Ind. Eng. Chem.*, **18**, 73.
59. Davies, B. L. (1934) *I.R.I. Trans.*, **10**, 176.
60. Davies, B. L. (1935) *India Rubb. J.*, **89**, 51.
61. Reiter, F. W. (1955) *TLARGI*, **14**, 29.
62. Scott, J. R. (1948) *J. Rubb. Res.*, **18**, 131.
63. Scott, J. R. (1949) *J. Rubb. Res.*, **17**, 67.
64. Fisher, D. G. and Scott, J. R. (1948) *J. Rubb. Res.*, **17**, 151.
65. Daynes, H. A. and Porritt, B. D. (1937) *I.R.I. Trans.*, **12**, 356.
66. Marchandise, R. (1929) *Encyclopédie du Caoutchouc et les Industries qui s'y rattachent* (Paris: Syndicat du Caoutchouc), p. 333.
67. Dieterich, E. O. and Gray, H. (1926) *Ind. Eng. Chem.*, **18**, 428.
68. Norman, R. H., Scott, J. R. and Westbrook, M. K. (1950) *J. Rubb. Res.*, **19**, 89.
69. Kemp, A. R. and Malm, F. S. (1935) *Ind. Eng. Chem.*, **27**, 141.
70. Scott, J. R. (1944) *J. Rubb. Res.*, **13**, 23.
71. Scott, J. R. (1950) *J. Rubb. Res.*, **19**, 128.
72. Fisher, D. G., Scott, J. R. and Willott, W. H. (1948) *J. Rubb. Res.*, **17**, 99.
73. Church, H. F. and Scott, J. R. (1949) *J. Rubb. Res.*, **18**, 13.
74. Fisher, D. G., Mullins, L. and Scott, J. R. (1949) *J. Rubb. Res.*, **18**, 37.
75. Scott, J. R. (1947) *J. Rubb. Res.*, **16**, 264.

CHAPTER XI

ANALYTICAL METHODS FOR RUBBER

by

F. C. J. POULTON

ANALYSIS of a rubber compound is generally undertaken to provide data on the original composition of a mixing, to gain some idea of the probable behaviour in service or to ascertain causes of failure or abnormal performance. The analysis may therefore be fairly elaborate to ensure an exact replica of the original compound, e.g. for costing purposes, or it may be sufficient to gain an idea of its composition in general terms so that a rubber compound of similar physical characteristics may be formulated using materials more readily available. A still more restricted examination may suffice when it is desired merely to explore a particular feature considered to arise from one or two of the principal ingredients, or when some aspect of service performance is ascribable to traces of deleterious materials.

It is probably true to say that prior to 1930 the analytical chemistry of rubber owed its basic scheme largely to the principles laid down by Weber in his classic work *Chemistry of Rubber Manufacture*. This state of affairs was due not only to the circumstance that the analytical techniques developed in recent years were not then available but also to the fact that rubber formulations were limited in their variety and based almost exclusively on natural rubber. Such a circumscribed field lent itself readily to a more or less rigid scheme of analysis which could be designed to reveal all the main features of conventional compounding. In the late 1920s a serious limitation of the classical system had already begun to appear with the advent of organic accelerators and anti-oxidants. Analysts were being criticised for being unable to throw much light on the very features of compounding that were becoming of increasing importance to the industry, and although numerous attempts were made to fill this gap, we now know that the breakdown of many accelerators under vulcanising conditions renders classical methods of little value in this particular branch of rubber analysis.

A second but more recent factor with far-reaching influence on the development of rubber analysis is the now widespread use of synthetic rubbers. From the point where almost every rubber product was based entirely on the natural material, the situation has been reached where natural rubber is now no more than a possibility in an array of likely polymers; furthermore, in an expanding field of technological endeavour there is no sign of finality having been reached in the variety of synthetic rubbers for specialised application, or in the development of analytical methods to deal with the new products. Rubber analysis today cannot therefore be confined to the formal application of standard text-book methods, nor does it readily conform to neat and tidy schemes which the untrained assistant can follow, leaving the interpretation of his results to a more experienced analyst. Analytical chemistry is now regarded as a part of applied physical chemistry, requiring also in the case of the rubber industry a substantial background of organic chemistry.

With these considerations in mind the aim in this chapter has been to present, first of all, those established methods of rubber analysis which are still of value notwithstanding recent technological development, together with any limitations of the methods revealed by recent experience. Equal emphasis, however, is laid on newer techniques, which often provide the only approach to many problems of the rubber analyst. In some instances these techniques must be regarded as specialised fields, and it would be presumptuous to attempt anything like complete treatment. A more limited but still, it is hoped, worthy objective will have been reached if the potentialities of such methods are indicated, and a survey given of the considerable amount of work already accomplished in these fields. Similarly, standard methods of conventional macro- and micro-analysis are not given in detail. It is deemed sufficient to refer to an appropriate text-book of recognised authority, but any special considerations arising from the application of the methods to rubber analysis are dealt with fully.

As new materials are continually being introduced, it is necessary to indicate the scope of this chapter. Some alignment of test methods with the nature of the product is an obvious if not strictly scientific course, and consequently rigid plastics have been excluded. The main emphasis has been given to natural rubber and rubber-like polymers. Border-line cases inevitably occur and here the author has made an arbitrary choice.

Technologically, and therefore analytically, the focus of the industry still resides in the main groups of hydrocarbon rubbers; test methods relating to these are considered in detail. These materials comprise natural rubber, synthetic polyisoprene, polybutadiene, styrene–butadiene rubbers, polyisobutylene and Butyl rubber. Nitrogen-containing polymers include the copolymers of vinyl pyridine and of acrylonitrile, and the isocyanate rubbers, while of the chlorine-containing polymers, the derivatives of natural rubber, polychloroprene, polyvinyl and polyvinylidene chloride will be treated as the main representatives. The testing of raw polymers has been omitted from this survey, primarily because the examination of such materials follows mandatory procedures, the details of which can generally be found in manufacturers' specifications.

The treatment of the specimen prior to analysis must depend primarily on the object of the investigation. If this object is to gain information regarding the general features of composition of the original mixing as a whole, considerations such as uniformity of sample, incorporation of any bloom and removal of extraneous matter are paramount. On the other hand, if the object is to study a local condition of the specimen it is important to isolate the affected region carefully, keeping the sample as small as possible, so as to increase the concentration of any significant component. In composite articles of laminated or fabric-reinforced construction it is especially necessary to ensure that the test specimen is not contaminated by another rubber compound. Laminated construction is readily revealed by taking a single oblique cut through the sample and observing the fresh surface for slight differences in colour or texture; samples from individual layers can then be obtained by the careful use of a scalpel or mounted razor blade. Fabric-reinforced articles are often assembled with an adhesive dip or spreading coat applied to the fabric as a thin layer which may be invisible in cross-section. Stripping the fabric rarely removes all this adhesive compound, and unless it is already known that an auxiliary coat has not in fact been used, it is advisable to remove a thin layer of rubber adjacent to the fabric.

The test specimen is homogenised by passing it between the cold rolls of a laboratory mill. Usually twelve passes of the folded and rolled rubber are sufficient, and excessive milling should be avoided. As the efficiency of the extraction processes used in the subsequent analysis depends, among other factors, on solvent penetration, it is obviously desirable to obtain a sample in as thin a sheet as possible. Both the BSI and ASTM procedures require the sheeted rubber to be 0·5 mm. thick or less. Differential-speed rolls are better than even-speed, since a porous and corrugated structure is imparted to the rubber, substantially increasing its effective surface area. Heavily loaded mixings tend to leave the mill as a coarse powder. Although the aggregates of such material may be several millimetres in diameter, it will usually be found that mechanical breakdown of the rubber is adequate for thorough penetration of the solvent. The prepared sample should be interleaved with glazed linen if the surface tends to be sticky, and should be stored in a stoppered jar.

For certain analytical procedures, particularly combustion or bomb methods in which a solid-phase reaction is initially involved, even milling to a thin sheet is not always sufficient to bring about intimate contact between the reactants. In order to produce the fine state of subdivision necessary, Haslam and Soppet [1] recommend a freezing technique in which the sample, already milled thinly, is cut into strips about 1 cm. wide, enclosed in a corked test-tube and immersed in a methanol–solid carbon dioxide mixture for 15 minutes to freeze the rubber. The strips are then taken quickly from the tubes and passed rapidly through a simple grinding device, such as a rotary pencil sharpener, which has also been chilled. Samples prepared in this manner are particularly susceptible to oxidation, and should not be unduly exposed to heat or to the atmosphere.

Cutting the rubber into minutes cubes by means of scissors is sometimes advocated, but this cannot be recommended as a satisfactory alternative to milling. Apart from the tedium of cutting even a few grams of rubber to pass a given sieve size, abnormal analytical results will almost certainly be obtained, since the rubber will not have undergone the severe mechanical rupture that tight milling produces.

In sampling rubberised fabrics, such as proofings, it is essential to separate the rubber from the cloth. Except for the crudest investigation, the uncertainties introduced by analysing the composite material are not permissible, even if some adjustment of the results is attempted by applying a factor based on the ratio of rubber to fabric. To assist stripping of the rubber the application of solvent to the fabric side of the sample has been recommended, but experience shows that if the solvent treatment is sufficient to be effective the composition of the rubber is altered. A better procedure in difficult cases is to remove a small quantity of the rubber in the dry state and apply micro-analytical methods.

Rubber solutions, cements and compounded latices are sampled by drying a thin film on a glass plate at 30–35° C, but it cannot be assumed that the rubber thus obtained will be of uniform composition. The dispersed powders in a compounded latex will frequently separate on standing, and in addition to thorough stirring of the original liquid sample it is necessary to homogenise the dried rubber by milling as described above.

EXTRACTION PROCEDURES

Exhaustive extraction with a suitable solvent provides a convenient means of dividing the prepared sample into two fractions, each of which, although still complex, can form a starting-point for more detailed analysis. This statement implies that the extraction process is fully quantitative, giving a clear-cut separation of soluble and insoluble components in all circumstances. In the case of vulcanised rubber, for instance, the aim would be to separate quantitatively the organic additions to the mixing from the rubber and fillers. It is common experience, however, that such a definite separation is very rarely obtained and, except fortuitously, the extract rarely agrees in amount with that expected from theoretical considerations: ingredients one would expect to find in the extract are sometimes not there, often being replaced by those considered nominally insoluble. Before embarking, therefore, on a description of the experimental procedures it may be as well to consider the factors which influence extraction.

The degree of separation achieved in any extraction procedure, that is, the extent to which the process approaches completion, is governed by three factors: (a) the nature of the material being examined; (b) the solvent; and (c) the experimental conditions of extraction. The first two factors are obviously related, and it is found in practice that a solvent suitable for removing soluble materials from one rubber system is not necessarily the best for removing the same materials from another system. There is little difficulty, for instance, in separating accelerators, antioxidants, and monomeric plasticisers from inorganic fillers, since the organic additions are usually readily soluble in a wide variety of solvents. Certain factors, such as the decomposition of accelerators, have to be taken into account, but this is essentially a matter of interpretation; the accelerator itself and its decomposition products are usually quantitatively extracted. On the other hand, the behaviour of polymeric substances of extended molecular-weight range (for example, the rubber itself or plasticisers, such as polypropylene adipate, factice and mineral rubber) is less predictable and largely governs the choice of the extracting solvent. A fully cross-linked polymer, although not dissolved, swells in the solvent, and the extent of this swelling determines the effectiveness with which other substances present are extracted. Familiar examples of this principle are the use of ether to swell rubber prior to aqueous extraction for the removal of HMT accelerator, and the removal of mineral rubber from a vulcanisate by a chloroform–acetone mixed solvent. Equally familiar, but less welcome to the analyst, is the tendency for lower molecular weight fractions of the elastomers themselves to be extracted along with other soluble substances: the same mechanism is at work, and one cannot expect to remove the larger molecules of a polymeric plasticiser and leave behind the lower molecular weight fractions of the rubber. The most satisfactory answer to this dilemma is still something of a compromise, and each case can be treated only on its merits.

Acetone is still the most common solvent for the examination of natural and styrene–butadiene rubbers, as it leaves the polymer itself virtually untouched unless severe oxidative degradation has taken place, in which case the molecular fragments are also extracted. Most monomeric plasticisers are taken out with acetone, which removes mineral oils and waxes, many saponifiable oils and waxes, esters, fatty acids and certain other organic acids, some grades of pine tar and many coal tar products.

The oil extenders now incorporated into some grades of styrene–butadiene rubbers are also separated by acetone, and Prem and Duke [2] have given details of an ultra-violet absorption method by which some processing oils may be characterised. Acetone also extracts organic accelerators and anti-oxidants from the rubber, together with their decomposition products, and acetone extraction consequently forms a preliminary step in a number of procedures for the identification and determination of these ingredients. In the presence of factice or bituminous substances, however, difficulties are encountered due to the extended molecular weight range of these materials. They are only partly extracted from rubber by acetone alone, and chloroform is used, either separately or as a mixed solvent with acetone, for more complete extraction. The free oils from factice increase the extract figures slightly, but factice itself is determined by treatment of the vulcanised rubber with alcoholic potassium hydroxide.

Elemental sulphur is also separated from the rubber by acetone extraction, and again this initial separation is the starting-point for a number of analytical procedures for the determination of free sulphur. Finally, acetone extracts the naturally occurring resins and fatty acid from natural rubber, and many of the additions made to synthetic rubber in the course of its manufacture.

Although acetone is the solvent most generally used in the analysis of vulcanisates, others are employed when more selective action is required. Ether is valuable in the examination of acrylonitrile–butadiene rubbers and vinyl chloride polymers, these materials being themselves dissolved by acetone. Ethyl alcohol is commonly used in the analysis of latex mixings when the question of soap additions is of some importance. This solvent is also able to distinguish between pine and coal tar, the former being soluble and the latter and its products generally insoluble. Bitumens of petroleum origin are also insoluble in alcohol. Chloroform is the preferred solvent for the extraction of bituminous materials, and since it dissolves depolymerised forms of rubber it reveals the presence of reclaim and badly aged natural rubber.

Water extracts a variety of constituents from natural and synthetic rubber mixings, but in practice its use is confined to the isolation of water-soluble accelerators, soaps and emulsifiers (principally in latex compositions) and traces of deleterious salts. Extraction with water will also reveal excessive protein, such as would arise from the addition of glue or casein.

Finally, the presence of partially saponifiable substances, such as factice, which are not extracted by acetone or chloroform, is indicated by treatment with alcoholic potash. The complete procedure, generally referred to as the " alcoholic potash extract ", is in fact a separation of the organic acids derived from the saponifiable substances.

Enough has been said of the interdependence of solvent and material being tested to make it clear why the third factor, the experimental conditions of extraction, must be chosen to give the closest approach to the theoretically correct amount of extractable material. Sixteen hours is regarded as a standard time for extracting most rubbers, but there seems no logical reason for this choice beyond the fact that extraction can be carried on overnight with a saving of operator's time. Lengthy extractions running into days are not to be recommended, since oxidative changes can set in, giving rise to a continuously increasing extract. It is for this reason that some workers carry out extractions of natural rubber in a dark cupboard or at least in subdued light. Four hours is generally considered adequate for the removal of all free sulphur, and most softeners can also be extracted with acetone or ether (according to the type of polymer present) in this time, except those softeners already mentioned, which are not extracted quantitatively. Most anti-oxidants are stable compounds and can be extracted by a hot solvent, but many accelerators are decomposed by heat, and should therefore be separated by cold extraction. It is often desirable also to use a solvent less reactive than acetone for the extraction of accelerators, and in such cases isopropyl alcohol is recommended.

These general remarks on extraction will perhaps make it clear why the precision of the various extraction procedures is never very high; two results often differ by as much as 5% of their mean value. The rate and duration of extraction, the heating and drying of the final extract are all important factors, and careful control of these operations is essential if results in line with accepted analytical standards are to be achieved.

Acetone extract

There are two types of apparatus in current use for the macro determination of acetone extractable matter, the Soxhlet type adopted in the BS method and the Underwriters' apparatus recommended by ASTM.

The former apparatus is made entirely of glass and designed so that the condensed extracting solvent in contact with the sample is at a temperature not much below its boiling point. A typical assembly is shown in Fig. 11.1a, the dimensions being appropriate to a 2-g. sample.

The sample is weighed, and wrapped in filter-paper, folded so that if the sample is sheeted, paper and rubber are interleaved, or if the sample is crumbed, particles cannot become detached and find their way into the extraction flask. The sample is then placed in the syphon cup of the extractor and extracted for a period considered adequate for the separation involved, preferably by heating on a water-bath. At the end of the extraction the column and condenser are replaced by a bent adapter and condenser and the bulk of the acetone removed by distillation, or the extracted sample can be removed from the syphon cup and the distilled acetone collected in the cup. If an electric hot-plate is used it is important to avoid overheating the extract, so the last few millilitres of acetone are removed on a water-bath. The flask and its contents are finally dried at a temperature of 70°–75° C for 1 hour, cooled and weighed. Where doubt exists regarding the completion of the extraction the original

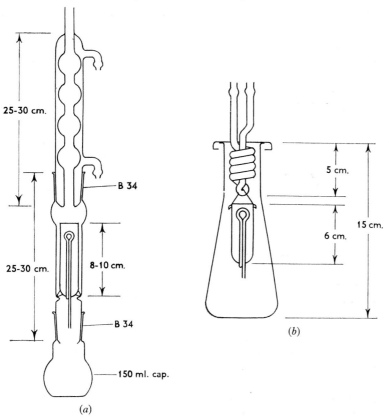

(a)

Fig. 11.1. (a) Extraction apparatus Soxhlet pattern. (b) Extraction apparatus Underwriters' pattern.

flask is replaced by a second and the extraction continued for a further period.

The Underwriters' apparatus advocated by ASTM is illustrated with recommended dimensions in Fig. 11.1b. The apparatus shown is suitable for a 2-g. sample which is folded in filter-paper, observing the same precautions as mentioned above. The more compact form of this extractor allows a higher extraction rate to be maintained, and this may reach 20 changes per hour in the syphon cup. After 16 hours the condenser and syphon cup are removed and the acetone carefully evaporated. The flask and extract are then dried and weighed as before.

When the available sample is restricted to a tenth of a gram or less neither the standard Soxhlet nor Underwriters' type of extractor is suitable, as the weight of the extract is too small by comparison with the weight of the flask to be measured accurately. Fig. 11.2*a* shows an apparatus, developed from that of Wyatt,[3] having a flask weighing only a few grams and suitable for the extraction of a 10–50-mg. sample. The flask is surmounted by a column containing a cold finger condenser from which the condensate drips on to the sample contained in an extraction

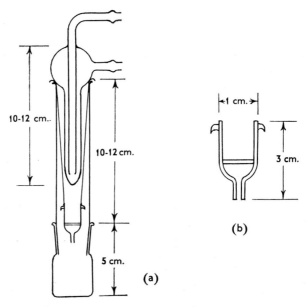

Fig. 11.2. Semi-micro extraction apparatus.

cup constructed as shown in Fig. 11.2*b*. This semi-micro apparatus does not operate on the syphon principle; the cup has a sintered-glass base which allows solvent extract to percolate into the flask. The weighed sample is placed directly in the cup and held there by a tightly fitting circle of filter-paper. Platinum wires suspend the cup from the rim of the glass column. With sample weights of the order of 20 mg., extractions comparable with the macro procedure can be effected in 2–3 hours.

A method recently developed by Kress[4] is also semi-micro in character, requiring sample weights of 100 mg. or less. The sample is heated under reflux with a 3 : 1 mixture (by volume) of methyl ethyl ketone and ethanol in a conical flask, the amount of extract being determined by weighing the rubber before and after extraction. With natural and styrene–butadiene rubber vulcanisates, for which the method is primarily intended, it is claimed that 30 minutes heating gives results equivalent to those obtained by the ASTM recommended 16-hour procedure.

The extract should be inspected carefully before evaporation of the acetone and in the dried state. The acetone extract from first-grade Hevea rubber gives a very pale straw-coloured solution and dries to a clear yellow oily liquid amounting to 3–3·5% of the weight of rubber. The extract from vulcanisates based on Hevea rubber is increased by soluble compounding ingredients, and these can be estimated by making a correction based on the rubber content of the compound. A brown solution indicates tars, bituminous materials or petroleum residues; pine tar and coal tar impart their characteristic odours to the dried extract. Petroleum residues, on the other hand, may be recognised by their dark colour and comparative freedom from odour. Mineral oils are revealed by their fluorescence, particularly under the ultra-violet lamp. A high proportion of free sulphur in the rubber will appear in the extract as a yellow crystalline solid.

Chloroform extract

The apparatus described for the determination of the total acetone extract is also suitable for chloroform extraction, which is almost invariably made on the acetone-extracted rubber. In practice, the first extraction flask with its acetone solution is replaced by a second weighed flask containing the requisite amount of reagent-grade chloroform. Four hours is generally sufficient to separate the remaining soluble matter, and at the end of this time the chloroform is distilled off and the extraction flask and its contents dried and weighed as before.

The exact interpretation of the chloroform extract is not always possible. Bitumen is recognised by the intense dark coloration it imparts to the wet and dried extract, and, if present alone, by the consistency of the dry material. In the absence of bitumen the extract will usually appear as a yellow oil consisting mainly of low-molecular-weight fractions of degraded natural rubbers; this is generally taken as indicating the use of reclaim.

Ether extract

Rubber compositions based on polychloroprene or copolymerised acrylonitrile and butadiene are extracted with ether to separate the plasticiser, which in these rubbers is frequently an ester of the dicarboxylic or phosphoric acid type. A Soxhlet type of extractor (see p. 881) is used, but 4 hours is generally sufficient for a quantitative extract. After weighing the extract, which may, of course, be a mixture of esters, characterisation of the plasticiser is carried out by conventional procedures of saponification, followed by identification of the constituent acid and alcohol.

The method of Rauscher and Clark [5] can be applied to many dicarboxylic esters. In this procedure the ester is heated under reflux with ethanolamine to give the alcohol and corresponding N : N'-di-β-hydroxyamide. The alcohol is removed by distillation and is characterised by physical constants and the preparation of a derivative, while the solid amide may be separated by filtration or solvent extraction, recrystallised and identified by melting point.

The analysis of plasticisers with special reference to those used in polyvinyl chloride compositions has been investigated by Haslam, Soppett and Willis [137] who put forward a scheme for the identification of many of the plasticisers found in commercial products. Three preliminary sorting tests are first advocated: the sodium fusion test for elements, the fluorescein or phenol phthalein test for phthalates, and the indophenol reaction for phenolic or cresylic compounds. Mixed plasticisers revealed by these tests may sometimes be separated by micro-distillation under reduced pressure and identified by physical constants, but more often it will be found that the components are so similar either in boiling point or chemical composition that they cannot be resolved by distillation. In these circumstances Haslam, Soppett and Willis saponify the ester with caustic potash in ethylene glycol, separate the alcohols by distillation and identify them from their infra-red spectra.

Water extract

Extraction with water is not usually considered a part of the conventional scheme for rubber analysis, mainly because the principal features it reveals, such as the presence of glue or casein, are more readily indicated by other tests. The importance of the water extract lies in its ability to reveal traces of undesirable water-soluble impurities in rubbers that have to fulfil certain performance requirements, and for this reason it is employed more as a specification test than as a means of investigating the composition of the rubber compound. It will generally be found, therefore, that the procedure for carrying out this test is agreed between the parties concerned, and does not necessarily follow the soundest scientific considerations.

The method recommended by BSI requires a 15-g. sample cut into cubes of $\frac{1}{8}$ in. side, which is boiled under reflux with distilled water for 1 hour. While cooling, precautions are taken to prevent the ingress of carbon dioxide; aliquots of the clear solution are taken for the determination of total water-soluble material, free acid or alkali, chloride and sulphate. For these determinations conventional methods of analysis are used.

Unsaponifiable matter

Unsaponifiable plasticisers, such as coal tar, mineral oil and wax, and paraffin wax, are generally determined on the dried acetone extract, the oil from oil-extended rubbers also being included in this fraction. Coal tar may be detected by the colour and odour of the extract, and mineral oil by its characteristic fluorescence; these properties are enhanced in the unsaponifiable portion of the extract, which is isolated and determined as follows:

About 25 ml. of approximately M alcoholic potash are added to a dried acetone extract and the mixture heated gently under reflux for 2 hours. The condenser is then removed, the alcohol evaporated to low bulk and the contents of the flask washed with a stream of hot water into a separating funnel. When cool the solution is repeatedly extracted with ether, using a few drops of ethanol to break stubborn emulsions which sometimes form at the interface. The collected ether extracts are washed with water until neutral, dried and evaporated, and the extracted material heated to $70°$ C for 30 minutes before the final weighing.

Alcoholic potash extract

A few plasticisers, the commonest being vulcanised oils, are not extracted from the vulcanisate by acetone or chloroform, but are revealed by alcoholic potash treatment of the rubber after extraction.

A 2-g. sample is extracted with acetone and chloroform, taken quickly from its filter-paper wrapping and placed in a flask with 25 ml. of approximately M alcoholic caustic potash. After heating under reflux for 4 hours the alkaline solution is run through a coarse filter into an evaporating dish, the rubber washed first with alcohol and then water, and the filtrate and washings are evaporated to dryness. The dried solids are dissolved in hot water and the solution transferred to a separating funnel in which it is acidified with hydrochloric acid and extracted with ether. The ether extracts are washed with water until neutral, dried by standing over anhydrous sodium sulphate and the ether carefully evaporated. The extract is heated to $70°$ C for 30 minutes and is then cooled and weighed.

IDENTIFICATION AND DETERMINATION OF POLYMER

The rapid commercial exploitation of synthetic rubbers coincided very closely with the acceptance of ultra-violet and infra-red spectroscopy as a recognised analytical tool in industry, and the recent history of the analytical chemistry of products based on these synthetic materials is largely an account of the development of spectroscopy applied to this field. Nevertheless, chemical methods still have their place not only because the older methods demand less-expensive equipment but also because they are, in general, rapid and require no special preparation of the sample. In control testing particularly, chemical tests are often preferred where it is required to confirm the identity of a known polymer or when it is necessary to decide between a limited number of known possibilities. In the analysis of totally unknown compounds, however, it is hazardous in the extreme to rely solely on chemical tests, and where a mixture of polymers is likely to occur the importance of weighing evidence from both chemical and spectroscopic examination cannot be too strongly emphasised.

It must also be accepted that an unequivocal identification of the polymer often necessitates eventually a fully quantitative examination of the rubber compound, at least as regards its major constituents, as only in this way is it possible to guard against the chance of overlooking an unsuspected component of the system. This interdependence of qualitative and quantitative work is reflected in the arrangement of this section on polymer analysis, where no sharp classification of the two aspects has been attempted.

Although in the early days of polymer analysis some success was achieved by applying a rigid series of analytical tests to the limited range of synthetic products then available, the wider variety of rubbers coming into use renders such schemes far less valuable than formerly, and at times even misleading. Apart from control analysis, every analytical investigation of an unknown vulcanisate must be considered individually and based primarily on a knowledge of the organic chemistry involved. Nevertheless, the analyst will find it of great assistance to have at his command at least a broad knowledge of the technology of the industry, and of the commercial possibilities in relation to the materials on which he is called upon to give an opinion.

General schemes of identification

Generally speaking, there is little difficulty in identifying a raw polymer as long as it is assignable to one of the recognised classes, but the processes of compounding and vulcanising often preclude the direct application of many tests of identification to finished products, and in any case increase the difficulties of interpretation of the results.

Dealing first with chemical tests of a general nature, the Lassaigne test for characteristic elements is still of value as a preliminary sorting test for polymer classification, providing certain limitations are borne in mind. It is essential to remove plasticisers, anti-oxidants, accelerators and sulphur by exhaustive extraction, and to take into account the possibility of such compounding ingredients as casein and factice. The Lassaigne reactions are, of course, entirely non-specific, their principal function being to act merely as pointers for further work.

Within the range of polymers at present commercially available the results of the Lassaigne test may be interpreted thus:

Nitrogen present

A strong positive response indicates the presence of polyacrylonitrile or polyvinyl pyridine. The test is not sufficiently sensitive to reveal the normal amounts of protein in natural rubber, but a weak positive is often given by casein or glue retained in products from stabilised latex compositions. A positive reaction is also obtained from the polyurethane rubbers.

Chlorine present

A precipitate in the chloride reaction is an indication of polychloroprenes, chlorinated or hydrochlorinated derivatives of natural rubber, chlorosulphonated polyethylene, polyvinyl chloride or polyvinylidene chloride. Since the chlorine-containing polymers are generally used as the exclusive basis of the compound, the precipitate obtained is usually copious and unmistakable; it is generally safe therefore to ignore traces of chlorine indicated by an opalescence of the solution, unless white factice is suspected. Chlorine and nitrogen occurring together may be taken as an indication of a polyvinyl chloride composition plasticised with acrylonitrile-butadiene copolymer. When nitrogen has first been detected therefore it is essential to remove cyanide before testing for chlorine.

Sulphur present

Large amounts of sulphur such as are responsive to the silver coin test are an indication of thioplasts. A somewhat weaker reaction is given by the sulphur in chlorosulphonated polyethylene, and none at all by the lesser amounts of sulphur arising from normal vulcanising systems. The more delicate nitroprusside variant of the test, however, will give a positive result with normally sulphur-vulcanised polymers.

Nitrogen, chlorine and sulphur absent

The absence of characteristic elements points to the use of natural rubber, styrene–butadiene rubbers and resins, polyisoprene, polybutadiene, polyisobutene and Butyl rubbers. It is, perhaps, in this group of polymers, often displaying widely different physical properties and technological function, that the analyst finds his greatest difficulties, and some guidance in their examination is given later in this section.

A scheme for identifying a restricted selection of unknown synthetic polymers has been proposed by Burchfield,[6] and has been embodied in a tentative standard procedure advocated by ASTM. In essence, Burch-field's scheme is based on a series of colour reactions and spot tests carried out on the pyrolysis products of the rubber. The first test registers the acid–base reaction of the pyrolysate in a buffered indicator solution (bromocresol green and metanil yellow) and the second depends on the formation of coloured reaction products with p-dimethylamino-benzaldehyde. Table 11.1 shows the response given by some common

TABLE 11.1

COLOUR REACTIONS OF PYROLYSATES (After Burchfield)

Material	Solution I		Solution II
	Initial colour	Colour after heating	Colour
Blank	Pale yellow	Pale yellow	Green
Polyvinyl chloride	Yellow	Yellow	Red
Chloroprene	Yellow	Pale yellow green	Red
Nitrile	Orange red	Red	Green
Chloroprene-nitrile	Orange red	Red	Yellow to red
Styrene	Yellow green	Green	Green
Natural rubber	Brown	Violet blue	Green
50 styrene–50 rubber	Olive green	Green blue	Green
Polyisobutylene	Yellow (droplet floats)	Pale blue green	Green
Polyvinyl acetate	Yellow	Pale yellow green	Yellow

elastomers to these tests. In the ASTM procedure another series of tests is carried out with reaction papers on the gaseous pyrolysis products obtained by local heating of the sample. Although to some extent complementary to the first series, these tests are rather less specific, and for some polymers offer little advantage over the Lassaigne test for characteristic elements. Thus the test for chloroprenes is based on yellow-red colour change of the indicator brought about by the liberated hydrochloric acid, and may therefore be expected to respond to all other chlorine-containing polymers. The test for nitriles is of value in that nitriles give the characteristic blue of copper cyanide (changed to green by the metanil yellow), while nitrogen in other forms does not. In two respects the Lassaigne test can claim some advantage over the ASTM pyrolysis procedure; first, the results from a mixture of polymers do not mutually interfere, and second, the results, being more objective in nature, rely less on the experience of the operator for their interpretation. Indeed, until judgement in assessing the results of the ASTM methods has been acquired it is essential to carry out parallel tests on known materials.

Other analytical schemes of a general nature have been put forward by Parker.[7, 8] The earlier one is based on the acid reaction time of the polymer, i.e. the time to incipient decomposition in a standard mixture of sulphuric acid, nitric acid and water; these times are fairly characteristic of polymers of many types, but the test fails with mixtures. Plasticisers and fillers interfere, and there is a considerable personal factor in judging

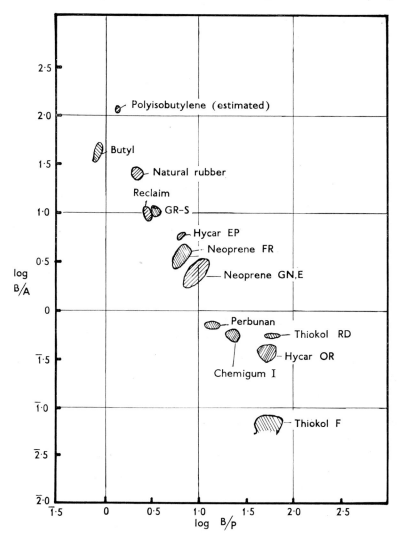

Fig. 11.3. Swelling ratio of polymers.

the exact moment when the reaction begins. The second procedure depends on the determination of the swelling ratio of the polymer, this term being applied to the ratio of the volume increase under standard conditions of immersion in benzene, light petroleum and aniline. The range of swelling ratios is extensive, and it has been found more convenient for graphical presentation of the results to plot their logarithms (see Fig. 11.3; the terms A, B and P in the co-ordinates represent the volume increase in aniline, benzene and light petroleum respectively). The shaded areas represent the extent of the variation given by each polymer in a number of different vulcanisates, and it will be seen that a reasonable degree of differentiation is possible; again, however, the hydrocarbon polymers tend to be grouped at one end of the range, so that distinction between different types is not so certain.

Finally, burning tests should be mentioned to complete the list of general methods, even if recommendations for their use must be somewhat guarded. The test merely consists in heating a portion of extracted sample in a test-tube or even at the edge of the bunsen flame. Natural rubber, styrene–butadiene rubbers, polyacrylonitriles, thioplasts, poly-acrylates and polyisobutenes all give characteristic odours, recognition of which, however, comes only with experience. The black-loaded vulcan-isates of the styrene and acrylonitrile copolymers tend to leave a dry char, while the Butyl types readily melt, with natural rubber giving a permanently sticky or greasy product somewhere between these two extremes. Chlorine-containing polymers do not give a characteristic " organic " odour, but are identified as a class by the liberation of hydro-chloric acid. Further evidence of these materials is given by their failure to support combustion and by the greenish mantle they impart to the flame while being heated. Thioplasts are readily identifiable, as they burn readily with the characteristic lambent blue flame of sulphur and give rise to copious fumes of sulphur dioxide.

The susceptibility of these tests to influence by unusual compounding ingredients, and their failure to deal with mixtures, are serious limitations on their usefulness.

Natural rubber

The best-known chemical test for natural rubber is that due to Weber,[9] who drew attention to the violet colour obtained when rubber is first brominated and then reacted with phenol. The test is carried out as follows:

A few milligrams of the extracted material is treated with 1 ml. of a freshly prepared solution of bromine in carbon tetrachloride (10% V/V) and heated in a boiling water-bath until most of the bromine has been removed. A small crystal of phenol is then added. With natural rubber a violet colour develops on further heating.

In general, the Weber reaction can be applied successfully to vulcan-isates, although the presence of carbon black darkens the solution, and the violet colour is then sometimes difficult to see. Where natural rubber has been used exclusively or forms the major component in a mixture a positive test is obtained. Polyisoprene gives an equally strong colour, as would be expected from Wake's [10] generalisation that an active methylene group adjacent to the double bond is normally required before a characteristic colour is obtained. A positive response is therefore not specifically indicative of natural rubber, but can be obtained whenever isoprene residues are present. The test does not give a colour with the other common elastomers, although purplish-brown tints are sometimes obtained which in inexperienced hands can be mistaken as an indication of natural rubber. It is insufficiently sensitive to detect the isoprene component of Butyl rubber, but gives a detectable colour with mixtures of Butyl and natural if the latter exceeds about 20% of the elastomer content. A similar sensitivity seems to be obtained with styrene–butadiene rubber/natural rubber mixtures. With regard to the application to materials allied to natural rubber, the colour is not given by alkali process reclaim, but the presence of a normal proportion of this material in a natural rubber compound does not inhibit the colour. Gutta-percha, balata, cyclised rubber and rubber hydrochloride all respond as natural, but chlorinated rubber does not give the colour.

A less-used colour reaction for natural rubber is also mentioned by Wake,[10] in which the rubber is fused with trichloracetic acid to give a yellow to red coloration. Some other elastomers also respond to this test, but may be distinguished by continuing the heating to the boiling point of the acid and then dissolving in water. Under these conditions natural rubber gives a pale greyish precipitate.

A number of tests have been suggested to distinguish between natural rubber and polyisoprene, and these are becoming of increasing value with the introduction of the " synthetic natural " rubbers. Basically the tests depend on the careful identification of a minor constituent of natural rubber which is not found in the synthetic product. It was suggested by Barnes *et al.*[12] that the presence of phosphorus might be used to establish the identity of natural rubber, but while the distinction is valid for raw polymer, it is subject to some uncertainty in dealing with compounded rubbers of unknown origin. A rather more specific indication lies in the detection of natural rubber protein. According to Tunnicliffe and Wilkinson [13] this is readily achieved by heating the acetone-extracted polymer with dilute hydrochloric acid to hydrolyse the protein and subjecting the hydrolysate to two-dimensional paper chromatography using a 75 butanol : 15 formic acid : 10 water mixture in the first dimension and an 80 phenol : 20 water mixture in the second. The resolved amino acids are detected in the usual way with ninhydrin reagent to give a characteristic and reproducible pattern. This procedure can be carried out on the semi-micro scale to reveal the protein in less than o·1 g. of natural rubber, and is applicable to fully compounded and vulcanised rubbers.

In quantitative analysis the proportion of elastomer in the compounded and vulcanised rubber may be calculated by the difference method, in which the sum of the added ingredients as determined analytically is taken from 100 after a correction has been made for non-rubber constituents of the raw polymer.

When it is known that new natural rubber is the only elastomer concerned the following formula recommended by the ASTM holds true:

$$\text{Natural rubber hydrocarbon } \% = \tfrac{94}{97}(100 - C)$$

where C represents the sum of the following: acetone extract, chloroform extract, alcoholic potash extract, unextracted sulphur (free or combined), total fillers, protein, cellulose.

The formula is based on the assumption that the crude rubber contains approximately 94% rubber hydrocarbon with about 6% of associated non-rubber constituents, of which roughly half will be included in the determination of the added compounding ingredients.   Strictly speaking, therefore, it applies only to those grades of rubber (the better-quality grades) for which the above assumptions are valid, and calculations can go seriously astray if it is applied to lower-grade rubbers or to vulcanisates containing a high proportion of reclaim, which would give rise to a high chloroform extract.   As in all difference methods, the reliability of the final figure can be no greater than that of the individual determinations used in its computation, and since in some methods of rubber analysis this is not very high, it is doubtful if the accuracy of the difference method reaches the standard implied by the formula.

The great value of a difference method lies in the ability to give in certain cases a guide to the total rubber content of the vulcanisate; further quantitative determination of individual polymers will then show if the polymer system has been fully elucidated.   The total polymer in mixtures of natural and styrene–butadiene rubber, and natural and Butyl is determinable by this method, and polybutadiene and polyisoprene also respond, but the method fails with the polyacrylonitrile rubbers, polychloroprenes and solvent-resistant types generally, largely owing to the difficulty of obtaining the total fillers free from polymer.

Methods of polymer determination based on the unsaturation of the molecule have been proposed,[11,14] but their application to vulcanised rubber has not been developed to a point where complete reliance on the results can be justified.   The shortcomings of unsaturation techniques arise partly from the difficulty of ensuring complete solution of the polymer and partly from the uncertain stoichiometry of the reactions involved.   It has also been shown that the reaction rate for a given polymer is markedly influenced by the nature of the solvent, and that conditions established for substantially complete addition and minimum substitution for one polymer system do not necessarily hold for another. Kemp and Peters [15] made a study of the possibilities of the technique in the evaluation of butadiene copolymers and developed a procedure to give results within a reasonable tolerance of theoretical in the case of styrene–butadiene copolymers of the GR-S type. It has since been applied [11] to natural rubber and to mixtures of natural and styrene–

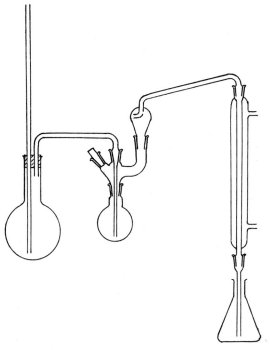

Fig. 11.4. Determination of natural rubber hydrocarbon.

butadiene rubber, but in the latter case it is necessary to know by an independent method either the amount of one of the components or the total elastomer present. The method is not suitable for polychloroprene or Butyl rubber.

The chromic acid oxidation method, as it has come to be known, is now far more widely used for the determination of natural rubber than any of the preceding methods. Based on the work of Kuhn and L'Orsa [16] on the determination of methyl groups attached to carbon, it has been adapted successfully to rubber analysis by Burger, Donaldson and Baty.[17] In outline the method is as follows (see Fig. 11.4):

A weighed portion of the rubber, containing about 0·3 g. of the hydro-carbon, is digested for one hour at 100° C with 50 ml. of an oxidising reagent prepared by adding 150 ml. of concentrated sulphuric acid to a solution of 200 g. chromic acid in 500 ml. water. Steam is then passed in from a generator until the volume of liquid in the digestion flask reaches 75 ml., and direct heat is then applied to maintain the volume at that level. When 500 ml. of distillate have been collected air is drawn through the distillate at a rate of 2 litres/min. for 30 minutes to remove carbon dioxide, and the distillate is then titrated with standard alkali. A blank determination is carried through in precisely similar conditions. The rubber hydrocarbon figure in unvulcanised compounds is calculated from the formula:

$$\text{Rubber hydrocarbon \%} = 0 \cdot 91 \times \frac{\text{Net corrected titration in ml. } 0 \cdot 1 \text{N alkali}}{\text{Weight of sample in grams}}$$

In ideal conditions the standard deviation of a single determination obtained on a given sample is about 0·5%, but substantial quantities of reclaimed rubber, ebonite dust or crumb can give rise to a much broader scatter of results.

The yield of acetic acid under the prescribed experimental conditions corresponds to 3 molecules acetic acid from 4 isoprene units, that is, a yield of 75% from natural rubber hydrocarbon. In addition to this empirical correction, allowance has to be made for the non-rubber con-stituents of the raw polymer, and where first-grade rubber is concerned the rubber hydrocarbon may be taken as comprising 94% of the natural rubber as a whole. The mechanism of the oxidation is not fully under-stood, and although analogies have been drawn between the behaviour of rubber in this reaction and that of other compounds,[18] no convincing explanation of the low but consistent yields of acetic acid has been put forward. Any component of the mixing which on oxidation yields an acid volatile in steam will be included as rubber in the calculation unless the appropriate correction can be made, and Burger, Donaldson and Baty have investigated a range of compounding ingredients and other elastomers with the object of assessing such interferences. A table embodying their findings is given on p. 895.

Most of the common rubbers are not oxidised by the chromic acid mixture, and apart from minor corrections indicated in the table the results for natural rubber usually remain valid even when a mixture of polymers is suspected. Mixtures of styrene–butadiene rubber and natural rubber over a wide range can be examined successfully, although the accuracy falls off appreciably when the synthetic component heavily preponderates. High-styrene copolymers appear to give a somewhat higher yield of volatile acid, and may reach a figure equivalent to 6% natural rubber. Acrylonitrile–butadiene copolymers interfere but slightly and the ter-polymer butadiene–styrene–vinyl pyridine is also without effect on the figure. In the analysis of mixtures of natural rubber and Butyl the accuracy of the result depends to a large extent on the ratio of the two constituents. If the natural rubber preponderates the oxidation

TABLE 11.2

EFFECT OF INTERFERENCES IN THE DETERMINATION OF NATURAL RUBBER

Material	Effect on Determination
Balata	Equivalent to rubber hydrocarbon
Carbon black	None
Cellulose	Equivalent to less than 2% rubber hydrocarbon
Dark factice	Negligible after extraction
Ebonite	Equivalent to about 50% rubber hydrocarbon
Gutta-percha	Equivalent to rubber hydrocarbon
SBR	Equivalent to about 3% rubber hydrocarbon
Hycar OR-15	Equivalent to $1\frac{1}{2}$–2% rubber hydrocarbon
Mineral rubber	If not extracted, equivalent to about 40% rubber hydrocarbon
Neoprene GN	Equivalent to 3% rubber hydrocarbon after allowing for halogen acids
Neoprene FR	Equivalent to 12% rubber hydrocarbon after allowing for halogen acids
Perbunan	Equivalent to $1\frac{1}{2}$–2% rubber hydrocarbon
Polyisobutene	Negligible

usually proceeds smoothly and quantitatively, and the natural rubber can be determined with a reasonable degree of accuracy, but when the ratio is reversed the discrepancy between the figure as determined by chromic acid oxidation, and the amount actually present becomes progressively greater as the proportion of Butyl increases. Mixtures in which the natural rubber amounts to only 10% or less of the total polymer may give a figure as low as 5%, while, in the extreme, the polyisoprene in raw Butyl, amounting to 2% of the total polymer, is virtually undetectable. This difficulty, which is due to the inert polyisobutene protecting the polyisoprene from attack by the acid, is not encountered in the examination of mixtures of natural rubber with other commonly used synthetics, since the polymer usually disintegrates completely in the acid.

Gutta-percha, balata and, of course, synthetic polyisoprene are quite indistinguishable from natural rubber in this test.

Wake [11] has examined the effect of combined sulphur on the recovery of acetic acid in this reaction. Since the addition of sulphur leads to some loss of unsaturation, the yield of acetic acid will be correspondingly reduced. For low combined-sulphur values, less than 2%, Wake concludes that the effect is negligible, but long experience of the method indicates that yields of 73% acetic acid are consistently obtained with soft-cured rubbers, and a more generally accepted figure for the rubber hydrocarbon is then given by the formula:

$$\text{Rubber hydrocarbon } \% = 0.93 \times \frac{\text{Net corrected titration } 0.1\text{N alkali}}{\text{Weight of sample in grams}}$$

Styrene–butadiene rubbers

Chemical methods for the identification and determination of styrene in the copolymers with butadiene are based on the conversion of the styrene to p-nitrobenzoic acid. These methods, particularly in quantitative work, have never been wholly satisfactory, and are yielding to spectroscopic techniques as equipment becomes more generally available. The quantitative procedure first appeared as a result of the introduction of the Buna-S type rubbers in the Second World War, and has since been adopted as a standard method by the ASTM. An outline of the method is as follows:

About 1 g. of the acetone extracted and dried sample is heated under reflux with concentrated nitric acid for about 6 hours. The solution is diluted with an equal volume of water, and 20% aqueous caustic soda added until it is just alkaline, followed by portions of 4% aqueous potassium permanganate until the characteristic pink colour is obtained. The mixture is heated on a steam bath over a period of 5 hours, with further additions of potassium permanganate solution to restore the colour. The precipitate is removed by filtration on a Buchner pad and the filtrate made just acid with dilute sulphuric acid. After any remaining pink colour has been discharged with sodium bisulphite the solution is transferred to a separating funnel, the p-nitrobenzoic acid extracted with ether and this is converted to the sodium salt by treatment with caustic soda. Reacidification of the alkaline extract with dilute sulphuric again liberates the free organic acid, which is extracted with ether and recovered by evaporation. The organic acid is assayed by titration with standard sodium hydroxide.

The method cannot be described as a general one, since the course of the main reaction seems to be very much influenced by extraneous factors, and the final product, nominally p-nitrobenzoic acid, is, in fact, an uncertain and non-reproducible mixture of acids. In the examination of raw styrene–butadiene rubbers containing about 25% styrene, reasonable agreement with the theoretical figure can be obtained, but when the method is extended to mixed polymers, carbon black stocks and vulcanisates, considerable investigatory work has failed to establish conditions for smooth oxidation without disruption of the benzene nucleus. In high styrene polymers the method fails completely.

The qualitative test follows the same general lines, but the oxidation stages can be reduced to about 15 minutes by using a 50–100-mg. sample. After oxidation with nitric acid and alkaline permanganate a single ether extraction is sufficient to give a few milligrams of the acid, which can be reduced to the amine by treatment with tin and hydrochloric acid. The normal procedure of diazotisation with chilled sodium nitrite and coupling with an alkaline phenol follow, to give a brilliant red dye if polystyrene is present in the original sample.

This test is perfectly satisfactory with raw styrene–butadiene rubber and its mixtures with natural rubber in uncured and cured stocks; it can also be carried out successfully in the presence of carbon black. Like the method for quantitative determination, however, it is not completely reliable when applied to high-styrene resins, sometimes giving a negative result when polystyrene is in fact present. When high-styrene resin is suspected it is better to carry out the test on the pyrolysate from the rubber. A small quantity of the thoroughly extracted material (100 mg. is ample) is heated in a small test-tube and two or three drops of the distillate, which collects on the upper walls of the tube, are transferred by a capillary pipette to a 5-ml. flask. The sequence of nitric acid and permanganate oxidation, followed by reduction, diazotisation and coupling, is then carried out on the distillate, and a red dye is obtained in the presence of styrene.

It is necessary to stress one final point concerning the qualitative test for styrene. Not only do traces of aromatic compounds remaining in the extracted rubber respond very readily to the test but also pyrolysis of natural rubber can form small quantities of cyclic compounds, which themselves give coloured solutions when examined in the way described. It is essential, therefore, to obtain a strong positive result before the presence of polystyrene can be affirmed by this test; a weak colour should be ignored except in so far as it may provide corroborative evidence of a small proportion of polystyrene.

Butyl rubber

Butyl rubber is characterised by its extreme inertness towards acids, and its presence in mixtures is often revealed by the jelly-like residue remaining in the digestion flask after a natural rubber determination by the direct oxidation method. This residue can be collected on a coarse filter, washed and dried, and the polyisobutene readily identified, either by the burning test, when a characteristic fatty odour is obtained, or by dissolving it in petroleum spirit and confirming its saturated nature by means of bromine water. Polyisobutene is unique among commercially available polymers in responding in the manner described, but like many

G G

other tests for polymers, the test becomes progressively less reliable as the proportion of the polymer in a mixture diminishes.

A useful confirmatory test when sufficient sample is available is based on the formation of a mercury derivative of the monomer, and is specific for isobutene. The test is made as follows:

> At least 1 g. of the extracted rubber is pyrolysed in a small test-tube fitted with a stopper and side-arm, and the volatile products are passed through an ice trap. The monomer passes through the trap and is absorbed in a methanolic solution of mercuric acetate (5% W/V). The methol is carefully evaporated and the crystalline mass treated with 20 ml. light petroleum ether. Insoluble matter is removed by passing through a Hirsch micro filter and the solution is evaporated to about 0·5 ml. in bulk. This solution is cooled strongly in ice and salt and the crystals filtered off and washed with 2 ml. chilled petroleum ether. The melting point of the methoxyisobutylmercuri-acetate is 55–56° C.

This test is reliable in the hands of the skilled analyst, but requires care and familiarity with micro-analytical operations. It behaves more satisfactorily if the polyisobutene can be separated from other elastomers, for example, by treatment with nitric or chromic acid.

A method for the determination of polyisobutene in mixtures of Butyl and natural rubber has been developed by Galloway and Wake [19] based on its resistance to acids and its solubility in petroleum.

> The finely divided or milled sample is placed in a crucible with a sintered-glass base and heated under reflux for about ten minutes with nitric acid in a simple form of extractor. The crucible and its contents are then removed, attached to a filter flask, washed with water, then alcohol, and returned to the original extractor for treatment with petroleum ether. The petroleum extract is poured off into a small weighed flask, and the crucible and its contents treated again in the extractor with nitric acid. Three such cycles of acidification and extraction are given and the combined petroleum extracts dried with anhydrous sodium sulphate, filtered and evaporated. Drying to constant weight then gives the polyisobutene content of the sample.

Rubber systems containing nitrogen

The nitrogen content of natural raw rubber is low, but reasonably constant, varying mainly according to the method of preparation of the rubber. Since the main source of the nitrogen is the protein constituent of the rubber, the lowest values encountered in commercial materials are in the deproteinised rubbers, which give figures usually about 0·1%, and exceptionally down to 0·05%. Centrifuged and electrodecanted latices contain 0·2 and 0·3% nitrogen and first-grade crêpe and smoked sheet between about 0·35 and 0·45%, since some protein is coagulated with the rubber. Evaporated concentrates containing all the protein will give somewhat higher figures, while skim rubber, that is rubber prepared from the serum after separation of centrifuged and electrodecanted concentrates, will, of course, have a correspondingly higher protein content and will even give nitrogen figures over 1%. A conversion factor of 6·3 is commonly accepted for calculating the protein content of the rubber from the nitrogen figure.

Higher proportions of nitrogen are indicative of a nitrogen-containing polymer. Isocyanate extended polyesters and polyethers give figures around 2%, while in acrylonitrile–butadiene rubbers the proportion of nitrogen will be higher still but varying according to the ratio of the two polymers. Some of the commercially produced acrylonitrile copolymers and their nitrogen contents are shown in Table 11.3.

TABLE 11.3

NITROGEN CONTENT OF ACRYLONITRILE–BUTADIENE COPOLYMERS

Rubber	Nitrogen
Perbunan 2818	7·4
2810	7·4
3310	8·7
3810	10·1
3805	9·2
Krynac 800	8·2
801	10·1
802	6·9
803	8·2
Hycar OR25	7·9
OR15	10·6
1022	7·9
1041	10·6
1042	7·9
Paracryl AJ	4·8
B	6·9
BJ	6·9
Chemigum 30N4NS	7·9
50N4NS	7·9
N-6	8·7
N-7	8·7
N3NS	11·8

A factor of 3·79 is used to convert the nitrogen content to acrylonitrile, but this figure in itself is of little interest, and to have value to the compounder it must be related to the total rubber content or to the polybutadiene present as its copolymer. Mixtures of acrylonitrile–butadiene copolymers with elastomer types other than polyvinyl chloride are not likely to occur, and in the majority of cases it is possible to analyse the vulcanisate by micro or semi-micro methods of ultimate analysis, from which the total polymer, the acrylonitrile–butadiene ratio and the proportion of carbon black can be computed. The nitrogen content of the extracted (plasticiser-free) rubber is first determined, and from this the acrylonitrile and the corresponding quantities of carbon and hydrogen may be calculated. The total hydrogen determined by ultimate analysis represents the sum of that due to butadiene and to acrylonitrile, and hence the hydrogen contributed by the butadiene can be obtained by difference and the figure used to calculate the amount of polybutadiene present. Since the carbon content of the butadiene can also be calculated, the difference between the total carbon as determined and the sum of the carbon contents of the two polymers gives the proportion of added carbon black.

A determination of the ash can either be made on a separate portion or, if the sample is limited, the combustion boat used in the carbon and hydrogen determination can be weighed before and after the test. Since the preliminary extraction with solvent can also be made on the semi-micro or micro scale, this procedure offers a route to the substantially complete analysis of acrylonitrile–butadiene rubbers in respect of the main constituents, and can be carried out in about 4 hours on a total sample weight of about 20 mg. The accuracy of the method suffers from the unfavourable conversion factor of hydrogen to butadiene, and this will affect the reliability of the figure for carbon black. Generally speaking, however, the method is capable of giving the acrylonitrile–butadiene ratio with sufficient accuracy to assign the polymer to one of the recognised grades, while the carbon black can be estimated to about $\pm 3\%$.

For the determination of nitrogen in natural rubber the Kjeldahl process is generally accepted, and for semi-micro work the Parnas–Wagner form of distillation unit is widely used. The general principles and operation of the Kjeldahl method are given in standard works on micro chemistry, and it is necessary to mention here only those points which have a direct bearing on its application to rubber.

For clearing the solution in the digestion stage several oxidation catalysts have been suggested, but three, copper, mercury and selenium and certain binary mixtures of these, appear to command greater favour. Providing the proper conditions are observed, there seems little to choose between the three, although in the presence of carbon black selenium is considerably more effective in discharging the colour. With raw rubber only, the digest with sulphuric acid and potassium sulphate clears comparatively rapidly (with copper catalyst in about 1 hour and with selenium catalyst in about 20 minutes using a 50-mg. sample). On the other hand, vulcanisates containing carbon black can be very stubborn, particularly with the less active catalyst, and there is a strong temptation to employ a rapidly acting type, such as selenium–mercury.   It has been shown, however, that prolonged treatment with such catalysts can lead to oxidation of the ammonia, but whether this takes place before the carbon black has entirely disappeared is an open question and requires further investigation.   In point of fact the presence of carbon as carbon black does not seem to affect the total recovery of ammonia, though there is admittedly a strong prejudice against its appearing in the distillation flask.   For the quantitative conversion to ammonia, therefore, it is necessary to observe both upper and lower limits for the digestion period, say 40–80 minutes for a 50-mg. sample, and to choose a catalyst, such as copper or copper–mercury, which will induce the maximum oxidation of carbon without loss of ammonia in that time.

The liberated ammonia can be absorbed in either standard hydrochloric acid or dilute boric acid.   In the former case a back titration is necessary, and thus two volumetric measurements, with their attendant errors, are necessary to obtain a single result.   When the boric acid method is adopted a direct titration of the absorbed ammonia is possible owing to its weak association with the boric acid, and it might be expected that a more accurate result would thereby be obtained.   In spite of this apparent advantage, however, titrations in boric acid are rather less reproducible than the conventional titration, presumably because some ammonia escapes absorption.

For the determination of nitrogen in acrylonitrile polymers both the Kjeldahl and the Dumas processes have been recommended, but some workers have obtained low and erratic results with the former, due, it is thought, to the loss of traces of cyanogen in the early stages of the acid digestion.   The micro-Dumas procedure follows closely the method suggested by Pregl, but the apparatus is modified to permit of the rapid introduction and withdrawal of the combustion boat.   A diagram giving details of the principal dimensions of the tube and its filling is given in Fig. 11.5.   For the determination of nitrogen in vinyl pyridine copolymers it is essential to determine nitrogen by micro-Dumas if a lengthy digestion, with the risk of loss of ammonia, is to be avoided.

Carbon and hydrogen can be determined by any recognised technique, the present-day tendency being to favour micro or semi-micro methods almost exclusively.   The apparatus shown in outline in Fig. 11.6 is a recent form of semi-micro combustion equipment, and although based on the classical procedure, incorporates features designed to give a high level of reproducibility in the results obtained.   Determinations are made on samples weighing 20–40 mg. in order to minimise the relative weighing errors of the full micro procedure.   Blanks are reduced to an exceptionally

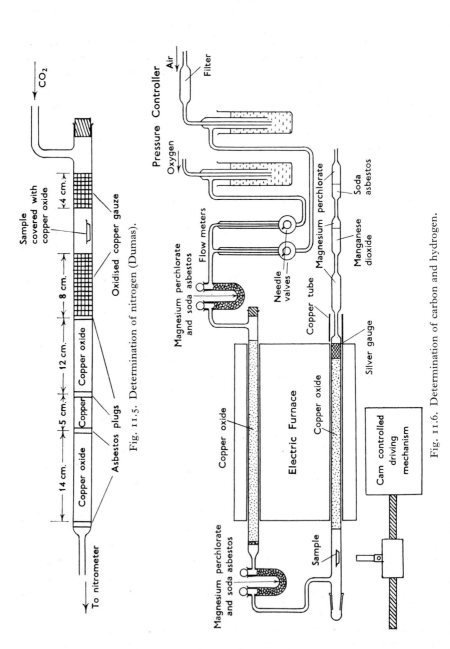

Fig. 11.5. Determination of nitrogen (Dumas).

Fig. 11.6. Determination of carbon and hydrogen.

low level by the pre-heating system, in which the oxygen and air supply is passed through a silica tube under conditions identical to those in the main combustion tube, and by absorbing impurities in a conventional scavenging train.   Combustion conditions are held constant by accurate temperature control of the furnace and by mechanical burner travel working to a cam-controlled programme.[20]   Oxides of nitrogen are removed by an external absorbent of pelletised manganese dioxide, and chlorine by a plug of silver wool.

Rubber systems containing chlorine

The chlorine content of natural rubber and of compounding ingredients likely to be associated with it is negligible, with the one exception that white factice can give rise to traces of chlorine in the sodium fusion test; more than this can be taken as evidence that synthetic materials are present.   These may be broadly classified according to general schemes of analysis already outlined, while the technological application of the rubber and its behaviour towards common solvents will frequently provide some guidance regarding its identity.   The vulcanised chloroprenes look and handle very much like natural rubber and, in the main, similar principles of compounding are used.   These points serve as a preliminary means of distinguishing the chloroprenes from the chlorinated derivatives of natural rubber and from polyvinyl chloride and allied polymers.   Polyvinyl chloride and polyvinylidene chloride are readily distinguished by the wide disparity in their chlorine contents, but the pyridine–soda test for polyvinyl chloride [21] and the morpholine test for polyvinylidene chloride [22] are usually adequate if only a rapid qualitative identification is needed. These two tests are made as follows:

Pyridine–soda test for polyvinyl chloride.   A small piece of the ether-extracted material is dissolved in 2–3 ml. pyridine by careful heating to the boiling point, and after slight cooling a few drops of 2% methanolic sodium hydroxide is added.   In the presence of polyvinyl chloride the solution gradually turns dark brown and a dark brown precipitate is formed.

Morpholine test for polyvinylidene chloride.   A small piece of the extracted polymer is heated with a few drops of morpholine.   Again a gradual darkening of the solution through red–brown–black takes place, and this is followed in the later stages by the separation of a dark-brown precipitate.

Polyvinyl chloride and related polymers may be quantitatively examined by the methods of Haslam and Newlands.[23]   The whole composition is treated with tetrahydrofurane at 100° C, and the mineral matter is removed by centrifuge.   The polymer is then precipitated by alcohol, filtered and dried, and is then available for examination by infra-red or chemical techniques. Alternatively, the finely shredded or milled composition is extracted with ether to remove plasticiser, and is then treated with tetra-hydrofurane or cyclohexanone to dissolve the polymer. The mineral matter is removed by centrifuge and the polymer is recovered by precipitation with alcohol or by evaporation of the solvent.

Vulcanised compounds based on the polychloroprenes are not amenable to this procedure, since the whole point of the use of these elastomers lies in their resistance to solvent action. It is rarely possible, therefore, to isolate the original polymer, and identification by chemical tests rests somewhat insecurely on inference from the sodium fusion test, the Burchfield reactions and behaviour towards acids and solvents. An estimate of the total rubber can be made by the difference method after determination of other compounding ingredients, and the chlorine content related to this will provide an indication as to whether the rubber is polychloroprene. Chemical tests here reach a limit of their usefulness, and it is essential to supplement the information they provide with evidence from spectroscopic or other sources.

Chlorine may be determined in the regenerated polymer by any standard procedure for the determination of chlorine in organic compounds. A bomb technique has been recommended for polyvinyl chloride and allied polymers,[24] but it is not suitable for softer elastomers owing to the difficulty of obtaining the material in a finely divided form. A more satisfactory method in such cases is based on that recommended by Belcher and Godbert,[25] in which the sample is heated in a current of moist oxygen, the products of combustion passed over an activated platinum surface and the hydrochloric acid absorbed in heated barium carbonate contained in the long combustion boat. After the combustion the barium carbonate is dissolved in dilute nitric acid and the chloride determined by a Volhard titration.

If the sample is restricted to a few milligrams, resulting in a small and correspondingly inaccurate titration in the Volhard procedure, the method recommended by Belcher, MacDonald and Nutten [26] can be applied. It has the advantage that neither sulphur nor nitrogen interfere, and the single standard solution employed, namely, potassium chloride, is extremely stable and is itself a primary standard. The determination is carried out as follows:

The apparatus consists of a horizontal tube formed of clear silica with a downwardly projecting vertical portion at the exit end containing glass beads. Combustion of the sample takes place in the horizontal portion, which also contains an etched platinum catalyst, and the hydrochloric acid liberated is absorbed in neutralised hydrogen peroxide held on the glass beads. The absorbing solution is run into a small flask and the beads rinsed with one or two portions of distilled water. After careful neutralisation of the solution with dilute alkali, mercuric oxycyanide is added, and sodium hydroxide is liberated according to the following reaction:

$$HgO \cdot Hg(CN)_2 + 2NaCl + H_2O = HgCl_2 + Hg(CN)_2 + 2NaOH$$

Instead of a single titration of the liberated alkali, which under these conditions is non-stoichiometric, the solution is first neutralised with dilute acid and identical amounts of acid, oxycyanide and methyl red–methylene blue indicator are added to a second flask. The volume of this solution is then adjusted to equal that of the first, and standard potassium chloride run in from a burette until the indicator colours in the two flasks match. The chloride in the sample and that added from the burette are then strictly equal.

This method also permits the simultaneous determination of chlorine and sulphur, and can thus be applied to the examination of sulphur-vulcanised chloroprenes and to chlorosulphonated polyethylene. In these applications a single alkalimetric titration of the absorbing solution gives the total of sulphur and chlorine, while the subsequent addition of mercuric oxycyanide and the titration with potassium chloride determines only the chlorine; sulphur is hence obtained by difference.

When the Lassaigne test has revealed both nitrogen and chlorine the presence of polyvinyl chloride and of acrylonitrile–butadiene copolymer used as a non-migratory plasticiser should be considered. These compositions cannot be treated by the dissolution method recommended by Haslam and co-workers, nor is it possible to remove completely the polyvinyl chloride component by continued extraction with a solvent, but a quantitative evaluation of the polymer system can be made from a determination of the chlorine and nitrogen by methods already outlined. Thus the polyvinyl chloride content may be calculated from the chlorine figure by applying a factor of 1·76, and acrylonitrile is given by a conversion factor of 3·79 applied to the nitrogen. A reasonable approximation to the amount of the butadiene component can then be made by the difference method after the fillers have been determined. Alternatively, further elementary analysis of the ether-extracted composition permits a somewhat more accurate reconstruction on lines analogous to those recommended previously for the analysis of acrylonitrile–butadiene rubbers. Thus from the chlorine content the hydrogen in the polyvinyl chloride can be calculated, while the nitrogen will indicate the hydrogen due to acrylonitrile. The total hydrogen in the extracted polymer less that contributed by the polyvinyl chloride and the acrylonitrile must then arise from the butadiene.   Added carbon black can also be determined by a similar calculation.

One final point in the determination of chlorine by combustion methods concerns the effect of heavy metals, whose presence is revealed by the residue of ash in the combustion boat at the end of the determination. These will retain some of the previously organically bound chlorine, thus giving rise to low results.   It is essential in such cases to add the residue in the boat to the solution prior to titration so that the chlorine content is restored to its full value.

Infra-red methods

The application of infra-red techniques to polymer analysis in the industrial laboratory derived its initial impetus from the now classical work of Barnes and his co-workers [27] and of Dinsmore and Smith,[28] and while instrumentation has advanced considerably in the last ten years, their experimental techniques still form a working basis for the infra-red examination of many polymers even today.   Obtaining an infra-red spectrum of the raw polymer is a comparatively straightforward matter, being mainly a question of presenting the sample to the instrument in a suitable form, generally deposited as a uniform film on rock-salt plates, as a solution in a solvent transparent to infra-red, or hot pressed between rigid silver chloride plates.   Considerable difficulties arise, however, in the examination of vulcanisates, since these usually contain substances which interfere either by masking significant portions of the spectrum or by excessive energy scattering.

Soluble constituents, such as softeners, accelerators and anti-oxidants, must be removed by exhaustive extraction, suitable solvents being acetone, chloroform, isopropyl alcohol or ether, but it is difficult in many cases to separate the polymer from mineral matter and carbon black without such severe degradation that the resulting spectrum is misleading or un-informative.   Dinsmore and Smith recommend heating the sample with o-dichlorobenzene at a relatively low temperature ($100°$ C) for 24 hours and removing the insoluble fillers by centrifuging or by filtration, assisted if necessary by a filter aid, such as Celite.   The solution is then vacuum concentrated before transfer to a rock-salt plate.   This procedure is reasonably satisfactory for vulcanisates based on natural rubber, poly-butadienes, polyisoprenes, styrene and Butyl rubbers, but other common rubbers, generally oil-resisting types, such as the chloroprenes and the acrylonitrile copolymers, are not completely dissolved.   A particular danger in mixed rubber systems is that some of the insoluble polymer is carried down with the carbon black or other filler, and the resulting frac-tionated solution as submitted for infra-red analysis is then not repre-sentative of the original system.   A variety of other solvents have been tried, but as their effectiveness as solvents is related directly to the oxidative degradation they induce, any improved solubility is a somewhat doubtful gain.

Harms [29] avoids the difficulties of separating the polymer by solution methods by a simple pyrolysis technique, claiming that the pyrolysate, although necessarily more complex in its chemical nature than the original polymer, gives nevertheless a spectrum of reproducible and identifiable pattern by which the original may usually be recognised. This is true in only the qualitative sense, and the pyrolysis technique will not, for instance, distinguish unequivocally between copolymers prepared from varying monomer ratios, such as the butadiene–acrylonitrile series.

Spectra are generally recorded over the frequency range 650–3,000 cm.$^{-1}$, a region which embraces most of the characteristic peak absorptions of commonly used polymers, and are compared with the spectra of known materials produced under identical experimental conditions with regard to sample preparation and instrumentation. It is not advisable, except for qualitative work, to make use of published spectra produced under unknown conditions, and it follows that an essential requirement for infra-red spectroscopy is a comprehensive library of reference spectra produced on one's own instrument. Concurrence of the spectra of the unknown and standard samples then gives the identity of the test material, but where direct comparison is not possible, reference to a correlation chart serves to classify the material on a basis of functional absorptions (see Fig. 11.7).

Apart from the C=C stretching band at about 1,650 cm.$^{-1}$ common to most diene polymers, natural rubber is best characterised by the hydrogen deformation band at 837 cm.$^{-1}$.[30] The absorption at 1,380 cm.$^{-1}$ due to CH_3 is also useful in the absence of polyisobutene, which gives a doublet in this region at 1,389 and 1,365 cm.$^{-1}$. Butyl rubber itself (not distinguishable from polyisobutene) gives a characteristic pattern having peaks at 1,226, 948 and 920 cm.$^{-1}$,[30] the first being useful for quantitative measurement.[28] Olefinic hydrogen deformations are also characteristic of polydienes as a group, giving peaks which serve to identify 1 : 2 and 1 : 4 addition in polybutadienes and polyisoprenes, and thus providing a means of distinguishing between normal and cold polymerisation techniques. Further evidence of polybutadiene and some of its copolymers are provided by absorption peaks at 995, 970 and 910 cm.$^{-1}$. The 970 band, in particular, usually remains strong and reasonably constant in frequency and can serve to identify the polymer in a wide variety of mixtures or copolymers.

Polystyrene may be characterised by the absorption in the aromatic region, particularly the peaks at 3,100 and 1,600 cm.$^{-1}$, while according to Davison and Bates [30] the absorption pattern over the frequency range

1,500–1,950 cm.$^{-1}$ is valuable in the identification of the mono-substituted benzene nucleus. Bands at 755 and 695 cm.$^{-1}$ are also available for the analysis of polystyrene, the latter being particularly useful for quantitative work.

Among the nitrogen containing polymers acrylonitrile suppresses the 995 band of butadiene and causes a shift in the 910-cm.$^{-1}$ band to 922-

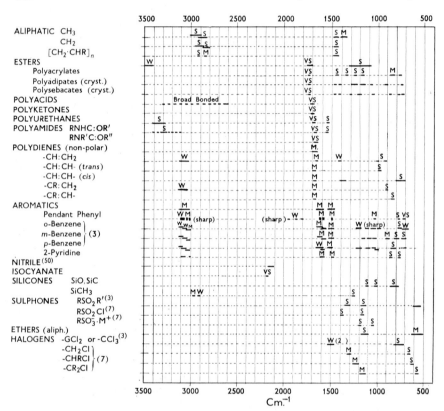

Fig. 11.7. Identification and determination of polymers. Correlation chart for polymers (after Davison and Bates).

cm.$^{-1}$; the broad band or doublet at 1,450 cm.$^{-1}$ is also considerably sharpened. The nitrile absorption at 2,240 cm.$^{-1}$ has been used by Dinsmore and Smith for quantitative analysis, and represents an isolated band unlikely to be confused by other features of the spectrum. Vinylpyridine shows a characteristic peak at about 1,470 cm.$^{-1}$ as well as aromatic absorptions which serve to distinguish it from acrylonitrile rubbers. Unfortunately aromatic isocyanate-extended polymers will also absorb in this region, but confusion is hardly likely to arise owing to the presence of absorptions assignable to the ester or ether groups. Probably the best absorption for characterising the polyurethanes, however, is the fairly strong band at 1,540 cm.$^{-1}$.

The spectrum of polychloroprene resembles that of natural rubber, as would be expected. The CH$_3$ band at 1,300 cm.$^{-1}$ disappears and is replaced by another distinctive absorption at 1,120 cm.$^{-1}$, while the 837 cm.$^{-1}$ hydrogen deformation band is shifted to 827 cm.$^{-1}$ presumably assignable to –CH:CCl–. Distinction between the chloroprene and chlorosulphonated polyethylenes is difficult by classical methods of analysis, but the bands at 1,160 and 1,060 cm.$^{-1}$ are specific to the latter. Polyvinyl chloride gives bands at 1,430, 1,250 and 960 cm.$^{-1}$, sufficient to distinguish it from other chlorine-containing polymers.

Harms,[29] whose work with pyrolysis techniques has already been mentioned, finds that certain changes are observable as compared with spectra from solutions in o-dichlorobenzene, and it is essential, therefore, to compile the reference spectra from pyrolysed samples. The strong 837-cm.$^{-1}$ band, for instance, disappears almost completely from natural rubber pyrolysates, but another occurs at about 889 cm.$^{-1}$; this latter absorption is, however, almost equally strong and constant and, taken in conjunction with a new absorption at 961 cm.$^{-1}$, gives an unmistakable indication of natural rubber. In butadiene–styrene rubbers many absorptions appear unchanged, but the 910-cm.$^{-1}$ band is useful in the quantitative analysis of mixtures with natural rubber, since its proximity to the 889-cm.$^{-1}$ band of natural rubber pyrolysate simplifies ratio measurements and base-line correction. Butyl rubber and its pyrolysate give very similar spectra, the characteristic features of which have already been mentioned, except that the pyrolysed material gives a pronounced unsaturation peak at about 880 cm.$^{-1}$. Pyrolysates from acrylonitrile polymers show the nitrile absorption at 2,240 cm.$^{-1}$ and useful bands at 1,730 and 1,600 cm.$^{-1}$, while the 965-cm.$^{-1}$ band, present in the original polymer, virtually disappears. For the identification of polychloroprene pyrolysates, Harms recommends the three peaks at 875, 813 and 746 cm.$^{-1}$.

TOTAL FILLERS

As in other sections of this chapter, it is necessary to begin by defining terms. The ASTM regards fillers as " those inorganic materials other than free sulphur and free carbon which have been added to the compound "—a definition which would appear to exclude cellulosic materials, such as wood flour. The BSI, on the other hand, takes a wider view and includes carbon black and organic materials along with mineral matter as making up the total fillers. The latter seems to be the more correct terminology, and will be accepted here, although the determination of carbon black as such is of sufficient importance to warrant a separate section.

For many purposes the direct determination of the carbon black, together with a reconstruction of the mineral matter from the ash, provides sufficient data to enable an evaluation of the total fillers to be made, but these tests will not reveal cellulose or other organic additions.   For this purpose it is necessary to dissolve the polymer, softeners, accelerator and anti-oxidant, and to separate the insoluble fillers by filtration or centrifuging.   From theoretical considerations, polymers should, in respect of their solubility be assignable to one of two groups: those which are not vulcanised in the conventional sense, and therefore remain soluble in an appropriate solvent, and the vulcanisable polymers.   The latter group are not soluble in the strict sense of the term after vulcanisation, owing to the formation of a three-dimensional structure, and their " solubilisation ", if the distinction be permitted, is dependent on the breakdown of the network into smaller units, generally in practice brought about by an oxidative mechanism.   This difference between linear and cross-linked polymers is of practical value to the analyst, who can determine the total fillers in a simple PVC composition with a good deal more confidence in his results than he expects from normal vulcanised materials.   Sufficient exceptions, however, to the general run of PVC compositions are encountered to justify a warning that straight solution methods may not always be applicable.   Acrylonitrile rubbers are, for instance, frequently incorporated as non-migratory procedures in PVC formulations.   In such cases it is useless to attack the compound with a solvent which in normal circumstances would dissolve the base polymer, for this merely achieves a partial separation which complicates rather than simplifies the subsequent quantitative work.   Experience shows that when qualitative analysis has revealed the presence of more than one polymer the only satisfactory course is to employ a solvent system which will dissolve the whole polymer network, if necessary degrading the rubber so that the fillers are obtained quite free from gel.

The difficulties of obtaining a true solution of the degraded rubber and a clear-cut separation of fillers are increased in the presence of carbon black, which often remains suspended in spite of lengthy centrifuging. Obviously in these circumstances a quantitative separation of the fillers is impossible, but an equally serious difficulty, and one not always easy to detect, arises from the formation of insoluble " carbon-gel " structures. This phenomenon not only vitiates the figure for insoluble matter but also tends to give a misleading picture of the polymer if the supernatent liquid is to be used for further investigations.   Precipitation of an insoluble fraction of rubber either from a homopolymer or by preferential precipitation of one polymer from a mixture is often aggravated by diluting the polymer solution with another solvent prior to centrifuging or filtration as is often done to hasten separation of the fillers.   In some cases there is sufficient polymer to separate as a gel-like fraction, which is immediately noticeable when the settled layer is carefully stirred. Often, however, it is only suspected when the insoluble matter has been separated and dried. Then, instead of a readily friable pad which can be broken up quite easily with a glass rod, the fillers are bound in a tough matrix which is noticeably resistant to grinding.

The final difficulty confronting the analyst arises from the necessity frequently to employ fairly drastic treatment to ensure as far as possible complete solution of the polymer. The factors which are particularly effective in this respect, such as a high temperature and oxidising conditions, are just those which are liable to alter the organic fillers both chemically and physically. In fact, it may be said that the more successfully a vulcanised polymer is brought into solution, the more likely the organic fillers are to be changed in character, and the more subject to error their quantitative determination will be. There is no simple answer to this problem, and the methods proposed by BSI and ASTM will not cope successfully with many of the newer polymers and mixtures which the analyst is likely to meet. In the methods outlined below the principle is to make the conditions for dissolving the polymer as mild as possible, consistent with giving a quantitative separation of the fillers, thus preserving as far as possible the original character of the insoluble organic additions. It is of some assistance that the cheaper cellulosic type of filler is not usually associated with the more intractable polymers, the so-called " specialist " rubbers of oil-resistant type, and the more drastic measures necessary to dissolve these polymers will not affect the fillers normally found with them.

Natural rubber

It is only to be expected that more investigations have been carried out into the determination of fillers in natural than in synthetic rubbers, and a wide variety of solvents and diluents have been proposed. Probably the earliest mention of a solvent for vulcanised rubber is by Weber, who used both α-nitronaphthalene and nitrobenzene. The latter is still in widespread use, and is perfectly satisfactory if the fillers consist solely of carbon black and inorganic materials. Any cellulose present, however, is seriously oxidised by nitrobenzene, and if a determination of the cellulose is to be made on the separated fillers the results will almost certainly be low.

The ASTM recommends dissolution of the rubber in mineral seal oil at a temperature of $150°-165°$ C, but oil to the specification required is not readily available in this country. It is suggested, however, that the solution finally obtained is less viscous than that given by many other solvents, and this permits rapid and more complete filtration. In the

ASTM procedure it is also pointed out that asbestos, and presumably other fibrous materials, can be separated from the rubber and the other compounding ingredients by passing through a fine screen which will retain the fibres but will permit the other dispersed powders to pass through. Further heating of the solution then causes further breakdown of the rubber colloid to give rapid settling of the remaining fillers. The analyst must decide for himself whether such a method of separating asbestos and similar materials is sufficiently accurate for his requirements.

Houblin criticises mineral oils as being too slow in their action unless the temperature reaches levels at which carbonaceous residues begin to form, and then high results are obtained.[31]   Houblin himself uses o-nitro-anisole and claims that vulcanised rubber will dissolve completely at a temperature of 115° C.   The method he advocates is as follows:

> 1 g. of the extracted rubber is broken into fragments and dropped into 25 ml. o-nitroanisole in a small conical flask.   The flask is heated on a small hot-plate at 115° C for 1 hour, then cooled and the contents diluted with a mixture of equal volumes of toluene and carbon tetra-chloride.   The solution is then passed through a fine filter which has been previously weighed, the insolubles are washed with carbon tetra-chloride, and then dried to constant weight.

Experience with Houblin's method indicates that, for normal vulcan-isates, such as tyre compounds and mechanicals, the conditions are far too mild for complete dissolution of the polymer; the rubber merely swells slightly and becomes a jelly-like mass from which the fillers refuse to separate.   Even prolonged heating at the recommended temperature is not wholly successful, and substantial improvement is obtained only if the temperature is raised to about 140°–150° C.   There is, of course, no harm in this unless cellulose is present, but it is possible that cellulose would be affected at that temperature.

The BSI recommend p-dichlorbenzene as a solvent after a preliminary swelling in carbon tetrachloride.   As alternatives, nitrobenzene and decahydronaphthalene are permitted in conjunction with the appropriate diluent, and in practice there seems little to choose between the three. The nitrobenzene method is as follows:

> 1 g. of the rubber is broken into fragments and dropped into 40 ml. boiling nitrobenzene.   Boiling is continued for 1 hour.   The flask is then cooled to room temperature and 100 ml. acetone is added with stirring.   Easier filtration is obtained if the flask is set aside for the fillers to settle;   the solution may then be carefully decanted through a fine filter which has previously been weighed.   The bulk of the solids are transferred to the filter by a jet from an acetone wash bottle, and

washing with acetone is continued until the washings are colourless. The filter and its contents are then dried to constant weight.

Butadiene–styrene rubbers and Butyl

Methods suitable for the determination of fillers in natural rubber can be applied equally well to butadiene–styrene and Butyl rubbers. With these materials Wake [32] has shown that it is even more important to create and maintain oxidising conditions during the dissolution process and suggests that failure to ensure this in the early stages will delay complete breakdown of the polymer. In the BSI procedure using p-dichlorbenzene, the presence of oxygen is ensured by blowing an occasional puff of air into the flask; otherwise the air is soon completely expelled by the vapour of the boiling solvent. The method is briefly as follows:

> 1 g. of the rubber is placed in a conical flask with 10 ml. carbon tetrachloride, and the flask loosely covered with a glass bulb or watch-glass. Gentle heat is applied to the flask until most of the liquid has evaporated, and then 100 g. p-dichlorbenzene are added to the flask. Heating is recommenced and the contents maintained just at the boiling point (173° C) until the rubber has completely disintegrated, blowing into the flask a puff of air from a hand bellows about every 15 minutes. When dissolution is complete, as indicated by absence of gel on testing with a glass rod, the flask is cooled to about 50° C, and 100 ml. carbon tetrachloride are added. The fillers are then removed by filtration, washed with hot carbon tetrachloride, dried and weighed.

Butadiene–acrylonitrile copolymers and polychloroprenes

These rubbers are, of course, far more difficult to dissolve than the hydrocarbon elastomers, and although the BSI method claims that p-dichlorbenzene will eventually dissolve them, for high-nitrile types, at any rate, the method is virtually useless. The ASTM method using mineral seal oil, according to the preamble, is not applicable to nitrile-type rubbers, " nor to any synthetic rubber compound that will not dissolve in the solvent oil "—an unassailable position!

The following method is a simpler version of that suggested by Kolthoff and Gutmacher,[33] and can be used for all nitrile-type rubbers. It is also suitable for polychloroprenes and has been applied successfully to chlorosulphonated polyethylene (Hypalon) although experience with this type of compound is more limited. Satisfactory results have also been obtained on polyurethane elastomers of the Adiprene C and Genthane S type, so the method can claim to be a good deal more versatile than any of those so far mentioned. It is not applicable to the fluorine-containing elastomers nor to silicone rubbers. The method is designed as a semi-micro procedure to deal with sample weights of 100–200 mg.

An accurately weighed portion of about 100–200 mg. is cut into small pieces and placed in a 50-ml. beaker with 10–15 g. *p*-dichlorbenzene. The temperature is raised to the boiling point and maintained at that temperature with magnetic stirring for 30 minutes to swell the polymer. It is then cooled to about 70° C, 5 ml. *tert*-butyl hydroperoxide is added, and the mixture is heated again at the boiling point with magnetic stirring until complete solution is attained. The contents of the beaker are diluted with 10 ml. *o*-dichlorbenzene, transferred to a centrifuge tube and after centrifuging and decanting the organic layer the residue is washed with several portions of benzene. The tube and its contents are dried at 100° C to constant weight.

Polyvinyl chloride and allied polymers

About 1 g. of the sample is first extracted with ether to remove soluble plasticisers and is then treated with about 40 ml. tetrahydrofurane or cyclohexanone in a centrifuge tube. If the mixture is stood overnight at room temperature the polymer will dissolve and the concentrated solution at the bottom of the tube should be dispersed by stirring. The mixture is then centrifuged until the fillers separate as a distinct layer, and the supernatant liquid is removed by gentle suction. The fillers are washed with two portions of solvent and two of acetone and are then dried to constant weight.

Carbon black is not commonly used in polyvinyl chloride compositions except as a pigment, and for this purpose the amount is usually quite small. Separation of a small amount of black, particularly the coarser grades, is not difficult in a high-speed centrifuge, but if large quantities are present it is not possible to separate the black quantitatively in the way described. The determination of black in this type of composition is best carried out by methods of ultimate analysis, in which determinations of carbon, hydrogen and chlorine are made on the plasticiser-free material. The carbon due to the polyvinyl chloride is calculated from the chlorine figure, and any carbon in excess of this indicates carbon black added as such to the original composition. Obviously, this method cannot compare for accuracy and reliability with a direct method, and depends above all on careful qualitative verification of the nature of the polymer. Account must also be taken of any carbonates present in the mineral matter, but in spite of these difficulties, the method does offer a route to at least an approximate figure for the carbon-black content.

Cellulose

No satisfactory direct method for the determination of cellulose in rubber is available. Both the BSI and ASTM recommend procedures based on acetylation of the separated fillers, but both methods include a warning that low results can be expected, mainly because cellulose in rubber is usually present in a degraded form, and hence partly soluble in the organic solvent used to dissolve the polymer. It has already been explained that further degradation of the cellulose is likely during the dissolution of the rubber.

Both methods commence with a separation of the total fillers which may be collected and dried to constant weight, and acid-soluble fillers are removed by treatment with hydrochloric acid. In the ASTM method the fillers and the asbestos pad are transferred from the crucible to a small beaker, where they are treated with 15 ml. acetic anhydride and 0·5 ml. sulphuric acid. The BSI however, recommends filtering the fillers on a sintered pad and treating the crucible directly with acetic anhydride and sulphuric acid. Acetylation of the cellulose is effected by heating the mixture on a water-bath for at least 1 hour, and here the ASTM stresses the importance of standardising the conditions of heating. The digest is then diluted with acetic acid and run through a second (weighed) crucible, washing first with acetic acid and then with acetone until the washings are quite colourless. The crucible is then dried and weighed, and the loss in weight represents the cellulose present in the sample.

It is usually more satisfactory to determine cellulose, or more correctly, organic fillers, by difference. Direct methods of determination exist for carbon black and for the various mineral constituents of the fillers; the sum of these taken from the total fillers gives a figure for the organic fillers which is more reliable than that derived by the direct method in the majority of cases.

Examination of fabric reinforced products

Unlike the determination of cellulose which has just been discussed, these methods are intended primarily for those instances where, quantitatively at any rate, rubber is the minor constituent. They are thus suitable for the chemical examination of belting, hose, fabric-reinforced diaphragms and even for such applications as the determination of resin dips on tyre cords, but the nature of the fibre in the reinforcing member, rather than the type of polymer used, may decide the solvent or the experimental conditions to be employed. It is, therefore, obviously impracticable to describe methods for every combination of fabric and polymer that the analyst may meet, and space permits only a selection of typical examples.

The following method, developed primarily for the examination of canvas reinforced polyvinyl chloride belting and hose, will not apply to products compounded with an insoluble non-migratory plasticiser such as an acrylonitrile–butadiene copolymer.

A small portion of the sample, weighing about 5 g., is cut so that it is accurately representative of the whole, and is placed inside a wire basket, about 2 cm. cube, made of 100-mesh stainless-steel gauze. The basket is attached to a length of wire which passes up the centre tube of a reflux condenser fitted to a 150-ml. extraction flask. About 100 ml. cyclohexanone are placed in the flask, in which the basket and its contents are immersed for several hours, preferably overnight. The solution is then gently refluxed on a small electric hot-plate, raising the basket periodically to observe the disintegration of the sample. Inorganic fillers are removed with the polymer, and although in practice the fabric may appear discoloured by a trace of residual carbon black, the amount retained is negligible. When the sample has completely disintegrated the basket is raised above the level of the liquid so that the condensed solvent acts as a rinse, and when the washings are colourless the apparatus is dismantled, the basket is detached, dried at 110° C, and weighed after appropriate conditioning. The weight of fabric can then be subtracted from the weight of the test portion, and the fabric-to-rubber ratio thus calculated.

It is, of course, possible to incorporate the above procedure into a more complete analytical scheme if the amount of sample is restricted. In these cases a preliminary extraction is made with ether to remove plasticisers. The same apparatus is used, but an extended extraction period may be required owing to the thickness of the test portion. The flask containing the ether solution is then replaced by one containing cyclohexanone, and the polymer and inorganic fillers are separated from the fabric as already described. The polymer solution and mineral matter are then transferred to a centrifuge tube, diluted with acetone and the fillers removed by centrifuging while the polymer may be recovered from the supernatant liquid either by evaporation of the solvent or by precipitation with alcohol.

Fabric reinforced mechanical goods range from those which employ conventional natural rubber compounds supported on cotton canvas to more specialised applications involving the use of synthetic rubbers in conjunction with man-made fibres. One of the newest of these, glass fibre, is, from the analyst's viewpoint, about the easiest to deal with, since virtually any solvent can be used to remove the rubber without having any detrimental effect on the reinforcing fabric. Probably the commonest form of reinforcement, however, is cotton, and then it becomes easier to remove this and weigh the rubber, rather than attempt to dissolve the rubber without altering the cotton in any way. An essential preliminary is the very thorough preparation of the sample, for it is important to ensure that the rubber cannot protect the cotton from attack by the aqueous solvent which is used. The best way of doing this is to cut the diaphragm into thin strips and place these in a high-speed macerator.

To determine the rubber-to-fabric ratio, about 0·5 g. of the disintegrated sample is placed in a small beaker and heated with 5 ml. concentrated hydrochloric acid. When the mixture has thickened appreciably about 50 ml. concentrated zinc chloride solution are added and the heating and stirring continued for a further 10 minutes. It is then diluted with water and filtered quickly through a weighed sintered filter. If the filter tends to clog it may be an indication that the cellulose has not completely dissolved, in which case the filtration is completed, the insoluble material sucked fairly dry, and returned to the beaker for a second treatment with zinc chloride. Finally, the filter is washed very thoroughly with hot water, dried and weighed.

A similar technique may be used for the examination of almost any combination of rubber and fabric, providing, of course, a solvent for the fabric is available. Oil-resisting acrylonitrile–butadiene rubbers supported on nylon are becoming quite common in aircraft components, but even qualitative analysis of such products is out of the question until the rubber is completely separated from the fabric. Nylon, however, can be dissolved in warm formic acid, and so by carrying through the above procedure, but using formic acid instead of zinc chloride, the rubber-to-fabric ratio can be determined, and sufficient rubber obtained for an analysis by microchemical methods.

Although the determination of adhesive dip on tyre cords and similar fabric can hardly be regarded as rubber analysis, it is a problem that often confronts the control laboratory, and the methods briefly outlined above will have an obvious application in that field. Since, however, rayon is the most important fibre to be considered here, it may be as well to give the method in a little more detail:

About 0·2 g. of the cord is cut into lengths about 1 cm. long, untwisted with forceps and heated in a weighing bottle for 30 minutes at 150° C. After cooling and weighing, the contents are tipped into a small beaker and the bottle reweighed. About 15 ml. formic acid are poured into the beaker which is warmed to 50° C and stirred for about 10 minutes. Then 4 ml. concentrated sulphuric acid are added, still with warming and stirring, and after 30 minutes a further 20 ml. formic acid. The mixture is filtered through a sintered-glass crucible which contains a 1-cm. layer of small glass beads above the pad; the insoluble material and filter are washed with hot water, and are then dried at 150° C and weighed.

SULPHUR

The determination of sulphur and its distribution in a vulcanisate is a cardinal feature of the examination of any rubber compound, and it is consequently not surprising that much attention has been given to the improvement of analytical methods. Before proceeding to a description of individual methods, however, it will be helpful to consider how data provided by analysis can be related to the distribution of sulphur in the original compound. At the same time it is desirable to define with some care the nomenclature used in this branch of rubber analysis, as the exact meaning of many of the terms is not without variation throughout the industry.

The term *total sulphur* refers to the total amount of sulphur in the rubber found by analysis regardless of its chemical form. Some authorities, expressly or by implication, exclude the sulphur combined in compounding ingredients, and in determining " total sulphur " aim at a figure that indicates only the amount of elementary sulphur added as such to the mixing. While it is true that the latter figure is important in formulating rubber compounds, it is unfortunate that the word " total " used in this connection has tended to lose its real meaning. The term *added sulphur* conveys the idea of the original addition of elementary sulphur accurately and unambiguously. This term is applied to the amount of elementary sulphur added originally to the mixing. It is not directly determinable by analysis, but in most rubber compounds can be taken as the sum of the sulphur combined with the rubber and the free sulphur, ignoring for all practical purposes the small amount of sulphur that forms zinc or other metallic sulphides and that which combines with the resins and saponifiable oils of natural rubber. In the so-called " sulphurless " curing systems vulcanisation is effected solely or mainly by labile sulphur from a thiuram polysulphide or an accelerator of similar character, and a determination of the sulphur combined with the rubber would in such compounds give a spuriously high figure for the added sulphur. Conversely, hot-air or open-steam cures are sometimes responsible for a loss of some of the elementary sulphur originally added, and consequently the sulphur combined with the rubber can be considerably less than the original addition. In these abnormal cases analysis is of little direct value, and estimation of the added sulphur is a matter for the compounder rather than the analyst, basing an opinion on the characteristics of the compound as a whole.

Rubber-combined sulphur. Before the introduction of organic accelerators the amount of sulphur combined with the rubber provided an indication of the degree of vulcanisation of the compound, and wide recognition was given to the " coefficient of vulcanisation ", which was simply the amount of rubber-combined sulphur calculated as a percentage of the rubber. Today this concept has largely fallen into disuse, and the main purposes of the determination are, first, in conjunction with information about the accelerators present, to give qualitative information about the vulcanising system being used, and secondly, to provide, after due correction for free sulphur, an estimate of the added sulphur.

In vulcanisates which do not contain inorganically combined sulphur of factice the rubber-combined sulphur is found by determining the sulphur in the rubber from which the free sulphur and organically combined sulphur, such as in accelerators, has been removed by solvent extraction. For this purpose methods recommended for the determination of total sulphur are suitable. Factice and mineral fillers are not extracted by the usual processes, however, and the sulphur figure in these cases will include that contributed by the compounding ingredients still retained in the rubber. If the nature of the inorganic additions is quite unknown the only safe course is to isolate the fillers and determine their sulphur content. The rubber-combined sulphur as normally determined can then be corrected by subtracting the sulphur in the separated fillers.

With regard to the sulphur in factice, Davis and Blake [34] suggest that this will be found in the alcoholic potash extract, the implication being that the rubber-combined sulphur can then be determined in the rubber after it has been treated with the alcoholic potash. Alkali treatment of the solvent-extracted rubber, however, not only saponifies the factice but also removes some of the sulphur generally regarded as being combined with the rubber, inasmuch as it is not extracted by acetone. It seems probable therefore that when factice is present an accurate determination of the rubber-combined sulphur is impracticable.

Total extractable sulphur. This is the term given to the total amount of sulphur in the material extracted from the rubber compound, usually by acetone; it is sometimes referred to as " sulphur in extract ". Although in some compounds the principal constituent of the total extractable sulphur is free sulphur, an assortment of ill-defined chemical substances, such as accelerator breakdown products and low-molecular-weight vulcanised resins and oils, may also be present. The sulphur figure obtained from such a mixture cannot be rigorously interpreted, and the fact that some of the analytical methods advocated for its determination are not quantitative merely adds to the confusion.

For control analysis, where a fixed relationship between the total extractable sulphur and the free sulphur can be safely assumed from a knowledge of the other compounding ingredients, the determination of total extractable sulphur survives as a chemical means of assessing the state of vulcanisation of the rubber compound, but even in such applications as these the same information could be gained by faster and more reliable analytical methods.

Free sulphur. The residue of the added sulphur remaining in the elementary form is generally small in vulcanisates and is known as " free sulphur ". The expression " true free sulphur " is sometimes used to distinguish it from the *total extractable sulphur*, but the qualification is unnecessary. From the analytical standpoint it is important that the method selected for the determination of free sulphur should not be susceptible to interference from sulphur which may be present in other forms, for example, as sulphur combined in accelerators.

Mineral sulphur. Inorganically combined sulphur appears in recognisable chemical compounds which remain substantially unchanged during processing and vulcanising. It is usually encountered as sulphide or sulphate, and is generally referred to as " mineral sulphur ". The determination of mineral sulphur is relatively straightforward, and since it remains for the most part in its original form, there is rarely any difficulty in relating the analytical results to the composition of the corresponding compounding ingredients.

TOTAL SULPHUR

The number and variety of methods proposed in the literature for the determination of total sulphur is perhaps some indication that the methods from time to time available for this important branch of rubber analysis leave much to be desired. Not all the methods will yield total sulphur in the sense in which it has been defined; indeed, some are expressly designed to avoid doing so, but as they follow broadly the same principles, they are conveniently grouped under this heading. The determination of rubber-combined sulphur can also be carried out by the same methods, having regard to their limitations in the presence of factice or mineral sulphur as already explained. With few exceptions, all employ the principle of oxidising the sulphur to sulphate, followed by a determination of the sulphate ion, and the variety of routes by which these stages may be accomplished leads to an almost bewildering choice of methods. A broad classification of the more representative methods provides a useful background against which the more detailed procedures given later may be considered.

Oxidation procedures for the conversion of sulphur to sulphate fall into three groups:

1. *Acid digestion methods.* In these methods the sample is treated with an oxidising acid, such as nitric or perchloric, and sometimes with auxiliary agents, such as bromine, either under normal atmospheric conditions or, as

in the Carius method, at an elevated temperature. Individual determinations by these methods tend to be lengthy because some forms of sulphur are not readily oxidised, and for the same reason quantitative oxidation of the sulphur is not always certain. On the other hand, the apparatus required is of the simplest, and a number of determinations can proceed side by side. Perhaps the greatest objection to these methods is that the high salt concentration in the final solution precludes the use of modern titrimetric finishes, and further time is then needed for the much more lengthy gravimetric determination of sulphate. The time required for a single result may thus extend over two days, a delay not always acceptable for production control purposes.

2. *Combustion methods.* Methods which depend on a rapid decomposition of the organic material in an atmosphere of oxygen have made considerable advances in recent years. Their two outstanding advantages are that they are extremely rapid, the actual combustion taking usually well under an hour, and that absorption of the sulphur oxides gives a relatively simple solution well suited to a rapid titrimetric assay. The need for an electric furnace with fairly close temperature control might be considered by some to be a disadvantage and, of course, with one unit only one determination at a time can be made.

3. *Bomb methods.* These procedures, in which the finely divided rubber is heated with a dry powdered oxidising mixture, combine some of the advantages and disadvantages of both the preceding groups. Thorough preparation of the sample is essential, and facilities for this are not always available, but the actual combustion is quite rapid. Insufficient work has been reported in the literature to indicate whether the method is quantitative in all circumstances, and the effect of such materials as antimony and zinc sulphides, for example, requires further investigation before the method can be regarded as a general one.

The techniques available for the determination of sulphate resulting from the oxidation stage may be classified in a similar way.

1. *Gravimetric determination of barium sulphate.* The traditional method of filtering and weighing sulphate as the barium salt is adopted by BSI [35] and ASTM [36] as a standard recommendation. In spite of its wide use, however, the difficulties surrounding the accurate assay of sulphate by this method are surprisingly little known, and the critical discussions offered by Fischer and Rhinehammer [37] and Frey [38] on the optimum conditions for precipitation of barium sulphate make a valuable contribution to the literature on this subject. The addition of picric acid as an agent for promoting the crystal growth of barium sulphate, now regarded as of doubtful value, was first proposed by Lindsly.[39] In more recent work by Belcher, Gibbons and West [40] the

precipitation of sulphate is followed by treatment with ethylenediamine-tetra-acetic acid to minimise interference from other cations, and in a later publication the same workers introduced a complexometric titration after the barium sulphate precipitation, thus providing an extremely rapid volumetric procedure for sulphate determination in which interference from a number of sources is eliminated.[41]

2. *Precipitation as an organic sulphate.* There have been many attempts to make the precipitation of sulphate with benzidine chloride and similar reagents fully quantitative, but no widely accepted procedure has yet emerged. The attraction of this approach lies in the possibility of filtering or centrifuging the organic sulphate from the solution and titrating the precipitate with an appropriate reagent. Such a procedure would obviously gain in time over gravimetric methods, but until recently the solubility of the organic sulphate was responsible for considerable errors. Outa[42] and Frey[43] have both developed methods directly applicable to rubber analysis in which benzidine is employed as the precipitant, Frey claiming that interference from cations can be overcome by passing the solution through a column of ion-exchange resin. Mahr and Kraus[44] have carried out similar work on precipitation methods with hexammine cobalti-bromide.

The situation with regard to organic precipitants for sulphate was completely changed by the introduction of *p*-chloro-*p'*-aminodiphenyl by Belcher, Nutten and Stephen.[45] The solubility of the sulphate formed by this reagent is given as 15 mg./litre compared with 98 mg./litre for benzidine sulphate, and the quantitative determination of sulphate reaches a high standard of accuracy. Bauminger[46] makes use of this reagent in the concluding stage of a combustion method for determining sulphur in rubber.

3. *Titrimetric methods.* The simplest of the direct methods consists in titrating with alkali the sulphuric acid formed on oxidative combustion and absorption in hydrogen peroxide. It is an extremely rapid procedure well suited to routine control when the main features of the rubber compound are known, but cannot be used in the presence of polymers containing chlorine or nitrogen.

Other methods employ the general principle of precipitating the sulphate by titration with a metal ion, the end point being detected with a metal-indicator. Tetrahydroxyquinone is a commonly used internal indicator, and the experimental conditions for its use with barium chloride have been studied by Siegfriedt, Wiberley and Moore.[47] A more specific application of the system to rubber analysis has been developed by Mahoney and Mitchell.[48] Other indicators suggested for this titration include Erythrosin B and sodium rhodizonate, but in these titrations the end point is often obscure, and Walters[49] has proposed titrating the solution with barium chloride to the point of maximum absorbence at 520–530 mμ as a means of overcoming this difficulty.

Outline descriptions of methods

The wet oxidation or fusion process is one of the oldest of the methods for the determination of sulphur and, with its many variations, is probably still the most widely used. The principle has been adopted in a standard method adopted by the BSI and by the ASTM, and for full working details reference should be made to the appropriate publications of these bodies. The essentials of the method are as follows:

About 0·5 g. of the finely sheeted rubber cut into small pieces is weighed into a porcelain dish, where it is covered with 15 ml. of bromine-saturated concentrated nitric acid. About 3 g. potassium nitrate are added and the mixture is heated gently at first and then steadily on a water-bath until a clear digest is obtained. The contents of the dish are then taken to dryness, about 5 g. anhydrous sodium carbonate stirred in with sufficient water to make a stiff paste, and the mixture again heated to dryness.

In the ASTM process the mixture is fused in the porcelain dish, but the BS method advocates transference to a nickel crucible at this stage; in both methods it is necessary then to heat with sulphur-free flame or in an electric furnace until a clear melt is formed. After cooling, the contents are leached out with hot water and the solution passed through a rapid filter. Silica is removed from this solution by evaporating to dryness, repeatedly treating the dry residue with hydrochloric acid, taking up in water and filtering. Sulphate is precipitated from the solution with barium chloride, and the barium sulphate is determined gravimetrically.

Addition of picric acid immediately before the precipitation of barium sulphate has been advocated as a means of accelerating the growth of barium sulphate crystals, and hence speeding up the final filtration. This modification is not universally accepted, however, and although mandatory in ASTM procedures, its use in British Standards referee methods is not permitted.

Although a lengthy method, the wet oxidation process requires no special equipment, lends itself to the analysis of many samples concurrently and determines the total of all forms of sulphur in the rubber.

A rather different oxidation procedure, known as the zinc–nitric acid method, is somewhat less general than the fusion method, since it will determine the total sulphur only when barium, antimony and lead compounds are absent. As it is slightly faster, however, it finds some favour as a control method, and forms one of the recommended procedures issued by the ASTM.

About 0·5 g. of the sheeted rubber is weighed into an Erlenmeyer flask, covered with 10 ml. of zinc–nitric acid reagent (1 litre concentrated nitric acid, 200 g. zinc oxide) and allowed to stand for at least 1 hour. 10 ml. fuming nitric acid are added slowly, the flask being cooled if necessary to retard the reaction. When the reaction is complete 5 ml. bromine water are added, the solution evaporated to a syrupy consistency and potassium chlorate added to remove any remaining specks of carbon.

The liquid is then evaporated to dryness over an asbestos mat and the mixture heated strongly until brown fumes have ceased. When cool the solids are dissolved in hydrochloric acid ($15\% \ V/V$), the solution filtered and the sulphate precipitated with barium chloride.

The Carius method may also be used for the determination of sulphur in rubber, and gives a result similar to that by the zinc–nitric acid method, i.e. the added sulphur, free sulphur, accelerator-combined sulphur and certain forms of mineral sulphur are included but not that due to barium sulphate.

Other wet oxidation methods use perchloric acid as the auxiliary oxidising agent,[50] concluding with the normal gravimetric procedure for the determination of sulphur as barium sulphate, but a recent development by Bethge [51] follows the perchloric acid oxidation with a reduction stage on the lines proposed earlier by Luke.[52] Bethge's method is briefly as follows:

The apparatus is assembled as in Fig. 11.8, which shows a 50-ml. digestion flask surmounted by an acid receiver, reflux condenser, and trap. After digestion of a 100-mg. sample with a mixture of perchloric and nitric acids the nitric acid is distilled and collected in the receiver. When the apparatus has cooled the reaction flask is removed, hydrobromic acid is added and a stream of inert gas passed through the liquid to remove excess bromine. For the reduction to hydrogen sulphide the flask is connected to the apparatus shown in the second figure and the solution treated with a mixture of hydriodic acid and hypophosphorous acid. The hydrogen sulphide is carried through on a stream of nitrogen, absorbed in sodium hydroxide solution and titrated iodometrically.

Although satisfactory for many rubber compounds, Bethge's method is liable to give low results in the presence of barium sulphate owing to the uncertain action of the reduction mixture, but other sulphur-containing inorganic fillers are quantitatively decomposed at the reduction stage.

Combustion methods

Because of their speed, much attention has been given in recent years to the development of combustion methods.   It is possible by using a rapid combustion technique to obtain a single result in less than 1 hour compared with a day or so by the older fusion and wet oxidation methods.

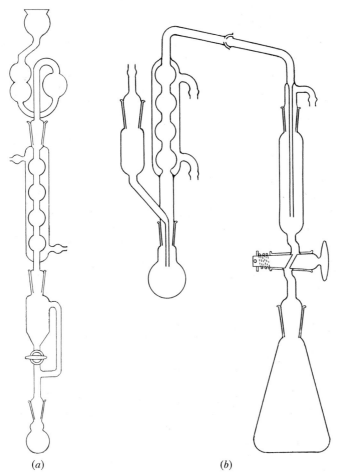

(a)   (b)

Fig. 11.8. (a) Determination of total sulphur (Bethge's method).   (b) Determination
of total sulphur (Bethge's method).

Another advantage of combustion techniques is that rather smaller samples can be used; 50–100 mg. of rubber are normally taken for each determination, but the methods generally operate quite successfully down to about 20 mg.   On the other hand, combustion methods involve the use of apparatus which, although by no means complicated, is certainly more expensive than the simple requirements of the fusion method, and they demand permanent bench space, which may be difficult to justify for only occasional use. Combustion methods, unlike classical methods, do not lend themselves readily to concurrent determinations, and the output of a single train reaches a practical limit of about six determinations per day with one operator.

One of the first accounts of a combustion procedure applied specifically to the determination of sulphur in rubber has been given by Gaunt,[53] but the technique did not gain wide recognition until its publication as a British Standard [54] in 1950. The following is a brief outline of the recommended procedure:

Oxygen from a cylinder is fed through a flow meter and purifying train of soda–asbestos and magnesium perchlorate into an electrically heated combustion tube suitable for temperatures up to 1,400° C. The sample is contained in a silica boat which can be manipulated within the combustion tube by a silica rod sliding in a rubber sleeve at the entrance to the tube. The effluent gases pass into an absorption system of three vessels charged with dilute hydrogen peroxide, the second incorporating a sintered-glass disk for efficient scrubbing of the gases. The considerable back-pressure set up in the system by the sintered disk is overcome by applying suction to the exit end of the absorber. By an arrangement of taps the vacuum line is made to draw the absorbing solutions into one vessel, where it is titrated when combustion is complete.

To carry out a determination, about 100 mg. of the sample are weighed into a combustion boat and covered with an inert material such as silica or alumina powder. When the temperature of the furnace has reached 1,350° C the oxygen flow is started at a rate of 500 ml./min., and the boat is pushed slowly along the combustion tube until it reaches the hot zone, where it rests for 15–20 minutes. At the end of this time the absorption system is disconnected, swept out with a stream of air to remove carbon dioxide and the collected absorbing solutions are titrated with standard alkali.

The combustion method outlined above will determine all the sulphur in a natural rubber compound with the exception of that combined in barium sulphate. A combustion temperature of 1,350° C is necessary for the decomposition of calcium sulphate, which may have been present originally or formed from calcium carbonate in the rubber and the sulphur dioxide in the effluent gas. In the absence of calcium compounds the furnace temperature can be lowered to 1,000° C. The method is not suitable for polymers containing chlorine or nitrile nitrogen, since these materials yield acid-forming gaseous products which interfere in the final alkalimetric titration.

Zimmerman and co-workers,[55] in an adaptation of the above procedure, modified the combustion conditions in an effort to determine the added sulphur independently of the mineral sulphur, but found considerable interference from certain fillers at a temperature of 480°–500° C. A similar technique is advocated by Stache,[56] who also noted the limitation imposed by chlorine-containing polymers.

In a semi-micro form of the combustion procedure, Bauminger[46] proposes heating the sample with a mixture of vanadium pentoxide and zinc oxide, since under these conditions barium and calcium sulphates are quantitatively decomposed at 1,000° C. Interference from chlorine and nitrogen is avoided by the use of p-chloro-p'-aminodiphenyl as a precipitant for the sulphate ion. With these modifications the method will determine the total sulphur in all rubber compounds based on the more common elastomers.

In a more recent paper Bauminger[57] recommends a complexometric determination of the sulphate. Details of the apparatus and procedure which form the basis of the current BSI recommended method[35] are as follows (see Fig. 11.9):

Metered and purified oxygen enters the combustion tube through a standard conical joint which can be disconnected to admit the combustion boat. The boat is propelled inside the tube by an iron cylinder activated externally by a magnet. The exit end of the combustion tube is bent vertically downwards to conduct the exit gases into the absorption system, whence the unabsorbed gases are drawn away on a vacuum line. A short winding of Nichrome wire carrying a regulated current heats the bend of the combustion tube sufficiently to prevent condensation of the issuing gases before they reach the primary absorber. The absorbers are charged with dilute hydrogen peroxide, which can be drawn off through the lower tap for the final titration.

A sample weight of 30–50 mg. is used for the determination, and after being placed in the boat the rubber is covered with about 1 g. of a mixture of 80% vanadium pentoxide and 20% zinc oxide. When the furnace temperature reaches 1,000° C and the temperature of the auxiliary heater is about 500° C oxygen is admitted at the rate of 50 ml./min. and the boat is pushed slowly into the hot zone, where it is heated for 30 minutes. The oxygen and vacuum lines are then disconnected and the absorbing solutions collected in a 50-ml. volumetric flask. If chlorine and nitrile polymers are known to be absent the determination of sulphur is concluded with an alkalimetric titration of the solution. In the presence of these polymers a 20-ml. aliquot is

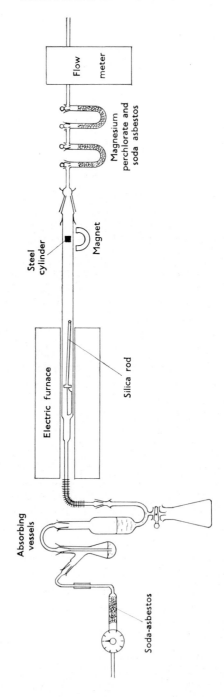

Fig. 11.9. Determination of total sulphur (Bauminger's method).

made slightly acid with hydrochloric acid and the sulphate precipitated with excess standard barium chloride.   To the cold solution, buffered with ammonium chloride and ammonium hydroxide, about 50 mg. zinc disodium ethylenediaminetetra-acetate are added, and the liberated zinc ions are titrated with a standard solution of disodium dihydrogen ethylenediaminetetra-acetate, using Eriochrome Black as indicator.   It is unnecessary to remove the precipitate of barium sulphate.   In the combustion of chlorine-containing polymers zinc is sometimes volatilised as the chloride, and this, collecting in the absorbers, interferes with the determination of the excess barium, but a correction can be made by titrating a second aliquot without the addition of barium chloride.

Methods depending on combustion in a bomb have been mentioned in the literature, but none has become sufficiently well established to gain acceptance as a standard procedure.

In these methods intimate mixing of the finely divided sample and the reacting mixture is essential; the usual preparation of the sample by milling thinly and then cutting with scissors is quite inadequate, and it is probable that many failures in the application of bomb methods to rubber analysis arise from neglect of this precaution.   A procedure for the determination of total sulphur in soft rubber vulcanisates is given in the *Parr Manual on the Peroxide Bomb*,[58] and is briefly as follows:

> 200 mg. of sample are treated with a mixture of potassium perchlorate, sucrose and sodium peroxide in a bomb of 22 ml. capacity. On cooling, the contents of the bomb are leached out with hot water, and barium sulphate is precipitated from the solution, collected and weighed in the conventional manner.

A modification of the above method which will deal with samples of a few milligrams in weight has been put forward by Siegfriedt, Wiberley and Moore,[47] who react the sample in a 1-ml.-capacity platinum cup placed inside a 40-ml. electrically fired bomb.   Sulphate in the final solution is determined volumetrically with standard barium chloride, using tetrahydroxyquinone as indicator.

Oxygen under pressure is used as the oxidant in a method proposed by Outa,[42] who concludes the determination with the precipitation of the sulphate with benzidine hydrochloride and an alkalimetric titration of the insoluble salt.

Dry oxidation methods allied to the bomb method but not operated under pressure generally make use of sodium peroxide as the oxidant, sometimes in admixture with sodium carbonate or carbon.   The reaction mixture is heated in a nickel or platinum crucible and the resulting

H H

sulphate determined in aqueous solution, either gravimetrically or by one of the numerous titrimetric procedures.

Yet another approach is suggested by Resnik,[59] whose method is of interest, since it eliminates completely the usual oxidation stage:

5–10 mg. of the finely divided sample are heated in a capillary tube with metallic potassium, and when cool the tube is broken under water in a small flask. The flask is assembled into a gas-evolution apparatus, the contents acidified and the hydrogen sulphide swept through on a stream of inert gas to be absorbed in sodium hydroxide solution. The sulphide is then determined iodometrically.

FREE SULPHUR

The term " free sulphur " as applied to vulcanisates should, strictly speaking, be reserved for that fraction of the elementary sulphur originally added to the mixing which remains uncombined with the rubber during vulcanisation. In the majority of rubber compounds it is not easy to obtain an exact measure of this fraction, as some of the sulphur reacts with metallic oxides to give small quantities of the corresponding sulphides, while some compounds, mainly accelerators and their breakdown products, contribute sulphur in a form which is difficult to distinguish analytically from elementary sulphur. Errors from the first of these sources are not likely to be great; the *in situ* formation of zinc sulphide, for instance, can for all practical purposes usually be ignored. The sulphur combined in many accelerators, on the other hand, if included as free sulphur can make an appreciable addition to the result, and this is recognised by the widespread use of the term " total extractable sulphur ". The importance of distinguishing between the free sulphur and the total extractable sulphur has already been stressed, and it follows that the choice of analytical method is no less important. In the procedures which follow, details of manipulation have been reduced to a minimum, while attention has been given to a critical evaluation of each method, particularly in the light of the foregoing considerations.

Methods for the determination of free sulphur which depend on prior extraction of the rubber with a solvent form an important group. Hot acetone is mainly used, and since it is non-selective in its action, many forms of sulphur, besides that in the elementary form, appear in the extract. Soxhlet extraction for 4 hours is generally adequate for normal vulcanisates, although overnight extraction (16 hours) is often preferred on the grounds of convenience. In unvulcanised and partly vulcanised compounds it is important not to exceed the 4-hour extraction time, and if incomplete extraction seems likely the tendency should be corrected by a reduction in sample weight rather than by longer extraction. There is the further consideration that many of the methods for the assay of free sulphur cannot handle quantitatively more than about 10 mg. of sulphur, and a reduction of sample weight is the only practicable way of observing this limit. As the determination of free sulphur is primarily a process control test with speed an important consideration, extraction methods show up rather unfavourably by comparison with non-extractive procedures.

Of the methods depending on prior extraction of the sulphur, the oldest and still one of the most firmly established procedures originated with Weber, who proposed the use of bromine as the oxidising agent. Although in principle the method is a simple one, bromine is rather slow as a reagent for oxidising sulphur, and often where the free sulphur content is abnormally high, globules of elementary sulphur will resist oxidation for lengthy periods. The action of bromine on some accelerators is similarly uncertain, less-stable types being readily attacked, so that their combined sulphur is included in the free sulphur figure.

The following version of Weber's method is recommended by BSI: [35]

A weighed portion of the sample is extracted with acetone, the extract carefully dried, and treated with bromine at 70° C until a colourless solution is obtained. Insoluble material is removed by filtration and the sulphate in the solution is precipitated, filtered and weighed as barium sulphate in the conventional manner.

Alternative methods employing stronger oxidants are advocated by both BSI and ASTM. The results by these methods include not only the free sulphur but also much of the sulphur combined in accelerators and their breakdown products, sulphur in the extractable portion of factice, in certain peptisers and in other acetone-soluble substances. The sulphur in these materials may, in the aggregate, exceed by several times the amount of free sulphur, and as this figure is required with some accuracy serious error can be introduced by applying a correction based on assumed values for other ingredients of the extract.

The BSI recommend the following procedure:

The acetone extract from a weighed portion of the sample is carefully dried and treated with concentrated nitric acid over a steam-bath for 4 hours. Small portions of solid potassium chlorate are introduced at intervals to hasten oxidation, and when clear the solution is evaporated, heated with hydrochloric acid to expel the nitric acid and diluted to give a solution from which the sulphate is recovered as the barium salt.

In the ASTM procedure [36] the acetone extract is treated with the zinc–nitric acid reagent on the lines described in the section on the determination of total sulphur. The oxidation is assisted with bromine and fuming nitric acid in the later stages, and the result probably represents the nearest approach to the concept of " total extractable sulphur " that can be achieved by normal wet oxidation methods.

With the introduction of organic sulphur-containing accelerators and an increasing awareness of the limitations of the older methods for free sulphur determination, attention was turned to more selective procedures. Still employing a preliminary extraction with acetone, Hardman and Barbehenn [60] recommended the use of metallic copper as a means of fixing the sulphur, leaving the other sulphur-containing ingredients of the extract unaffected. While there is no doubt that many common accelerators are stable towards copper in acetone solution, it is also true that some compounds containing co-ordinately linked sulphur are more readily decomposed.[61] In such cases some of the accelerator-combined sulphur will appear as elementary sulphur, but even so, the interference is substantially less than in other conventional methods of free-sulphur determination.

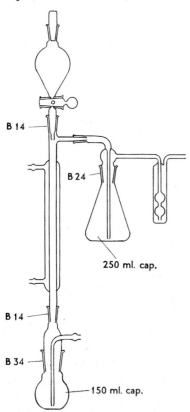

Fig. 11.10. Determination of free sulphur.

In a study of the copper spiral method as presented in BS 903 : 1950, Lancaster and Tarrant [62] showed that the recovery of sulphur varied between 94 and 96%, and suggested improvements whereby a more uniform level of 99·5% could be achieved. Their revised apparatus is shown in Fig. 11.10, the main differences from the earlier form being the use of glass joints, reduction of the internal surface area of glass and the use of air-free nitrogen dipping under the surface of the liquid in the reaction flask. They also found it was more satisfactory, after the extraction of the sulphur by acetone, to draw off the solvent through a filter stick, rather than pour it through a paper, to retain loose particles of copper sulphide. The modifications suggested by Lancaster and Tarrant form the basis for the revised BSI method [35] which in outline is as follows :

A test portion of the sample is extracted with acetone using a Soxhlet form of extractor which has a spiral of chemically clean copper gauze in the extraction flask. After at least 4 hours a second piece of copper gauze is added to the extract and after 30 minutes heating is examined to see if further deposition of copper sulphide has occurred; if it has and the second piece of gauze is appreciably blackened, it can be taken as an indication that the amount of free sulphur is greater than the method can accurately determine, and the extraction should be repeated with a smaller test portion.

If the second gauze remains clean in the extract the acetone solution is drawn off through the filter stick and the gauze rinsed with several portions of acetone. After the receiving flask and guard tubes have been charged with cadmium acetate the gas evolution apparatus is assembled as shown in the figure and is swept through with nitrogen. Hydrochloric acid is added from the tap funnel, the reaction flask gently heated at the boiling point and the flow of nitrogen maintained for about 30 minutes. Iodine (approximately 0·05N) is added to the receiving flask, and when the cadmium sulphide has dissolved the solution is titrated with sodium thiosulphate.

The same workers have investigated the influence of " rubber resins " and certain accelerators, and conclude that the former are without apparent effect, but some accelerators of the thiuram class cause a slight positive error.

The copper spiral method has been adapted to the micro scale by Lancaster and Tarrant, and by this procedure amounts of sulphur down to about 5 μg, corresponding to a free sulphur level of about 0·05% on a 10-mg. sample, can be determined with an accuracy equal to that of the standard macro process. Brief details of the method are as follows:

A 10-mg. sample of the rubber is extracted with acetone in a micro extractor with a piece of chemically clean copper gauze about 1 cm.² in the extraction flask. 2–4 hours is sufficient to extract normal amounts of sulphur, but to confirm that the extraction is complete a second piece of copper gauze is added to the flask and the heating continued for another 30 minutes. If the gauze remains clean the acetone solution is drawn off by suction through a filter stick, and the flask containing the gauze and the filter stick is attached to the gas-evolution apparatus shown in Fig. 11.11.

The apparatus is flushed with a stream of oxygen-free nitrogen prepared by passing the commercial product through alkaline pyrogallol and then over copper turnings maintained at 500° C. A scrubber containing concentrated sulphuric acid is interposed to dry the nitrogen, but this and the pyrogallol can be dispensed with if a purer grade of nitrogen is available. After metering, the gas stream enters the gas-evolution apparatus through a side arm which also admits acid for the decomposition of the copper sulphide, and the effluent gas stream leaves through a reflux condenser, carrying the hydrogen sulphide into a

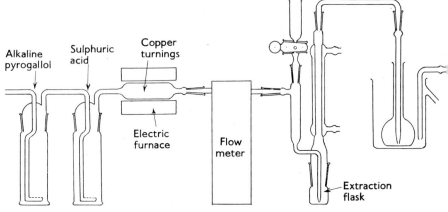

Fig. 11.11. Micro determination of free sulphur.

standard volumetric flask, where it is absorbed by a 2% W/V solution of zinc acetate.

When the apparatus is completely assembled as shown in the figure, air is expelled by passing nitrogen at a fairly rapid rate for 10–15 minutes. Acid is then added through the side arm, the gas flow reduced to about 10 ml./min. and the flask heated with a micro burner until the copper sulphide is completely decomposed. The absorption flask and its delivery tube are then disconnected from the rest of the apparatus, a few millilitres of p-aminodimethylaniline dissolved in sulphuric acid are added, followed by a few drops of ferric chloride solution. The methylene blue colour reaches its maximum intensity in about 15 minutes and remains stable for at least 12 hours. After 15 minutes, therefore, the solution is diluted to standard volume (50 ml.) and the absorbence is measured at about 670 mμ.

Lancaster and Tarrant found that calibration curves prepared directly from sodium sulphide were not reproducible. The method they recommend is to take known volumes of a standard solution of sulphur in iso-propyl alcohol, reflux in the presence of copper gauze and then to follow through the complete procedure of acidification, absorption of the hydrogen sulphide in zinc acetate and formation of methylene blue. The curve obtained is not strictly linear, a feature which supports the contention of other workers [63] that the methylene blue complex does not follow Beer's Law.

The reaction between potassium cyanide and elementary sulphur to give the thiocyanate has also been proposed as the basis of a method for the determination of free sulphur. In a development of this principle by Minatoya, Aoe and Nagai [64] the dried acetone extract is refluxed with alcoholic potassium cyanide, taken to dryness and treated with acetone to dissolve the thiocyanate. The insoluble residue is removed by filtration and the acetone evaporated off. The solids are then taken up in water and the solution titrated with silver nitrate. Both these methods are claimed to be selective towards elementary sulphur in the presence of the common accelerators.

Of the many methods proposed for the determination of free sulphur, probably the most selective are those based on the polarographic reduction of sulphur. Provided an appropriate base solution is available, the polarographic wave for any reducible ion is unique, and other substances in the solution, even if reduced, cannot interfere. The first use of the polarograph in rubber analysis was reported by Proske,[65] and in a method for the determination of free sulphur he recommended an extraction of the rubber with pyridine to remove the sulphur, followed by reduction in an acetic acid–sodium acetate base solution with methyl cellulose as a maximum suppressor. Poulton and Tarrant, however, found difficulty in making Proske's method fully quantitative, and noted some interference from accelerators. In an improved method, suggested by Poulton and Tarrant,[66] a return is made to acetone for the initial extraction, and reduction takes place in a four-component electrolyte of pyridine, methanol, sodium acetate and acetic acid using an external calomel electrode. These workers also investigated the polarographic response of many accelerators and anti-oxidants and were able to show that sulphur could be well separated from most of these materials and accurately determined (see Table 11.4).

The polarographic method recommended by Poulton and Tarrant is briefly as follows:

About 0·2–0·4 g. of the sample is extracted on the semi-micro scale with acetone and the dried extract warmed with 5 ml. pyridine. 10 ml. methanol are then added, followed by 5 ml. of a sodium acetate–acetic acid buffer (0·35M), and after removal of oxygen the solution is polarographed over the range $-0·3$ to $-1·0$ V at 25° C. The half-wave potential of sulphur in this electrolyte is $-0·63$ V against the saturated calomel electrode.

The method is calibrated by measuring wave-heights for known concentrations of sulphur dissolved in pyridine.

Non-extractive methods for free-sulphur determination have an advantage in that the preliminary separation with acetone is replaced

TABLE 11.4

POLAROGRAPHIC BEHAVIOUR OF SOME COMMON ACCELERATORS AND ANTI-OXIDANTS

Accelerator or anti-oxidant	Half-wave potential v. S.C.E.	Remarks on polarographic behaviour
Diphenylguanidine (DPG)		No wave in pyridine electrolyte
Di-o-tolylguanidine (DOTG)		,,
Triphenylguanidine (TPG)		,,
Hexamethylenetetramine (HMT)		,,
Mercaptobenzthiazole (MBT)	Uncertain	Wave from zero volts and is completed before sulphur wave. Suitable for estimating accelerator
Benzthiazyl disulphide (MBTS)	,,	,,
Thiocarbanilide (TCA)	,,	,,
Zinc isopropylxanthate (ZIX)	,,	Wave from zero volts and extending beyond sulphur wave. Irregular shape in this electrolyte, unsuitable for measurement
Zinc diethyldithiocarbamate (ZDC)	−0·4	Sharp wave formed which does not interfere with sulphur determination. Suitable for estimating accelerator
Tetramethylthiuram disulphide (TMT)	−0·5	Behaves similarly to ZDC
Tetraethylthiuram disulphide (TET)	−0·55	Behaves similarly to ZDC
Diphenylguanidine with derivative of mercaptobenzthiazole (Ureka)	−0·32, −0·5	Double wave suitable for estimating accelerator. No interference with sulphur
Diphenylguanidine phthalate with derivative of mercaptobenzthiazole (Ureka DD)	−0·33, −0·53	Similar to Ureka
Phenol–aldehyde–amine type (Nonox NSN)	−0·3, −0·97	Double wave of regular shape suitable for estimating anti-oxidant. No interference with sulphur wave.
Nonox HF	−0·3, −0·9	Similar to Nonox NSN, but second wave poorly formed
Phenyl-2-naphthylamine (Nonox D)	0·3	No interference with sulphur wave. Suitable for estimating anti-oxidant
Phenyl-1-naphthylamine (Nonox A)	Uncertain	Wave from zero volts, completed before sulphur wave
Condensation product of aldol, and aldol-2-naphthylamine (Nonox S)	,,	Poor wave form, which does not interfere with sulphur determination
s-Di-2-naphthyl-p-phenylene-diamine (Agerite White)	,,	Poor wave which masks the sulphur wave
Piperidinium pentamethylene-dithiocarbamate (PPD)	,,	No interference with sulphur wave
Diphenylcarbamyldimethyldithio-carbamate (ONV)	,,	,,
Aldehyde derivative of a Schiff's base (A11)	,,	,,
Reaction product of aniline with two different aliphatic aldehydes (A16)	,,	,,
Reaction product of butyraldehyde and butylidene (A32)	,,	,,
Triethyltrimethylaminetriamine (Trimene base)	,,	,,
Benzthiazyl-2-monocyclohexyl sulphenamide (Santocure)	−0·52	Wave suitable for measurement

by direct treatment of the rubber with a reagent capable of bringing the elementary sulphur into a form suitable for assay, thus gaining considerably in time over extractive methods. Again the aim is to distinguish between the elementary sulphur and other sulphur compounds in the rubber, but it may be said at once that in this respect the non-extractive methods are less successful than the copper spiral or polarographic methods, although considerably more reliable than the bromine, zinc–nitric acid or nitric acid–potassium chlorate methods.

An early paper of Bolotnikov and Gurova [67] described the use of sodium sulphite for the determination of free sulphur in rubber, depending on the reaction between the sulphite and sulphur to give thiosulphate. A number of accelerators interfered. Mackay and Avons [68] modified the method so that it remains valid in the presence of many common accelerators, but it is still subject to interference from some accelerators of the thiuram class. The method now forms the basis of a recommendation by ASTM, and is briefly as follows:

A 2-g. prepared sample is boiled gently with aqueous sodium sulphite for 4 hours in the presence of a small quantity of sodium stearate to assist wetting. Strontium chloride is added to precipitate fatty acids and cadmium acetate to precipitate mercaptobenzthiazole, and the solids are removed by filtration. Excess sulphite in the solution is removed with formaldehyde, and the thiosulphate is titrated with iodine.

A non-extractive method following different lines has been advocated by Brock and Osborn.[69] The finely divided rubber is boiled gently in an acetone solution of triphenylphosphine and excess of the reagent is titrated with iodine using the " dead-stop " end point. The method is claimed to be suitable for the examination of natural rubber, butadiene–styrene and butadiene–acrylonitrile types and Butyl, and to be substantially unaffected by other compounding ingredients. Interference from accelerators is said to be no greater than in the sulphite method.

A somewhat similar procedure is followed by Taranenko and Zakharova [70] using diethylamine as the reagent. The finely divided rubber is heated under reflux with aqueous diethylamine, acidified iodate–iodide solution added, and the liberated iodine titrated with thiosulphate. No mention is made of possible interference by sulphur-bearing accelerators.

MINERAL SULPHUR

A survey of all possible sulphur-containing inorganic compounding ingredients would include a number of very slight importance in present-day rubber technology, and attention is confined therefore to those in common use, viz. the sulphates of barium and calcium and the sulphides of zinc, antimony and cadmium. Interpretation of the analytical data, which in the earlier part of this chapter warranted considerable discussion, is not so difficult when dealing with the mineral sulphur, because the chemical compounds in which this sulphur occurs are unaltered under vulcanising conditions. Furthermore, as metallic sulphides are generally added as pigments, and the sulphates often as pigment extenders, their identity is usually obvious from the colour of the rubber compound.

The usual course in reconstructing the filler system is to determine the total amount of sulphur combined in the fillers and to relate this to the metals revealed by analysis of the ash. Generally a stoichiometric ratio is found which suffices to identify the original filler, but in some rubber compounds, particularly where a mixture of sulphide and sulphate is suspected, it is advisable to determine also the sulphur present as sulphide. The inorganic sulphate can then be found by difference, and since this is present as the barium or calcium salt, the reconstruction can be completed.

For the determination of total sulphur in the fillers, these are first separated from the rubber with a high-boiling rubber solvent, and the sulphur is determined on a weighed portion by one of the methods already described for total sulphur in rubber. It is particularly important to select a method which will include sulphur in barium sulphate if this is present, and the choice is thus limited to the fusion method and Bauminger's combustion method. In the fusion method about 0·5 g. of the separated and dried fillers are weighed into a porcelain dish and treated with brominated nitric acid and potassium nitrate. After the addition of sodium carbonate and taking to dryness, the mixture is fused and then leached out with water. Sulphate is determined gravimetrically in the solution. In Bauminger's combustion method also, no modification to the procedure already recommended is necessary. About 10–15 mg. of the fillers are heated in oxygen in a silica boat under a layer of vanadium pentoxide–zinc oxide mixture, and the oxides of sulphur absorbed in hydrogen peroxide. Sulphate is determined by titration with ethylene-diaminetetra-acetic acid after the precipitation of barium sulphate.

Sulphur present as sulphide is best determined by a gas-evolution process, and the apparatus and procedure described for the determination of free sulphur in rubber are suitable. Again, an upper limit of about 10 mg. of sulphur should be observed by adjusting the weight of the test portion. The determination may be made on the original rubber (after milling or other means of sample preparation) or on the fillers separated by hot solvent, as in the case of the total sulphur in fillers. An appropriate quantity is weighed into the reaction vessel and heated with about 20 ml. dilute hydrochloric acid while a slow stream of nitrogen is passed through the apparatus. The hydrogen sulphide is absorbed in buffered cadmium acetate and titrated iodometrically.

INORGANIC CONSTITUENTS

Memmler [71] lists some twenty-eight inorganic compounds which may be incorporated into rubber as inorganic fillers, and while some of these, such as powdered glass and tin oxide, could be excluded from a list of modern compounding ingredients, additions in recent years bring the number up to well over thirty. For the purpose of analysis most of these may be regarded as based on the following elements: aluminium, antimony, barium, cadmium, calcium, iron, lead, magnesium, silicon, titanium and zinc. The reduction of about thirty substances to the determination of a dozen elements raises the problem of the interpretation of the analytical results, since the analyst is required to provide not a list of chemical elements, but a working formula for the original mixing. In this he is helped by a knowledge of compounding practice, and consoled by the reflection that the number of principal mineral ingredients in any composition is rarely more than four or five, and is frequently restricted to one or two.

An essential preliminary to any scheme of analysis of the mineral matter, qualitative or quantitative, is to separate it from the organic components of the mixing. Although not necessary in all cases, it is a wise precaution first to extract the sample with an organic solvent, since phosphate- and chlorine-containing plasticisers, if not removed, can cause difficulties in the subsequent analysis. After extraction, three techniques are in common use for removal of the insoluble organic components: direct or dry ashing, wet oxidation and rubber solvent methods.

Direct ashing

Direct or dry ashing is the term used to denote the procedure by which the organic material is expelled by destructive distillation or pyrolysis, usually from an open silica or porcelain crucible. It is generally accepted that inflaming of the crucible contents is undesirable, and so heating in the early stages is usually by the application of a small bunsen flame, transferring then to a furnace for completing the ignition at a temperature not exceeding 550° C.

Linnig, Milliken and Cohen [72] have proposed a rapid ashing method in which the sample is wrapped in filter-paper, placed in the crucible and then heated directly in a closed muffle furnace maintained at 550° C. Although primarily intended for ash determination in raw styrene–butadiene polymer, it would seem to be applicable to a number of other polymers, although no work appears to have been carried out on vulcanisates generally.

Since heating is carried out under strongly oxidising conditions, the inorganic compounds in most cases revert to the more thermo-stable forms, with the tendency generally towards oxide formation. Compounding ingredients added as oxides will remain as such, and thus in rubber compounds containing only silica, zinc oxide, titanium oxide, magnesium oxide and iron oxide, dry ashing can be used as a rough quantitative check on these substances unless other features of the mixing cause interference. Litharge is readily reduced to the metal under normal ashing conditions, but the other oxides, including zinc, are not reduced by carbon, whether this originates as carbon black or as residual carbon from decomposition of the polymer. The sulphides of zinc, antimony and cadmium tend to form the corresponding oxides even at 550° C, but the decomposition of carbonates is less definite; magnesium carbonate forms the oxide reasonably quickly at 450° C, but at temperatures below 800° C calcium carbonate loses its carbon dioxide extremely slowly.[73] This partial conversion at lower temperatures is primarily responsible for the poor reproducibility of the ash figure usually encountered when whiting is present. The combined water of clay, asbestos and talc is released quickly at temperatures over 400° C to give the anhydrous silicates. Calcium and barium sulphates are not affected by ashing temperatures up to 550° C.

The direct ashing method is suitable for rubbers based on the hydrocarbon polymers and on the acrylonitrile polymers, but in chlorine-containing polymers the volatility of zinc and possibly other metal chlorides invalidates the direct method; in neoprene compounds, for instance, it is necessary to turn to wet oxidation or even to a dissolution method if recovery of the fillers as such is required. Even in the case of mixings based on the hydrocarbon polymers, however, it would be wrong to claim that dry ashing is a precise operation, as the foregoing discussion will show, and although both the BSI and ASTM include recommended methods for dry ashing in their publications, great stress is laid on the control of experimental conditions. In the ASTM referee method, in particular, elaborate precautions are taken to ensure close reproducibility with regard to time of heating, rate of temperature rise and positioning of thermocouples in the furnace.

Wet oxidation

Some limitations of the dry ashing procedure are overcome by the wet oxidation process in which the organic material is destroyed by heating with strongly oxidising acids. The possibility of losing volatile metals is very much reduced, and there is no risk of small losses arising from the ash constituents reacting with the material of the crucible. The acids generally employed for wet oxidation are sulphuric and nitric, but as these do not usually produce a perfectly clear solution, it is common practice to heat with a few drops of hydrogen peroxide or perchloric acid in the final stages of the digestion. Needless to say, the wet oxidation process introduces a few disadvantages of its own, chief among which are the rather longer time factor and the high concentration of sulphuric acid in the final solution. There is the further objection that as considerable volumes of acids are used in the course of the oxidation, unless these are of the highest standards of purity, undesirably high concentrations of trace metals may be introduced.

Apart from the siliceous components of the rubber which are not completely broken down by acids, metals are taken into solution as their sulphates, and hence wet oxidation is a suitable technique when the examination of cations is the primary consideration, as for example, in the determination of trace metals. It is of less value in the study of major mineral constituents generally, but may be required when conditions are abnormal, as in the examination of compounded polychloroprene.

The weight taken for wet combustion should not exceed 1 g. for major constituents, and the test portion is cut into pieces about 1 cm.^{2} and placed in a Kjeldahl flask with a mixture of 4 ml. concentrated sulphuric acid and 5 ml. concentrated nitric acid. A vigorous reaction usually starts or is promoted by gentle warming, and when this has gone to completion further heating is given until the liquid darkens. After cooling, 1 ml. concentrated nitric acid is added and heating recommenced. The liquid will lighten somewhat and then darken again as the nitric acid is boiled off. The cycle of cooling and addition of nitric acid is repeated until the solution no longer chars with continued boiling. At this stage the solution is usually pale yellow, but before the final treatment with hydrogen peroxide or perchloric acid is given the neck of the Kjeldahl is washed down with distilled water to return any volatile but undecomposed organic material to the bulk of the solution. Failure to rinse at this stage may have the following effects:

(a) The remaining oxidation stages are unduly prolonged by traces of organic matter running from the neck into the flask.

(b) An explosion may result from the premature use of perchloric acid.

(c) The subsequent analysis in respect of some cations may be upset by traces of organic matter.

After rinsing, the solution is boiled to fuming, 1 ml. nitric acid added and the solution again heated until it remains a pale yellow colour. Then, after cooling, 1 ml. 100 volume hydrogen peroxide or 1 ml. concentrated perchloric acid is added, and heating recommenced. The final solution should be colourless, but a second treatment with hydrogen peroxide is occasionally required. Traces of nitric acid are then removed by one or two successive additions of 5-ml. portions of water, alternating with boiling the solution down to fuming. The solution is then ready for analysis.

Rubber solvent methods

The advantages of separating the mineral ingredients in substantially their original form have led to many suggestions for dissolving the rubber in a suitable agent and collecting the insoluble residue by centrifuging or filtration. Details of various experimental procedures are given elsewhere, and it only remains here to point out the features of this technique in so far as it is applied to the inorganic fraction.

There is the overriding consideration that many of the newer rubbers show a pronounced resistance to solvent attack, and prolonged treatment with a strongly degradative solvent is sometimes necessary. Further, as this technique separates the total fillers from the rubber, a second separation is often necessary to isolate the mineral matter from insoluble organic material and carbon black. Sometimes, as when the insoluble organic fillers consist of cork or leather dust, advantage may be taken of the difference in density between the organic and inorganic fractions to separate the two by a flotation method. A portion of the insoluble material is moistened with alcohol, water is added with stirring, and after settling, the lighter organic fraction is skimmed from the top of the liquid. If a second treatment is given to the separated material any trapped inorganic material is released and the organic filler again collects at the surface of the liquid. The inorganic portion is collected by filtration and dried at low heat.

Since the hot-solvent method separates the fillers in their original form, a microscopic examination can with advantage precede the normal chemical analysis. This is an essential step when silicate materials such as clay, asbestos or slate powder are present, as dry ashing destroys the characteristic structure of these substances on which their identification mainly depends. It is also possible to make direct determinations of carbon dioxide and sulphur on the separated mineral matter to provide data on which a reconstruction of the filler system can be based.

QUALITATIVE EXAMINATION

In unknown compositions the time taken in the analysis of the mineral matter can be substantially reduced if the quantitative procedures are preceded by a short qualitative examination. It is obviously unnecessary to apply a full quantitative scheme to the determination of only one or two components, while an even greater time saving will be shown and a higher degree of accuracy achieved if specific methods for these components can be applied. In the brief outline of methods given below qualitative tests of high sensitivity have been avoided, since it is assumed that interest lies chiefly in the inorganic compounding ingredients added as such to the original rubber compound. Adventitious traces, apart from copper and manganese, are generally of no importance, but when they are, standard works [74] applicable to this specialised field should be consulted.

The colour of a rubber product often gives a guide to the nature of the pigment. Many of the brighter colours are today produced by the use of organic pigments, but the traditional inorganic pigments, usually oxides or sulphides, are still in widespread use for the more subdued tones, and may be recognised by their greater stability towards heat and high-boiling organic solvents.

Some mineral fillers of natural origin lose their characteristic crystalline form on heating, and to assist the identification of these substances it is necessary to carry out a microscopic examination on a specimen of the mineral matter isolated by the hot solvent process. Talc, clay, asbestos and some forms of silica are usually recognisable under the microscope, whereas their chemical composition is not sufficiently distinctive for positive identification by analysis. A rapid check with dilute hydro-chloric acid should also be carried out on the mineral matter to detect the presence of sulphide or carbonate. The presence of a sulphide can be taken as confirmation of an inorganic pigment, while carbonate generally originates from the calcium or magnesium compound.

If the qualitative examination is to be taken further, a convenient division into two fractions can be made with dilute hydrochloric acid. Insoluble material will include silica, substantially all the clay if the acid treatment is not prolonged, barium sulphate, titanium dioxide and possibly some iron oxide, while the soluble portion will contain antimony, aluminium, calcium, cadmium, iron, lead, magnesium and zinc. After this initial separation the soluble and insoluble fractions are tested to reveal the main constituents. By the use of semi-micro techniques the whole qualitative procedure can be carried out on a few milligrams of material in about 30 minutes.

Acid-insoluble portion

About 2–3 mg. of the material insoluble in hydrochloric acid are heated with 0·5 ml. concentrated sulphuric acid in a micro-centrifuge tube, cooled and centrifuged to clarify the supernatant liquid. One drop of the clear solution is withdrawn by capillary pipette and added to 1 ml. water on a black tile. A white turbidity indicates barium, present as sulphate in the original mineral matter. To the remainder of the sulphuric acid digest is added a little ammonium sulphate, and the mixture is reheated to dis-solve any titanium dioxide. After centrifuging again another drop of the clear liquid is withdrawn and added to dilute hydrogen peroxide on a white glazed tile. If titanium is present the yellow colour of pertitanic acid is produced. An insoluble residue after this treatment indicates silica or silicates.

Acid-soluble portion

About 0·5 ml. of the hydrochloric acid solution of the mineral matter is diluted five-fold with water, and hydrogen sulphide is passed in from a micro-generator. Antimony gives an orange-red precipitate under these conditions, and cadmium in sufficient concentration gives a yellow precipitate. Lead sulphide is not precipitated, but its occurrence with either antimony or cadmium is most unlikely. The precipitation of antimony as sulphide is a sufficiently sensitive test to establish its presence in the original rubber, but a confirmatory test for cadmium is sometimes desirable, since often a small proportion of cadmium sulphide used as a tinting agent leads to extreme dilution in the test solution, from which the sulphide fails to precipitate. In these circumstances a more sensitive spot test, such as that with di-*p*-nitrophenylcarbazide, is required. A drop of the diluted acid solution is mixed on a white glazed tile with one drop of 10% sodium hydroxide solution and one drop of 10% potassium cyanide solution. One drop of the reagent (0·1% alcoholic solution of d-*p*-nitrophenylcarbazide) is added, followed by two drops of formalin, and a bluish-green precipitate forms in the presence of cadmium.

Iron and aluminium are found in the filtrate from the antimony and cadmium precipitation. Iron, when present in more than a trace, is revealed by the intense colour of the ash, and further qualitative evidence is usually unnecessary. Aluminium in quantity is revealed by its insoluble hydroxide precipitated by ammonia, but a more sensitive test on the semi-micro scale is based on its reaction with morin. The slightly acid solution is spotted on to a filter-paper, and one drop of a saturated solution of morin in methyl alcohol is added to it. A brilliant green fluorescence readily visible under an ultra-violet lamp is obtained when aluminium is present.[75] The iron-free solution may now be tested for lead with hydrogen sulphide and for zinc by means of the spot reagent "zincon", 2-carboxy-2'-hydroxy-5'-sulphoformazyl benzene. This reacts specifically with zinc to form a blue complex over the pH range 8·5–9·5. To one drop of the dilute acid solution sodium carbonate is added until it is alkaline to phenolphthalein. 2% boric acid is added very slowly until the pink colour is almost discharged, and then one drop of the freshly prepared reagent is added. A clear blue colour is obtained in the presence of zinc, which contrasts strongly with the orange-coloured reagent. The zincon reagent is prepared by dissolving 0·15 g. of the solid in 2 ml. N NaOH and diluting with water to 100 ml.

Calcium is introduced into rubber mixings as its sulphate, carbonate or, more rarely, hydrated oxide. As sulphate it is associated with antimony sulphide and is unlikely to occur otherwise, while the carbonate will be revealed in the preliminary test with dilute acid. Generally, the oxalate precipitation is adequate to detect calcium in the test solution, but if the concentration is extremely low it is advisable to apply a more sensitive reaction, such as that with dihydroxytartaric acid ozazone.[76] Finally, magnesium is detected by its ability to form characteristically coloured lakes with a number of organic dyestuffs, that produced by thiazole yellow being probably the most widely known.[77]

QUANTITATIVE ANALYSIS OF INORGANIC CONSTITUENTS

Quantitative determination of the inorganic constituents should be undertaken in the light of the results of the qualitative examination. It is rarely necessary to follow a comprehensive analytical scheme, and recent work has tended to concentrate on specific and accurate methods for single constituents or groups of associated constituents. Foremost in this connection are the wide application of titrimetric methods based on the strongly complexing reagent ethylenediaminetetra-acetic acid, and the advances in physico-chemical methods. Although, therefore, complete schemes of analysis are given in outline at the end of this section, the main purpose in the following survey is to indicate quantitative methods which are most suited to the determination of single elementary species.

Aluminium. Prepared hydrated alumina may be used as such in compounding, but alumina can also arise from clay, by treatment of the ash or mineral matter with hydrochloric acid. Aluminium may also be obtained from other complex silicates and from alumina-based pigments. Clays and other silicates do not decompose in a uniform manner on acid treatment, and this leads to an indeterminate division of the aluminium between acid-insoluble and acid-soluble portions of the ash. The temperature of ashing also seems to have a bearing on the degree of subsequent acid attack on clays, and it is generally known that strong heating decreases the solubility of alumina. If the figure for total alumina is required, therefore, it is necessary to take into account both the acid-soluble and acid-insoluble material. For the determination of aluminium in the acid-insoluble material, the silicate is first decomposed by alkali fusion. Experimental details of this procedure are dealt with under silica (p. 950).

Soluble aluminium is still generally determined by the classical gravimetric procedure as recommended by ASTM, in which the hydroxide is precipitated, filtered, ignited and weighed as aluminium oxide. Owing to the highly adsorptive nature of the aluminium hydroxide precipitate, it is usually advisable to make a double precipitation, particularly if traces of other metals are to be determined subsequently. A method which avoids the difficulties of the hydroxide precipitation has been proposed by Smales,[78] who has established the optimum conditions for the quantitative precipitation of aluminium as the benzoate. Smales recommends precipitation from a solution buffered at pH 3·5–4 to eliminate interference from zinc.

A direct titrimetric method has been developed by Theis,[79] who employs Chromazurol S as an internal indicator with ethylenediaminetetra-acetic acid. This indicator gives its sharpest colour change at pH levels above 4 but in these circumstances the precipitation of aluminium hydroxide can sometimes be troublesome. Theis overcomes the difficulty by the continual addition of sodium acetate to raise the pH as the concentration of ionic aluminium is progressively lowered, thus sharpening the end point. Blenkin has modified the procedure suggested by Theis and has developed a method by which iron and aluminium can be determined together in one solution.[80]

Antimony. The trisulphide and pentasulphide are incorporated into rubber compounds as pigments and are then frequently associated with calcium sulphate. Their use is declining in favour of organic dyestuffs, but antimony oxide is occasionally used as a fireproofing agent. It is essential to determine antimony on the mineral matter separated by high-boiling rubber solvent or on the solution obtained by wet oxidation of the original rubber; dry ashing must be avoided because of the volatility of antimony compounds.

For frequent or series determinations the electrolytic methods are rapid and accurate, and probably the most suitable is that of Lindsey and Tucker using the principle of controlled potential.[81] By a slight modification of this method lead may also be determined. Most laboratories, however, require to make only occasional determinations of antimony, and the methods recommended by BSI and ASTM are then preferable. The rubber is first decomposed by treatment with an oxidising acid mixture, and the resulting digest is diluted and adjusted to about 2N with respect to hydrochloric acid. Antimony is precipitated as sulphide from this solution by vigorously passing hydrogen sulphide, and the sulphide removed by filtration. The sulphide is then taken up in hydrochloric acid, the antimony reduced to the trivalent form with sodium sulphite and then titrated with potassium bromate.

Barium. Many pigments are produced in an extended form with barium sulphate as a diluent. It is also used as a pigment in its own right, or simply as a high specific gravity filler.

In the analysis of the mineral matter, barium sulphate is generally encountered in the acid-insoluble portion, often in the presence of clay, and sometimes also as a mixture with titanium dioxide. The problem therefore is usually one of separation rather than determination, since for the latter purpose the classical method of reconversion to barium sulphate has not been improved upon.

The ASTM procedure for the determination of barium in the presence of other insoluble substances is to fuse a portion of the rubber ash with a mixture of sodium carbonate and sodium nitrate, thus converting the barium to carbonate. On leaching out with water the insoluble material is collected on filter-paper, dissolved in hydrochloric acid and the barium precipitated by the addition of slight excess of sulphuric acid. The barium sulphate is determined gravimetrically.

A minor modification of the above procedure designed to eliminate the final lengthy gravimetric stage has been suggested by Frey,[82] who titrates the solution of barium with a standard solution of sodium sulphate to the point of maximum turbidity as measured on a suitable photo-electric instrument.

An entirely different approach is adopted by Blenkin,[80] in which the insoluble constituents are heated with concentrated sulphuric acid to dissolve the barium sulphate. On pouring into water the barium sulphate reprecipitates and is removed by filtration. In the freshly precipitated condition barium sulphate readily dissolves in the ammonium salt of ethylenediaminetetra-acetic acid and the determination is then completed by titrating the excess complexone with magnesium chloride.

Cadmium. From the analytical standpoint many of the reactions of cadmium are closely similar to those of antimony and lead, and considerable difficulties might arise in their separation, were it not for the fact that, as pigments, they are rarely found together in a rubber compound.

Since any cadmium present forms a constituent of the soluble portion of the ash, the most satisfactory method for its determination is to precipitate it as the sulphide from very dilute acid solution, and apply the complexometric method of Kinnunen and Wennerstrand,[83] in which the cadmium is titrated with 0·01M ethylenediaminetetra-acetic acid using Eriochrome Black as indicator.

Calcium. Calcium may be incorporated into rubber as the carbonate, silicate or, more rarely, as the hydrated oxide. It may be found as sulphate in association with antimony sulphide, and may also appear in traces in clays and other naturally occurring silicates.

In classical analysis calcium is precipitated from ammoniacal solutions as the oxalate, but as the reaction is not at all specific, it is necessary first to remove heavy metals, aluminium and zinc from the solution. The calcium oxalate is then removed by filtration, preferably on a sintered-silica crucible and may be weighed as the oxalate, carbonate or oxide, depending on the subsequent conditions of heating. Peltier and Duval give the following data on the progressive decomposition of calcium oxalate: [73]

Below 100° C	Monohydrate is stable
100°–226° C	Loses water of crystallisation
226°–346° C	Anhydrous salt is stable
346°–420°	Transition $Ca(CO_2)_2 \rightarrow CaCO_3$ with loss of carbon monoxide
420°–660° C	Calcium carbonate is stable
660°–840° C	Transition $CaCO_3 \rightarrow CaO$ with loss of carbon dioxide
Above 840° C	Calcium oxide is stable

It should be borne in mind that the evolution of carbon dioxide is dependent on the vapour pressure exerted above the carbonate; the data given above relate to heating in an open crucible, i.e. with immediate removal of the liberated carbon dioxide.

As an alternative to the gravimetric determination, the oxalate may be dissolved in warm dilute sulphuric acid and titrated with standard potassium permanganate.

Among recently developed physical methods, that developed by Frey [84] is directly applicable to rubber analysis and is extremely rapid. Essentially, the method consists in precipitating the calcium as oleate, stabilising the dispersion and measuring the calcium oleate nephelometrically. A turbidimetric method using the oxalate, but otherwise on similar lines, has been put forward by Hunter and Hall,[85] and enables operations to be reduced to the semi-micro scale. A great deal of work has been carried out recently on the complexometric determination of calcium, and it would be both superfluous and invidious to refer to particular contributions to the very extensive literature on the subject. Robertson,[86] however, has made a direct adaptation of the principle to rubber analysis, in which calcium, magnesium and zinc may be determined in a single solution. In the determination of calcium the ash solution, free from heavy metals, iron and alumina, is rendered alkaline with caustic soda, potassium cyanide is added to suppress interference by zinc and the solution is titrated with ethylenediaminetetra-acetic acid using Murexide as indicator. Since magnesium is not complexed at the pH of this titration, calcium can be determined in the presence of both zinc and magnesium.

Iron. Apart from being widespread as an impurity in many naturally occurring mineral fillers, iron in quantity generally points to the addition of an iron oxide pigment.

In the commonly used analytical procedure iron and aluminium are precipitated as the mixed hydroxides, which are ignited to the oxides and then weighed. As it is usually evident from visual inspection which metal predominates, the approximate figure thus obtained for either component generally suffices, but if individual determinations of iron and alumina are required, further analysis can be carried out after a fusion of the mixed oxides with potassium hydrogen sulphate or, more directly, on a solution of the freshly precipitated hydroxides in hydrochloric acid. By either method the iron may be determined by potassium dichromate titration and the aluminium by precipitating and weighing the oxinate complex formed with 8-hydroxyquinoline. Recently, however, more rapid methods for separate iron and alumina determinations, based on compleximetry and ion-exchange, have become available.

Blenkin has developed a particularly rapid method in which the iron and aluminium are successively titrated with ethylenediaminetetra-acetic acid. The mixed hydroxides are first dissolved in dilute hydrochloric acid and the solution heated just to boiling. Three or four drops of 2% salicylic acid in ethanol are added as indicator and then sufficient 2M sodium acetate solution to give a purple colour to the solution. The solution is then titrated with ethylenediaminetetra-acetic acid until the solution is colourless, when a further 2 ml. sodium acetate solution is added. If the purple colour returns the titration is continued until further portions of sodium acetate produce no redevelopment of the colour. The iron content is calculated from the total titration. Aluminium is determined by continuing the titration with Chromazurol S as indicator in the manner already described (p. 946).

The separation of iron and aluminium lends itself particularly well to selective adsorption methods. Kakihama and Kojima [87] describe the successive elution of iron and aluminium from a column of Amberlite IR120 ion-exchange resin, and the determination of iron and aluminium in the separate eluates. A semi-micro-scale separation on acidified Amberlite IRA140 resin is proposed by Teicher and Gordon.[88] The method is particularly useful where aluminium heavily preponderates, and consists basically in complexing the iron as thiocyanate, which is held on the resin, while the aluminium is readily eluted and can be determined by any standard procedure.

Lead. The main use of lead compounds in rubber technology is as a pigment, when it is frequently used as the chromate, but litharge still finds some application in high density compounds. In dry ashing procedures lead compounds tend to be readily reduced to the metal and also to fuse into the glaze of the crucible. When lead is present therefore it is advisable to carry out the analysis on the mineral matter separated by the hot solvent method or on the solution obtained by wet oxidation. After separation of the mineral-matter constituents insoluble in hydrochloric acid the soluble portion is taken to fuming with sulphuric acid, and to the well-cooled solution is added a mixture of equal volumes of ethanol and water. The precipitated lead sulphate is then collected on a sintered filter and weighed.

Magnesium. Apart from the use of the oxide and carbonate as compounding ingredients, magnesium appears in the acid-soluble portion of the ash as a decomposition product of the magnesium silicates (talc, asbestos, etc.). In this connection it is worth noting that the magnesium compounds decompose much more rapidly than the aluminium silicates under acid attack, to give a correspondingly higher figure for soluble magnesium.

The ASTM recommend that magnesium be determined by precipitation as magnesium ammonium phosphate, which, after filtration, is ignited to the pyrophosphate and weighed. This still remains one of the most accurate procedures for the determination of magnesium, but since many other metals interfere, and must therefore be removed before the magnesium is precipitated, more direct methods are coming into favour. In a recent paper by Kobrova, for instance, magnesium is estimated in the presence of much larger quantities of calcium by titrating with a standard solution of 8-hydroxyquinoline with Eriochrome Black as indicator.[89] Magnesium is also readily complexed with ethylenediaminetetra-acetic acid, and a considerable literature deals with its determination by this means. The application of these methods to rubber analysis has been the subject of recent work by Robertson [86] and Blenkin; [80] the essentials of these procedures have been given under calcium (p. 948).

Silica. Silica in the free state is finding increasing use as a reinforcing filter in rubber, but it is more often encountered by the analyst in the form of naturally occurring complex silicates, such as clay, talc and asbestos, or in the manufactured silicates of aluminium and calcium. Small amounts of silica in the ash will arise from the rubber itself or as impurities in some compounding ingredients, while appreciable quantities of silicate can be introduced by the free use of dusting powders during rubber-processing operations.

Hydrochloric acid attacks silicates to a degree which varies widely with such factors as acid concentration, time and temperature of acid treatment, and even with the time and temperature of heating in the actual ashing operation. The data in Table 11.5 shows the losses sustained by various silicates after heating at different temperatures and digesting with acid, and demonstrate the importance of standardising the experimental conditions if consistency in the analytical results is to be achieved.

The classical procedure for the determination of silica is to fuse the portion of the ash or mineral matter which is insoluble in hydrochloric acid with a mixture of sodium and potassium carbonates, dissolve in water and then filter off the insoluble carbonates. The filtrate is taken to dryness, baked repeatedly with hydrochloric acid and finally taken up in slightly acid solution. The silica is filtered and weighed after ignition. In the ASTM modification of the above method the fusion stage is omitted and the original ash treated directly with hydrochloric acid and baked. The insolubles by this procedure may contain, therefore, not only silicates but also barium, lead and titanium compounds. Silica is estimated by difference after treating the insolubles with a mixture of hydrofluoric and sulphuric acids, it being assumed that silica is completely volatilised, while barium and lead salts revert to the sulphate. The method also assumes that the final form of the residual compounds is gravimetrically identical with that before hydrofluoric acid treatment.

TABLE 11.5

EFFECT OF ACIDS ON SILICATES

	% loss with 0·1N hydro-chloric acid	% loss with 1·0N acetic acid		% loss with 1·0N hydrochloric acid			% loss with conc. sulphuric acid
	After heating to 600° C	Before heating	After heating to 600° C	Before heating	After heating to 600° C	After heating to 900° C	Before heating
China clay (i)	4·8	0·8	2·2	0·4	12·3	1·0	3·5
China clay (ii)	11·6	0·6	4·2	1·6	23·9	2·5	14·4
Bentonite clay	7·2	3·4	10·0	5·5	10·3	2·5	7·5
French chalk	15·0	1·8	3·4	1·1	46·1	23·8	26·8
Asbestos	29·7	7·8	48·3	24·7	64·6	70·9	46·1
Calcium silicate	8·9	21·9	8·5	22·9	14·4	24·3	29·8

Blenkin avoids the uncertain response of silicates towards hydrochloric acid by a direct application of Wilson's method [90] to the ash. The procedure is fully volumetric and extremely rapid, but demands careful adherence to the optimum experimental conditions. In outline the method is to fuse the ash with caustic soda in a nickel crucible, cool and dissolve out the contents with hot water. (Care is necessary at the fusion stage, as the reaction between caustic alkali and silica-rich materials can be violent; the use of a safety screen is recommended.) After adjusting the pH to about 2 with hydrochloric acid, ammonium molybdate is added, followed by more hydrochloric acid to reduce the pH to 1·5, at which level silicomolybdic acid forms quantitatively. The addition then of quinoline hydrochloride precipitates the silica as the quinoline silicomolybdate, and this product is filtered, dissolved in caustic soda and the excess alkali is titrated with hydrochloric acid.

Titanium. In rubber compounds titanium invariably appears as the oxide, and the stability is such that it retains this form throughout the ashing operation. Titanium dioxide is not readily attacked by hydrochloric acid, and in the conventional scheme of separation it will be found in the acid-insoluble portion together with barium sulphate and the silicates. Titanium dioxide will, however, dissolve on prolonged heating with concentrated sulphuric acid, and its dissolution can be hastened by raising the temperature of digestion by the addition of potassium or ammonium sulphate; the determination may then be concluded by gravimetric, redox or colorimetric methods.

In the gravimetric procedure titanium is precipitated as the hydroxide, filtered and subsequently ignited to the oxide, in which form it is weighed. Since the hydroxide begins to precipitate at about pH 4, careful control of the pH at the point of precipitation enables a separation to be made between titanium and aluminium. In practice, however, unless the aluminium is present in only a small proportion relative to the titanium co-precipitation readily occurs, necessitating a double or even treble precipitation of the mixed hydroxides. Redox volumetric methods avoid this difficulty, and a typical procedure is given by Vogel.[91] The diluted solution of titanium sulphate is passed through a Jones reductor and the resulting titanous salt collected in an excess of ferric alum solution. The ferrous salt thus generated is titrated with potassium dichromate or potassium permanganate. The usual preliminary treatment of the ash with hydrochloric acid ensures the absence of interfering substances. Colorimetric procedures are more suitable for the determination of smaller quantities of titanium, and are both simple and rapid. Again the solution of titanium in sulphuric acid is taken, and is treated with hydrogen peroxide. Yellow pertitanic acid is formed, and the absorbence of the solution measured at about 405 mμ is linearly related to the concentration of titanium over the range 10–100 mg. TiO_2 per litre.

Zinc. In chlorine-containing polymers zinc must be determined on the mineral matter separated by solvent treatment or in the solution of the inorganic constituents obtained by wet oxidation. For the determination of zinc in other polymers dry ashing can be used providing the ignition temperature does not exceed 600° C. Above this temperature and in the presence of clay, zinc forms a silicate which is not readily attacked by subsequent treatment with hydrochloric acid, and methods for the determination of zinc which are applied to the acid-soluble portion of the ash are no longer fully quantitative.

The majority of classical methods require a prior separation of the zinc as sulphide, either from slightly ammoniacal solution or from a solution buffered at pH 2·6 with sodium acetate and chloracetic acid. The latter modification gives a granular precipitate which filters more readily. The sulphide is then ignited to the oxide and weighed, or is redissolved in hydrochloric acid and precipitated as zinc ammonium phosphate, which is then converted to the pyrophosphate for weighing. Frey [92] recommends a gravimetric determination as the anthranilate, again, however, after separation from other metals.

Among volumetric methods, that involving titration with potassium ferrocyanide using uranyl acetate as indicator is recommended by ASTM. Internal redox indicators are considered to hold an advantage, however, and in these systems the titrant consists of potassium ferrocyanide and a small amount of ferricyanide. Diphenylamine, diphenylbenzidine and, more recently, 3-3'-dimethylnaphthidine have in turn been advocated as indicators for this titration. Zinc is also readily complexed by ethylene-diaminetetra-acetic acid, and may be titrated directly using Eriochrome Black as indicator, providing other titratable metals are absent. This condition would involve in most cases a sulphide separation, but considerable ingenuity has been shown recently in establishing conditions in which zinc may be estimated without removal of other interfering ions. Thus Brown and Hayes [93] titrate zinc in a solution maintained at pH 6 by a maleate buffer using Eriochrome Black as indicator, and then proceed to estimate magnesium in the same solution by raising the pH to about 10 and continuing the titration. Calcium invalidates this method. In a second paper [94] the same authors describe a modification for dealing with larger quantities of magnesium than their original procedure can cope with. After first complexing the zinc with cyanide the mixture is passed through a column of Amberlite IR120 (sodium form) to remove most of the magnesium. The zinc cyanide complex in the filtrate is then decomposed with formaldehyde and the zinc, now in the cationic form, is titrated with EDTA at pH 6·8.

Flaschka and Franschitz,[95] in a modification of the Brown and Hayes technique, claim that greater accuracy is obtained by the use of a ferrocyanide titration for zinc with 3-3'-dimethylnaphthidine as a redox indicator, after complexing other metals with EDTA. This method allows the determination of zinc in the presence of a considerable preponderance of alkaline-earth metals. A complexometric procedure is also proposed by Kinnunen and Merikanto,[96] but using zincon as indicator; a back-titration procedure permits the determination of zinc in the presence of a number of other metals.

COMPREHENSIVE SCHEMES OF ANALYSIS

In general, it may be said that a composite scheme of quantitative analysis is required only when the mineral fillers of the rubber compound are completely unknown and the direct application of methods for individual components outlined in the preceding sections is not practicable. Similarly, in cases where a variety of mineral ingredients have been incorporated it may ultimately be less time-consuming to carry through a complete scheme of quantitative analysis. Three composite schemes in current use will be described briefly.

1. Probably the most widely used comprehensive scheme is that based on the classical sequence of analytical groups. It is almost entirely gravimetric in character, and consequently demands no specialised apparatus; furthermore, only a single portion of the ash (from 1–2 g. of the rubber) is required for the complete analysis. On the other hand, the whole procedure is lengthy and can occupy several days.

The material taken for analysis is obtained by dry ashing or by separation from the rubber by hot solvent. In the latter case a dry-ashing stage may also be necessary to remove organic additions or carbon black. The contents of the crucible are heated at 95°–100° C with 5 ml. concentrated hydrochloric acid for about 30 minutes and then taken just to dryness. After moistening with hydrochloric acid water is added, the solution boiled, and filtered. The insoluble matter containing barium sulphate, silica or silicates and titanium dioxide, is fused with alkali carbonate, and a subsequent leaching with water separates the titanium dioxide and barium carbonate from the soluble decomposition products of the silicates. Barium and titanium are determined in the insoluble residue by the methods already indicated, while silica is recovered from the water-soluble portion by repeated baking and treatment with hydrochloric acid. After removal of the silica the solution is added to the original acid-soluble portion of the ash for the remainder of the analysis.

Antimony, cadmium and lead are removed by diluting the solution and passing hydrogen sulphide, determining cadmium and lead in the precipitate, but using another test portion of the rubber for the determination of antimony. After expulsion of hydrogen sulphide from the solution by boiling, iron is oxidised with a few drops of nitric acid, and iron and aluminium are then precipitated as the hydroxides by adding ammonia. The mixed hydroxides are usually filtered off, ignited and weighed as the combined oxides, but methods for the determination of the individual metals are available and have already been mentioned. Zinc, and possibly traces of lead, are then precipitated as their sulphides, either by means of hydrogen sulphide or ammonium polysulphide, removed by filtration and then determined, and the filtrate is freed from hydrogen sulphide for the precipitation of calcium as oxalate under mildly ammoniacal conditions. After the calcium oxalate has been filtered off, ammonium salts are removed from the solution by adding excess nitric acid and taking to dryness, and finally magnesium is determined by dissolving the residue in dilute hydrochloric acid and precipitating as magnesium ammonium phosphate. The double salt is filtered, ignited to the pyrophosphate and weighed.

2. The ASTM scheme, although differing in detail from the classical system outlined above, follows broadly the same sequence with regard to analytical group separations. The modifications introduced have the effect of making the whole scheme somewhat shorter than the older arrangement, but it requires three portions of ash, each from about 1 g. of rubber. These are examined for, respectively (2.1) silica and insoluble matter, lead, iron oxide and alumina, calcium and magnesium; (2.2) zinc oxide; (2.3) total barium.

Should antimony also be present a fourth test portion of the rubber (0·5 g.) is required.

2.1. The ash from 1 g. of the rubber is digested with hydrochloric acid to obtain insoluble and soluble fractions. The former is used for the determination of silica by volatilising with hydrofluoric acid, a procedure subject to errors which have already been discussed. Lead is determined as the sulphate, iron and alumina as the mixed oxides, calcium by oxalate precipitation and magnesium as the pyrophosphate, using the acid-soluble portion of the ash. Methods for these determinations have already been given.

2.2. A second portion of rubber is ashed and treated similarly with hydrochloric acid, but iron and aluminium hydroxides are precipitated with ammonia and filtered off together with the siliceous matter. Zinc is then determined in the filtrate by titrating with potassium ferrocyanide using uranyl acetate as external indicator.

2.3. For the determination of total barium a third portion of ash is fused with sodium carbonate–nitrate mixture, afterwards leaching out the soluble material with water and filtering. The residue of insoluble carbonates is taken up in hydrochloric acid, and lead is removed by passing hydrogen sulphide through the solution after careful adjustment of the acidity (0·2N HCl). Barium is then determined in the filtrate.

In the ASTM procedure provision is also made for the determination of acid-soluble barium compounds.

3. The integrated scheme of analysis devised by Blenkin makes almost exclusive use of volumetric procedures based on titration with ethylene-diaminetetra-acetic acid. It is much faster than the gravimetric scheme and has the further advantage that only one standard solution is required. Three portions of ash are needed, but the possible components determined in each are grouped according to their occurrence in the usual type of rubber mixing; it is not always necessary therefore to apply the scheme in full. The mineral ingredients are determined in the three portions as follows:

3.1. Aluminium, calcium (acid-soluble and insoluble forms), iron, magnesium (acid-soluble and insoluble forms), zinc oxide, zinc sulphide.

3.2. Barium sulphate, titanium dioxide.

3.3. Total silica.

3.1.1. Determination of zinc, calcium and magnesium as oxides or carbonates. 1 g. of the rubber is ashed in a porcelain crucible and the ash brought just to boiling with N acetic acid. The insoluble material is filtered off, ignited and retained for further tests, while the filtrate is just neutralised with caustic soda and divided into two portions. One of these is used for the determination of zinc by adding sodium maleate buffer to pH 6·8 and titrating with the disodium salt of ethylenediaminetetra-acetic acid using Eriochrome Black as the indicator. If the titrant is standardised in terms of zinc the zinc oxide content of the ash can be calculated.

After titration of the zinc the same solution is made strongly alkaline with ammonia and the titration is continued to the next end point. The extra titration is equivalent to the calcium and magnesium present, and these can be calculated if the calcium and magnesium equivalents of the disodium ethylenediaminetetra-acetate are known.

To the second portion of the filtrate potassium cyanide is added to complex the zinc, and the pH is adjusted to about 11·5 with caustic soda (thymol violet used as an external indicator is convenient). Then murexide indicator is added and the solution is titrated with disodium ethylenediaminetetra-acetate to the blue end point to give the calcium content. The magnesium figure is then obtained by difference.

3.1.2. Determination of zinc sulphide. The insoluble residue, ignited after separation from the acetic acid solution, is heated with 25 ml. 100 volume hydrogen peroxide for 1 hour. The insoluble material is again filtered off, ignited and reserved for the determination of iron, aluminium and magnesium. After boiling the filtrate to remove excess hydrogen peroxide, about 0·5 g. ammonium chloride is added and then a slight excess of ammonia. Titration of the solution with disodium ethylenediaminetetra-acetate with Eriochrome Black as indicator gives the zinc content, present in the original mineral matter or ash as sulphide.

3.1.3. Determination of iron and aluminium. The iron determined by this procedure will be that originally present in the rubber as pigment, together with traces originating as impurity in other compounding materials. The aluminium will include that derived from any clay present.

The ignited residue from the hydrogen peroxide treatment is fused in a nickel crucible with about 1 g. caustic soda pellets. After cooling, the solids are washed out with hot water, the solution made slightly acid with hydrochloric acid and, after filtering off any undissolved residue, made up to standard volume. A measured volume of this solution is taken for the determination of iron and alumina according to the details already given under iron (p. 948), i.e. by first titrating the iron with ethylenediaminetetra-acetic acid using salicylic acid as indicator in the presence of sodium acetate, and continuing the titration with Chromazurol S as indicator for aluminium.

3.1.4. Determination of insoluble calcium and magnesium. The calcium found in this fraction represents that present in calcium silicate, while the magnesium results from the decomposition of talc, asbestos and chemically allied products.

The determination is carried out on a further portion of the filtrate after the caustic-soda fusion, following the experimental conditions given under 3.1.1.

3.2.1. Determination of barium. This method can be applied directly to the ash, when it will determine total barium, or to the insoluble residue after acetic acid treatment of the ash, when barium sulphate only is determined.

5 ml. concentrated sulphuric acid are added to the ash in the crucible which is then heated to fuming for about 5 minutes, stirring occasionally with a glass rod. After cooling the acid is poured into about 75 ml. cold water, the rinsings being added to the same solution. The insoluble matter is removed on a pad of filter-paper pulp retaining the filtrate and washings for the determination of titanium (3.2.2.).

The pad is returned to the original beaker, broken up with water and ammonium hydroxide, and an excess of ammonium ethylenediamine-tetra-acetate added. After-warming and stirring to dissolve the barium sulphate, the solids are removed on another pad of filter-paper pulp and excess ammonium ethylenediaminetetra-acetate in the filtrate titrated with magnesium chloride, using Eriochrome Black as indicator. The concentration of the magnesium chloride solution must, of course, be established by titration with the ammonium ethylenediaminetetra-acetate.

3.2.2. Titanium dioxide. The final insoluble residue from the barium estimation is dried, ignited and cooled, and is then heated for 30 minutes with 10 ml. concentrated sulphuric acid with the addition of 5 g. ammonium sulphate. When cool, the solution is poured into cold water and filtered. This filtrate and that from the corresponding stage of the barium determination are combined and made up to a standard volume for the colorimetric determination of titanium. An aliquot of the solution, judged to contain 10–100 mg. TiO_2/litre is taken, and two drops 100 volume hydrogen peroxide added to produce the yellow colour of pertitanic acid. The absorbence of this solution is measured at 405 mμ.

3.3.1. Silica and silicates. Silica is determined by fusing the ash with caustic soda, and forming the quinoline silico-molybdate complex. Details have already been given in the Section dealing specifically with *silica*.

DETERMINATION OF TRACES OF COPPER, MANGANESE AND IRON

Although the deleterious effects of certain metals, notably copper and manganese, on natural rubber have been recognised since the beginnings of the industry, no completely satisfactory explanation of the way they act has been put forward. It is well known, for instance, that the different forms in which copper is chemically bound vary widely in their activity towards rubber. Copper sulphide and some forms of complexed copper, as in phthalocyanine dyestuffs, are virtually harmless, while copper introduced as a soap, such as stearate or oleate, rapidly degrades natural rubber. Manganese behaves rather similarly, the interstitial manganese in some naturally occurring silicate fillers is quite without effect, even when its concentration in the rubber may be much higher than that from a more active compound, such as naphthenate or linoleate. The same considerations apply equally to other metals, such as nickel, cobalt and vanadium, but as these occur less commonly, they tend to remain unsuspected as possible causes of rapid degradation of rubber in service.

The second factor influencing the oxidation rate is the environment of the metal catalyst. Again it is common knowledge that an excessive amount of copper is a far more serious matter in an unvulcanised latex rubber than in a solid rubber compound. The explanation commonly put forward is that the sulphur present in vulcanised stocks by the preferential formation of copper sulphide prevents or delays the formation of the more catalytically active rubber-soluble copper compounds. It is further suggested that the higher proportion of serum constituents present in latex rubber brings any copper present into a more soluble form. Heavy loadings of black and fillers diminish the susceptibility of the rubber towards copper, and certain anti-oxidants are recognised as being able to confer a degree of protection specifically against copper ageing.

The third factor influencing the rate of deterioration is, of course, the conditions of service in which the rubber operates.

These considerations have a direct bearing on the interpretation of analytical results, for the analyst is frequently asked two questions: (a) how much of the total copper is capable of causing rapid deterioration of the rubber, i.e. is catalytically active? and (b) what can be regarded as a safe limit for the copper content?

No single answer can be given to either of these questions. There is at the moment no means of distinguishing between harmless and aggressive forms of copper. The practice of extracting the rubber with an aqueous medium such as dilute sulphuric acid and regarding only the extracted copper as chemically active is manifestly wrong, since the most dangerous forms of copper are not soluble in such a medium. Much more hope lies in the direction suggested by Wake,[97] in which the swollen rubber is extracted with an organic solvent and copper determined in the extract. The distinction between organically soluble and insoluble copper may not be a rigid one with regard to its catalytical activity, but it is at any rate broadly in line with the behaviour of copper towards rubber. There is, however, no certainty that the inactive forms of copper will remain so, since certain constituents of the rubber, such as the organic acids, could conceivably bring the copper into a soluble, and therefore active, form. What the technologist really requires to know is the amount of copper that would, under stated conditions of service and in a specific rubber compound, change to the aggressive form. The answer to this dilemma is obviously outside the sphere of analytical chemistry, and where deterioration due to copper is suspected there is at present no sound alternative to the determination of total copper.

The permissible limit for copper is dependent on the nature of the rubber compound, and no specific recommendation can be given with confidence. It is widely accepted, however, that on rubber prepared from 60% latex concentrate a copper content of 10 p.p.m. or over is inadmissible (some users specify that the sum of copper and manganese must not exceed 10 p.p.m.). As it is in this form of rubber that copper has its most devastating effect, it is probably safe to conclude that in other rubbers the copper content can rise above this figure without serious consequences.

Copper. Methods for the determination of copper and manganese have recently undergone considerable revision at the hands of the BSI Sub-committee dealing with this aspect of rubber analysis. The work of Poulton and Tunnicliffe [98] showed that wet oxidation is not always essential for the quantitative recovery of copper, and accurate results can be obtained by the simple dry ashing technique. Although Poulton and Tunnicliffe's investigations were directed primarily at natural raw rubber and latex, it was later shown that the conclusions were also valid for most synthetic polymers and, indeed, for many vulcanised compounds. This method is briefly as follows:

5 g. rubber are ashed in a silica crucible with magnesium oxide as ashing aid. After dissolving the ash in hydrochloric acid–nitric acid mixture ammonium citrate is added to complex the iron and the solution is made just ammoniacal. The reagent consists of a chloroform solution of zinc diethyldithiocarbamate which forms with copper a yellow-brown compound. A measured quantity of this reagent is added to the ammoniacal solution, and after shaking and then separating off the organic layer, copper is determined by measuring the absorbence of the chloroform solution at about 435 mμ and referring this reading to a calibration curve.

When substantial quantities of silica or silicates are present in the rubber the dry ashing method is no longer applicable, as copper silicate is readily formed, from which the copper is not extracted by subsequent acid treatment.   Low results can also be obtained in the presence of chlorine due to volatilisation of copper chloride by dry ashing.   In these special cases the organic matter is removed by wet oxidation, and this procedure can thus claim to be a more general method.   In practice, of course, the need for copper determinations in these compounds does not often arise, and for the majority of investigations involving the determination of copper the dry ashing technique is quite satisfactory.   The general method applicable to heavily compounded stocks and to chlorine-containing rubbers is as follows:

The solution in concentrated sulphuric acid is prepared by wet oxidation as already described.   It is diluted with an equal volume of water and decanted through a filter-paper, leaving as much insoluble material in the flask as possible.   About 5 ml. of 5N hydrochloric acid are added to the flask, the solution is heated to incipient boiling, cooled somewhat and passed through the filter-paper.   The flask and insoluble material are washed with two portions of hot water, the washings passed through the filter-paper and the original filter and washings collected in a 100-ml. conical flask.   If on cooling crystals of calcium sulphate form, the flask and its contents are cooled to below $10°$ C and again filtered through paper, washing the flask and calcium sulphate with two portions of ice-cold water.   5 ml. of 50% citric acid are added to the filtrate, which is then neutralised with ammonia and transferred to a separating funnel, making a final addition of a further 2 ml. of ammonia.   25 ml. of a chloroform solution of zinc diethyldithiocarbamate are measured into the solution and the mixture shaken vigorously for 2 minutes.   After separation of the two layers the chloroform layer is drawn off into a dry flask containing about 0·1 g. anhydrous sodium sulphate, making further additions until the solution becomes perfectly clear.   The solution is decanted through a pad of glass wool into the cell of a photoelectric absorptiometer and the optical density measured at about 435 mμ.

Manganese.   Most methods for the determination of small quantities of manganese conclude with a colorimetric stage following the oxidation of manganese to permanganate.   A number of oxidising agents are available for this purpose, but the two most frequently used are ammonium persulphate and potassium periodate.   The method as a whole presents little difficulty, but fading of the permanganate colour immediately prior to or during the final measurement is occasionally encountered.   This trouble seems to be due to traces of organic matter that have escaped the initial combustion, or that have been introduced subsequently by the use of poor-quality distilled water or by filtration through paper. Traces of halides are also responsible for fading, and high salt concentrations are said to retard the development of the permanganate colour.

Wet oxidation for the removal of organic matter is best avoided in the determination of manganese in favour of dry ashing, as traces of the organic material are sometimes trapped in the neck of the flask by volatilisation or acid spray, and thus escape complete oxidation. Any filtration required should be through asbestos pulp rather than paper, and instead of normal laboratory distilled water " stabilised water " prepared by distilling from water containing a trace of sulphuric acid and potassium permanganate should be used throughout. Glassware, particularly the absorption cells, should be freed from every trace of organic matter by washing with acetone and rinsing first with dilute potassium permanganate and then with stabilised water. Probably the best medium for extracting manganese from the ash is hydrochloric acid, but it is essential to remove all residual halogen by subsequent vigorous fuming with sulphuric acid. The alternative is to avoid the use of acid extractants completely and adopt a fusion procedure with potassium bisulphate. While this complicates and lengthens the procedure slightly, results are more consistent and tend to come slightly higher than those obtained by acid extraction.

The method involving dry ashing and acid extraction is recommended by BSI, and is briefly as follows:

10 g. of the sample are ashed in a silica crucible over a small gas flame, completing the ignition in a muffle furnace at 550° C. After cooling, 4 ml. concentrated hydrochloric acid are added and the contents of the crucible are evaporated to dryness. Then 1 ml. concentrated sulphuric acid is added and the mixture is again taken almost to dryness with copious fuming. 4 ml. o-phosphoric acid and 2 ml. water are added when cool, and insoluble matter is removed on a small sintered filter or asbestos pad. The filtrate is heated to boiling with 0·3 g. potassium periodate and is maintained at 90°–100° C for 10 minutes. It is then cooled, made up to standard volume and the absorbence of the solution measured in a suitable photoelectric instrument. The absorption cells should be cleaned with acetone, rinsed with dilute permanganate, stabilised water and the test solution, in that order, and finally filled with the test solution for measuring the optical density at about 525 mμ. The reagent blank is also determined and the corrected value for the manganese concentration read off from a calibration curve.

The following modification of the above process puts greater emphasis on the complete removal of organic matter and eliminates the use of acid extraction.   As it is the most general method so far devised it is well suited to the determination of manganese in compounded rubbers.

A 10-g. test portion is cut into small pieces which are added separately to a silica crucible, heated over a low bunsen flame.   Combustion is completed in a muffle furnace at 550° C.   Concentrated sulphuric acid is added dropwise to the cooled crucible and the mixture heated to dryness with repeated small additions of sulphuric acid as necessary to produce a clean ash.   Finally, the ash is heated to fuming with sulphuric acid, is again cooled and 5–10 g. potassium bisulphate, depending on the amount of the ash, is added to the crucible, which is then heated at 600°–700° C until the molten mixture is clear or until all reaction has finished.   When cool, the melt is dissolved in dilute sulphuric acid and transferred to a small beaker, filtering off any insoluble matter through an asbestos pad.   Any iron present is complexed by adding phosphoric acid in portions of 1 ml. until the solution is colourless, and then 0·3 g. potassium periodate is added, the solution raised to boiling and heated at 90°–100° C for 10 minutes to ensure full development of the permanganate colour.   The solution is finally made up to standard volume and the absorbence measured at about 525 mμ.

A blank determination is carried out on the reagents and the calibration curve is prepared by measuring the absorbence of a range of solutions of known manganese content.

Iron.   The usual method of precipitating iron as hydroxide and igniting to oxide is not sufficiently sensitive for the small quantities that are of interest in the examination of synthetic rubbers.   The following colorimetric procedure has proved satisfactory:

3–5 g. of the rubber are weighed into a silica or porcelain crucible heated over a burner to remove volatile organic matter, and then ignited at 550° C in a furnace until free from carbon.   When cool the ash is heated on a water-bath with 2 ml. of a mixture containing 1 volume concentrated nitric acid, 2 volumes concentrated hydrochloric acid and 3 volumes of water, and is then washed into a 50-ml. flask containing 5 ml. 10% citric acid.   Ammonia is added to bring the pH to about 10, and the red colour of ferrous thioglycollate is produced by adding 5 ml. of a 2% aqueous solution of thioglycollic acid, afterwards making the solution up to 50 ml.   The absorbence is measured at about 535 mμ and after correcting for the reagent blank the concentration of iron in the test solution is determined from a calibration curve.

CARBON BLACKS

Methods for the determination of black have developed almost exclusively along two lines: those in which the rubber is destroyed or removed by acid or solvent attack, the chemical inertness of the black enabling it to be recovered substantially in its original form, and dry distillation or combustion methods, in which the rubber and other volatile organic material is removed by pyrolysis. Essentially, the determination of carbon black is a quantitative separation, and to the extent that other compounding ingredients resemble carbon black, the difficulties of its accurate determination in any particular rubber compound will be increased. Inert fillers have always constituted a problem in black determinations, whether these be inorganic, such as clay, or organic, such as leather, wood dust or cellulose. Today, as in other branches of rubber analysis, the situation is further complicated by the increasing use of polymers that are themselves resistant to acid or solvent breakdown, or are incompletely volatile. Over the whole range of polymers with which black may be associated it is generally accepted that the best of the wet methods are probably more general in the application, but for a limited range of polymers the combustion methods are undoubtedly faster and more accurate.

The oldest of the wet degradation methods for carbon black estimation is that of H. Williams-Jones,[99] and is so well known as not to require detailed instructions. Nitric acid is used as a medium for destroying all ingredients of the mixing, including the rubber itself, other than carbon black and siliceous fillers. The undissolved material is collected on an asbestos pad, which is then dried and weighed and the loss in weight after oxidising the black by ignition in a muffle furnace represents carbon black. The figure thus obtained is consistently higher by about 5% than the theoretically calculated value, due to organic residues adsorbed on the carbon, and an empirical correction factor is usually applied.

A number of modifications have been made over the years to minimise the errors in this basic procedure and to render it applicable to some of the recently developed polymers. Hammond[100] tackled the question of filtration, observing, as others have done, that some types of black showed a pronounced tendency to percolate through the asbestos pad. His remedy was to incorporate ignited kieselguhr in the acid digest to act as a filter aid, and to augment the asbestos pad with a cup-shaped layer of kieselguhr before filtering. These recommendations have been incorporated in the current BSI method.[101] Hammond further suggested that by a suitable wash treatment to remove adsorbed organic substances, the empirical correction factor of 0·95 could be eliminated. The wash sequence proposed was as follows: hot concentrated nitric acid, hot water, boiling acetone–chloroform azeotrope, hot 2N caustic soda, hot 2N hydro-chloric acid, hot water and alcohol.   Unfortunately many people find that this elaborate washing redisperses the black so that it readily penetrates the pad, thus losing the advantages conferred by the kieselguhr.   It is not surprising therefore that Hammond's latter recommendations, unlike his more practical suggestion with regard to kieselguhr, are no longer used.   Nevertheless, a washing with hot chloroform seems desirable in order to remove mineral rubber which is not taken out in the original extraction.   Later workers have found that by heating the separated black to the relatively high temperature of 200°–300° C before the first weighing the adsorbed substances are driven off, and no correction factor is then necessary.

Another source of error arises from certain types of mineral matter. Carbonates, oxides and sulphides dissolve in nitric acid, but clays, hydrated silicas and aluminas, and lead compounds all change in weight on heating to the temperature at which the carbon is oxidised, and this loss, if regarded as carbon, will contribute a substantial error.   Lead compounds can be removed by washing with hot hydrochloric acid (ASTM) or with hot ammonium acetate, in either case testing the neutralised final washings with potassium chromate.   The error due to silicates and similar com-pounds containing combined water can be assessed if the amount of such material in the rubber and the proportion of water it contains is known. Such a correction, however, can never be more than approximate, and the method cannot be seriously recommended when these materials are present, except possibly in control analysis when the composition of the clay is accurately known and the water correction can be applied with an acceptable degree of confidence.

A more satisfactory means of determining the carbon in the presence of combined water is to convert it to carbon dioxide and weigh as such after absorption in soda asbestos.   The contents of the crucible are trans-ferred to a silica combustion boat, removing the last specks of carbon from the walls of the crucible with a small pad of asbestos wool.   The boat is then placed in the combustion tube of a semi-micro furnace and the carbon determined by any standard procedure for the determination of carbon in organic compounds.[102]   The BSI recommend a rather simpler technique, in which the boat and contents, after placing in a hard glass tube, are heated, presumably without a catalyst filling at an unspecified temperature in an atmosphere of oxygen.   Not surprisingly, erratic results are obtained by this procedure, due to incomplete oxidation of the carbon.   Combustion of organic compounds without the aid of a catalyst has been the subject of much recent study, and empty tube techniques, as they are called, are now a well-established alternative to the conventional copper oxide filling, but the essential factors for complete oxidation under these conditions, such as a high combustion temperature ($900°-1,000°$ C) and a rapid flow of oxygen, must be observed.

There still remains the difficulty of relating the fixed carbon figure as obtained by analysis to the amount of carbon black actually present in the rubber. Obviously there cannot be a simple answer to this, since the proportion of fixed carbon in rubber grades of black varies from type to type. It is, however, related inversely to the volatile matter of the carbon black, and thus if the type of black is known, as it would be in control testing, the proportion of fixed carbon would also be known or could be determined, and the necessary correction applied to the determination of black in the rubber. Where the nature of the black is not known before-hand, it is possible to assign it to one of several broad classes based on its volatile content. Bauminger and Poulton [103] have made an approach to this problem by determining the volatile matter released from the black over the temperature interval $600°-900°$ C, but as their work is primarily associated with a combustion method for the determination of black, its detailed discussion is left until later.

The nitric acid method outlined above can be used for the determination of black in polybutadiene rubbers, SBR and natural rubber, while simple modifications will enable it to be used for some of the other synthetics. Thus for polychloroprene vulcanisates Scott and Willott [104] recommend swelling the rubber with nitrobenzene prior to the acid digestion. Their full procedure is as follows:

0·5–1 g. of the finely divided rubber is extracted with acetone and chloroform and then dried under vacuum. 20 ml. nitrobenzene are added and the mixture heated on a small hot-plate until swollen (about 30 minutes), whereupon 20 ml. dilute nitric acid (75 ml. water/25 ml. concentrated nitric acid) are added and the heating continued for about 1 hour longer. After cooling, 100 ml. xylene are added and the black removed on an alundum or prepared Gooch crucible, and washed with hot xylene and acetone. After drying at $150°$ C and weighing, the crucible is ignited in a muffle furnace and reweighed, the loss being regarded as carbon.

Scott and Willott make no recommendation regarding a correction factor, but results appear to come slightly high; unfortunately no systematic work appears to have been done by which the recovery of black can be accurately assessed. A second obvious recommendation, particularly as the method is primarily intended for polychloroprene compounds, would be the insertion of an ammonium acetate wash prior to the first weighing to remove lead compounds.

A further advance along essentially similar lines was made by Louth,[105] who uses tetrachlorethane in conjunction with nitric acid as a digesting medium and introduces ether to improve filtration conditions. Louth recommends the following procedure:

About 0·1–0·15 g. of the sample is weighed into a 150-ml. beaker, 10 ml. tetrachlorethane added and the mixture heated gently on a hot-plate until the sample is noticeably swollen and softened. 15 ml. of boiling nitric acid (S.G. 1·42) are added and the heating continued until the rubber is disintegrated and the black completely dispersed (usually less than 1 hour; the nature of the rubber and of the other ingredients are the principal factors involved). When the solution has been cooled to below 20° C in running water or ice, 25 ml. ether are stirred in, and as soon as two layers have been formed the upper one is decanted through a prepared Gooch crucible. The treatment with further portions of ether is repeated until a clear upper layer is obtained, and then the sides of the beaker are washed down with a small quantity of acetone. The crucible is filled with ether and the suction reduced to a point where the ether just percolates through the pad, and then slowly the contents of the beaker are poured into the crucible, maintaining by repeated additions of ether, an ether–acetone ratio of at least 2 : 1. The beaker and crucible are washed with ether–acetone mixture, drained as much as possible, dried in an oven at 250°–300° C, cooled and weighed. The carbon is burnt off in a muffle furnace at 900° C and the crucible cooled and reweighed. The loss in weight represents free carbon.

Louth finds, in common with other workers, that if the black is dried at a minimum temperature of 200° C before ignition, volatile absorbed substances are driven off and the need for a correction factor is eliminated. Figures quoted by Louth indicate a high degree of fidelity with known additions of black, results ranging only between 99·6 and 100·4% for a number of channel and furnace blacks recovered from natural, SBR, butyl, chloroprene and acrylonitrile rubbers. Louth's method, therefore, is probably the most general of the variations of the nitric acid method, although all manipulative difficulties are by no means eliminated. The composition of the solvent at the filtration stage, for instance, is quite critical, and its control demands a high degree of care on the part of the analyst. The possibility of a violent reaction between the ether and nitric acid has also been mentioned as an objection to the method, but there seems little danger of this if the nitric acid digest is well cooled before adding the ether and if contact between the two is not unduly prolonged.

Before leaving methods based on nitric acid, mention should be made of that due to Galloway and Wake,[106] designed specifically for the determination of black in butyl compounds. Details have already been given elsewhere in this chapter. The principle of the method is to attack the polyisoprene component with nitric acid and then dissolve the poly-isobutene in petroleum ether. The residual black, which is collected on a sintered filter, is determined by loss in weight on oxidation or by combustion and weighing the carbon dioxide.

As an alternative to acid-digestion methods, dissolution in organic solvents has been suggested, the main advantage being that filtering is easier. The chief objections to solvent methods are the uncertainty of ensuring complete removal of the polymer and the possibility of polymer precipitation on dilution. No doubt it is for these reasons that solvent methods have not displaced entirely the older nitric acid procedure.

Roberts,[107] working with natural rubber, advocates heating with cresol for 3–4 hours at 160°–165° C or overnight at 140°–145° C to dissolve the polymer, but this method is interesting not for the solvent treatment but for the method of determining the carbon. After the insoluble material has been collected on asbestos, acid washings remove soluble sulphides and carbonates, and the dry residue is heated strongly over a burner in a Rose's crucible in an atmosphere of nitrogen. The crucible is cooled, weighed and reheated in air to the same temperature in order to oxidise the carbon, and finally is cooled and reweighed. The loss in weight represents carbon, and is independent of the combined water in clays or other substances.

The difficulties of removing the rubber by solvent treatment have been successfully overcome in the case of some polymers at least, by Kolthoff and Gutmacher.[108] They chose p-dichlorobenzene as the initial solvent and induced the oxidative breakdown of the polymer with tert-butyl hydroperoxide and osmium tetroxide. Their procedure in outline is as follows:

0·25 g. of the rubber is heated gently under reflux with 20 g. p-dichlorobenzene for 30 minutes. After the mixture has been cooled slightly 5 ml. tert-butyl hydroperoxide are added and 1 ml. osmium tetroxide in benzene solution (0·08 g. in 100 ml. benzene). The mixture is reheated to 120° C for 30 minutes, then cooled and diluted with 25 ml. benzene. The black is separated through asbestos, washed with warm benzene and dilute nitric acid, and then with distilled water. The crucible is dried at 325°–350° C for 30 minutes, cooled and weighed. After igniting in an oxidising atmosphere at 750°–800° C the crucible is cooled and weighed again to obtain the loss in weight due to carbon.

Designed essentially for the determination of black in masterbatches, the method is claimed by Kolthoff and Gutmacher to be suitable for natural rubber, SBR, Butyl and polychloroprene.

Methods based on the removal of the polymer by pyrolysis have attracted the attention of control chemists particularly, on account of their speed, although in their early form no high degree of accuracy could be claimed for them. With recent refinements, however, and as applied to a limited number of polymers, they can equal the wet methods in accuracy, but if they are to be used with confidence it is essential to know the nature of the polymer with which the black is associated.

The earliest of the dry pyrolysis methods is probably that due to Namita.[109] Namita merely heated approximately 1 g. of the sample in a Rose's crucible in an inert atmosphere of carbon dioxide or nitrogen to remove by pyrolysis all the volatile ingredients of the rubber compound. After being cooled and weighed, the crucible was reheated in an oxidising atmosphere to remove the carbon and again cooled and weighed.

This simple technique assumes a negligible carbonaceous residue from other compounding ingredients, and also in practice suffers from errors due to the essential crudity of the apparatus. It is, for instance, very difficult to exclude oxygen completely from the crucible, and slight oxidation of carbon after heating in nitrogen is often evident. Nevertheless, Namita's method has provided a starting-point for more elaborate studies, among which that of Bauminger and Poulton [103] considers the various problems involved in greater detail. An outline of their method is as follows:

> About 0·1 g. of the sample is extracted with acetone and chloroform by one of the standard procedures. After drying, the rubber is placed in a silica combustion boat which is inserted into the cool end of a combustion tube heated in its centre portion to 600° C, and through which a stream of oxygen-free nitrogen is passed. The boat is propelled slowly forward by means of a hooked wire or silica rod into the hot zone, and after 5 minutes is withdrawn to its original position, where it is cooled for about 10 minutes with nitrogen still passing. The boat is cooled in a desiccator and then weighed. The boat is then transferred to a second combustion tube heated at 900° C and through which a slow stream of oxygen is passed. The evolved carbon dioxide is collected in a soda–asbestos tube which is weighed before and after the determination. The boat is withdrawn from the combustion tube, cooled in a desiccator and reweighed.

Incomplete pyrolysis of the polymer or any of the organic compound ingredients will lead in the above method to a carbonaceous residue, which will be subsequently converted to carbon dioxide along with the black, and hence will give rise to a fictitiously high carbon figure. Bauminger and Poulton considered the magnitude of this error for a variety of polymers (see Table 11.6), from which it became evident that interference from this source can be classified at three levels:

(1) polymers in which carbon formation is very low and substantially constant;

(2) polymers in which carbon formation is appreciable but reasonably constant;

(3) polymers in which carbon formation is high and variable.

Pyrolysis methods are well suited to materials in the first group—which includes natural rubber, synthetic polyisoprene, polybutadiene, Butyl and

TABLE 11.6

CARBONACEOUS RESIDUE FROM POLYMERS

Type of polymer	Residual carbon, %
Natural rubber, pale crêpe	0·27
Natural rubber, smoked sheet	0·23
Natural rubber, film from 60% centrifuged latex concentrate	0·28
Synthetic polyisoprene (Ameripol SN)	0·28
Synthetic polyisoprene (Coral rubber)	0·23
Polybutadiene	0·18
Polyisobutene	0·08
Butyl rubber	0·10
Styrene–butadiene rubber (Intol 1500)	0·23
Styrene–butadiene rubber (Krylene)	0·20
Styrene–butadiene rubber (oil-extended—Krynol)	0·21
Acrylonitrile–butadiene rubber (Krynac 800)	3·4
Acrylonitrile–butadiene rubber (OR15)	3·7
Acrylonitrile–butadiene rubber (Paracril AJ)	2·0
Thioplast (Thiokol FA)	2·8
Polyvinyl acetate	2·6
Polyvinyl chloride	5·5–6·2
Polychloroprene (Neoprene GN)	12–15

SBR, can be used with caution in the second group if the nature of the polymer is known, but are unsuitable for polymers in the third group— which consists primarily of the chlorine-containing rubbers.

It will be noticed that in this method the loss in weight of the boat and its contents on heating in oxygen, and the weight of carbon as calculated from the carbon dioxide produced, are both determined. The divergence between these two values represents the non-oxidisable portion of the volatile matter released from the surface of the black between the temperatures 600° and 900° C, and is a characteristic of the black, although not necessarily a unique one. Table 11.7 gives the values of this component for a number of typical commercial rubber blacks. The figures are shown in Column 3 as a percentage of the difference in weight before and after heating in nitrogen, and the distinction between the main classes of black is clearly evident. Having identified the type of black, it is then possible to make a correction for the volatile matter, which can be added to the fixed carbon figure to give the original carbon black content.

Column 4 in the same table shows the amount of fixed carbon in the same range of blacks.

Inorganic fillers which change in weight between 600° and 900° C will also introduce an error into this method, and although corrections for this effect can usually be calculated from an analysis of the inorganic compounds, the results do not reach an acceptable level of accuracy with heavy

TABLE 11.7

VOLATILE MATTER AND FIXED CARBON IN CARBON BLACKS

Type	Name	Non-oxidisable volatile matter, %	Fixed carbon, %
Channel	Micronex	6·0	91·6
	Kosmobile H.M.	5·6	91·3
	Spheron 4	5·3	93·8
	Spheron 6	7·9	90·7
	Spheron 9	5·7	91·7
	Dixiedensed	6·7	90·8
Lamp	Magecol	0·2	97·4
	Champion	0·8	98·1
Furnace	Statex 93	0·0	99·3
	Statex K	3·4	96·0
	Furnex	2·3	95·4
	Philback O	2·5	96·5
Thermal	P33	0·7	96·5
	Seval	2·3	97·1

loadings of filler. China clay and whiting are probably the most likely ingredients to give trouble of this nature. Clay has been found to lose about 2% of its weight between 600° and 900° C, and the error after applying a calculated correction to the apparent loss in weight of the black between the same two temperatures will obviously not be very great. Whiting, however, loses approximately 44% of its weight in similar conditions, and the correction in this case, therefore, is less exact.

Identification of black

Almost as important as the amount of black present in a rubber compound is information regarding its type. Without going deeply into theories of black reinforcement, it can be said that in characterising a black the analyst is assessing some property that shows a reasonable correlation with the physical properties conferred by the black on vulcanised rubber. There is, of course, no single property that does this, and methods of black identification based on such a characterisation are bound, sooner or later, to strike anomalies, but particle size and surface structure are generally accepted as having a dominant effect on reinforcement, and a useful classification can therefore be made by studying these features.

When the choice lay between channel and lamp black, with their great disparity in particle size, their qualitative identification was relatively straightforward.   A simple test for these two was to compress a small portion of the black, separated by the solvent or acid process, on a sheet of unglazed paper and to draw a steel spatula blade over the surface.   The fine channel blacks under this test show a dense glossy sheen, while lamp blacks give a much greyer shade with distinctly less gloss.   With the wider range of blacks now available, manufactured mainly by the furnace process, this test loses a good deal of its value, but in the analysis of an unknown black comparison with a set of standard blacks can be of considerable assistance, especially if the range of possibilities can be narrowed by other considerations, such as the physical properties of the rubber.

A method based on the determination of the volatile content of the black has already been described.   Incidental to the determination of black by the method of Bauminger and Poulton a knowledge of the volatile matter enables a broad classification to be drawn showing the distinction between the highly adsorptive channel blacks and the coarser lamp and furnace grades.

A more recent approach utilises the colour index of the black, and although the information so far published [110] relates primarily to characterising black as a raw material, an extension of the work to the identification of black in a rubber compound appears feasible.   In the present context the colour index relates to dispersions of black at very high dilution, and may be defined as the ratio of the absorbences of the dispersion with respect to violet and red light.

It is common knowledge that channel black in dilute aqueous dispersion tends to give a reddish hue to transmitted light, whereas the coarser blacks give a bluish-grey colour.   The colour produced is not specifically related to the particle size of the black but to the size of the dispersed aggregates, and thus the accepted theory of light scattering by spherical particles does not apply.   Nevertheless, with few exceptions, a constant but again empirical correlation has been shown to exist between the colour given by a black in dilute dispersion and the degree of reinforcement it confers on a rubber compound.   Corresponding to the colours of the transmitted light, the fine-particle blacks absorb more strongly in violet, while larger-particle blacks absorb relatively more strongly in the red, and quantitative expression can be given to this effect by measuring on a suitable spectrophotometer the absorption in the two regions and calculating the ratio of these absorbences.

The colour-index method, unlike the combustion method, requires a specimen of the black recovered from the rubber, and is on that account a much lengthier procedure.   On the other hand, it enjoys two advantages in that, provided the black can be separated by acid or solvent treatment, the method is independent of the polymer system and indeed of the other ingredients of the mixing, and only a few milligrams of the black are required.   Experimentally the method depends on the accurate and reproducible preparation of a stable black dispersion, and this is ensured by adopting a strict routine with regard to grinding and dilution.   A satisfactory procedure is to grind 1 mg. of the black in a small agate mortar with one or two drops of gum acacia for a fixed time, say 2 minutes, and then gradually dilute first with mucilage and then with water with constant grinding and stirring to 100 ml.   Exact details are not important, provided they are consistently followed and will ensure a concentration for absorbence measurement of about 10 mg. of black per litre.

Previous workers [111] have shown that black recovered from rubber is not materially affected in regard to particle or aggregate size, and it has now been established that the colour index of the black remains reasonably constant also.   Table 11.8 shows a range of values for the colour index

TABLE 11.8

COLOUR INDEX OF CARBON BLACK

Polymer	Carbon black	Colour index	
		Free state	Recovered from rubber
Natural rubber	Vulcan 3	1·61	1·60
	Philblack E	1·92	1·90
	Philblack I	1·73	1·75
	Statex 93	1·22	1·23
	Lampblack	0·96	0·95
	Pelletex	1·17	1·17
	P33	1·06	1·07
Butyl	Micronex	1·92	1·90
	Vulcan 3	1·61	1·63
	Pelletex	1·17	1·22
Polybutadiene	Philblack O	1·54	1·60
Styrene–butadiene (Krylene)	Philblack O	1·54	1·57
Styrene–butadiene oil extended (Krynol)	Philblack A	1·36	1·41
Acrylonitrile–butadiene (Krynac 800)	Spheron 9	1·98	1·94
Acrylonitrile–butadiene (Hycar OR15)	Philblack O	1·54	1·58
	Philblack A	1·36	1·36
Acrylonitrile–butadiene (Paracril AJ)	Thermax	0·91	0·90
Polychloroprene (Neoprene GNA)	Philblack O	1·54	1·58
	Vulcan 3	1·61	1·64
Hypalon	Philblack O	1·54	1·62
	Philblack A	1·36	1·33
Polyurethane	Philblack O	1·54	1·61

of some currently used types of black, both in the free state and after separation from a wide range of polymeric materials.   These values are not, of course, independent of local experimental factors, and must be established under the operating conditions in each individual laboratory.

The black is separated from vulcanised rubber by a hot solvent procedure known to be effective for the polymer system being examined. Probably the most generally applicable is the following modification of Kolthoff and Gutmacher's method:

About 0·1 g. of the finely sheeted rubber is extracted with acetone–chloroform and placed in a small beaker with 10–15 g. *p*-dichlorobenzene. The temperature is raised slowly to the boiling point for 30 minutes with magnetic stirring to soften and swell the polymer. It is then cooled to about 70° C, 5 ml. *tert*-butyl hydroperoxide are added and the mixture reheated to the boiling point with stirring for 1–2 hours. After cooling slightly and diluting with 10 ml. *o*-dichlorobenzene the contents of the beaker are transferred to a centrifuge tube, in which the black is separated. Washing is carried out first with *o*-dichlorobenzene and then benzene. The dried black is then crushed in a small agate mortar, returned to the centrifuge tube, where it is treated with hot dilute (1 : 1) nitric acid, washed with water and dried at 100°–110° C. It is then free of polymer and soluble fillers and is dispersed as already described. Finally, the dispersion is run into the cell of a photoelectric absorptiometer and the absorbence measured at the extremes of the visible spectrum.

ACCELERATOR AND ANTIOXIDANT

The identification and determination of accelerator and antioxidant in vulcanisates has always been one of the more difficult problems in rubber analysis, but the application of modern techniques has in many cases provided means at least to classify the ingredient, if not to identify it specifically. The quantitative determination of accelerator or antioxidant is often possible by spectroscopy or by colorimetric methods once it has been shown by qualitative tests to be present, but it by no means follows that the amount found after vulcanisation is the same as that originally added. In practice, however, an exact measure of the agent is rarely necessary, since for a given rubber compound the accelerator and antioxidant system is generally decided from technological considerations.

The customary starting-point for an investigation into the accelerator and antioxidant system of a rubber compound is the acetone extract, but hot or cold alcohol or benzene have also been used as solvents to separate these ingredients from the vulcanisate. Two points should be borne in mind in choosing a solvent: the reactivity of acetone towards the soluble ingredients of the extract, with its possible effect on the pattern of accelerator fragments disclosed by analysis, and, in low-temperature vulcanising systems, the prolongation of effective curing time by hot extraction.

For the identification and assay of the accelerator or antioxidant in the extract, colour reactions and absorption spectroscopy have largely displaced older gravimetric methods, which were in any case of severely limited application. Sometimes tests are applied directly to the extract, but generally speaking, more reliable results are obtained by further resolution of the solvent extract by adsorption or partition chromatography.

A survey of the colour reaction of about forty commercially available antioxidants was made by Endoh,[112] as a result of which he was able to classify the more important of them (which at that time did not include the phenolic types) into about nine groups. A clear distinction between the groups is possible by the use of nine reagents based on sulphuric acid. Many of the tests reviewed by Endoh were further investigated by Deal,[113] but work by both authors was confined to the free antioxidant. It is, of course, essential to compare the results obtained from an unknown vulcanisate with the colour produced by a known specimen of the accelerator or antioxidant, but in doing so it is essential to remember that many break down during vulcanisation into fragments which provide no certain indication of the chemical identity of the original substance, and that their association with other ingredients of the rubber often tends to confuse the results of analytical tests. Shimada [114] followed Endoh's work with an investigation into the reactions of some accelerators with metallic oleates in benzene.

The colour reactions of a number of accelerators with aqueous copper salts have been investigated by Schaefer.[115] Commencing with the response given by the free substance, the tests were extended first to 5% accelerator masterbatches and then to vulcanisates containing about 1% accelerator. Identification was possible in all cases, but the vulcanisate used was a very simple composition containing no added softener, antioxidant or carbon black; the colour tests were therefore applied in nearly ideal conditions which are rarely experienced in practice.

Schaefer's work was extended by Budig,[116] who applied the colour reactions developed by the former worker to a series of typical vulcanisates containing a variety of common compounding ingredients extractable by acetone. The range of accelerators studied was the same as in the earlier investigation; colour changes were noted on addition of the copper reagent and again after standing for 2 hours, but the results were far less characteristic than in the case of the free accelerators or masterbatches. Where accelerator mixtures are concerned the tests fail completely, Budig suggesting that the " ultra " component, giving a more intense colour, completely masks the second accelerator.

A major contribution was made by Burchfield and Judy,[117] who were about to identify about 12 of the commoner amine antioxidants. Briefly the scheme of identification proposed by these authors is based on the following reactions:

1. Oxidation of many diarylamines and naphthylarylamines by nitrous acid in association with stannic chloride in benzene medium to give highly coloured products. The aldehyde–amine accelerators give very weak colours with this test and are not likely to interfere.

2. Diarylamine ketone condensation products form intensely coloured compounds (arylmethane chlorostannates) with benzotrichloride in the presence of stannic chloride. The test is carried out in ethylene dichloride.

3. Amine-type antioxidants will readily couple with diazonium compounds to give colours ranging from yellow to strong cherry red. The test is in no way specific, and results must be checked against the reactions of a known compound. The coupling reagent recommended by Burchfield and Judy is p-nitrobenzene diazonium chloride.

4. Another oxidation reaction useful for subdividing antioxidants falling into the first group depends on the use of benzoyl peroxide. Orange yellow colours are given by aryl-substituted p-phenylenediamines, and in certain instances the colour is modified to violet or blue by stannic chloride addition.

5. Primary and secondary amines in general give a green colour with p-phenylenediamine and ferric chloride. Phenyl-α- and β-naphthylamines give pale yellow and red colours respectively in this reaction, but acetone–aniline condensation products give a greenish colour, and hence may be distinguished by this test from phenyl-β-naphthylamine. Aldehyde amines respond as primary amines.

The tests are applied to rubber samples after a short initial extraction of the antioxidant with a suitable solvent. Two or three tests are usually sufficient to characterise the antioxidant. Table 11·9 gives a summary of the colours given under the specified conditions.

In connection with the extraction and identification of the guanidines Humphrey [118] suggested that acidified acetone is necessary for complete extraction. Dufraisse and Houpillart [119] also failed to detect guanidine accelerators in the extract from vulcanisates. Shimada found that distinctive colours, ranging from pink to purple, were obtained when cobalt oleate was added to guanidine-type accelerators extracted from rubber by acetone. Reddish-violet colours seem to be confined to the reaction with guanidines, but the hue is influenced not only by the specific nature of the guanidine but also to some extent by the state of cure of the vulcanisate. Among other tests for guanidines, the well-known reaction

TABLE 11.9

COLOUR REACTIONS OF AMINE ANTIOXIDANTS
(After Burchfield and Judy)

Antioxidant	1	2	3	4	5
Phenyl-α-naphthylamine	Green	Yellow	Reddish-violet		_Yellow_
Phenyl-β-naphthylamine	_Green_	Yellow	_Red_		_Red_
Agerite Stalite (allyl substituted diphenylamine)	Blue-green	Yellow	Yellow		Blue-green
BLE (diphenylamine-acetone condensation product)	Blue-green	_Violet_	Yellow	Yellow	Blue-green
Betanox (phenyl-β-naphthylamine-acetone condensation product)	_Greenish-yellow_	_Green_	_Orange-red_	Yellow	Violet
N : N'-diphenyl-β-phenylene diamine	Blue-violet	Yellow	Yellow	_Orange-violet_	Orange-red
Agerite White (N : N'-di-β-naphthyl-p-phenylene diamine)	_Blue_	Yellow	Orange-red	Orange-blue	Orange
Flectol A (acetone–aniline condensation product)	Yellow	Yellow	_Red_		Blue-green
Stabilite (N : N'-diphenyl-ethylene diamine)	Red ppt.	Yellow	_Orange-red_		Reddish-violet
Santoflex B (acetone–p-amino-diphenyl condensation product)	Yellow	Yellow	Yellow	_Reddish-violet_	_Reddish-violet_
VGB (aniline–acetaldehyde condensation product)	Yellow	Greenish-yellow	Yellow		_Green_

Underlines indicate strong colour.

with sodium hypochlorite giving intense violet-red colours is often of value, but sometimes fails on account of its low sensitivity when applied to vulcanisates. The formation of a picrate is now largely discredited as a test for guanidines because so many other substances give a similar response.

Shimada extended his investigations with cobalt oleate to some dithio-carbamate accelerators extracted from vulcanisates with benzene; all gave yellowish-green colours. He also found that vulcanisates cured with thiuram mono- and disulphide gave the characteristic yellowish-green colour with cobalt oleate and suggested that these accelerators transform to dithiocarbamates during vulcanisation. This view was supported by Jarrijon [120] after an investigation by ultra-violet spectroscopy into the mechanism of thiuram acceleration.

A quantitative investigation into the transformation of the thiuram sulphides was made by Hilton and Newell.[121] Their procedure for the determination of dithiocarbamates is to extract with ethanol, treat with phosphoric acid and absorb the liberated carbon disulphide in dimethyl-amine for spectroscopic measurement at 287 mμ. Thiuram disulphides are first reduced with sodium bisulphite. In order to determine both accelerators, therefore, and hence to assess the degree of conversion, after the first distillation from the acidified ethanol the residual solution is neutralised with dilute sodium hydroxide and treated with aqueous sodium bisulphite. The distillation, absorption and determination of carbon disulphide are then carried out as before.

Many qualitative tests have been proposed for 2-mercaptobenzthiazole (MBT) based on its reaction with heavy metals to form coloured compounds or insoluble salts, but not all are acceptable as a means of detecting the accelerator in rubber. One of the earliest methods was proposed by Wistinghausen,[122] who recommended precipitation of the copper salt by copper oleate followed by filtration and weighing. Although useful as a qualitative test, as the heavy orange precipitate is very characteristic, Wistinghausen's quantitative procedure has now largely been superseded by colorimetric and spectrophotometric methods. Bismuth nitrate gives a bright yellow coloration with MBT,[123] which is extremely sensitive, but which can obviously suffer interference from many other possible ingredients of the extract.

MBT may also be detected by its reaction with copper dibutylphthalate, to give a yellow colour,[124] and with 2 : 6-dibromoquinonechlorimide. The latter reagent is prepared by grinding the solid into an aqueous suspension and is used as a spot reagent on a white tile or filter-paper. One drop of the alcoholic or acetone solution of the accelerator is added to the reagent, and at the junction of the liquids a brick-red colour is produced immediately in the presence of MBT. Accelerators chemically allied to MBT, such as dibenzthiazyl-2-disulphide (MBTS) and N-cyclo-hexyl-2-benzthiazyl sulphenamide, fail to respond to the colour reactions of the parent substance, but since these compounds generally decompose during vulcanisation to give MBT as one of the products, a positive reaction is usually obtained whenever a member of the benzthiazyl series has been used as accelerator. Dufraisse and Houpillart [119] found that MBT or MBTS introduced singly to the rubber compound would produce a mixture of both as a result of vulcanisation. These workers also found difficulty in extracting these accelerators from partially vulcanised mixings and postulated the formation of an acetone-insoluble intermediate product. The reaction between MBT and nickel salts in which a reddish-brown compound is formed has been exploited by Bauminger and Poulton [125] to form the basis of a quantitative method for the determination of accelerators in vulcanisates. These workers also noted the partial oxidation of MBT to the disulphide, and their procedure includes a reduction stage to ensure reconversion to the original form.

Burmistrov [126] points out that many of the colour reactions given by MBT with copper and bismuth reagents are also shown by the thiuram disulphides, and in dealing with mixtures of these accelerators recommends that the thiuram be decomposed by treating the extract with aqueous caustic soda. The MBT may then be extracted from the acidified digest with benzene and tested either with the usual reagents or by converting it to orthanilic acid, which is detected by a diazo reaction and coupling.

Chromatographic methods

Recent workers have allied liquid-phase chromatography with the colour reactions of accelerators and antioxidants, and have thus produced a useful tool for their identification, and for the analysis of the extract generally. Chromatography is particularly suited to the separation and, if necessary, isolation of minor constituents of a mixture and at the same time demands only simple apparatus. On the other hand, it must be regarded essentially as a practical art, since the results it gives can rarely be stated in strict quantitative terms. Inevitably this leads in the litera-ture to lengthy and detailed accounts of the behaviour or response of the test material under specified experimental conditions, but even the best efforts of the various authors in this direction are no substitute for first-hand acquaintance with the effects produced. To derive full benefit from the technique of chromatography it is essential to build up a background of experience based on the analysis of known compounds, rather than to rely completely on the well-meant but often inadequate picture presented by other workers.

Bellamy, Lawrie and Press [127] apply the technique of adsorption chromatography to the identification of five of the commoner accelerators and nine antioxidants in vulcanised rubber. In the case of acccelerators the basis of their method is generally to isolate the accelerator by means of a column of activated alumina, develop a colour with cobalt oleate reagent and fractionate the coloured derivative on a second alumina column. Separation of the accelerator from other ingredients of the acetone extract relies on the fact that wax, sulphur and mineral oil are readily eluted from the column by benzene, while fatty acids and tar are much more firmly held. After removal of the benzene-eluted fraction the accelerator can be washed steadily down the column with 95% benzene–5% alcohol and collected in the eluate. Most accelerators move down the column as a distinct but faintly coloured single band and are removed by evaporation of the eluting solvent, but DPG is an exception in that it forms a series of coloured bands on the column sufficiently distinctive to identify this accelerator without further testing. The other accelerators, MBT, MBTS, zinc diethyldithiocarbamate (ZDC) and tetramethylthiuram disulphide (TMT), are treated with copper oleate in benzene solution and chromatographed on a second alumina column again using 95% benzene–5% alcohol as the developing agent. The behaviour of the colour complex on the second column is unique and serves to characterise the original accelerator.

The separation of antioxidants follows similar lines, except that most are comparatively weakly held on alumina and, on washing with benzene, tend to move down the column as a diffuse band behind the wax and mineral oil fraction. Flectol H (2-2-4-trimethyl-1-2-dihydroquinoline), however, is largely retained as a brown zone, which is then eluted without further resolution by 90% benzene–1% alcohol. Movements of the antioxidant can be followed by observing the column in ultra-violet radiation, since most antioxidants fluoresce strongly, but " streak " reagents form a more reliable guide, both to the position and to the chemical nature of the antioxidant. For this purpose the moist column is extruded carefully from the tube and the assumed position of the antioxidant confirmed by drawing a fine streak of reagent across the zone by means of a capillary. Table 11.10 shows the response of the antioxidants to a series of spot-test reagents. When the position of the antioxidants on the column has been established its identity is confirmed by cutting the column transversely and washing off the adsorbate from the indicated position with warm benzene. This benzene solution is then concentrated by evaporation of the solvent and the confirmatory colour test applied by the addition of the appropriate drop reagent on a white tile.

Adsorption methods are also advocated for the separation of 6-phenyl-1-2-dihydro-2-2-4-trimethylquinoline (Santoflex B), BLE (a condensation product of diphenylamine and acetone), N : N'-diphenyl-p-phenylenediamine (JZF), and phenyl-β-naphthylamine, by Hively and co-workers.[128]

Two columns are used, one of active alumina and the second of a de-activated grade. The acetone extract from the vulcanisate is evaporated to dryness and systematically chromatographed using a variety of eluting solvents. The weight of the fractions eluted by successive 40-ml. portions of solvent indicates the presence of the maximum component, the identity

TABLE 11.10

COLOUR REACTIONS OF ANTIOXIDANTS
(After Bellamy, Lawrie, and Press)

Antioxidants	Sulphuric acid	1% ammonium vanadate in sulphuric acid	1% potassium dichromate in sulphuric acid	Nitric acid–sulphuric acid 1 : 3
Phenyl-α-naphthylamine	Faint green	Vivid green	Green-blue	Green
Phenyl-β-naphthylamine	Pale yellow	Very faint green-yellow	Brown-green	Red
Agerite White	Green	Prussian blue	Red, changing to Prussian blue	Purple
Flectol H	Nil	Faint red-brown	Faint red-brown	Bright red
Agerite Stalite	Nil	Nil	Strong brown ochre	Green
BLE	Nil	Green	Green	Deep violet
Nonox S	Faint brown-green	Brown	Nil	Brown
Vulcaflex A	Green	Dark blue-green	Dark green-blue	Crimson
Neozone HF	Brown-green	Emerald green	Red—changing to emerald green	Red

of which is established by melting-point determination and ultra-violet absorption spectroscopy.

Parker and Berriman [129] advocate partition methods using a column filling of " Celite " and silica-gel mixture in place of the more adsorptive alumina. A careful study was made of the chromatographic behaviour and colour reactions of a number of currently used accelerators and anti-oxidants, and the colours obtained from a number of streak reagents are shown in Table 11.11. As would be expected, chemically related compounds are not distinguished by the colour reactions, but some differences in the behaviour on the column towards a range of developing solutions enables tentative deductions to be drawn regarding the identity of certain individuals. Applying their preliminary work to the detection of the same accelerators and antioxidants in vulcanisates, Parker and Berriman examined a variety of rubber compounds and found that the accelerators thiocarbanilide (TCA), tetramethylthiuram di- and mono-sulphides,

TABLE 11.11

COLOUR REACTIONS OF ACCELERATORS AND ANTIOXIDANTS
(After Parker and Berriman)

Compound	30% W/V sodium hypochlorite	5% W/V aqueous $CuSO_4.5H_2O$	5% W/V $Bi(NO_3)_3$ in 0·5N nitric	Bismuth nitrate in 0·5N nitric acid, after reduction	5% W/V aqueous $Pb(C_2H_3O_2)_2.3H_2O$	Aqueous lead acetate after reduction	1% W/V $(NH_4)VO_3$ in 60% W/W sulphuric acid	Mixture of conc. HNO_3 (1 vol.) and conc. H_2SO_4 (3 vols.)	0·5% W/V selenium dioxide in conc. sulphuric acid
Vulcafor DOTG	Dark reddish-brown	Nil	Nil	Nil	Nil	Nil	Nil	Nil	Nil
,, DPG	Dark reddish-brown	Nil	Nil	Nil	Nil	Nil	Nil	Nil	Nil
,, TPG	Reddish-brown	Nil	Nil	Nil	Nil	Nil	Nil	Nil	Nil
,, TC	Pale orange on standing	Light brown	Yellow	Yellow	Nil	Nil	Nil	Pale violet fades rapidly	Nil
,, MBT	Nil	Faint yellow	Bright chrome-yellow	Bright chrome-yellow	Lemon yellow	Lemon yellow	Faint green	Nil	Faint yellow
,, MBTS	Nil	Nil	Nil	Bright chrome-yellow	Nil	Lemon yellow	Nil	Nil	Nil
,, TMT	Nil	Bright yellow-green	Pale lemon-yellow	Pale lemon-yellow	Nil	Nil	Very pale green to faint blue	Nil	Nil
,, MS	Nil	Strong yellow	Pale yellow	Pale yellow	Nil	Nil	Very pale green to faint blue	Nil	Nil
,, TET	Nil	Bright yellow-green	Pale lemon-yellow	Pale lemon-yellow	Nil	Nil	Very pale green to faint blue	Nil	Nil
Santocure	Nil	Nil	Nil	Bright chrome-yellow	Nil	Lemon yellow	Faint green	Nil	Nil
Phenyl α-naphthylamine	Light orange to orange-yellow	Nil	Nil	Nil	Nil	Nil	Prussian blue	Dark olive green	Blue on standing
Phenyl β-naphthylamine	Orange	Nil	Nil	Nil	Nil	Nil	Dark brown	Green rapidly turning brown	Pale greenish-yellow
Agerite White	Orange-pink	Nil	Pale green or pale blue	Nil	Nil	Nil	Dark greenish-blue	Mauve	Deep blue
m-toluylene diamine	Orange-brown	Yellow-green	Nil	—	Nil	—	Pink-brown on standing	Faint orange	Nil
N:N'-diphenyl p-phenylene diamine	Pale orange-yellow	Nil	Light blue	—	Nil	—	Crimson	Magenta	Purple

tetraethylthiuram disulphide (TET) and Santocure could no longer be detected. Discussing some of the apparent discrepancies, Parker and Berriman point to the conflicting reports regarding recovery of the substituted guanidines, suggesting that their own positive result supporting the earlier work of Wistinghausen and Humphrey may in fact be due to the detection of breakdown products, whereas other workers applied tests responsive only to the original substances. The transformation of MBT, MBTS and Santocure is also discussed, their own results falling into line with the experience of other workers in that MBT was the only identifiable accelerator in the extract from a vulcanisate compounded with one of the other derivatives. TMT could not be detected as such owing to its conversion to the dithiocarbamate. Of the anti-oxidants tested, phenyl-α- and -β-naphthylamines, N : N_1-di-β-naphthyl-p-phenylene-diamine (Agerite White), N : N'-diphenyl-p-phenylenediamine (DPPD), Flectol H and Nonox S (an aldol–naphthylamine condensation product) were all detected in the extract from vulcanised rubber.

A later contribution by the same authors [130] is devoted entirely to the detection by adsorption chromatography of the individual members of the dithiocarbamate group of accelerators. Although the characteristics of the members of this series are not clearly developed by direct chromatography of the accelerators themselves, the behaviour of the corresponding copper derivatives is sufficiently unique to permit identification. After acetone extraction the dried extract is treated with benzene or carbon tetrachloride, the copper derivative formed by reaction with aqueous copper sulphate and the organic solution applied to the column. Development is carried out with a mixture of ethyl ether and carbon tetrachloride.

In addition to its value as a direct contribution to the methods of antioxidant and accelerator analysis, the work of Parker and Berriman is important because it emphasises very clearly the need for acquiring an exact knowledge of the breakdown products of these materials. Not only during processing of the rubber but also in the course of the subsequent extraction with hot acetone, significant changes in the chemical nature of many accelerators are induced; only by a clear understanding of these phenomena is it possible to arrive at a useful diagnosis of the accelerator system of the rubber compound.

In many respects partition chromatography on paper offers certain advantages for accelerator and antioxidant detection over column methods, since it combines the simplicity and speed of the earlier technique with a facility for dealing with even smaller quantities of the test material. The paper support also provides a suitable medium for the application of colour-test reagents, and this avoids the irksome procedure of extracting the moist adsorption column from its glass envelope before further tests can be carried out. Fluorescence of the separated zones can be observed in ultra-violet radiation somewhat more readily than when a glass tube is interposed. Its greatest advantage, however, is that another means of identification is provided by determining the Rf value (rate of travel of the test substance relative to that of the solvent front).

A comprehensive treatment of the subject applied to the identification of accelerators and antioxidants has been given by Zijp,[131] who first classifies the materials according to their chemical composition and then develops partition methods appropriate to each class, making use of colour reactions for identification. The members of the guanidine group naturally give rather similar colours but have markedly different Rf values, ranging from 0·35 for o-tolylguanidine to 0·85 for triphenylguanidine. Diphenyl and di-o-tolylthioureas are detected by forming the corresponding guanidine by ammoniation in the presence of lead oxide. MBT and associated accelerators form another group, and while clear identification was obtained in some cases, it is pointed out that many accelerators of this class decompose to give MBT, which is revealed on the chromatogram by the bismuth nitrate reaction. Some guidance as to the nature of the original substance may be gained by identifying other residues from the accelerator. A third section of Zijp's paper deals with the dithiocarbamates and thiuram series. Since some dithiocarbamates are not themselves water-soluble, better chromatographic separation is obtained by conversion to the respective amines. Identification is then possible by reconversion to the dithiocarbamate followed by the formation of the copper compound. A second test with ninhydrin distinguishes between diethylamine and piperidine which have the same Rf value in acidified butanol. Zinc methyl- and zinc ethyl-dithiocarbamates do not give identifiable amines under the above conditions, and diazotisation and coupling followed by chromatography of the dye is recommended.

Amine anti-oxidants are identified by their Rf value when chromatographed on a fully acetylated paper with a mixture of benzene and alcohol as the mobile phase, and by their response to a reagent consisting of benzoyl peroxide in benzene. Table 11.12 shows the data from both tests and gives an idea of the degree of differentiation attainable between products of like composition. The identification of individual phenolic antioxidants is more difficult, and generally demands the running of two chromatograms with different mobile phases. Even so, the Rf values are in many cases rendered imprecise by pronounced tailing of the spot. Tollens' reagent and Millen's reagent are two solutions suggested for confirmatory testing but neither is specific for individual antioxidants.

Zijp also puts forward a scheme for the identification of the accelerator and antioxidant in rubber mixes and vulcanisates of unknown composition based on the classification of these substances outlined above. As each

TABLE 11.12

PAPER CHROMATOGRAPHIC DETECTION OF ANTIOXIDANTS

(After Zijp)

Systematic name	Trade name	Colour reaction product	Identification limits in 10^{-6} g.		Rf values
			Before chromatography	After separation	
1. Phenyl-α-naphthylamine	Neozone A Nonox A Alterungsschutzmittel P.A.N.	Light yellow	5	10	0·64
2. Phenyl-β-naphthylamine	Neozone D Nonox D Alterungsschutzmittel J.Z.F.	Blue-grey	5	20	0·64
3. Diphenyl-p-phenylenediamine	Alterungsschutzmittel P.B.N.	Yellow-orange	1	2	0·56
4. Phenyl-cyclohexyl-p-phenylene diamine	Alterungsschutzmittel 4010	Yellow	1	10	0·73
5. Di-β-naphthyl-p-phenylenediamine	Agerite White Santowhite C. I. Nonox C.I. Alterungsschutzmittel D.N.P.	Pink	1	5	0·55 (Tailing)
6. p-Isopropoxydiphenylamine	Antioxidant 123 E.g. in Agerite Hipar, a mixture of 2, 3 and 6	Yellow-brown	—	—	0·73
7. p:p'-Dimethoxydiphenylamine	E.g. in Thermoflex A, a mixture of 2, 3 and 7	Brown-pink	—	—	0·68
8. p-(p-Tolylsulphonylamino)-diphenylamine	Aranox	Brown-red	1	5	0·65
9. p-(p-Tolylsulphonylamino)-phenyl-p-tolylamine	M.U.F.	Red	1	5	0·65
10. Mono- and diheptyldiphenyl-amine	Agerite Stalite	Green	—	—	0·81; 0·91
11. 2:4-Diaminodiphenylamine	Oxynone	Brown	1	10	0·38
12. p:p'-Diaminodiphenylmethane	Tonox	Red-brown	2	40	0·50
13. Diphenylethylenediamine	Stabilite	Red-brown	10	80	0·65
14. Di-o-tolylethylenediamine	Stabilite Alba	Red-brown	10	80	0·67

class is treated as a separate entity, the total weight of sample required is considerable, amounting to some 17 g. for the full scheme when applied to unknown samples, but for control analysis where a number of possibilities can be eliminated rather less sample will suffice. Briefly the procedure is as follows:

(*a*) *Detection of guanidines and amines.* An acetone extract from 5 g. of the rubber is boiled with 2N hydrochloric acid, cooled and filtered. The solution is evaporated and divided into two parts; one part is dissolved in water and chromatographed for the identification of the amines, while the other is neutralised with ammonia, again evaporated, placed on the paper in acetone solution and chromatographed to give the guanidines. The acid-insolubles are taken up in acetone, treated with ammonia in the presence of lead oxide and heated to dryness. Acetone is again used to separate insolubles and the filtrate is evaporated, boiled with 2N hydrochloric acid and chromatographed as before to give guanidines obtained from thiourea derivatives originally present.

(*b*) *Mercapto group.* The acetone extract from 5 g. of the rubber is heated with 4N ammonium hydroxide, fatty acids are precipitated with strontium chloride and removed by filtration. The filtrate is evaporated, neutralised with dilute hydrochloric acid, taken to dryness and dissolved in acetone. Two chromatograms are developed from the acetone solution, one on unbuffered paper and the other on paper buffered at pH 10. Bismuth nitrate is used as the indicating reagent, but the difference in Rf values on the two papers enables a clear distinction to be drawn between MBT and MBTS.

(*c*) *Antioxidants.* The acetone extract from 5 g. of the rubber is dissolved in 96% ethanol, the solution treated with strontium chloride and ammonia and the precipitate removed by filtration. The filtrate is evaporated to small volume and chromatographed on acetylated paper by the ascending method. Amine antioxidants are detected with benzoyl peroxide, and phenolics by Tollens' and Millen's reagents.

(*d*) *Dithiocarbamates and thiurams.* The acetone extract from 2 g. of the rubber is adjusted to a volume of 10 ml., and to 5 ml. of this solution are added a few drops of aqueous copper sulphate. A brown colour indicates dithiocarbamate. The remaining 5 ml. is boiled with phosphoric acid to decompose the dithiocarbamate, and is neutralised with 25% caustic soda. Sodium bisulphite is then added, followed by ammonia and ammonium citrate, and the solution is divided. Chloroform is added to both portions and a few drops of copper sulphate to one. On shaking, the development of a brown colour in the second portion (using the portion without copper as a reference solution) indicates a thiuram in the original sample.

Spectroscopic methods

A comprehensive study by Mann [132] deals with the examination of accelerators and antioxidants in vulcanisates by infra-red spectroscopy. Reference spectra of a number of accelerators and antioxidants were prepared from mulls of the purified materials in liquid paraffin, and these served as a basis of comparison for the spectra of fractions from the acetone extract of the rubber. Separation of the accelerator and antioxidant from the other components of the extract is achieved by adsorption chromatography on alumina columns, following the procedure recommended by Bellamy, Lawrie and Press. Frequently, the reaction products of accelerators with cobalt oleate are also examined.

Mann comments on the excessive reactivity of alumina for this work, a feature which tends to obscure the results of the subsequent examination of the eluted fractions. Thus both MBTS and Zenite are converted wholly to MBT and, indeed, the thiazole group as a whole (MBT, MBTS, Santocure and zinc 2-mercaptobenzthiazole (Zenite)) is detected only by the absorption spectrum of the parent substance.

ZDC cannot be detected by a direct chromatography of the extract; it is found only after the addition of cobalt oleate. The green compound formed by this reagent gives rise to two zones on the alumina column, one of which is eluted by benzene and gives a spectrum sufficiently close to that of ZDC itself to be used in identifying the accelerator. Zinc pentamethylene dithiocarbamate (ZPD) and diethyl ammonium dithiocarbamate (DEAD) behave somewhat similarly, and their conversion products can be readily identified, but piperidine pentamethylene dithiocarbamate (PPD), as noted by other workers, cannot be detected after vulcanisation. Mann has also obtained further evidence of the conversion of TMT and TET to ZDC on vulcanisation in the presence of zinc oxide, and again therefore, these accelerators cannot be detected in their original form. They can, however, be detected spectroscopically after extraction from unvulcanised mixings. Xanthates also decompose completely under vulcanising conditions, and no characterisation of their products seems possible.

Guanidines are recognised by chromatography of the benzene solution of the extract as carried out by Bellamy, Lawrie and Press, but additional evidence is obtained from the spectra of eluted fractions and of picrate derivatives. Mann finds that the identification of aldehyde–amine types of accelerator is likely to be particularly difficult, since they often consist of complex mixtures and are frequently found in association with antioxidants of somewhat similar chemical nature. It has been found also that certain grades of pine tar also interfere seriously in the detection of accelerators of this class.

Antioxidants examined included Flectol H, PBN, Agerite White, p-phenyl phenol (Parazone), Nonox NS (a phenol formaldehyde amine condensation product) and Nonox HF. All are extracted from vulcanisates by acetone, and the extracted mixture is applied to the column in benzene–alcohol mixture. The progress of the zones is followed by their fluorescence under ultra-violet radiation. On elution the successive fractions are examined spectroscopically, and Mann reports close similarity between these spectra and the corresponding spectra of the unprocessed antioxidants.

Kress [133] has applied ultra-violet spectroscopy as a control test in the quantitative analysis of accelerator masterbatches, basing his investigation on seven of the commoner accelerators representative of the main classes commercially available. A direct solution method is used, i.e. taking the whole of the matrix into solution, and it has been shown in the accelerators selected for examination that spectral interference from the rubber or antioxidant can be disregarded. The technique is equally suitable for dual-accelerator systems, and is particularly applicable to factory control analysis. In collaboration with Mees,[134] the same worker has developed a scheme for the recovery of a wide range of accelerators from vulcanisates and uncured stocks and their subsequent identification by ultra-violet spectroscopy. The method dispenses with chromatography as a means of isolating the accelerator from the extract, and the rubber is treated directly with aqueous reagent. Either the aqueous solution or its ether extract is then examined spectroscopically over the range 220–380 mμ, and the resulting spectra are compared with those of known specimens.

Digestion with 1% barium hydroxide extracts thiazoles, thiurams, thiocarbamates, oximes, thiocarbanilides and azolines, and if the solution is extracted with ether interfering substances, such as guanidines, certain amines and antioxidants, will be removed. The spectrum of the alkaline solution is taken and the accelerator identified by characteristic maxima. Acidification of a portion of the extract generally produces a shift in these maxima to shorter wavelengths, and this also serves to identify thiazoles, oximes, azolines and thiocarbanilides. Thiurams and dithiocarbamates are identified individually by the spectroscopic examination of a chloroform solution of the copper compound formed by reacting the original barium hydroxide extract with aqueous copper sulphate. Sulphenamides are not directly identifiable, since they are decomposed by the acid to give the thiazole and an amine hydrochloride; their identification depends on the characteristic spectrum given by the corresponding dithiocarbamate formed from the amine.

A second portion of the rubber sample is treated for 2 hours with dilute hydrochloric acid in order to extract guanidines, aldehyde amines, sulphenamides, azolines and thiocarbanilides. The acid digest is first washed with ether or chloroform to remove azolines, antioxidants and traces of thiazoles and is then made ammoniacal to free the guanidines and the amines derived from sulphenamides. Characteristic spectra are obtained for the guanidines, both in the aqueous acid medium and as a free base in ether, but identification of the amine, and hence the sulphenamide, depends on the formation of the corresponding dithiocarbamate. This is achieved by evaporating the dry chloroform solution of the amine to small bulk and heating with carbon disulphide and a few milligrams of caustic soda. After evaporation of the organic solvents the mixture is taken up in a little water and the spectrum is obtained.

Aldehyde amines are also found in the aqueous acid extract, but their direct identification by absorption spectroscopy will be obscured by guanidines if these are also present. Such a mixture is unlikely, but if suspected the amine can be separated and identified by the formation of the dithiocarbamate on the lines already given.

A somewhat similar approach to the problem of identifying accelerators and antioxidants has been made by Brock and Louth,[135] who base their methods on the fact that the majority of commercially available materials contain at least one of the following: carbon disulphide, ammonia, guanidine and a thiazole derivative. They therefore promote the decomposition of the accelerator by digesting the rubber with acidified ethanol and identify the breakdown products by means of X-ray crystallography and ultra-violet spectroscopy. Thus, after acid digestion, the amine is distilled from the solution made alkaline, and the hydrochloride of the amine identified by X-ray diffraction. Further separative treatment of the alkaline solution provides a neutral fraction containing antioxidants, an acidic group which includes the thiazoles and a basic fraction in which the guanidines are found. The identification procedures recommended are X-ray diffraction for the guanidines and ultra-violet spectroscopy for antioxidant and thiazole groupings. Any carbon disulphide formed during the initial digest is trapped in alcoholic caustic potash and revealed by the copper xanthate reaction. From the results of these tests, collected in Table 11.12, a wide range of commercial accelerators may be characterised and their presence detected in a rubber compound.

The determination of phenolic antioxidants is a problem that has come to the fore with the wider use of synthetic rubbers and the emphasis on non-staining compounds. Difficulties in their determination arise from the fact that their absorption maxima occur at shorter wavelengths than those of amines and their absorptivities are only about one-tenth as great. Wadelin,[136] however, makes use of the shift in the maximum that occurs in alkaline solution to select the absorption due to phenol from that arising from other ingredients of the raw polymer extracted by ethanol. In the case of Wingstay S, for example (an alkylated phenol), the peak absorptivity moves from 279 mμ in neutral solution to 301 mμ in alkali, with an increase in the level of absorptivity from 8·4 to 14·8. Other antioxidants to which the technique can be successfully applied are 2246 (methylene-*bis*-2-2$_1$-(6-*tert*-butyl 4-methylphenol) and Ionol (2 : 6-di-*tert*-butyl-4-methylphenol).

References

1. Haslam, J. and Soppet, W. W. (1948) *J. Soc. chem. Ind.*, **67**, 33.
2. Prem, D. and Duke, J. (1955) *Rubb. World*, **133**, 383.
3. Wyatt, G. H. (1941) *Analyst*, **66**, 362.
4. Kress, K. E. (1956) *Rubb. World*, **134**, 709.
5. Rauscher, W. H. and Clark, W. H. (1948) *J. Amer. chem. Soc.*, **70**, 438.
6. Burchfield, H. P. (1945) *Ind. Eng. Chem., Anal. Ed.*, **17**, 806.
7. Parker, L. F. C. (1944) *J. Soc. chem. Ind.*, **63**, 378.
8. Parker, L. F. C. (1945) *J. Soc. chem. Ind.*, **64**, 65.
9. Weber, C. O. (1900) *Ber.*, **33**, 791.
10. Wake, W. C. (1945) *Analyst*, **70**, 175.
11. Wake, W. C. (1945) *I.R.I. Trans.*, **21**, 158.
12. Barnes, R. B., Williams, V. Z., Davis, A. R. and Giesecke, P. (1944) *Ind. Eng. Chem., Anal. Ed.*, **16**, 9.
13. Tunnicliffe, M. E. and Wilkinson, G. L., Dunlop Research Report.
14. Bloomfield, G. F. (1944) *J. chem. Soc.*, **117**, 120.
15. Kemp, A. R. and Peters, H. (1943) *Ind. Eng. Chem., Anal. Ed.*, **15**, 453.
16. Kuhn, R. and L'Orsa, F. (1931) *Z. angew. Chem.*, **44**, 847.
17. Burger, V. L., Donaldson, W. E. and Batey, J. A. (1943) *Rubb. Chem. Technol.*, **16**, 660.
18. Barthel, W. F. and La Forge, F. B. (1944) *Ind. Eng. Chem., Anal. Ed.*, **16**, 434.
19. Galloway, P. D. and Wake, W. C. (1946) *Analyst*, **71**, 505.
20. Hollins, P. H. and Skidmore, D. W. (1958) *J. Sci. Inst.*, **35**, 378.
21. Shaw, T. P. G. (1944) *Ind. Eng. Chem., Anal. Ed.*, **16**, 541.
22. Wechsler, H. (1953) *J. Polymer. Sci.*, **11**, 233.
23. Haslam, J. and Newlands, G. (1950) *J. Soc. chem. Ind.*, **69**, 103.
24. Haslam, J. and Soppet, W. W. (1948) *J. Soc. chem. Ind.*, **67**, 33.
25. Belcher, R. and Godbert, R. L. (1945) *Semi-micro Quantitative Organic Analysis* (London: Longmans Green), p. 101.
26. Belcher, R., Macdonald, A. M. G. and Nutten, A. J. (1954) *Mikrochim. Acta*, (i), 104.
27. Barnes, R. B., Linsell, U. and Williams, V. Z. (1943) *Ind. Eng. Chem., Anal. Ed.*, **15**, 83.
28. Dinsmore, H. L. and Smith, D. G. (1948) *Anal. Chem.*, **20**, 11.
29. Harms, D. L. (1953) *Anal. Chem.*, **25**, 1140.
30. Davison, W. H. T. and Bates, G. R. (1954) Paper 39, 3rd Internat. Rubber Technology Conference, London.
31. Houblin, R. A. (1940) *Rev. gén. Caoutch.*, **17**, 49.
32. Wake, W. C. (1947) XIth International Congress Pure and Applied Chem., Proceedings p. 365.
33. Kolthoff, I. M. and Gutmacher, R. G. (1950) *Anal. Chem.*, **22**, 1002.
34. Davis, C. C. and Blake, J. T., *Chemistry and Technology of Rubber* (New York: Rheinhold Publishing Corporation), p. 867.
35. British Standard Methods of Testing Vulcanised Rubber, BS 903 Parts B6–B10 : 1958.
36. ASTM Standards on Rubber Products; American Society for Testing Materials, Designation: D297–54T, p. 86.
37. Fischer, R. B. and Rhinehammer, T. B. (1953) *Anal. Chem.*, **25**, 1544.

38. Frey, H. (1952) *Anal. Chim. Acta*, **6**, 126.
39. Lindsly, C. H. (1936) *Ind. Eng. Chem., Anal. Ed.*, **8**, 176.
40. Belcher, R., Gibbons, D. and West, T. S. (1954) *Chem. Ind.*, (5), 127.
41. *Ibid.*, p. 850.
42. Outa, M. (1948) *An. Asoc. quim. Brazil*, **7**, 159.
43. Frey, H. (1951) *Anal. Chim. Acta*, **5**, 375.
44. Mahr, C. and Kraus, K. (1948) *Anal. Chem.*, **20**, 477.
45. Belcher, R., Nutten, A. J. and Stephen, W. I. (1953) *J. chem. Soc.*, 1334.
46. Bauminger, B. B. (1956) *Analyst*, **81**, 12.
47. Siegfriedt, R. K., Wiberley, J. S. and Moore, R. W. (1951) *Anal. Chem.*, **23**, 1008.
48. Mahoney, J. F. and Mitchell, J. H. (1942) *Ind. Eng. Chem., Anal. Ed.*, **14**, 97.
49. Walters, R. N. (1950) *Anal. Chem.*, **22**, 1332.
50. Frey, H. (1952) *Anal. Chim. Acta*, **6**, 28.
51. Bethge, P. O. (1956) *Anal. Chem.*, **28**, 119.
52. Luke, C. L. (1943) *Ind. Eng. Chem., Anal. Ed.*, **15**, 602.
53. Gaunt, R. (1915) *Analyst*, **40**, 9.
54. British Standard Methods of Testing Vulcanised Rubber, BS 903 : 1950, p. 27.
55. Zimmerman, E. W., Hart, V. E. and Horowitz, E. (1955) *Anal. Chem.*, **27**, 1606.
56. Stache, W. (1955) *Plaste u. Kautschuk*, **2**, 161.
57. Bauminger, B. B. (1956) *I.R.I. Trans.*, **32**, 218.
58. Parr Manual No. 121, Parr Instrument Co., Moline, Ill., U.S.A.
59. Resnik, B. (1950) *Zavodskaya Lab.*, **16**, 363.
60. Hardman, A. F. and Barbehenn, H. E. (1935) *Ind. Eng. Chem., Anal. Ed.*, **7**, 103.
61. Mann, J. (1950) *J. Rubb. Res.*, **19**, 72.
62. Lancaster, P. and Tarrant, L. W. (1951) Dunlop Research Report.
63. Ambler, J. A. (1931) *Ind. Eng. Chem., Anal. Ed.*, **3**, 341.
64. Minataya, S., Aoe, I. and Nagai, I. (1935) *Ind. Eng. Chem., Anal. Ed.*, **7**, 414.
65. Proske, G. E. (1947) *Z. angew. Chem.*, **59**, 121.
66. Poulton, F. C. J. and Tarrant, L. W. (1951) *J. appl. Chem.*, **1**, 29.
67. Bolotnikov, V. and Gurova, V. (1933) *J. Rubb. Ind., U.S.S.R.*, **10**, 61.
68. Mackay, J. G. and Avons, C. H. J. (1940) *I.R.I. Trans.*, **16**, 117.
69. Brock, M. J. and Osborn, T. W. (1955) *Rubb. Age, N.Y.*, **77**, 84.
70. Taranenko, I. T. and Zakharova, I. A. (1955) *Zavodskaya Lab.*, **21** (10), 1163.
71. Memmler, K., *The Science of Rubber* (New York: Reinhold Publishing Corporation).
72. Linnig, E. J., Milliken, L. T. and Cohen, R. I. (1951) *J. Res. nat. Bur. Stand.*, **47**, 135.
73. Peltier, S. and Duval, C. (1947) *Anal. Chim. Acta*, **1**, 345.
74. Feigl, F., *Spot Tests*, Vol. 1—*Inorganic Applications*. Amsterdam Elsevier Publishing Company.
75. Schantl, E. (1924) *Mikrochemie*, **2**, 174.
76. Feigl, F., *Spot Tests*, Vol. 1—*Inorganic Applications*, p. 208.
77. Johnson, W. C. (Ed.), *Organic Reagents for Metals* (London: Hopkin and Williams), p. 182.
78. Smales, A. A. (1947) *Analyst*, **72**, 14.
79. Theis, M. (1955) *Z. anal. Chem.*, **144**, (2), 106.
80. Blenkin, J. (in press).
81. Lindsey, A. J. and Tucker, E. A. (1954) *Anal. Chim. Acta*, **11**, 260.
82. Frey, H. E., *Methoden zur chemischen analyse von Gummischungen* (Berlin: Springer-Verlag).
83. Kinnunen, J. and Wennerstrand, B. (1954) *Chem. Anal.*, **43** (2), 34.
84. Frey, H. E. (1951) *Anal. Chim. Acta*, **5**, 317.
85. Hunter, J. G. and Hall, A. (1953) *Analyst*, **78**, 106.
86. Robertson, C. M. (1957) *I.R.I. Trans.*, **4**, 97.

87. Kakihama, H. and Kojima, S. (1953) *Japan Analyst*, **2**, 421.
88. Teicher, H. and Gordon, L. (1951) *Anal. Chem.*, **23**, 930.
89. Kobrova, M. (1954) *Chem. Listy*, **48** (8), 1167.
90. Wilson, H. N. (1949) *Analyst*, **74**, 243.
91. Vogel, A. I., *Text-book of Quantitative Inorganic Analysis* (London: Longmans Green).
92. Frey, H. E. (1951) *Anal. Chim. Acta*, **5**, 313.
93. Brown, E. G. and Hayes, T. J. (1953) *Anal. Chim. Acta*, **9**, 6.
94. *Ibid.*, p. 408.
95. Flaschka, H. and Franschitz, W. (1955) *Z. anal. Chem.*, **144**, 421.
96. Kinnunen, J. and Merikanto, B. (1955) *Chem.-Anal.*, **44** (2), 50.
97. Wake, W. C., Communication to the International Organisation for Standardization, T.C.45—*Rubber*, Düsseldorf, 1955.
98. Poulton, F. C. J. and Tunnicliffe, M. E. (1950) *I.R.I. Trans.*, **26**, 235.
99. Williams-Jones, H. (1914) *Proc. 4th International Rubber Conference*, London.
100. Hammond, G. L. (1934) Research Association of British Rubber Manufacturers, Technical Note No. 37.
101. British Standard Methods of Testing Vulcanised Rubber, BS 903 : 1950.
102. Belcher, R. and Godbert, R. L., *Semi-micro Quantitative Organic Analysis* (London: Longmans Green).
103. Bauminger, B. B. and Poulton, F. C. J. (1949) *Analyst*, **74**, 351.
104. Scott, J. R. and Willott, W. H. (1941) *India Rubb. J.*, **101**, 177.
105. Louth, G. D. (1948) *Anal. Chem.*, **20**, 717.
106. Galloway, P. D. and Wake, W. C. (1946) *Analyst*, **71**, 505.
107. Roberts, J. B. (1940) *Rubb. Age, N.Y.*, **47**, 319.
108. Kolthoff, I. M. and Gutmacher, R. G. (1950) *Anal. Chem.*, **22**, 1002.
109. Namita, K. (1930) *J. Rubb. Soc. Japan*, **2**, 255.
110. Fiorenza, A. (1956) *Rubb. Age, N.Y.*, **80**, 69.
111. Parkinson, D. (1940) *I.R.I. Trans.*, **16**, 87.
112. Endoh, H. (1935) *J. Soc. Chem. Ind. Japan, Suppl. binding*, **38**, 618.
113. Deal, A. J. A. (1947) *I.R.I. Trans.*, **23**, 148.
114. Shimada, K. (1932) *J. Soc. Rubb. Ind. Japan*, **5**, 420.
115. Schaefer, W. (1948) *Kautsch. u. Gummi*, **1**, 149.
116. Budig, K. H. (1948) *Kautsch. u. Gummi*, **1**, 305.
117. Burchfield, H. P. and Judy, J. N. (1947) *Anal. Chem.*, **19**, 786.
118. Humphrey, B. J. (1936) *Ind. Eng. Chem., Anal. Ed.*, **8**, 1953.
119. Dufraisse, C. and Houpillart, J. (1942) *Rev. gén. caoutch.*, **19**, 207.
120. Jarrijon, A. (1943) *Rev. gén. caoutch.*, **20**, 157 and 177.
121. Hilton, C. L. and Newell, J. E. (1953) *Anal. Chem.*, **25**, 530.
122. Wistinghausen, L. von (1929) *Kautschuk*, **5**, 77.
123. Spacu, G. and Kuras, M. (1936) *Z. anal. Chem.*, **102**, 108.
124. Turk, E. and Reid, E. E. (1945) *Ind. Eng. Chem., Anal. Ed.*, **17**, 713.
125. Bauminger, B. B. and Poulton, F. C. J. (1953) *I.R.I. Trans.*, **29**, 100.
126. Burmistrov, S. I. (1948) *Zavodskaya Lab.*, **14**, 787.
127. Bellamy, L. J., Lawrie, J. H. and Press, E. W. S. (1947) *I.R.I. Trans.*, **22**, 308.
128. Hively, R. A., Cole, J. O., Parks, C. R., Field, J. E. and Fink, B. (1955) *Anal. Chem.*, **27**, 100.
129. Parker, C. A. and Berriman, J. M. (1952) *I.R.I. Trans.*, **28**, 279.
130. Parker, C. A. and Berriman, J. M. (1954) *I.R.I. Trans.*, **30**, 69.
131. Zijp, J. W. H. (1958) *Rec. Trav. chim.*, **77**, 129.
132. Mann, J. (1951) *I.R.I. Trans.*, **27**, 232.
133. Kress, K. E. (1951) *Anal. Chem.*, **23**, 313.
134. Kress, K. E. and Mees, F. G. S. (1955) *Anal. Chem.*, **27**, 528.
135. Brock, M. J. and Louth, G. D. (1955) *Anal. Chem.*, **27**, 1575.
136. Wadelin, C. W. (1956) *Anal. Chem.*, **28**, 1530.
137. Haslam, J., Soppett, W. W. and Willis, H. A. (1951) *J. appl. Chem.*, **1**, 112.

CHAPTER XII

PART ONE

THEORIES OF VULCANISATION

by

J. GLAZER and F. H. COTTON

VULCANISATION AND CROSS-LINKING THEORY

ALTHOUGH it is now generally agreed that the process of vulcanisation consists of the introduction of cross-links in the rubber matrix, the nature of these cross-links is still a matter of considerable speculation, and intense experimentation is still occurring in this field. The statistical theory of rubber elasticity is based upon the concept of long-chain molecules whose mobility is limited by a number of cross-links situated at random in the polymer. While these cross-links may be comparatively few in number, they are sufficient to prevent the unrestricted flow of *whole* molecules past neighbouring ones. A vulcanised rubber is, in this sense, a solid and will retain its shape from birth (i.e. its shape from the moment of vulcanisation). At the same time, the low intensity of cross-links implies that the vast majority of the segments making up the long-chain molecule are free to move by virtue of kinetic energy. Vulcanised rubber may therefore be regarded as a number of flexible molecules whose flow is prevented only by occasional cross-links along their length.

Based upon this concept, the statistical theory is able to provide mathematical relationships between the intensity of cross-links and measurable physical properties, such as equilibrium modulus and degree of swelling. Equations have been developed which permit the calculation of cross-link intensity from a knowledge of the stress–strain or swelling properties of the vulcanisate. These equations are proving of great benefit to rubber science and technology. Not only do they present a quantitative physical picture of vulcanisation network, they are also being used to establish the chemical and physical nature of the cross-linking process.

Cross-link intensity and swelling

When a vulcanisate is placed in contact with a suitable solvent (i.e. a solvent in which the non-vulcanised rubber dissolves completely) appreciable swelling occurs. The solvent passes into the rubber by a process akin to osmosis and extends the three-dimensional network until the deformation stresses are sufficiently large to resist any further overall passage of solvent into the swollen gel. At this point the rate of imbibition of solvent becomes equal to the rate of expulsion of solvent by the deformed network, and no further swelling occurs. The extent of swelling, at this stage, is known as the *equilibrium swelling* of the system. Although in practice it is rare for a rubber to reach an equilibrium swelling condition owing to oxidative fission of the molecules, it is easily possible to overcome this complication by standard extrapolation methods. The equilibrium swelling is related to the structural parameters of the network by the following equation: [1]

$$- \ln(1 - v_r) - v_r - \mu v_r^2 = \rho V_0 \left\{ \frac{1}{M_c} - \frac{2}{M} \right\} \left(v_r^{\frac{1}{3}} - \frac{v_r}{2} \right) \quad (12.1)$$

where v_r is the volume fraction of rubber in the swollen system, μ a polymer–solvent interaction coefficient, ρ the density of the non-swollen rubber, V_0 the molar volume of the solvent, M_c the average molar weight of polymer between cross-links and M the average molecular weight of the rubber before vulcanisation. This rather formidable equation may be simplified in certain circumstances. By choosing conditions whereby the primary molecular weight (M) is large in comparison with M_c, i.e. under normal " technological cure " conditions, where M~200,000 and M_c~10,000, the term $\left(\frac{1}{M_c} - \frac{2}{M} \right)$ approximates to $1/M_c$, then eqn. 12.1 becomes:

$$- \ln(1 - v_r) - v_r - \mu v_r^2 = \rho \frac{V_0}{M_c} \left(v_r^{\frac{1}{3}} - \frac{v_r}{2} \right) \quad . \quad (12.2)$$

By working at high degrees of swelling (e.g. v_r~0·1) a further approximation becomes of interest: $v_r/2$ becomes small compared with $v_r^{\frac{1}{3}}$, and eqn. 12.2 reduces to

$$- \ln(1 - v_r) - v_r - \mu v_r^2 = \rho \frac{V_0}{M_c} \cdot v_r^{\frac{1}{3}} \quad . \quad . \quad (12.3)$$

This last equation is widely known as the Flory–Rehner equation.[2] It preceded the more exact eqn. 12.1 of Flory. It is evident that the essential difference between eqn. 12.2 and 12.3 is the additional $-v_r/2$ term, and in practice,[3] it has been found that the $-v_r/2$ correction is of less importance than the primary molecular weight term $\left(\frac{1}{M_c} - \frac{2}{M} \right)$, consequently some workers prefer to make use of the following swelling equation:

$$- \ln(1 - v_r) - v_r - \mu v_r^2 = \rho V_0 \left(\frac{1}{M_c} - \frac{2}{M} \right) \cdot v_r^{\frac{1}{3}} \quad (12.4)$$

K K

for determining cross-link intensities (no. of cross-links/g.).　Since it has recently been suggested [88] to the present authors that the inclusion of the $- v_r/2$ term in eqn. 12.1, 12.2 is incorrect, the continued use of eqn. 12.3, 12.4 is to be preferred until the question of the validity of this term has been settled.

Cross-link intensity is inversely related to M_c, as can be seen from Fig. 12.1, which represents a portion of cross-linked rubber.　It can be seen that each chain segment (of weight M_c) is terminated by two cross-

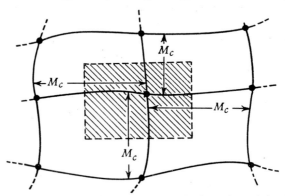

Fig. 12.1. Portion of cross-linked rubber.　M_c is the molar weight of rubber between adjacent cross-links.

links, one at each end.　Clearly, the central cross-link completely " possesses " one-half only of each of the four chain segments emanating from it (shaded area).　Hence, such a cross-link has associated with it $2M_c$ of polymer, i.e. $2M_c$ of polymer contains one cross-link.　One gram of polymer therefore contains $1/2M_c$ cross-links; this is the cross-link intensity.

Cross-link intensity and stress–strain properties

According to the statistical theory of rubber elasticity, the force (f) necessary to maintain a sample of vulcanised rubber at an elongation ratio, α, during simple extension, is [4]

$$f = \rho RT\, A_0 \left(\frac{1}{M_c} - \frac{2}{M} \right)\left(\alpha - \frac{1}{\alpha^2} \right) \quad . \quad . \quad . \quad (12.5)$$

where A_0 is the cross-sectional area of the undeformed sample and α is the ratio of the length of the elongated specimen to its original length; ρ, M and M_c are as previously described, and R and T are the gas constant and absolute temperature respectively.　When the primary molecular weight of the rubber is high, eqn. 12.5 simplifies to

$$f = \frac{\rho RT}{M_c}\, A_0 \left(\alpha - \frac{1}{\alpha^2} \right) . \quad . \quad . \quad . \quad (12.6)$$

It must be emphasised that these relationships are strictly applicable only under conditions of thermodynamic equilibrium. It is well known that hysteresis effects exist and that the retractive force depends markedly on the rate of extension of the system. For physical testing purposes, it is usually sufficient to specify the rate of extension in an attempt to overcome the effects of hysteresis. However, this is clearly insufficient for the estimation of cross-link intensity, and the problem has been tackled either by swelling the vulcanisate after elongation, followed by solvent removal before measuring the retractive force,[5, 6] or by direct stress measurements on the swollen specimen.[7,15]

For small elongations, the so-called Young's modulus (E) may be related, very simply, to the cross-link intensity, thus: E is defined as $f \cdot l/A_0 \cdot \Delta l$, where l is the unstrained length and Δl is the elongation. Expressing E in terms of α, we have $E = f/A_0(\alpha - 1)$. Substituting for f in eqn. 12.6, we obtain:

$$E = \frac{\rho RT}{M_c} \frac{\left(\alpha - \dfrac{1}{\alpha^2}\right)}{(\alpha - 1)}$$

It can easily be shown that for very small extensions, i.e. as α approaches unity, so $(\alpha - 1/\alpha^2)/(\alpha - 1)$ approaches 3, whence

$$E = 3\rho RT/M_c$$

Some workers [9,10] prefer to use this expression for calculating cross-link intensities.

Cross-link intensity and tensile strength

The technological importance attached to tensile strength makes it desirable to relate this property to the cross-link intensity. Although it is now well established that tensile strength is strongly dependent upon the cross-link intensity of the specimen, it is also apparent that it depends on other factors, among which is the amount of orientated crystallinity in the vulcanised, stretched rubber at the moment of fracture.

The relationship between tensile strength and cross-link intensity was first investigated by Gee,[11] who studied sulphur and accelerated-sulphur cures of natural rubber. In view of the complexity of the chemical nature of the sulphur cross-link, it is advantageous to consider non-sulphur systems first. Fig. 12.2 presents collectively the results obtained by Flory, Rabjohn and Shaffer,[12] who used decamethylene-*bis*-methyl azodicarboxylate, by Cuneen,[13] who used *bis*-thioladipic acid, and by Morrell and Stern,[14] who used *tert*-butyl peroxide. The tensile strengths refer to the cross-sectional area at break, since it is at the break-point that the strength is measured. The cross-link intensities for the azodicarboxylate system were determined indirectly by chemical deduction, while those for the *bis*-thioladipic acid and *tert*-butyl peroxide systems were based upon swelling measurements in benzene. It can be seen that in all cases the tensile strength increases almost linearly up to *ca.* 5×10^{-5} moles cross-links per g. Both the azodicarboxylate and the *tert*-butyl peroxide systems then exhibit maxima, at cross-link intensities of *ca.* 5×10^{-5} and *ca.* 7×10^{-5} respectively. Because the latter value was obtained from equilibrium swelling in benzene according to the manner discussed above and using $\mu = 0.395$, it is of interest that a more reliable

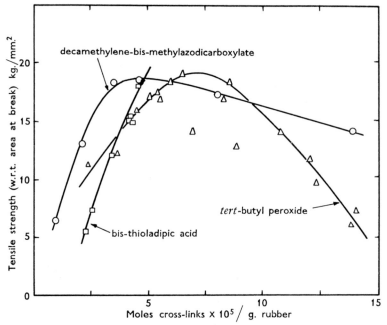

Fig. 12.2. Dependence of tensile strength on cross-link intensity for natural rubber vulcanised by non-sulphur agents.

value [15] for the polymer–solvent interaction coefficient $\mu = 0.422$ allows us to recalculate the cross-link intensity at maximum tensile strength. When this is done for the *tert*-butyl peroxide system, we obtain 5.2×10^{-5}, a value which is remarkably close to that found for the azodicarboxylate system, where a completely independent (i.e. chemical) method of cross-link assessment was used. This value corresponds to *ca.* one cross-link per 300 isoprene residues.

At cross-link values greater than *ca.* 5×10^{-5}, tensile strength falls with increasing cross-links. This is not apparent in Fig. 12.2 for the *bis*-thioladipic acid system because sufficiently high cross-link intensities were not investigated. The discovery of this maximal tensile-strength region, which is not to be confused with the so-called technological optimum cure, is stimulating, since it directs attention to factors other than cross-link intensity, e.g. orientated crystallisation, which is discussed in the next section. However, before passing on, it is worthwhile to compare the above results with those obtained for curing systems containing sulphur. These are re-presented in Fig. 12.3, where tensile strength at break is plotted against cross-link intensity for a non-accelerated

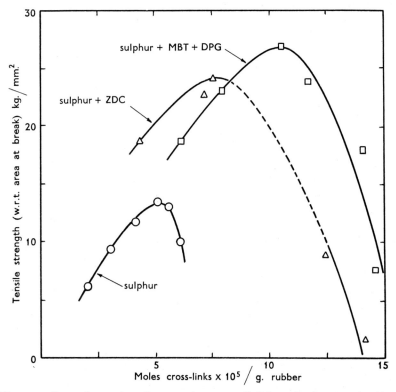

Fig. 12.3. Dependence of tensile strength on cross-link intensity for natural rubber vulcanised by sulphur system (Gee) [11].

sulphur system, a zinc diethyldithiocarbamate (ZDC)–accelerated sulphur system and a mercaptobenzthiazole (MBT)–diphenylguanidine (DPG)–accelerated sulphur system. Both accelerated systems contain zinc oxide and stearic acid. The most striking impression from Fig. 12.3 is the low value (13·5 kg./mm.²) of the maximum tensile strength for the non-accelerated system compared with the values (*ca.* 25 kg./mm.²) obtained for the accelerated systems. Indeed, the non-accelerated system is outstandingly bad in this respect, when compared with both accelerated sulphur and non-sulphur systems. It is clear that the function of the accelerator is more than one of mere catalysis, and the extent to which accelerators (or accelerator fragments) are incorporated chemically into the network is discussed in more detail later.

It is noteworthy that in the region of low cross-link intensities all of the curves tend to be superimposable. In view of the wide range of vulcanising systems involved, this suggests that the relationship between tensile strength and cross-link intensity is independent of the chemical nature (but not the number) of cross-links in the network and depends only on the physico-chemical properties of the polymer molecule. In this region the increase in tensile strength with cross-link intensity follows directly from the concept that an unvulcanised rubber is a liquid and will relax completely under stress by a flow mechanism, whereas a vulcanised rubber is a three-dimensional network which cannot relax under stress—unless, of course, cross-link or chain scission occurs. Thus, with increasing cross-link intensity the rubber, under stress, becomes less subject to viscous flow, and stress dissipation by this means becomes correspondingly less; instead, the stress is supported by an increasing amount of cross-linked polymer, and the rubber matrix is eventually able to withstand successfully the applied stress. The purpose of the cross-links, then, is to prevent flow, and their presence is a necessary condition for the existence of rubbery elasticity.

Tensile strength and orientated crystallisation

It has long been known that natural rubber crystallises on stretching.[19] Field [20] and, later, Goppel [21] attempted to measure the extent of crystallisation, during simple extension, as a function of the elongation. Their results showed considerable discrepancy, and since the method of Goppel was the more refined, his results are now generally accepted. Furthermore, Goppel's results agree much better than Field's with independent estimates based on the volume contraction undergone by rubber during crystallisation.[22, 23] Some pertinent results are presented in Fig. 12.4, which summarises the results obtained from *tert*-butyl peroxide and accelerated-sulphur cures by using X-ray-diffraction and volume-contraction methods. Although the agreement is not striking, the results may be considered satisfactory in view of the different experimental techniques involved and the different vulcanising agents. In any event, it is clear that the extent of crystallisation increases from zero up to *ca.* 30% over an elongation range from 200 to 600%. It must be emphasised that extension results in *orientated* crystallisation, and X-ray studies show conclusively that the crystallites are orientated with their long axis along the direction of stress.

It is instructive to attempt a correlation between tensile strength and extent of orientated crystallisation, based upon the results of Goppel and

Arlman,[18] who obtained tensile strength values for those compounds examined for crystallisation. The appropriate values are plotted in

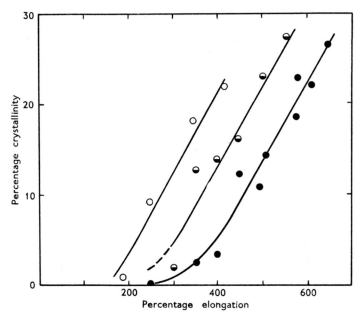

Fig. 12.4. Crystallinity plotted against elongation for natural rubber vulcanisates, in simple extension.

○ *tert*-butyl peroxide cure (volume change method).[23]
● *tert*-butyl peroxide cure (X-ray method).[23]
◒ accelerated sulphur cure (X-ray method).[21]

Fig. 12.5 for a gum-stock containing natural rubber 100, sulphur 5, zinc oxide 3 and DPG 1 part, cured for varying times at 142° C. Although highly desirable, it is clearly not possible to measure the degree of crystallinity at the break-point, consequently the values obtained at 450% elongation have been used; the tensile strength values are calculated with respect to the cross-sectional area at break. It can be seen from Fig. 12.5 (left-hand ordinate) that the tensile strength appears to be linearly related to the degree of crystallinity in the vulcanisate. This conclusion receives support from some results reported by Dogadkin and Karmin,[17] who attempted a similar correlation for natural rubber vulcanisates under simple extension. Unfortunately, these workers used the method of Field (*loc. cit.*) for crystallinity estimation. However, by applying a correction factor (obtained by direct comparison of the results of Goppel with those of Field), this difficulty can be overcome, and the result is shown in Fig. 12.5 (right-hand ordinate), where it is seen that the linear relationship is confirmed. The crystallinity values of Dogadkin and

Karmin refer to an elongation of 500%; this undoubtedly explains the shift of their figures towards higher crystallinity, compared with those of Goppel and Arlman. A similar investigation confirms the qualitative

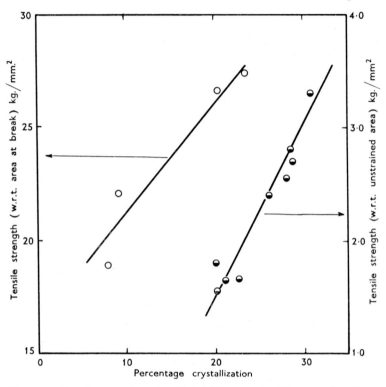

Fig. 12.5. Tensile strength v crystallinity (X-ray method) for natural rubber vulcanised by sulphur and accelerator.

○ Goppel and Arlman.[18]
◑ Dogadkin and Karmin.[17]

dependence of tensile strength on degree of crystallinity for natural rubber vulcanisates sulphur-cured with DPG, MBT and TMTD accelerators.[16]

In Fig. 12.6 are plotted the results of Morrell and Stern,[14] who studied the tensile-strength and crystallisation properties of a series of natural rubber vulcanisates cured by *tert*-butyl peroxide. This system has the advantage that no zinc oxide is present, so that any possibility of vacuole formation, at the zinc oxide–rubber surface during extension, is eliminated. These workers were able to extrapolate their crystallinity values (volume-contraction method) to the break-point, thereby increasing the validity of the procedure. Once again, a linear relationship between tensile strength and degree of crystallinity can be seen to hold.

While the results presented above undoubtedly show that tensile strength is directly proportional to the degree of crystallinity in the rubber at the break-point, the extent to which orientated crystallinity contributes to the magnitude of the tensile strength is not known quantitatively.   Thus Flory,[26] in his investigation of Butyl-rubber vulcanisates, preferred to relate his tensile-strength results to the " active fraction " of the network, which he defined as the fraction of the network subjected to permanent orientation by stretching.[27]

A plausible explanation for the above results can now be attempted, along the lines suggested by Flory [27] and Gee.[11]   At very low degrees of

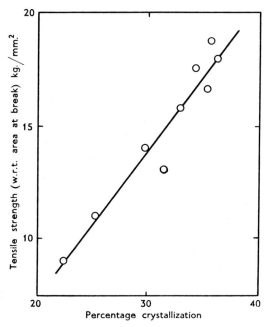

Fig. 12.6. Tensile strength v crystallinity (volume change method) for natural rubber vulcanised by *tert*-butyl peroxide, from curves of Morrell and Stern.[14]

cross-linking (*ca.* $1 \cdot 0 \times 10^{-5}$ cross-links/g) the rubber is too plastic to allow orientation to occur during extension.   It is easier for the system to react to the deformation stress by viscous flow than by crystallisation, with the result that the stress is dissipated before it is sufficiently large to effect reorientation and crystallisation.   At medium degrees of cross-linking ($1 \cdot 0 \times 10^{-5}$ to 5×10^{-5} cross-links/g.), a complete network has been formed and elongation-at-break values of *ca.* 900% are found,[14] and it is clear that viscous flow is no longer feasible.   Over this region, appreciable molecular adlineation occurs during extension, and a large rise in degree of crystallisation is made manifest.   Paralleling this rise is the increase in tensile strength, which may improve to values of 20–25 kg./mm.^{2} (w.r.t. area at break). Since the network structure is now complete, any further insertion of cross-links can only result in the " tightening " of the network. This, in turn, imposes an increasing number of restrictions on any molecular segment attempting to adlineate with a neighbouring segment. The overall effect is that the degree of orientated crystallisation now falls and a concomitant drop in tensile strength is observed. It can be objected that the application of a sufficiently high stress should eventually produce adlineation and crystallisation, no matter how " tight " the network is. It appears, however, that rupture occurs well before such a high stress can be applied. This is not surprising in view of the high stress values required to extend highly cross-linked rubbers.

The above explanation receives support from the well-known fact that butadiene–styrene rubbers, whose gum-stocks possess notoriously low tensile strengths, do not crystallise on extension, whereas Butyl and polyurethane gum-stocks, which show high degrees of orientated crystallinity on extension, exhibit high tensile strengths. Moreover, the tensile strength of natural rubber vulcanisates is markedly reduced when the system is swollen with a solvent.[11] This is to be expected, since the presence of solvent molecules between the chain segments of the rubber will reduce crystallisation tendencies. Increasing the test temperature exerts a similar effect.[11, 28]

In this discussion no attempt is made to explain why a highly crystalline matrix should possess a greater inherent strength than a corresponding amorphous system. Any explanation would necessitate a greater knowledge of the mechanism of rupture, concerning which comparatively little is known at present.

Vulcanisation and chemical cross-links

The development of the statistical theory of rubber elasticity has been well justified by the impetus it has given to the development of new synthetic rubbers which are chemically unrelated to natural rubber, and by the consequent rationalisation of such rubber properties as modulus, swelling, tensile strength, crystallinity, etc., in terms of the cross-link intensity of the rubber. In only two cases,[3, 6] however, has the degree of cross-linking—as determined physically by swelling or modulus—been checked by independent chemical means. In both cases, it is gratifying to note, agreement has been very satisfactory. Since the process of cross-linking is of necessity a chemical one (although the chemical reaction involved may be induced physically, e.g. by high energy radiation), it is of great interest to summarise some of the chemical evidence for the cross-linking theory of vulcanisation. This theory is now generally accepted, although certain workers still believe that the cross-links are wholly [29] or partially [30] due to van der Waals attraction between neighbouring chains. The major purpose of this section is to establish that the chemical cross-links are essentially covalent, although the presence of zinc oxide in olefine rubbers invariably introduces the possibility of ionic, salt-like cross-links. In attempting this, it is desirable to outline the organic chemistry involved in the cross-linking reactions. Indeed, such chemical knowledge is essential to an understanding of the processes involved. It must be freely admitted at the outset that—in principle, at least—a sufficiently strong van der Waals attraction may constitute a cross-link, and therefore give rise to vulcanisation effects indistinguishable from those due to covalent, chemical bonds. However, the uncertainty may be by-passed by postulating that vulcanisation involves the cross-linking of neighbouring molecules in such a way that these cross-links are not destroyed when the vulcanisate is subjected to mild variations in physical conditions or environment. For example, a cross-link defined in this manner will be quite stable towards a swelling fluid, towards stresses of all types and towards elevated temperatures (short of bond destruction). It is known that these influences do not destroy covalent bonds, and we shall be justified in concluding that a cross-link detected by swelling or modulus methods must, in general, be a covalent one. In the event of a

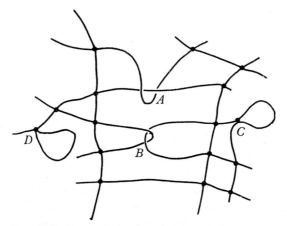

Fig. 12.7. Cross-linked network showing chain-entanglements A, B and intra-molecular covalent bonds C, D.

cross-link being destroyed by swelling and/or stress application it will not constitute a true cross-link, indeed it will not be detectable by the usual physical methods. It should be mentioned, however, that chain-entanglements, such as shown in Fig. 12.7, qualify for inclusion in the above definition, and indirect means must be used for assessing their relative importance. On the other hand, a covalent bond may be inserted in the rubber during vulcanisation which cannot be detected by normal physical methods, e.g. Fig. 12.7, C and D. In fact, most of the discrepancies found between chemical and physical estimations of cross-link intensities are ascribed to irregularities of these types.

Coupling of simple molecules by vulcanising agents

The study of molecular models for vulcanisation investigations is now well established, but results obtained by their use should be applied to rubber with caution, owing to the polymeric nature of rubber. For example, polyisoprene can undergo intramolecular re-actions that are not possible with " monomer " polyisoprene: 2-methyl-butene ($CH_3 \cdot CMe \vdots CH \cdot CH_3$). Furthermore, the reactivity of the functional group may be radically affected by the replacement of the end hydrogen atoms of the molecule by long-chain groups R, e.g. $R \cdot CH_2 \cdot CMe \vdots CH \cdot CH_2 \cdot R$. Nevertheless, model compounds have played a great part in the development of chemical theories of vulcanisation, and some of the more important cases are now presented in the course of a summary of pertinent studies of vulcanisation. These studies are all eventually concerned with natural rubber vulcanisation, although in certain cases parallel studies have been made with butadiene–styrene rubbers.

Sulphur monochloride. This reagent, which vulcanises rubber even in the cold, is known to effect the coupling of simple olefines, e.g. ethylene, by a reaction which is believed to be:

$$2CH_2{=}CH_2 + S_2Cl_2 \longrightarrow S \underset{CH_2-CH_2-Cl}{\overset{CH_2-CH_2-Cl}{\diagup \diagdown}} + S$$

although the reaction is undoubtedly not as straightforward as this (see later).

Sulphur. The importance of sulphur warrants a separate discussion (see later). It is sufficient to note here that simple olefines are coupled by sulphur, with the formation of polysulphide bridges to yield dimers and higher polymers. Taking isobutylene as a model, the following reaction has been shown to occur:

$$2(CH_3)_2C \vdots CH_2 + S_x \longrightarrow (CH_3)_3C \cdot S_x \cdot CH_2 \cdot C(CH_3) \vdots CH_2$$

bis-Thiol acids. The reactions of thiol compounds (RSH) with model olefines and natural rubber have been investigated.[31] In all cases, the thiol was found to undergo an addition reaction in a sense opposite to Markownikov's Rule, and the reaction is catalysed by peroxides and ultra-violet light. This is invariably diagnostic of a non-polar, free radical process. Methylcyclohexene reacts with thiolacetic acid,[32] thus:

$$CH_3\text{-cyclohexene} + CH_3 \cdot CO \cdot SH \longrightarrow CH_3\text{-cyclohexyl-}CH \cdot S \cdot CO \cdot CH_3$$

while the difunctional *bis*-thiol acids [13] give rise to a coupling reaction:

$$2\ CH_3\text{-cyclohexene} + HS \cdot CO(CH_2)_x \cdot CO \cdot SH \longrightarrow$$

It was similarly found that natural rubber reacted with thiolacetic acid to give the appropriate derivative:

$$\left(-CH_2-CH-CH-CH_2- \right)_n \quad (CH_3;\ S \cdot CO \cdot CH_3)$$

which is quite soluble in solvents and has none of the characteristics of a vulcanisate. When natural rubber was treated, under the same conditions, with difunctional *bis*-thiol acids, however, a ready reaction ensued at 100° C which resulted in a product having all of the general properties (elasticity, insolubility, swelling) of a vulcanised rubber. The reaction product, by analogy with the above, may be legitimately described as containing a certain number of cross-links of the following type:

$$
\begin{array}{c}
\overset{\displaystyle CH_3}{\underset{|}{}} \\
-CH_2-CH-CH-CH_2- \\
\underset{|}{} \\
S-CO \\
\underset{|}{} \\
(CH_2)_x \\
CH_3 \quad S-CO \\
\underset{|}{} \quad \underset{|}{} \\
-CH_2-CH-CH-CH_2-
\end{array}
$$

(I)

although this is evidently an oversimplification, since *ca.* 55% of the available thiol acid remained uncombined when all reaction with rubber had ceased. Moreover, the unreacted acid was found to have undergone polycondensation, resulting in products of the type

$$HS \cdot CO \{(CH_2)_4 \cdot CO\}_n SH$$

This is unfortunate, since it precludes the explicit determination of the number of inserted cross-links by chemical means (combined S). However, Cuneen was able to measure the cross-link intensities of his products

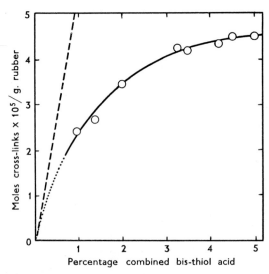

Fig. 12.8. Cross-link intensity *v* combined *bis*-thioladipic acid in vulcanisation of natural rubber (results of Cuneen [13]). Interrupted line: theoretical for 1 mol. thiol acid per cross-link.

by swelling measurements in benzene, and his results are of interest in that they illustrate departures from ideal behaviour similar to other vulcanising systems.   Fig. 12.8 shows cross-link intensity plotted against the percentage of combined *bis*-thioladipic acid in the vulcanisate.   As a comparison, the theoretical relationship for one mole of combined acid per mole cross-link is included as an interrupted line.   It can be seen that as the combined acid increases the cross-linking efficiency (i.e. the no. of moles of cross-links produced by one mole of vulcanising agent) becomes progressively smaller and eventually approaches zero at *ca.* 5% combined thiol acid.   On the other hand, by attempting an extrapolation (dotted line, Fig. 12.8) of the experimental curve back to zero combined thiol acid at the commencement of the reaction, it is evident that the experimental curve approaches the theoretical, and this suggests that the vulcanisation commences with an efficiency of unity, i.e. that the first cross-links inserted are indeed as depicted by formula I.   Should this be so, one can surmise that, as the vulcanisation proceeds, progressively more *bis*-thiol acid is incorporated in the rubber without contributing to the network structure. This could be due to mono-attachments of the type:

$$-CH_2-\overset{\overset{\displaystyle CH_3}{|}}{CH}-\underset{\underset{\displaystyle S \cdot CO(CH_2)_4 \cdot CO \cdot SH}{|}}{CH}-CH_2-$$

or to ring formation as a result of an intramolecular reaction:

$$-CH_2-\overset{\overset{\displaystyle CH_3}{|}}{CH}-CH-CH_2-CH_2-\overset{\overset{\displaystyle CH_3}{|}}{CH}-CH-CH_2-$$

(with the bridge: S—CO—(CH$_2$)$_4$—CO—S)

although the possibility of autoxidation catalysis by the thiol acid should not be overlooked.   A concurrent progressive degradative reaction of this type would result in low cross-linking efficiency.

   bis-Azodicarboxylates.   The use of this type of reagent constitutes a classical example of the application of simple models to the problem of rubber vulcanisation.   It is of additional interest, since it is one of the very few systems investigated where it has proved possible to check quantitatively the predictions of the statistical theory by chemical means, and the results were extremely gratifying and serve to show the essential correctness of both the elasticity theory and the chemical-model method.

   The vulcanising potentiality of this type of reagent was established by showing that diethyl azodicarboxylate reacted with 2-methyl-2-butene thus:[33]

$$CH_3 \cdot CMe \text{:} CH \cdot CH_3$$
$$+$$
$$\underset{\parallel}{N \cdot CO_2Et}$$
$$N \cdot CO_2Et$$

$$\longrightarrow$$

$$CH_2 \cdot CMe \text{:} CH \cdot CH_3$$
$$|$$
$$N \cdot CO_2Et$$
$$|$$
$$NH \cdot CO_2Et$$

The chemical structure of the adduct was proved by ozonolysis and hydrogenation. It was further found that natural rubber reacted similarly to form a stable, soluble adduct:

$$-CH_2-\underset{\underset{CH_3}{|}}{C}=CH-CH_2-$$
$$+$$
$$\underset{\parallel}{N \cdot CO_2Et}$$
$$N \cdot CO_2Et$$

$$\longrightarrow$$

$$-\underset{\underset{N \cdot CO_2Et}{|}}{CH}-\underset{\underset{CH_3}{|}}{C}=CH-CH_2-$$
$$|$$
$$NH \cdot CO_2Et$$

Soon afterwards it was shown that when a difunctional analogue was used it could cause the coupling of two molecules of 2-methyl-2-butene.[6] Furthermore, when decamethylene-bis-methylazodicarboxylate was allowed to react with natural rubber it resulted in an insoluble adduct having all the properties of a vulcanised rubber. By analogy with the above chemical models, the following chemical structure was ascribed to the cross-links:

$$CH-N-NH-CO-O-(CH_2)_{10}-O-CO-NH-N-\cdots-CH$$

$$CH_3-\underset{\parallel}{C} \quad CO_2CH_3 \qquad\qquad CO_2CH_3 \quad \underset{\parallel}{C}-CH_3$$

$$CH \qquad\qquad\qquad\qquad\qquad\qquad\qquad CH$$

$$CH_2 \qquad\qquad\qquad\qquad\qquad\qquad\qquad CH_2$$

(II)

Conditions were established to allow the reaction to proceed quantitatively. Thus by choosing the appropriate amount of bis-azodicarboxylate and allowing the reaction to proceed to completion, these workers were able to produce vulcanised rubbers of any required degree of cross-linking and, for the first time anywhere, of explicitly known cross-link intensity. Some important aspects of the experimental technique are as follows: (a) natural rubber of high primary molecular weight was chosen so as to allow the use of the simplified modulus eqn. 12.6; (b) vulcanisates were prepared by mixing the reactants in benzene solution, by solvent removal followed by careful de-gassing and vulcanising in air at 60° C for 2 hours; (c) the absence of rubber degradation during cross-linking was satisfactorily established by control experiments using diethylazodicarboxylate, during which no significant fall in viscosity occurred, and (d) equilibrium values of retractive force under simple extension were assured by pre-swelling the elongated specimen in petroleum ether. These precautions permit great reliance to be placed upon the results.

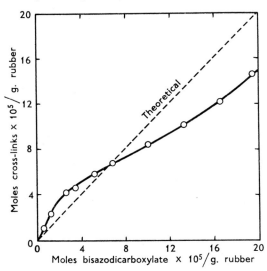

Fig. 12.9. Natural rubber vulcanised by *bis*-azodicarboxylate. Ordinate: cross-link intensity by retractive force and eqn. 12.6. Abscissa: cross-link intensity by chemical means. (Flory, Rabjohn and Shaffer [6].)

Using this technique, it was possible to measure the retractive force, at 100% elongation, for a series of natural rubber (and butadiene–styrene rubber) vulcanisates of known cross-link intensity. The values thus obtained were compared with values calculated from eqn. 12.6 and, in general, remarkable agreement was found. Results for natural rubber vulcanised with decamethylene-*bis*-methylazodicarboxylate are summarised in Fig. 12.9, in which the cross-link intensity—from retractive-force measurements—is plotted against the known, chemical cross-link intensity. The interrupted line refers to the theoretical relationship to be expected if every physical cross-link is of the type, shown above (II).

It will be recalled, from the previously discussed results of Figs. 12.2 and 12.3, that optimum tensile strength is generally attained in the range 5×10^{-5} to 10×10^{-5} moles cross-links/g. of rubber, and from Fig. 12.9 it is evident that over this important range the statistical theory provides cross-link assessments that do not differ by more than $\pm 20\%$ from chemical assessments. These differences are not unexpected and have been ascribed to network complications not taken into account in the statistical theory. Positive deviations at low cross-link intensities are probably due to chain entanglements (Fig. 12.7, *A* and *B*), which exert the same elastic effect as chemical cross-links and give rise to a higher number of physically effective cross-links than theoretical. Negative deviations at high cross-link intensities probably result from increased intramolecular reactions (Fig. 12.7, *C* and *D*) which result in a lower number of physically effective cross-links than theoretical.

It may be concluded that the statistical theory provides an essentially correct picture of the physical nature of vulcanised rubber and that its quantitative predictions concerning assessment of cross-link intensities (i.e. degree of cure) may be satisfactorily relied upon. Provided, then, that suitable experimental precautions are taken to obtain equilibrium conditions, " modulus " measurements may be relied upon to provide a reasonably correct assessment of the effective physical cross-links in vulcanised rubber networks.

tert-Butyl peroxide. Although this reagent is not incorporated chemically in the rubber during vulcanisation, it results in the coupling of two, originally distinct, olefine units, and hence qualifies for inclusion in this discussion of polyfunctional reagents with olefines. In a series of chemical studies of the reaction between *tert*-butyl peroxide and olefines, it was satisfactorily established that dimers (and higher polymers) were formed from the olefine.[34] These workers concluded from their own and previous [35] studies that *tert*-butoxy radicals, resulting from homolytic scission of the peroxide, react either by direct dehydrogenation of the α-methylene groups of the olefine with concomitant *tert*-butanol formation, or by decomposition to acetone and methyl radicals which themselves cause similar dehydrogenation. As a result, the olefine radicals combine to yield coupled poly-olefines, and *tert*-butanol, acetone, methane and ethane are formed as by-products. The overall reaction is shown schematically below:

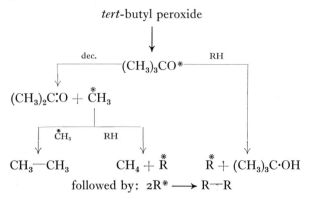

followed by: $2R^* \longrightarrow R{-}R$

where RH represents an olefine possessing an α-methylene group. They further showed that the coupled olefines contain no combined oxygen and retain, virtually unchanged, the original unsaturation. They suggested the following process, here illustrated with methylcyclohexene as the isoprene model:

$$
\begin{array}{ccc}
\text{CH}_3 & & \text{CH}_3 \\
| & & | \\
\text{C} & & \text{C} \\
\diagup\diagdown & & \diagup\diagdown \\
\text{CH}_2 \quad \text{CH} \quad + (\text{CH}_3)_3\text{C·O*} & \longrightarrow & \text{CH}_2 \quad \text{CH} \quad + (\text{CH}_3)_3\text{C·OH} \\
| \qquad | & & | \qquad |* \\
\text{CH}_2 \quad \text{CH}_2 & & \text{CH}_2 \quad \text{CH} \\
\diagdown\diagup & & \diagdown\diagup \\
\text{CH}_2 & & \text{CH}_2
\end{array}
$$

$$
2 \;
\begin{array}{c}
\text{CH}_3 \\
| \\
\text{C} \\
\diagup\diagdown \\
\text{CH} \quad \text{CH}_2 \\
| \qquad | \\
\text{CH}_2 \quad \text{CH*} \\
\diagdown\diagup \\
\text{CH}_2
\end{array}
\longrightarrow
\begin{array}{cc}
\text{CH}_3 & \text{CH}_3 \\
| & | \\
\text{C} & \text{C} \\
\diagup\diagdown & \diagup\diagdown \\
\text{CH}_2 \quad \text{CH} & \text{CH} \quad \text{CH}_2 \\
| \qquad | & | \qquad | \\
\text{CH}_2 \quad \text{CH}\!-\!\!\text{CH} & \text{CH}_2 \\
\diagdown\diagup & \diagdown\diagup \\
\text{CH}_2 & \text{CH}_2
\end{array}
$$

This dimer may subsequently undergo dehydrogenation and further polymerisation. Although the above methylcyclohexenyl radical may couple in its alternative mesomeric form, the nature of the cross-link remains unchanged.

With polyisoprenes, the reaction is somewhat more involved. For example, with 2 : 6-dimethylocta-2 : 6-diene the same reaction sequence is envisaged, although an intermediate cyclisation stage appears to occur (reduced unsaturation in the coupled olefine). However, the incursion of cyclisation does not affect the eventual extent of coupling in so far as one carbon–carbon cross-link still results from the combination of every pair of isoprenyl radicals,[3] thus:

$$
\begin{array}{c}
*\text{CH} \\
\diagup\diagdown \\
\text{CH} \quad \text{CH}_2 \\
\| \qquad | \\
(\text{Me})_2\text{C} \quad \text{CMe} \\
\diagdown\diagup \\
\text{CH·Me} \\
\\
\text{(III)}
\end{array}
\xrightarrow{\text{resonance}}
\begin{array}{c}
\text{CH} \\
\diagup\!\!\diagdown \\
\text{CH} \quad \text{CH}_2 \\
| \qquad | \\
(\text{Me})_2\text{C*} \quad \text{CMe} \\
\diagdown\!\!\diagup \\
\text{CH·Me} \\
\\
\text{(IV)}
\end{array}
\xrightarrow{\text{cyclisation}}
\begin{array}{c}
\text{CH} \\
\diagup\!\!\diagdown \\
\text{CH} \quad \text{CH}_2 \\
| \qquad | \\
(\text{Me})_2\text{C} \quad *\text{CMe} \\
\diagdown\diagup \\
\text{CH·Me} \\
\\
\text{(V)}
\end{array}
$$

(interrupted curved arrows represent single electron transformations) followed by:

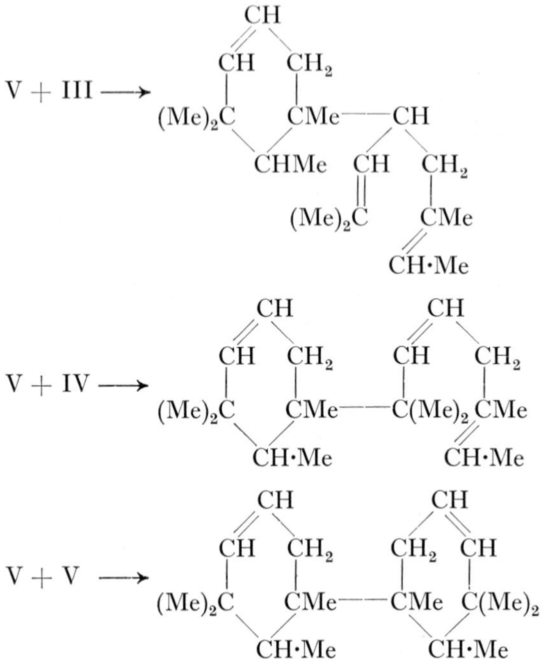

$$V + III \longrightarrow$$

$$
\begin{array}{c}
CH \\
CH \quad CH_2 \\
(Me)_2C \quad\quad CMe\text{---}CH \\
CHMe \quad CH \quad CH_2 \\
(Me)_2C \quad\quad CMe \\
CH\cdot Me
\end{array}
$$

$$V + IV \longrightarrow$$

$$
\begin{array}{c}
CH \quad\quad\quad CH \\
CH \quad CH_2 \quad CH \quad CH_2 \\
(Me)_2C \quad CMe\text{---}C(Me)_2 \quad CMe \\
CH\cdot Me \quad\quad\quad CH\cdot Me
\end{array}
$$

$$V + V \longrightarrow$$

$$
\begin{array}{c}
CH \quad\quad\quad CH \\
CH \quad CH_2 \quad CH_2 \quad CH \\
(Me)_2C \quad CMe\text{---}CMe \quad C(Me)_2 \\
CH\cdot Me \quad\quad\quad CH\cdot Me
\end{array}
$$

At the same time, Farmer and Moore showed that *tert*-butyl peroxide was capable of vulcanising rubber under conditions identical with those necessary for the coupling of simple olefines. Some characteristic properties of the vulcanisates are collected in Table I, and it is clear that classical vulcanisation has been effected by this reagent.

TABLE 12.1

VULCANISATION CHARACTERISTICS OF NATURAL RUBBER/*tert*-BUTYL PEROXIDE CURES (6 hr. at 140° C) [34]

tert-*Butyl* peroxide (%)	Moles × 10^5 cross-links/g.	Tensile strength (kg./cm.²)	Modulus 300% (kg./cm.²)
1·0	6·8	155	14
1·45	7·4	206	16
1·7	7·4	190	17
3·1	17	22	—
3·95	23	16	—
51·5	114	—	—

From this investigation, it appeared that the *tert*-butyl peroxide system would be eminently suitable for confirming the validity of the statistical theory, subject to satisfactory means being developed to provide reliable chemical assessment of cross-link intensities. The results of such a study have recently been announced.[3] Cross-link intensities were obtained (a) by swelling measurements in n-decane and the application of eqn. 12.4, and (b) by chemical analysis of the by-products of vulcanisation, i.e. by determining the amounts of *tert*-butanol and methane liberated during cure. The vulcanisation was performed over a temperature range of 110°–140° C in an enclosed system to ensure absence of oxygen and to prevent the loss of volatile by-products. *tert*-Butanol was estimated by an infra-red method and methane by a volumetric gas method after fractional distillation. A consideration of the reaction scheme depicted on p. 273 shows that every act of formation of a radical R* is accompanied by the formation of either one molecule of *tert*-butanol or one molecule of methane. Since every cross-link results from the combination of two such radicals, it follows that the number of cross-links is equal to

$$\frac{1}{2}\{\text{molecules } \textit{tert}\text{-butanol} + \text{molecules methane}\}.$$

It should be mentioned that, unless the period of vulcanisation was excessive, virtually all of the peroxide could be accounted for in terms of unreacted peroxide and liberated *tert*-butanol and acetone. Furthermore, it was found that [acetone] $\simeq$ [methane] + 2[ethane] as required by the postulated reaction scheme.

The results are summarised in Fig. 12.10, where the cross-link intensity, determined by swelling, is plotted against the cross-link intensity determined chemically. It is readily seen that the deviation from theoretical (i.e. the relationship to be expected if every physical cross-link were caused by simple, radical combination: $2R* \longrightarrow R–R$) is largely due to a positive intercept of $2·9 \times 10^{-5}$ moles cross-links/g. rubber at zero chemical cross-link intensity. This result is ascribed to the existence of molecular entanglements (Fig. 12.7, A and B) which are " frozen " into the vulcanisate by the chemical cross-links. If this is so it is to be expected that, at very low degrees of cross-linking, the experimental line should curve down to the origin (Fig. 12.10, dotted line), because a molecular entanglement exists only by virtue of both of its component chain segments being terminated by cross-links. Consequently, as zero cross-link intensity is approached, the possibility of a molecular entanglement possessing such chain segments approaches zero, and no entanglements should therefore exist at zero cross-link intensity. Indeed, this is a logical necessity for a completely uncured rubber in contact with a solvent.

Further reference to Fig. 12.10 shows that a second deviation from theoretical is present. This is the somewhat greater slope of the experimental line compared with the theoretical. This implies that, after allowance has been made for entanglements, the addition of each chemical cross-link is accompanied by the addition of slightly more than one (1·2) physical cross-links.   The reason for this is obscure.

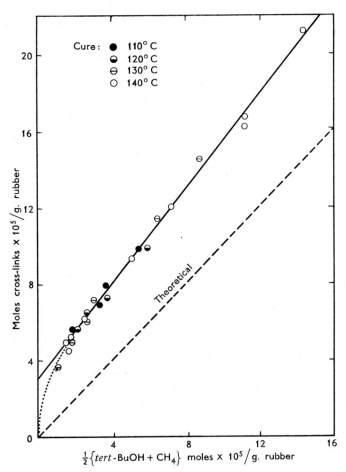

Fig. 12.10. Natural rubber vulcanised by *tert*-butyl peroxide. Ordinate: cross-link intensity by swelling and eqn. 12.4. Abscissa: cross-link intensity by chemical means. (Moore and Watson [3].)

Notwithstanding these two, theoretically minor deviations, the results of this excellent investigation are a clear vindication of the statistical theory of rubber elasticity as applied to the measurement of cross-link intensities by equilibrium swelling methods with the use of eqn. 12.4.

Summary.   The examples discussed so far are sufficient to convince that reagents able to couple simple olefines are also able to vulcanise rubber. In all of the cases mentioned the cross-links have resulted from the coupling of separate rubber molecules by classical covalent bonds. More-over, with the *bis*-azodicarboxylates and *tert*-butyl peroxide the evidence is overwhelmingly in favour of the conclusion that all of the physically effective cross-links, *inserted by the vulcanising agent*, are exclusively covalent in nature. The italicised qualification serves to accommodate the existence of physically effective cross-links arising from chain-entangle-ments in the network. It follows that, in these cases, secondary valency forces play no part in the cross-link pattern of the elastic network. This is not to say that strongly polar groups are ineffective in modifying certain physical properties of vulcanisates. On the contrary, it is known, for example, that diethylazodicarboxylate profoundly modifies the tensile strength of *bis*-azodicarboxylate-cured rubber, although it plays no part in cross-link insertion.[12] This is not surprising in view of the quite different factors that contribute to high tensile strength and high modulus.

Vulcanisation Systems

Support for the theory that intermolecular van der Waals attractive forces are responsible for vulcanisation appears to be based upon the pub-lished work of Williams[30] and of Stiehler and Wakelin,[29] who relied on the following evidence for their views: (a) accelerated-sulphur vulcanisates are peptised when heated in the presence of piperidine or an excess of piperidinium pentamethylenedithiocarbamate. Intermolecular covalent bonds should not be affected and, therefore, these workers suggested that the cross-links are due to weaker, secondary forces which are easily dispersed by basic peptisers. (b) The secondary valency forces were due to the highly polarised thioketone groups resulting from α-methylene attack by sulphur. Infra-red evidence[36] (band at 10·4 μ) was quoted as favouring the existence of thio-ketone groups.

These views constituted a serious criticism of the covalent bond theory, but may now be disregarded, since subsequent reports show that the peptisation effect is wholly ascribable to molecular oxygen.[37] In the absence of oxygen no peptisation occurs whether piperidine is present or not. This result shows rather that oxidative fission of covalent bonds is the cause,[38] and thus serves to strengthen the covalent bond theory. Moreover, further investigation[39] has led to a re-assignment of the 10·4μ band which is now known to be associated with the CRH:CRH group.

Vulcanised latex appears to be exceptional in that, while each latex globule is internally cross-linked by covalent bonds, neighbouring globules are held together by weaker, secondary forces. As expected, such a system is very easily dispersed mechanically when highly swollen in benzene.[40]

Non-accelerated sulphur system

Researches [41] on the reactions of olefines with oxygen and sulphur have unfortunately led to the wide acceptance of a free radical chain mechanism in which the following stages are said to occur:

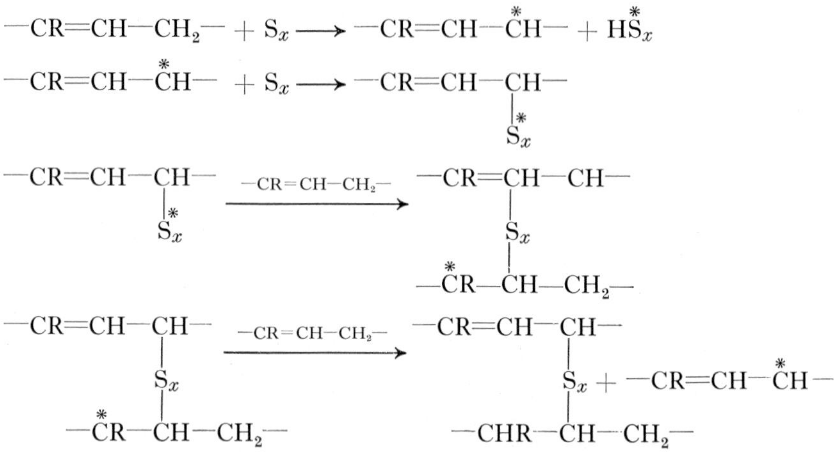

$$-CR=CH-CH_2- + S_x \longrightarrow -CR=CH-\overset{*}{C}H- + H\overset{*}{S}_x$$

$$-CR=CH-\overset{*}{C}H- + S_x \longrightarrow -CR=CH-CH-$$
$$\underset{\overset{|}{\overset{*}{S}_x}}{}$$

$$-CR=CH-CH- \xrightarrow{-CR=CH-CH_2-} -CR=CH-CH-$$

with the products leading to

$$-\overset{*}{C}R-CH-CH_2-$$

$$-CR=CH-CH- \xrightarrow{-CR=CH-CH_2-} -CR=CH-CH-$$

$$-\overset{*}{C}R-CH-CH_2- \qquad -CHR-CH-CH_2- \;+\; -CR=CH-\overset{*}{C}H-$$

The evidence supporting this mechanism is indirect, however, since it relies entirely on: (a) the α-methylene reactivity exhibited by certain olefines towards free radical reagents such as oxygen, and (b) the analytical establishment of the main product of sulphuration to consist of alkyl-alkenyl (poly) sulphides. Certainly, there appears to be no direct evidence for the free radical nature of the reaction, let alone evidence sufficiently convincing to permit acceptance of the above detailed mechanism. While the evidence may be said to be permissive of such a mechanism, it is by no means compelling, and it is as well to reconsider the chemical evidence in the light of more recent studies of sulphur and model olefine systems.

When *iso*butylene or *cyclo*hexene was heated with sulphur at 140° C these mono-olefines were found to give rise to bimolecular polysulphides whose carbon–hydrogen ratio was the same as the original olefine but whose unsaturation had been reduced by half.[42] Similar results were obtained using the di-isoprenic 2 : 6-dimethylocta-2 : 6-diene, except that the product appeared to contain a monomolecular cyclised monosulphide (VI) in addition to bimolecular polysulphides (VII).

(VI)

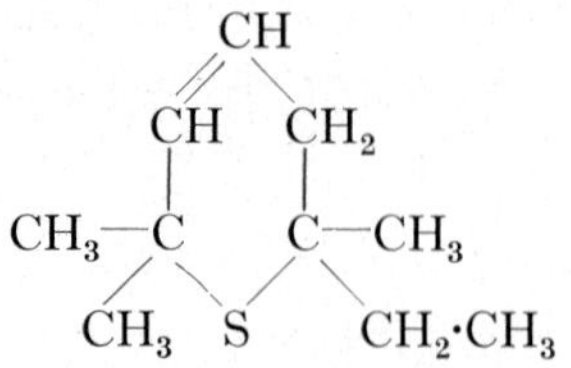

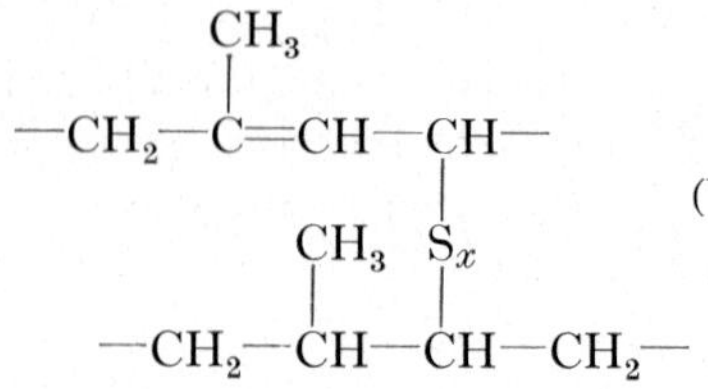

(VII)

A more detailed re-investigation [43] of this reaction has shown that the structures VI and VII are no longer acceptable. The cyclic monosulphide is now regarded as a mixture of the compounds VIII, IX, X and XI,

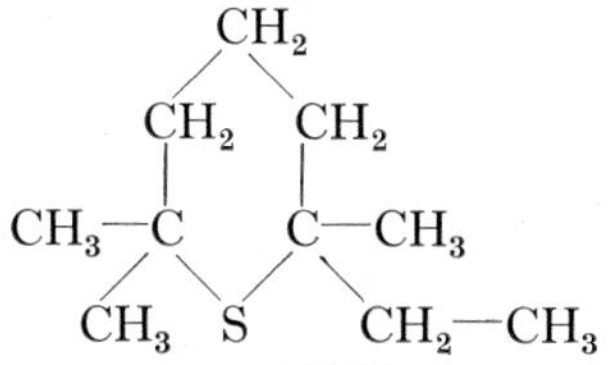

(VIII) 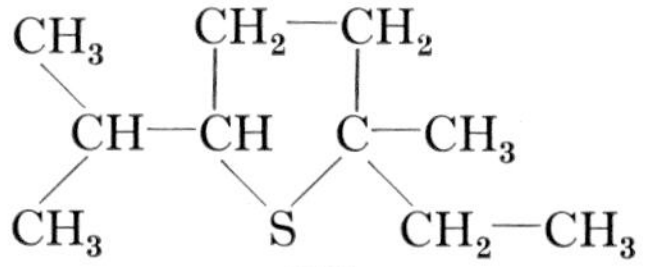   (IX)

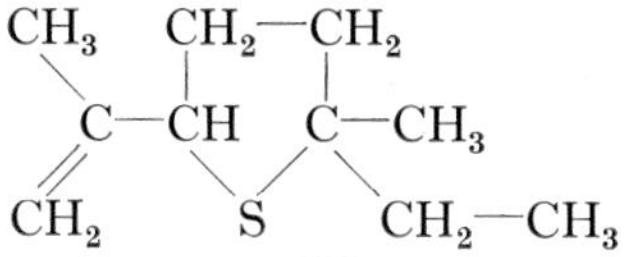

(X) 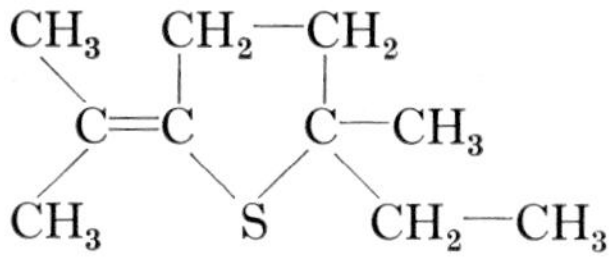   (XI)

and the bimolecular polysulphide as containing structures of the types XII and XIII in addition to VII, after prolonged heating.

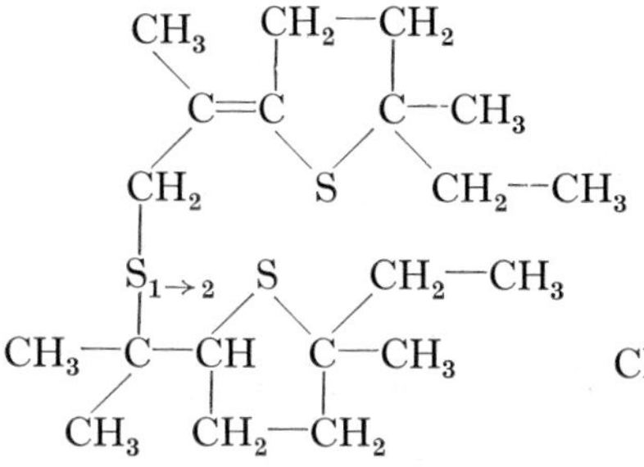

(XII) 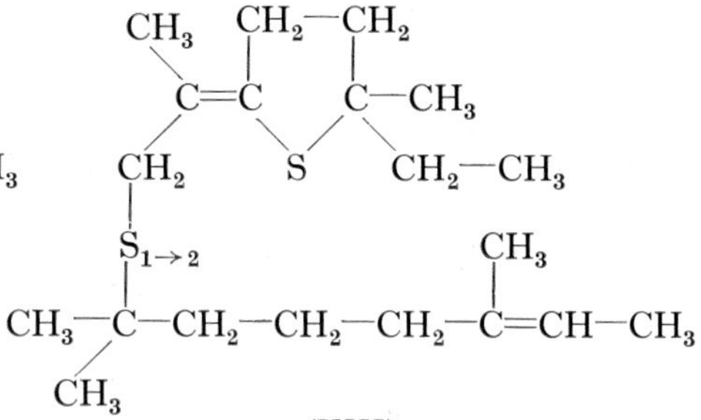   (XIII)

The evidence for the structures VIII to XI is based upon the following observations made on the cyclic monosulphide mixture: (*a*) After chromatographic fractionation on silica gel, the mixture gave a product free from VIII. Catalytic hydrogenation of this product gave a single compound IX, which was identified by comparison with an independently synthesised sample. (*b*) The presence of X was shown by an infra-red absorption band at 11·3 μ, which is characteristic of the $CR_2 : CH_2$ group. (*c*) VIII was identified by its infra-red absorption spectrum. (*d*) XI was identified by its possession of an ultra-violet absorption band 2290–2300 Å, corresponding to the $-C=C-S-$ group, the absence of a double-bond absorption band in the infra-red—this absence being characteristic of the group $CR_2:CR_2$—and the absorption of one mole of hydrogen per $C_{10}H_{18}S$ unit to give pure IX.

The relative amounts of VIII to XI were found to be markedly time-dependent, see Table 12.2, a result that accentuates the complexity of the

overall process. Thus, after 50 hours, X has undergone further re-
action(s), as a result of which VIII has become the major product, XI has
increased somewhat in amount and X has almost completely disappeared.
The details of these reactions are, as yet, matters for speculation, although
it has been shown that the transformation X ⟶ XI can be effected by
base catalysis of elemental sulphur (S_x) thus:

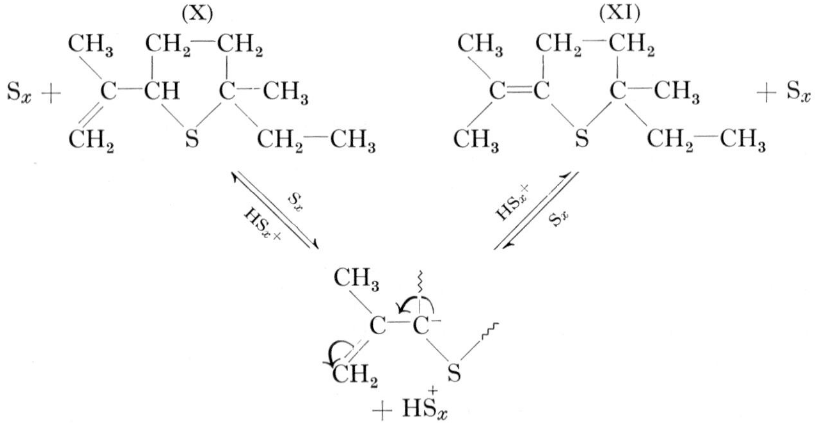

To explain the presence of X, and therefore the ultimate presence of
XI, as a major reaction product, a polar mechanism has been suggested
along the following lines:

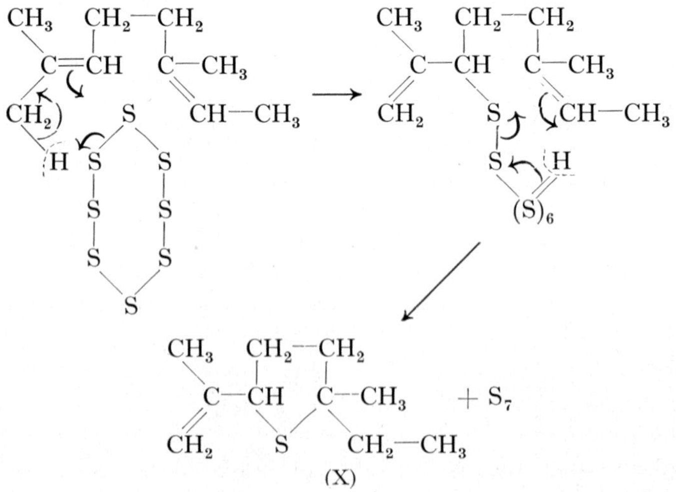

where the curved arrows represent electron pair transformations. Support for the concept of a polar reaction, as distinct from a free radical

reaction, comes from observations that the reaction is accelerated by free radical reaction inhibitors and by polar additives.[44]

TABLE 12.2

TIME DEPENDENCE OF REACTION PRODUCTS OF 2 : 6-DIMETHYLOCTA-2 : 6-DIENE WITH SULPHUR AT 140° C [43]

Time, hour	VIII	IX	X	XI
5	Zero	Small	50%	25%
50	60%	Small	4%	31%

The large amount of the six-membered ring compound VIII found after 50 hours reaction, is attributed to the polar addition of H_2S to the original olefine followed by an intra-molecular cyclisation, according to the following:

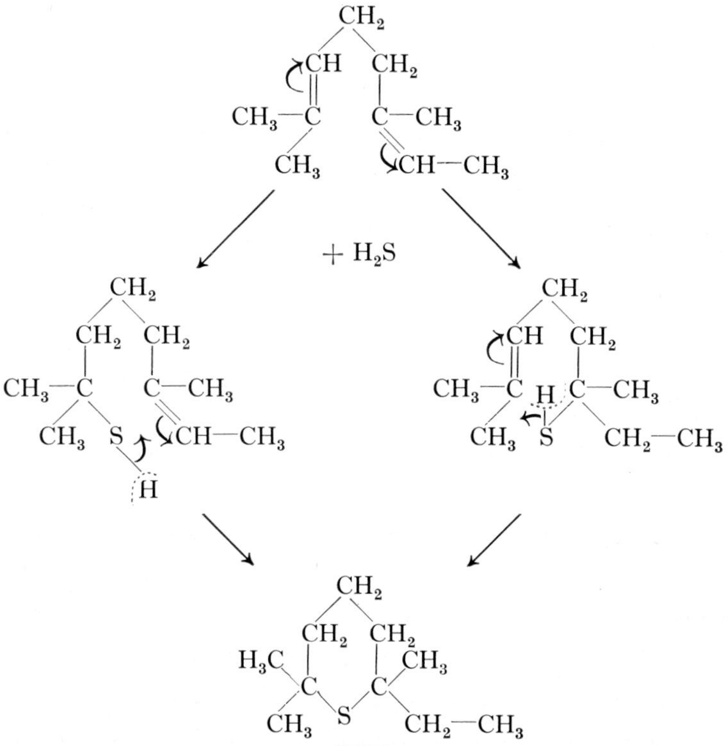

$$CH_3-C \quad C-CH_3$$

+ H_2S

(VIII)

The H_2S is presumed to be formed by side reactions.

It was also found that the constitution of the bimolecular polysulphide fraction is time dependent. The situation appears to be more complex here, and the products have not been unambiguously characterised;

however, the experimental evidence shows that after 5 hours of reaction the C_{20} molecule contains, on average, 5 sulphur atoms. A proportion of this sulphur is present as polysulphide in the cross-link, since hydrogenolysis with lithium aluminium hydride results in the formation of hydrogen sulphide according to the process

$$\text{R—S—S}_x\text{—S—R} \xrightarrow{\text{LiAlH}_4} 2\text{RSH} + x\text{H}_2\text{S}$$

After 50 hours reaction, the C_{20} molecule contains, on average, 3–4 sulphur atoms, of which 1–2 atoms are present in cyclic sulphide structures, the remainder being in the form of mono- and disulphide cross-links. It appears therefore that after short reaction periods the cross-linked product is of the linear polysulphide type (VII), and that prolonged reaction involves the transfer of sulphur from the polysulphide cross-links to adjacent isoprene units, thus resulting in the formation of cyclic structures. This process of sulphur transfer and simultaneous cyclic–sulphide formation ends with the eventual formation of types XII and XIII, in which the actual cross-link itself contains between 1 and 2 sulphur atoms only.

Concurrent with the reactions occurring *within* each group of compounds, as discussed above, there occurs an increase in the cyclic monosulphide fraction at the expense of the cross-linked polysulphide. This observation [45] is summarised in Table 12.3 and shows how the combined

TABLE 12.3

TRANSFER OF COMBINED SULPHUR FROM CROSS-LINKED POLYSULPHIDE TO CYCLIC MONOSULPHIDE

During the reaction of 2 : 6-dimethylocta-2 : 6-diene (100 parts) with sulphur (10 parts) at 141° C [45]

Reaction time, hours	Total combined sulphur, %	Cross-linked product, Cyclic product w/w
1·5	1·4	5·6
3·0	3·0	4·4
6·0	3·8	2·9

sulphur becomes increasingly inefficient as a cross-linking agent while the reaction proceeds. This effect is not necessarily related to technological " reversion ", however, since no evidence is presented to suggest that cross-links are irreversibly broken during the process of sulphur transfer.

The transfer of polysulphidic sulphur to neighbouring isoprene units— or even completely independent isoprene units—had been suspected for some time. Several years previously it was shown [46] that when di-allyl tetrasulphides were heated with olefines at 140° C a transfer of combined sulphur from the tetrasulphide to the olefine occurred, e.g.

$$R—S—S—S—S—R + 2\underset{\underset{CH_2—CH}{CH_2}}{\overset{\overset{CH=CH}{CH_2}}{\big|}}CH_2$$

$$\downarrow$$

$$R—S—S—S—\underset{\underset{CH_2—CH_2}{CH}}{\overset{\overset{CH=CH}{\big|}}{\big|}}CH_2 + \underset{\underset{CH_2—CH_2}{CH_2}}{\overset{\overset{S—R}{\big|}{\overset{CH—CH_2}{\big|}}}}CH_2$$

In this connection it is noteworthy that studies [47] of radioactive sulphur exchange between organic polysulphides and elemental S^{35} have established that exchange occurs between these provided the sulphide bridge contains more than two sulphur atoms, e.g.

$$R—S—S—S—R \xrightarrow{\ S^{35}\ } R—S—S^{35}—S—R$$

It was further shown that exchange occurred between polysulphides, even in the absence of free sulphur, e.g.

$$R—S—S—S—R \xrightarrow{\ R'—S—S^{35}—S—R'\ } R—S—S^{35}—S—R$$

in addition to formation of polysulphides of higher and lower sulphur contents. In these systems no exchange was detectable with mono- or disulphides. However, the latter compounds were found to undergo sulphur exchange freely with organic thiols, e.g.

$$R—S^{35}—S^{35}—R \xrightarrow{\ R—SH\ } R—S^{35}—S—R$$

It was also reported that exchange reactions, presumably of similar types, occurred with vulcanised rubber, and the work accentuates, even further, the complexity of the vulcanisation process. It can no longer be doubted that sulphuration reactions continue to occur when the combined sulphur in the system becomes constant, and even continues when all of the free sulphur has combined with the rubber.

No mechanistic conclusion concerning the vulcanisation of rubber in non-accelerated sulphur systems would be complete without kinetic evidence to support it. It is regrettable, therefore, that no satisfactory

evidence of this nature has been published * since the original investigation
of Spence and Young,[48] who showed that when natural rubber is heated
with sulphur the rate of sulphur combination is linear with respect to
time, see Fig. 12.11.   This result, which implies that the rate-determining
stage does not directly involve the sulphur molecule, contradicts their
further finding that the rate of sulphur combination depends strongly on
the initial sulphur concentration.   We can only conclude that the experi-

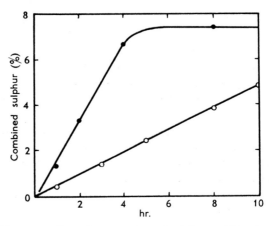

Fig. 12.11. Rate of non-accelerated sulphur combination.

● 2-methyl-2-butene (7·4% S) at 141° C.[49]
○ natural rubber (10% S) at 135° C.[48]

mental technique used was insufficiently sensitive to distinguish between
an auto-catalytic type of reaction and a reaction of zeroth order.   This is
not surprising in view of the laborious analytical methods required for
determining combined sulphur.   It is pertinent to note that an investigation [49] of the rate of combination of sulphur with the model compound
2-methyl-2-butene appears to indicate a similar zeroth order reaction.
The results are shown in Fig. 12.11, whence it can be seen that, after due
allowance is made for different temperatures, the rate of sulphur combination with 2-methyl-2-butene is about twice that with natural rubber.   A
more strict kinetic investigation of the whole problem is required before
mechanistic conclusions can be reliably made, but such an investigation
might be premature until the chemical nature of the sulphur linkages
in the rubber are unequivocally established.

The extreme complexity of the results obtained for the reaction of
sulphur with the di-isoprenic-2 : 6-dimethylocta-2 : 6-diene, as previously
discussed, probably precludes any expectation of the analogous rubber
system behaving in a simple fashion.   Thus, although it has satisfactorily

* See, however, reference [44].

been shown that one double bond disappears for every atom of sulphur that combines with rubber,[50] it would be optimistic to suggest that this results from a reaction of the following type:

$$2 \quad -CH_2-\underset{\underset{CH_3}{|}}{C}=CH-CH_2- \; + \; S \longrightarrow \quad -CH_2-\underset{\underset{CH_3}{|}}{C}=CH-\underset{\underset{S}{|}}{C}H-$$

$$-CH_2-\underset{\underset{CH_3}{|}}{C}H-\underset{}{C}H-CH_2-$$

even though careful analytical data show that the C–H ratio remains unaltered during sulphuration.[51] Indeed, the apparent simplicity of this result must, for the present, be regarded as fortuitous in view of the large variety of potential sulphuration processes that have been shown to occur with the model olefine systems discussed above.

It was at one time hoped that the use of methyl iodide as an analytical reagent for detecting thio-ether groups would lead to the chemical identification of the sulphur cross-link. Thus it was shown [52] that rubber vulcanisates behave abnormally in liberating trimethylsulphonium iodide when treated with methyl iodide. It was further shown that this abnormal reaction also occurred with model systems provided the sulphur was present in the form of a di-allyl thio-ether, e.g.

$$CH_2\text{:}CH\text{·}CH_2\text{·}S\text{·}CH_2\text{·}CH\text{:}CH_2 + 3CH_3I \longrightarrow 2CH_2\text{:}CH\text{·}CH_2I + (CH_3)_3\overset{+}{S}\,\overset{-}{I}$$

However, later investigations [53] showed that the model di-allylic systems were far less reactive towards this reagent than vulcanised rubber; simultaneous investigations [54] showed that allyl-*tert*-alkyl and di-*tert*-alkyl thio-ethers behave in a similar abnormal fashion with methyl iodide. As a result of these qualifications, much of the force of the original argument is lost, and it no longer warrants serious consideration.

Taking the above investigations as a whole, it must be concluded, on the basis of evidence deduced from purely organic chemical methods, that the non-accelerated reaction of sulphur with rubber is a complex one consisting of the chemical incorporation of sulphur in the form of intramolecular monosulphides and intermolecular polysulphides. None of the intramolecular sulphur and only part of the intermolecular sulphur is directly involved in the cross-link structure. The overall relationship of one double bond consumed for every sulphur atom combined appears to be fortuitous in view of the latest evidence, which suggests that the sulphur bridge contains from one to two sulphur atoms and that each cross-link has associated with it one or two five-membered cyclic sulphide structures (XII, XIII). After prolonged reaction, a further structure (VIII), resulting from H_2S addition, becomes apparent—although the origin of the H$_2$S is not explicitly known. The detailed structures of the sulphide products are inconsistent with a free radical sulphuration process and are in fact indicative of a polar-type reaction between sulphur and olefine.

Bearing in mind the above results, sulphur should not be expected to be an efficient agent of vulcanisation, since only a small fraction of the combined sulphur is directly involved in the chemical cross-links. This is borne out by the results now to be described. It has proved possible to measure the efficiency of sulphur as a cross-linking agent during its

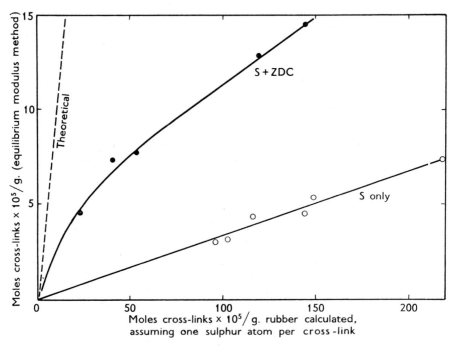

Fig. 12.12. Inefficiency of non-accelerated sulphur vulcanisation of natural rubber, from results of Gee [11].

non-accelerated reaction with natural rubber, by physical assessment of the cross-link intensity as a function of the combined sulphur content and by comparing these results with the theoretical intensity calculated on the basis of one sulphur atom per cross-link. The relationship, shown in Fig. 12.12, is based upon the assessment of cross-link intensities by equilibrium modulus measurements on vulcanisates swollen in light petroleum.[11] It is readily seen that, on average, one cross-link is formed for every *ca.* 30 sulphur atoms combined with the rubber. The theoretical relationship, to be expected if one cross-link is formed for every combined sulphur atom, is shown in Fig. 12.12 as an interrupted line. The low cross-link efficiency of non-accelerated sulphur may be compared with that of a ZDC-accelerated system, results for which are included in Fig. 12.12. It can be seen that while the latter system is far from being 100% efficient, it does tend to approach such behaviour at low cross-link intensities. As already mentioned above, chemical evidence obtained with model systems suggests that, *at its least efficient stage*, each cross-link should have *ca.* 4 sulphur atoms associated with it. The physically determined value of *ca.* 30 is indirect, but nevertheless compelling, evidence for the existence of a high proportion of combined sulphur in sulphide structures that do not contribute to the elastic network. It should be mentioned, in conclusion, that none of the non-accelerated systems discussed above contain zinc oxide or zinc stearate. There is consequently no question of zinc sulphide being included in the combined sulphur values.

Accelerated sulphur systems

As a result of the analytical difficulties attending any investigation of the chemical structure of vulcanised rubber, it may be remarked that most of our present knowledge concerning the detailed modes of sulphur combination has resulted from the use of model olefines. It is fitting, therefore, that this section is opened by considering the present state of knowledge of the chemistry of the accelerated sulphuration of model olefinic systems. It must be admitted that, until quite recently, virtually nothing was known of either the products or the mechanism of this type of reaction, but the last few years have witnessed investigations that may provide the key to future understanding. The complexity of the non-accelerated reaction must act beneficially as a sobering influence in so far as it shows the need for stricter and more detailed chemical methods, both analytical and synthetic, if significant results of lasting value are to be obtained.

Model systems. Earlier investigations with 2 : 6-dimethylocta-2 : 6-diene and sulphur showed that accelerators and activators, such as mercaptobenzthiazole, zinc oxide and zinc propionate, led to increased amounts of cross-linked polysulphides at the expense of the cyclic monosulphide, in addition to an increase in the overall rate of sulphuration.[45]   Under similar conditions 2-methyl-2-butene (which, being a mono-olefine, cannot form cyclic monosulphide) was found to give increased yields of cross-linked monosulphide at the expense of the cross-linked polysulphides.[55] These results are indicative of the ancillary agents acting so as to increase the cross-linking efficiency of sulphur. " Maximum " efficiency requires cyclic monosulphide to be absent and all cross-linked material to be monosulphidic, and although this situation has never been achieved in practice, it is noteworthy that, in the reaction of 2 : 6-dimethylocta-2 : 6-diene with sulphur, the presence of diphenylguanidine, zinc oxide and

L L

zinc propionate increases the ratio of cross-linked to cyclic material up to a value greater than 40. The corresponding value for the non-accelerated reaction is *ca.* 5. However, there is no noticeable tendency for the cross-linked product to become monosulphidic.

More recently the sulphuration of *cyclo*hexene, methyl*cyclo*hexene, 2 : 6-dimethylocta-2 : 6-diene and related olefines by sulphur in the presence of diethylamine at 140° C have been investigated.[56] The inclusion of the amine serves to indicate the possible modes of action of base-like technological accelerators. These studies show that the presence of the amine results in the production of *saturated* products consisting predominantly of mono- and disulphides. Moreover, the constitution of these products satisfactorily establishes the dominant reaction to be of the polar type, leading to addition products in accord with Markownikov's Rule. Thus, the mono-olefines undergo a series of reactions, shown below, which appear to result from the polar addition of hydrogen sulphide

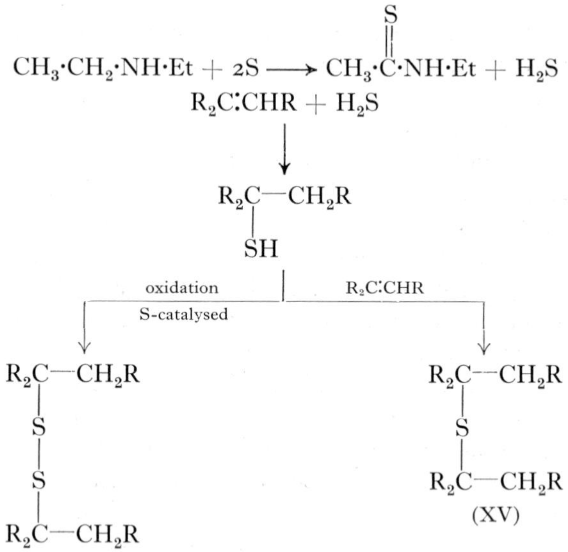

$$CH_3 \cdot CH_2 \cdot NH \cdot Et + 2S \longrightarrow CH_3 \cdot \overset{\overset{\displaystyle S}{\|}}{C} \cdot NH \cdot Et + H_2S$$

$$R_2C \text{:} CHR + H_2S$$

$$\downarrow$$

$$R_2C - CH_2R$$

$$|$$

$$SH$$

oxidation $R_2C \text{:} CHR$

S-catalysed

$$R_2C - CH_2R \qquad\qquad\qquad R_2C - CH_2R$$
$$|\qquad\qquad\qquad\qquad\qquad\qquad |$$
$$S\qquad\qquad\qquad\qquad\qquad\qquad S$$
$$|\qquad\qquad\qquad\qquad\qquad\qquad |$$
$$S\qquad\qquad\qquad\qquad\qquad R_2C - CH_2R$$
$$|\qquad\qquad\qquad\qquad\qquad\qquad (XV)$$
$$R_2C - CH_2R$$
$$(XIV)$$

to the olefine, followed by (*a*) the sulphur-catalysed oxidation of the intermediate thiol to give bimolecular disulphide XIV, together with (*b*) the polar addition of the intermediate thiol to the olefine to give the bimolecular monosulphide XV. The hydrogen sulphide is believed to arise by dehydrogenation of the amine, forming N-ethylthioacetamide as a major side-product. Unreacted hydrogen sulphide is eventually isolated as diethylammonium hydrogen sulphide. The results of this investigation contrast markedly with the non-accelerated sulphuration of mono-olefines, where the major products have been identified as unsaturated polysulphides of the alkyl alkenyl type (R–S_x–R' where $x \simeq 4$, on average), and demonstrates vividly how the presence of the amine alters the character of the reaction in the direction of increased cross-link efficiency. It was further noted that *sym*-disubstituted olefines give rise to a product consisting predominantly of XV, while the trisubstituted olefines— possibly for reasons of steric hindrance—produce predominantly XIV. This suggests that, under similar sulphuration conditions, butadiene polymers should tend towards monosulphidic and isoprene polymers towards disulphidic cross-links.

Extension of this study to the sulphuration of the di-olefinic 2 : 6-dimethylocta-2 : 6-diene (XVI) in the presence of diethylamine at 140° C has shown that cyclic monosulphides are formed along with complex bimolecular polysulphides. The cyclic monosulphide fraction contains products VIII to XI, i.e. identical with those found in the non-accelerated system and, consequently, a similar mechanism has been suggested involving: (*a*) the polar addition of hydrogen sulphide, followed by cyclisation to yield VIII, and (*b*) the electrophilic attack by sulphur at the double bond of the olefine to yield X and XI. The complex bimolecular polysulphides, however, unlike their non-accelerated analogues, were found to be predominantly saturated, and are regarded as being formed *via* the intermediate cyclic monosulphide (X) by the series of polar and oxidative reactions given on p. 1028.

The extent to which each of the above component processes is time-dependent is unknown at present. By way of amplification of this series of reactions, it should be mentioned that the bimolecular polysulphides are strikingly similar to those found in the non-accelerated reaction. The only, but nevertheless important, difference is the absence of unsaturation in the cyclic components of XVIII, XIX and XX. The exclusively mono- and disulphidic nature of the actual cross-link in the latter compounds is in conformity with the similar cross-links (see XIV and XV) formed by the mono-olefines, and throws into relief the importance of hydrogen sulphide and thiol (XVII) addition reactions as well as oxidative reactions under accelerated sulphuration conditions.

Characterisation of cure. In normal technological practice it is usually sufficient to gauge the extent of vulcanisation by measuring a single physical property. The choice of property depends, *inter alia*, upon the ease of measurement, the magnitude of the change undergone during cure and the eventual service conditions of the rubber product. While such cure assessment may be ideally suited to the needs of commerce from the point of view of speed and specification fulfilment, it is usually unsuitable for use during diagnostic investigation of vulcanisation mechanisms. The reason for this should be clear by now; before vulcanisation can be assessed it must be defined, and very often the choice of definition is governed by the method available for assessing cure. This, in turn, may be determined by the consumers' specification. "Hand" or "pencil" tests [57] may be quoted as extreme examples of cure-assessment methods that may be of

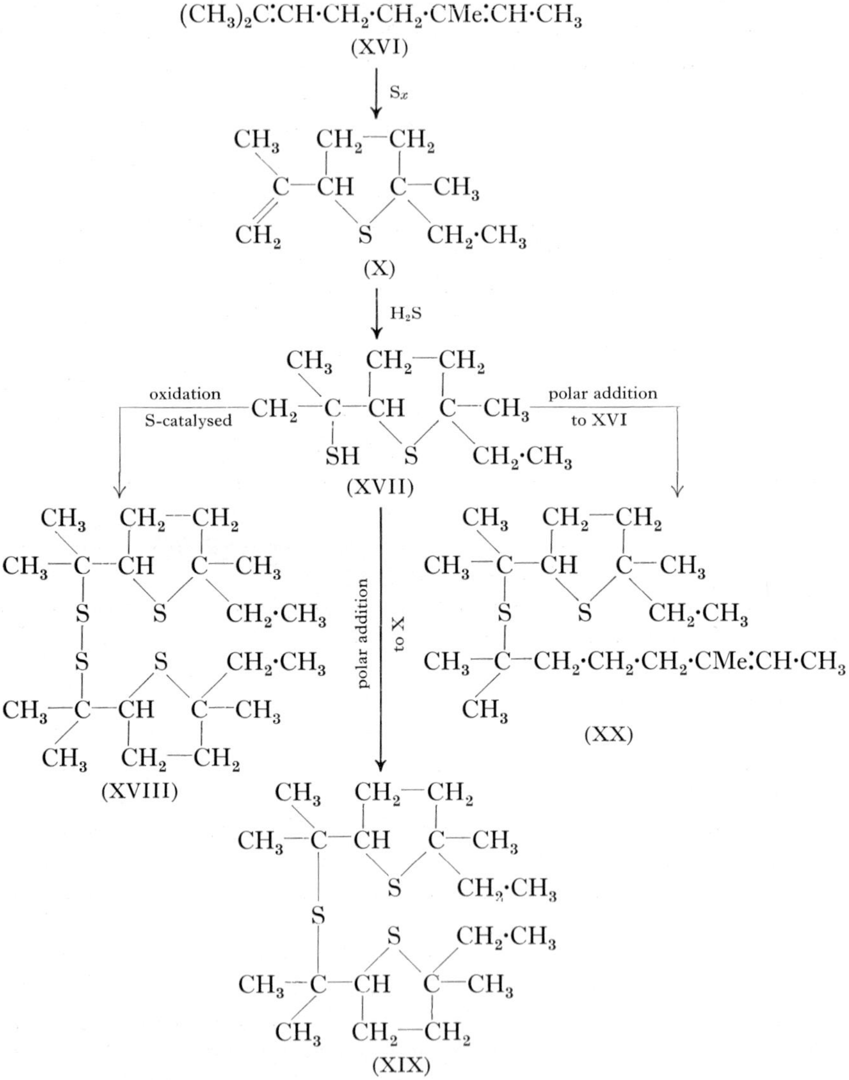

$$(CH_3)_2C\!:\!CH\cdot CH_2\cdot CH_2\cdot CMe\!:\!CH\cdot CH_3$$

(XVI)

$$\downarrow S_x$$

(X)

$$\downarrow H_2S$$

(XVII)

oxidation, S-catalysed ⟶

polar addition to XVI ⟶

(XVIII)

(XX)

polar addition to X

(XIX)

considerable convenience from the point of view of production efficiency but which cannot be used quantitatively and which are too dependent upon the individual test operator for widespread use.

In line with the evidence presented in the opening sections of this chapter, it is advantageous to define vulcanisation as the process of building up a three-dimensional network in the rubber matrix. Since this involves the insertion of cross-links into the system, we can accept this process as truly representative of the phenomenon of vulcanisation. As a result, any legitimate method for measuring cross-link intensity is potentially suitable for assessing quantitatively the extent of cure. The degree of suitability will depend upon the particular method chosen for measuring cross-link intensity and, as mentioned in previous sections, equilibrium swelling and/or equilibrium stress–strain properties have been found to be eminently suitable for this purpose. This is not to say that the measurement of ancillary properties, such as tensile strength, combined sulphur, elongation, etc., are without value. Indeed, such measurements are very often highly indicative of the existence of secondary processes (i.e. processes other than cross-linking) during cure, and, in certain circumstances, there is no reason why a property such as tensile strength, " Goodbrand " modulus or elongation should not be used when the relationship between the appropriate property and cross-link intensity has been satisfactorily established for the system. As an illustration, tensile strength could be used with fair reliability, at low cross-link intensities, for certain types of natural rubber gum-stock systems as a result of the empirical relationships established in Figs. 12.2 and 12.3. It must be borne in mind, however, that any physical assessment of cross-link intensity will include the non-chemical type of cross-link arising out of the presence of chain entanglements. The relative importance to be attributed to this effect will depend on whether the investigation is concerned with the gross number of cross-links or with the cross-links specifically inserted by the vulcanising agent.

It must be evident that the theoretical justification for using swelling and/or modulus measurements at equilibrium is somewhat offset in practice by the time-consuming nature of these measurements, and it is not surprising that other methods have been promulgated to overcome this disadvantage. For example, " Goodbrand " modulus has been used as a measure of cross-link intensity—but only after calibrating this property against the equilibrium modulus.[11] It is futile to use a single (non-equilibrium) modulus measurement for assessing the rate coefficient of cure, but two such measurements should be sufficient.[58] However, this can be acceptable only when the reaction is demonstrably of the first-order kinetic type and when the modulus has been satisfactorily related to the true cross-link intensity, as determined by equilibrium methods. Other workers [51] prefer to make use of the elongation at a fixed stress in conjunction with a second-order type kinetic relationship, although the existence of such a relationship has been questioned.[60] It has recently been shown that elongation measurements at fixed stress (5 kg./cm.^{2}) may be empirically related to 100% modulus measurements on natural rubber gum-stocks and that cure may therefore be characterised by strain measurements at this stress.[61] It has likewise been established [14] that elongation at break is linearly related to cross-link intensity over the range 0–15×10^{-5} moles cross-links/g. of rubber, for natural rubber cured with *tert*-butyl peroxide. The legitimate use of the (non-equilibrium) 100% modulus as a criterion of cure has been established empirically by demonstrating that the following relationship holds for natural rubber gum-stocks:

$$\frac{10^5}{M_c} = \frac{1}{3 \cdot 27} \left\{ F_{100} - 1 \cdot 31 + \left(\frac{105}{V_c + 18 \cdot 7} \right) \right\} \quad . \quad (12.7)$$

where F_{100} is the (non-equilibrium) modulus at 100% extension, V_c is the Mooney viscosity of the uncured compound and the numerical parameters arise out of the non-ideal elastic behaviour of the rubber system.[61] For a compound of known Mooney viscosity, eqn. 12.7 reduces to

$$F_{100} = A \cdot n + B . \quad . \quad . \quad . \quad . \quad (12.8)$$

where n is the no. of moles cross-links/g. and A, B are empirical constants. From eqn. 12.8 it is seen that the 100% modulus is linearly related to the cross-link intensity, and it may therefore serve as a satisfactory, secondary standard for assessing degree of cure.

It is to be concluded that when equilibrium swelling and/or equilibrium modulus results are not available, non-equilibrium values may be justifiably used provided that the relationship between such non-equilibrium values and the cross-link intensity is known. Other parameters, such as combined sulphur, tensile strength and elongation, are only wholly acceptable when they have been explicitly related to cross-link intensities. In general, the non-availability of such relationships requires that caution be exercised in attempting any correlation between the parameter and the extent of vulcanisation, although it would clearly be unwise to reject wholly the many results of investigations where these relationships have not been established. In the latter cases the results may very well be of qualitative and even semi-quantitative significance.

Oxidising agents. The isolation of compound XVIII during the amine-accelerated sulphuration of 2 : 6-dimethylocta-2 : 6-diene has led to the suggestion that the oxidation of a thiol intermediate results in dilsulphide cross-links according to

$$2R\text{—}SH + Ox \longrightarrow R\text{—}S\text{—}S\text{—}R + OxH_2$$

where R–SH is the thiol intermediate and Ox is an oxidising agent.[56] The idea of oxidising processes occurring during sulphur vulcanisation is by no means novel. For example it was suggested [55] that intermediate thiols, in the presence of soluble zinc, form zinc mercaptides and that these may be oxidised by sulphur to form disulphide cross-links. This suggestion has since been extended by observations on systems of varying zinc contents.[51, 62] As a result, it is now accepted that in the absence of cross-link degradation [63] the following oxidation occurs in curing systems containing little or no zinc:

$$2R-SH + S \longrightarrow R-S-S-R + H_2S$$

and gives rise to a disulphide cross-link together with one molecule of hydrogen sulphide; in systems of high zinc content, however, this oxidation proceeds *via* the intermediate zinc mercaptide and produces a molecule of zinc sulphide for each disulphidic cross-link:

$$R-S-Zn-S-R + S \longrightarrow R-S-S-R + ZnS$$

Thus it was shown [55] that the 200% modulus is linearly related, over an appreciable range, to the amount of zinc sulphide formed in mercapto-benzthiazole-accelerated natural rubber gum-stocks containing zinc oxide and zinc laurate, see Fig. 12.13. Apart from deviations at low sulphide

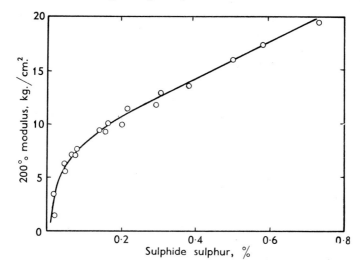

Fig. 12.13. Modulus *v* sulphide sulphur for the compound: rubber 100, zinc oxide 5, zinc laurate 7, MBT 0·5, sulphur variable (0·75 to 6·0). (Armstrong, Little and Doak [55].)

concentrations, the linear relationship holds well. The significance of this result depends upon the assumption that the non-equilibrium modulus is a reliable measure of cross-link intensity. In view of subsequent investigations,[11] which have shown that low-extension, non-equilibrium moduli are almost linearly related to cross-link intensities, this assumption is qualitatively valid. We conclude, therefore, that over the linear region of Fig. 12.13, the continued formation of cross-links is accompanied by a proportionate liberation of zinc sulphide. Moreover, when eqn. 12.6 is applied to this linear region it is found that one cross-link is inserted for every 0·8 molecules of liberated zinc sulphide—a result in excellent conformity with the above-suggested mechanism. Extrapolation of the linear portion to zero liberated sulphide gives a positive intercept on the modulus axis. This intercept must correspond to the number of cross-links that have been inserted by processes other than the above oxidation of the zinc mercaptides. These may be chemical in nature or even due to chain entanglements (see Fig. 12.10).

Further support for the existence of thiol oxidation processes in accelerated–sulphur vulcanisation emerges from the fact that excellent technical cures are obtained when organic oxidising agents replace zinc oxide in accelerated-sulphur mixes.[64] The absence of zinc oxide precludes the possibility of intermediate zinc mercaptide formation and ensures the dominance of simple, thiol oxidation:

$$2RSH \xrightarrow{\text{ox.}} R\text{—}S\text{—}S\text{—}R \quad [51]$$

Some typical results are shown in Fig. 12.14, where the extent of vulcanisation, characterised by the (non-equilibrium) 200% modulus, is plotted

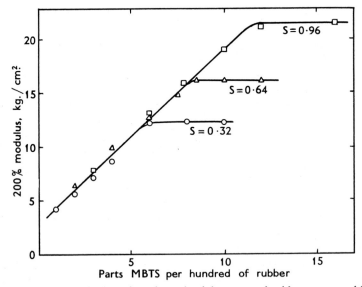

Fig. 12.14. Vulcanisation of accelerated-sulphur, natural rubber compound by dibenzthiazole disulphide (MBTS), (Barton [64]).

as a function of the added disulphide (dibenzthiazole disulphide). The incursion of degradative processes was minimised by curing at 100° C, while the completion of vulcanisation was ensured by curing for 32 hours.

The mix consists of natural rubber 100, zinc diethyldithiocarbamate 2, dibenzylamine 1, sulphur 0·32, 0·64 and 0·96 with varying amounts of dibenzthiazole disulphide. It can be seen that, in the absence of dibenzthiazole disulphide, the extent of vulcanisation is small. The presence of the disulphide gives rise to increased vulcanisation, and its maximum degree depends upon both the sulphur and disulphide contents of the mix. With 10 parts of disulphide and 0·96 parts of sulphur the modulus developed equals that of a typical gum-stock containing zinc oxide. This result accords well with the oxidation hypothesis, and the process probably occurs in two exchange stages, thus

$$R{-}S{-}H \; + \; \underset{\text{benzthiazolyl}}{\overset{N}{\underset{S}{\diagup\diagdown}}}C{-}S{-}S{-}C\underset{S}{\overset{N}{\diagdown\diagup}}$$

$$\downarrow$$

$$R{-}S{-}S{-}C\underset{S}{\overset{N}{\diagup\diagdown}} \; + \; \underset{S}{\overset{N}{\diagup\diagdown}}C{-}SH$$

$$\downarrow \; R{-}SH$$

$$R{-}S{-}S{-}R \; + \; \underset{S}{\overset{N}{\diagup\diagdown}}C{-}SH$$

where R–SH is an intermediate thiol derivative of rubber formed during accelerated sulphuration (cf. XVII). In line with this explanation is the isolation of mercaptobenzthiazole as a major reaction product when natural rubber or cyclohexene is heated with dibenzthiazole disulphide,[46, 64] and the frequent demonstration that exchange reactions occur between thiols and disulphides.[47] Final support is evidenced by vulcanisation of a thiolated natural rubber by dithiazole disulphides in the total absence of elemental sulphur, accelerator and zinc oxide.[64] Cross-linking was unequivocally demonstrated by swelling measurements.

The description of the thiol-to-disulphide process as one of oxidation is used here on grounds of common usage. Strictly speaking, a chemical species is oxidised only when it loses one or more electrons from its valency shell. This does not occur in the process under consideration here, which is an exchange reaction or, more precisely, a hydrogen transfer reaction.

Non-rubber components of natural rubber. The well-known fact that purified rubber hydrocarbon has somewhat inferior physical properties and cures at a slower rate than whole rubber is not yet explained. Clearly no completely satisfactory explanation is possible until the mechanisms of sulphur acceleration have been established. However, a recent study [65] shows that small amounts of base-like components are probably acting as classical accelerators. Some pertinent results for three classified grades of rubber are shown in Table 12.4. It can be seen that the fastest cure is that

TABLE 12.4

SOME CHEMICAL PROPERTIES OF CLASSIFIED NATURAL RUBBER
(Veith [65])

Rubber grade	Cure rate	% ash	% N	% N *	% fatty acid	pH ash slurry
Red	Slow	0·19	0·36	0·36	1·47	7·9
Yellow	Medium	0·22	0·39	0·37	1·40	8·0
Blue	Fast	0·37	0·49	0·48	2·00	9·4

* After acetone extraction.

by the rubber possessing the greatest alkaline ash and nitrogen contents. It is noteworthy that almost all of the nitrogen is retained in the rubber after acetone extraction, showing it to be of peptide origin. A little earlier it was found that the tensile strength at optimum cure of natural rubber increased during storage of the raw rubber, and it was suggested that lecithin and cephalin components of the non-rubber fraction decomposed, during storage, to form the bases choline and colamine and that these functioned as base-like accelerators.[66]

The role played by the natural fatty acids present in raw rubber is not known. It may be conjectured that, in the presence of zinc oxide, they serve to solubilise zinc,[25] and thus allow the formation of zinc mercaptides during vulcanisation. The same may be true of the carboxylic and phosphoric acid groups present in the protein and phospholipid fraction. In addition to their functioning as bases, the amines may serve as zinc solubilisers in the form of zinc–amine complexes. In this connection, it has been shown that rubber, substantially freed from amino acids by proteolytic enzymes, gives products of inferior mechanical properties unless additional fatty acids are added.[67]

Effect of organic bases. The essentially base-like nature of all technical accelerators leads inevitably to the conclusion that accelerated sulphuration involves base catalysis. It is surprising, therefore, that comparatively little attention has been given to the correlation of basicity with accelerating capacity. In a recent study [68] it has been shown that, in a standard compound of natural rubber 100, sulphur 7·5 and organic base x moles, the amount of combined sulphur after a fixed period of cure at 148° C is directly related to the base strength of the organic base. Owing to the large range of acceleration involved, it was not possible to compare the bases at a single fixed period of cure and at a single concentration. Instead, a convenient cure time and concentration (see Table 12.5) was chosen for each of a series of bases, and it was shown that, under these conditions, the amount of combined sulphur is related to the pK_A within each amine series.

TABLE 12.5

Base series	Base concentration and time of cure at 148° C
A. Aniline	0·04 mole for 90 minutes
Diphenylaniline	,, ,, ,,
Triphenylaniline	,, ,, ,,
B. Aniline	0·01 mole for 90 minutes
Methylaniline	,, ,, ,,
Dimethylaniline	,, ,, ,,
C. o-, m-, p-Toluidine	,, ,, ,,
D. o-, m-, p-Phenylenediamine	0·04 mole for 60 minutes
E. Phenylguanidine	0·02 mole for 30 minutes
Diphenylguanidine	,, ,, ,,
Triphenylguanidine	,, ,, ,,

Results are shown in Fig. 12.15. where increasing pK_A corresponds to increasing basic strength. The bases investigated were all aromatic and are shown in Table 12.5 Although comparisons cannot be made *between*

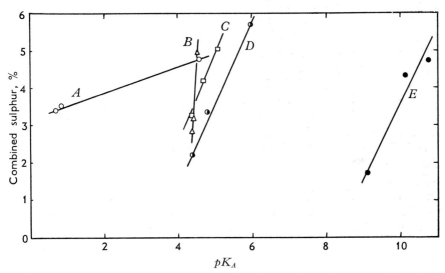

Fig. 12.15. Combined sulphur v pK_A for series of bases (Kratz, Young and Katz [68]).

series, it can be seen that *within* each of the series, increased basicity results in increased sulphur combination. It would be unwise at this stage to ascribe this effect completely to base-catalysis. Clearly the presence of amines may introduce new modes of sulphuration, although a recent investigation [56] indicates that dimethylaniline-accelerated sulphuration is similar to the non-accelerated reaction and differs significantly from diethylamine-accelerated sulphuration, where the role of the amine appears to involve hydrogen sulphide formation. The very important part played by diethylamine in this connection has been discussed more fully in a previous section, although its strictly catalytic role has not yet been clearly established. Furthermore, nothing is known of the mechanism of the key reaction:

$$CH_3 \cdot CH_2 \cdot NH \cdot Et + 2S \longrightarrow CH_3 \cdot CS \cdot NH \cdot Et + H_2S$$

Rate of vulcanisation. Since all of the usual methods of vulcanisation require the use of chemical agents, kinetic methods should lead to fruitful results in the elucidation of vulcanisation mechanisms. Although this type of investigation is proving successful with Butyl rubber, [69,70] the incursion of reversion effects and intramolecular sulphuration introduces complications with natural rubber systems. Nevertheless, it has been shown [61] that the rate of cross-link insertion follows a first-order kinetic law. Since cross-link insertion is invariably accompanied by degradation processes (reversion) in accelerated-sulphur mixes, the overall rate of increase of cross-links is regarded as resulting from two consecutive first-order processes. Having established that cross-link intensities could be assessed from 100% modulus measurements with the aid of eqn. 12.7, these workers were able to undertake their kinetic investigation. A typical kinetic run for a reverting compound (ACS1) is shown in Fig. 12.16, where the reversion effect is very apparent. In the same figure is shown the increase of combined sulphur, and it is significant that the first-order rate coefficient for cross-link insertion is more than three times greater than that for sulphur combination: k_1 for cross-link insertion $= 0.18$ min.$^{-1}$, k_1 for sulphur combination $= 0.05_6$ min.$^{-1}$. Such a situation is kinetic proof of the complexity of the system under consideration, and speculation regarding possible reaction schemes would be premature until more information is available concerning the different types of cross-link present and the proportion of sulphur combined as zinc sulphide.

The noteworthy result that sulphur combination obeys a first-order kinetic law is in contrast with the alleged zeroth-order nature of the non-accelerated sulphuration,[48] and shows that sulphur is involved in the rate-determining stage. Were this not so, then the rate law observed would need to be ascribed either to diffusion difficulties as the network develops or to the existence of a particular type of reactive centre in the rubber which becomes exhausted at the completion of cure. The former explanation appears unlikely in view of the high activation energy found for the process (*ca.* 18 kcal./mole), while the latter explanation may be discounted in the absence of independent supporting evidence.

It is significant that the 100% modulus appears to be negative at the beginning of the reaction and rises to zero only after a definite (although small) amount of sulphur combination has occurred. This effect results directly from the finite molecular weight of the primary rubber molecules,

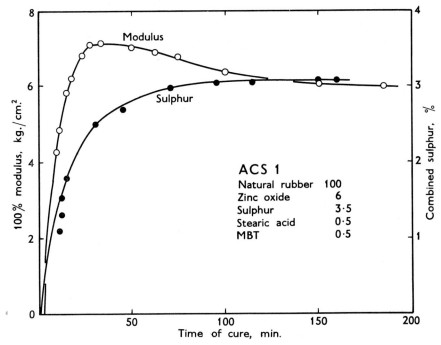

Fig. 12.16. Rate of vulcanisation of MBT—accelerated natural rubber at 140° C. (Gee and Morrell [61].)

and is a reflection of the cross-linking that must occur before the whole of the rubber matrix participates in the three-dimensional network (see also Fig. 12.20). In this connection it has been noted [71] that in an extreme case, where the primary molecular weight was *ca.* 20,000, the rubber remained plastic even when containing 3–4% of combined sulphur.

Mercaptobenzthiazole acceleration. The results mentioned above were obtained with compound ACS1, a typical mercaptobenzthiazole-accelerated compound. Similar compounds, based on mixes of natural rubber with sulphur, zinc stearate and mercaptobenzthiazole have been investigated kinetically, and an attempt has been made to isolate and characterise the effect of each of these ingredients.[63] Cross-link intensities were determined: (*a*) by equilibrium modulus measurements on vulcanisates swollen in benzene, using the relationship

$$f = \frac{\rho R T A_0}{M_c \, v_r^{\frac{1}{3}}} \left(\alpha - \frac{1}{\alpha^2} \right) \qquad . \qquad . \qquad . \qquad (12.9)$$

where these symbols are as previously defined, and (*b*) by equilibrium swelling measurements on vulcanisates swollen in benzene, using eqn. 12.2 with $\mu = 0.437$. It can be seen that eqn. 12.9 is equivalent to eqn. 12.6, but modified to allow for the dilution effect of the swelling liquid. Good agreement was stated to have been found between cross-link intensities obtained by both of these methods. In the course of this study the effect of progressive addition to the mix of zinc stearate and mercaptobenzthiazole on the rate and extent of cross-link insertion was demonstrated. Some results are summarised in Fig. 12.17, where it can be

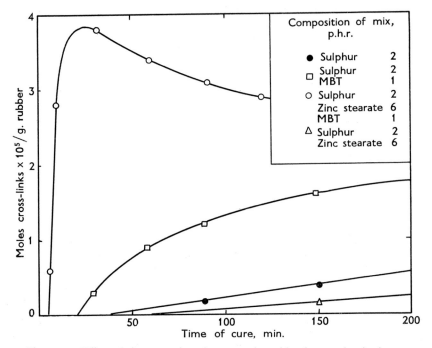

Fig. 12.17. Effect of zinc stearate and mercaptobenzthiazole on vulcanisation at 138° C. (Adams and Johnson [63].)

seen that the overall rate of cross-linking of natural rubber by sulphur is: (*a*) reduced somewhat by zinc stearate; (*b*) increased appreciably by mercaptobenzthiazole; and (*c*) increased remarkably by mercaptobenzthiazole in the presence of zinc stearate. In the last case the incursion of reversion is very evident.

In attempting an appreciation of these results the first question requiring an answer is whether the mercaptobenzthiazole is acting truly catalytically or whether it is chemically incorporated in the vulcanisate. In this connection, some results of Auerbach [72] are of interest. This author studied the consumption of mercaptobenzthiazole (1 part) and radioactive sulphur S^{35} (3 parts) during the vulcanisation of natural rubber (100 parts) in the presence of zinc oxide (3 parts) and showed that chemical combination of the accelerator undoubtedly occurred.   Some results are presented in Fig. 12.18, where the organically combined sulphur (i.e. excluding zinc sulphide) is plotted against the combined mercaptobenzthiazole during cure.   It can be seen that some accelerator appears to have been consumed at zero sulphur combination.   This probably results from the chemisorption of accelerator at the surface of the zinc oxide.   For the major part of the sulphuration the molecular ratio of combined sulphur to combined mercaptobenzthiazole remains fairly constant at *ca.* 170, but drops

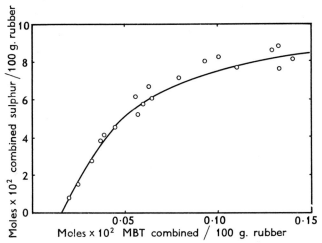

Fig. 12.18. Combination of sulphur *v* mercaptobenzthiazole during vulcanisation (Auerbach [72]).

off considerably during the later stage of the reaction.   Chemical combination of accelerator appears, therefore, to be considerable, in that up to 25% of the mercaptobenzthiazole initially present has been consumed during the uptake of 85% of the elemental sulphur.   However, since *ca.* 170 atoms of sulphur combine with the rubber for every mercaptobenzthiazole consumed, it is evident that the reaction is overwhelmingly one of sulphur combination, and the accelerator may with justification be regarded as a catalyst.

The question next to be considered is whether the catalytic effect of the mercaptobenzthiazole is specific to the cross-linking process or whether it extends to the intramolecular sulphuration.   It can readily be understood that an accelerator which catalyses the cross-linking process exclusively, leaving unaffected the intramolecular sulphuration, will favour the formation of cross-links at the expense of the intramolecular reaction.   Such an effect should be accompanied by a corresponding increase in cross-linking efficiency on the part of the sulphur. Conversely, an accelerator which catalyses equally all sulphuration reactions will have no effect on the cross-linking efficiency. Based on data by Adams and Johnson, it may be calculated that *after long times of cure* the non-accelerated vulcanisate possesses—on average—31 combined sulphur atoms per cross-link while the mercaptobenzthiazole–zinc stearate-

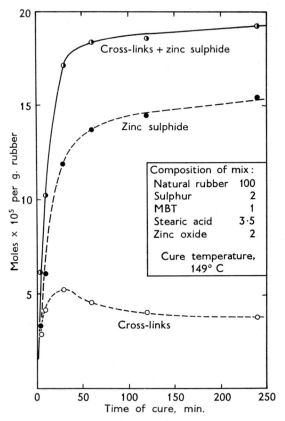

Fig. 12.19. Development of cross-links and zinc sulphide during cure (Adams and Johnson [63]).

accelerated vulcanisate possesses 15 combined sulphur atoms per cross-link. Thus mercaptobenzthiazole, in the presence of zinc stearate, increases the rate of cross-link insertion by a factor of *ca.* 100 (see Fig. 12.17) while increasing the overall cross-linking efficiency by a factor of only 2. Similar calculations based on independent studies [73] with a similar system —that of natural rubber, sulphur, mercaptobenzthiazole, stearic acid and zinc oxide—show that the ancillary agents have the effect of reducing the overall number of combined sulphur atoms per cross-link from *ca.* 30 for the non-accelerated down to *ca.* 10 for the accelerated system, i.e. the overall efficiency is increased by a factor of *ca.* 3. On the basis of these results, it might be concluded that the dominant effect of the mercapto-benzthiazole is to increase the rate of cross-linking without a proportionate increase in the cross-linking efficiency. This conclusion would be misleading, however, since the efficiency is markedly dependent on the time of cure, and some further results of Adams and Johnson (see below) show that the efficiency is very high (*ca.* 2 atoms of combined sulphur per cross-link) for the accelerated reaction *at short times of cure.*

The replacement of zinc stearate by zinc oxide and stearic acid leads to substantially the same type of cure phenomena.[63] The effect is illustrated in Fig. 12.19 for a typical mercaptobenzthiazole-accelerated mix containing zinc oxide and stearic acid, the results for which may be compared with the analogous curve of Fig. 12.17, for a mix containing both mercaptobenzthiazole and zinc stearate. The rates of cross-link insertion, the optimum cross-link intensities and the extents of reversion are all similar. From Fig. 12.19 it may be further observed that cross-link insertion, at all times during cure, is accompanied by zinc sulphide formation. The latter process continues even when reversion has set in. The cross-linking efficiency for this mix is shown in Fig. 12.20, where the

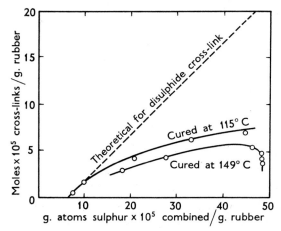

Fig. 12.20. Cross-links intensity *v* combined sulphur for MBT-accelerated mix. For composition of mix, see Fig. 12.19 (Adams and Johnson [63]).

cross-link intensity is plotted as a function of the organically combined sulphur. Cure was effected at 115° C so as to reduce reversion effects and a parallel cure at 149° C is presented for comparison. The effect of the finite molecular weight of the rubber is manifested as an intercept along the combined sulphur axis and, allowing for this effect, the theoretical relationship to be expected for a disulphidic cross-link is shown as an interrupted line.   For the vulcanisate cured at $115°$ C, it can be seen that 2 atoms of sulphur combine for every cross-link inserted during the early part of cure.   As cure proceeds, the cross-linking efficiency decreases progressively until, at high degrees of cure, *ca.* 20 atoms of sulphur combine for every additional cross-link inserted.   For the higher temperature product the curve passes through a maximum and reversion becomes dominant.

These results show conclusively that vulcanisation commences with a high cross-linking efficiency and to the complete exclusion of intra-molecular sulphuration processes, if it is assumed that the cross-link is disulphidic.   As cure proceeds, the sulphur requirements for each additional cross-link increases, and this may be due to: (*a*) the incursion of intramolecular sulphuration; (*b*) the incursion of cross-link degradation to form intramolecular cyclic sulphides and/or thiols; and (*c*) the oxidative scission, of the rubber molecules *at random* along the chain.   The last possibility may be disregarded in view of the fact that it has been shown, by stress relaxation kinetics, that the scissions occurs at (or near) the cross-link and not at random.[74]   The remaining possibilities are presented diagrammatically below:

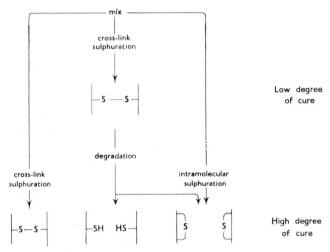

With the evidence available at present, it is not possible to do more than suggest which of these are likely.   The formation of thiol groups by disulphide hydrogenation cannot account for the above results, since, in the presence of soluble zinc, they should remain wholly effective as cross-links in the zinc mercaptide form: R–S–Zn–S–R.   In fact, the formation of zinc sulphide during cure has been attributed by some[55] to the formation of disulphidic cross-links *via* the zinc mercaptide (see p. 281).   This is virtually the reverse of the proposed degradation process involving thiol formation, which may therefore be discounted. The suggestion of cyclic sulphide formation seems not unreasonable in view of the successful demonstration that such groupings occur during sulphuration of model polyolefines (see pp. 1017, 1028). But it is not known whether they result from direct sulphuration or from cross-link degradation.

Whatever the reason for the increasing inefficiency of sulphur during continued reaction, it is evident from Fig. 12.20 that, in the early stage of the reaction, the cross-linking process is very much favoured in comparison with the intramolecular reaction, and it must be concluded that the catalytic effect of mercaptobenzthiazole, in the presence of zinc stearate, is specific to the cross-linking process.

The final topic to be discussed in connection with mercaptobenzthiazole acceleration is the high specificity of the accelerator towards the cross-linking component of the sulphuration process. Reverting again to Fig. 12.17, it is evident that the presence of the accelerator produces a modest catalytic effect in the absence of zinc stearate, although the cross-linking efficiency remains low (33 atoms of combined sulphur per cross-link). The additional presence of zinc stearate is necessary if the full potential of the system is to be made manifest. This well-known technological fact cannot be due to a separate zinc stearate catalytic effect, since this material, in the absence of mercaptobenzthiazole, retards the cross-linking process (Fig. 12.17) and even reduces the cross-linking efficiency (46 atoms of combined sulphur per cross-link). These facts can be rationalised by the hypothesis that the non-specific catalysis of mercaptobenzthiazole is directed into specificity by the zinc stearate. A possible mechanism for this effect may be suggested, based on results obtained for the sulphuration of $2 : 6$-dimethylocta-$2 : 6$-diene,[43, 56] discussed earlier. It will be recalled that the sulphurated products were postulated as being formed by: (a) the intramolecular addition of the intermediate thiol at the adjacent double-bond to form cyclic monosulphide; (b) the intermolecular addition of the intermediate thiol at the double bond of a neighbouring molecule to form bimolecular monosulphide; and (c) the intermolecular sulphur-catalysed oxidation of the intermediate thiol to form a bimolecular disulphide. This immediately suggests a possible selective mode of action of zinc stearate (or, indeed, any rubber-soluble zinc salt [63]), for it is clear that zinc cannot catalyse either of the above thiol-addition reactions each of which involves electrophilic attack at a double-bond. On the other hand, there is reason to suppose that zinc will form a bimolecular bridge of the zinc mercaptide type: R–S–Zn–S–R. The formation of this bridge should facilitate the subsequent oxidation by sulphur to form a disulphide bridge with the simultaneous liberation of zinc sulphide:

$$R\!-\!S\!-\!Zn\!-\!S\!-\!R + S_x \longrightarrow R\!-\!S\!-\!S\!-\!R + ZnS + S_{x-1}$$

for in the absence of such a bridge, the oxidation would require a ter-molecular collision. This mechanism accounts for: (i) the effect of zinc in reducing intramolecular, cyclic monosulphide formation; (ii) the predominantly disulphidic nature of the cross-link; and (iii) the frequently observed relationship between cross-link intensity and zinc sulphide formation.[75] The role of zinc, as outlined here, results from the intermediate formation of a rubber thiol in the accelerated reaction. Since evidence derived from the sulphuration of 2 : 6-dimethylocta-2 : 6-diene shows that such rubber thiols are not involved in the non-accelerated reaction, the negative activity of zinc—in the absence of mercaptobenz-thiazole—is readily explained.

The precise chemical mode of action of mercaptobenzthiazole remains unknown, although it may react with sulphur to form an active precursor to vulcanisation,[69] either by a free radical process, e.g.

$$\text{C—SH} \rightleftharpoons \text{C—S* + H*}$$

$$\text{C—S* + S—S} \rightleftharpoons \text{C—S—S} \quad \overset{*}{\text{S}}$$

or by a polar process, e.g.

$$\text{C=S, S—S} \rightleftharpoons \text{(H on N), S, S} \rightleftharpoons \text{C—S, S⁻ S} \quad + \text{H}^+$$

However, the postulation of such precursors is wholly speculative, and precise chemical knowledge on this subject must await further investigation.

Thiuram disulphide vulcanisation

Although it is well known that tetramethylthiuram disulphide (TMT) vulcanises rubber in the total absence of added sulphur, it is not known whether the reaction involves the intermediate formation of elemental sulphur or whether the disulphide itself is the active agent. Thiuram disulphides are unique vulcanising ingredients in that their use in sulphur-less mixes produces excellent vulcanisates of extremely low sulphur content. In Fig. 12.21, some results are shown for the cross-linking efficiency of TMT as a vulcanising agent. The cross-link intensities, originally obtained by swelling in benzene and using $\mu = 0.395$, have been recalculated using the more acceptable value 0·422.[15]   It is strikingly evident that the reaction is far more efficient than even the most efficient, accelerated-sulphur cures (cf. Figs. 12.12, 12.20) so much so that some of the experimental points correspond to *ca.* 4 cross-links per atom of combined sulphur.   Although too much significance should not be

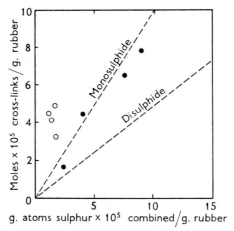

Fig. 12.21. Cross-link intensity *v* combined sulphur for TMT vulcanisation.

○ Zno 2, TMT 3 p.h.r. (Gee [11]).
● Zno 5, TMT variable (Russell [73]).

Interrupted lines are theoretical relationships for mono- and disulphide cross-links.

attached to this value, the situation is nevertheless suggestive that some cross-links are being formed with no corresponding sulphur combination. This, together with the excellent ageing properties associated with thiuram vulcanisates, suggests that direct carbon to carbon cross-links are contributing to the network structure.   In this connection, it is significant that a TMT mix was chosen for illustrating the kinetics of cross-link formation in a non-reverting system.[61]   A more detailed kinetic study of the process involving the simultaneous measurement of cross-link intensity, consumed TMT, liberated ZDC (see below) and combined sulphur is now required.

A comprehensive, kinetic study of thiuram disulphide vulcanisation has recently been made, in the course of which the fate of the thiuram disulphide has been partly elucidated.[79]   It appears that, under cure conditions and in the presence of zinc oxide, two-thirds of the thiuram disulphide invariably appears eventually as the zinc dithiocarbamate, i.e.

$$3 \ R_2N\cdot CS\cdot S\cdot S\cdot CS\cdot NR_2 \xrightarrow[\text{rubber}]{\text{ZnO}} 2 \ R_2N\cdot CS\cdot S\cdot Zn\cdot S\cdot CS\cdot NR_2 + ?$$

This result holds over wide variations of temperature, thiuram disulphide and zinc oxide concentration,[80] and has even been demonstrated with the model di-isoprene, geraniol.[81] The location and nature of the remaining proportion of thiuram disulphide remains unknown at present. Part is undoubtedly incorporated chemically in the rubber, but detailed analytical figures for chemically combined thiuram fragments are not available.

Whatever the fate of every third molecule of thiuram disulphide, the vulcanisation process can be seen to be complex, since the rate of thiuram disulphide consumption is, in general, two to three times faster than the rate of zinc dithiocarbamate formation. This result is illustrated in Fig. 12.22, where the rates of TMT consumption and zinc dimethyl-

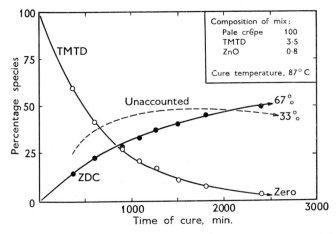

Fig. 12.22. Rate of consumption of TMT (○) and rate of formation of ZDC (●) during vulcanisation of natural rubber by TMT at 87° C. Interrupted line shows " unaccounted " TMT, (Scheele, Lorenz and Dummer [79]).

dithiocarbamate (ZDC) formation are shown together with the " unaccounted " TMT. The comparatively low temperature (87° C) has been chosen here so as to increase the fraction of experimentally observed reaction.

The following points are noteworthy: (a) both the consumption of TMT and the formation of ZDC follow first-order rate laws; (b) TMT consumption proceeds ca. 3 times faster than ZDC formation and, furthermore, from cross-link intensity studies [61] on a similar system, the rate of cross-link insertion proceeds ca. 3 times faster even than TMT consumption; and (c) the " unaccounted " TMT passes through a maximum at ca. 48% and eventually drops to 33% of the original amount. All of these kinetic features are indicative of a complex series of reactions, and it may be speculated that the following free radical processes may occur to varying extents during cure:

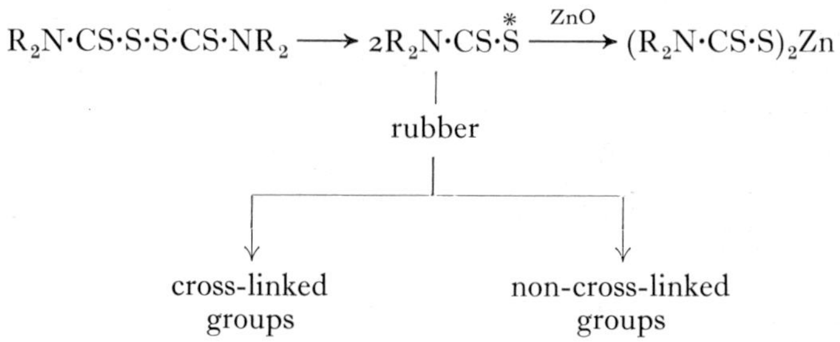

$$R_2N{\cdot}CS{\cdot}S{\cdot}S{\cdot}CS{\cdot}NR_2 \longrightarrow 2R_2N{\cdot}CS{\cdot}\overset{*}{S} \xrightarrow{\;ZnO\;} (R_2N{\cdot}CS{\cdot}S)_2Zn$$

rubber

cross-linked   non-cross-linked
groups   groups

The cross-linked groups, although possibly linked by direct C–C bonds, may still contain thiuram fragments, e.g.

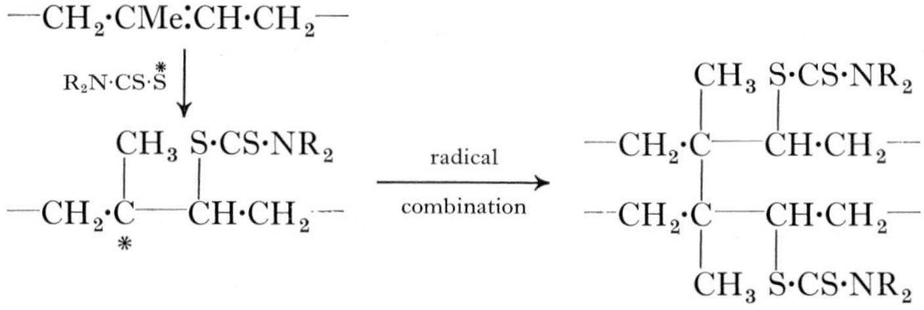

—CH$_2$·CMe:CH·CH$_2$—

$R_2N{\cdot}CS{\cdot}\overset{*}{S}$

CH$_3$ S·CS·NR$_2$

—CH$_2$·C——CH·CH$_2$—

$\xrightarrow[\text{combination}]{\text{radical}}$

CH$_3$ S·CS·NR$_2$

—CH$_2$·C——CH·CH$_2$—

—CH$_2$·C——CH·CH$_2$—

CH$_3$ S·CS·NR$_2$

but, in view of the low combined sulphur content of TMTD vulcanisates, an appreciable amount of the following type of process must occur simultaneously:

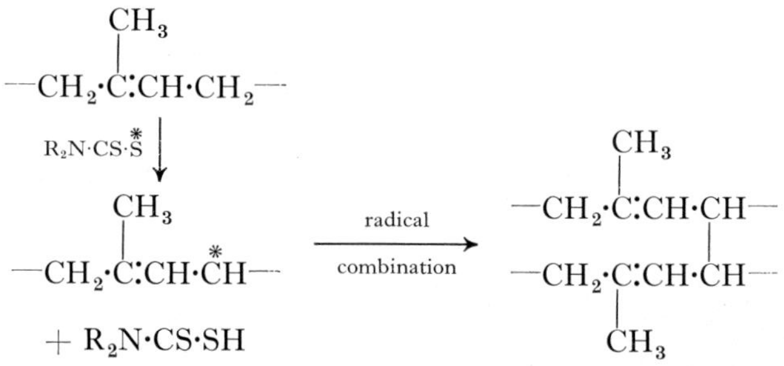

CH$_3$

—CH$_2$·C:CH·CH$_2$—

$R_2N{\cdot}CS{\cdot}\overset{*}{S}$

CH$_3$

—CH$_2$·C:CH·CH—

$\xrightarrow[\text{combination}]{\text{radical}}$

CH$_3$

—CH$_2$·C:CH·CH—

—CH$_2$·C:CH·CH—

CH$_3$

+ R$_2$N·CS·SH

Similarly, the non-cross-linked groups may contain varying amounts of thiuram fragments, e.g.

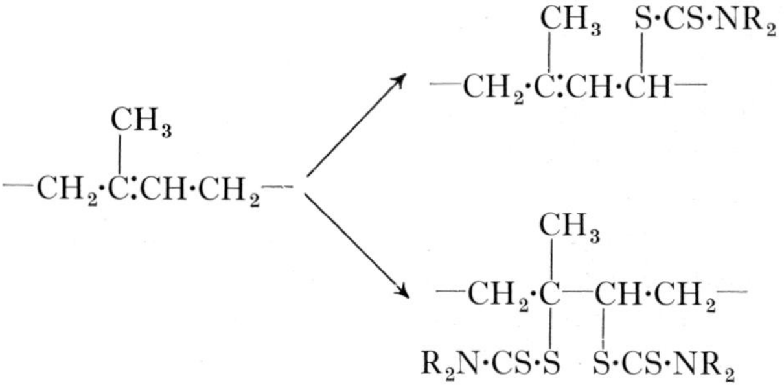

CH$_3$

—CH$_2$·C:CH·CH$_2$—

CH$_3$ S·CS·NR$_2$

—CH$_2$·C:CH·CH—

CH$_3$

—CH$_2$·C——CH·CH$_2$—

R$_2$N·CS·S S·CS·NR$_2$

In all cases when thiuram fragments have combined with the rubber the dithiocarbamic acid may be subsequently liberated by the following type of elimination reaction:

$$\begin{array}{c} S \cdot CS \cdot NR_2 \\ | \\ -CH-CH_2- \end{array} \longrightarrow -CH{=}CH- + R_2N \cdot CS \cdot SH$$

which presents a possible explanation for the continued formation of ZDC after the disappearance of the TMT (Fig. 12.22).

The examination [82] of the products formed when 2 : 4-dimethylpent-2-ene (3 moles) was treated with TMT (1 mole) in the presence of zinc oxide confirmed that ZDC was the main product of thiuram decomposition, although the presence of a small amount of tetramethylthiourea was also reported. No trace of olefine dimerisation products could be found, although products which appeared to be alkyl alkenyl mono- and disulphides were isolated.

It has been suggested [83] that thiuram disulphides function, during cure, by decomposition to yield active sulphur and, *inter alia*, ZDC, which together constitute an accelerated sulphur system.[24] The following overall stoicheiometric relation was suggested in an attempt to explain the invariable two-thirds yield of ZDC during vulcanisation in the presence of zinc oxide:

$$12(CH_3)_2N \cdot CS \cdot S \cdot S \cdot CS \cdot N(CH_3)_2 + 10ZnO$$

$$\downarrow$$

$$8(CH_3)_2N \cdot CS \cdot S \cdot Zn \cdot S \cdot CS \cdot N(CH_3)_2 + 2(CH_3)_2N \cdot CO \cdot O \cdot Zn \cdot O \cdot CO \cdot N(CH_3)_2 \\ + 2(CH_3)_2N \cdot CS \cdot N(CH_3)_2 + CO_2 + CS_2 + 12(S)$$

When we note that a popularly held opinion in the past has been that TMT vulcanises *via* the intermediate formation of tetramethylthiuram monosulphide (TMTM) and " active " sulphur [84] and that, more recently, virtually the reverse has been suggested,[85] i.e. that TMTM vulcanises in the presence of sulphur via the intermediate formation of TMT, then it is evident that much remains yet to be settled in this field.

Benzoyl peroxide vulcanisation

The structural similarity shown by the thiuram disulphides, containing the $-CS \cdot S \cdot S \cdot CS-$ group, and benzoyl peroxide, containing the $-CO \cdot O \cdot O \cdot CO-$ group has led to the investigation of the kinetics of benzoyl peroxide decomposition during the peroxide vulcanisation of natural rubber.[86] The results show many aspects similar to thiuram disulphide decomposition.

Sulphur monochloride vulcanisation

This vulcanising agent, unlike sulphur, cures at room temperature, and advantage has been taken of this to investigate kinetically its reaction with rubber in solution by a dilatometric method.[8, 76] It has been shown that the reaction is speeded up by accelerators of sulphur vulcanisation and that these are most effective when they possess an active hydrogen atom. In addition, it has been shown that simple mercaptans, amines and alcohols of the type R–XH (where R is organic and X = S, N or O) serve as effective accelerators, and their activity is attributed to their ability to undergo the following type of reaction.

$$R-XH + Cl-S-S-Cl \longrightarrow R-\overset{*}{X} + HCl + \overset{*}{S}-S-Cl$$

For the non-accelerated process, the following stages have been suggested:

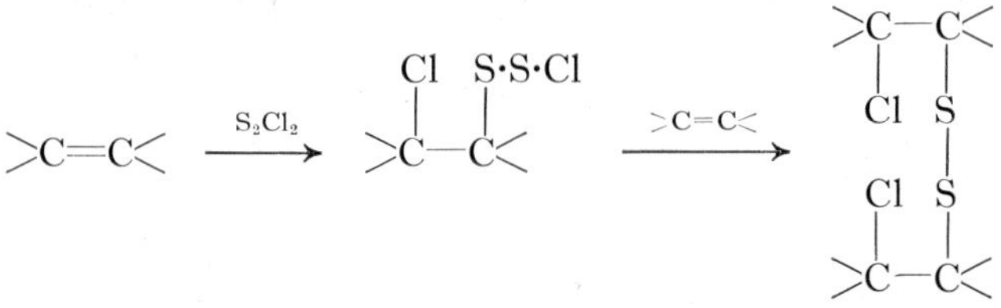

although the evidence presented, to date, does not permit a choice to be made between a polar or free radical mechanism.

The accelerated process possibly proceeds by a free radical mechanism of the following type:

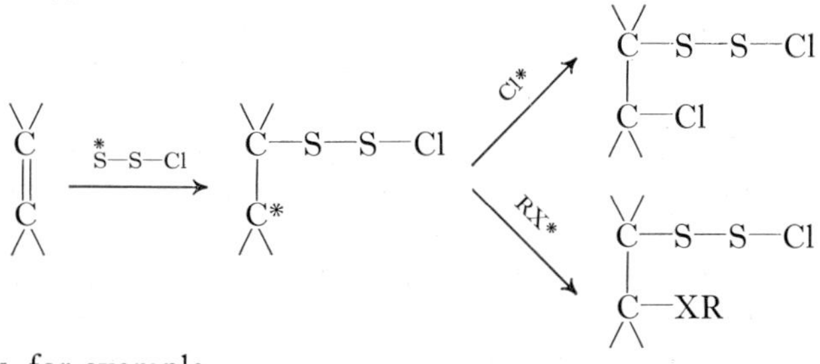

followed by, for example,

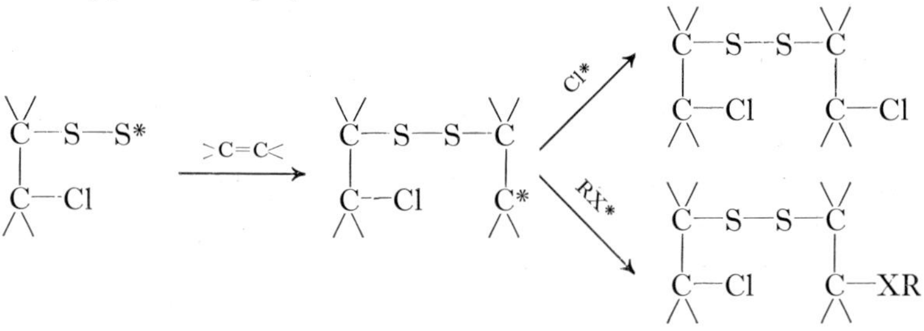

Until analytical data are available to support these structures, however, it would be unwise to regard these processes as more than speculative, although unpublished data [77] on model systems now shows that the cross-link is indeed disulphidic, in spite of previous assertions to the contrary.[78]

References

1. Flory, P. J. (1950) *J. chem. Phys.*, **18**, 108.
2. Flory, P. J. and Rehner, J. (1943) *J. chem. Phys.*, **11**, 521.
3. Moore, C. G. and Watson, W. F. (1956) *J. Polymer Sci.*, **19**, 237.
4. Flory, P. J. (1944) *Chem. Rev.*, **35**, 51.
5. Gee, G. (1946) *Trans. Faraday Soc.*, **42**, 585.
6. Flory, P. J., Rabjohn, N. and Shaffer, M. C. (1949) *J. Polymer Sci.*, **4**, 225.
7. Gee, G. (1946) *Trans. Faraday Soc.*, **42B**, 33.
8. Glazer, J. (1951) *Nature*, **167**, 404.
9. Charlesby, A. and Groves, D. (1954) *Proc. Third Rubber Technol. Conf., London*, 317.
10. Novikov, A. S., Bartenev, G. M. and Galil-Ogly, F. A. (1954) *Doklady Akademii Nauk SSSR*, **94**, 253.
11. Gee, G. (1947) *J. Polymer Sci.*, **2**, 451.
12. Flory, P. J., Rabjohn, N. and Shaffer, M. C. (1949) *J. Polymer Sci.*, **4**, 435.
13. Cuneen, J. I. (1952) *J. appl. Chem.*, **2**, 353.
14. Morrell, S. H. and Stern, J. (1953) *I.R.I. Trans.*, **28**, 17.
15. Gumbrell, S. M., Mullins, L. and Rivlin, R. S. (1953) *Trans. Faraday Soc.*, **49**, 1495.
16. Lukin, B. V. and Kasatochkin, V. I. (1946) *J. Technical Physics*, **16**, 1383.
17. Dogadkin, B. and Karmin, B. (1947) *Colloid J. U.S.S.R.*, **9**, 348.
18. Goppel, J. M. and Arlman, J. J. (1948) *Appl. sci. J.*, **A1**, 462.
19. Meyer, K. H. and Mark, H. (1928) *Ber.*, **61**, 1939.
20. Field, J. (1941) *J. appl. Phys.*, **12**, 23.
21. Goppel, J. M. (1947) *Appl. sci. J.*, **A1**, 3.
22. Treloar, L. R. G. (1941) *Trans. Faraday Soc.*, **37**, 84.
23. Nyburg, S. C. (1954) *Brit. J. appl. Res.*, **5**, 321.
24. Craig, D., Davidson, W. L., Juve, A. E. and Geib, I. G. (1951) *J. Polymer Sci.*, **6**, 1.
25. Craig, D., Juve, A. E. and Davidson, W. L. (1951) *J. Polymer Sci.*, **6**, 13.
26. Flory, P. J. (1946) *Ind. Eng. Chem.*, **38**, 417.
27. Flory, P. J. (1953) *Principles of Polymer Chemistry* (New York: Cornell Univ. Press), p. 461.
28. Boonstra, B. S. T. T. (1949) *India Rubb. World*, **121**, 299.
29. Stiehler, R. D. and Wakelin, J. H. (1947) *Ind. Eng. Chem.*, **39**, 1647.
30. Williams, I. (1947) *Ind. Eng. Chem.*, **39**, 901.
31. Cuneen, J. I. (1947) *J. chem. Soc.*, 36.
32. Cuneen, J. I. (1947) *J. chem. Soc.*, 134.
33. Rabjohn, N. (1948) *J. Amer. chem. Soc.*, **70**, 1181.
34. Farmer, E. H. and Moore, C. G. (1951) *J. chem. Soc.*, 131, 142, 149.
35. Raley, J. H., Rust, F. F. and Vaughan, W. E. (1948) *J. Amer. chem. Soc.*, **70**, 88, 1336.
36. Sheppard, N. and Sutherland, G. B. B. M. (1945) *Trans. Faraday Soc.*, **41**, 261.
37. Dogadkin, B. and Tarasova, Z. (1947) *J. gen. Chem. U.S.S.R.*, **17**, 1401.
38. Dogadkin, B., Tarasova, Z. and Pasynskii, A. (1947) *J. gen. Chem. U.S.S.R.*, **17**, 2222.
39. Sheppard, N. and Sutherland, G. B. B. M. (1947) *J. chem. Soc.*, 1699.
40. Humphreys, N. C. H. and Wake, W. C. (1950) *I.R.I. Trans.*, **25**, 334.

41. Farmer, E. H. (1946) " Vulcanization " in *Advances in Colloid Science*, Vol. II, ed. H. Mark and G. S. Whitby (New York: Interscience), p. 299.
42. Farmer, E. H. (1947) *J. Soc. chem. Ind.*, **66**, 86; Farmer, E. H. and Shipley, F. W. (1947) *J. chem. Soc.*, 1519; see also Armstrong, R. T., Little, J. R. and Doak, K. W. (1944) *Ind. Eng. Chem.*, **36**, 628 for similar olefine systems.
43. Bateman, L. C., Glazebrook, R. W., Moore, C. G. and Saville, R. W. (1954) *Proc. Third Rubb. Technol. Conf., London*, 298.
44. Private communication: Moore C. G.; Ross, G. W. (1958) *J. Chem. Soc.*, 2856.
45. Bloomfield, G. F. (1949) *J. Soc. chem. Ind.*, **68**, 66.
46. Bloomfield, G. F. (1947) *J. chem. Soc.*, 1547.
47. Guryanova, E. N., Vasilyeva, V. N. and Kuzina, L. S. (1955) *Proc. Conf. Acad. Sci. U.S.S.R. on Peaceful Uses of Atomic Energy*, 163.
48. Spence, D. and Young, J. (1912) *Koll. Z.*, **11**, 28.
49. Selker, M. L. and Kemp, A. R. (1947) *Ind. Eng. Chem.*, **39**, 895.
50. Bloomfield, G. F. (1945) *J. Soc. chem. Ind.*, **64**, T274.
51. Bloomfield, G. F. (1948) *J. Soc. chem. Ind.*, **67**, 14.
52. Kemp, A. R. and Selker, M. L. (1944) *Ind. Eng. Chem.*, **36**, 16, 20.
53. Selker, M. L. (1948) *Ind. Eng. Chem.*, **40**, 1467.
54. Naylor, R. F. (1947) *J. chem. Soc.*, 1106; Bloomfield, G. F. (1948) *Proc. Second Rubber Technol. Conf., London*, 79.
55. Armstrong, R. T., Little, J. R. and Doak, K. W. (1944) *Ind. Eng. Chem.*, **36**, 628.
56. Moore, C. G. and Saville, R. W. (1954) *J. chem. Soc.*, 2082, 2089; Glazebrook, R. W. and Saville, R. W. (1954) *ibid.*, 2094.
57. Juve, A. E. (1954) " Physical Test Methods and Polymer Evaluation " in *Synthetic Rubber*, Ed. G. S. Whitby (New York: Wiley), p. 506.
58. Thirion, P. (1951) *Rev. gen. Caoutch.*, **28**, 563.
59. Stiehler, R. D. and Roth, F. L. (1948) *India Rubb. World*, **118**, 367; *idem* (1948) *J. Res. Nat. Bureau Stand.*, **41**, 87; Schade, J. W. (1952) *India Rubb. World*, **126**, 67.
60. Newton, R. G. (1952) ASTM Spec. Publicn., No. 138.
61. Blackwell, R. F. (1952) *I.R.I. Trans.*, **28**, 75; Fletcher, W. P., Gee, G. and Morrell, S. H. (1952) *ibid.*, **28**, 85; Blackwell, R. F., Fletcher, W. P. and Gee, G. (1952) *ibid.*, **28**, 93; Gee, G. and Morrell, S. H. (1952) *ibid.*, **28**, 102.
62. Hull, C. M., Olsen, S. R. and France, W. G. (1946) *Ind. Eng. Chem.*, **38**, 1282.
63. Adams, H. E. and Johnson, B. L. (1953) *Ind. Eng. Chem.*, **45**, 1539.
64. Barton, B. C. (1950) *Ind. Eng. Chem.*, **42**, 671.
65. Veith, A. G. (1952) ASTM Spec. Publicn., No. 138.
66. Altman, R. F. A. (1948) *Ind. Eng. Chem.*, **40**, 241.
67. Scott, J. R. (1948) *J. Rubb. Res.*, **17**, 48.
68. Kratz, G. D., Young, H. H. and Katz, I. (1949) *Ind. Eng. Chem.*, **41**, 399.
69. Gordon, M. (1951) *J. Polymer Sci.*, **7**, 485.
70. Zapp, R. L., Decker, R. H., Dyroff, M. S. and Rayner, H. A. (1951) *J. Polymer Sci.*, **6**, 331.
71. Verghese, G. T. (1949) *I.R.I. Trans.*, **24**, 280.
72. Auerbach, I. (1953) *Ind. Eng. Chem.*, **45**, 1526.
73. Russell, E. W. (1951) *Trans. Faraday Soc.*, **47**, 539.
74. Berry, J. P. and Watson, W. F. (1955) *J. Polymer Sci.*, **18**, 201.
75. Barton, B. C. and Hart, E. J. (1952) *Ind. Eng. Chem.*, **44**, 2444.
76. Glazer, J. and Schulman, J. H. (1954) *J. Polymer Sci.*, **14**, 169; Glazer, J. (1954) *ibid.*, **14**, 225.
77. Glazer, J. and Vidwans, L., unpublished evidence.
78. Meyer, K. H. and Mark, H. (1928) *Ber.*, **61**, 1948.
79. Scheele, W., Lorenz, O. and Dummer, W. (1954) *Kautsch. u. Gummi*, **7**, WT 273; *idem* (1955) *ibid.*, **8**, WT 2, WT 27.

80. Scheele, W. and Lorenz, O. (1956) *Kautsch. u. Gummi*, **9**, WT 27; Scheele, W. and Stange, P. (1956) *ibid.*, **9**, WT 110.
81. Scheele, W. and Lorenz, O. (1955) *Kautsch. u. Gummi*, **8**, WT 85.
82. Farmer, E. H., Ford, J. F. and Lyons, J. A. (1954) *J. appl. Chem.*, **4**, 554.
83. Craig, D. (1956) *J. Polymer Sci.*, **20**, 197.
84. Craig, D., Davidson, W. L. and Juve, A. E. (1951) *J. Polymer Sci.*, **6**, 177.
85. Scheele, W. and Bielstein, G. (1955) *Kautsch. u. Gummi*, **8**, WT 251.
86. Lorenz, O. and Scheele, W. (1955) *Kautsch. u. Gummi*, **8**, WT 273.
87. Zapp, R. L. (1948) *Ind. Eng. Chem.*, **40**, 1508.
88. Private communication from G. N. Welding.

CHAPTER XII

PART TWO

PRACTICAL VULCANISATION

by

L. R. MERNAGH

SINCE the day 120 years ago when Goodyear first heated a mixture of rubber and sulphur on a domestic stove and so discovered vulcanisation, this action of heat and sulphur has remained the standard method of converting crude rubber, with all its limitations, into a commercially usable product, giving it the qualities of resistance to heat and cold in addition to considerable mechanical strength.[1]

Goodyear also conjured up the word " cure " for vulcanisation, and this has become the recognised term in production circles. Readers interested in the early experiments on vulcanisation are referred to Goodyear's [2] and Hancock's [3] original works. It should be mentioned here that claims to have discovered vulcanisation have been made in almost every country of the civilised world, for example, van Gouns [4] claimed to have discovered it in Holland in 1833.

If the concept of vulcanisation has remained essentially unchanged the technological processes involved in its execution have continuously improved. Sources of heat include hot air or inert gas, hot water, steam, electrical energy through (*a*) resistance heating, (*b*) induction and (*c*) dielectric, while cold curing under atmospheric conditions without elevated temperatures is widely practised. More modern forms of energy employed experimentally include ultra-violet and atomic radiation.

Common sulphur is adequate for all normal curing purposes, the essential condition being that it must be in the form of a fine dry powder. Where bloom is to be avoided insoluble sulphur costing 8 times as much is employed. The Peachey process, which forms elemental sulphur *in situ* by mixing sulphuretted hydrogen and sulphur dioxide, is confined to the cold curing of thin-walled articles, and is now only of academic interest. A more practical method of obtaining the same result involves the use of sulphur chloride in liquid or vapour phase. It is estimated that 60,000 tons/year of sulphur are used in the vulcanising of rubber. Substitutes for sulphur in vulcanisation include two elements closely associated chemically with sulphur, selenium and tellurium, which have specialised uses of some importance. Organic peroxides as curing agents have not attained production status. Neoprene is quite exceptional in using metallic oxides (e.g. zinc oxide) as vulcanising agents, though sulphur is employed as the secondary accelerator or activator.

Principles of vulcanisation

Before reviewing types of equipment it is necessary to understand the qualities desired in the vulcanisate and to appreciate the problems involved in their attainment. Vulcanisation as a practical proposition is a process whereby a material of variable composition and a bad conductor of heat is subjected to the process with the intention of producing a *uniform* product having improved physical properties. That such a result is obtained day in and day out with either natural or synthetic rubber is a tribute first of all to improved compounding materials permitting a wide range of cure without deleterious effect and also to engineering design and " plumbing " which permit uniform heating. The possibilities of varia-bility are so many and so serious that it is essential that the utmost control be exercised, firstly, on the uniform quality of the raw materials and the uniform dispersion of the sulphur and the other ingredients, and secondly, on the time, pressures and temperatures used in the operation.

Conditions of cure will vary over a very wide range according to the type of vulcanisate required and the facilities available. Many factors must be pre-determined, including the desired hardness of the product, its thickness, the turnover required and treatment of the rubber stock ahead of cure. Hardness will normally be determined by the composition of the stock, but it can also be influenced materially by the state of cure.

The thickness of the article will obviously be highly significant, due to the necessity of providing heat in the interior of a bad conductor and preserving a uniform state of cure through the cross-section.

There are two recognised methods of dealing with thick rubber articles. The first is by " stepped " or step-up cures, in which more than one tem-perature is employed; the principle being that the whole article is raised to near vulcanising temperature (say 120° C) before further heat to reach the curing temperature of 138° C is applied. A better technical, if more expensive, method of attaining this objective is to pre-heat the article outside the mould by di-electric which gives uniform heat throughout the mass of the article.

The second method depends upon the reverse effect, namely a slow external cooling in place of a slow heating. Heat is discontinued before cure is complete and the article is held under pressure in the mould, free from draughts or other cooling influences, while the heat penetrates to the interior. This is " soak " cure.

The heat transfer during vulcanisation of thick sheets of rubber has been analysed,[5] and a method of calculating the extra time for thicker sheets has been put forward. A somewhat similar study has been made for blocks $\frac{1}{2}$ to $1\frac{1}{2}$ in. thick.[6] An increase in dimensions necessitates a reduction in curing temperature, with increased time to obtain uniformity throughout the product.

For hollow articles, particularly those with a complicated cross-section such as a tyre, resort is made to two further expedients. Heat is applied simultaneously to the inside and outside, and the various components are compounded of stocks having different rates of cure to ensure a balanced cure for the whole. It is a severe test of the compounder's art that the centre of the bead area and the top of the carcass under the shoulders, which represent the thickest portions of the tyre, shall cure in the same time as the thin sidewall, particularly in the light of present-day emphasis on a steadily increasing modulus from the inside to the outside of a tyre. A typical cure for a bus tyre might read:

Internal

170 lb. stream pressure	15 minutes	
165° C water	125	,,
Blow down	10	,,
Total:	150	,,

External

120° C circulating steam	40 minutes	
138° C vent	5	,,
138° C circulating	25	,,
120° C	80	,,
Total:	150	,,

" Post " cure

Just as rubber is slow to build up temperature during cure, so it is equally reluctant to lose it after the article is removed from the curing equipment. Therefore until this temperature is " killed " cure will continue. This has obvious advantages, for in the case of high-temperature cures only a small fraction may take place in the equipment and the remainder after removal. This suggests a simple method of obtaining maximum efficiency from expensive equipment, but a certain minimum time for cure under pressure is required, otherwise the product is liable to be porous and may " blow ". Subsequent curing would not be uniform unless protection is given against draughts, etc., and the shape of the article might give varying rates of cooling. It is a common practice in the industry to cure partly in a mould and to complete the cure in open steam. Quite apart from the obvious risks of the parts not getting their second cure due to error, sufficient cure must be given initially to pass the porous point (see Fig. 12.23). The results of curing the same article using three different moulding times at high temperature is shown, the first barely passes the porosity line before removal from the mould, yet during its normal cooling to room temperature it becomes overcured. An extra minute in the curing time in the mould eliminates the risk of porosity but causes a worse overcured condition. The third condition, involving a reduction in temperature to " kill " the cure before the article leaves the mould, provides the ideal cure.

It is a well-established axiom that low-temperature–long-time cures

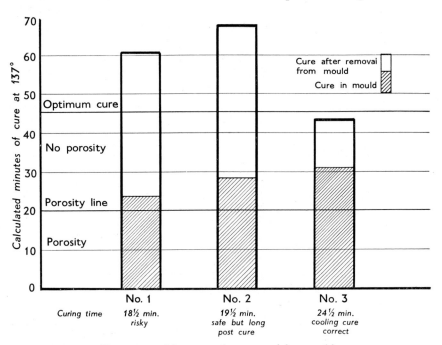

Fig. 12.23. After-cure after removal from mold.

give the best products. It must be understood that the terms short and long applied to curing times are purely relative, because what represents long times by modern standards would have been ultra-short cures in bygone days. Pressure from managements and production men who are so conscious of the need for maximum turn-over from curing equipment makes the putting into practice of this axiom more and more difficult.

Minimum curing time is fixed by two considerations. The first is the maximum safe temperature to which rubber should be subjected (150° C for natural and 163° C for SBR), although there are plenty of examples where these temperatures have been exceeded appreciably, particularly where finished appearance is not a criterion. The second limitation arises from the necessary processing of the article before cure. Heat treatment due to calendering or extruding may restrict the choice of curing agents in order to prevent incipient cure, pre-cure, or what is more commonly called " scorch ". In setting curing conditions we tend to take too much advantage of the plateau effect of modern accelerators, which allows a wide range of conditions without adversely affecting the quality of the product to an obvious extent. This tolerance should be allowed only in those cases where a composite article has to be cured, and should not be used to compensate for day-to-day variations in steam pressure. The subject of temperature coefficient of vulcanisation has been studied by Lowenstein and Rollins,[7] who make quite clear the importance of accurate temperature control.

Gross under- or over-cures are readily detected, but minor irregularities which may, however, adversely affect the service of the product are difficult or impossible to detect under normal testing procedure. Some of the causes of bad temperature control are enumerated below:

(a) Inadequacy of generating equipment, e.g. boilers which have to be operated at maximum load to satisfy normal production and fall short immediately some adverse condition arises.

(b) Equipment which may have sufficient calculated capacity, but not when a number of curing units are started up together, e.g. after a meal break.

(c) Additions to original layout which involve tortuous piping, e.g. with bends which collect condensed steam.

(d) Inadequacy of traps allowing water to collect in steam lines. These require frequent inspection.

(e) Use of pressure controllers and gauges in preference to thermometers and temperature controllers. A steam line can become waterlogged through faulty trap operation without pressure being affected. Temperature and pressure bear a direct relationship only when the steam is dry, and it may not be possible to ensure that the steam is dry. It is temperature which determines the rate of cure, and it is this which should be measured at the curing unit.

(f) Bad location of temperature recorders. Recorders which may indicate specified conditions when located at the steam generator may tell a different story at the curing press after the steam has travelled an appreciable distance through unlagged or badly lagged piping. If the source of steam supply is some distance from the vulcaniser it is preferable to use steam with a few degrees of superheat to cater for heat losses and reduce condensation to a minimum before the steam reaches the vulcaniser.

(g) Even in well-instrumented organisations there may occur water-

M M

logged platens and steam cavities while the thermometers show correct curing temperature due to their being located in the supply or return steam lines and not in the individual press or mould. All equipment should be fitted with inlets permitting the insertion of mercury-in-glass thermometers for spot checking.

(*h*) Dirty moulds which prevent good contact at the rubber–metal face or poor contact between metal faces where heat transfer is by conduction, which is impeded by dirt or loose connections.

Steam lines can be connected to presses either in parallel or in series. Series ensures that steam flows through all cavities, but gives greater temperature difference between inlet and outlet. Temperature uniformity is generally obtained with parallel piping, but poor circulation may result in one of the branches without indication.

Further, a decision has to be taken on what constitutes a correct differential in temperature between the supply and return lines of a curing unit. Too little means low circulation, whereas too great a differential indicates waste of heat by conduction or radiation and irregular cure through the product.

Optimum cure

Determinations of optimum cure and rate of cure are essential prerequisites in the selection of stocks for particular articles. These are generally obtained by first curing samples at say 140° C and determining modulus, tensile strength and hardness at various cure times.

Attempts have been made to define optimum cure,[8] but while it may normally be fixed from the curves obtained by plotting modulus and tensile strength against cure times, optimum cure may be selected on hardness, tear strength, abrasion, flex-cracking or other physical quality, according to the nature of the projected service of the article. Many operators, particularly American, lean towards optimum modulus in deciding optimum cure,[9] but maximum tensile strength is more generally used in Great Britain. A rate-of-cure chart for natural rubber is shown in Fig. 12.24, comprising three curves based on physical determinations, namely ultimate tensile strength, 300% modulus and hardness, together with one based on chemical determination (i.e. free sulphur) for comparison. The point of optimum cure is picked out on the three physical charts by:

(*a*) *Tensile strength.* The point on the curve which has a tangent based on a slope of 10 lb. increase in tensile strength per minute of cure. Result: 46 minutes.

(*b*) *Modulus.* A point on the curve which has a tangent based on a slope of 20 lb. increase in modulus per minute of cure. Result: 43 minutes.

(c) *Hardness.* A point on the curve which has a tangent based on a slope of $\frac{1}{5}°$ increase in hardness per minute of cure. Result: 48 minutes.

The optimum cure of such a stock would be quoted at 45 minutes at 138° C.

Hardness is less specific than the other constants, and because of this is less frequently used.

Different operators will use different slopes for determining the various points. The Research Association of British Rubber Manufacturers defines optimum cure [10] to the nearest five minutes " as a mean of tensile strength, modulus and hardness optimum times, the mean being weighted in favour of the tension strength value ". For most natural rubber mixes the optima for the various properties are defined arbitrarily as the times at which the property–time of vulcanisation curves have the following upward slopes: tension strength 6 lb./m.²/min.; modulus $8\frac{1}{2}$ lb./in.²/min.; hardness $\frac{1}{6}$ B.S. min.". Morrell [11] suggests a method of reducing the considerable amount of work involved in these determinations by adopting a quick method for determining optimum based on modulus, which is referred to later on under " Cure Control ", and then applying a factor for optimum based on tensile strength which will remain constant for similar types of stock.

A method [12] of determining optimum cure by means of minimum hysteresis loss depends upon plotting the hysteresis loops for a series of cures. The ratio for load at 50% elongation on deformation against the same figure on recovery is determined, and the minimum quotient indicates optimum cure.

The information on the previous pages relates essentially to natural rubber and does not necessarily apply to SBR, with which, for instance, hardness and modulus continue to increase beyond the optimum cure point. Tear resistance, cut growth and permanent set, however, have been used to determine the optimum cure of SBR. Methods based on hysteresis are not suitable for synthetic rubbers. [9]

Selecting a *practical* cure after optimum has been determined is a matter of personal judgement, and may depend upon the slope of the curve, a definite percentage of optimum or on empirical bases. Similar judgement is required in selecting the type of curing equipment to be used. Allowance will have to be made for the subsequent cure which the article may undergo in service, particularly where it is likely to be subjected to appreciable heat, due principally to internal friction.

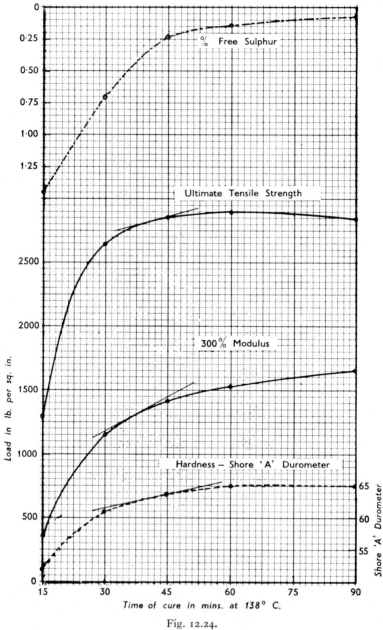

Fig. 12.24.

Control of production cures

The following methods are in general use:

1. Specific gravity, which is easily determined by finding the zinc chloride solution of known gravity in which the sample just floats. This is not strictly a check on cure but on materials, which may affect cure.

2. The simplest check on cure is by a hardness determination, i.e. durometer reading. Reliable hardness readings can be obtained only when the article is cold, which means from four to twenty-four hours after cure. Any test which is operative only after many hours delay obviously starts with a considerable handicap as a routine or spot test on continuous production. In consequence, attempts are made to carry out hot testing. With experience a sufficiently close allowance for temperature change can be made to distinguish between good and scrap material, though not good enough to ensure the exact specified hardness. Experience has shown that hot testing is less reliable with SBR than with natural rubber. Hot testing may lead to the rejection of articles which will be satisfactory when cold. Any success with hot testing depends upon it being carried out at the same temperature, e.g. immediately the article has been removed from the mould.

3. Cutting up of scrap production may provide information on undercured conditions, trapped air, etc.

4. Thermocouple tests at various locations in platens and the surface of the product and in the interior of it provide the most reliable information concerning the state of cure and its uniformity. In the case of tyres six temperature readings may be taken between tyre and mould at both shoulders and at the centre line at locations 180° apart, the hot junctions being an interference fit in suitable vent holes in the mould. Additional readings inside the tyre can be taken in the centre of the sidewall and under both shoulders. A timing device may be incorporated permitting readings to be taken at fixed intervals, say every 6 seconds.

The platens of presses should be checked frequently for regularity of temperature throughout their area by having a metal plate of the same area as the platen with a machined surface drilled to accommodate thermocouples in a variety of locations. This is preferable to inserting thermocouples between platen and mould. Platens should also be checked at say six monthly intervals with a search plate to ensure flatness within 0·002 in.

5. Compound parts, such as rubber-to-fabric bonded articles, e.g. tyres, belts, and rubber-to-metal bonded goods can be tested by determining the adhesion between the rubber and the non-rubber face. For typical rubber-to-metal parts the strength should be of the order of 250 lb./in.^{2}.

6. Some articles lend themselves to a tear-resisting test as a measure of cure.

7. Chemical analysis for free sulphur provides one of the most generally accepted methods of determining state of cure. The limits set for each particular stock based on experience may then be used to compare future samples against control. Free-sulphur figures, however, will show only the final state of cure, and are useless as a guide in preventing the removal of articles from hot moulds before the porosity line has been passed.

8. A swelling test for estimating the degree of vulcanisation is described in BS 1673.[13]

9. Where the article concerned is sufficiently large a sample should be taken to determine the physical qualities of most interest, for example, modulus or tensile strength.

Types of equipment used

The total time of vulcanisation can be broken down into two stages:

    (*a*) the time taken to heat the article to curing temperature; and

    (*b*) the time to cure after curing temperature has been reached.

The latter is fixed for any given temperature, consequently the relative efficiency of various types of equipment will depend upon the time saved during warm-up. The continuous vulcanisers described in the following pages make a strong appeal on these grounds.

A shorter curing time does not necessarily mean the use of less steam, since unit weight of rubber requires a definite quantity of heat. The secret of high efficiency with any hot cure is to keep it running continuously. In open types of cure using air or inert gas, time can be reduced considerably by circulating the heating medium, since a cold article cools the gas in direct contact with it and then acts as an insulator. Where saturated steam under pressure is used, the cold surface causes steam to condensed, at the same time giving up its large content of latent heat. The condensation causes a reduction of pressure, attracting more steam to the area. Hence steam always tends automatically to correct for any cold spot.

No one process will possess all the virtues, and those which may appear to be the most desirable may be rejected on grounds of high initial cost and maintenance. A variety of methods of cure will now be described:

Hot-air cures

Hot-air cures may be divided into open-air cures at atmospheric pressure and oven cures. Open-air cures are suitable for sheet goods and dipped goods. The former are skimmed on a horizontal spreading machine and cured by passing over the heated coils of the drying unit. Dipped goods which are cured on formers are made by dipping in a rubber solution containing a super-accelerator and when dry, cured in hot air. The drying off and curing operations can be combined to make the process continuous, the usual conditions being an air cure rising from 80° to 120° C through $\frac{3}{4}$ hour.

Hot-air curing is normally conducted in horizontal vulcanisers, which may vary between 12 and 40 ft. in length, and 5 and 8 ft. in diameter. They will be lagged and either jacketed or lined with steam pipes. Air pressures of 15–40-lb./in.² are applied before the curing temperature is reached. Fans are needed for circulation. Air cure is used when a glossy finish is required without tack, and normally it is limited to thin-gauge materials because of the difficulty of securing uniform heat distribution. This includes such articles as dipped goods, clothing textiles and footwear. Temperature is raised gradually at a controlled rate, say over 60 minutes, to a maximum of 130° C. The process can be made continuous for cloth by allowing it to enter a heated chamber at a controlled rate from a festoon device. The entry is made through a trap-slot in the wall at one end of the oven and leaves through a corresponding exit at the other.

Footwear, after being built up on formers, may be cured in a hot-air oven using 15–40 lb./in.² pressure ahead of heat. The rise will take 30–60 minutes, followed by a similar period at 130° C. An unusual form of air cure has been described. This is a gas-fired unit 252 ft. long by 10 ft. 3 in. wide and 18 in. deep, which is mounted on rollers to allow for expansion. The rubber mix is conveyed on an endless glass fabric belt through the oven, which is kept at a thermostatically controlled temperature of 177° C. Seven direct-fired gas-burner units are used for producing hot gases which pass over the rubber articles.[15] The project was started on the basis of economy, low capital cost, cleanliness and ease of control.

Extruded or cut thread is normally cured in long hot-air chambers. The initial temperature is 95° C, rising to 200° C, using inert gas containing steam to replace air.

Open steam cures

This method, by which articles are subjected to dry steam under pressure in horizontal heaters, is the " work-horse " of the rubber industry. A wide variety of materials is handled in this way, including rubber hose, footwear, small mechanicals, tubed goods, insulated wire and cable, and hard rubber, in addition to tyre repairs and remoulds. The method is also employed to finish off cures started in presses in order to increase the turnover of the moulds concerned. This last practice is attended by risks owing to the possibility of mistakes which result in articles missing their second cure or having more than one. The cooling from the first cure may also be irregular through the cross-section of the article, and thereby lead to an irregular final cure. Furthermore, if the article is removed from the mould too soon it will show porosity and separation.

A hose cured in open steam is generally surrounded by talc, while other items are covered with a liner to protect the surface. The liner is also useful in exerting pressure due to shrinkage when wetted. Where porosity is a possibility, the pressure inside the heater is increased by using air together with steam, for example, steam at $115°$ C (10 lb./in.^{2}) plus 50 lb./in.^{2} air. The use of open steam for vulcanising rubberised fabric has not been replaced to any extent by newer methods which would appear to be more efficient. 50–300-yard rolls are wound on a hollow steam drum to a thickness of $1\frac{1}{2}$ in. and tightly wrapped with the liner.

Certain inflated rubberised fabric products, such as life-saving rafts, are cured by this method. They are kept during cure in their normal inflated shape. The inflation set-up has a balancing mechanism which keeps the internal and external pressures equal. Near the end of the cure air is turned into the steam to give a slow drop in pressure. Sheet rubber may be cured by this method by placing it between stainless-steel plates, which are then placed inside a rubberised-fabric blanket bag. This method produces sheet rubber with a glossy finish.

V-belts mounted on corrugated drums and wrapped are commonly cured by this method. Hose may be cured by passing it rapidly before cure through a " lead press " which covers it with a thin casing of lead, which acts as a mould. The lead-covered hose is then rolled on large reels. Each hose is filled with water at 100 lb./in.^{2} to maintain shape.

A description has been given of one of the largest pot heaters having dimensions of 55 ft. $\times$ 15 ft.[16] The latest method for curing rubber-insulated cable is by a continuous open steam vulcanising unit (Fig. 12.25). The two main processes of insulating and sheathing can both be handled in this equipment at a very high rate. The extruder in a layout of this type is usually cold fed, because the compound is so fast curing that a change in temperature which affects plasticity might also produce scorching. The covered cable passes along a jacketed vulcanising tube 150 ft. long having a telescopic inlet end with bayonet fixing to extruder die. A water trough 48 ft. long is mounted above the curing tube to cool the cable during its return passage to the driven capstan wheel and hence to the wind-up. Saturated steam at 200 lb./in.^{2} is used, the passage through the curing tube averaging 16 seconds.

In the tyre industry open steam curing is the old method of curing tubes. The uncured extruded tubes were blown on to either straight or curved mandrels and cured for periods of about 30 minutes. Cycle tubes are still

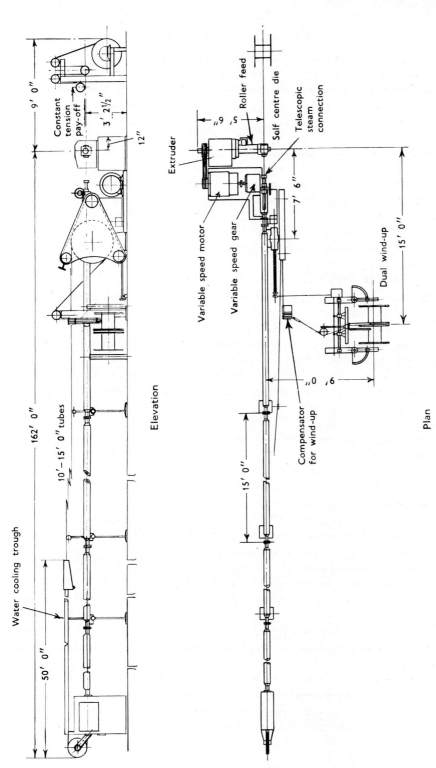

Water cooling trough

162' 0"

10'–15' 0" tubes

50' 0"

Elevation

9' 0"

Constant tension pay-off

3' 2½"

12"

Extruder

Variable speed motor

Variable speed gear

5' 6"

Roller feed

Self centre die

Telescopic steam connection

7' 6"

Dual wind-up

15' 0"

6' 0"

Compensator for wind-up

15' 0"

Plan

Fig. 12.25. Open steam cable vulcanising unit.

manufactured to some extent by this method, although some of these and all larger-sized tubes are now manufactured by a moulded method, whereby lapped splices are eliminated and a tube of correct shape is obtained.

Platen-press cure

Platen-press cure has been throughout the years the standard method of dealing with that vast assortment of items known as general rubber goods and such diverse products as belting, sponge, flooring, hot-water bottles, cycle and other small pneumatic tyres, soles and heels, and mechanicals.[17] When operated by a single hydraulic ram, common platen sizes are 28 in. × 28 in. and 32 in. × 32 in., but using multi-rams size is virtually unlimited, machines accommodating 32 ft. of belt at a time having been produced.

Most of the normal-sized presses have multiple daylights, i.e. they are capable of handling 6 or 7 moulds at a time. Fig. 12.26 shows a 28-in. × 28-in. 6-daylight footwear press. This is shown with a hydraulically operated loading table of adjustable height. The number of daylights in use has been steadily falling with the lower cure times of modern compounds, otherwise mould changing time would become entirely disproportionate. When a press has x daylights it is quite common practice to operate with $x + 1$ moulds, which increases efficiency, because the press is in full operation while the additional mould is being worked. This practice, known as " floating-mould technique ", is criticised in some quarters due to its possible effect on quality by continually applying and relieving pressure. The practice of " bumping ", i.e. relieving the pressure momentarily immediately after closing the mould, as a final assurance that air has been eliminated is criticised similarly, and also on the basis of wear and tear on the press.

Rams may have up or down stroke, and while the former is much the more common, the latter has the advantage of providing a fixed working height.

A 32 in. × 32 in. press will have a ram of about 27 in. diameter, the stroke, and consequently the daylight, between platens varying according to type of work, the average figure lying between 12 and 15 in. This would have a capacity of 500 tons operating with 2,000 lb./in.² hydraulic pressure. Low-pressure hydraulic of the order of 350 lb./in.² is used to close the press, after which the higher pressure takes over. Corresponding figures for a 48-in. × 48-in. press would be 1,000 tons capacity, 36-in. ram and 3-in.-thick platens.

Platens need a " fine machine " finish being machined from the solid, the holes being accurately spaced by drilling, and may be fitted with baffles internally to cause the steam to take a serpentine course. Steam pressures of up to 100 lb./in.² are usual for natural rubber work.

Steam is the favoured heating medium, although electrical-resistance heating has been used in presses up to 48 in. × 48 in. Where a battery of steam-heated presses is already working to the capacity of the boilers and

Fig. 12.26. Self contained multi-daylight press with lifting table.

additional production is required an electrically heated press may be the answer, particularly if higher-temperature cures are required. Steam or water have obvious advantages when " cooling cures " are required. Whether or not electricity is used for heating, it may replace the hydraulic system and enable the press to be closed by a mechanical toggle system.

This type of operation is more flexible than hydraulic and permits quicker cycles of operation. It also lends itself more easily to automatic time control and " cut out " in case of overload.

When platen presses are used for " continuous " cure, such as belting which is moved along length by length, it is usual to taper off the temperature at the ends of the press where the overlap of the belt is subjected to a second cure. Thus the body of the platen may be at 135° C while the ends would be at 110° C. Platen presses are used for the continuous cure of sponge rubber made from extruded stock. This is passed between liners between the platens.

Where moulds are used with platen presses they fall into one of two categories, either compression type or transfer. Transfer is the newer method and generally preferred for precision parts, and is faster loading and unloading, particularly if some excess spew is tolerated, enabling all cavities of the mould to be interconnected with rubber and to be stripped as a " mat " in one motion.

Where rubber-to-metal bonded parts are produced, experience has shown that compression-type moulds are preferable. The explanation may be the partial setting up of the stock as it moves down the cavity, thereby reducing the effective pressure, or alternately, the cement may be wiped from the metal parts by this action, which results in a higher proportion of parts showing poor adhesion. Because of freedom from this danger, compression moulds can be operated at 10° C higher temperature, thereby reducing the cycle.

Shrinkage of cured articles is an important factor when designing moulds. Type of stock used, type of mould and temperature of cure all have an influence. These are lumped together and an arbitrary figure of $1\frac{1}{2}$–3% chosen for the general run of mechanicals, but for accurate work, such as gaskets, a study may be required, and considerable help can be obtained from a Government publication.[18]

Services to the press, additional to the hydraulic already mentioned, comprise steam up to 120 lb./in.² pressure, the line falling vertically one side of the press and returning the other side to drain with suitable trap. The take-off lines for the various platens are in parallel. Circulation of the steam may be assisted by means of an aspirator.

It is impossible to record typical cures because of the wide diversity of products handled due to their size and the quality of stock used. Anything from a few minutes to an hour or longer is quite common, with temperatures ranging from 135° to 180° C. This last high figure is too high for a quality product.

The influence of material thickness on cure has already been the subject of comment. Mechanical goods of substantial volume often demand long cures at low temperatures to ensure first of all, that the porosity point is passed before removing the article from the mould, and secondly, that the post mould cure is not excessive.

Curing by platen presses using multi daylights has given way to the fixed-mould type of unit press during recent years, but this latter depends for success upon lengthy runs avoiding the necessity for mould changing. A platen press is still the most convenient machine for handling varied short-run work and for articles which have to be stripped after removal from the press, e.g. hot-water bottles from their large cores, and for deeply drawn work, such as battery boxes. More attention is now being given to

Fig. 12.27. Hand-operated press for small mouldings.

preforming rubber blanks, so providing the moulder with material which has the correct shape and weight, thus assisting moulding and reducing " spew ".

The use of high-frequency (di-electric) heating of uncured rubber slugs—for example, heels—prior to curing has achieved some progress and on technical grounds has considerable merit. The initial outlay which must include some form of automatic or semi-automatic handling of parts from heater to mould is considerable. Power consumption and equipment upkeep are important items in running costs.

Multiple presses as distinct from single presses with multiple daylights extend the usefulness of platen presses enormously. Fig. 12.27 shows a hand-operated press for small mouldings. It may be provided with steam or electrically heated platens measuring 6 in. × 6 in.; and varying day-lights to suit the nature of the work. Six such presses are shown mounted on a bench with an upper member carrying eccentric cams which are operated by hand levers. These are suitable for women workers.

Fig. 12.28. Hydraulic belt press with gripping and stretching gear.

At the other end of the scale, Fig. 12.28 shows a hydraulic belt press with gripping and stretch gear having twelve rams of 20 in. diameter and 18 in. stroke, the platen size is 32 ft. × 3 ft. 6 in., with a daylight of 18 in.; working pressure 1,700 lb./in.².

Unit vulcanisers for general rubber goods

Unit vulcanisers (fixed-mould presses) are superseding daylight platen presses for the curing of that multitude of rubber articles known as general rubber goods. Efficient operation depends upon long runs of particular parts to avoid down time through mould changing. Efficiency is helped by tray-loading outside the mould, the use of automatic ejectors after cure and preferably pre-heated rubber parts. It is normal practice to work hot cures, i.e. moulds remaining continually at the curing tempera-ture throughout. The presses cover a range of platen sizes, for example, 10 in. × 16 in., 18 in. × 18 in., and 32 in. × 32 in. are common types, the moulds being bolted to the top and bottom platens, one of the smaller types being shown in Fig. 12.29. On opening, the top platen may move vertically for about 4 in. before tilting back to take up its normal open position, or alternatively, may have a horizontal sheer stripping action.

Fig. 12.29. Fixed mould press.

The opening and closing of the mould is performed by electrically operated toggle action, no hydraulic being employed, the lower platen remaining motionless throughout. The total pressure may vary from 50 to 400 tons, with adjustments down to zero accommodating a range of mould thicknesses from 4 to 12 in. Steam platen pressures up to 70 lb./in.^{2} are used.

Instrumentation makes the operation as nearly as possible automatic, each press being fitted with time–steam temperature recorders. Cure times may be only 75% of those used with conventional platen presses owing to the lower heat loss. Specialised use of such presses is the manufacture of hollow articles, such as tennis balls and small pneumatic tyres, when internal pressures up to 160 lb./in.^{2} may be used according to number of cavities and size. More uniform cures may be anticipated from this type of operation compared with platen presses, as permanent contact is maintained between platen and mould, there is less variation from cavity to cavity and no warpage of moulds which arises from the use of different-size moulds in different daylights of platen presses, while working time during which heat is lost is minimised. The hard labour of removing moulds from the press, stripping, reassembling and returning to press is obviated. Efficiency is improved by having cavities cut in the mould backs through which steam circulates.

Special equipment for tyre curing

(a) Pot heaters

Curing in pots, heaters or autoclaves is the same process using different names for the equipment used, and is the original method for the mass production of tyres, and a very large proportion of today's tyres are still produced by this method, although few new batteries have been installed in recent years.

Pots are vertical vessels which can be sealed to withstand steam pressure and in which any number up to twenty tyre moulds are stacked one above the other. They are supported on a hydraulic ram which seals the moulds against the lid of the heater, the curing temperature being obtained primarily by steam circulation round the moulds. All tyre sizes up to the very largest can be cured in this equipment.

For ease of working, heaters are generally set up in excavations below ground level. In view of the substantial investment in installations, there is natural reluctance to scrap such equipment in favour of more modern methods and consequently many improvements have been effected over the years.

Initially only air under pressure was used inside the tyre, but shorter cure times and better-balanced cures have been obtained by using hot water, steam or both internally. In fact, the following combinations have been used:

1. High-pressure air.
2. High-pressure steam followed by higher-pressure air.
3. High-pressure steam followed by lower-pressure steam.
4. High-pressure steam followed by dead end cold water.

5. High-pressure steam followed by dead-end hot water.

6. Circulated hot water.

7. High-pressure steam followed by low-pressure steam followed by dead-end cold water.

Commencing a cure with high-pressure air or high-pressure steam enables a test to be made for internal leaks before the external steam is applied.

Most improvements have been directed towards taking some of the hard labour out of the operation, for originally moulds were largely man-handled. Now gravity conveyors, electric hoists and mechanical mould openers and closers and tyre stripping devices have taken some of the toil out of the operation, but it still remains an arduous job.

The disadvantages of the process are obvious. Cure time is long judged by present standards. It is wasteful of hydraulic water and heating steam, using 60% more of the latter than in the most modern tyre-cure practice and 50% more than is standard for jacket-type presses. The method does have the advantage of not consuming heat when cure is not in operation. To operate such units efficiently it is essential to fill the heaters completely with moulds containing tyres, and this may necessitate a wide variety of sizes and types. All must have the same cure, that is an average cure, which means that some may be over- and some under-cured. Steam circulation will not be perfect. There may be eddies and pockets of poor circulation, giving irregular cures between one tyre and another or between different parts of the same tyre. A failure in the hydraulic or even in one steam or air connection may ruin a whole " heat " of tyres. This stratification of the inside atmosphere may be overcome by modifying the locations and dimensions of steam valves. If necessary an outlet valve can be installed in the vulcaniser which is controlled thermostatically and which will remain open during the steam-filling period, permitting the air inside the vulcaniser to escape. It will then close automatically at a temperature below that of vulcanisation. It is often advantageous to have autoclaves fitted with steam sample lines to which the temperature controllers and thermometers are attached. These sample lines are fitted with aspirators at the outlet to ensure that there is a constant flow of steam along the line so that the temperature in the line is representative of that in the heater. The controllers and recorders can then be installed in a place remote from the vulcaniser, where they will not be damaged and where they can be conveniently supervised.

Other limitations of pot-heater curing include the high proportion of non-productive time that is time spent in working the heaters and the many men tied up with this operation. There is considerable dependence on the human element in the control of time, temperature and pressure, although fully automatic autoclaves have been described [19] which operate on a push-button basis and in the event of a power failure can revert to manual control.   Control panels incorporating all the necessary instruments are available commercially.

A typical heater has a diameter of 66 in., is operated by a 24-in.-diameter ram having a 14-ft. stroke.   This allows 13 ft. 1 in. for moulds.   It is designed to work with a steam pressure of 100 lb./in.^{2} and hydraulic of 2,240 lb./in.^{2}.   Steam is admitted through a 2-in. inlet near the bottom of the heater, the orifices being arranged tangentially to provide circulation.

The one favourable feature of pot-heater curing is freedom from curing faults and blemishes.   The mould is relatively cold when the tyre is laid,

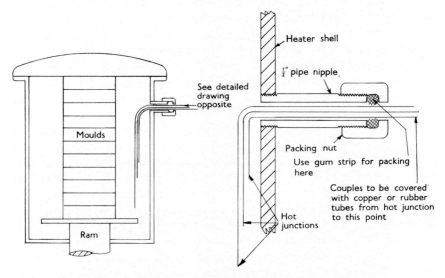

Fig. 12.30. Method of installing couples to check temperature of external steam between mould stack and heater shell.

and this is fully shaped before external heat is applied.   The gradual warming-up process is much less rigorous than those methods in which the mould is maintained at the curing temperature.

A typical cure for a passenger tyre is 40 minutes at 143° C external temperature, using hot water or steam internally.   Fig. 12.30 shows a method of inserting thermocouple leads at three or more heights to obtain a representative figure for curing temperature.

Recent installations have avoided deep excavations because of the prohibitive costs involved, and vessels of considerably less depth accommodating one to three moulds have become more common.

A pot-heater vulcaniser for handling tyres measuring 88 in. × 33 in. and weighing 2,500 lb. has been described.[20]

(b) Airbags

Until the introduction of Bagomatic presses airbags (air containers to fit the inside of the uncured tyre) were a necessary evil, their manufacture representing a non-productive operation, as after curing a limited number of tyres they have to be scrapped and replaced by new; the weight of the stock concerned being on average 25 lb. for passenger sizes and 60 lb. for giant tyres.

Many efforts have been made to dispense with airbags, these being mainly based on rendering the inside of the tyre air- and water-proof, generally by the use of insoluble gelatine coatings or of cured or semi-cured inner liners. After optimistic experimental runs they have not survived in production. The cost of airbags, although high, is appreciably less than that of the tyres they service, and the risk of producing defective tyres by other methods is too high. It needs only a minute area in a cover to remain uncoated to permit an attack by air or steam which will cause a scrap tyre due to separation. Other difficulties with non-airbag cures include the problem which arises through the tyre beads having to seal against the rings during inflation, yet at the same time they must be free to rotate, otherwise buckled or mis-shapen beads result. Furthermore, the inside of the tyre will tend to be rough and pitted and not have the smooth finish of an airbag tyre. Balanced cures are difficult using such methods, because 170 lb./in.^{2} is the absolute minimum necessary for internal pressure, and this corresponds to 190° C temperature, yet it is impossible to increase the external steam temperature beyond 166° C. Finally, there is the problem of the condensate which forms inside the tyre and which must be removed.

The composition of airbag stocks varies over very wide limits, and often to the regret of the user very poor-quality and workaway stocks are used. Low-grade rubbers, i.e. rubbers of low modulus, are desirable for easy extrusion and limitation of subsequent growth. In other words, a " dead " stock is required, and consequently reclaim suggests itself as an ingredient. Although not generally used, reclaim has stood the test of time and may be incorporated satisfactorily. Some slight loss of life might result from its use, but it is insufficient to be assessed by the rough and ready methods available for computing airbag life. Stocks are generally highly loaded with clay, SRF black, mineral rubber, etc. Large-sized bags are frequently extruded in two parts for convenience. One section is the solid base, the other a hollow section forming the body of the bag. These sections are united during cure. This method eases the problem of pre-cure or scorching, but it presents a point of attack for flexcracking in service and also increases the extruding time necessary for bag manufacture.

Tyre designers demand heavy bases in bags in order to keep tyre beads in position during processing. These heavy bases often cause problems during extrusion owing to their thickness combined with a slow rate of extrusion and consequent difficulty of cooling. These heavy bases are in contact with the thickest section of the tyre. This is undesirable from the point of heat transfer. In consequence, tyre-curing times and temperatures have to be set to meet this state of affairs, thereby becoming the major obstacle to reducing curing times.

Three methods of splicing airbags are in general use:

1. A butt splice produced by cutting both ends of the bag with a hot knife and pressing the exposed edges together.

2. An angled butt splice, generally made by operating a hand knife through a guide. The cutting angle produces a larger area of contact between the surfaces it is desired to join.

3. A lap splice, which must, of necessity, be bulky and which produces a heavy spot round the circumference of the bag, often leading to localised under-curing of the tyre.

The splice of an airbag is the first vulnerable point for breakdown. The second is the valve. High-temperature operation alternating with sudden cooling is bound to exercise a powerful disturbing influence on any metal–rubber bond, and brass or steel valves, whether bonded chemically to the rubber or held in place mechanically by clamp-in methods, are bound to work loose in time. Many devices, some quite ingenious, have been produced which postpone the evil day when leaks around the valve become apparent. Probably the best arrangement is a brass valve bonded to a natural rubber base, which, in turn, is vulcanised to the bag. To permit circulation of the steam or hot water in the bag during cure a second valve is sometimes fitted, one acting as an inlet and the other as outlet. Despite the technical advantage of this system, it is a practice not generally followed, partly due to the risk of valve leaks being doubled.

Government Technical Missions which visited Germany immediately after the War were enthusiastic over the Manschetta valve.[21] Strictly this is not a valve at all, but a rubber tube having heavy tapering walls fitted to the inside of the bag and projecting about 1 in. into the interior. The bore of the tube is a tight fit on the steam connection which is pushed inside it, and as pressure builds up in the bag this is exerted on the rubber tube to produce a seal between it and the metal connection. Experience in this country has shown that the occasional scrap tyre has made its use unpopular, although it is still in wide use on the Continent.

The third vulnerable part of an airbag is its internal surface. Conditions are nearly perfect for early destruction. Where air is the medium either for the initial cure of the bags or in the production of tyres, oxygen is available, heat is always present and the bags are subjected to frequent flexing. It is common practice to protect the inner surface of airbags with glycerine and to add reducing agents such as sodium sulphite. These are of little avail when the contents are flushed out every cure, as in steam and water cures. Oxidation leads to cracking and flaking, and before the bag is finally rejected trouble may well have been experienced with " coffee grounds " produced from loose oxidised rubber stopping up the connections.

The outside of the bag will also have deteriorated by heat, oxidation and over-cure, despite the dopes used on the bag and on the inside of the tyre to prevent sulphur migration.

Fine cracks and indentations appear in service, and when they become too bad the existing surface can be buffed off and replaced by a recover. It is highly questionable if such a practice is economical, but it is quite certain that if the amount of rubber removed is not replaced exactly in weight and location with new rubber, cure problems will result. It is the generally accepted practice nowadays merely to burn lightly and buff or scrape bags frequently to prevent cracks developing and to abandon the bags when this process ceases to have beneficial effect.

Taking all these hazards into account, airbags may be considered satisfactory if they complete an average life of 300 tyre cures for passenger sizes and 200 for giants, but these figures can vary within wide limits, depending upon the standard demanded of inside tyre appearance.

Designers are by no means agreed on the optimum stretch of airbags, that is the amount the periphery of the airbag is less than the inside periphery of the cured tyre. This figure expressed as a percentage is generally accepted at 2–3%, although figures considerably higher have been used. The smaller the airbag, the easier it is to handle when inserting in the tyre, and it should not be accepted that once a bag has been cured in a tyre it permanently assumes the internal dimensions and shape of the tyre. Recovery occurs for some considerable time, but eventually the bag grows, and this feature constitutes a constant problem. The greater the growth, the greater the difficulty with cracks.

For satisfactory curing, bags must be completely freed from the water resulting from its use as such, or by condensate of steam. This constitutes a problem for the normal one-valve bag. One of two methods is employed. A siphon can be inserted in the valve and the operation of emptying started automatically by the pressure still available inside the bag, or the pressure may be created by an airline. The alternative is to suck the water from the bag by means of a vacuum line connected to the valve which is stationed in its lowest position. Neither method can be guaranteed to provide complete evacuation without care and attention, but it is essential this be done owing to the adverse effect on the cure of the next tyre if cold water remains.

In view of its resistance to oxidation, Butyl suggests itself as a likely material for airbag manufacture. Considerable interest was shown in this material in the U.S.A. a few years ago, but it has not been sustained, possibly owing to the declining interest in airbags generally with the introduction of Bagomatic cure. Efforts have, however, been made to cover the inside surface of natural rubber bags with Butyl in order to make the best use of the two materials. Butyl airbags are difficult to splice, and this may be the reason for limited interest.

Airbags are normally cured alongside the tyres in which they are used, so that a typical pot-heater cure would be 40 minutes at 144°–150° C, using steam or hot water internally.

The airbag's present-day successor, the bladder used inside tyres in Bagomatic cure, is made from Butyl accelerated by dimethylol-phenol to improve its heat resistance. It is prepared in one of two ways. It is either extruded as a slug, then spliced into a circle of the appropriate diameter, or alternatively, it is calendered in thin strips, plied up on a resin circular former, thereby avoiding the necessity for a splice and reducing the risk of trapped air, which is likely to occur when extruding thick sections. It is then press moulded to produce a circular form corresponding very much to the shape of an uncured tyre. Such a bladder can be seen in Fig. 12.31 in the right-hand mould. The gauge of the bladder is of the order of $\frac{3}{8}$ in., which is considerably thinner than the conventional airbag. It is cured from 15 to 30 minutes at temperatures in excess of 150° C. The rate at which the mould can be closed and the danger of blisters and trapped air determine the minimum conditions of cure. They eventually fail from cracks or buckles. The avoidance of premature failures is greatly helped by the absence of any form of splice or valve which might break down at the high temperatures employed. A reasonable life for such a bladder is something over 700 cures for tyres.

(c) Unit vulcanisers for tyres and tubes

Modern tyre and tube vulcanisation depends upon unit presses curing one or at the most two tyres simultaneously. These permit short cures taking full advantage of modern fast accelerators, the moulds generally remaining hot throughout their use, thereby saving the time of cooling and reheating moulds and the fuel involved in the latter operation. It is, however, possible to operate cooling cures with this equipment. With automatic release or ejection of the tyre after cure, the labour saving over the pot-heater method is substantial, one man operating eight to ten presses. Cured giant tyres may be unloaded and replaced with " green " tyres within 5 minutes, consequently moulds are in almost continuous use.

The outstanding advantage, however, is quality. A tailor-made cure can be worked out for each individual tyre, and this can be controlled accurately with the instruments available. Once the airbag connection has been made correctly the possibility of human error is virtually eliminated, because the operation is " push button ", the mould closing and subsequently opening automatically after the prescribed time. Presses are of three main types :

1. Those designed to accept moulds having integral steam cavities.
2. Those having domes integral with the presses which convert them into " one-mould pot heaters ".
3. Steam-heated platen type, where the external heat is transferred to the mould by conduction through good metallic contact.

In the first type the stand or press is used primarily to provide the necessary mechanical pressure to keep the two halves of the mould closed during cure and to ensure automatic and positive opening of the mould after cure. It also protects against heat losses through radiation, conduction or convection. The necessary curing temperature is obtained from steam contained in a cavity integral with the mould. In its original or simplest form each half mould is a single casting containing a mould cavity with a steam cavity behind it. A more flexible arrangement is to have mould backs or " masters " which act as steam cavities and which will accept a variety of sizes of tyre moulds which can be bolted in to render the backs steam-tight. The equipment is expensive and provides problems, for example, in the provision of vents which have, of necessity, to be taken through the steam cavity. Such presses are generally operated on hot cures. Frequently the stands are designed to accommodate two moulds, one on top of the other or in the same horizontal plane, but both must obviously operate on the same time–temperature cycle.

The second type of press with domes has all the good points of pot-heater type plus the advantage of a specialised cure for the particular tyre concerned. Automatic mould opening and closing and timing are available. These presses may operate on the loose bead ring principle, which allows the lower bead ring to lift vertically during the late movements of press opening, thereby extracting the tyre from the stationary lower half of the mould. Alternatively, one of the halves of the mould may slide transversely out of adjustment with its counterpart during the opening of the press.

Presses having platens are similar in type and operation to the Bago-matic presses, which are described in greater detail later on, but they lack some of the automatic features and necessitate the use of airbags.

The modern method of curing inner tubes depends upon the use of this type of press where the mould halves are bolted to the top and bottom platens respectively. It is customary for this purpose to have additional steam or electrical heating in the valve area because of the extra thickness of material at this point. Tube cures are of quite short duration due to the thin gauges employed, 5 minutes being a typical time for a passenger tube. Temperatures may go up to 180° C, depending upon the polymer used.

(d) Bagomatic presses

At the time of writing Bagomatic and Autoform represent the most modern methods of curing tyres. Provision is made for all sizes from bicycle tyres up to 12·00–20, and while giant tyres are being cured regularly in production by this method, more experience has been obtained with passenger tyres, and although this type will be described, the principle is the same for tyres large and small.

Bagomatic is a press-cure method combining many operations previously conducted individually, such as tyre shaping, bagging, laying, curing and de-bagging. The outstanding advantage is that the heavy and somewhat unsatisfactory airbag previously used has given way to a much lighter " bladder " which permits shorter cures, particularly when coupled with the higher curing temperatures made possible by the use of Butyl in the bladder and synthetic stocks in the tyre. It eliminates airbag tubing, building, curing, the bagging machine, airbag connections, the de-bagging machine, airbag testing, doping, etc.

The time for curing small passenger tyres, which was previously about 40, has now been reduced to as low as 18 minutes, although there has been some retraction from this very low figure in order to obtain a more balanced cure from inside to outside of the tyre.

External heat is provided either by transfer from a steam-heated platen or by circulating live steam in a dome. Platens are general for passenger tyres, with some movement towards domes, which are standard for giant tyres. Presses are of dual formation, operating two moulds in the same horizontal plane. In consequence, two tyres are cured simultaneously. Temperatures up to 163° C are used externally, internally either steam or hot water circulates. Steam pressures up to 250 lb./in.^{2} are possible, though 175–200 are more normal, from which it follows that most of the heat for the cure comes from the inside. Hot-water cures are based on 177° C water at 300 lb./in.^{2} pressure.

All operations are automatic, the operator's duty being limited to laying two tyres over their bladders, pressing a button and, when the mould has opened automatically, removing the cured tyres. Already the whole operation has been made fully automatic in the U.S.A., with the tyres being fed to the mould and removed after cure by automatic means. A battery of such presses worked by one operator represents a highly efficient unit. Success depends on excellent maintenance, accurate timing and, particularly in the case of short cures, dry steam at exactly the right temperature.   An accurately built tyre is an essential—in particular, it must be free from trapped air.

The service lines to the press comprise:

(a) Shaping steam at 15–25 lb./in.^{2}
(b) High-pressure steam up to 200 lb./in.^{2}.
(c) 100 lb./in.^{2} steam.
(d) Cooling water at 32° C, 100–200 lb./in.^{2} pressure.
(e) Air or hot water for bladder stripping and tyre ejection.
(f) Main drain for cooling water and condensate.
(g) Steam and condensate drain from platens.
(h) Vacuum for evacuating the bladder.

Instrumentation will include temperature recorders for internal and external steam and cooling water in addition to pressure recorders for internal steam, shaping steam and a vacuum gauge.   These are all mounted on a panel controlling the whole battery.   Individual presses have timed programme controllers (described under Instruments), with thermometers on every mould for external steam recording and pressure gauges for internal.

The cycle of events after the button has been pressed comprises the following operations:

The lid of the mould closes slowly and at the same time a blower is set in operation which removes excess dusting powder from the outside of the tyre and inside of the mould.   Meanwhile shaping steam is beginning to fill out the bladder and expand the tyre.   As soon as the mould is closed high-pressure steam takes over from the shaping steam and the curing time commences.   At a fixed time during the cure high-pressure steam gives way to 100-lb./in.^{2} steam or high-pressure water.   In the former case the process is gradual, taking 3–5 minutes.   Since the high-pressure line is closed and the 100-lb./in.^{2} line open, the latter comes into operation only as the high-pressure steam condenses.   This 100-lb./in.^{2} steam is in turn replaced by cooling water, which is ultimately blown down and run off.   Thereafter the mould opens, the cured tyre is lifted from the bottom half of the mould, the bladder collapses and lifting arms free the tyre from the bladder.   Sudden changes in temperature and pressure are to be avoided, since they lead to " shatter " separations in the tyre, particularly if the changes are made at high temperatures.   A typical steam cure with the platens at 163° C is as follows:

170-lb./in.^{2} steam	12·5	minutes
100 lb./in.^{2} steam	4·4	,,
80° C cooling water	0·2	,,
Blow down	0·4	,,
Run off	1·0	,,

The Autoform Unit is very similar in principle to the Bagomatic, the main distinction being the operation of the bladder, which during the tyre-laying operation is withdrawn into a well in a somewhat similar manner to the airbag in a modern bagging machine.

Already experiments are afoot to eliminate the bladder entirely and use the inside of the tyre as the container of the internal heat medium. The

Fig. 12.31. Bagomatic press.

introduction of the tubeless tyre already renders the inside of a tyre impervious to air, which is an appreciable step towards rendering it resistant to steam and water.

In view of the rapid turn-over of tyres cured by this method, an alert technical service must always be available to limit defects.

A 40-in. press suitable for passenger tyres is shown in Fig. 12.31. The right-hand mould shows a bladder collapsed and ready to receive a tyre, while the left-hand mould shows an uncured tyre in position over its bladder and ready for the button to be pushed.

(e) Tyre remoulding

This rapidly expanding industry has grown up, performing for tyres a similar function to that which the shoe repairer performs for footwear, namely the replacement of the more expendable portion of the product. One in three tyres manufactured, whether passenger or giant, finds its way eventually to the retreading factory, many returning more than once. Various titles have been given to the process, e.g. top-capping, recapping, retreading, rebuilding, remoulding and reconditioning, and while there are distinctions between them, the lines of demarcation are not always clear. Top-capping is the minimum process of adding a rectangular section of new rubber to the top of the old buffed tread, which has the advantage of requiring minimum heat, and consequently is the least harmful to the carcass.

Remoulding renews the tyre from bead to bead, providing a new tread and either new sidewalls or veneers over existing ones. The result is a tyre almost indistinguishable in appearance from new.

The industry has been helped enormously by the introduction during recent years of improved and lower stretch textiles in tyre construction, thereby limiting tyre growth in service, ensuring that worn tyres will fit standard moulds and that treads will not crack in service. The generally accepted limitation of not fitting remoulded tyres to the front wheels of buses becomes less necessary with the availability of wire cord and tubeless tyres.

It is impossible to summarise the types of equipment used for vulcanising remould tyres because of the wide variety involved. Technically there is no reason why new tyre-production moulds should not be used, as indeed they are, although a slightly larger cavity may be preferred for re-moulding. The objection to this method is the large investment required to cover every size and type of tyre together with the time lost in mould changing. The retreader has not the long or continuous runs on one and the same size which are a feature of the mass production of the original tyres. In consequence, the accent is on equipment of a flexible nature permitting a variety of tyre sizes to be handled with a minimum of disruption, and considerable ingenuity has been exercised in this direction subsequent to the original use of spacer rings of varying width in the centre of the tread to accommodate tyres of different cross-sections. Emphasis has also been given to expediting mould opening and consequent quick release of tyres after cure. Initially all equipment was of American origin, but with the rapid expansion of business other manufacturers have entered the market, and continental makers are especially active.

The principle of remould vulcanisation follows that of new tyres, with the exception that internal heat is not generally employed, air at 120–200 lb./in.² pressure being the medium in the airbag. Steam temperatures and pressures are generally lower, despite the accent on quick cures and turnovers. One limitation is the compound used, which must have good shelf-ageing properties, a quality which operates against fast-curing stocks. At the time of writing all remould material (" camelback ") is made from natural rubber, synthetic not yet having found a market, despite its universal acceptance in the U.S.A. and other countries, and its facility for shorter cures based on higher permissible curing temperatures.

Fig. 12.32. Earthmover tyres after Vaculug treatment.

Owing to the difficulty of removing all moisture from a used carcass sent in for remoulding, it is usual to restrict the temperature of the carcass to something under the boiling point of water to minimise the risk of carcass separations. 148° C (50 lb./in.² external steam) is the generally accepted curing temperature, and curing times are based on 5 minutes for every $\frac{1}{32}$ in. of camelback gauge. A small passenger tyre therefore requiring retread material of $\frac{10}{32}$ in. gauge would require 50 minutes curing time. In an industry which encompasses all sizes and conditions of production units from the little man having one or two moulds to the large factories turning out hundreds per day, one would not expect to find uniformly good conditions of piping and temperature control, but the best conditions are in line with original tyre manufacture in regard to instrumentation and attention to detail.

One process which stands apart from the others in method is the system in which the tyre carcass with its new recap solutioned to the buffed old tread is contracted within a steam-heated ring which vulcanises the stock and produces a simple tread pattern. Internal pressure is provided by air contained in a conventional inner tube. The process is simple, the cure short and the old tyre carcass is not damaged by further heating.

One further method employed is that intended for farm-tractor, earth-mover and similar tyres having prominent tread patterns. After the relics of the old tread pattern have been removed by buffing, the pattern is restored by reforming each bar of the pattern by applying the cemented

Fig. 12.33. Five 11-36 tractor tyres submitted for Vaculug processing prior to curing.

sections piece-meal by hand. The bars are made from lug stock—an extruded stock of approximately rectangular section subsequently cut to length. Curing is by open steam in a horizontal heater, the tyres being rotated during the process to prevent loss of shape. Tyres up to 100 in. × 30 in. may be retreaded by this method. Fig. 12.32 shows two of these large earthmover tyres after Vaculug treatment. Fig. 12.33 shows five somewhat smaller tyres ready for processing. For average-sized tyres in the classes concerned cure is 40 minutes at 140° C, air at 20 lb./in.² being applied before steam pressure is admitted.

(f) Tyre repairing

Tyre repairing comprises everything from effacing minor superficial blemishes in new tyres to the major operation of applying multi-ply patches to giant tyres damaged accidentally. The vulcanisation equipment varies accordingly.

Many " spot " repairers are available for minor jobs, the pressure being applied mechanically, the heat for vulcanising being obtained by firing a predetermined quantity of alcohol or metaldehyde or preferably by electrical resistance, as this permits control over the quantity of heat applied.

Major repairs are carried out in equipment based on new-tyre principles. A sectional mould representing one-fifth or one-sixth of the circumference of the tyre, being heated externally with steam and internally also if desired, although most sectional airbags contain air only under pressure. Such a repair may require up to 3 hours heating using 50 lb./in.^{2} steam externally and 100 lb./in.^{2} air inside.

Continuous vulcanisers

The continuous vulcaniser now considered is a somewhat specialised type of machine which is finding increased acceptance in both the rubber and plastic industries. With its use a wide variety of plain or embossed sheet goods can be cured continuously in a wide strip. Typical rubber products are coated fabrics, doubled fabrics, flooring, shoe soleing and belting, different models being available for different widths up to 80 in. The machine was invented by an Englishman, Gray of the India Rubber and Gutta Percha Company and patented in 1903. Subsequent development took place in Germany (Berstoff) and the U.S.A. (Boston Woven Hose). Full descriptions of these machines are available in the rubber literature.[22, 25]

In comparison with hydraulic press cure by stages or the cure of material wrapped in liners in open steam, continuous cure shows substantial savings in time, labour, power, space and investment. The following description of the component parts of such a vulcaniser is extracted from the makers' (Berstoff) literature:

(a) A large steel cylinder closed at both ends arranged to be heated internally by means of steam and equipped with the instruments necessary to accurately control the temperature. This cylinder is balanced, turned, precision ground and polished to a fine finish, then chromium plated all over.

(b) An endless pressure belt made of spirally wound high-tension steel-wire cable, woven into a flat band and coated on the operative side with a heat-resisting elastic composition.

(c) Reversing steel guide rollers supported in adjustable bearings in such a way that the pressure belt is guided over a large portion of the circumference of the above-mentioned heated cylinder.

(*d*) A tensioning roller coupled with hydraulic cylinders and pump, built integrally with the machine, to regulate the tension on the endless pressure belt and thereby the pressure on the material being heat treated or processed.

(*e*) A variable-speed gear to control the rate at which the material to be heat treated passes through the machine, and therefore the time during which it is processed.

The drive is applied to the machine through the top guide roller, which has a very wide speed range. Both this and the bottom guide roller are readily adjustable to permit change of drums. A steam-heated pre-

Fig. 12.34. Let-off and wind-up arrangements on continuous vulcaniser.

heating table may be set ahead of the machine for warming the bottom ply of thick materials. The life of the pressure belting is claimed to be 5–10 years. Fig. 12.34 shows the let-off and wind-up arrangements reading from left to right, while Fig. 12.35 shows the progress through the vulcaniser in the opposite direction. Continuous cure obviates the dis-advantage of the over-lapping which necessarily results from length-by-length cure in a hydraulic press by eliminating the different colours, textures and finish which may result at the junctions, and more important still by eliminating service defects resulting from over-cure at the over-laps.

In comparison with hot air or steam curing a roll of material in a liner which might require 5 hours at 120°–145° C in a hot-air oven would proceed through the continuous vulcaniser in 9–12 minutes at 160° C. The essential difference between the German and the American machine is that the latter employs an endless steel belt, which is the secret of its success. This permits heat to be applied to both faces of the rubber material and allows articles up to $1\frac{1}{4}$ in. thick to be handled. The Boston Woven Hose Company discovered that most of the high pressure believed to be required for vulcanising certain products could be applied to form them before they

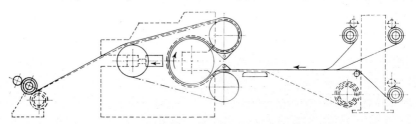

Fig. 12.35. Progress of material through continuous vulcaniser.

are vulcanised and is not required during the actual cure. An unvulcanised transmission belt is approximately 25% thicker than the same belt after cure. 200 lb./in.² will compress the unvulcanised product, and this pressure is applied to the lowest of the three idler rolls, which, like the others, is steam heated. Stretch is applied by a system of gears to give a regular percentage of length increase.

A continuous method has also been described for hollow goods such as tennis balls.[22] After some preliminary shaping they travel in two piece moulds on a chain conveyor through a 80° C zone in which the inflating material functions, releasing the gas which completes the shaping, after passing through two further zones (120° and 150° C) the moulds return to the cold zone for unloading. The heating unit is steam piping at 200 lb./in.², with fans to circulate the hot air. The production mentioned is 20,000 articles in 24 hours.

Di-electric heating

There are two distinct classes of resistance heating:

1. Using resistances of suitable construction which are heated by the passage of electric current, and the heat which is generated, transferred by conduction, radiation and/or convection.[26,27]

2. Di-electric heating where the heat is generated in insulating materials by high-frequency current.[28,29]

High frequencies are necessary in order to cause internal friction within the molecule. These can be obtained economically only by the use of electronic tubes, hence this method is also referred to as electronic heating. Materials treated by this method will under certain conditions lose heat by radiation or conduction, consequently, contrary to more conventional methods of cure, the interior of objects may be cured faster than the outside.

The main advantage claimed for di-electric heating conducted under proper conditions is the uniformity of effect produced, since the whole article is heated throughout its mass. Because of this a wider choice of stocks is possible, as heat transfer will not have to be taken into account when drawing up the formula.

The limitations are that the process is of little use for thin sheets, and a poor dispersion of carbon black will cause " hot spots ". Curing units need to be purchased for specific jobs and thereby lack flexibility, consequently they are much more suitable for continuous operation than for batch processes. Maintenance can be expensive due to the cost of tubes and their limited life, and the services of a qualified electronic engineer are necessary. Further, it is necessary to ensure that radiation is not causing a nuisance to the immediate neighbourhood.

Pre-conditioning of stock reduces wear on moulds and lowers ram pressures. High frequency finds more use for heating than for curing. Some examples of the application of di-electric in the industry include:

1. As a source of heat for drying, e.g. removing moisture from fabrics before calendering, and drying off foamed latex products.

2. Pre-heating solid rubber stocks before milling or curing. It has been established that by pre-heating natural rubber compounds $1\frac{1}{4}$ in. thick for $2\frac{1}{2}$ minutes it is possible to treble the output of presses. A mould formed of wood impregnated with synthetic resin or with a silicone has a di-electric loss factor substantially equal to that of the material being vulcanised, and hence both the mould and its contents are equally heated.[30] Hard rubber wheels can have cure times reduced by as much as 40% and yet not blow.

3. The curing of foamed latex is a very good example, as foam is difficult to heat by conventional methods.

Cold cures

Nascent sulphur. A simple and ingenious method which has not lived up to its early promise is the Peachey process.[31, 33]

Sulphur monochloride. This may be a true cold cure, or more frequently vapour at 27° C is used. Cloth is passed over a roller immersed in sulphur chloride in an inert solvent which is " printed " on to the rubber face and then passed round a steam-heated drum. Small articles

N N

may be dipped for a few seconds and the solvent dried off. The same treatment can be used to remove tackiness on a cured rubber surface.

Sulphur cures at room temperature. These are based on the use of ultra accelerators. They are used for curing proofed goods, and for special repair patches.

Miscellaneous methods of curing

1. *Curing* in situ. An example of this is the splicing of belts in position on a conveyor. This may be a cold cure made by a solution of sulphur chloride or by a highly accelerated self-curing cement, or alternatively, a portable press electrically heated might be used for a conventional cure.

2. *Infra-red radiation.* Infra-red rays may be used in the vulcanisation of rubberised fabric sheeting and belting, enabling belting coated with latex to be dried and vulcanised simultaneously. This can be made a continuous process when radiation is applied on both sides of rubber-coated cloth while the latter is moving.

3. *Ultra-violet light.* Vulcanisation by ultra-violet has only a surface effect and is of no commercial value.

4. *Atomic-energy radiation.* Natural rubber and some synthetic polymers when subjected to atomic-energy radiation become cross-linked —a process equivalent to vulcanisation—without the aid of extraneous chemicals. The degree of cross-linking is proportional to the radiation dose. It is too early to state whether this method has any industrial value, and consequently this process is not enlarged upon in this section, which deals with commercially practical methods. There are numerous technical papers available for consultation.[34-40] In one of these [38] compounding data and physical properties are given for natural rubber, SBR, neoprene, Thiokol, etc., when treated with gamma radiation from cobalt 60. No residual radiation remains in the article.

5. *Immersion in liquids.* Where porosity is a problem it is possible to vulcanise film-like materials by immersion in hot water or saline solutions. The film must be dry and contain no water-soluble pigments which would leach out. Rubber mixtures containing fillers are vulcanised in a bath containing a water-soluble metal salt of a dithiocarbamic acid as accelerator, cures for which are 1 hour at boiling point. To obviate the formation of bubbles the liquid should be in a pressure vessel covered with a gas. Saline solutions, say at 110° C, may be used in preference to steam for curing the rubber lining of chemical vessels.

6. *Localised electric heating.* Localised heat may be generated in a particular section of an article by passing an electric current through electrically conducted rubber adjacent to or integral with the article. Alternatively, heating pads similar to electric blankets may be applied

selectively. An example of this is the use of an electric " booster " when making a repair on the inside of a tyre at the same time as other work, such as retreading, is being carried out.

Instrumentation

Vulcanisation is too important an operation to be left to human control, however experienced and conscientious. Instrumentation makes controlled cure possible, and in consequence instrument engineering is a highly important function in the modern rubber factory, skilled attention

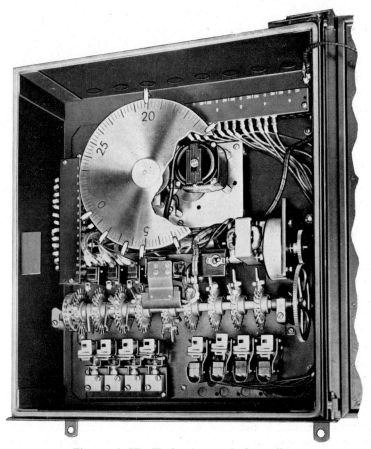

Fig. 12.36. The Taylor Automatic Controller.

being necessary, not only in the maintenance of the instruments but also in their siting. There are instruments available which will indicate, record or control all the services involved in vulcanisation, including time, temperature and pressure, and are capable of setting in motion such operations as the opening and closing of moulds and, in general, will control any process variable which is capable of being converted into an electric charge or pneumatic or hydraulic pressure impulse.

The latest type of instrument available is capable of controlling the whole cycle of a complicated cure, including mould opening and closing and a multitude of other services, such as three steam pressures, cooling water, blow down, vacuum, etc. The Taylor instrument shown in Fig. 12.36 and Fig. 12.37 is a programme type of instrument for the repetitive

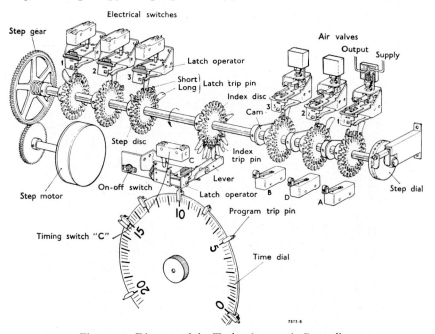

Fig. 12.37. Diagram of the Taylor Automatic Controller.

on–off operation of electrical and pneumatic process functions according to any desired time programme.

The instrument consists of two basic sections, the time-measuring components and the process-actuating components. Time-measuring components include a synchronous-speed time motor and a gear train which gives the time dial an extremely accurate rate of rotation. The process programme is set on the direct-reading time dial by means of programme trip pins clamped at the required time graduations. The process-actuating components include the electrical switches and the air valves, their step discs and the non-synchronous step motor. This motor, through the step-trip pins, operates the electrical and pneumatic functions according to the process programme set on the time dial.

The time-dial mechanism, through its trip pins, initiates the operation of the step discs by closing the timing switch to start the step motor.   The step discs, moving quickly through a predetermined arc, carry the step trip pins that open or close the electrical switches and air valves for controlling the process functions.   When the timer has completed its desired programme cycle the step discs and the time dial are automatically returned to the zero start position.

The pilot light mounted on the door is lighted during each timing cycle of the instrument.

Product defects

Defects occur in finished product.   Some of these are due entirely to conditions of vulcanisation and some only partly due to the vulcanisation process.   The following table enumerates major defects, their probable causes and remedies to be applied:

(a) Superficial defects

The product has the appearance in places of not having contacted the mould. " Light " moulding defects:

1. *Cause*	*Remedy*
Insufficient material to fill out the cavity, or material wrongly distributed.	Revise volume and shape of uncured article.
Air trapped between rubber and mould surfaces.	Study dimensions of uncured article. Often a modification of dimensions of component will reduce flow and avoid air trapping.
	Add more overflow channels to mould cavities. Pin vents are very useful. " Bumping." Useful for press-cured article. Consist of momentarily releasing hydraulic pressure. This allows air to escape between rubber and mould.
	Increase the moulding pressure; external in case of press cures; internal in case of tyres or hollow articles.
	Increase the stiffness of the external rubber surface by modifying composition, changing processing temperatures and increasing ageing between processing and curing.
	Use dusting powder on surface of article.
	Addition of wax to formula is often useful.
Surface moisture.	Keep uncured article at temperature slightly above atmospheric to prevent moisture condensation on surface. Avoid steam leaks around and in the vulcaniser.
	If surface cooling water is used for cooling after processing, make sure this is all evaporated.

Cause   *Remedy*

2. *Cracks at mould*

Junctions known as " back rinds ".

Insufficient or fluctuating hydraulic   Increase pressures if practical.
pressure. Fluctuating internal pres-   Eliminate causes of pressure variation.
sure (when used).

3. *Surface cracks and fold-over defects*

Stock flow during early part of cure   Modify shape and distribution of rubber
combined with surface contamination.   to reduce flow to a minimum, and also
                                                  to allow all parts to contact mould
                                                  surface almost simultaneously.
                                              Avoid deep grooves and high ridges on
                                                  surface of uncured article where these
                                                  do not conform to mould design.
                                              Remedies for air trapping are also
                                                  applicable.
                                              Increase external hydraulic pressure
                                                  and internal pressure (if used) to
                                                  reduce flow time to a minimum (i.e.
                                                  so that it is completed before vul-
                                                  canisation commences. Reduce
                                                  mould temperatures or modify curing
                                                  characteristics of rubber for the same
                                                  reason.
                                              Avoid any distortion of article after final
                                                  assembly and prior to curing. Keep
                                                  rubber surfaces scrupulously clean.
                                                  It is very difficult to clean rubber
                                                  surfaces after they have been con-
                                                  taminated.
                                              Plastic sheeting placed on susceptible
                                                  places immediately after assembling
                                                  the article and kept on until the
                                                  article is placed in the mould will
                                                  keep the surface clean.
                                              Avoid use of dusting agents on the
                                                  surface.
                                              Reduce mould lubricant to a minimum.
                                              Brush the area where cracks appear and
                                                  clean with solvent prior to cure.

(b) Blisters

Generally due to air trapped during pro-   Modify processing temperatures or
cessing of the rubber (calendering or   pressures.
extruding) and during building or   Make sure there is always sufficient
assembling of component parts.   feed at calenders and extruders.
                                              Use sufficient pressure in assembling
                                                  components.
                                              Pricking visible blisters in uncured un-
                                                  processed material and assemblies
                                                  will eliminate many blisters in cured
                                                  articles.
                                              Bleeder cords between components can
                                                  often be used advantageously.

Cause	Remedy
Moisture or volatile liquids in material or on surface.	Avoid moisture in raw material. If surface cooling water is used after extrusion make sure that this is all evaporated before final assembly.

(c) Tears and Snags

Cause	Remedy
Over-vulcanisation.	Reduce curing time and/or temperature. Modify composition of rubber to reduce speed of cure.
Mould temperature too high.	Rubber is very brittle at high temperatures, particularly some types of synthetic. Reduce curing temperatures or cool mould before removing article.
Insufficient mould lubrication.	Use more powerful or more concentrated lubricant. Apply lubricant to surface of article itself at places where tears occur.
Defective mould design.	Avoid sharp corners on outside of mould design which will tear the rubber on removal. Avoid sharp angles on inside of mould design to reduce adhesion of rubber to mould surface.
Method of removal of article from mould:	Tears can sometimes be eliminated by change of method of opening and mould and the way the article is taken out.

(d) Porosity

Cause	Remedy
Moisture or volatile substances in rubber or compounding ingredients.	Test all material for moisture content to determine the source. Avoid use of raw material containing anything volatile.
Moisture contamination of processed part. Excess of volatile solvents or rubber solution used for washing or making surfaces tacky.	Use a minimum of solvent or solution. Allow to dry thoroughly before covering up. Keep processed material in warm dry atmosphere.
Insufficient material in the mould.	Check volumes and shapes of component parts.
Insufficient internal pressure (is used).	Increase pressure if possible. Keep pressure uniform at all times.
Undercure. Dissolved and trapped gases expand on release of external pressure. These cause porosity if the rubber is undercured and not strong enough to resist the expansion.	Check curing conditions and composition of components affected. If persistent, increase curing times or temperature or use faster-curing composition.

(e) Separation and lack of adhesion of component parts

It is often very difficult to obtain satisfactory adhesion of components differing considerably in composition. The relative amounts of sulphur and accelerators and the types of accelerators used in the various parts influence the union of the surfaces of two parts different in composition. These must be chosen so that there is no under- or over-vulcanisation of the surface layers at the union due to migration of curing ingredients from one to the other. A layer of junction material of intermediate composition is sometimes necessary.

To get rubber-to-fabric adhesion the fabric must be quite dry, and it must be treated with solutions or " dips " to increase the strength of the union.

Butyl rubber compositions require special treatment in order to obtain satisfactory adhesion to natural rubber and other synthetics.

Defective adhesion occurs from accidental causes. The major ones are given below:

Cause	*Remedy*
Contamination of united surfaces with dirt, dust or " bloom ".	Keep surfaces of components clean at all times. Keep covered up at all times except when work is being done on them.
	Wash surfaces with solvent or use rubber solution.
	Some synthetic rubbers give surfaces which lack cohesion, and even if clean they require application of rubber solution containing special resins.
	Sulphur bloom can be eliminated by using insoluble sulphur. Waxy softeners will often give surface bloom on uncured stock. Replace by material with greater solubility in uncured rubber.
	Excess antioxidant (particularly DPPD) causes bloom which can be prevented by reducing proportions or substitutes of another antioxidant.
Surface scorching or pre-vulcanisation of a component.	Modify mixing formula or processing conditions.
Surface moisture.	Avoid exposure to cold, damp air. If external cooling water is used in processing, make sure this is thoroughly dried off.
	If solvents or solutions are used for cleaning or tackifying, their evaporation has a cooling effect which deposits moisture in a cool atmosphere. Do this work in a comparatively dry, warm atmosphere.
	Use of slower-drying solvent is sometimes necessary.
Exposure to sunlight or ultra-violet light.	With some types of accelerator surface vulcanisation occurs very quickly on exposure to light. Keep all surfaces covered as much as possible. Never expose any surface to direct sunlight or in close proximity to ultra-violet light.
Accidental use of wrong material.	Examine the defective parts. If possible, test the product to see if correct material has been used. Natural rubber and some synthetics if contaminated with small amounts of Butyl rubber give a laminated condition, the lamination showing poor adhesion.

Cause	*Remedy*
Undercure in articles containing fabric.	Check curing conditions and material used. If necessary, lengthen curing cycles or increase temperatures. Use faster-curing composition.
	Separations in articles containing fabric are frequently caused by a combination of circumstances. Undercure is only one of these.

Lubricants, dusting agents and mould-release agents

One of the necessary evils of rubber processing is in the use of lubricants to allow free movement at rubber-to-rubber and rubber-to-metal faces.

The term " release agent " has come to be accepted as a general term describing all the materials used for assisting in release of articles from moulds. The term, however, cannot completely cover dusting powders, which have been used through the ages not only for preventing rubber sticking to hot metal but also to prevent uncured rubber sticking to uncured rubber. Many dry lubricants have been tried in the past, and those which have stood the test of time are french chalk, soapstone, talc, mica, cornstarch and zinc stearate. Zinc stearate should be divorced from the others for two very good reasons. The first is that it has the outstanding advantage of dissolving in hot rubber, and the second that it is infinitely more expensive than the other materials mentioned. No agreement has been obtained or is likely to be reached on an order of merit of the above powders. In fact, it is general practice to ring the changes and try different materials at different times due to some new variable entering the scheme of things which upsets processing and produces an unfavourable situation which is relieved by change of lubricant.

Dusting powders function by forming a coat on the uncured surface which is wiped or blown off before cure and with it the dirt and dust which have become deposited and which, if not removed, will cause cracks or laminations by preventing clean surface of rubber to come together and unite after displacement during the mould-closing operation. A good mould-release agent should have the following qualities:

(1) it should release easily;
(2) have no adverse effect on the rubber product;
(3) cause no contamination of the mould;
(4) be non-toxic and unobjectionable on any similar ground.

Unfortunately, these ideals are extremely hard to obtain. Inorganic powders are dusty, and so operate against good housekeeping. Organic materials such as oils and soaps build up appreciably in moulds. The material which has made a very substantial advance on any of its pre-decessors over the last few years is that known as silicone. This has become a firm favourite because of its efficiency, simplicity of application (being generally sprayed in moulds) and slow build-up. It has but two minor limitations: it prevents the application of a water-base paint on the cured article in any uniform condition, as it tends to form rivulets, and when used too freely will prevent rubber knitting together in a mould and may cause laminations or tears. Silicone is available in two forms: (1) The emulsion which is generally used is a 35% emulsion of dimethyl-silicone in water; this is diluted with water to a concentration as low as $0\cdot1\%$. (2) Fluid which is 100% silicone and can be diluted with organic solvents such as carbon tetrachloride, naphtha and alcohol. This may be applied to the uncured product in concentrations of $0\cdot5-1\%$.

The timing of the introduction of silicon distracted attention from wetting agents of the detergent type which represent an enormous advance on their predecessors and which are the preferred materials in those cases where silicone is unsuitable.

REFERENCES

1. (1953) *History of the Rubber Industry*, Chapter 2.
2. Goodyear, C. (1853) *Gum Elastic*.
3. Hancock, Thomas (1857) *Personal Narrative*.
4. Jorissen, W. P. (1914) *Chem. Weekblad*, **11**, 852–7; (1915) *ibid.*, **12**, 799–804; (1919) *ibid.*, **16**, 527–536, 1014–8.
5. Bott, E. C. C. (1952) *Industr. Chem.*, **28**, 534.
6. (1952) *Vanderbilt News*, **18**, No. 5.
7. Lowenstein, J. G. and Rollins, J. H. (1956) *Rubb. Age, N.Y.*, **78**, 543–6.
8. Schade, J. W. (1952) *India Rubb. World*, **126**, 67–72.
9. Juve, A. E. (1954) *Synthetic Rubber* (Whitby), pp. 395–8.
10. (1952) R.A.B.R.M., C.I.R., Sheet 2.
11. Morrell, S. H. (1952) *R.A.B.R.M. Bulletin*, **6**, 114–16.
12. (1951) *Rubb. Chem. Technol.*, Vol. xxiv, No. 4, 820.
13. BS 1673 Part 4 : 1953 *Evaluation of Vulcanising Characteristics*.
14. Warne, W., and Co. and N.T. Gas Board (1952) *Gas Times*, 311–12.
15. Freeman, H. A. (1953) *India Rubb. W.*, **129**, 354–7.
16. Soderquist, L. E. (1952) *Rubb. Age, Lond.*
17. (1954) *The Services Rubber Investigations*, 124 *et seq.*
18. (1955) *Rubb. Age, N.Y.*, **78**, 310.
19. Willshaw, H. (1956) *Engineering*, 144.
20. (1945) *Production and Performance of German Synthetic Tyres*, Rubber Bureau, W.P.B., pp. 43–5.
21. Reece, W. H. (1950) *Continuous Vulcanizing Processes*, I.R.I. *Trans.*, **26**, 137–50.
22. Bierer, J. M. and Knowland, T. M. (1939) *India Rubb. J.*, **98**, 257.
23. Bierer, J. M. (1950) *I.R.I. Trans.*, **26**, 257–80.
24. Kirkpatrick, D. W. (1953) *India Rubb. W.*, **128**, 501.
25. Brit. Elec. Devl. Assoc. (1953) *Elec. and Productivity Series* 5, 126.
26. (1953), *India Rubb. J.*, **125**, 514.
27. (1948) *The Vanderbilt Rubber Handbook*, p. 60 *et seq.*

28. Kumakawa, F. and Aoki, J. (1949) *J. Soc. Rubb. Ind. (Japan)*, **22**, 129–45.
29. Pat. Apln. 30439 U.S.A., May 2, 1947, F. H. Mason and G. P. Bosomworth.
30. Harrison, H. C. (1952) *India Rubb. J.*, **122**, 142–4.
31. B.P. 129,826.
32. (1954) *Synthetic Rubber* (Whitby), p. 809.
33. Charlesby, A. and Groves, Miss D. (1954) *Proc. Third Rubber Tech. Conf.*, 317.
34. Charlesby, A. (1952) *Proc. roy. Soc.*, **215**, 187.
35. Charlesby, A. and Rose, M. (1953) *Chem. Age*, **69**, 743–4.
36. Charlesby, A. (1954) *Atomics*, **5**, 12–21, 27.
37. Jackson, W. W. and Hale, D. (1955) *Rubb. Age, N.Y.*, **77**, 865–71.
38. Jackson, W. W. and Hale, D. (1955) U.S.A.F., Wright Air Devl. Centre Materiel Lab. Tech. Report 55–57, Dayton, O.
39. Davidson and Geib (1948) *J. appl. Phys.*, **19**, No. 5, 427.

CHAPTER XIII

PART ONE

RUBBER AGEING: FUNDAMENTAL STUDIES

by

J. F. SMITH

IN spite of the extensive work that has been carried out on the fundamental aspects of rubber deterioration, it can be said that more remains unknown than known. There have been many obstacles to progress, not the least of which is that the word " rubber " describes a physical state rather than any one substance. Every rubber mix represents a mixture of different chemical structures which has become more complex with the growth in the number of synthetic polymers and compounding ingredients now available. The main developments in the study of ageing have been:

1. The recognition that substances such as rubber, cellulose, wool, silk, etc., are polymers and that their peculiar physical properties are dependent on this fact.

2. The analysis of the detailed chemical structures of high polymers.

3. The accurate mathematical expression of physical properties in terms of chemical structure.

4. The recognition of the principal factors which cause deterioration. These consist of heat, light, mechanical " fatigue ", oxygen, ozone and the catalytic effect of certain trace elements. Many other chemicals will, of course, degrade rubber, but this type of degradation is not usually classified as ageing.

5. The identification of the chemical reactions involved in deterioration. Usually this is obtained by analogy, from the study of " model " compounds of progressively increasing complexity and increasing similarity to the structure of rubber. Unfortunately even the simplest (and least " rubberlike ") model compounds undergo a most complex series of chemical reactions with even a single agency of deterioration.

6. The prevention, or marked reduction in the rate, of deterioration based on the above knowledge.

Step 6 is the practical goal, which up till now has been achieved, ironically though it may be, more from *ad hoc* practice than by sound scientific method.

This section of the chapter is concerned mainly with item 5 in the above list and certain aspects of item 6.

Simple " model " compounds—olefins

Natural rubber consists mainly of an unsaturated polymeric hydro-carbon; therefore the simplest and most logical model compound to consider is a low-molecular-weight mono-olefin such as ethylene.

The fact that ethylene is so stable towards oxygen at room temperature should perhaps have discouraged the early formulation [1] of olefin aut-oxidation (i.e. by molecular oxygen) as a simple addition of oxygen to the C:C double bond, since on this basis the higher homologues of ethylene (even propylene) would not be expected to autoxidise so much more readily than ethylene itself. This is not the only conflicting evi-dence. Thus the autoxidation of olefins displays the phenomenon of autocatalysis which cannot be explained by direct oxygen addition to the double bond. Furthermore, the loss in unsaturation is usually negligible compared with the amount of oxygen absorbed. One might have ex-pected structural investigations to have shed light on the structure of the " peroxide ". The first formed " peroxide " from olefin autoxidation, however, is not particularly stable, and is thus a rather difficult subject to study. It was not until 1939 [2,3] that the structure of an olefin " peroxide " was satisfactorily elucidated. The absorption of oxygen by cyclohexene was shown to result initially in the production of Δ^2-cyclohexenyl hydro-peroxide (I) with retention of the original double bond. This led, how-

(I)   (II)   (III)

ever, to a further complication in that straightforward addition of oxygen to the olefin was no longer conceivable as a reaction mechanism, since the α-methylenic hydrogen atom must first be severed from the rest of the molecule.

From this stage the concept of α-methylenic reactivity of olefins de-veloped, initially from the classic work [4-21] of E. H. Farmer and his colla-borators. The concept was further developed by the investigations of the chemical kinetics of olefin autoxidation at the British Rubber Producers Research Association.[22-44] This concept of α-methylenic olefin reactivity must have appeared quite revolutionary in its early days, because addition at the double bond had long been considered characteristic of olefin reactions. In contrast, recent years have seen the acceptance of α-methylenic reactivity to a degree which later work has shown not to be warranted.[44]

The early workers did not consider their work to present a complete picture of rubber ageing in terms of simple molecules, but unfortunately many have been too ready to extrapolate the results even as far as vulcanised rubber. This has been shown to be quite unjustified.

Farmer [4] extended the work of Criegee [2] and confirmed the hydroperoxide structure (I), because on mild reduction with sodium sulphite it gave Δ^2-cyclohexenol (II), or by catalytic hydrogenation, cyclohexanol (III). This would have been inconceivable had the first formed product of autoxidation been the addition of oxygen to the double bond. Other examples of α-methylenic olefin hydroperoxides which have been extensively studied are derived from:

(a) *Linoleic acid* [14]

$$CH_3(CH_2)_3—CH=CH—CH_2—CH=CH—(CH_2)_7COOH \qquad (IV)$$

which as the ester gives the hydroperoxide

$$CH_3(CH_2)_4—CH=CH—\underset{\underset{OOH}{|}}{CH}—CH=CH—(CH_2)_7—COOCH_3 \quad (V)$$

(b) *Linolenic acid* (VI), which gives a mixture of hydroperoxides derived from attack at the two starred carbon atoms,

$$CH_3\cdot CH_2—CH=CH—\overset{*}{CH_2}—CH=CH—\overset{*}{CH_2}—CH=CH(CH_2)_7—COOH$$
$$(VI)$$

(c) *Tetralin* (VII), which gives, on autoxidation, mainly products (alcohol and ketone) derived from the hydroperoxide (VIII),

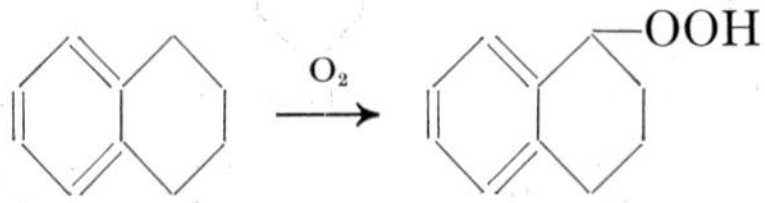

(VII)   (VIII)

(d) *Cumene* (IX), which gives the hydroperoxide (X) and incidentally is the basis of a commercial process for producing acetone and phenol by hydrolysis of this hydroperoxide

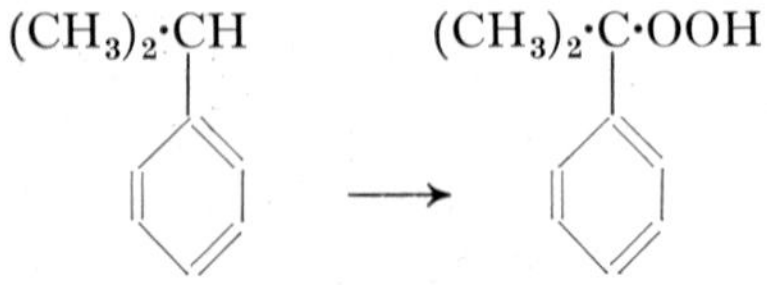

(IX)   (X)

While the process of α-methylenic hydroperoxidation undoubtedly represents the major mode of attack by molecular oxygen on a wide range of olefins which have α-methylenic hydrogen atoms, its importance as a general principle has been over-emphasised for two main reasons: (*a*) the analytical methods for –OOH groups used by the early workers, unknown to them, gave high results and consequently the impression that α-methylenic hydroperoxide accounted for nearly 100% of the oxygen absorbed. In fact, by using a much more accurate analytical method,[45] it has been shown [44] that hydroperoxide accounts for only 80% or so of the *initial* oxygen uptake, i.e. before any extensive decomposition of the first formed products has taken place.

(*b*) Bolland chose an ester of linoleic acid as most suitable for kinetic measurements, because it in fact gave the α-methylenic hydroperoxide as the exclusive product.

It is perhaps advisable at this stage to indicate how this α-methylenic reactivity of olefins arises and why it is so strongly developed in the case of ethyl linoleate.

Autoxidation of olefin is a free-radical reaction, as shown by all the characteristic features; e.g. (*a*) the reaction proceeds at a faster rate in the presence of substances (benzoyl peroxide, azo-*bis*-isobutyronitrile) which are known to dissociate into free radicals, (*b*) the reaction is inhibited by substances (certain phenols and aromatic amines) which combine with free radicals, (*c*) exceptionally high quantum yields are observed in the photochemical autoxidation. These features will be discussed in greater detail later (p. 1107). The key reaction is the abstraction of an α-methylenic hydrogen atom to form the free radical (XI):

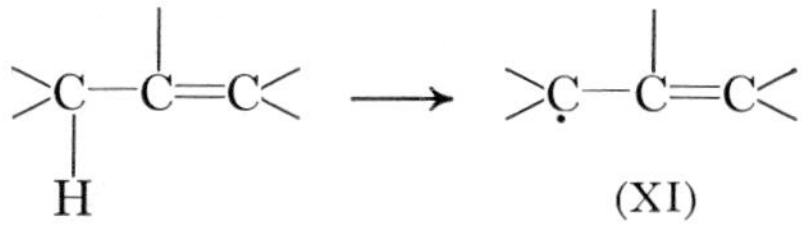

By merely shifting the position of the double bond another structure (XII) can be written for this radical:

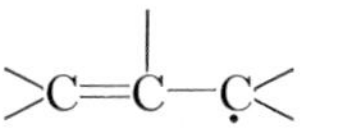

When more than one structure for a substance can be written *without any change in the position of the atomic nuclei* (or at least with only a very small change), then the chemical behaviour of the substance is better represented as a " blurred " combination of the two structures than by either individual structure. What is more important, however, is that the energy of this " hybrid " structure is lower than the expected energy of either individual structure, i.e. the molecule is " resonance stabilised ". An alternative picture derived from the " molecular orbital " theory also predicts a lowering of the energy due to a delocalised orbital instead of a localised orbital or normal double bond.

It is because α-methylenic hydrogen abstraction results in a radical with this resonance, or delocalisation energy, that the α-methylenic hydrogen atoms are most prone to attack. It is also a qualitative feature of " resonance " theory that the more hybrid structures, or canonical forms, that can be written down, the lower will be the energy of the molecule. This explains why ethyl linoleate has such a strongly developed α-methylenic reactivity. This radical XIII can be written down as structures XIV, XV, XVI and XVII.

$$—CH=CH—\overset{\cdot}{C}H—CH=CH—\qquad (XIII)$$

$$—CH=CH—CH=CH—\overset{\cdot}{C}H—\qquad (XIV)$$

$$—\overset{\cdot}{C}H—CH=CH—CH=CH—\qquad (XV)$$

$$—\overset{\cdot}{C}H—CH—CH=CH—CH—\qquad (XVI)$$

$$—\overset{\cdot}{C}H—CH=CH—CH—\overset{\cdot}{C}H—\qquad (XVII)$$

(excited structures)

and the high reactivity results from the labile hydrogen atom being in the α-methylenic position to *two* double bonds or in other words from the substance being a 1 : 4-diene. It is, perhaps, fortunate that natural rubber is a 1 : 5-polydiene!

A consequence of the resonance phenomenon above is that although hydrogen abstraction is predominantly confined to the α-methylenic position, the addition of an oxygen molecule (which is itself a diradical) at one end of the oxygen molecule to this radical can take place at any position which is a free-radical centre (represented by C) in structures XIII and XVII. Thus although it was stated on p. 1102 that the hydroperoxide (XVIII) was the principal structure, in fact this is not true, all of the peroxides represented by structures XVIII–XX having been identified.[5,14,18,19]

$$\overset{OOH}{\underset{|}{—CH=CH—CH—CH=CH—}}\qquad (XVIII)$$

$$\overset{OOH}{\underset{|}{—CH=CH—CH=CH—CH—}}\qquad (XIX)$$

$$\overset{OOH}{\underset{|}{—CH—CH=CH—CH=CH—}}\qquad (XX)$$

This double-bond shift is in fact characteristic of olefin autoxidation, and the fact that cyclohexene gives rise to only one hydroperoxide is because of the complete equivalence of the two hybrid structures of the radical (XXI, XXII). 1 : 2-dimethylcyclohexene (XXIII) by contrast gives rise to two hydroperoxides [20] (XXIV, XXV).

It should be noted that whereas the original olefin structure of linoleic acid was unconjugated, two of the hydroperoxides involve a conjugated pair of double bonds. This might be expected to give rise to a K band

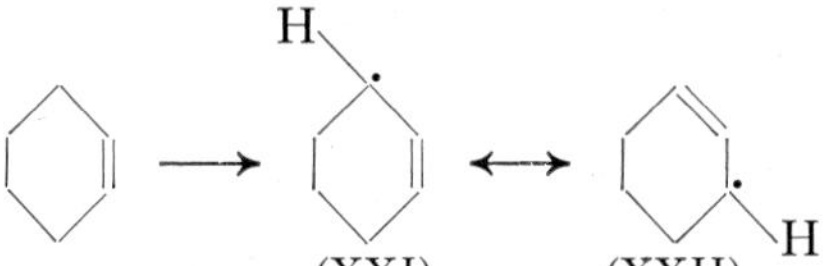

(XXI) ⟶ (XXII)

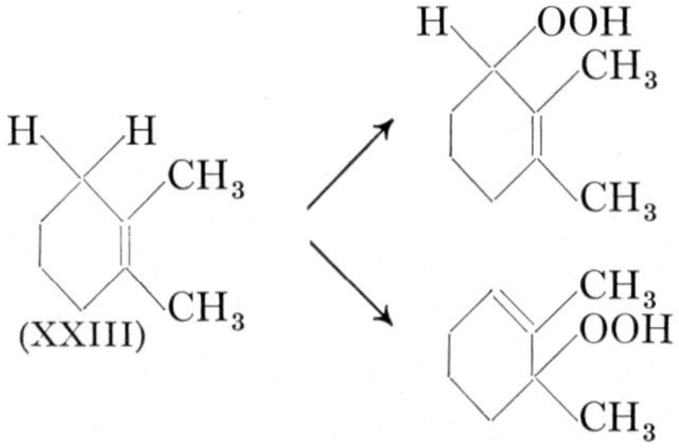

(XXIII) → (XXIV) / (XXV)

in the ultra-violet absorption spectrum at 205–230 mμ, and in fact during autoxidation there is an increase in the light absorption in this region,[14,18] but the complete picture of increased light absorption is probably more complex than this.[43] Furthermore, –C=O, –OOH and –OH groups have a distinctly auxochromic effect which may obscure the increased absorption due to the development of conjugation.

Since natural rubber is 1 : 5-polydiene, and although 1 : 4-dienes are convenient for kinetic work, in view of their high reactivity and almost exclusive α-methylenic attack, it is essential to consider 1 : 5-dienes.[8]

Simple compounds of this class which are fairly easily obtained include dihydromyrcene (XXVI), dihydrofarnesene (XXVII) and squalene (XXVIII).

$$H\!-\!(CH_2\!-\!\overset{\overset{\displaystyle CH_3}{|}}{C}\!=\!CH\!-\!CH_2)_2\!-\!H \quad (XXVI)$$

$$H\!-\!(CH_2\!-\!\overset{\overset{\displaystyle CH_3}{|}}{C}\!=\!CH\!-\!CH_2)_3\!-\!H \quad (XXVII)$$

$$H\!-\!(CH_2\!-\!\overset{\overset{\displaystyle CH_3}{|}}{C}\!=\!CH\!-\!CH_2)_3\!-\!(CH_2\!-\!\overset{\overset{\displaystyle CH_3}{|}}{C}H\!=\!C\!-\!CH_2)_3\!-\!H \quad (XXVIII)$$

Extensive structural work[21] supported by kinetic evidence[34] suggests structure XXIX for the first isolatable hydroperoxide.

The reactivity of 1 : 5-dienes is, as expected, somewhat lower than 1 : 4-dienes, but higher than mono-olefins.

Although conjugated polyolefins are of little importance as useful polymers (they would be quite black incidentally), it is of interest to note that they show a quite different type of reactivity. Hydroperoxides are not formed, but rather ring and polymeric diperoxide linkages.[19,46] These are not analysed by the ordinary methods for hydroperoxides, since di-

$$-CH_2-\underset{\underset{CH_3}{|}}{C}=CH-\overset{\overset{\displaystyle O-O}{\big|}}{CH}-CH_2-CH_2-\underset{\underset{OOH}{|}}{\overset{\overset{\displaystyle CH_3}{|}}{C}}-CH-CH_2- \qquad \text{(XXIX)}$$

peroxides in general are more stable. Diperoxides, furthermore, do not undergo electron transfer reactions with heavy metal ions (see later). In consequence, unlike other olefins, the autoxidation of conjugated polyenes is not catalysed by trace metals.[46] This reactivity of conjugated polyenes is probably much more like the normal addition reactions of olefins (e.g. towards bromine) and probably involves the following sequence of reactions:

$$>\!C\!=\!\underset{H}{C}-\underset{H}{C}\!=\!C\!< + O_2 \longrightarrow >\!C\!-\!\underset{\underset{OO\cdot}{|}}{\overset{\displaystyle \cdot}{C}}-\underset{H}{C}\!=\!C\!< \xrightarrow[\text{olefin}]{+ \text{ conjugated}}$$

$$\begin{array}{c} >\!C\!-\!\underset{\underset{\underset{\displaystyle >C-\underset{H\ H}{\overset{\cdot}{C}}-C=C<}{|}}{O_2}}{\overset{\displaystyle \cdot}{C}}-\underset{H\ H}{C}\!=\!C\!< \end{array} \xrightarrow{O_2} \text{diperoxide cross-linked polymer}$$

as well as the diperoxide cyclising reaction,

$$>\!C\!-\!\underset{\underset{O_2\cdot}{|}}{\overset{\displaystyle \cdot}{C}H}\!-\!CH\!=\!C\!< \longrightarrow >\!C\!-\!CH\!=\!CH\!-\!\underset{\underset{O-O}{|\_\_\_\_\_}}{\overset{|}{C}}\!<$$

The type of reactivity in conjugated polyenes undoubtedly arises from the resonance stabilisation of the radical resulting from the hybrid structures (XXX, XXXI).

$$>\!C\!-\!\underset{\underset{OO\cdot}{|}}{\overset{\displaystyle \cdot}{C}H}\!-\!CH\!=\!C\!< \longleftrightarrow >\!C\!-\!\underset{\underset{OO\cdot}{|}}{CH}\!=\!CH\!-\!\overset{\displaystyle \cdot}{C}\!<$$

$$\qquad\qquad \text{(XXX)} \qquad\qquad\qquad\qquad \text{(XXXI)}$$

The longer the conjugated chain, the more structures will be available. This type of resonance stabilisation is not available for radical addition to other polyenes beyond the 1 : 3 series or for mono-olefins. This type of reaction, however, is now known to take place to a limited extent for these other olefins,[44,47] since polymeric products become deposited (though late in the reaction) during autoxidation and the initial hydroperoxide yields are not 100% with reference to the oxygen absorbed. Although this type of reactivity is only of *minor chemical significance* outside the range of conjugated olefins, it is in all probability of *great significance in determining changes in the physical properties of polymers* during autoxidation. This is because although simple hydroperoxidation may be expected to have little influence on physical properties, the above minor reactions represent cross-linking of the polymer, a small amount of which can drastically alter the physical properties.

In general, reactions of minor *chemical significance can be* of major significance in terms of *physical* properties.

Unconjugated olefins—autoxidation kinetics

Rate of oxygen absorption

The following reaction scheme satisfies the observed rate of *oxygen absorption* under all experimental conditions (concentration of reactants, oxygen pressure, temperature within limits and light intensity).

Reaction rate.

$$ROOH \xrightarrow[\text{or } h\nu]{\text{Thermal}} ROO\cdot + H\cdot \qquad v_1 = r_1$$

$$ROO\cdot + RH \longrightarrow ROOH + R\cdot \qquad v_2 = k_2(RO_2\cdot)(RH)$$

$$R\cdot + O_2 \longrightarrow RO_2\cdot \qquad v_3 = k_3(R\cdot)(O_2)$$

$$R\cdot + R\cdot \longrightarrow \text{inactive products} \qquad v_4 = k_4(R\cdot)^2$$

$$RO_2\cdot + R\cdot \longrightarrow \text{inactive products} \qquad v_5 = k_5(RO_2\cdot)(R\cdot)$$

$$RO_2\cdot + RO_2\cdot \longrightarrow \text{inactive products} \qquad v_6 = k_6(RO_2\cdot)^2$$

Assuming a stationary concentration of free radicals and that under this condition

$$r_1 = v_4 + v_5 + v_6,$$

also if the chain length is great,

$$v_2 = v_3$$

then

$$(RO_2\cdot)^2 = \cfrac{r_1}{\dfrac{k_4 k_2}{k_3{}^2}\dfrac{(RH)^2}{(O_2)^2} + \dfrac{2k_4 k_2(RH)}{k_3(O_2)} + k_6}$$

Now

$$\frac{d(O_2 \text{ absorbed})}{dt} = v_3 = v_2 \text{ under long-chain conditions} = k_2(RO_2\cdot)(RH)$$

substituting for $(RO_2\cdot)$ above,

$$\frac{d(O_2 \text{ absorbed})}{dt} = \frac{r_1^{\frac{1}{2}}}{\left(\dfrac{k_4}{k_3^2(O_2)^2} + \dfrac{k_6}{k_2^2(RH)^2} + \dfrac{2k_5}{k_2 k_3(RH)(O_2)}\right)^{\frac{1}{2}}}$$

If it is assumed that $k_4 k_6 = k_5^2$, then

$$\frac{d(O_2 \text{ absorbed})}{dt} = \frac{r_1^{\frac{1}{2}}}{\left(\dfrac{k_4^{\frac{1}{2}}}{k_3(O_2)} + \dfrac{k_6^{\frac{1}{2}}}{k_2(RH)}\right)}$$

Thus at " high " oxygen pressures

$$\frac{d(O_2 \text{ absorbed})}{dt} = r_1^{\frac{1}{2}}\frac{k_2(RH)}{k_6^{\frac{1}{2}}}$$

and at " low " oxygen pressures

$$\frac{d(O_2 \text{ absorbed})}{dt} = \frac{r_1^{\frac{1}{2}} k_3(O_2)}{k_4^{\frac{1}{2}}}$$

Since the rate of oxygen absorption is proportional to the square root of the rate of initiation, some inconsistency appeared to be involved when the rate was found to be proportional to the first power of (ROOH), unless the decomposition of ROOH was second order. This has been shown to be true by studying the decomposition of Δ^2-cyclohexenyl hydroperoxide in an inert solvent, the decomposition arising from a small concentration of hydroperoxide dimer.[40]

$$2ROOH \rightleftharpoons (ROOH)_2 \longrightarrow \text{free radicals}$$

The author and A. J. Chalk [48] have shown a similar process to occur in certain catalysed systems, where the initiation reaction can be represented as

$$ROOH + A \rightleftharpoons ROOH\cdot A \longrightarrow \text{free radicals}$$

In this case A, the catalyst, ranged from carboxylic acids to zinc salts of carboxylic acids and even ferric salts of carboxylic acids.

In contrast to the above, other possible initiators show the expected square-root dependence.[31] The same square-root dependence on the intensity of illumination in the photochemical reaction is also observed.[32, 33]

While the above rate equation for oxygen absorption is obeyed for 1 : 5-olefins and 1 : 5-polyenes, the mechanism must be somewhat different, owing to the fact that the first isolatable peroxide (XXIX, p. 1106) contains two oxygen molecules. In all probability step 3 in the reaction sequence is replaced by a two-stage process

$$-CH_2-\overset{|}{C}=CH-\overset{\cdot}{C}H-CH_2-\overset{|}{C}=CH-CH_2-$$

$$\downarrow$$

$$-CH_2-\overset{|}{C}=CH-\underset{\overset{|}{O_2\cdot}}{CH}-CH_2-\overset{|}{C}=CH-CH_2-$$

$$\downarrow$$

$$-CH_2-\overset{|}{C}=CH-\underset{\underset{O}{\big|\rule{3em}{0pt}}}{CH}-CH_2-\overset{\cdot}{\underset{\underset{O}{\big|}}{C}}-CH-CH_2- \longrightarrow$$

$$-CH_2-\overset{|}{C}=CH-\underset{\underset{O}{\big|\rule{3em}{0pt}}}{CH}-CH_2-\underset{\overset{|}{O_2\cdot}}{\overset{|}{C}}-CH-CH_2$$

Even with the above modification, the scheme is quite inadequate to explain the changes which take place in natural rubber on autoxidation. Some of the discrepancies are enumerated below:

(a) Hydroperoxidation of the polymer chain of itself can be expected to modify the physical properties to only a minor degree.

(b) Cross-linking of the polymer, which is known to take place (see later), is only vaguely formulated in the termination reactions. Other reactions, although of minor chemical significance, may represent a major proportion of the cross-linking.

$$CH_2=\overset{\overset{\displaystyle CH_3}{|}}{C}-CH=CH_2$$

(XXXII)

$$-CH_2-\overset{\overset{\displaystyle CH_3}{|}}{C}=CH-CH_2-CH_2-\overset{\overset{\displaystyle CH_3}{|}}{C}=CH-CH_2-$$
Normal head-to-tail union

$$-CH_2-CH=\overset{\overset{\displaystyle CH_3}{|}}{C}-CH_2-CH_2-\overset{\overset{\displaystyle CH_3}{|}}{C}=CH-CH_2-$$
Head-to-head union

$$-CH_2-\overset{\overset{\displaystyle CH_3}{|}}{C}=CH-CH_2-CH_2-CH=\overset{\overset{\displaystyle CH_3}{|}}{C}-CH_2-$$
Tail-to-tail union

(c) Chain scission reactions which are also known to take place (see later) *are not even represented.*

(d) Although natural rubber has predominantly a "head-to-tail" I : 5-polyene structure, there are a small but finite number of points in the rubber chain where "head-to-head" and "tail-to-tail" union of isoprene (XXXII) instead of the normal "head-to-tail" structure pertains. Furthermore, although a conjugated diene such as isoprene normally polymerises across the I : 4 positions to give a I : 5 polyene, a small amount of I : 2 and 3 : 4 polymerisation undoubtedly exists, as shown by infra-red spectroscopy. These minor amounts of anomalous structure can be the "weak points" of the polymer chain.

(e) Since the rubber polymer has this "mixed" structure, the system undergoing autoxidation can be regarded as a multi-component system. Now it has been shown that a two-component system such as cumene and tetralin undergoing competitive autoxidation presents some unusual features.[49] This was attributed to the greater facility of the termination reaction between a radical derived from cumene and one from tetrain, than the termination reactions between radicals derived from the same parent olefin. This gives rise to a marked minimum rate of oxygen absorption as the molar proportions of the two olefins are varied. In fact, certain centres of anomalous structure may be responsible for the antioxidant present in natural rubber.

(f) Probably the most serious deficiency in the scheme is that it is virtually irrelevant to sulphur vulcanisates (see later), where the centre of attack is undoubtedly the sulphur cross-links.

In summary, hydroperoxidation is undoubtedly of major chemical significance in olefin autoxidation. It is, however, merely a precursor (if not irrelevant) to the physically important scission and cross-linking processes. With this statement in mind, the significance of the work described in the next section can be better appreciated in so far as it refers to polymer degradation.

Individual rate coefficients

By studying merely the rate of oxygen absorption of an olefin it is not possible to extract the values for the rate coefficients of the individual reaction steps. Since olefins vary considerably in their reactivity towards oxygen, it is of great interest to know which step in the reaction sequence is most influenced by variations in olefin structure. To decide this the individual rate coefficients must be determined, and in consequence considerable effort has been devoted to this end.

The value of r_1, the rate of initiation, is the only parameter in the equation for oxygen absorption which can be directly determined, since it can be studied in isolation. The initiating species can be not only the spontaneously formed hydroperoxide but also deliberately added substances which are known to dissociate into free radicals. There are, however, pitfalls in this approach. Thus there is the implicit assumption that the free-radical-producing initiator will decompose at the same rate in the liquid olefin as in an inert solvent. While this is true for azo initiators, it is manifestly untrue for benzoyl peroxide.[39] The study of hydroperoxides as initiators in isolation is by no means simple.[40] Thus only the early stages of the decomposition obey simple kinetics, because of the separation of water later in the reaction and the consequent onset of a heterogeneous reaction. Further, in the absence of oxygen a chain decomposition takes place in olefin media. The reaction order in the early stages is only pure second order with respect to (ROOH) in an inert solvent such as benzene. It has to be assumed that the chain decomposition of hydroperoxides is suppressed during autoxidation.

Although the decomposition of hydroperoxides is second order in benzene, over the range of hydroperoxide concentrations which can be accurately analysed the autoxidation of certain olefins [42] strongly suggests that at very low (ROOH), when the hydroperoxide exists almost entirely in the monomeric form, the decomposition is first order. The range of hydroperoxide concentration over which this change in order takes place varies from olefin to olefin. This leads to considerable uncertainty in the rate of olefin autoxidation at zero hydroperoxide concentration. This rate at zero (ROOH) would be most useful to know, since some mechanism must operate at zero (ROOH). Experiments, however, to determine this rate are futile, since under conditions of varying reaction order it is impossible to extrapolate back to zero (ROOH) with any accuracy. All that exists is speculation about the mechanism at zero (ROOH), but the following reactions *may* represent the mechanism:

$$>\!\!C\!-\!\overset{|}{C}\!\!=\!\!C\!\!<\; +\;O_2 \;\longrightarrow\; >\!\!\overset{\cdot}{C}\!-\!\overset{|}{C}\!\!=\!\!C\!\!<\; +\;HO_2\cdot$$

$$>\!\!\underset{H}{\overset{|}{C}}\!-\!\overset{|}{C}\!\!=\!\!C\!\!<\; +\;O_2 \;\longrightarrow\; >\!\!\underset{H}{\overset{|}{C}}\!-\!\overset{|}{C}\!-\!\overset{\cdot}{\underset{O\cdot}{\overset{O}{C}}}\!\!<$$

There is not a direct way of determining k_2, k_3, k_4 or k_6 in the oxygen absorption equation as there is with r_1. By determining, however, the rate of oxygen absorption at " high " oxygen pressures (in the region where there is no longer a dependence of rate on oxygen pressure) we have

$$\frac{d(O_2 \text{ absorbed})}{dt} = r_1^{\frac{1}{2}} \frac{k_2(\text{RH})}{k_6^{\frac{1}{2}}}$$

so that if r_1 is separately determined it is possible to evaluate $k_2/k_6^{\frac{1}{2}}$. Also, if the reaction is studied at " low " oxygen pressures and even extrapolated to zero oxygen pressure, since under these conditions

$$\frac{d(O_2 \text{ absorbed})}{dt} = r_1^{\frac{1}{2}} \frac{k_3(O_2)}{k_4^{\frac{1}{2}}}$$

it is possible to evaluate $k_3/k_4^{\frac{1}{2}}$. In practice, this latter expression is difficult to obtain, since at low oxygen pressure the diffusion of oxygen into the liquid can easily become rate determining. Furthermore, the measurements cannot be made on the more volatile olefins.

In order to separate k_2 and $k_6^{\frac{1}{2}}$ non-stationary initiation rates must be produced. The only practicable way of doing this is in the photochemical autoxidation, where the rate of initiation can be suddenly started or stopped by the simple process of switching the source of illumination.

A particularly useful development of this idea is the rotating-sector technique.[50] This depends on illuminating the autoxidising system and shutting off the illumination for equal intervals, which is most conveniently done by placing a rotating-sector wheel between the light source and the reaction vessel. As the speed of the wheel increases, at first there is little change in the rate of oxygen absorption, but when the period of illumination corresponds to the mean lifetime of the radicals, a fairly abrupt change in the rate of oxygen absorption takes place, followed by little further change. Provided termination takes place solely by radical–radical interaction, it is possible to formulate this in precise mathematical terms, although the treatment becomes more complicated when the " dark " rate is more than negligible compared with the " light " rate.[32, 33]

In addition to the rotating-sector technique it is possible to derive the mean lifetime of the radicals by observing the decay in the rate of oxygen absorption as soon as the source of illumination is cut off or the rise in the rate when the illumination is switched on.[38] In this case considerable experimental finesse is required to " catch " the decay or growth process.

Having determined τ, the average lifetime of the radicals, it is possible to evaluate k_6 because

$$\tau = \frac{\text{Total radical concentration}}{\text{Rate of radical destruction}}$$

and under " high " oxygen pressure $RO_2 \cdot$ represents the major part of the radical population

$$\therefore \quad \tau = \frac{(RO_2 \cdot)}{k_6 (RO_2 \cdot)^2} = \frac{1}{k_6 (RO_2 \cdot)}$$

Now since
$$(RO_2 \cdot)^2 = \frac{r_1}{k_6},$$

$$k_6 = \frac{1}{r_1 \tau^2}$$

and since $\dfrac{k_2}{k_6^{\frac{1}{2}}}$ can be derived experimentally, k_2 can therefore also be extracted.

Since these rate coefficients have to be derived by such a circuitous process, great accuracy cannot be expected even from very careful work. Nevertheless, Bolland and his colleagues were able to show from this work that the variation in overall reactivity from one olefin to another resided in reaction 2, the hydrogen abstraction reaction from the α-methylenic position,

$$ROO \cdot + RH \longrightarrow ROOH + R \cdot$$

rather than in the termination reaction. Thus for a number of olefins k_2 ranged from 0·03 MLS units in the case of oct-1-ene to 5·7 MLS units in the case of ethyl linoleate. On the other hand, k_6 ranged only from about 0·2 × 10^6 MLS units in the case of oct-1-ene to about 0·9 × 10^6 MLS units in the case of cyclohexene. In consequence, it is unnecessary to resort to this length to determine the α-methylenic reactivity of an olefin. The readily obtainable $k_2/k_6^{\frac{1}{2}}$ is a reasonable measure of this reactivity.

By using this criterion of α-methylenic reactivity, Bolland [36] was able to formulate some simple rules regarding α-methylenic reactivity deduced from a range of olefins that would have involved a prohibitive amount of work in determining the absolute rate coefficients. These rules are as follows. Consider propene (XXXIII)

$$
\begin{array}{ccc}
(a) & (b) & (c) \\
CH_3 - CH & : CH_2
\end{array}
$$
(XXXIII)

At 45° C he concludes that at " high " oxygen pressures:

(i) Replacement of 1 or 2 hydrogen atoms at (a) and/or (c) by alkyl groups increases k_2 by 3·3^n, where n is the total number of substituents. Similar replacement at (b) is without effect.

(ii) Replacement of a hydrogen atom at (a) by a phenyl group increases k_2 by 23 fold.

(iii) Replacement of a hydrogen atom at (a) by an alk-1-enyl group increases k_2 by 107 fold.

(iv) The value of k_2 appropriate to a cyclic structure is 1·7 times that in an analogous acyclic structure.

Certain exceptions to this are noted, particularly when steric effects intervene as in 2 : 4-dimethylpent-2-ene.[43] Furthermore, it is difficult to approach " high " oxygen pressure conditions with very reactive olefins owing to the facility of

$$ROO\cdot + RH \longrightarrow ROOH + R\cdot$$

compared with

$$R\cdot + O_2 \longrightarrow RO_2\cdot$$

in this case. This leads to a relatively high concentration of R· radicals and a consequently greater termination by

$$R\cdot + R\cdot \longrightarrow \text{inactive products}$$

and

$$RO_2\cdot + R\cdot \longrightarrow \quad ,, \qquad ,,$$

compared with

$$RO_2\cdot + RO_2\cdot \longrightarrow \quad ,, \qquad ,,$$

An olefin of this type is [41] 2 : 6-dimethylhepta-2 : 5-diene.

Unconjugated olefins—antioxidants

A characteristic of chain reactions, and one that often leads to widely divergent results, is that the overall rate can be drastically reduced by the presence of quite small amounts of materials which can react with free radicals to produce species of much lower reactivity. It would have been a great triumph for fundamental chemistry if, following the characterisation of olefin autoxidation, the practical application of the principle had led to the use of antioxidants. Unfortunately for the academic chemist but fortunately for the rubber technologist antioxidants (albeit without an understanding of their mode of action) had been in use for many years.

Considering first phenolic antioxidants, the simplest picture of their mode action is illustrated by the following example:

$$RO_2\cdot + HO\!\!-\!\!\langle\ \rangle\!\!-\!\!OH \longrightarrow ROOH + \cdot O\!\!-\!\!\langle\ \rangle\!\!-\!\!OH$$

the semiquinone radical then being too stable to abstract an α-methylenic hydrogen atom from the olefin.

It was expected and to a large measure found [29] that inhibitor efficiency and redox potential of a number of compounds of this class should be closely related.   In fact, on plotting $\log_{10}$ (relative efficiency) [a measure of energy difference] against the redox potential of the inhibitor a straight-line relation was obtained for a series of phenolic antioxidants.

To be precise, had such a correlation not been obtained, the proposed mode of action would not have been completely disproved.   The reaction of $RO_2\cdot$ radicals with an inhibitor is a *rate* process, and as such is controlled by the energy of *activation* rather than by the free energy of *reaction*.   The redox potential of an inhibitor is determined by the free energy of *reaction* in oxidising the inhibitor.   Although activation energies and free energies of reaction often run parallel, they are not compelled to in theory.   In fact, when steric and entropy requirements of the transition state become exceptional the parallelism disappears.

At the ends of the redox potential range of phenolic inhibitors, as Bolland and Ten Have found, the parallelism breaks down for another reason.   Thus phenols of high redox potential produce semiquinone radicals which are quite capable of propagating the reaction chain.   Also phenols of very low redox potential are readily dehydrogenated, and thus effectively removed, by molecular oxygen.

Waters [51] has shown that the relationship between redox potentials and antioxidant efficiency in benzaldehyde autoxidation, using various quinones, holds only for quinones which are closely related structurally.

Certain sterically hindered phenols have come into prominence in recent years as antioxidants for rubber and petroleum because, while they have an efficiency comparable with amine antioxidants, they cause practically no staining.   Bickel and Kooyman [52] attribute the effectiveness of these sterically hindered phenols to the fact that they do not undergo radical transfer with the substance being protected.

$$A\cdot + RH \longrightarrow AH + R\cdot$$

rather than by a high rate of termination.

$$AH + RO_2\cdot \longrightarrow A\cdot + ROOH$$

Product analysis is complicated by the small amounts of inhibitor used and by the multiplicity of products (often of high molecular weight) which result from inhibited autoxidation.   Such results, however, as are available show that the reaction must be more complicated than the simple abstraction of the oxygen-bound hydrogen atom in the phenol to give a semiquinone.   Often too, the isolated products are far removed from the primary products of inhibition.   Thus it has been shown that *p*-cresol results in diphenyl derivatives for which the following mechanism was proposed: [53]

Di-*ortho*-substituted *p*-cresols, however, appeared to involve hydrogen abstraction from the *p*-methyl group to give dibenzyl derivatives.

Bickel and Kooyman believed that under conditions of high (ROO·) an adduct is formed between di-*ortho*-substituted *p*-cresols and the ROO· radical, a view also shared by Boozer and Hammond [55] for certain amine antioxidants, since even amines without a labile hydrogen on the nitrogen atom are good inhibitors. The mode of action of amine inhibitors appears to be particularly complicated. It has been suggested [30, 56] that they act by decomposing hydroperoxides by a mechanism not resulting in the production of free radicals.

Hydroperoxide decomposition

Having stated that the deterioration of the physical properties of high polymers and the hydroperoxidation of simple olefins are not as closely correlated as once thought and that reactions of minor chemical importance may be of major physical significance, the decomposition of hydroperoxides might be the significant feature of polymer degradation. While this is possibly true, several pitfalls await the unwary speculator:

1. In an inert medium the hydroperoxide and its decomposition products will interact with one another and with oxygen.[57] In an olefinic medium the hydroperoxide and its decomposition products react preferentially with the olefin owing to the large concentration of the latter.

2. Since certainly part of the autoxidation is an alternative to the mechanism originally proposed by the BRPRA,[44] chain and cross-link scission and cross-link formation may not necessarily proceed via the hydroperoxide.

3. Sulphur vulcanisates probably degrade by a different mechanism (see later).

The following are some of the speculated reactions of hydroperoxides which could explain the presence of the observed products and also molecular-weight changes of polymeric olefins:

$$2ROOH \longrightarrow RO\cdot + RO_2\cdot + H_2O$$

$$\begin{array}{c} R' \\ | \\ -CH{=}CH{-}C \quad (\text{i.e. } RO\cdot) \\ | \\ O\cdot \end{array}$$

$$\begin{array}{c} O \\ \| \\ -CH{=}CH{-}C{-}R + H\cdot \end{array} \qquad -CH{=}CH{-}CH{=}O + R'\cdot$$

$$\downarrow O_2$$

$$\begin{array}{c} -CH{=}CH{-}C{=}O \\ | \\ OOH \end{array}$$

$$\downarrow$$

$$-CH{=}CH{-}C{\big\langle}^{O}_{OH}$$

$$RO\cdot + ROOH \longrightarrow ROH + RO_2\cdot$$

Other products of hydroperoxide decomposition whose origins are not clear include epoxides and carbon dioxide.

In summary, it is not difficult to decide what reactions are possible, but to assess the relative importance of these reactions presents a serious problem, being, in all probability, sensitive to changes in the character of the medium.

Catalysis of olefin autoxidation

It has been known for a long time that minute traces of certain heavy metals (Cu, Fe, Mn, etc.) catalyse autoxidation reactions. In certain instances (paint driers) this has been put to good effect, while in others (fats, petroleum, rubbers) these catalysts have a great nuisance value. In spite of rigorous analytical control and clean processing, this catalysis all too often rears its ugly head.

Until the general features of *uncatalysed* olefin autoxidation had been elucidated, little progress could be made in understanding catalysed autoxidation.

When the exact role of hydroperoxides in olefin autoxidation had been realised, another topic which had been studied in great detail appeared relevant. This was the metal-catalysed decomposition of hydrogen peroxide, which has been reviewed by Weiss [58] and by Baxendale.[59] Although precise agreement on the relative importance of the various reactions has, even now, not been reached, the significant reactions appear to be:

$$M^{++} + H_2O_2 \longrightarrow HO_2\cdot + M^+ + H^+$$

$$M^+ + H_2O_2 \longrightarrow OH\cdot + M^{++} + OH^-$$

$$M^+ + HO_2\cdot \rightleftharpoons M^{++} + HO_2^-$$

$$M^+ + OH\cdot \longrightarrow M^{++} + OH^-$$

$$M^{++} + HO_2\cdot \longrightarrow M^+ + H^+ + O_2$$

$$H_2O_2 \rightleftharpoons H^+ + HO_2^-$$

$$HO_2\cdot \rightleftharpoons H^+ + O_2^-$$

$$OH\cdot + H_2O_2 \rightleftharpoons H_2O + HO_2\cdot$$

$$M^{++} + O_2^- \rightleftharpoons M^+ + O_2$$

Where M^+ represents the method in its lowest valency state and M^{++} the next higher valency state.

The decomposition of organic hydroperoxides in *aqueous solution* was shown [60, 70] to exhibit similar behaviour, but is complicated by the rearrangement and disproportionation reactions outlined earlier in this chapter.

In non-polar solutions there is a dearth of work on catalysed hydroperoxide decomposition.[65, 71] Similar mechanisms may be expected to operate, but may be modified by the following factors:

1. Ionisation process will be strongly suppressed.

2. The metal ions will not be co-ordinated by water molecules as they are generally in aqueous solution.

3. The redox potential of the metal may be very different from that in water by virtue of 2.

Applied studies on metal catalysis of autoxidation are very numerous and involve considerable disagreement owing to the many conditions (type of vulcanisate, composition of catalyst, presence of impurities) which must be defined to give reproducible results.

Fundamental studies on metal-catalysed autoxidation of olefins are relatively scarce. George and Robertson[72, 73] visualise the initiation reaction as a catalyst–oxygen interaction, deduced presumably from the independence of the rate of autoxidation on the hydroperoxide concentration. In the case of the ferric-iron-catalysed autoxidation of cyclohexene, however, the author[74] and his co-workers have shown that complex formation between the catalyst and the hydroperoxide takes place and the initiation reaction is the decomposition of this complex into free radicals. Since the concentration of the catalyst is usually very small (of the order of parts per million), the concentration of hydroperoxide, which no longer controls the rate of autoxidation, can also be very small if the complex is a tight one. In fact, the hydroperoxide concentration can be high enough before the first measurements can be made. The case of ferric iron in cyclohexene is fortunate in that the complex is not so tight that it precludes observation of hydroperoxide dependence of rate. With copper and cobalt,[48] the combination of high catalytic activity and tight complex formation precludes the observation of hydroperoxide dependence except at low temperatures (*ca.* 30° C) compared with those used for ferric iron (*ca.* 60° C). It seems likely that George and Robertson's results can be reinterpreted on this basis. Kern and Willersinn have come to a similar conclusion[75] to that of the author and his colleagues in the case of the catalysis of unsaturated ester autoxidation by copper salts.

The choice of a suitable catalyst for autoxidation studies is not easy. Thus the oil-soluble naphthenates are of variable and complex compositions while the stearates are liable to micelle formation. The author and his colleagues[48, 74] have avoided this by using the heptoates, the *o*-bromo-benzoates and the *o*-toluates of the metals. Kern and Willersinn have similarly used the octoates.[75] Bawn, Pennington and Tipper[76] avoided this catalyst complication by using the acetates and studying autoxidation in glacial acetic acid, in which both hydrocarbon and catalyst are soluble. It has been emphasised,[74] however, that unlike rubber, this is a strongly polar system.

Bawn's reaction scheme was obtained by combining the uncatalysed scheme of autoxidation with a simplified scheme of hydroperoxide decomposition as catalysed by metal salts.

$$ROOH + M^{++} \longrightarrow ROO\cdot + M^+ + H^+$$
$$ROOH + M^+ \longrightarrow RO\cdot + M^{++} + OH^-$$
$$ROO\cdot + RH \longrightarrow ROOH + R\cdot$$
$$R\cdot + O_2 \dashrightarrow RO_2\cdot$$
$$2RO_2\cdot \longrightarrow \text{inactive products}$$

The author and A. J. Chalk [48] have shown this to be an inadequate representation in non-polar media for a number of reasons:

1. The catalyst is depicted as a free ion, which apart from being unlikely in non-polar media, does not permit the influence of groups in the coordination sphere of the metal to be considered.

2. The reaction order with respect to catalyst and hydroperoxide should be $\frac{1}{2}$ in both instances at long chain length and high hydrocarbon concentration. In fact it soon becomes independent of (ROOH).

3. It does not explain the inhibitory effect of manganous manganese.

To account for (1) and (2) it is necessary to depict the metal ion more precisely as a complex with its anion, the medium and added complexing agents. Furthermore, the initiation reaction must first be preceded by one or more hydroperoxide molecules entering the co-ordination sphere of the metal. This will largely be determined by the stability and lability of the metal complex with its anion, medium and added complexing agents.

The activity of the metal as a catalyst will depend on the redox potential of the metal (but with the same reservations as for inhibitor action). Since this depends, sometimes most strikingly, on groups in the co-ordination shell, the catalytic activity of the metal [48] is strongly dependent on the anion, the medium and added substances. It is not surprising that reproducible results are the exception rather than the rule with such a variable material as vulcanised rubber.

In order to explain the inhibitory action of certain metals (manganous manganese, in particular, *in cyclohexene*) it was found necessary [48] to add to Bawn's scheme a termination reaction involving the metal; for instance

$$RO_2\cdot + Mn^{++} \longrightarrow RO_2^- + Mn^{+++}$$

although other termination reactions can also be postulated. This type of reaction is well known in hydrogen peroxide decomposition and accounts for the stoichiometric analysis of hydrogen peroxide by ferrous salts at high $[Fe^{++}]/[H_2O_2]$ ratios.

$$Fe^{++} + H_2O_2 \longrightarrow Fe^{+++} + OH\cdot + OH^-$$
$$OH\cdot + Fe^{++} \longrightarrow Fe^{+++} + OH^-$$

In order to produce strong catalysis the catalyst must be soluble in the medium. In fact, the activity of insoluble catalysts can be expressed in terms of the number of surface atoms of catalyst. Colloidally dispersed catalysts, however, may have a very high activity comparable with soluble catalysts.

Sequestering agents

The term " sequestering agent " is a comparatively new addition to the rubber chemists' vocabulary, and there has been considerable confusion about its exact meaning.[77] It is quite superfluous to use the term as synonymous with complexing or chelating agent, and the author prefers the following definition which is consistent with the etymology of the term: " A sequestering agent is a substance which prevents the participation of a metal or its compounds in a chemical reaction." [78]

A complexing agent is a molecule (in the widest sense of the word) which is chemically bound to a metal. The binding may be electrostatic, covalent or even of the weak van der Waals type. If the molecule is bound to the metal at more than one centre it is described as a chelating agent. A complexing or chelating agent may *sequester* or *activate* the metal in any particular reaction. The factors which determine in which way a complexing agent will behave have recently been investigated (but not exhaustively so) by Chalk and Smith.[79]

Chelating agents are in general better sequestering agents than monofunctional complexing agents, because for a given overall formation constant (10^{10} say), the chelating agent produces a much lower concentration of the " free " metal ion: Assuming a concentration of the complex of $M/1000$,

For a monofunctional complexing agent X

$$\frac{[MX_2]}{[M][X]^2} = 10^{10} \text{ and since } [X] = 2[M], M = 3 \times 10^{-5}.$$

For a bifunctional (i.e. bidentate) chelate Y

$$\frac{[MY]}{[M][Y]} = 10^{10} \text{ and since } [M] = [Y], M = 3 \times 10^{-7}.$$

Occasionally the addition of a complexing agent to a system containing the metal will result in the precipitation of the complex. This is, however, not the general mode of action of sequestering agents because, while solubility is an important factor governing catalysis, many complexes are soluble though inactive.

There has in the past been some confusion between sequestering agents and inhibitors (i.e. antioxidants). An inhibitor becomes consumed

o o

during its mode of action. A sequestering agent (or at least an idealised one) is not consumed. Some inhibitors, however, may also act as sequestering agents, and *vice versa*. In fundamental studies using inhibitors it has not always been realised that the inhibitor can combine or otherwise react with the metal catalyst as well as with free radicals. This fact makes the interpretation of inhibited rates in the presence of metal catalysts somewhat uncertain.

Inhibitors which are not accompanied by a sequestering action are rapidly consumed in the presence of very active catalysts. In consequence, it is preferable in practical applications to use inhibitors which also have a sequestering action.

One of the most obvious suggestions about the mode of action of sequestering agents is that they act by a " blocking " effect, since it has been shown that the hydroperoxide molecule must enter the co-ordination shell of the metal before electron transfer can take place.[48] This can, however, not be the sole factor, since it does not explain the activating effect of certain complexing agents. This activating effect probably results from a shift in the redox potential towards an optimum value for the most efficient catalysis. Analogously some sequestering agents may act by shifting the redox potential *away* from the optimum value.

The activating effect and blocking effects acting in opposite directions are illustrated by the following example.[79]

Ferric heptoate is a weak catalyst for the autoxidation of cyclohexene. In the presence of 1 : 3-*bis*-(salicylideneamino)propane (XXXIV) the catalysis becomes as strong as with unchelated copper compounds.

$$CH{=}N{-}CH_2 {\cdot} CH_2 {\cdot} CH_2 {-} N{=}CH$$
$$OH \qquad\qquad HO$$
(XXXIV)

This can be explained by a change in the redox potential on chelation, plus the fact that only four of the six co-ordination positions of ferric iron can be chelated by this compound.

If instead of (XXXIV), one adds 1 : 3-*bis*-(salicylideneamino) 2 : 2'-*bis*-(salicylidene aminomethyl) propane (XXXV), no activation of the ferric iron is observed. Now the compounds are so similar that the redox potential changes may also be expected to be similar. Compound (XXXV), however, can complex all the co-ordination positions around the ferric ion and prevent catalysis by a blocking effect.

Compound XXXIV sequesters cupric heptoate in the autoxidation of cyclohexene, probably by a redox potential change. Thus while copper is usually taken to have a maximum co-ordination number of four, it can actually co-ordinate weakly at a fifth position. This weakly bound co-ordination appears to be sufficiently strong for catalysis to take place, as when triethylenetetramine (XXXVI), a strongly co-ordinated quadri-dentate chelate, activates cupric heptoate in the above system.[79]

$$
\begin{array}{c}
N\!=\!CH\!-\!\bigcirc \\
| \\
CH_2 \ \ HO\diagup \\
\bigcirc\!-\!CH\!=\!N\!\cdots\!CH_2\!-\!\overset{|}{\underset{|}{C}}\!-\!CH_2\!-\!N\!=\!CH\!-\!\bigcirc \\
\diagdown OH \quad\quad CH_2 \quad\quad\quad HO\diagup \\
| \\
\bigcirc\!-\!CH\!=\!N \\
\diagdown OH
\end{array}
$$

(XXXV)

$$NH_2 \cdot CH_2 \cdot CH_2 \cdot NH \cdot CH_2 \cdot CH_2 \cdot NH \cdot CH_2 \cdot CH_2 \cdot NH_2$$

(XXXVI)

Another sexidentate chelating agent which does not activate ferric iron is 1 : 8-*bis*-(salicylideneamino)-3 : 6-dithia octane (XXXVII). These sexi-dentate agents also sequester cobalt salts which have a co-ordination number of six. Lower chelates fail to do so.

Manganese does not appear to be sequestered, but in certain instances (at low (ROOH)) long induction periods may give the impression that sequestering has taken place. This catalysis may result from manganese compounds being able to form a transient 7-co-ordinated complex.

$$
\bigcirc\!-\!CH\!=\!N\!-\!CH_2\!-\!CH_2\!-\!S\!-\!CH_2CH_2\!-\!S\!-\!CH_2\!-\!CH_2\!-\!N\!=\!CH\!-\!\bigcirc
$$
$$\diagdown OH \qquad\qquad\text{(XXXVII)} \qquad\qquad HO\diagup$$

To be precise, the concept of an " optimum redox potential " for efficient catalysis lacks theoretical justification. Electron-transfer catalysis is a rate process, whereas the redox potential is an equilibrium property, and although the two often run parallel, there is no compelling reason why they should do so. In consequence, when the technique of measuring redox potentials in non-polar media is developed, the correlation with catalytic activities might be found to be very poor.

There are some important aspects of sequestering-agent solubility and rate of complex formation which must be considered. For instance, in aqueous solution the sodium salts of ethylenediaminetetracetic acid are often efficient sequestering agents. These salts are not soluble in cyclo-hexene or rubber and do not sequester copper in these media. By form-ing the *bis*-(cetyltrimethyl ammonium) salt, an oil-soluble sequestering agent [79] can be obtained. This does not, however, sequester copper in non-polar solution, unless heated with the copper salt for some time, because of the slow formation of the complex under these conditions.

Ozone

One of the most remarkable forms of rubber deterioration is ozone cracking. The average ozone concentration in the atmosphere is roughly 0·04 parts per million, but in spite of this extremely low concentration, severe cracking of stretched rubber can occur over a period of some months. In some articles this cracking determines the useful life.

Although it had been known for a very long while that ozone could cause stretched rubber to crack, Newton [80] was the first clearly to elucidate the role of atmospheric ozone. The problem had been confused previously with the phenomenon of light crazing, which takes place on the surface of unstretched or stretched rubber, but is randomly oriented with respect to the applied stress. Ozone cracking always takes place at right angles to the applied stress. Furthermore, the chemical changes produced by ozone on solid rubber are confined to a layer probably not more than 100 Å thick, whereas light crazing results in a resinous film which is obvious on unaided inspection. In light crazing it is the brittle nature of this resinous film that causes the random crazing on exposure to strong light.

The fact that ozone reacts with rubber is not surprising. Ozone is one of the most reactive oxidants known, and will quite readily attack even saturated paraffins, and even more readily a highly unsaturated material such as natural rubber. As might be expected with such a powerful oxidant, the rate of reaction of ozone with an olefin is almost instantaneous. Until now this has prevented any systematic investigation of the reaction mechanism.

The products of ozone attack on an olefin are quite well known though often complex. In fact, ozonolysis (i.e. combined ozone attack followed, often inevitably, by hydrolysis) is one of the most powerful investigational tools for the distribution of unsaturation in organic molecules.[81] Harries pictured the initial product of ozone attack on a double bond as follows: [82]

$$>C=C< \xrightarrow{\text{O}_3} \quad >C \underset{|}{\quad} C< $$
$$O-O-O$$

However, Staudinger's formula,[83]

$$>C \overset{O-O}{\underset{O}{<\quad>}} C<$$

is now generally accepted as being more in accord with the hydrolysis and decomposition products of ozonides.

This formula poses some very problematical questions of mechanism.

1. The σ carbon–carbon bond must be broken without the molecule " falling into two pieces ".

2. The ozone molecule is also severed.

The most likely mechanism for ozone attack is as follows,

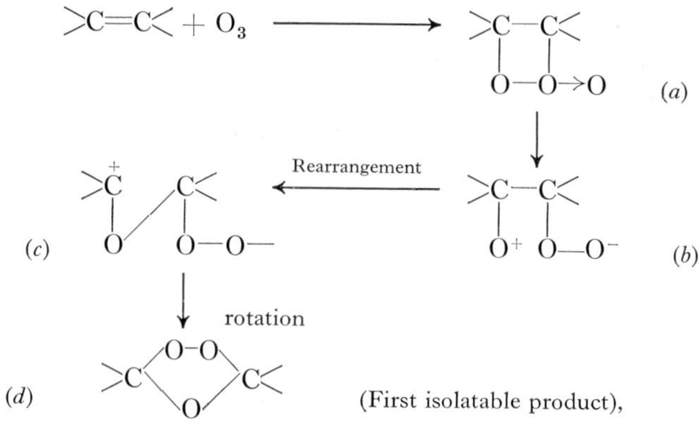

(First isolatable product),

although the initial *cis*-addition of the ozone molecule is contrary to the usual *trans*-addition at double bonds.

This mechanism is substantiated by the work of Criegee and his co-workers,[84] who showed that by choosing a compound, 9 : 10-octalin (XXXVIII), where the rearrangement and rotational stages of the above scheme are sterically impossible, a new type of ozonide (XXXIX) was formed:

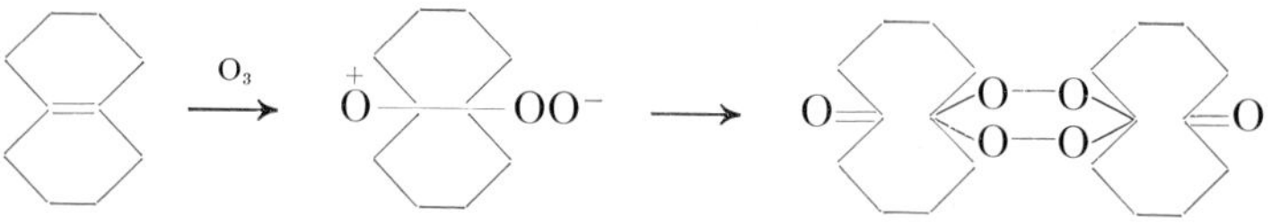

(XXXVIII)   (XXXIX)

Even if the mechanism of ozone attack on olefins is ever established, the crucial question (*a*) why does ozone cause *cracking*? and (*b*) why is simultaneous stress necessary? will still have to be answered. After all, many chemicals will attack the double bond, but none produces the type of cracking characteristic of ozone.

The problem would, in all probability, then resolve itself into one of surface chemistry. Kendall and Mann [85] have shown by infra-red spectroscopy that the reaction is confined to a very thin layer of the order of 200 Å thick. Knowledge of the physical properties of this ozonide film may be all important, as the following speculative picture shows. The ozonide film may be impermeable to ozone, and if brittle in nature will crack on stretching. The fresh rubber surface formed by cracking will further react with the ozone. Since the stress is concentrated at the bottom of cracks, a crack once initiated will then tend to grow as continuously fresh surface is exposed.

Other explanations in terms of the stress preventing radical recombination have been presented.[86] On this picture, however, the addition of antioxidants should strongly enhance cracking, although in practice they usually have little effect. Furthermore, extensive work by Wibaut and his colleagues [87] indicates that ozone attack is electrophilic rather than free radical in nature.

The concept of strain energy weakening the chemical bonds has been repeatedly rejected on the grounds that the strain energy is infinitesimal compared with bond energies. Strains, however, are anything but uniform at the molecular level, and the occasional presence of a highly strained bond may be sufficient to cause cracking. This aspect may be significant at the rearrangement stage of ozone attack ($b \rightarrow c$), where the transition state must cause considerable weakening of the bonds. Physical strain may be sufficient to cause rupture of the molecule at this stage and thus incipient cracking.

Autoxidation of simple sulphides

In spite of the importance of this problem in relation to vulcanised rubber, it has not been investigated until recently.[88-99] The cause of this neglect is not hard to seek. Until the mode of sulphur combination in vulcanisation had been explained there could be no rational selection of model compounds. Only somewhat less recently, and by the same school, has the chemistry of vulcanisation been to some extent clarified.[93] From these studies it became apparent that saturated and Δ^2-unsaturated monosulphides would conveniently form the starting-point for fundamental studies relevant to vulcanised rubber.

Saturated sulphides [90] do not readily autoxidise, but unsaturated sulphides autoxidise generally more rapidly than simple mono-olefins. One feature, however, immediately distinguishes the autoxidation of mono-olefins and unsaturated sulphides. This is the intense inhibitory effect of the products of sulphide autoxidation which brings the autoxidation to a standstill after a percentage of reaction which varies widely from compound to compound but is usually quite small (Figs. 13.1, 13.2, 13.3, 13.4). It is also difficult to prevent a heterogeneous reaction occurring with sulphides. In fact, reproducible results cannot be obtained unless silica vessels are used. This feature, which is only mildly displayed with olefin autoxidation, may have serious implications in the deterioration chemistry of rubber vulcanisates in view of the widespread use of a variety of technological fillers.

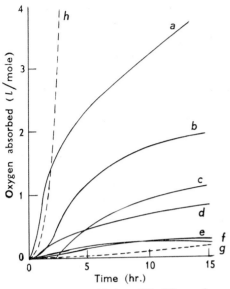

FIG. 13.1. Autoxidation of Bu^{n}SR at 75°.

R = (a) CHPh:CH·CH$_2$·, (b) CHMe:CH·CHMe·, (c) CH$_2$:CH·CHMe·, (d) CHMe:CH·CH$_2$·, (f) CH$_2$:CH·CH$_2$·. *Curves (e), (g), and (h) refer to diallyl sulphide, methyl oleate, and ethyl linoleate respectively.*

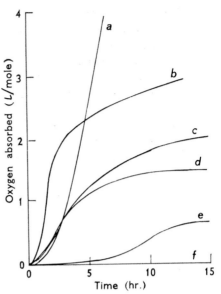

FIG. 13.2. Autoxidation of CHMe:CH·CHMe·SR at 75°.

R = (a) Ph, (b) Me, (c) Bu^n, (d) Pr^n, (e) Pr^i, (f) Bu^t (*no uptake*).

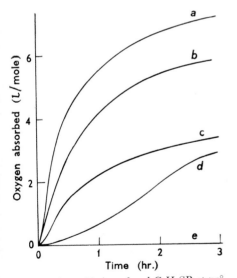

FIG. 13.3. Autoxidation of *cyclo*C$_6$H$_9$SR at 75°.

R = (a) Me, (b) Et, (c) Ph, (d) Pr^i, (e) Bu^t (*no uptake*).

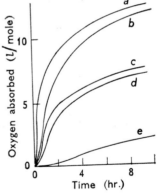

FIG. 13.4. Autoxidation of unsaturated cyclic sulphides at 55°.

(a) 2-*Methyl*-5-iso*propylthiacyclopent-2-ene.*
(b) 2-*Methylthiacyclohex-2-ene.*
(c) *Thiacyclohex-2-ene.*
(d) *Thiacyclohex-3-ene.*
(e) 2 : 3-*Dimethylthiacyclohex-2-ene.*

The rate of autoxidation of allylic sulphides is remarkably sensitive to substitution in the allylic grouping (Fig. 13.1), but although of greater magnitude, is similar to the effect of substitution in simple olefins.[36]   In allylene–alkyl sulphides substitution in the alkyl grouping also has a powerful effect on the rate of autoxidation (Fig. 13.2, 13.3).   Cyclic sulphides autoxidise much more rapidly than acyclic sulphides (Fig. 13.4) and show less auto-inhibition.

The autoxidation of organic sulphides displays all the characteristic features of a free-radical-chain reaction.   Thus the reaction is catalysed by the free-radical-generating molecule $\alpha\alpha'$-azoisobutyronitrile.   Surprisingly, however, the reaction is not catalysed by peroxides or hydroperoxides, but ultra-violet light considerably accelerates it.   Furthermore, the usual rubber antioxidants have a strongly inhibitory effect on the autoxidation.

The rate of autoxidation of an allylic sulphide is so large compared with that of a mono olefin, that double activation of the α-methylenic hydrogen atom (i.e. by the double bond and by the sulphur atom) appears likely and comparable with ethyl linoleate, where two double bonds activate the α-methylenic hydrogen atom.   Bateman and Cuneen[90] have proposed with some reserve the following scheme to account for the autoxidation of organic sulphides.

$$\text{CHR}=\text{CH}-\text{CH}_2-\text{S}-\text{R}' \xrightarrow{-\text{H}} \text{CHR}=\text{CH}-\overset{\bullet}{\text{C}}\text{H}-\text{S}-\text{R}' \quad . \quad . \quad (1)$$

$$\text{CHR}=\text{CH}-\overset{\bullet}{\text{C}}\text{H}-\text{S}-\text{R}' + \text{O}_2 \longrightarrow \text{CHR}=\text{CH}-\underset{|}{\text{CH}}-\text{S}-\text{R}' \quad . \quad . \quad (2)$$
$$\text{O}-\text{O}\cdot$$

$$\text{CHR}=\text{CH}-\underset{|}{\text{CH}}-\text{S}-\text{R}' + \text{CHR}=\text{CH}-\text{CH}_2-\text{S}-\text{R}' \quad . \quad . \quad (3)$$
$$\text{O}-\text{O}\cdot$$

$$\text{CHR}=\text{CH}-\underset{|}{\text{CH}}-\text{S}-\text{R}' + \text{CHR}=\text{CH}-\overset{\bullet}{\text{C}}\text{H}-\text{S}-\text{R}'$$
$$\text{O}-\text{OH}$$

$$\text{CHR}=\text{CH}-\underset{|}{\text{CH}}-\text{S}-\text{R}' \longrightarrow \text{CHR}=\text{CH}-\underset{|}{\text{CH}}-\text{S}-\text{R}' + \text{OH}\cdot \quad (4)$$
$$\text{O}-\text{OH} \qquad\qquad\qquad \text{O}\cdot$$

$$\text{CHR}=\text{CH}-\text{CH}_2-\text{S}-\text{R}' + \text{OH}\cdot \longrightarrow \text{CHR}=\text{CH}-\overset{\bullet}{\text{C}}\text{H}-\text{S}-\text{R}' + \text{H}_2\text{O} \quad (5)$$

$$\text{CHR}=\text{CH}-\underset{|}{\text{CH}}-\text{S}-\text{R}' \longrightarrow \text{CHR}=\text{CH}\cdot\text{CHO} + \text{R}'-\text{S}\cdot \quad . \quad (6)$$
$$\text{O}\cdot$$

$$2\text{R}'-\text{S}\cdot \longrightarrow \text{R}_2\text{S}_2 \quad . \quad . \quad . \quad . \quad . \quad . \quad . \quad (7)$$

In many instances substantial yields of sulphoxide are formed, but the above scheme does not explain this.

Bateman and Hargrave [89] have shown, however, that hydroperoxides can rapidly oxidise sulphides to sulphoxides thus—

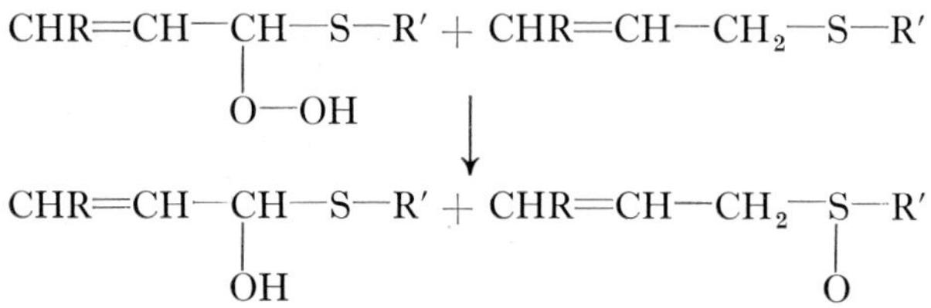

$$CHR{=}CH{-}\underset{\underset{O-OH}{|}}{CH}{-}S{-}R' + CHR{=}CH{-}CH_2{-}S{-}R'$$

$$\downarrow$$

$$CHR{=}CH{-}\underset{\underset{OH}{|}}{CH}{-}S{-}R' + CHR{=}CH{-}CH_2{-}\underset{\underset{O}{|}}{S}{-}R'$$

This reaction appears deceptively simple in mechanism. In polar solvents it is quantitative, but the solvent can be shown to play an important role [88]

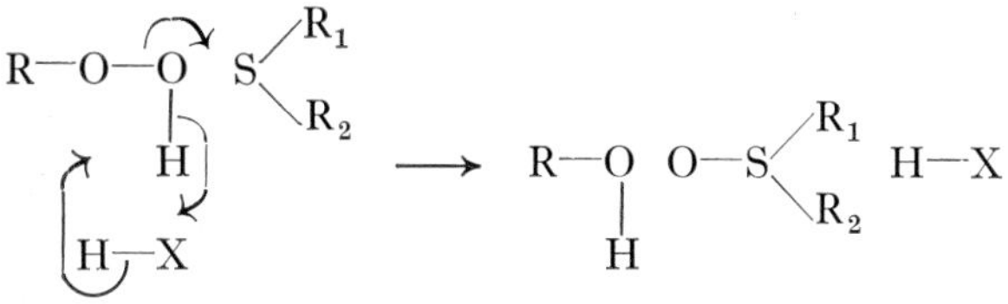

where HX is the solvent.

In non-polar solvents some hydroperoxides (e.g. Δ^2-cyclohexenyl hydroperoxide) also react quantitatively to give sulphoxide. Here a further molecule of the hydroperoxide appears to fulfil the role of the solvent in polar solutions

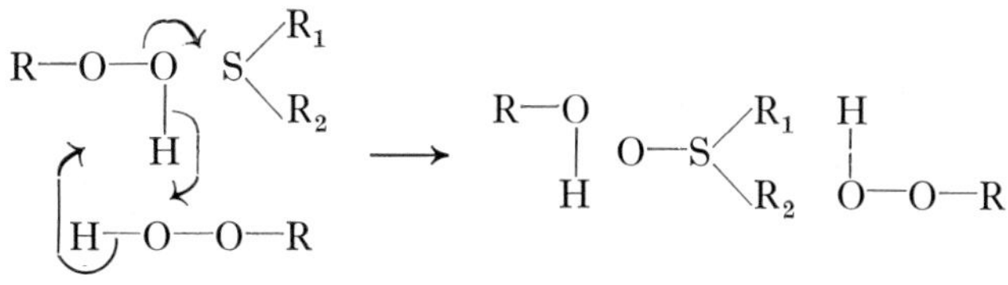

Other hydroperoxides (e.g. *tert*-butyl hydroperoxide) undergo a much more complicated reaction with organic sulphides in non-polar media. Thus the reaction becomes catalysed by oxygen and the reaction is no longer bimolecular. The acidity of the hydroperoxide appears to determine whether the reaction will be of the above simple type (where a further molecule of the hydroperoxide fulfils the role of the solvent in polar systems) or whether the complicated behaviour will be characteristic of *tert*-butyl hydroperoxide in non-polar solvents.

This latter behaviour exhibits free radical characteristics so that the formation of sulphoxide in the autoxidation of allylic sulphides may occur as follows:

$$CHR{=}CH{-}\underset{\underset{O{-}O\cdot}{|}}{CH}{-}S{-}R' + CHR{=}CH{-}CH_2{-}S{-}R'$$

$$\downarrow$$

$$CHR{=}CH{-}\underset{\underset{O\cdot}{|}}{CH}{-}S{-}R' + CHR{=}CH{-}CH_2{-}\underset{\underset{O}{\downarrow}}{S}{-}R'$$

$$CHR{=}CH{-}\underset{\underset{O\cdot}{|}}{CH}{-}S{-}R' + CHR{=}CH{-}CH_2{-}S{-}R'$$

$$\downarrow$$

$$CHR{=}CH{-}\underset{\underset{OH}{|}}{CH}{-}S{-}R' + CHR{=}CH{-}\overset{\cdot}{C}H{-}S{-}R'$$

The scheme above does not provide any clear reason for the strong auto-inhibition observed in the autoxidation of allylic sulphides. In a subsequent paper Bateman and Shipley [91] obtained evidence for the formation of the following compounds, as well as those already expected, in the autoxidation of cyclohex-2-enyl methyl sulphide,

also possibly

Therefore the following additional reactions were postulated:

The compounds

were synthesised and found to have a powerful inhibitory action on the autoxidation, thus explaining the powerful auto-inhibitory nature of the autoxidation kinetics of organic sulphides.

It is evident that the autoxidation of simple organic monosulphides is considerably more complicated than that of simple mono olefins, and many new kinetic features arise. This should discourage the all too commonplace attempts to fit the observed features of the ageing of sulphur vulcanisates into the autoxidation scheme of simple olefins. Although they are possible, by the exercise of speculative ingenuity, comparisons of this type are obviously meaningless.

At the time of writing the autoxidation of organic sulphides is still being studied, but the study must be based on more rubber-like structures and polysulphide linkages, before they can be applied to rubber vulcanisates. Even then, considerable reserve may be necessary because reactions of minor chemical significance may be all important in determining the physical significance of cross-linking and scission processes.

Model compounds for synthetic rubbers

The model compounds discussed so far are relevant to the ageing of synthetic rubbers if these have structural features in common. Thus butadiene–styrene copolymers (e.g. SBR) have hydrogen atoms in the α-methylenic position to double bonds and may be expected to exhibit similar autoxidative reactivity to natural rubber.

Many of the modern synthetics have been " tailor made " with very slow ageing as the goal. In this class are neoprene, silicone rubbers, urethane rubbers, chloro-sulphonated polyethylene, Butyl rubber and plasticised polyvinyl chloride. The thermal ageing properties of these are generally so good that even if good model compounds could be selected, they would autoxidise too slowly for convenient measurement at temperatures comparable with those used under service conditions. At considerably higher temperatures autoxidation could no doubt be induced, but the mechanism in all probability would be completely different. Virtually the whole of this chapter has been concerned with one elastomer, natural rubber, and this being so, one can understand the reluctance of workers to study the multitude of synthetic elastomers in anything like the same detail. Furthermore, the failings of these synthetic elastomers do not lie in their ageing properties but rather in one or other of their physical or chemical characteristics. Thus the low tensile strength of silicone rubbers, the difficult processing of Butyl rubber and the awkward moulding of polyvinyl chloride have stimulated more research than their ageing properties.

In oxidative stability SBR compares with natural rubber, and some fundamental studies have been made.[94-96] Some of the structures which can occur in SBR are represented in the hypothetical unit

$$-CH-CH_2-CH_2-CH=CH-CH_2-CH-CH_2-CH-CH_2-$$

(with phenyl substituents on the first and third $-CH-$ groups, and on the final $-CH-$ group: CH double-bonded to CH_2)

Shelton and his co-workers studied various molecules having structural features in common with this hypothetical unit (XL–XLII)

$$\text{C}_6\text{H}_{11}-CH_2-CH_2-CH=CH-CH_3 \qquad (XL)$$

$$\text{C}_6\text{H}_{11}-CH_2-CH_2-CH_2-CH=CH-CH_3 \qquad (XLI)$$

$$\text{C}_6\text{H}_{11}-CH_2-CH_2-CH-CH=CH_2 \qquad (XLII)$$
$$\qquad\qquad\qquad\qquad\quad CH_3$$

These workers showed that the main products of XL on autoxidation were hydroperoxides, ketones and esters. The ketone and hydroperoxide oxygen rose to a maximum early in the reaction and then declined. The ester oxygen content continuously rose. It was concluded that a hydroperoxide was the initial product, which then broke down, mainly to ketone. This in turn was further oxidised to esters.

Saturated polymers autoxidised thermally very slowly indeed. Wibaut [97] has shown the low-temperature autoxidation of paraffins to be similar to olefins, with the point of attack being favoured in the increasing order primary C< secondary C< tertiary C provided steric hindrance does not intervene. In n-paraffins, owing to the similar reactivity at many carbon atoms, a multiplicity of products is obtained.

Polythene, although expectedly inert to thermal autoxidation, is very susceptible to photochemical autoxidation, and this appears to be due to the presence of ketonic impurities in the polymer chains which photosensitise the polymer to autoxidation.[98]

Fundamental studies on polymers

The distinction between fundamental and applied studies on polymers is arbitrary. This section is devoted to studies capable of reasonable interpretation at the molecular level.

The absorption of oxygen by polyene polymers is autocatalytic, but is often preceded by a short phase of auto-inhibition. Unvulcanised rubber autoxidises with the production of hydroperoxides,[12] and vulcanised rubber gives similar oxygen absorption curves. In view, however, of the complexities of sulphide autoxidation, it is unwise at present to infer reactions similar to simple olefins from oxygen-absorption studies on sulphur vulcanisates, even though the oxygen absorption curves have features of similarity. One feature of dissimilarity between unvulcanised natural rubber and simple olefins is that the rate of oxygen absorption of natural rubber is dependent on the pressure of oxygen. The exact reason for this is not clear, but may be due to the retardation of termination reactions in viscous media such as rubber.

Comparisons between simple olefins and natural rubber are also rendered uncertain because of natural impurities in the latter which are difficult to remove.

During autoxidation both cross-linking and scission reactions take place simultaneously. Depending on the balance between these two types of reaction, the polymer will either soften or harden during autoxidation. These changes in the average molecule weight between cross-links are reflected in the solubility of an initially unvulcanised polymer and in the equilibrium swelling of a vulcanised polymer. These properties have been used to follow the net effect of these aggregative and disaggregative reactions,[99-101] but care is necessary to avoid further degradation during the process of solution or swelling.

According to the theory of rubber elasticity the stress–strain relationship

$$f = SkT\left\{\frac{l}{lu} - \left(\frac{lu}{l}\right)^2\right\}$$

holds for a vulcanisate,

where f = stress (calculated in original cross-section);
lu = unstretched length;
l = stretched length;
T = absolute temperature;
k = Boltzmann constant;
S = number of network chains per c.c.

This formula applies, however, only after the relatively weak non-valency forces between chains have had time to relax, and at room temperature this can take considerable time. The ordinary rubber testing machine gives anything but a static test. In principle, the above formula suggests several ways of following the changes in physical properties of elastomers on ageing:

(a) At constant length the changes in stress may be followed (stress relaxation).

(b) At constant stress the change in length may be followed (creep).

(c) The stress produced by a given elongation after various ageing intervals may be followed (removing the strain in between tests).

(d) The elongation produced by a given stress may be followed under the same conditions as in (c).

It must be stated again, however, that unless the relaxation time of non-valency forces between polymer chains is small compared with the time of testing and unless negligible ageing takes place during this test time, no reliable conclusions can be drawn about the cross-linking and scission which have taken place. Unfortunately this reservation has not always been appreciated, and much confusion has resulted.

With these reservations, observations of type (a) above are a measure of original cross-links which have become severed, since any new cross-links formed are formed in their equilibrium position and do not therefore support stress. The intermittent observations of types (a) and (b) above are a measure of the total degree of cross-linking in the polymer at any time. A combination of continuous stress relaxation and intermittent measurement should therefore provide a measure of the relative amounts of cross-linking and scission which take place on ageing.[102-105]

In its simplest form, S in the above equation is taken to undergo unimolecular decay

$$S = S_0 l^{-k_1 t}$$

where $S_0 = S$ at time $(t) = 0$ and k_1 is the rate coefficient. Under conditions (a) above, substitution in the rubber elasticity equation leads to

$$f = f_0 l^{-k_1 t}$$

At low temperatures the relaxation time of non-valency forces between polymer chains causes a marked deviation from this equation in the early stages. This can also be caused by the early scission of easily degraded cross-links.

The above theory can be refined to include specific cross-link scission, random and specific cross-linking and random and specific chain scission.[106]

The future holds considerable promise that physical studies of this type combined with refined mathematics and chemical research will shed much light on the complexities of rubber ageing.

Fundamental and applied studies conclusions

It is interesting to speculate how many of the researches quoted in this chapter would have been conducted if the complex nature of rubber ageing had been as evident 20 years ago as it is today. The initial choice of model compounds was naturally the simplest. With each additional complexity of structure the complexities of reactions and kinetics have manifoldly increased.

New accelerators and antioxidants have been introduced, though mainly by trial and error, which have considerably improved the physical properties and ageing resistance of natural rubber. In the future the use of metal sequestrants, formulated on principles derived from fundamental work, and light stabilisers may be expected to become common practice. Of these the mode of action of light stabilisers is virtually unknown. It is not simply that they absorb light. Since on this basis there is no distinction between stabilisers and sensitisers. Fundamental studies on the primary action of light, in initiating reaction chains, are woefully inadequate to give a clear picture of energy transfers within a molecule after it has absorbed a quantum of light.

The cost of fundamental research, if pursued vigorously, is very high. Unless fundamental research *is* pursued vigorously, it is not worthwhile. Even then, it is hard to estimate its value. Taken over all industry, it is of inestimable value, if not to the sponsor then to someone else, and, if not today, then tomorrow.

REFERENCES

1. Dufraisse, C. (1937) *Chemistry and Technology of Rubber*, ed. C. C. Davis and J. T. Blake, p. 440 (N.Y.: Reinhold); Markley, (1947) *Fatty Acids* (N.Y.: Interscience).
2. Criegge, R., Pilz, H. and Flygare, H. (1939) *Ber.*, **72**, 1799.
3. Hock, H. and Neurwirth, A. (1939) *Ber.*, **72**, 1562.
4. Farmer, E. H. (1942) *Trans. Faraday Soc.*, **38**, 340.
5. Farmer, E. H., Bloomfield, G. F., Sundralingham, A. and Sutton, D. A. (1942) *Trans. Faraday Soc.*, **38**, 348.
6. Farmer, E. H. and Sutton, D. A. (1942) *J. chem. Soc.*, 116.
7. Farmer, E. H. and Sundralingham, A. (1942) *J. chem. Soc.*, 121.
8. Farmer, E. H. and Sutton, D. A. (1942) *J. chem. Soc.*, 139.
9. Farmer, E. H. and Narracott, E. S. (1942) *J. chem. Soc.*, 185.
10. Farmer, E. H. and Michael, S. E. (1942) *J. chem. Soc.*, 513.
11. Farmer, E. H. and Sutton, D. A. (1943) *J. chem. Soc.*, 119.
12. Farmer, E. H. and Sundralingham, A. (1943) *J. chem. Soc.*, 125.
13. Bloomfield, G. F. (1943) *J. chem. Soc.*, 356.
14. Farmer, E. H., Koch, H. P. and Sutton, D. A. (1943) *J. chem. Soc.*, 541.
15. Sutton, D. A. (1944) *J. chem. Soc.*, 242.
16. Bateman, L. and Koch, H. P. (1944) *J. chem. Soc.*, 600.
17. Farmer, E. H. (1945–46) *I.R.I. Trans.*, **21**, 122.
18. Bolland, J. L. and Koch, H. P. (1945) *J. chem. Soc.*, 445.
19. Farmer, E. H. (1946) *Trans. Faraday Soc.*, **42**, 228.
20. Farmer, E. H. and Sutton, D. A. (1946) *J. chem. Soc.*, 10.
21. Bolland, J. L. and Hughes, H. (1949) *J. Chem. Soc.*, 492.
22. Bateman, L. (1945–46) *I.R.I. Trans.*, **21**, 118.
23. Bolland, J. L. and Orr, W. J. C. (1945–46) *I.R.I. Trans.*, **21**, 133.
24. Bolland, J. L. and Gee, G. (1946) *Trans. Faraday Soc.*, **42**, 236.

25. Bolland, J. L. (1946) *Proc. Roy. Soc. A.*, **186**, 218.
26. Gee, G. (1946) *Trans. Faraday Soc.*, **42**, 268.
27. Bolland, J. L. and Ten Have, P. (1947) *Trans. Faraday Soc.*, **43**, 201.
28. Bateman, L. (1947) *J. Polymer Res.*, **2**, 1.
29. Bolland, J. L. and Ten Have, P. (1947) *Disc. Faraday Soc.*, No. 2, 252.
30. Bateman, L. and Bolland, J. L. (1947) *Proc. int. Congr. Pure and Applied Chem.* (*London*), **11**, 325.
31. Bolland, J. L. (1948) *Trans. Faraday Soc.*, **44**, 669.
32. Bateman, L. and Gee, G. (1948) *Proc. roy. Soc. A.*, **195**, 376.
33. Bateman, L. and Gee, G. (1948) *Proc. roy. Soc. A.*, **195**, 391.
34. Bolland, J. L. and Ten Have, P. (1949) *Trans. Faraday Soc.*, **45**, 93.
35. Bolland, J. L. (1949) *Quart. Rev.*, **3**, 1.
36. —— (1950) *Trans. Faraday Soc.*, **46**, 358.
37. Bateman, L., Bolland, J. L. and Gee, G. (1951) *Trans. Faraday Soc.*, **47**, 338.
38. Bateman, L., Gee, G., Morris, A. L. and Watson, W. F. (1951) *Disc. Faraday Soc.*, No. 10, 250.
39. Bateman, L. and Morris, A. L. (1952) *Trans. Faraday Soc.*, **48**, 1149.
40. Bateman, L. and Hughes, E. H. (1952) *J. chem. Soc.*, 4594.
41. Bateman, L. and Morris, A. L. (1953) *Trans. Faraday Soc.*, **49**, 1026.
42. Bateman, L., Hughes, H. and Morris, A. L. (1953) *Disc. Faraday Soc.*, No. 14, 190.
43. Bateman, L. (1954) *Quart. Rev.*, **8**, 147.
44. Hargrave, K. R. and Morris, A. L. (1956) *Trans. Faraday Soc.*, **52**, 89.
45. Barnard, D. and Hargrave, K. R. (1951) *Analyt. chim. acta*, **5**, 476.
46. Kern, W., Heinz, A. R. and Stallman, J. (1955) *Makromol. Chem.*, **16**, 21.
47. Swern, D., Knight, H. B., Scanlan, J. T. and Ault, W. C. (1945) *J. Amer. chem. Soc.*, **67**, 1132.
48. Chalk, A. J. and Smith, J. F. (1957) *Trans. Faraday Soc.*, **53**, 1214.
49. Russell, G. A. (1955) *J. Amer. chem. Soc.*, **77**, 4583.
50. Burnett, G. M. and Melville, H. W. (1954) *Chem. Rev.*, **54**, 225.
51. Dunn, J. R. and Waters, W. A. (1953) *J. chem. Soc.*, 2993.
52. Bickel, A. F. and Kooyman, E. C. (1956) *J. chem. Soc.*, 2215.
53. Moore, R. F. and Waters, W. A. (1954) *J. chem. Soc.*, 243.
54. Bickel, A. F. and Kooyman, E. C. (1953) *J. chem. Soc.*, 3211.
55. Boozer, C. E. and Hammond, G. S. (1954) *J. Amer. chem. Soc.*, **76**, 3861.
56. Shelton, J. R. and Cox, W. L. (1953) *Ind. Eng. Chem.*, **45**, 392.
57. Smith, J. F. and Bevan, M. A.   R.A.B.R.M. unpublished work.
58. Weiss, J. (1952) *Advances in Catalysis*, **4**, 343 (N.Y.: Academic Press Inc.).
59. Baxendale, J. H. (1952) *Advances in Catalysis*, **4**, 31 (N.Y.: Academic Press Inc.).
60. Kharasch, M. S., Fono, A. and Nudenberg, W. (1950) *J. Org. Chem.*, **15**, 748, 763.
61. Kharasch, M. S., Fono, A. and Nudenberg, W. (1951) *J. Org. Chem.*, **16**, 128.
62. Kharasch, M. S., Fono, A., Nudenberg, W. and Bischof, B. (1952) *J. Org. Chem.*, **17**, 207.
63. Orr, R. J. and Williams, H. L. (1953) *J. phys. Chem.*, **57**, 925.
64. —— and —— (1954) *J. Amer. chem. Soc.*, **76**, 3321.
65. Fordham, J. W. L. and Williams, H. L. (1950) *J. Amer. chem. Soc.*, **72**, 4465.
66. —— and —— (1950) *Canad. J. Res.*, **28**B, 551.
67. —— and —— (1951) *J. Amer. chem. Soc.*, **73**, 1634.
68. Wise, W. S. and Twigg, G. H. (1953) *J. chem. Soc.*, 2172.
69. Hawkins, E. G. E. and Young, D. P. (1950) *J. chem. Soc.*, 2804.
70. Kolthoff, I. M. and Medalia, A. I. (1949) *J. Amer. chem. Soc.*, **71**, 3789.
71. Robertson, A. and Waters, W. A. (1948) *J. chem. Soc.*, 1578.
72. George, P. and Robertson, A. (1946) *J. Inst. Petrol.*, **32**, 382.
73. —— and —— (1946) *Trans. Faraday Soc.*, **42**, 217.

74. Banks, G. L., Chalk, A. J., Dawson, J. E. and Smith, J. F. (1954) *Nature*, **174**, 274.
75. Kern, W. and Willersinn, H. (1955) *Makromol. Chem.*, **15**, 6.
76. Bawn, C. E. H., Pennington, A. H. and Tipper, C. F. H. (1951) *Disc. Faraday Soc.*, **10**, 282.
77. Smith, R. L. (1956) *Chem. & Ind. Rev.* 320.
78. Chalk, A. J. and Smith, J. F. (1956) *Chem. & Ind. Rev.*, 462.
79. —— and —— (1957) *Trans. Faraday Soc.*, **53**, 1235.
80. Newton, R. G. (1945) *J. Rubb. Res.*, **14**, 27.
81. Harries, C. D. (1916) *Untersuchung uber das ozon und seine Anwirkung auf organische Verbindungen* (Berlin: J. Springer).
82. Long, L. (1940) *Chem. Rev.*, **27**, 437.
83. Staudinger, H. (1925) *Ber.*, **58**, 1088.
84. Criegee, R. (1950) *Fortschr chem. Forsch.*, **1**, 527; Criegee, R. and Wenner, G. (1949) *Ann.*, **564**, 9.
85. Kendall, F. H. and Mann, J. (1956) *J. Polymer Sci.*, **19**, 503.
86. Smith, D. M. and Gaugh, V. E. (1953) *I.R.I. Trans.*, **29**, 219.
87. Wibaut, J. P., Sixma, F. L. J., Kampschmidt, L. W. F. and Boer, H. (1950) *Rec. Trav. chim.*, **69**, 1355.
88. Bateman, L. and Hargrave, K. R. (1954) *Proc. roy. Soc. A.*, **224**, 389.
89. —— and —— (1954) *Proc. roy. Soc. A.*, **224**, 399.
90. Bateman, L. and Cuneen, J. I. (1955) *J. chem. Soc.*, 1596.
91. Bateman, L. and Shipley, F. W. (1955) *J. chem. Soc.*, 1996.
92. Barnard, D. (1956) *J. chem. Soc.*, 489.
93. Bateman, L. C., Glazebrook, R. W., Moore, C. G. and Saville, R. W. (1954) *Proc. Third Rubb. Technol. Conf. London*, 298.
94. Mitchell, G. R. and Shelton, J. R. (1953) *Ind. Eng. Chem.*, **45**, 386.
95. Lawrence, J. W. and Shelton, J. R. (1950) *Ind. Eng. Chem.*, **42**, 136.
96. Warner, W. C. and Shelton, J. R. (1951) *Ind. Eng. Chem.*, **43**, 1160.
97. Wibaut, J. P. and Strang, A. (1952) *Proc. Koninkl Ned. Akad. Wetenschap*, **55**, 207.
98. Pross, A. W. and Black, R. M. (1950) *J. Soc. Chem. Ind.*, **69**, 113.
99. Cole, J. O. and Field, J. E. (1947) *Ind. Eng. Chem.*, **39**, 174.
100. Halpern, J. and Winkler, C. A. (1950) *Canad. J. Chem.*, **28**, 5.
101. Coffman, J. A. (1952) *Ind. Eng. Chem.*, **44**, 1421.
102. Tobolsky, A. V., Metz, D. J. and Mesrobian, R. B. (1950) *J. Amer. chem. Soc.*, **72**, 1942.
103. Tobolsky, A. V., Prettyman, I. B. and Dillon, J. H. (1944) *J. appl. Phys.*, **15**, 380.
104. Tobolsky, A. V. and Andrews, R. D. (1945) *J. chem. Phys.*, **13**, 3.
105. Andrews, R. D., Hofman-Bang, N. and Tobolsky, A. V. (1948) *J. Polymer Sci.*, **3**, 669.
106. Berry, J. P. and Watson, W. F. (1955) *J. Polymer Sci.*, **18**, 201.
107. Horne, S. E., Kiehl, J. P., Shipman, J. J., Folt, V. L., Gibbs, C. F., Wilson, E. A., Newton, E. B., Reinhart, M. A. (1956) *Ind. Eng. Chem.*, 784.

CHAPTER XIII

PART TWO

PRACTICAL AGEING

by

J. M. BUIST

ENGINEERS and architects now realise that rubber-like polymers can be used as constructional materials in machinery and buildings, despite the fact that they have long tended to think first of metals, stone, brick, asphalt and cement as their basic raw materials. These prejudices, however, are beginning to diminish, since engineers in the automobile and aircraft industries have come to rely on rubber parts.

Successful performance in these applications gives designers the necessary confidence to consider rubber parts for other tasks, and a great deal of experimental work is being done throughout many industries.

With each new development the question, " How long will this rubber component last?" must be answered. The answer, however, is seldom a simple one, for the reasons given in the earlier part of this chapter. The life of a rubber article is obviously governed not only by the type of rubber used and the quality of the rubber article employed but also by the service conditions. Under certain conditions some synthetic rubbers can perform satisfactorily for longer periods than natural rubber—for example, at high temperatures or in the presence of oil. The qualities of a rubber article are legion, and can be varied to produce an infinite balance of properties: tensile strength, hardness, resilience and abrasion resistance. This balance of properties will change with age, and it is the understanding of the correct balance of qualities required by a particular application and the various methods of retaining or prolonging that balance which makes this field of study so important to both the rubber compounder and the rubber user.

Service data, obtained under conditions where the effects of oxygen, ozone, heat, light, etc., have been produced simultaneously, are sparse, but interesting information on the longevity of natural rubber articles has been published.[1] These authors divide rubber applications into three classes:

(*a*) relatively static with little wear, e.g. tank linings, cables, jointings;

(*b*) static with heavy wear, e.g. hot-water bottles, rubberised clothing, hose, flooring, and roads;

(*c*) dynamic wear, e.g. vibration mountings, springs, shock absorbers, belting, tyres.

From the point of view of durability the last class would be expected to have the shortest life.   It is stated in this paper that rubber railway buffer springs are expected to have a life of 12 years, rubber-covered rollers in use for 25 years in America were still giving satisfactory service, rubber paving was in good condition after 30 years, rubber flooring laid in 1898 was still good.   These examples, and that of a tyre which was serviceable after 23 years, illustrate that natural rubber articles can be made to have a long life.   Information on the life of synthetic rubber articles is naturally of shorter duration, but some claims made for synthetic rubber articles, lasting 20 years appear to be substantiated.[2]   The lack of precise and comprehensive data obtained over long periods in service is a great handicap for the technologist who is forced to extrapolate from data obtained under laboratory conditions.   Normally in the laboratory the test conditions are chosen in such a way that the effect of oxygen, ozone, heat, light, stress, etc., are controlled, and frequently attempts are made to study each of these factors independently.   The difficulties associated with studying each factor independently have been discussed,[3] and it has been pointed out that although the general effects of these factors are known, the technologist cannot yet integrate them and forecast with assurance the life of a rubber article under service conditions.   In other words, this field is still one where the methods used are empirical, and the successful extrapolations which have been made in the case of many new rubber applications should not be allowed to encourage complacency.

The rail-pad application demands that rubber compounds be made to pass a stringent specification [4] containing clauses for compression modulus and compression set.   It has been suggested that rail pads should have a life of the order of 20 years, but there is no adequate clause in the specification to enable the life to be assessed.   It is doubtful whether sufficient long-term service data exists to enable such a clause to be drafted.   Certainly there is no published data available to show that after x years a compound is performing satisfactorily although the compression modulus has increased by $y\%$ and the compression set increased to $z\%$.   A similar unsatisfactory state of affairs exists in many other new applications.

The position with established applications, e.g. tyres, is still highly empirical but not so unsatisfactory, since it is known with certainty that some compounds have a satisfactory long life.   The performance of these compounds under controlled accelerated ageing conditions is also known, and new compounds, normally, must have a performance equal to or better than the established compounds under accelerated ageing conditions before they are selected for fuller evaluation in wheel tests and road tests. In this way accelerated ageing tests are used as " screening " or " sorting " tests and perform a useful function, but their value would be further enhanced if a closer correlation with service could be established.

Types of ageing

Recently the writer [3] classified the various ageing processes to which rubbers are subject and suggested that in all 6 categories the fundamental reaction responsible for ageing is always the same, namely the oxidation of the rubber hydrocarbon by oxygen, but in each case the reaction is " triggered " or activated by a different force, different in nature and magnitude. This classification is given in Table 13.1.

TABLE 13.1

CLASSIFICATION OF TYPES OF AGEING

Type of ageing	Activating force
1. Shelf ageing or " normal " oxidation	No activation (in the ideal case)
2. Metallic poisoning	Catalytic activation
3. Heat ageing	Thermal activation
4. Light ageing	Photo activation
5. Flexcracking	Mechanical activation
6. Atmospheric cracking	Molecular activation

In the Monograph on Ageing and Weathering [3] the author points out that this classification is clearly an over-simplification, but nevertheless the scheme has the basic merit of covering the known facts and at the same time suggests two possible means of preserving rubber from deterioration, either by inhibiting or retarding the basic oxidative reaction, irrespective of the nature or magnitude of the activating force, or by " deactivating " the latter. The above classification " precludes neither the possible discovery of a counter-oxidant to combat ozone attack, nor the use of ' metal sequestering ' agents as a means of minimising the deterioration of rubber in the presence of copper and manganese ".[3] Recent work on ozone-protective agents, a field where it has hitherto been generally assumed that conventional antioxidant types were ineffective, vindicates the usefulness of the above classification.

In the case of heat ageing the changes produced in the properties of natural and synthetic rubbers are largely the sum of two effects: (1) continued vulcanisation (or cross-linking), and (2) oxidative chain breakdown, and the relative rates and magnitudes of the two effects govern the amount of change in each property. Chain breakdown usually causes a fall in modulus and an increase in breaking elongation, whereas continued cross-linking has the reverse effect. One difference between natural and synthetic rubbers is the contribution of after-vulcanisation to ageing. For example, several workers [5-8] find that after-vulcanisation is of much greater importance in the case of synthetic rubbers, such as SBR and neoprene GN, than with natural rubber. It has been claimed [9] that after-vulcanisation is of less importance when low amounts of sulphur are used with natural rubber. Equally if the curing system for natural

TABLE 13.2

HIGH-TEMPERATURE AGEING OF NATURAL RUBBER VULCANISED WITH QUINONE DIOXIME

	Compound A				Compound B	
Smoked sheet	100				100	
Zinc oxide	5				5	
Kosmos 45	50				50	
Stearic acid	1				1	
Vulcafor BQN	4				—	
Vulcafor ZDC	2				—	
Sulphur	—				2·5	
Vulcafor MBT	—				0·75	
Vulcanisation time at 141° C	45 minutes				45 minutes	
	Unaged	*1 day oven at 125° C*	*2 days oven at 125° C*	*1 week oven at 100° C*	*Unaged*	*1 week oven at 100° C*
Tensile strength, kg./cm.²	190	115	42	145	239	49
Elongation, %	470	290	183	298	520	83
Modulus, 100%	27	27	16	36	28	—
Modulus, 300%	115	124	—	97	120	—

rubber is altered radically a different balance of the after-vulcanisation and oxidative scission effects are obtained. The results [10] given in Table 13.2 show that natural rubber compounds vulcanised with quinone dioxime can be made to have high-temperature ageing resistance of the same order as many synthetic rubber compounds.

Temperature coefficients

The difficulties associated with attempts to use results of accelerated ageing tests at elevated temperatures in an effort to estimate the degree of deterioration at another temperature are well known and have recently been summarised.[3, 11] Attempts to predict long-term effects at low temperatures from the relatively short-term effects at higher temperatures have never been successful. There are several reasons for this lack of success. If one were dealing with a simple chemical reaction the Arrhenius equation could be used to calculate the effects of temperature, but the application of this equation is extremely limited, since the temperature coefficients are not constant over a wide temperature range and vary in magnitude for different compounds and for different properties. This is illustrated by data on temperature coefficients given in Table 13.3.[3]

TABLE 13.3

TEMPERATURE COEFFICIENTS

Type of polymer	Property studied	Temperature range, °C	Temperature coefficient per 10° C	Ref.
Air oven ageing:				
Natural rubber	Tensile strength and elongation	Room temp. and 70	3·21 * approx.	12
,, ,,	Stress–strain	,,	2·6–3·3 *	13
,, ,,	,, ,,	,,	2·88–3·02 *	14
,, ,,	Tensile strength and elongation	,,	2·54–4·04	15
,, ,,	Tensile strength, modulus and elongation	,,	2·77 *	16
,, ,,	Stress–strain	70–100	2·65–2·73 *	17
,, ,,	,, ,,	70–100	2·6 *	17
SBR	,, ,,	100–132	2·0	6
,,	Elongation and modulus	90–127	2·0	7
,,	Tensile strength and elongation	70–121	2·2	18
,,	Elongation and modulus	70–100	2·1	8
,,	Tensile strength, elongation, modulus and hardness	15–100	2·25	19
	Stress–strain	80–100	1·97–2·09	20
,, Nitrile	Elongation	121–149	2·0	21
Oxygen bomb ageing:				
Natural rubber⎫ Neoprene ⎬	Stress–strain	70–80	1·63–3·88	22
Natural rubber	Tensile strength	70–85 60–80 60–110	2·0 2·38 2·5	23 24 25
Natural rubber	Stress–strain	70–80	2·0–2·2	17
SBR	,, ,,	70–100	2·63–3·09	20

* Values for coefficients calculated from data published, assuming when required, a shelf ageing temperature of 26° C.

The Arrhenius equation can be used only to foretell the rate of change of a system at any temperature from the kinetics established at any other two temperatures. Implicit in the application of this equation is the assumption that the ageing curves are linear. In fact, this condition seldom applies, and it can be shown [11] that in many cases the " energy of activation " is not independent of the stage of ageing.

For example, Schoch and Juve,[26,27] who obtained extensive data with natural rubber, SBR, Butyl, neoprene GN, Hycar OR-15 and Perbunan 26 at room temperature and elevated temperatures, calculated temperature coefficients for those products which showed comparable changes at each ageing temperature. These authors conclude that " the ability to extrapolate the results of accelerated ageing tests to higher or lower temperatures depends on: (*a*) whether the accelerated test temperature and the

TABLE 13.4

DEPENDENCE OF TEMPERATURE COEFFICIENT ON DEGREE OF AGEING

Compound	Polymer	Physical property	Change in property, %	Temperature range, °C	Temperature coefficient, 10° C
I	SBR 60 minutes cure	Tensile strength	−10	100−121	2·92
			−20	100−121	2·71
		Elongation	−20	30−121	2·47
			−40	30−121	2·60
		Modulus	+60	30−121	2·43
			+100	30−121	2·59
I	SBR 90 minutes cure	Tensile strength	−10	70−121	2·62
			−20	100−121	2·95
		Elongation	−30	30−121	2·05
		Modulus	+40	25−121	2·18
			+80	25−121	2·22
II	Natural rubber 45 minutes cure	Tensile strength	−10	30−100	2·70
			−20	30−100	2·61
		Elongation	−10	30−100	2·40
			−20	30−100	2·64
III	Neoprene 45 minutes cure	Elongation	−12	30−121	2·31
		Modulus	+10	30−121	2·16
			+24	30−121	2·31
IV	GR-I 20 minutes cure	Tensile strength	−30	70−121	2·24
		Elongation	−40	70−121	2·72
	GR-I 30 minutes cure	Tensile strength	−20	70−121	2·66
		Elongation	−30	70−121	2·60
V	Nitrile 45 minutes cure	Elongation	−20	30−121	2·55
		Modulus	+30	30−121	2·55
V	Nitrile 90 minutes cure	Elongation	−20	30−121	2·52
		Modulus	+20	30−121	2·41

desired extrapolated temperature are in the range over which essentially the same deteriorating mechanisms prevail and (*b*) a knowledge of the temperature dependence of the rate limiting reaction ". Their view is that for SBR, nitrile rubbers and neoprenes extrapolation can be carried out between room temperature and 150° C; with natural rubber the temperature range would be room temperature and 100° C; with Butyl rubber, which behaves differently at each temperature, extrapolation is not possible. Recently their data has been re-examined,[11] and it is shown in Table 13.4 that the temperature coefficient is influenced by the degree of ageing, and these calculations confirm the suggestion made by the writer [3] that " the assumption often made that the same temperature co-efficient applies to a compound over a reasonably wide temperature range is unjustified ". In other words, ageing at a high temperature does not necessarily produce the same effects as ageing at a lower one.

Another important factor which must be stressed is that temperature coefficients between 2·0 and 3·0 must be determined with at least 10% accuracy for prediction of the ageing of a sample at 20° C, not to be in error by more than 50% when these predictions are estimated from data obtained at 80° C. If a temperature coefficient of 2·0–3·0 per 10° C is accepted, then a temperature tolerance of $\pm$ 1° C corresponds to a tolerance of 15–22% in the time scale. Before predictions can be made therefore it is necessary to control the temperature within close limits and determine the coefficients accurately, and even then the other factors discussed earlier may invalidate the predictions made.

Accelerated ageing tests

The six types of ageing listed in Table 13.1 have been studied by many investigators, and considerable thought has been given to the design of suitable accelerated ageing tests. It is difficult to use the accelerated ageing tests, which will be described, in a way that only one activating force is acting; in practice, unless very special precautions are taken, more than one activating force is normally acting, and the full implications of this complication are not always appreciated. One example will serve to illustrate the difficulty. It is well known that certain materials which protect rubbers against ozone attack under static exposure are not effective under dynamic stressing. Naturally attempts have been made to design suitable dynamic tests for evaluating ozone protective chemicals, but if the dynamic conditions (mechanical activation) are made severe there is a real danger that the test will not evaluate ozone cracking (molecular activation) but flexcracking (mechanical activation).

The main types of accelerated ageing tests used by the industry are:

(1) oven test developed by Geer [29] in 1916;
(2) oxygen bomb test, developed by Bierer and Davis in 1924 [30];
(3) air bomb, developed by Booth [31] in 1932;

(4) ozone test, developed by Kearsley [32] in 1930;

(5) ultra-violet tests, used by Williams [33];

(6) humidity and steam tests.[3, 34]

The degradation produced in an oven, oxygen bomb or air bomb is that of oxidation (credit should be given to Stevens,[35] 1919, for providing the first direct proof that the oxygen in the air played a part in the ageing of rubber), and the essential difference between the three methods is the rate factor. For example, it has been suggested [3, 36] that the degradation produced by years of natural shelf ageing corresponds to weeks exposure in the oven at 70° C, days exposure in the oxygen bomb at 70° C with an oxygen pressure of 300 lb./in.^{2} and to hours exposure in the air bomb at 126° C with an air pressure of 80 lb./in.^{2}

Basic precautions

Certain basic precautions [37-39] which are necessary in accelerated ageing tests, and have been accepted by Committee ISO/TC/45, are reproduced below, since all concerned with accelerated ageing tests should apply these precautions.

General

(a) After curing, all test pieces should be stored in the dark until the commencement of the accelerated ageing test.

(b) Care should be taken to ensure that the test pieces have a good, smooth finish and are free from blemishes and other flaws.

(c) Distinction should be made between different types of ageing, which should be evaluated separately.

Atmospheric or ozone cracking tests

(d) In accelerated atmospheric cracking tests exposure to ozone should be made in the dark so as to reduce skin formation and crazing; similarly, in outdoor tests the stretched rubbers should be shielded from light.

(e) In development work, compounds for evaluation by exposure to ozone or to the atmosphere should contain at least a small percentage of black to minimise the effects of incidental exposure to light.

(f) Cracking should be judged against a series of graded photographs or standard samples.

Sunlight or accelerated light tests

(g) It is unnecessary and serves no useful purpose to test the light resistance of black stocks.

(h) The rubber should be unstressed.

(i) When comparing different types of polymer for light resistance only, vulcanisates of the same colour and transparency should be used.

Note. All possible sources of variation are not covered in recommendations (*g*)–(*i*), but until further work fulfilling the above conditions has been carried out it is not possible to evaluate other factors, such as deposition of foreign matter on the surface of the test pieces, atmospheric variations (e.g. rain, temperature, etc.) or ozone (either in the outdoor atmosphere or produced by a source of artificial light).

Accelerated light tests

(*j*) An enclosed arc lamp with an intensity distribution as near as possible to that of sunlight should be employed.

(*k*) The total intensity of radiation should be measured. Radiation of excessive intensity should be avoided so as to prevent overheating of the test pieces.

Oven and bomb tests

(*l*) Oven and bomb tests should be used to accelerate the type of degradation which takes place either indoors in the absence of light (as in drawer or shelf ageing) or outdoors, either with rubbers containing black or with unstressed test pieces in the dark. As ovens and bombs do not simulate natural ageing in the presence of either light or ozone when the rubbers are stretched, they should not be used for these purposes.

(*m*) When oven and bomb tests are used as service tests the physical properties of the rubber should be measured at the ageing temperature.

(*n*) High temperatures lead to heterogeneity of the test piece, and therefore oven and bomb tests should be carried out at the lowest practicable temperature.

(*o*) In such tests standard dimensions should be specified for the test pieces, and results should be compared only between samples of similar shape.

(*p*) The test pieces should be aged in special individual containers.

(*q*) To follow the progress of oven or bomb ageing satisfactorily, at least two physical properties should be measured.

(*r*) As a general criterion of oven or bomb ageing, elongation at break, in the absence of reversion, is most suitable. Modulus values, however, should be checked for indications of reversion, and if the latter is found, tensile strength is to be preferred to elongation at break.

Oven ageing

Temperature of test and thickness of test piece

The conventional oven ageing test [40,41,42,43,44,45] carried out with natural rubber is performed at 70° C, but tests with synthetic rubbers at this temperature have to be carried out for longer periods, since they are inherently more stable to air or oxygen attack. Temperatures above 70° C are frequently employed with synthetic rubbers. At elevated temperatures oxidation occurs in the outer layer, causing surface hardening with most vulcanised rubbers; it has been suggested [46] that there is a critical temperature below which the rubber dissolves oxygen uniformly throughout its mass and above which the absorption of oxygen by vulcanised rubber is so rapid in relation to the rate of diffusion of oxygen that it can penetrate only to a small depth before being absorbed: and the centre of the sample may be devoid of oxygen. Examples of non-homogeneity occurring in natural rubber due to these effects [3,27,37] are well known, but, even at temperatures above 70° C, the tendency for non-homogeneity is less with synthetic rubbers than with natural rubber at lower temperatures. This is thought to be due to synthetic rubbers in general having slower rates of reaction than natural rubber and in certain cases higher oxygen diffusion rates. In these circumstances effects found with natural rubber at elevated temperatures do not necessarily apply to synthetic rubbers. For example, non-homogeniety of natural rubber has been demonstrated [11] by measuring the change in tensile properties and studying the effect of thickness of test piece on the rate of ageing. It was found that the apparent resistance to ageing increases as thickness of test piece increases and the temperature is raised above 100° C. The effect of thickness is reduced, however, by including antioxidants,[37,46] and in general as the inherent ageing resistance is improved so the effect of thickness is reduced. In the case of the heat-resistant natural compound, referred to in Table 13.2, no trace of inhomogeneity could be found after ageing for 2 days at 125° C. This reasoning leads to the belief that the effect of thickness should be less important with synthetic rubbers, e.g. SBR, due to their inherently better ageing resistance.

It is clear, however, that when studying the effects of high-temperature ageing on bulk properties it is important to ensure that the test-piece dimensions, particularly thickness, correspond to the dimensions of the service article. On the other hand, if the conditions are so severe that the deterioration is mainly produced at the surface, e.g. air bags, then the effects can be reproduced in the accelerated test by employing test pieces as thin as is practicable.[11]

In the various national specifications for oven ageing it is usually specified that the temperature at various points in the oven should not vary by more than $\pm 1°$ C. This tolerance of 2° C applies over the range of temperature 70°–200° C. It can be argued that a tighter tolerance is required for temperatures at 150° C and above, but accurate data to support this contention is lacking. The importance of maintaining adequate temperature control within a 2° C tolerance has been fully discussed.[3,47,48]

Two ovens have been described [47,48] which employ the principle that the best and only practicable method of maintaining a constant and uniform temperature throughout an air space is to maintain the boundary walls at that temperature. " If this is done, nothing within the walls can depart from that temperature whether by conduction, convection or radiation. If the temperature of the walls is not constant and uniform, temperature gradients in the air space are inevitable, and not even the most vigorous stirring will eliminate them. Moreover, solid bodies (e.g. rubber samples) attain by radiation a temperature which may easily differ from that of the air with which they are in contact, by as much as a degree or two. It is therefore important that for a satisfactory control of temperature in an air oven it must be immersed in a medium of constant temperature and high heat capacity." [3]

Individual containers

Adequate evidence has been published [3,26,48,49] to show that when different compounds are aged together in the same oven or container there is a distinct possibility that some cross contamination will occur between compounds, especially if the compounds age at different rates. For accurate work therefore it is recommended that individual containers be used for each compound. Suitable designs of equipment have been described, [47,48,50] and the latter two papers show how existing ovens can be modified quite simply. New equipment, however, should conform with the following broad description of " cell type ovens ", which has been accepted by Committee ISO/TC/45 [3]:

The apparatus shall consist of one or more cylindrical vertical cells having a minimum height of 30 cm. The cells shall be surrounded by a thermostatically controlled good transfer medium (aluminium block, liquor bath, saturated vapour). The design of the apparatus shall be such that heated air may enter the bottom of the cell and shall be exhausted out of the top of it without being recirculated. Air passing in one cell shall not enter other cells. Provision is made for a slow circulation of air through the cells of not less than three changes in 1 hour. The incoming air shall be heated by the same heat-transfer medium up to the temperature of the oven before entering the cell. The temperature of each of the test cells shall be uniform in time and space within $\pm 1°$ C of the specified temperature. Suitable means should be provided for controlling and measuring the temperature.

The problem of contamination can be overcome by using the test-tube method, [51] which was developed in America for high-temperature ageing at temperatures up to $150°$ C. The test pieces are suspended in large test-tubes provided with vent tubes and heated by immersion in an oil-bath or heated aluminium block, [52] which as sources of heat permit good control of temperature. It would be expected that the test-tube method would be more reproducible than the standard oven test, and in fact the variations between laboratories have been found to be less.[27] This is an important point, since the results of co-operative tests with standard ovens [3] emphasised " that even in skilled hands ageing equipment is not controlled sufficiently closely for adequate reproducibility in rates of deterioration to be produced in several laboratories ".

Air circulation

Most national specifications (and the international methods) include a clause defining the rate of air circulation in oven tests. Normally it is also specified that the rubber test pieces should not occupy more than 10% of the free space in the oven, and in these cases an air circulation rate of 0·2 change per hour is required to replenish the oxygen.[53] In the international method [54] and BS 903 [40] it is specified that there should be a slow circulation of air at not less than three changes in 1 hour.

Oxygen bomb and air bomb

Oxygen bombs are widely used with natural rubber compounds,[40] but apparently this method is not employed to any great extent with SBR compounds in America. The American delegation to Committee ISO/TC/45 have pointed out that oxygen bomb ageing at 70° C under an oxygen pressure of 300 lb./in.^{2} is not used with SBR because the compounds are stable under these conditions and only slight deterioration occurs. The method, however, is specified in ASTM D572–53. It is difficult to accept this view without further examination.

In *The GR-S Manual* [55] data are presented for oxygen bomb and oven ageing of SBR, and the changes in physical properties of a typical SBR reinforcing black compound on ageing in air at 70° and 100° C and in the oxygen bomb at 70° C and 300 lb./in.^{2} pressure of oxygen are summarised in Table 13.5.

The oxygen bomb is not as vigorous with SBR as it is with natural rubber, but the initial rate of hardening is a little greater than is obtained in the air oven at 70° C, and from the data in Table 13.5 there is evidence of softening in the oxygen bomb, e.g. modulus at 300%.

A comparison of the ageing of a SBR and a natural rubber tread-type compound is given in Table 13.6.

Although the air oven at 100° C produces more deterioration in a shorter time than the oxygen bomb with SBR, the degree of deterioration in the oxygen bomb is still appreciable.

Other work [20] has shown that oxygen bomb ageing at 100° C results in a greater drop in tensile strength and a smaller increase in modulus than

TABLE 13.5

AGEING OF SBR REINFORCING BLACK COMPOUND

	Period of ageing, days	Tensile strength, kg./cm.²	Elong. at break, %	Modulus at 100%, kg./cm.²	Modulus at 300%, kg./cm.²	IR Hardness, Degrees	Resilience at 50° C, %	Tear resistance, kg./cm.²	Comp. set at 70° C, %	Swelling in benzene, % volume change
Oven ageing:										
Unaged	None	192	500	20	82	70	42	64	33	—
Aged at 70° C	7	166	357	28	130	78	46	70	25	—
	14	166	352	32	146	79	45	52	20	—
	28	147	258	44	—	79	48	34	23	—
Aged at 100° C	1	139	278	38	—	74	49	63	15	—
	2	142	259	44	—	77	52	60	18	—
	4	131	208	50	—	80	49	54	17	—
	8	123	162	73	—	82	51	36	18	—
Oxygen bomb ageing (70° C/ 300 lb./in.² oxygen):										
Unaged	None	192	500	20	82	69	42	—	—	288
Aged	4	159	435	30	108	76	41	—	—	262
	8	151	428	28	104	76	42	—	—	254
	12	152	443	34	106	78	40	—	—	262
	16	83	348	34	76	77	32	—	—	282

oven ageing at 100° C.   It has been argued [58] that this data indicates that the rate of chain scission, as measured by fall in tensile strength, increases with increase in oxygen pressure, and the rate of cross-linking, determined from the increase in modulus, is approximately independent of oxygen

TABLE 13.6

AGEING OF SBR AND NATURAL RUBBER TREAD COMPOUNDS

	Tensile strength, kg./cm.²		Elong. at break	
	SBR	Natural rubber	SBR	Natural rubber
Oxygen bomb at 70° C:				
0 days	217	254	506	540
4 ,,	175	154	369	430
6 ,,	152	—	273	—
8 ,,	142	117	267	345
10 ,,	118	—	220	—
12 ,,	—	78	—	290
Air oven at 100° C:				
0 days	217	254	506	540
2 ,,	165	242	230	430
4 ,,	124	225	161	330
6 ,,	122	109	146	190

pressure.   The conclusion reached [58] was " since the nature of the changes in the physical properties of SBR during ageing at elevated temperatures varies with oxygen pressure, the use of the oxygen bomb ageing test for the practical evaluation of the ageing of SBR would seem inadvisable ".   As the oxygen pressure can be controlled easily (300 ± 10 lb./in.²), the above recommendation is too sweeping.

Another anomaly concerns the air bomb,[31] which is no longer included in BS 903 because the method is not widely used by British Industry. This method is still included in ASTM D454–53, and due to the high-temperature used (126° C) deterioration occurs more rapidly than in an oxygen bomb at 70° C.   The air bomb appears to be quite widely used in America, and it is strange that the objections raised against the oxygen bomb have not been applied to the air bomb.

Temperature

The need for accurate temperature control in bomb equipment is the same as for ovens, but general experience [3] is that it is easier to operate to a tolerance of 2° C with commercial bomb equipment than with commercial oven equipment.   This has been attributed to the fact that the heating of bombs follows the basic principle of getting the walls of the containers at a uniform temperature.   It is recommended that the pressure and the temperature inside the bomb should both be recorded continuously throughout any period of ageing.

Individual containers

The only practical method devised so far for utilising the individual container principle with oxygen bombs is to reduce the size of the bombs so that in effect each bomb is used only for the ageing of single compounds. A very small bomb of 250 c.c. capacity which is suitable has been designed in France.[58]

An obvious point which cannot be emphasised too much is the necessity to clean thoroughly the inside of bombs and ovens. Volatile ingredients from compounds and oxidative products can accumulate on the inside of containers, and contamination of compounds aged subsequently in the equipment can occur and vitiate the improvements which would otherwise result from the use of individual containers.

Ozone and atmospheric exposure tests

The misconception that light is necessary for atmospheric cracking has been perpetuated in the name " sun-checking ", and has been strengthened by confusion with crazing, which requires light, and also by the fact that atmospheric cracking occurs at a slower rate indoors, owing not to absence of sunlight but to dissipation, by contact with indoor surfaces, of the active agents present in indoor air. The critical elongation of 10–20% at which atmospheric cracks reach maximum size is explained by the dependence of the rates of crack formation and growth on elongation.[59] A similar effect is found with ozone cracks, and this and other similarities, which have been enumerated,[3] have suggested that ozone alone is responsible for atmospheric cracking. Ozone is certainly a major factor but as early as 1945 it was suggested [37] that it " may not be the only one . . . for it is possible that other atmospheric oxidising agents may act in a similar way ". Later work,[60] which confirmed that certain peroxides could produce the same type of cracking in rubber, supports this view. Nevertheless, there is no doubt that ozone is one of the most efficient agents for producing cracking in strained rubber, and exposure to an atmosphere of ozonised air is the normal accelerated test employed by the rubber industry.

The concentration of ozone in the outside atmosphere varies a great deal, and depends on many factors.[3, 59, 61–67]. Nevertheless, it has been shown [59] that the product of ozone concentration and the time to crack a sample right through was fairly constant, ranging between 0.6×10^{-3} and 4×10^{-3}, which means a period between 10 and 70 days are required to crack through rubber samples, taking the normal concentration of ozone in the atmosphere as 4×10^{-8} c.c./c.c.

Extensive work has been carried out on ozone and atmospheric exposure tests, particularly during the last fifteen years, and although many valuable papers have been published,[3, 28, 56, 59, 61, 65, 68, 69, 70] much more fundamental work is still required before the position can be regarded as satisfactory. The main purpose of these tests is the assessment of how rubber compounds will withstand exposure and the evaluation of methods and chemicals for improving resistance to atmospheric and ozone cracking. The mechanism of ozone attack is still a debatable subject,[3] which will not

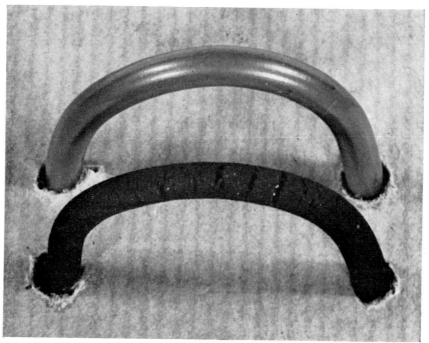

Fig. 13.5. Protection offered by Vulcaprene lacquer to natural rubber cable exposed to ozonised air.

be discussed here, but a brief discussion of the modes of protecting rubber compounds is appropriate, since it has a bearing on the methods of testing.

Microcrystalline waxes [59, 61, 71, 72] are recommended as protective agents, and under static conditions they are often satisfactory. The mode of action is for the wax to bloom to the surface of the rubber, and the effectiveness of the wax depends on its forming a continuous film. The bloom is easily damaged and breaks if the rubber is extended above about 25% extension. Another method is to apply an ozone-resistant film to the surface and Vulcaprene (polyester rubber) lacquers or veneers are often employed (see Fig. 13.5 [28]). Various other surface treatments, such as

P P

light catalysed oxidation,[73] hydrogen peroxide,[61] bromine [61] and nitrogen peroxide,[61] are also claimed to be effective for a time.   Of the above treatments, the polyester film is the only one with the advantage that the film is extensible and more difficult to damage.   In all cases once the barrier film is broken cracking proceeds very quickly at that point.   More recently an advance has been made in that certain types of aromatic amines [28,56,74,132] which are added during compounding have been shown to give protection not only under static but also under dynamic conditions.   A further contribution is that these materials and polyester films can be applied to the surface of cracked rubber and delay further cracking on subsequent exposure.[75]   Some of the amines referred to are weak anti-oxidants for natural rubber and SBR, and although they seem to have some specific anti-ozone activity, it is still necessary to bring them to the surface of the rubber where ozone attack occurs.   It has been noted that some amines, e.g. N : N'-di-*sec.*-butyl-*p*-phenylenediamine, sweat to the surface readily,[28] whereas with some others the addition of wax to aid migration to the surface is recommended.[74]   Many members of this class of amine are toxic and/or dermatitic to some degree, and some are volatile, which reduces their effectiveness under certain conditions.

Five important characteristics for a protective agent against ozone have been listed [74] as:

(*a*) Specific anti-ozone activity.

(*b*) Non-toxic under conventional processing conditions.

(*c*) Low vapour pressure, so as to be retained in the rubber during processing and later service.

(*d*) Resistant to heat ageing up to 212° F.

(*e*) Limited solubility in the polymer to provide gradual continual migration to the surface, where it can be effective, since ozone attacks rubber only at the surface.

The following further points are now suggested for addition to this list.

(*f*) The bloom formed in (*e*) should not be of an objectionable nature or appearance.

(*g*) No effect on scorching properties during processing.

(*h*) Provision of adequate anti-flexcracking properties in addition to the other attributes.

The provision of anti-flexcracking properties is added because until a class of chemicals is found which combines resistance to flexcracking with resistance to atmospheric cracking the problem is not solved completely. At present some compounders are tending to improve resistance to atmospheric cracking at the expense of resistance to flexcracking.

In other words, the tests for atmospheric and ozone cracking should be supplemented by toxiological tests on the chemicals employed, vapour pressure tests, solubility tests and flexcracking tests in the case of tyre compounds.

Atmospheric exposure tests

Static exposure tests outdoors are carried out either on stretched rubber strips, wedge shaped dumb-bells [59] with which a range of strains can be studied or by exposing bent test pieces in special racks. The dimensions of a suitable shaped dumb-bell are given in Fig. 13.6, and the exposure of

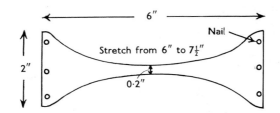

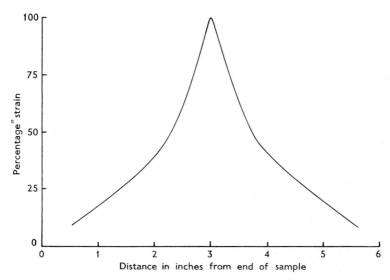

Fig. 13.6. Dumb-bell test piece for outdoor exposure and exposure to ozone.

bent test pieces is illustrated in Fig. 13.7. For accurate work the number and size of the cracks can be determined with a microscope,[59] but for routine work most laboratories compare the exposed test pieces with photographs of test pieces at various stages of cracking. So far it has not been possible to get a scale of cracking which would be acceptable to all

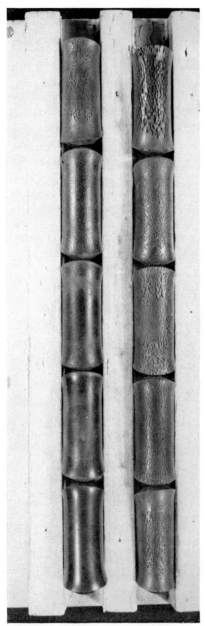

Fig. 13.7. Bent test piece exposed outdoors.

workers, and some of the difficulties associated with this problem have been discussed.[3, 59, 61, 76]

Because the ozone concentration in the atmosphere varies from day to day and from place to place, and because of many other factors which can affect the "normal" ageing of the rubber, thereby having an influence on its resistance to ozone or atmospheric attack, these outdoor exposure tests cannot be expected to give reproducible results. It is therefore essential to include a standard rubber compound of known performance in each set of compounds evaluated. The problem of comparing the results between sets remains as a great difficulty, and in the case of fine differences between particular compounds it is essential to obtain a side-by-side comparison.

In addition to the static outdoor exposure test there is a need for an outdoor dynamic test. The tests so far described [28, 77–80] have not been supported by the extensive data illustrating their usefulness, which would be required before they were adopted widely. To return to the classification of types of ageing, here is a case where it is necessary to employ two activating forces, one mechanical and the other molecular, and quite a lot of work remains to be done before the correct balance can be found and controlled.

In 1957 it was reported [56] that flexing in ozonised air resulted in two types of cracking; one type similar to normal flexcracking occurred in the groove whereas in the rubber adjacent to the groove, where smaller strains apply, the cracks were similar in appearance to those obtained in a static exposure test in the ozone cabinet. Flexing tests such as the De Mattia carried out in an atmosphere of ozonised air were too severe since cracking occurred so quickly that little discrimination between compounds was possible, and the presence of the two types of cracking indicated that both flexcracking and ozone attack were occurring simultaneously. Much better discrimination was obtained by modifying the conditions of test so as to reduce the strain in the test piece. This was done by using straight strip test pieces, without a moulded groove, where the maximum strain produced is in the region of 15 per cent (cf. 136 per cent with grooved test piece). Using the modified test piece good correlation was reported between tests carried out with the De Mattia machine outdoors and on a De Mattia machine enclosed in an atmosphere of ozonised air in the laboratory. More extensive work in the same organisation has been completed [132] and fully justifies the original hope that this method would correlate with the results of service exposures.

Ozone exposure tests

It has been pointed out [3] that experience in America [81] and in Great Britain [82, 83] with ozone testing equipment has not been entirely satisfactory. The method most widely adopted [84] uses an ultra-violet lamp as the source of ozone, with the test pieces being completely protected from the light of the lamp. The ASTM apparatus [85] (Fig. 13.8) consists essentially of a cabinet divided into an upper compartment containing the test pieces and a lower compartment housing an ultra-violet lamp. A stream of air is drawn over the ultra-violet lamp into the upper compartment through a system of baffles which act as a light trap. The air in the upper compartment is sampled through a hard rubber tube, the sample being drawn at a measured rate through an absorption vessel, where the incoming air is mixed with a mist of buffered potassium iodide solution which is recirculated within the vessel. The concentration of ozone employed is 25 ± 5 parts per 100,000,000. As pointed out earlier, the rate at which cracking occurs depends on the ozone concentration, with very high concentrations causing cracking so quickly that the degree of discrimination between materials is impaired.[67, 84]

Certain difficulties associated with the method have been discussed,[3] and at present the delegations to Committee ISO/TC/45 are interchanging their experience with this and other techniques. In general, opinion is that the method, while useful for development work in a single laboratory, gives poor reproducibility between laboratories, and for this reason is not suitable for specification purposes. The ozone exposure apparatus described in ASTM method D1149-55T has a number of deficiencies, the

principal being the lack of a sufficient flow of ozonised air through the test
chamber, and adequate agitation of this air to prevent stratification. The
method employs an ultra-violet light source and unless an automatic ozone
concentration control system is used in conjunction, the method can be
criticised on the ground that there will be a decreased output of ultra-violet

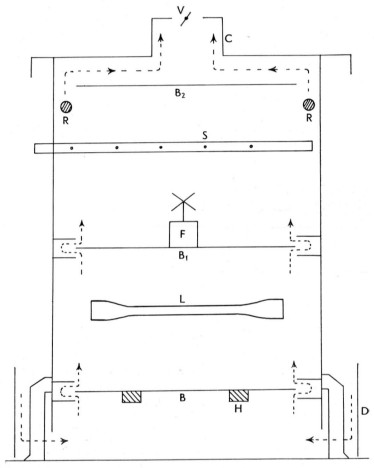

Fig. 13.8. Ozone test chamber.

light with ageing of the tube, thereby affecting the ozone concentration.
The use of a silent discharge method appears to be preferable since it gives
uniform output over a long period. The method of controlling the ozone
concentration employed usually depends on the type of ozone generator.
When an ultra-violet source is used, control can be obtained by adjusting
the voltage applied, shielding part of the ultra-violet tube exposed to the
air flow, or by the use of an automatic control system which brings into

operation an auxiliary ultra-violet source, as required. When a silent discharge generator is used, a two-stage dilution of the ozonised air is generally
necessary, and control of the concentration is obtained by accurate metering
of the air, which is a fairly simple matter.

Fig. 13.9. Apparatus for exposing test pieces to ozonised air.

The level of ozone concentration in the cabinet is affected by the presence
of rubber test pieces and it is reasonable to limit the number of test pieces
to give a maximum surface area of test piece to volume of cabinet ratio of
1 : 10. In addition, unless a rapid flow of ozonised air is used, it will be

found that variations in concentration occur at different levels in the test chamber. A flow rate giving several complete changes of ozonised air in the test chamber per minute obviates any necessity for additional stirring and appears to be satisfactory.

The I.C.I. method [56] for assessing ozone resistance complies with the above principles. The apparatus, together with absorption vessel for determining the ozone concentration, shown in Fig. 13.9, consists of a silent discharge ozone generator, producing ozonised ozygen of a high concentration which is diluted with air in two stages and fed into the exposure cabinet. Oxygen from a cylinder is dried and passed through the ozone generator at a constant rate of 30 litres per hour, which results in the formation of ozone at a concentration of approximately 0·3 per cent. The ozonised oxygen is then mixed with clean dry air and a small proportion of this ozonised air (10 litres per hour) is mixed with the main air flow at the point of entry to the exposure cabinet. The main air flow is controlled at 9·6 cu. metres/hour and passes over an electric heater before being mixed with the ozonised air. This rate of air flow ensures that there is a complete change of air in the cabinet every 14 seconds.

One method used for the determination of ozone concentration is essentially that given in ASTM D49-55T, namely, the absorption of ozone by a buffered solution of potassium iodide in water, and measurement of the iodine liberated by titration with sodium thiosulphate.

A great deal of collective experience on ozone testing is being obtained by several delegations to Committee ISO/TC/45 and no doubt this will lead to refined and improved methods being evolved.

Only three papers have been published [56,86,132] where flexing tests have been carried out in an atmosphere of controlled ozone concentration. The provision of technological data obtained under these conditions is of great assistance to compounders.

Light ageing

Increased interest in methods for assessing resistance to light ageing of rubber articles has been encouraged by developments in the non-staining antioxidant field. As powerful non-staining antioxidants have been discovered, so light-coloured rubbers have been employed in more varied applications.

Two types of test are employed: exposure of unstrained test pieces outdoors and exposure of unstrained test pieces to light from an artificial light source. The difficulties associated with obtaining reproducible results in the outdoor test are obvious; variations in the sunlight intensity from day to day and from place to place not only give rise to erratic results but also make it difficult to set a " target " for reproduction under controlled conditions in the laboratory. Many different types of artificial light source have been studied, but the correlation with outdoor tests is normally poor, and the ideal source has still to be found.

ASTM Method D750-55T gives details of an accelerated light resistance test, but some of the basic precautions listed earlier in this chapter for a light-exposure test have not been included. This method employs a carbon-arc light source, and definite steps are taken to eliminate the presence of ozone. The ASTM are doing a great deal to help in this field, and in a proposed revision of Specification E42 they list seven types of machine operating carbon-arc lamps—single enclosed carbon arc, twin enclosed carbon arc, single open-flame sunshine carbon arc—and state that the apparatus shall include equipment necessary for measuring and controlling arc current, arc voltage, black panel temperature, water-spray temperature, operating schedule or cycle, and exposure time. It is significant that the warning is given in this specification that " satisfactory correlation can be expected between different machines of the same type when operated according to this procedure. Comparisons should not be made between effects of exposure in different types of apparatus unless correlation has been established for the particular material ".

In ASTM D750 the amount of radiation is measured by the uranyl oxalate actinometer method, in which the amount of oxalic acid decomposed by the light is determined. The suggestion [87] that this technique can be used only for checking the constancy of a given source and not for comparing different light sources may not be strictly true. An improved method based on ASTM D750 has been investigated by certain delegations to ISO/TC/45, and from the preliminary results of this co-operative work the uranyl sulphate–oxalic acid method appears to be suitable for assessing the light intensity of particular types of light sources. Another method, developed by the National Bureau of Standards, uses light-sensitised papers for checking light intensity by comparing the exposed papers with a set of master papers of known exposure.[88] It has also been suggested [3] that improvements might result if limits of intensity were established.

In the 12th Foundation Lecture [56] the view was expressed that " better methods of measuring light dosage, better exposure lamps, and a better understanding of the fundamental factors involved in staining of rubber may all be required before a satisfactory light ageing test can be specified ". The same paper drew attention to work in the textile field, pointing out that enclosed carbon arc sources did not have spectral distributions similar to sunlight [133] and suggested that Xenon lamps which do have spectral distributions similar to sunlight should be investigated in the light ageing of polymers. Three types of light source (a) carbon-arc lamps, (b) mercury discharge lamps, (c) tungsten filament lamps, have been compared [133] and the authors' conclusions were:

Q Q

" None of the light sources investigated had a spectral distribution similar to sunlight. The enclosed flame arc resembled sunlight only to the extent that the proportion of radiant power omitted in the region 3000–4300 A was approximately the same as that on noon summer sunlight. In other regions of the spectrum the proportions omitted by the arc differed considerably from those given by the sun. The two principal factors affecting the distribution of energy in the spectrum of the enclosed flame arc were the composition of the surrounding atmosphere and asymmetrical burning of the arc. The total radiation depended upon the electrical power input, which should vary as little as possible in both current and voltage. Fume deposited on the globe from the arc caused the radiation to be diffused rather than absorbed.

" The high-intensity arc was of all the light sources examined the nearest to noon sunlight in its spectral characteristics. This type of arc, however, cannot be left to burn unattended for periods of several hours."

Various laboratories are now employing Xenon sources and the general impression is that these sources give the best hope of finding a satisfactory light source.

At the moment deterioration is assessed by visual examination, and it is helpful to define some of the terms used to distinguish various phenomena. If coloration is defined as the colour of the vulcanisate after cure, discoloration is the change in colour which occurs on the surface on exposure to light.[89] Discoloration can be assessed against standard scales[3] or compared with a control compound. Visual assessment of this kind introduces an operator error which can be quite high, depending on the experience and ability of the individuals. For greater reliability, especially where fine differences are concerned, precise colour measurements with spectrometers are required, and for more routine work photoelectric reflectance meters have been employed.

Apart from discoloration, another effect produced by exposure to light, is crazing. It has been shown that the amount of crazing produced depends on the colour of the vulcanisate,[28] and therefore it can be inferred that the amount of discoloration plays a complicating role in this type of change. The degree of crazing produced in the surface is also difficult to assess visually, and it is most difficult to prepare a standard set of test pieces showing a comprehensive graduated scale of crazing.

Exposure of thin films of rubber (e.g. proofings) to light produces stiffening, and a simple bend modulus test[90] has been recommended. The authors recommend that a control test piece be exposed under the same conditions as the materials under test, and their data show that the errors associated with this method are quite high. Experiments with proofings varying in composition, colour and thickness demonstrated that these factors may interact strongly, so that in studying variations in one factor the others must be kept constant. Recent co-operative work [56] between different laboratories showed poor reproducibility, and it is clear that some factors in the method need to be defined more closely and perhaps other factors, at present not controlled, need to be included in the method.

Newton and Wake [90] considered that the light stiffening of proofing should only be carried out in natural light and concluded that the ultra-violet component of the solar radiation was responsible for the bulk of the stiffening and that the effect decreased progressively as the wavelength increased. Above a wavelength of 540 mμ (green) no stiffening occurred. The use of plastic filters, which had been used successfully in the fading of fabrics,[134] has been employed to investigate the spectral regions responsible for the development of staining in rubber compounds.[135] This work suggests that the stain developing out of doors in sunlight is due to ultra-violet radiation in the case of a white rubber compound containing no antioxidant, or a phenolic antioxidant and due partly to ultra-violet and partly to visible radiation in the case of a compound containing an amine type antioxidant.

A problem allied to discoloration is staining by migration,[89] which is the discoloration which becomes apparent on a surface which has been in contact with a rubber surface. Many automobile manufacturers have their own specifications for studying staining by migration to car enamels, and technological data in this field has been published.[89, 91, 92] ASTM D925-55 describes two procedures which are of interest. The rubber test piece is placed on a lacquered test panel and exposed to light from an artificial source and examined to see whether a stain develops beyond the area in direct contact. In cases where the interest is in contact staining, Method D925-55 specifies that the rubber test piece be held between two test panels and exposed to a temperature of 175° F in a circulating air oven. It is important to realise that in the latter test some materials will migrate into the test panel under these conditions but will not necessarily stain unless the panel is subsequently exposed to light. Once again the test conditions have therefore to be chosen after careful consideration is given to the conditions applying in service.

Humidity and steam tests

Moist tropical ageing involves exposure to light, oxygen and ozone at higher temperatures than those met in this country, and published data [28, 93] suggests that moisture can act as a catalyst of oxidation. The effects of humidity on the ageing of a range of rubbers over periods of up to two years exposure in an oven at 40° C and in a humidity oven at 40° C with 75% RH have been studied, and the results obtained for tensile strength and elongation at break are given in Figs. 13.10 and 13.11.[28] Attention is drawn to the increased deterioration of the carbon black compounds in the presence of moisture.

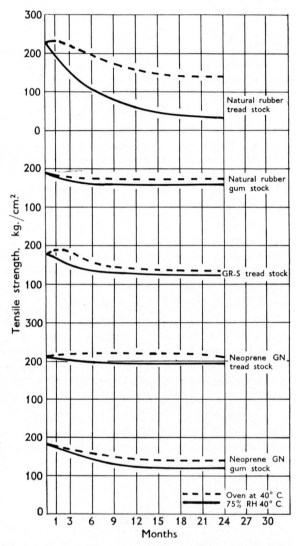

Fig. 13.10. Ageing results.

Humidity cabinets used to simulate tropical conditions are normally operated in the range 30°–40° C and 60–90 RH. There are considerable daily climatic variations in the Tropics, and the accuracy with which these should be reproduced is often debated. Under dry desert conditions

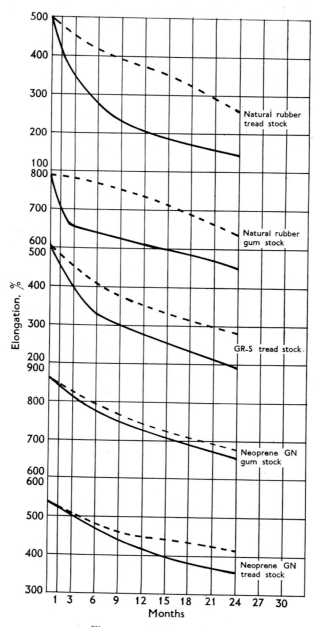

Fig. 13.11. Ageing results.

there can often be a sudden fall in temperature at night, and frost may be formed. A German specification [94] uses a temperature of $40°$ C at a relative humidity of 90%, but introduces cycles where the temperature falls to $+ 15°$ C (with a relative air humidity of 45%) in order to produce dew formation on the surface of the test pieces.

With the development of polyester rubbers, e.g. Vulcaprene A,[95] the I.C.I. steam ageing test [34] was introduced so that compounders had a method of checking whether articles made from this rubber had been processed and cured correctly. It is claimed [3] that the method is useful in research work to find polyester rubbers with improved hydrolytic stability and data on the " steam lives " of Vulcaprene A, " Vulkollan " [96] and " Moltopren " [97] have been published. The same writer emphasises very strongly that the results of this test should not be used to calculate the life of articles in service.

Additional methods of assessing ageing

The six main types of accelerated ageing discussed above are not the only ones which are used to study ageing, and many applications require the ageing characteristics to be studied in circumstances where the main agencies are combined in a controlled manner, e.g. heat + light + oxygen. A large variety of semi-service tests have been developed, and it is not possible to describe them here, but reference should be made to *Rubber in Engineering* [98] for an excellent discussion of the problem as seen from the point of view of engineering applications.

Immersion in fluids

Reference must be made, however, to a few of the more important test methods which are used to evaluate the stability of vulcanisates. For example, the ageing of polymers immersed in fluids is of considerable importance in several applications. It can be considered that swelling has a similar effect upon the physical properties of a vulcanisate as a rise in temperature;[98] as swelling occurs the rubber is strained, and tensile strength, modulus and hardness decrease, whereas resilience increases. The swelling media can provide some protection against ageing due to the exclusion of oxygen; a neoprene compound which showed surface cracks on bending after 80–100 hours at $150°$ C in air lasted 600–800 hours at the same temperature when immersed in a heavy engine oil.[98] In addition to this longer life at a given temperature, immersion in fluids often means that a rubber, resistant to the immersion fluid, can be used at higher temperatures than when exposed to hot air. In the case of diaphragms, where one surface may be immersed and the other surface exposed to hot air, failures sometimes occur due to the immersion fluid diffusing to the air–polymer surface. If this surface has hardened appreciably the strains set up by the swelling action of the diffused fluid may produce cracks.

The question of working with standard test fuels in laboratory tests has been discussed in Chapter IX. The purity of these test fuels can be very important, for cases are known where rubber parts, e.g. petrol hose, have failed due to the preferential absorption of some deleterious impurity, e.g. piperidine.[99] Different properties are affected to different extents by swelling and the complications that arise, due to this, when assessing the " oil resistance " of chloroprene [100] and butadiene–acrylonitrile rubbers [101] have been reviewed. Methods of measuring the physical properties of swollen rubbers are not entirely satisfactory, and refinements in technique are required.[99] In the case of rubbers such as SBR and natural rubber it is essential to protect them from splashes of oil and solvents when they are under strain. Catastrophic effects can easily be demonstrated by holding a ring test piece of these rubbers under strain in a tensile machine and applying a drop of high-swelling liquid to the surface.[102]

Oil-resistant rubbers are not the only ones to be used in conditions where the rubber part is immersed in fluid, and the lining of chemical plant presents a growing field where natural rubber, ebonite and to an increasing extent Butyl rubber find application. In the case of chemical-plant linings there are many associated problems, such as bonding of the lining, and

TABLE 13.7

CHEMICAL RESISTANCE OF RUBBERS—% SWELLING AFTER 14 DAYS AT 70° C

	Butyl	Neoprene GN	Nitrile rubber
Aniline	12	284	Perished
p-Butylaniline	33	400	550
Naphthylamine	7·5	549	466
Pyridine	12	282	354
Nitrobenzene	14	210	250
Octyl phenol	6	19	150
Tricresyl phosphate	o	130	170
Ethylacetoacetate	6	250	225
Methylmethacrylate	19	130	130
Isopropenylacetate	18	70	150
Creosote	100	270	280
C-Chloraniline	3·5	300	450

The above data were obtained using vulcanisates containing 50 parts of EPC black on 100 parts of elastomer.

although the tensile strength of the lining may be unimportant, the tear strength may be very important. As the strength properties are affected by the degree of swelling, and although it involves a simplification, a useful indication of the performance and ageing of rubbers for chemical-plant linings can often be obtained from swelling data only. Information on the chemical resistance of a range of rubbers as assessed by swelling data is given in Table 13.7.

Oxygen Absorption

The oxidation of rubber can be studied either by measuring the amount of oxygen or oxidation products present in the rubber after ageing or by the rate of absorption of oxygen. The gravimetric method is seldom used, and two methods of measuring rates of absorption are employed. In the manometric method [46,103,104] the drop in pressure as oxygen is absorbed is measured, and in the volumetric method [46,105-111] the change in volume at constant pressure is measured. The volumetric method appears to be the one preferred,[3,109] since it has the advantage that the pressure is constant throughout the test, and it has been found to be the more reproducible method.

The interpretation of the results of oxygen absorption tests is never a simple matter. Absorption measurements are sensitive [112] to compounding and processing factors, the state of vulcanisation, the previous history of the compound and the presence of deactivators [113] in the compound. Interpretation of oxygen-absorption data is further complicated by the shape of the oxygen-absorption curve, which for most rubber compounds is part of a general three-stage type of curve.[112] Normally the oxygen-absorption data used for correlation with other ageing data has been the second-stage quasi-linear rate, but it has been suggested [112] that the third stage should be used for assessing antioxidants. In view of the above difficulties it is not surprising to find that efforts to correlate oxygen-absorption measurements with measurements of changes in physical properties produced by the more conventional ageing tests should have led to several conflicting opinions.[3] Many take the view that they correlate better with the oxygen-bomb test than with oven tests.[109,112,114]

There does not appear to be a simple relationship between oxygen uptake and loss of tensile strength. Two papers [115,116] point out that the lower the temperature of ageing, the larger the percentage of oxygen which can be combined without loss of tensile strength. For example, the amount of combined oxygen required to reduce the tensile strength of a natural rubber compound by approximately one-half varies from 1·2% at 60° C to 0·65% at 110° C. This is confirmation that the process of ageing depends upon the temperature of test or service and emphasises that studies of the initial rates of oxygen absorption at one temperature cannot provide sufficient data to forecast how compounds will oxidise under a variety of conditions.

It has been suggested [3] that the provision of a standard volumetric method would help comparison of results between different laboratories, but at the same time such a method should not be included in purchasing specifications.

Stress relaxation and creep tests

Tobolsky *et al.*[117-121, 138-141] developed a theory, relating oxidation to stress relaxation at constant strain, which suggested that stress-relaxation measurements could be used for the evaluation of the stability of rubbers to ageing. A ring test piece of thin cross-section is used, and the stress is measured either by a beam balance or an inclined-plane type of instrument. Designs of apparatus, varying in detail but following the same principles, have been published.[122-125]

The use of stress-relaxation methods as a means of assessing accelerated ageing has been reviewed, and claims [126] for improved ability to discriminate between materials may well have been premature. Certainly some of the difficulties associated with the interpretation of this type of test data, where complex chemical reactions are involved, have not been properly appreciated.

There is no doubt that within a certain temperature range stress decay occurs by means of oxidative chain scission. In the case of natural rubber stress relaxation can be reduced a thousandfold by carrying out the test in an atmosphere of very highly purified nitrogen (instead of air) [118] or reduced by the addition of antioxidants [127-129] or increased by light activation.[120, 121, 126] Conclusions have been drawn from the results of stress relaxation and creep measurements about the nature and the site of the bond involved in oxidative scission,[118] but some of these conclusions have been questioned, since important deviations in relaxation behaviour were revealed by the use of a refined technique.[125] It is essential to remember that the measurement of physical changes produced by chemical reactions involved in the degradation of polymeric networks is generally employed in cases where direct chemical investigation is impracticable. An indirect procedure, such as interpreting stress-relaxation measurements in terms of chemical changes, imposes a strict discipline in interpretation. Some of the uncertainties present in interpreting stress-relaxation data are clear from the statement [125] that the relation between " total number of monomeric units at which scission has occurred (total number of cuts) to the number of effective chains cut at least once (effective cuts) " is important, since " the former is the measure of degradation given by chemical means and the latter is related to the corresponding change in physical properties ". The same authors also emphasise that with sulphur vulcanisates effective chains are being produced concurrently with chain scission, and in these circumstances it is essential that two types of measurement be made, e.g. under intermittent and continuous conditions of stressing. This distinction was recognised in the early work, and the originator of the method has reviewed [130] the extensive work carried out in a paper deserving close study.

An interesting new test for ozone resistance [131] measures the continuous creep of ring test pieces. A load sufficient to give an initial extension of 20% is hung from each ring and because of the high ratio of surface to volume of the test piece, the loss of supporting cross sectional area accompanying ozone cracking, results in lengthening of the loading ring. The authors attribute the observed creep almost entirely to ozone cracking as opposed to oxidative deterioration. Another method of assessing the relative ozone resistance of rubbers [137] measures the difference in tension modulus between an uncracked and cracked rubber strip and it is claimed that normal stress relaxation and creep are automatically eliminated. For quantitative treatment, it is essential that there be a large number of very small cracks, and therefore the test should be carried out at high strain. Equipment for more conventional stress relaxation in ozonised air [138] has also been described.

The present position [3] is that although stress-relaxation techniques are undoubtedly useful research tools for studying the process of oxidative scission, the method should not be used as a routine test to compare results from widely different compounds until a great deal more is known about the complex chemical reactions which are involved.

REFERENCES

 1. Messenger, T. H. and Graham, P. C. C. (1953) *Rubber Developments*, **6**, 1, 2.
 2. (August 1955) *Neoprene Notebook No. 65*.
 3. Buist, J. M. (1956) *Ageing and Weathering of Rubber* (Cambridge: W. Heffer).
 4. (January, 1955) Specification of Société National des Chemins de Fer Français No. 667E.
 5. Scott, J. R. (1945) *I.R.I. Trans.*, **21**, 157.
 6. Harrison, S. R. and Cole, O. D. (1944) *Ind. Eng. Chem.*, **36**, 702.
 7. Juve, A. E. and Garvey, B. S. (1944) *Ind. Eng. Chem.*, **36**, 212.
 8. Baum, A. A., Sturgis, B. M. and Vincent, J. R. (1944) *Ind. Eng. Chem.*, **36**, 348.
 9. Dufraisse, C. (1937) *Chemistry and Technology of Rubber*, Davis and Blake, Chapter 13 (N.Y.: Reinhold Publishing Corporation), p. 497.
10. Habgood, B. J., Private Communication.
11. Williams, G. E. (1957) *I.R.I. Proc.* **4**, 37
12. Geer, W. C. and Evans, W. W. (1921) *India Rubb. World.*, **64**, 887.
13. Krall, S. (1930) *Rubb. Chem. Technol.*, **3**, 148.
14. Follansbee, E. M. (1929) *Ind. Eng. Chem.*, **21**, 1012.
15. Tener, R. F., Smith, W. H. and Holt, W. L. (1927) Tech. Paper 342, Nat. Bur. Standards.
16. Nellen, A. H. and Sellars, H. M. (1929) *Ind. Eng. Chem.*, **21**, 1019.
17. (1948) *Vanderbilt Rubber Handbook*, p. 451.
18. Massie, G. E. and Warner, A. E. (1944) *Ind. Eng. Chem.*, **36**, 720.
19. Scott, J. R. (1945) *I.R.I. Trans.*, **21**, 78.
20. Shelton, J. R. and Winn, H. (1947) *Ind. Eng. Chem.*, **39**, 1133.
21. McCarthy, G. D. *et al.* (1945) *ASTM Bull.* No. 132, 33.

22. Neal, A. M., Bimmerman, H. G. and Vincent, J. R. (1942) *Ind. Eng. Chem.*, **34**, 1352.
23. Ingmanson, J. H. and Kemp, A. R. (1936) *Ind. Eng. Chem.*, **28**, 889.
24. —— —— (1938) *Ind. Eng. Chem.*, **30**, 1168.
25. Kemp, A. R., Ingmanson, J. H. and Mueller, G. S. (1939) *Ind. Eng. Chem.*, **31**, 1472.
26. Schoch, M. G., Jr. and Juve, A. E. (1949) *ASTM Spec. Pub. No.* 89, 59.
27. Juve, A. E. and Schoch, M. G. Jr. (1954) *ASTM Bull.*, **195**, 54.
28. Buist, J. M. (1954) *Rev. gen. Caoutch.*, **31**, 479.
29. Geer, E. G. and Evans, W. W. (1921) *India Rubb. J.*, **61**, 113.
30. Bierer, J. M. and Davis, C. C. (1924) *Ind. Eng. Chem.*, **16**, 711.
31. Booth, E. W. (1932) *Ind. Eng. Chem.*, **24**, 555.
32. Kearsley, E. P. W. (1931) *Rubb. Chem. Technol.*, **4**, 13.
33. Williams, I. (1926) *Ind. Eng. Chem.*, **18**, 367.
34. *The Vulcaprene Manual*, I.C.I. Ltd.
35. Stevens, H. P. (1919) *J. Soc. chem. Ind.*, **38**, 192T.
36. Buist, J. M. (1953) *History of Rubber Industry* (Cambridge: W. Heffer), p. 152.
37. Buist, J. M. and Welding, G. N. (1945) *I.R.I. Trans.*, **21**, 49.
38. *The Services Rubber Investigations Users' Memorandum No.* U16.
39. (1954) *The Services Rubber Investigations Users' Memoranda and Addenda* (H.M.S.O.).
40. BS 903 : Part A19 : 1956.
41. ASTM D573-53.
42. Italian Specification UNI2031.
43. French Specification T46-004.
44. German Specification DIN53508.
45. Netherlands Specification N1001.
46. Morgan, L. B. and Naunton, W. J. S. (1938) *Proc. Rubb. Tech. Conf. London*, 599.
47. Milligan, A. G. and Shaw, J. E. (1934) *J. Sci. Inst.*, **11**, 10.
48. Eccher, S. and Oberto, S. (1951) *I.R.I. Trans.*, **27**, 325.
49. Fackler, M. B. and Rugg, J. S. (1951) *Anal. Chem.*, **23**, 1646.
50. Blackwell, R. F. (1954) *India Rubb. J.*, **127**, 1188.
51. ASTM D865-57.
52. Bradbury, E. J. and Clark, R. A. (1956) *Rubb. World*, **134**, 872.
53. Scott, J. R., Communication to Committee ISO/TC/45.
54. Committee ISO/TC/45, Recommendation No. 171
55. (1947) *The GR-S Manual* (I.C.I. Ltd.).
56. Buist, J. M. (1957) *I.R.I. Trans.*, **33**, 102.
57. Cole, J. O. (1954) in *Synthetic Rubber*, ed. G. S. Whitby (N.Y.: J. Wiley; London: Chapman and Hall), Chapter 13.
58. Anon. (1951) *Rev. gen. Caoutch.*, **28**, 851.
59. Newton, R. G. (1945) *J. Rubb. Res.*, **14**, 27.
60. Crabtree, J. and Biggs, B. S. (1953) *J. Polymer Sci.*, **11**, 280.
61. Crabtree, J. and Kemp, A. R. (1946) *Ind. Eng. Chem.*, **38**, 278.
62. Kearsley, E. P. W. (1930) *Rubb. Age, N.Y.*, **27**, 649.
63. Gluckauf, E. (1944) *Quart. J. roy. Met. Soc.*, **70**, 13.
64. Reynolds, W. C. (1930) *J. Soc. chem. Ind.*, **49**, 168.
65. Van Rossem, A. and Talen, H. W. (1931) *Kautschuk*, **7**, 79, 115.
66. Gluckauf, E. and Paneth, F. A. (1941) *Nature*, **147**, 614.
67. Garvey, B. S. and Emmett, R. A. (1944) *Ind. Eng. Chem.*, **36**, 209.
68. Powell, E. F. and Gough, V. E. (1945) *I.R.I. Trans.*, **21**, 102.
69. Smith, D. M. and Gough, V. E. (1953) *I.R.I. Trans.*, **29**, 219.
70. Rugg, J. S. (1952) *Anal. Chem.*, **24**, 818.
71. Harrison, H. C. (1945) *I.R.I. Trans.*, **21**, 93.
72. Best, L. L. and Moakes, R. C. (1951) *I.R.I. Trans.*, **27**, 103.
73. Williams, I. (1926) *Ind. Eng. Chem.*, **18**, 367.

74. Shaw, R. F., Ossefort, Z. T. and Touley, W. T. (1954) *India Rubb. World*, **130**, 5, 636.
75. Buist, J. M., Williams, G. E. and I.C.I. Ltd., Patent Pending.
76. Werkenthin, T. A. (1946) *Rubb. Age, N.Y.*, **59**, 697.
77. Throdahl, M. C. (1947) *Ind. Eng. Chem.*, **39**, 514.
78. Ford, H. W. and Cooper, L. V. (1950) *India Rubb. World*, **124**, 696; **125**, 55.
79. Creed, K. E., Jr., Hill, R. B. and Breed, J. W. (1952) *Rubb. Age, N.Y.*, **70**, 756.
80. Fielding, J. H. (1947) *Rubb. Chem. Technol.*, **20**, 1020.
81. Juve, A. E. (20 June 1951) Report of Subcommittee XV of ASTM D11.
82. Moakes, R. C. (1951) *Res. Assoc. Brit. Rubber Mfrs. Bull.*, **5**, 92.
83. Kendall, F. H., *Res. Assoc. Brit. Rubber Mfrs. Research Memorandum* R.386.
84. Crabtree, J. and Kemp, A. R. (1946) *Ind. Eng. Chem. Anal. Ed.*, **18**, 769.
85. ASTM D1149-55T.
86. Eccher, S. (1940) *Rubb. Chem. Technol.*, **13**, 566.
87. Bowditch, F. T., Greider, C. E. and Ollinger, C. G. (1942) *Amer. Soc. Test. Mat. Proc.*, **42**, 845.
88. Moses, F. L. and Rodde, A. L. (1948) *India Rubb. World*, **119**, 201, 260.
89. Haworth, J. and Pryer, W. R. (1949) *I.R.I. Trans.*, **25**, 265.
90. Newton, R. G. and Wake, W. C. (1950) *J. Rubb. Res.*, **19**, 16.
91. Williams, G. E. (1956) *I.R.I. Proc.*, **3**, 43.
92. Buist, J. M. (1955) *Chim. e Industr.*, **37**, 1044.
93. Soden, A. L. and Wake, W. C. (1951) *I.R.I. Trans.*, **27**, 223.
94. VDI2026.
95. Harper, D. A., Smith, W. F. and White, H. G. (1948) *Proc. Second Rubb. Tech. Conf. London*, p. 61.
96. Bayer, O., Muller, E., Petersen, S., Piepenbrink, H. F. and Windemuth, E. (1950) *Rubb. Chem. Tech.*, **23**, 812.
97. Hochtlen, A. (1952) *Kunstoffe*, **42**, 303.
98. (1946) *Rubber in Engineering* (H.M.S.O.).
99. Buist, J. M. 1947 The Fundamentals of Rubber Technology, I.C.I. Ltd., 138. W. J. S. Naunton, *The Third I.R.I. Foundation Lecture*, 1948, p. 22.
100. De Puy, R. E. (14 November 1952) *Symposium on Oil Resistance of Rubber, Sveriges Gummitekniska Forenings Hostmote.*
101. Duke, N. C. and Mitchell, W. A. (14 November 1952) *Symposium on Oil Resistance of Rubber, Sveriges Gummitekniska Forenings Hostmote.*
102. Morris, R. E., Mitton, P., Montermoss, J. C. and Werkinthin, T. A. (1943) *Ind. Eng. Chem.*, **35**, 646.
103. Dufraisse, C. (1938) *Rubb. Chem. Technol.*, **11**, 268.
104. Van Amerongen, G. J. (1946) *Rubb. Chem. Technol.*, **19**, 170.
105. Dufraisse, C. and Le Bras, J. (1938) *Proc. Rubb. Tech. Conf. London*, 555.
106. Dufraisse, C. (1938) *Proc. Rubb. Tech. Conf. London*, 547.
107. Shelton, J. R. and Winn, H. (1944) *Ind. Eng. Chem.*, **36**, 728.
108. —— —— (1946) *Ind. Eng. Chem.*, **38**, 71.
109. Shelton, J. R. (1949) *ASTM Spec. Tech. Publication No. 89*, 12.
110. Milligan, A. G. and Shaw, J. E. (1938) *Proc. Rubb. Tech. Conf. London*, 537.
111. Stafford, R. L. (1948) *Proc. Rubb. Tech. Conf. London*, 94.
112. —— (1954) *Third Rubb. Tech. Conf. London*, 253.
113. Le Bras, J. (1944) *Rev. gen. Caoutch.*, **21**, 3.
114. Pollack, L. R., McElwain, R. E. and Wagner, P. T. (1949) *Ind. Eng. Chem.*, **43**, 2280.
115. Kemp, A. R., Ingmanson, J. H. and Mueller, C. S. (1939) *Ind. Eng. Chem.*, **31**, 1472.
116. van Raamsdonk, G. W. (May 1955) *Symposium on Ageing of Rubber, Swedish Rubber Institute.*
117. Tobolsky, A. V., Prettyman, I. B. and Dillon, J. H. (1944) *J. appl. Phys.*, **15**, 380.
118. Tobolsky, A. V. and Andrews, R. D. (1945) *J. Chem. Phys.*, **13**, 3.

119. Andrews, R. D., Tobolsky, A. V. and Hanson, E. E. (1946) *J. appl. Phys.*, **17**, 352.
120. Mesrobian, R. B. and Tobolsky, A. V. (1947) *J. Polymer Sci.*, **2**, 463.
121. Mochulsky, M. and Tobolsky, A. V. (1948) *Ind. Eng. Chem.*, **40**, 2155.
122. Mooney, M., Wolstenholme, W. E. and Villers, D. S. (1944) *J. appl. Phys.*, **15**, 324.
123. Berry, D. S., *Research Assoc. Brit. Rubber Mfrs. Research Memorandum No.* R.394.
124. Pedersen, H. L. and Nielsen, B. (1951) *J. Polymer Sci.*, **7**, 97.
125. Berry, J. P. and Watson, W. F. (1955) *J. Polymer Sci.*, **18**, 201.
126. Throdahl, M. C. (1949) *ASTM Special Technical Publication No. 89*, p. 35.
127. Throdahl, M. C. (1948) *Ind. Eng. Chem.*, **40**, 2180.
128. Baxter, S., Potts, P. D. and Vodden, H. A. (1955) *Ind. Eng. Chem.*, **47**, 1481.
129. Robinson, H. W. H. and Vodden, H. A. (1955) *Ind. Eng. Chem.*, **47**, 1477.
130. Tobolsky, A. V. (1956) *J. appl. Phys.*, **27**, 673.
131. Leeper, H. M. and Gable, G. L. (1956) *Ind. Rubb. World*, **134**, 703.
132. Thornley, E. R. and Watts, J. T. (1950) *Proc. Int. Rubb. Conf. Washington DC*, 190.
133. Cooper, B. S. and Hawkins, F. S. (1949) *J. Soc. Dyers and Colourists*, **65**, 12, 585.
134. McLaren, K. (1956) *J. Soc. Dyers and Colourists*, **72**, 86.
135. Buswell, A. G. (1960) *I.R.I. Trans.* In the press.
136. Edwards, D. C. and Storey, E. B. (1959) *Rubber Age*, **85**, 478.
137. Vodden, H. A. and Wilson, M. A. (1959) *I.R.I. Trans.*, **35**, 82.
138. Mercurio, A. and Tobolsky, A. V. (1959) *J. polym. Sci.*, **36**, 467.
139. Hillmer, K. H. and Scheele, W. (1958) *Kaut. u. Gummi*, **11**, WT210.
140. Dunn, J. R. and Scanlan, R. (1958) *I.R.I. Trans.*, **34**, 228.
141. Dunn, J. R., Scanlan, R. and Watson, W. F. (1959) *Trans. Faraday Soc.*, **55**, No. 436, Pt. 4, 667.

NAME INDEX

1186　　　　　NAME INDEX

SUBJECT INDEX